# The Cosmic Perspective

## SECOND EDITION

**Jeffrey Bennett**
*University of Colorado at Boulder*

**Megan Donahue**
*Space Telescope Science Institute*

**Nicholas Schneider**
*University of Colorado at Boulder*

**Mark Voit**
*Space Telescope Science Institute*

Addison
Wesley

San Francisco, California   Reading, Massachusetts   New York
Harlow, England   Don Mills, Ontario   Sydney   Mexico City   Madrid   Amsterdam

Acquisitions Editor: *Adam Black*
Executive Editor: *Ben Roberts*
Market Developer: *Chalon Bridges*
Marketing Manager: *Christy Lawrence*
Publishing Associate: *Liana Allday*
Developmental Editor: *Laura Maria Bonazzoli*
Production Coordination: *Joan Marsh*
Production: *Mary Douglas, Rogue Valley Publications*
Photo Research: *Myrna Engler*
Graphic Artists: *Joe Bergeron, John Goshorn/Techarts,*
    *Blakeley Kim, Emiko-Rose Koike/fiVth.com,*
    *Quade Paul/fiVth.com*
Copyeditor: *Mary Roybal*
Text Designers: *Blakeley Kim, Andrew Ogus*
Partial Cover Photo: Quade Paul/fiVth.com; PhotoDisk; and
    Hubble Space Telescope
Cover Designers: Quade Paul/fiVth.com and Emiko Rose
    Koike / fiVth.com
Composition: *Thompson Type/Alma Bell, Lori Shranko,*
    *Janice Adamski*
Cover Printer: *Coral Graphics*
Prepress Services: *H&S Graphics, Inc./Tom Andersen,*
    *Mike Tambellini, Lori Jewell, Dave Frank*
Printer and Binder: *Von Hoffmann Press*

For permission to use copyrighted material, grateful acknowledgment is made to the copyright holders on pp. C-1–C-3, which are hereby made part of this copyright page.

Many of the designations used by manufacturers and sellers to distinguish their products are claimed as trademarks. Where those designations appear in this book, and the publisher was aware of a trademark claim, the designations have been printed in initial caps or all caps.

Library of Congress Cataloging-in-Publication Data--2nd ed.
The cosmic perspective / Jeffrey O. Bennett . . . [et al.].
    p.   cm.
   Includes index.
   ISBN 0-8053-8044-2
   1. Astronomy.   I. Bennett, Jeffrey O.
  QB43.3.C68   2001
  520—dc21                   2001045214

2 3 4 5 6 7 8 9 10—VHP—04 03 02 01

*We shall not cease from exploration*
*And the end of all our exploring*
*Will be to arrive where we started*
*And know the place for the first time.*
  T. S. ELIOT

## Dedication

TO ALL WHO HAVE EVER WONDERED about the mysteries
of the universe. We hope this book will answer some of your
questions—and that it will also raise new questions in your
mind that will keep you curious and interested in the ongoing
human adventure of astronomy.

And, especially, to the members of the "baby boom" that
has occurred among the authors and editors during the writing of this book: Michaela, Emily, Rachel, Sebastian, Elizabeth,
Nathan, Grant, Georgia, Brooke, and Brian. The study of the
universe begins at birth, and we hope that you will grow up in
a world with far less poverty, hatred, and war so that all people
will have the opportunity to contemplate the mysteries of the
universe into which they are born.

# BRIEF CONTENTS

# DETAILED CONTENTS

# PREFACE

We humans have gazed into the sky for countless generations, wondering how our lives are connected to the Sun, Moon, planets, and stars that adorn the heavens. Today, through the science of astronomy, we know that these connections go far deeper than our ancestors ever imagined. This book tells the story of modern astronomy and the new perspective—*The Cosmic Perspective*—with which it allows us to view ourselves and our planet. It is written for anyone who is curious about the universe, but it is designed primarily as a textbook for college students not planning to major in mathematics or science.

## Approach

This book grew out of our experience teaching astronomy both to college students and the general public over the past 20 years. During this time, a flood of new discoveries fueled a revolution in our understanding of the cosmos, but the basic organization and approach of most astronomy textbooks remained unchanged. We felt the time had come to rethink how to organize and teach the major concepts in astronomy. This book is the result. Several major innovations in organization set this book apart.

### A "Big Picture" Context Throughout the Book.

Many traditional textbooks begin with the sky as viewed by the ancients and gradually work through to the expanding universe and modern ideas of cosmology at the very end of the book. The potential advantage to this traditional organization is that, if students fully absorb it, they recreate for themselves the thought patterns and paradigm shifts that led from ancient superstitions about the sky to modern understanding of the universe. Unfortunately, this potential advantage is very difficult to realize in practice, because it means that students must learn a sequence of successive paradigms, why each was rejected, and why the next one followed, before finally arriving at what we now consider the correct understanding. That is, students must essentially recreate the thinking produced over thousands of years by some of the greatest minds in history, all with just a few hours of study per week over one or two course terms. Not only is such a process unrealistic for most students, but it also tends to lead to confusion among the various paradigms, thereby preventing students from understanding either the modern view or how we arrived at it. We have therefore chosen a different approach in which we begin the book with a broad overview of modern scientific understanding of the cosmos, and then use the rest of the book to help students understand how and why we have reached this understanding and what gaps remain in our knowledge. We believe that, for the vast majority of students, this approach enables them to understand the scientific process much better than they would with the historical approach, because knowing the end goal helps them focus their studies. We maintain this "big picture" context throughout the book by always telling students where we are going when we introduce new topics, and by reviewing the context at the end of each chapter (in the end-of-chapter sections called *The Big Picture*).

### Stronger Emphasis on the Scientific Process.
Nearly all astronomy textbooks emphasize the scientific process, but we believe that our approach allows us to go beyond what is possible with a more traditional, historical approach to astronomy. In particular, by starting with the context of modern astronomy, we are able to focus clearly on how science works (Chapter 3) and on key physical principles that apply universally (Chapters 4 through 6). For example, we use the concept of conservation of energy over and over throughout the text to show how it helps explain everything from whether planets are geologically active to the processes that govern the lives of stars.

### Fully Integrated History.
Most introductory astronomy textbooks lump the historical development of astronomy, from the Greeks through the Copernican

revolution, into a single segment (for example, one or two chapters) of text. While the chronological flow of this approach certainly has aesthetic appeal, we have found that it also tends to encourage students to memorize the history for the test and then quickly forget it afterward. We therefore believe it is far more effective to integrate historical development throughout the narrative so that each historical topic appears in the context of how it helped lead to particular modern topics. This is precisely the approach to history that helped make Carl Sagan's *Cosmos* series so popular and informative, and we have found that it works equally well in the college classroom. Moreover, because it spreads the historical topics throughout the text, it actually allows us to have *more* coverage of the history of astronomy than can comfortably fit in most other astronomy texts. (Also, we have taken extraordinary care to make sure that our historical discussions are based on the most current understanding of history; to help ensure accuracy, noted historian of science Owen Gingerich reviewed our historical material.)

*True Comparative Planetology.* We offer a true comparative planetology approach, in which the discussion emphasizes general principles that apply to planetary geology and planetary atmospheres as opposed to simply describing one planet at a time. This approach has several crucial advantages over the more common, planet-by-planet approach. For example, by focusing on planetary processes rather than simply on morphological features, we strengthen students' grasp of how a few key physical principles apply throughout the universe, thereby furthering our goal of helping students understand the scientific process. In addition, long after the course is over, students are much more likely to retain the understanding of physical processes built in this way than they are of any particular planetary features that they memorize through a planet-by-planet approach. Perhaps most important, the comparative planetology approach helps students see the relevance of planetary science to their own lives by enabling them to gain a far deeper appreciation of our own unique world.

*An Evolutionary Approach to Galaxies and Dark Matter.* Over the past few decades, a revolution has occurred in our understanding of galactic evolution. For example, whereas quasars were once considered a distinct class of objects, the evidence now strongly contradicts this idea; instead, it now appears that quasars represent an unusually active stage of life in the centers of some young galaxies. Despite this revolution in scientific understanding, most introductory textbooks still present galaxies in the order that made sense when early galaxy classification schemes were first developed a half-century ago. We have

taken an approach that teaches about galaxies in a way that closely parallels how nearly all textbooks (including ours) teach about stars: we begin with our own galaxy as a paradigm (Chapter 18), then discuss the variety of galaxies and how we determine key parameters such as distances (Chapter 19), and then discuss how we've arrived at the current state of knowledge regarding galaxy evolution (Chapter 20). Because dark matter plays such an important role in this evolutionary understanding, we then devote an entire chapter (Chapter 21) to its study.

*An Integrated Approach to Cosmology.* Ultimately, one of the primary goals of astronomy is to understand our cosmic origins, which means understanding cosmology. Most introductory textbooks present cosmology only in a final chapter. We integrate the study of cosmology throughout much of the text. Students first encounter modern cosmological ideas, including the notion of the Big Bang and the idea of an expanding universe, as part of our big picture overview in Chapter 1. Our entire presentation of galaxies is steeped in cosmology, since the study of galactic evolution cannot be effectively separated from cosmological ideas. Thus, we do not have a single cosmology chapter in the traditional sense, but instead we have a chapter devoted to the Big Bang theory (Chapter 22) that builds upon the understanding students develop throughout the text.

*Supplementary Chapters on Relativity and Quantum Mechanics.* It is impossible to teach a class in astronomy without receiving questions such as: Why can't we go faster than the speed of light? What is the universe expanding into? What is a black hole? The common thread to these questions is that the answers, or possible answers, can be understood only through relativity. We believe that the ideas of relativity can be made accessible to anyone and have therefore included two chapters (Chapters S2 and S3) covering basic ideas of special and general relativity. We have also included a chapter on quantum mechanics and its astronomical implications (Chapter S4). These three chapters will enable students to understand stars, galaxies, and cosmology in much greater depth than they could otherwise. And, from our teaching experience, students will find the topics of relativity and quantum mechanics to be among their favorite topics in the course. However, recognizing that many instructors will not have the time or inclination to cover these chapters, we have made them supplemental chapters—covering them will enhance student understanding of the chapters that follow, but they are not prerequisite to the remaining chapters.

## Pedagogical Features

Besides the main narrative, the book includes a number of pedagogical features designed to enhance student learning:

### End-of-Chapter Questions, Problems, and Projects.
The following four sets of questions appear at the end of each chapter:

- *Review Questions.* The Review Questions replace a standard chapter summary. Like a summary, they review the important concepts from the chapter. However, they are more effective as a study tool than a standard summary because they require students to think rather than enabling mindless use of a highlight pen. While it is possible to assign review questions as homework, these questions generally can be answered with little more than a quick re-reading of the relevant sections of the text.

- *Discussion Questions.* These questions are meant to be particularly thought provoking and generally do not have objective answers. As such, they are ideal for in-class discussion.

- *Problems.* Each chapter includes several problems of varying levels of difficulty that are designed to be assigned as written homework. Problems are generally arranged from easier to harder, and to the extent possible follow the order of presentation in the chapter. Problems with an asterisk require mathematical manipulation, generally following methods described in Mathematical Insight boxes.

- *Web Projects.* Each chapter ends with one or more Web Projects, which are designed for independent research. The projects typically ask students to learn more about a topic of relevance to the chapter, such as a current or planned mission. Students can find useful links for all the Web Projects at The Astronomy Place (www. astronomyplace.com).

### Time Out to Think.
This feature gives students the opportunity to reflect on important new concepts. It also serves as an excellent starting point for classroom discussions. Answers or discussion points for all the Time Out to Think questions can be found in the Instructor's Guide.

### Common Misconceptions.
These boxes address and correct popularly held but incorrect ideas related to the chapter material. In a few cases in which the boxes focus on misconceptions perpetrated by television or movies, the boxes carry the title "Movie Madness."

### Mathematical Insights.
These boxes contain most of the mathematics used in the book, and they can be covered or skipped depending on the level of mathematics that you wish to include in your course.

### Thinking About.
These boxes contain supplementary discussion of topics related to the chapter material but not prerequisite to the continuing discussion.

### The Big Picture.
This end-of-chapter feature helps students put what they've learned into the context of the overall goal of gaining a new perspective on ourselves and our planet.

### Cross-References.
When we discuss a concept that is covered in greater detail elsewhere in the book, we include a cross-reference in brackets. For example, [Section 5.2] means that the concept being discussed is covered in greater detail in Section 5.2.

### Glossary.
A detailed glossary makes it easy for students to look up unfamiliar terms.

### Appendices.
The appendices include a number of useful references, including summaries of key constants (Appendix A), key formulas (Appendix B), and a brief review of key mathematical skills such as working with scientific notation and operating with units (Appendix C).

### Star Charts (Appendixes I, J).
The list of constellations and the star charts help interested students learn their way around the night sky.

## Alternate Versions of the Book

*The Cosmic Perspective* is available in four versions tailored to particular course types:

- *The Cosmic Perspective, Second Edition* (full version, ISBN 0-8053-8044-2) This is the most complete version of the book, containing sufficient material for astronomy courses ranging in length from one quarter to a full year.

- *The Solar System: The Cosmic Perspective, Second Edition, Volume 1* (ISBN 0-8053-8544-1) This version contains Chapters 1–13 and Chapter S1 of the full version of the book. It is designed for courses that focus on the solar system rather than on stars, galaxies, and cosmology.

- *Stars, Galaxies, and Cosmology: The Cosmic Perspective, Second Edition, Volume 2* (ISBN 0-8053-8557-6) This version contains Chapters 1, 4–7, 14–22, and S2–S5 of the full version of the book. It is designed for courses that focus on stars, galaxies, and cosmology.

■ *The Cosmic Perspective, Brief Edition*
(ISBN 0-201-69734-3)
This is a condensed version of the full book, designed primarily for use in courses that provide an overview of all of astronomy but at a lower level of depth than offered in the full version of the book.

## Supplements and Resources

*The Cosmic Perspective* is much more than just a textbook; it is a complete package of resources designed to help instructors and students. Here, we've broken the resources into two categories, the first designed to help students directly and the second designed to help instructors prepare course materials and lectures.

### Resources To Help Students Learn

The following resources are designed to reinforce the content knowledge students will learn from the textbook.

*The Astronomy Place* (*www.astronomyplace.com*). This Web site is designed specifically to accompany *The Cosmic Perspective* textbooks. Among its constantly growing list of features, instructors and students will find:

■ A complete set of student study resources for each chapter in the textbook; the resources include chapter summaries, additional information on Common Misconceptions and Mathematical Insights, self-assessment quizzes, and chapter-specific links (including links for the end-of-chapter Web Projects). In addition, all Time Out To Think questions and all end-of-chapter Problems are digitized for online assignments. The entire textbook is available on-line in XML and can be browsed by topic.

■ A suite of interactive tutorials that build understanding through a carefully constructed, step-by-step process based on the type of interaction and discussion that typically would occur during office hours.

■ Ten 5-minute animated and narrated mini-movies that provide engaging summaries of key topics.

■ Activity worksheets to be used with the *SkyGazer, College Edition* software packaged with the textbook.

■ On-line versions of the textbook glossary and appendices.

■ Updates on the latest astronomy news.

*Carl Sagan's Cosmos Series.* The newly released *Best of Cosmos* (ISBN: 0-8053-8571-1) and complete, revised, enhanced, and updated *Cosmos* series (Video ISBN: 0-8053-8570-3, DVD ISBN: 0-8053-8572-X) are available free to qualified adopters of *The Cosmic Perspective.*

*SkyGazer, College Edition.* Based on *Voyager III,* one of the world's most popular planetarium programs, *SkyGazer, College Edition* makes it easy for students to learn constellations and explore the wonders of the sky through interactive exercises. The *SkyGazer* CD is packaged free with all new copies of the textbook. It can also be ordered separately (CD-ROM ISBN: 0-8053-8022-1).

*The Astronomy Tutor Center.* This center provides one-to-one tutoring by qualified college instructors in any of four ways—phone, fax, email, and the Internet—during afternoon/evening hours and on weekends. The tutor center instructors will answer questions and provide help with examples, exercises, and other content found in *The Cosmic Perspective.* Students who register to use the astronomy tutor center can receive as much tutoring as they wish for the duration of their course. Registration is free with purchase of a new textbook or can be purchased separately; see www.aw.com/tutorcenter for more information.

### Course Preparation Resources

*Instructor's Resource Guide.* (ISBN: 0-8053-8559-2) Includes an overview of the philosophy of the text, discussion of strategies for teaching astronomy, suggestions on preparing an astronomy course, sample syllabi for courses of different length and emphasis, a reference guide for integrating the *Cosmos* video series and the Astronomy Place Web tutorials and movies with this textbook, a chapter-by-chapter commentary with notes and teaching hints, answers or discussion points for all the Time Out to Think questions in the book, and solutions to end-of-chapter problems.

*The Astronomy Place Instructor Resources* (*www.astronomyplace.com*). The Astronomy Place has numerous resources designed specifically for instructors, including:

■ A digitized version of the Instructor's Resource Guide (not including solutions to problems).

■ Syllabus Manager, an easy to use on-line course management system. It can be used to build and maintain one or more syllabi on the Web. The system also allows you to receive and grade student assignments on-line.

- Customization resources that allow you to use the content of The Astronomy Place in WebCT, BlackBoard, or CourseCompass. If you are interested in these customized options, please contact your local Addison Wesley sales representative.

*Printed Test Bank.* (ISBN: 0-8053-8545-2) Includes over 1500 multiple-choice, true/false, and free-response questions for each chapter.

*TestGen EQ CD-ROM.* (ISBN: 0-8053-8045-0) Provides identical questions from the Printed Test Bank on one CD-ROM (Windows/Mac compatible). Allows the instructor to view and edit questions, add questions, and create and print different versions of tests. A built-in question editor creates graphs, imports graphics, and inserts text.

*Transparency Acetates.* (ISBN: 0-8053-8546-0) A selection of over 200 figures from the text printed on full-color transparency acetates.

*Addison Wesley Science Digital Library.* (ISBN: 0-8053-8569-X) This cross-platform CD-ROM includes illustrations, tables, and star charts from the book and many animations/video clips from the Web site that can be customized for lecture presentation.

### Acknowledgments

A textbook may carry author names, but it is the result of hard work by a long list of committed individuals. We could not possibly list everyone who has helped, but we would like to call attention to a few people who have played particularly important roles. First, we thank our editors and friends at Addison Wesley Longman who have stuck with us through thick and thin, including Ben Roberts, Adam Black, Robin Heyden, Sami Iwata, Bill Poole, Linda Davis, Joan Marsh, Stacy Treco, Christy Lawrence, Nancy Gee, Liana Allday, and Tony Asaro. Special thanks to our production team, especially Mary Douglas, Myrna Engler, and Mary Roybal; our art team, led by Blakeley Kim and Emiko-Rose Koike; and our Web team, led by Claire Masson, Jim Dove, and Ian Shakeshaft.

We've also been fortunate to have an outstanding group of reviewers whose extensive comments and suggestions helped us shape the book. We thank all those who have reviewed drafts of the book in various stages, including:

Christopher M. Anderson, University of Wisconsin
Peter S. Anderson, Oakland Community College
John Beaver, University of Wisconsin at Fox Valley
Priscilla J. Benson, Wellesley College

Eric Carlson, Wake Forest University
Supriya Chakrabarti, Boston University
Dipak Chowdhury, Indiana University–Purdue University at Fort Wayne
Robert Egler, North Carolina State University at Raleigh
Robert A. Fesen, Dartmouth College
Sidney Freudenstein, Metropolitan State College of Denver
Richard Gelderman, Western Kentucky University
Richard Gray, Appalachian State University
David Griffiths, Oregon State University
David Grinspoon, University of Colorado
Jim Hamm, Big Bend Community College
Charles Hartley, Hartwick College
Joe Heafner, Catawba Valley Community College
Richard Ignace, University of Iowa
Bruce Jakosky, University of Colorado
Kurtis Koll, Cameron University
Kristine Larsen, Central Connecticut State University
Larry Lebofsky, University of Arizona
Patrick Lestrade, Mississippi State University
David M. Lind, Florida State University
Michael LoPresto, Henry Ford Community College
William R. Luebke, Modesto Junior College
Marie Machacek, Massachusetts Institute of Technology
Marles McCurdy, Tarrant County College
Steven Majewski, University of Virginia
Phil Matheson, Salt Lake Community College
Barry Metz, Delaware County Community College
John P. Oliver, University of Florida
Jorge Piekarewicz, Florida State University
Harrison B. Prosper, Florida State University
Christina Reeves-Shull, Richland College
Elizabeth Roettger, DePaul University
John Safko, University of South Carolina
James A. Scarborough, Delta State University
Joslyn Schoemer, Denver Museum of Nature and Science
James Schombert, University of Oregon
Gregory Seab, University of New Orleans
Mark H. Slovak, Louisiana State University
Dale Smith, Bowling Green State University
John Spencer, Lowell Observatory
Darryl Stanford, City College of San Francisco
John Stolar, West Chester University
Jack Sulentic, University of Alabama
C. Sean Sutton, Mount Holyoke College
Beverley A. P. Taylor, Miami University
Donald M. Terndrup, Ohio State University
David Trott, Metra State College
Darryl Walke, Raritan Valley Community College
Fred Walter, State University of New York, Stony Brook
Mark Whittle, University of Virginia
Jonathan Williams, University of Florida

J. Wayne Wooten, Pensacola Junior College
Arthur Young, San Diego State University
Dennis Zaritsky, University of California, Santa Cruz

*Historical Accuracy Reviewer*—Owen Gingerich,
   Harvard–Smithsonian

   In addition, we thank the following colleagues
who helped us clarify technical points or checked the
accuracy of technical discussions in the book:

Thomas Ayres, University of Colorado
Cecilia Barnbaum, Valdosta State University
Rick Binzel, Massachusetts Institute of Technology
Howard Bond, Space Telescope Science Institute
Humberto Campins, University of Florida
Robin Canup, Southwest Research Institute
Mark Dickinson, Space Telescope Science Institute
Jim Dove, Metropolitan State College of Denver
Harry Ferguson, Space Telescope Science Institute
Andrew Hamilton, University of Colorado
Todd Henry, Georgia State University
Dave Jewitt, University of Hawaii
Hal Levison, Southwest Research Institute
Mario Livio, Space Telescope Science Institute

Mark Marley, New Mexico State University
Kevin McLin, University of Colorado, Boulder
Rachel Osten, University of Colorado, Boulder
Bob Pappalardo, Brown University
Michael Shara, American Museum of Natural
   History
Glen Stewart, University of Colorado
John Stolar, West Chester University
Dave Tholen, University of Hawaii
Nick Thomas, MPI/Lindau (Germany)
John Weiss, University of Colorado, Boulder
Don Yeomans, Jet Propulsion Laboratory

   Finally, we thank the many people who have
greatly influenced our outlook on education and our
perspective on the universe over the years, including
Tom Ayres, Fran Bagenal, Forrest Boley, Robert A.
Brown, George Dulk, Erica Ellingson, Katy Garmany,
Jeff Goldstein, David Grinspoon, Don Hunten,
Catherine McCord, Dick McCray, Dee Mook, Cheri
Morrow, Charlie Pellerin, Carl Sagan, Mike Shull,
John Spencer, and John Stocke.

*Jeff Bennett*
*Megan Donahue*
*Nick Schneider*
*Mark Voit*

# HOW TO SUCCEED IN
# YOUR ASTRONOMY COURSE

Most readers of this book are enrolled in a college course in introductory astronomy. If you are one of these readers, we offer you the following hints to help you succeed in your astronomy course.

## Using This Book

Before we address general strategies for studying, here are a few guidelines that will help you use *this* book most effectively.

- Read assigned material twice.

  - Make your first pass *before* the material is covered in class. Use this pass to get a "feel" for all the material and to identify concepts that you may want to ask about in class.

  - Read the material for the second time shortly after it is covered in class. This will help solidify your understanding and allow you to make notes that will help you study for exams later.

- Take advantage of the features that will help you study.

  - Always read the *Time Out to Think* features, and use them to help you absorb the material and to identify areas where you may have questions.

  - Use the *cross-references* indicated in brackets in the text and the *glossary* at the back of the book to find more information about terms or concepts that you don't recall.

  - Go to The Astronomy Place at **www. astronomyplace.com** to find additional study aids, including tutorials and quizzes with answers.

- It's your book, so don't be afraid to make notes in it that will help you study later.

  - Don't highlight—<u>underline!</u> Using a pen or pencil to <u>underline</u> material requires greater care than highlighting and therefore helps keep you alert as you study. And be selective in your underlining—for purposes of studying later, it won't help if you underlined everything.

  - There's plenty of "white space" in the margins and elsewhere, so use it to make notes as you read. Your own notes will later be very valuable when you are doing homework or studying for exams.

- After you complete the reading, and again when you study for exams, make sure you can answer the *Review Questions* at the end of each chapter. If you are having difficulty with a review question, reread the relevant portions of the chapter until the answer becomes clear.

## Budgeting Your Time

One of the easiest ways to ensure success in any college course is to make sure you budget enough time for studying. A general rule of thumb for college classes is that you should expect to study about 2 to 3 hours per week *outside* of class for each unit of credit. For example, based on this rule of thumb, a student taking 15 credit hours should expect to spend 30 to 45 hours each week studying outside of class. Combined with time in class, this works out to a total of 45 to 60 hours spent on academic work—not much more than the time a typical job requires, and you get to choose your own hours. Of course, if you are working while you attend school, you will need to budget your time carefully.

As a rough guideline, your studying time in astronomy might be divided as shown in the table at the top of p. xix. If you find that you are spending

| If Your Course Is: | Time for Reading the Assigned Text (per week) | Time for Homework Assignments (per week) | Time for Review and Test Preparation (average per week) | Total Study Time (per week) |
|---|---|---|---|---|
| 3 credits | 2 to 4 hours | 2 to 3 hours | 2 hours | 6 to 9 hours |
| 4 credits | 3 to 5 hours | 2 to 4 hours | 3 hours | 8 to 12 hours |
| 5 credits | 3 to 5 hours | 3 to 6 hours | 4 hours | 10 to 15 hours |

fewer hours than these guidelines suggest, you can probably improve your grade by studying more. If you are spending more hours than these guidelines suggest, you may be studying inefficiently; in that case, you should talk to your instructor about how to study more effectively.

### General Strategies for Studying

■ Don't miss class. Listening to lectures and participating in discussions is much more effective than reading someone else's notes. Active participation will help you retain what you are learning.

■ Budget your time effectively. An hour or two each day is more effective, and far less painful, than studying all night before homework is due or before exams.

■ If a concept gives you trouble, do additional reading or studying beyond what has been assigned. And if you still have trouble, ask for help: You surely can find friends, colleagues, or teachers who will be glad to help you learn.

■ Working together with friends can be valuable in helping you understand difficult concepts. However, be sure that you learn *with* your friends and do not become dependent on them.

■ Be sure that any work you turn in is of *collegiate quality*: neat and easy to read, well organized, and demonstrating mastery of the subject matter. Although it takes extra effort to make your work look this good, the effort will help you solidify your learning and is also good practice for the expectations that future professors and employers will have.

### Preparing for Exams

■ Study the review questions, and rework problems and other assignments; try additional questions to be sure you understand the concepts. Study your performance on assignments, quizzes, or exams from earlier in the term.

■ Try the quizzes available on the text Web site at **www.astronomyplace.com**

■ Study your notes from lectures and discussions. Pay attention to what your instructor expects you to know for an exam.

■ Reread the relevant sections in the textbook, paying special attention to notes you have made on the pages.

■ Study individually *before* joining a study group with friends. Study groups are effective only if every individual comes prepared to contribute.

■ Don't stay up too late before an exam. Don't eat a big meal within an hour of the exam (thinking is more difficult when blood is being diverted to the digestive system).

■ Try to relax before and during the exam. If you have studied effectively, you are capable of doing well. Staying relaxed will help you think clearly.

# ABOUT THE AUTHORS

*Jeffrey Bennett* received a B.A. in biophysics from the University of California at San Diego in 1981 and a Ph.D. in astrophysics from the University of Colorado in 1987. His thesis research focused on Sun-like stars, but he now specializes in mathematics and science education. He has extensive teaching experience at the elementary and secondary levels and has taught more than fifty college courses in astronomy, physics, mathematics, and education. He led the development of the Colorado Scale Model Solar System (pictured here) and proposed and served as a co–principal investigator on the Voyage scale model solar system for the National Mall. Besides his astronomy textbooks, he has written textbooks in mathematics (Bennett and Briggs, *Using and Understanding Mathematics,* Addison Wesley, 2002) and statistics (Bennett, Briggs, & Triola, *Statistical Reasoning for Everyday Life,* Addison Wesley, 2001), a popular book (*On the Cosmic Horizon,* Addison Wesley, 2001), and is currently working on children's books. When not working, he enjoys participating in masters swimming and hiking the trails of Boulder, Colorado, with his family.

*Megan Donahue* is an astronomer at the Space Telescope Science Institute in Baltimore, Maryland. After growing up in rural Nebraska, she obtained an S.B. in physics from the Massachusetts Institute of Technology in 1985 and a Ph.D. in astrophysics from the University of Colorado in 1990. Her thesis on intergalactic gas and clusters of galaxies won the Robert J. Trumpler Award (1993). She continued her research as a Carnegie Fellow at the Observatories of the Carnegie Institution in Pasadena, California, and later was an Institute Fellow at the Space Telescope Science Institute. She is an active observer, using ground-based telescopes, the Hubble Space Telescope, and orbiting X-ray telescopes. Her research focuses on questions of galaxy evolution, the nature of intergalactic space, large-scale structure formation, and dark matter and the fate of the universe. She married Mark Voit while in graduate school and they are the parents of two children, Michaela and Sebastian.

*Nicholas Schneider* is an associate professor in the Department of Astrophysical and Planetary Sciences at the University of Colorado and a researcher in the Laboratory for Atmospheric and Space Physics. He received his B.A. in physics and astronomy from Dartmouth College in 1979 and his Ph.D. in planetary science from the University of Arizona in 1988. In 1991, he received the National Science Foundation's Presidential Young Investigator Award. His research interests include planetary atmospheres and planetary astronomy, with a focus on the odd case of Jupiter's moon Io. He enjoys teaching at all levels and is active in efforts to improve undergraduate astronomy education. Off the job, he enjoys exploring the outdoors with his family and figuring out how things work.

*Mark Voit* is an astronomer in the Office of Public Outreach at the Space Telescope Science Institute. He earned his A.B. in physics at Princeton University in 1983 and his Ph.D. in astrophysics at the University of Colorado in 1990. He continued his studies at the California Institute of Technology, where he was Research Fellow in theoretical astrophysics. NASA then awarded him a Hubble Fellowship, under which he conducted research at the Johns Hopkins University. His research interests range from interstellar processes in our own galaxy to the clustering of galaxies in the early universe. Occasionally he escapes to the outdoors, where he and his wife, Megan Donahue, enjoy running, hiking, orienteering, and playing with their children. Mark is also author of the popular book *Hubble Space Telescope: New Views of the Universe.*

# PART I
# Developing Perspective

# CHAPTER 1
# Our Place in the Universe

Far from city lights on a clear night, you can gaze upward at a sky filled with stars. If you lie back and watch for a few hours, you will observe the stars marching steadily across the sky. Confronted by the seemingly infinite heavens, you might wonder how the Earth and the universe came to be. With these thoughts, you will be sharing an experience common to humans around the world and in thousands of generations past.

Remarkably, modern science offers answers to many fundamental questions about the universe and our place within it. We now know the basic content and scale of the universe. We know the age of the Earth and the approximate age of the universe. And, although much remains to be discovered, we are rapidly learning how the simple constituents of the early universe developed into the incredible diversity of life on Earth.

In this first chapter, we will survey the content and history of the universe, the scale of the universe, and the motions of the Earth in our universe. We'll thereby develop a "big picture" perspective on our place in the universe that will provide a base on which we can build a deeper understanding in the rest of the book. You may wish to begin by studying the two paintings that appear in the first few pages of the chapter, summarizing (respectively) our cosmic address and cosmic origins.

the universe

the Local Supercluster

the Local Group

**FIGURE 1.1** Our place in the universe. This painting illustrates our cosmic address: The Earth is one of nine planets in our solar system; our solar system is one among more than 100 billion star systems in the Milky Way Galaxy; the Milky Way is one of the two largest of about 30 galaxies in the Local Group; the Local Group lies near the outskirts of the Local Supercluster; and the Local Supercluster fades into the background painting of structure throughout the universe.

Earth

## 1.1 A Modern View of the Universe

If you observe the sky carefully, you can see why most of our ancestors believed that the heavens revolved about the Earth. The Sun, Moon, planets, and stars appear to circle around our sky each day, and we cannot feel the constant motion of the Earth as it rotates on its axis and orbits the Sun. Thus, it seems quite natural to assume that we live in an Earth-centered, or *geocentric*, universe.

Nevertheless, we now know that the Earth is a planet orbiting a rather average star in a vast cosmos. (In astronomy, the term *cosmos* is synonymous with *universe*.) The historical path to this knowledge was long and complex, involving the dedicated intellectual efforts of thousands of individuals. In later chapters, we'll encounter many of these individuals and explore how their discoveries changed human understanding of the universe. We'll see that many ancient beliefs made a lot of sense and changed only when people were confronted by strong evidence to the contrary. We'll also see how the process of science has enabled us to acquire this evidence and thereby discover that we are connected to the stars in ways our ancestors never imagined.

First, however, it's useful to have at least a general picture of the universe as we know it today. This big picture will make it easier for you to understand the historical development of astronomy, the evidence for our modern ideas, and the mysteries that remain. Let's begin by examining what modern astronomy has to say about our cosmic location and origins.

### Our Cosmic Address

Take a look at Figure 1.1 on the preceding pages. Going counterclockwise from Earth, this painting illustrates the basic levels of structure that describe what we might call our "cosmic address."

Earth is a planet, by which we mean that it is a reasonably large object that orbits a star—our Sun. Our **solar system** consists of the Sun and all the objects that orbit it: nine planets (including Earth) and their moons, the chunks of rock that we call asteroids, the balls of ice that we call comets, and countless tiny particles of interplanetary dust.

Our Sun is a star, just like the stars we see in our night sky. The Sun and all the stars we can see with the naked eye make up only a small part of a huge, disk-shaped collection of stars called the **Milky Way Galaxy**. A galaxy is a great island of stars in space, containing from a few hundred million to a trillion or more stars. The Milky Way Galaxy is relatively large, containing more than 100 billion stars. Our solar system is located a little over halfway from the galactic center to the edge of the galactic disk. Many of the stars in the Milky Way are grouped together in

---

### Basic Astronomical Definitions

*Star*  A large, glowing ball of gas that generates energy through nuclear fusion in its core. The term *star* is sometimes applied to objects that are in the process of becoming true stars (e.g., protostars) and to the remains of stars that have died (e.g., neutron stars).

*Planet*  An object that orbits a star and that, while much smaller than a star, is relatively large in size. There is no "official" minimum size for a planet, but the nine planets in our solar system are all at least 2,000 kilometers in diameter. Planets may be rocky, icy, or gaseous in composition, and they shine primarily by reflecting light from their star.

*Moon* (or *satellite*)  An object that orbits a planet. The term *satellite* is also used more generally to refer to any object orbiting another object.

*Asteroid*  A relatively small, rocky object that orbits a star. Asteroids are sometimes called *minor planets* because they are similar to planets but smaller.

*Comet*  A relatively small, icy object that orbits a star.

*Star system*  One or more stars and any planets or other material that orbits them. The term *solar system* refers to our own star system (*solar* means "of the Sun"). Many star systems contain two or more stars that orbit each other; two-star systems are called *binary star systems*.

*Star cluster*  A group of stars (ranging in number from a few hundred to a few million) that are closely associated in space. In general, all the stars in a star cluster were born at roughly the same time from the same cloud of interstellar gas.

*Galaxy*  A great island of stars in space, containing from a few hundred million to a trillion or more stars.

*Galaxy cluster*  A collection of galaxies held together by gravity. Small clusters are generally called *groups* (such as our Local Group), with the term *cluster* reserved for collections of hundreds or thousands of galaxies.

*Supercluster*  A giant structure encompassing many groups and clusters of galaxies.

*Universe* (or *cosmos*)  The sum total of all matter and energy. By current understanding, only part of the universe is observable to us even in principle; we call this our *observable universe*.

**star clusters**; on a clear night, you can see many beautiful star clusters with a pair of binoculars.

Many galaxies congregate in groups; groups that contain more than a few dozen galaxies are called **galaxy clusters**. Our Milky Way belongs to a group of 30 or so galaxies called the **Local Group**.

On the largest scale, the universe has a frothlike appearance in which galaxies and galaxy clusters are loosely arranged in giant chains and sheets. In some places the galaxies and galaxy clusters are more tightly packed than in others; we call these giant structures **superclusters**. The supercluster to which our Local Group belongs is called, not surprisingly, the **Local Supercluster**. Between these vast structures lie huge voids containing few, if any, galaxies.

Finally, the **universe** is the sum total of all matter and energy. That is, it encompasses the superclusters and voids, and everything within them. As you progress through the text, you will learn much more about the different levels of structure in the universe. To keep the hierarchy straight, you might imagine how a far-away friend would address a postcard to someone on Earth (Figure 1.2).

quick overview of the scientific story of creation, as summarized in Figure 1.3.

As we'll discuss shortly, telescopic observations of distant galaxies show that the entire universe is *expanding*. That is, average distances between galaxies are increasing with time. If the universe is expanding, everything must have been closer together in the past. From the observed rate of expansion, astronomers estimate that the expansion started somewhere between 12 billion and 16 billion years ago. Astronomers call this beginning the **Big Bang**.

The universe has continued to expand ever since the Big Bang, but not without important changes. Until about a decade ago, astronomers assumed the overall expansion had slowed with time because of gravity, which attracts all objects to all other objects. However recent evidence suggets that the expansion might instead be accelerating, a strange idea that we'll discuss in

**FIGURE 1.2** A postcard from a distant friend.

**TIME OUT TO THINK** *Some people think that our tiny physical size in the vast universe makes us insignificant. Others think that our ability to learn about the wonders of the universe gives us significance despite our small size. What do you think?*

### Our Cosmic Origins

How did we come to be? Much of the rest of this text discusses the scientific evidence concerning our cosmic origins, and we'll see that humans are relative newcomers in an old universe. For now, let's look at a

Chapter 21. Regardless of how the overall expansion has changed, gravity has clearly drawn matter together on smaller scales. In structures such as galaxies and clusters of galaxies, gravity has won out against the overall expansion. That is, while the universe as a whole continues to expand, individual galaxies and their contents do *not* expand.

Most galaxies, including our own Milky Way, probably formed within a few billion years after the Big Bang. Within galaxies, gravity drives the collapse of clouds of gas and dust, forming stars and planets. Stars have limited lifetimes, and when they die they may spew much of their content back into interstellar space. This material can then become part of new clouds of gas, which gravity collapses into new star

The universe has
been expanding
ever since its hot
and dense beginning
in the Big Bang. Each
of the three cubes represents
the same region of the universe,
showing how the region expands with time.

**FIGURE 1.3** Our cosmic origins: All the matter and energy in the universe was created in the Big Bang. This sequence of paintings shows the progression of that matter and energy from the Big Bang to human life. Note that the elements from which we are made were produced in stars that shined long ago, and these elements formed the Earth, thanks to the recycling role played by our galaxy.

The Earth was built with elements
produced in stars that lived and died
in the Milky Way before our solar system
formed.

Within a few billion years after the Big Bang, gravity caused local concentrations of matter to collapse into galaxies even while the universe as a whole continued to expand.

Galaxies like the Milky Way act as cosmic recycling plants: Stars are made from the material in clouds of gas and dust within the galaxy, and stars return material to interstellar space when they die.

A star forms at the center of a collapsing cloud of gas and dust, and planets may form in the spinning disk that surrounds the young star.

Massive stars explode when they die, scattering the elements they've produced into space.

Stars shine with the energy produced by nuclear fusion in their cores; the fusion also creates heavier elements from lighter ones.

systems. Thus, galaxies function as cosmic recycling plants, recycling material expelled from dying stars into subsequent generations of stars and planets.

Not only is material recycled, but its chemical nature also changes with time. All the matter in the universe was created in the Big Bang, but the early universe contained only the simplest chemical elements: hydrogen and helium (and trace amounts of lithium). All other elements were manufactured by stars through **nuclear fusion**, in which lightweight elements fuse (i.e., their nuclei join together) to form heavier elements. The energy released by nuclear fusion, which occurs deep in stellar cores, is what makes stars shine. For most of their lives stars shine by fusing hydrogen into helium, but near the ends of their lives the more massive stars generate energy with advanced fusion reactions that produce elements such as carbon, oxygen, nitrogen, and iron. Many of these massive stars die in titanic explosions that release these heavy elements into space, where they mix with other gas and dust in the galaxy to be incorporated into later generations of star systems.

The processes of heavy-element production and cosmic recycling had already been taking place for several billion years by the time our solar system formed, about 4.6 billion years ago. The cloud that gave birth to our solar system was about 98% hydrogen and helium; the other 2% contained all the other chemical elements. The small rocky planets of our solar system, including the Earth, were made from a small part of this 2%. We do not know exactly how the elements on the Earth's surface developed into the first forms of life, but we do know that life was already flourishing on Earth more than 3.5 billion years ago. Biological evolution took over once life arose, leading to the great diversity of life on Earth today.

In summary, all the material from which we and the Earth are made (except hydrogen and most helium) was created inside stars that died before the birth of our Sun. We are intimately connected to the stars because we are products of stars. In the words of astronomer Carl Sagan (1934–96), we are "star stuff."

### Images of Time

We study the universe by studying light from distant stars and galaxies. Light travels extremely fast by earthly standards: The speed of light is 300,000 kilometers per second, a speed at which it would be possible to circle the Earth nearly eight times in just 1 second. Nevertheless, even light takes a substantial amount of time to travel the vast distances in space. For example, light takes about 1 second to reach the Earth from the Moon and about 8 minutes to reach the Earth from the Sun. Light from the stars takes many years to reach us, so we measure distances to the stars in units called **light-years**. One light-year is the distance that light can travel in 1 year—about 10 trillion kilometers, or 6 trillion miles. Note that a light-year is a unit of *distance*, not of time.

The brightest star in the night sky, Sirius, is about 8 light-years from our solar system, which means that it takes light from Sirius about 8 years to reach us. Thus, when we look at Sirius, we see light that left the star about 8 years ago. The Orion Nebula, a star-forming region visible to the naked eye as a small, cloudy patch in the sword of the constellation Orion, lies about 1,500 light-years from Earth. Thus, we see the Orion Nebula as it looked about 1,500 years ago—about the time of the fall of the Roman Empire. If any major events have occurred in the Orion Nebula since that time, we cannot yet know about them because the light from these events would not yet have reached us.

Because it takes time for light to travel through space,

*the farther away we look in distance, the further back we look in time.*

If we look at a galaxy that lies 10 million light-years away, we see it as it was 10 million years ago. If we observe a distant cluster of galaxies that lies 1 billion light-years away, we see the cluster as it was 1 billion years ago.

### Mathematical Insight 1.1    How Far Is a Light-Year?

It's easy to calculate the distance represented by a light-year if you recall that

$$\text{distance} = \text{speed} \times \text{time}$$

For example, if you travel at a speed of 50 kilometers per hour for 2 hours, you will travel 100 kilometers. A light-year is the distance covered by light, traveling at a speed of 300,000 kilometers per second, in a time of 1 year. In the process of multiplying the speed and the time, you must convert the year to seconds in order to arrive at a final answer in units of kilometers.

$$1 \text{ light-year} = (\text{speed of light}) \times (1 \text{ yr})$$

$$= \left(300,000 \, \frac{\text{km}}{\text{s}}\right) \times \left(1 \, \text{yr} \times \frac{365 \text{ days}}{1 \text{ yr}}\right.$$

$$\left. \times \frac{24 \text{ hr}}{1 \text{ day}} \times \frac{60 \text{ min}}{1 \text{ hr}} \times \frac{60 \text{ s}}{1 \text{ min}}\right)$$

$$= 9,460,000,000,000 \text{ km}$$

That is, "1 light-year" is just an easy way of saying "9.46 trillion kilometers" or "almost 10 trillion kilometers."

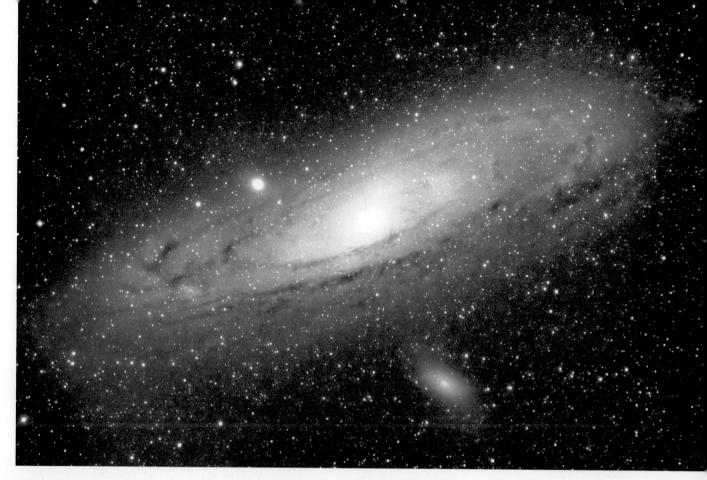

**FIGURE 1.4** M31, the Great Galaxy in Andromeda, is about 2.5 million light-years away, so this photo captures light that traveled through space for 2.5 million years to reach us. Because the galaxy is 100,000 light-years in diameter, the photo also captures 100,000 years of time in M31: We see the galaxy's near side as it looked 100,000 years later than the time at which we see the far side.

Ultimately, the speed of light limits the portion of the universe that we can see. For example, if the universe is 12 billion years old, then light from galaxies more than 12 billion light-years away would not have had time to reach us. We would say that the **observable universe** extends 12 billion light-years in all directions from Earth. (As we'll discuss in Chapter 19, this explanation is somewhat oversimplified, but it captures the basic point that our *observable* universe may not include the *entire* universe.)

It is amazing to realize that any "snapshot" of a distant galaxy or cluster of galaxies is a picture of both space and time. For example, the Great Galaxy in Andromeda, also known as M31, lies about 2.5 million light-years from Earth. Figure 1.4, therefore, is a picture of how M31 looked about 2.5 million years ago, when early humans were first walking the Earth. Moreover, the diameter of M31 is about 100,000 light-years, so light from the far side of the galaxy required 100,000 years more to reach us than light from the near side. Thus, the picture of M31 shows

## Common Misconceptions: Light-Years

A recent advertisement illustrated a common misconception by claiming "It will be light-years before anyone builds a better product." This advertisement makes no sense, because light-years are a unit of *distance*, not a unit of time. If you are unsure whether the term *light-years* is being used correctly, try testing the statement by remembering that 1 light-year is approximately 10 trillion kilometers, or 6 trillion miles. The advertisement then reads "It will be 6 trillion miles before anyone builds a better product," which clearly does not make sense.

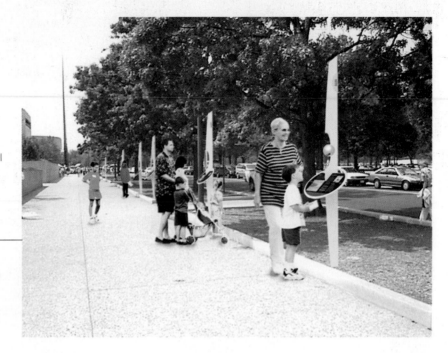

**FIGURE 1.5** This artist's rendering shows the locations of the Sun and inner planets in the *Voyage* scale model solar system on the National Mall in Washington, DC (opening Fall 2001). Voyage was created for the National Mall and other locations around the world by the Challenger Center for Space Science Education, the Smithsonian Institution, and NASA.

100,000 years of time. This single photograph captured light that left the near side of the galaxy some 100,000 years later than the light it captured from the far side. When we study the universe, it is impossible to separate space and time.

## 1.2 The Scale of the Universe

We've given some numbers in our description of the size and age of the universe, but these numbers probably have little meaning for you—after all, they are literally astronomical. In this section, we will try to give meaning to incredible cosmic distances and times.

### A Walking Tour of the Solar System

One of the best ways to develop perspective on cosmic sizes and distances is to start with a scale model of our solar system. Let's imagine a walk through a model with a scale of 1 to 10 billion, such as the Voyage scale model solar system on the National Mall in Washington, DC (Figure 1.5); that is, diameters and distances in the model are *one ten-billionth* ($10^{-10}$) of actual diameters and distances in the solar system (Table 1.1). Figure 1.6 shows the sizes of the Sun and the planets on this scale.

Pages 12–23 take you on a virtual walk through a model solar system. Each page represents one stop, starting from the Sun and continuing to each of the planets. We also include stops for asteroids and comets. After you complete the 12-page tour, be sure that you have noticed the following key ideas about the scale of the solar system:

- The Sun is roughly the size of a grapefruit, while the planets range in size from dust-speck-size Pluto to marble-size Jupiter. Earth is about the size of a pinhead.

- The inner planets (Mercury, Venus, Earth, Mars) are all located within a couple of dozen steps of the Sun, with the Earth located 15 meters from the Sun. The outer planets (Jupiter, Saturn, Uranus, Neptune, Pluto) are spread much farther apart, with Pluto located about 600 meters (just over $\frac{1}{3}$ mile) from the Sun. Walking the full length of the model would take about 10 minutes, not including stops.

- Perhaps the most striking feature of the solar system is its *emptiness*. Although our model shows the planets laid out in a straight line from the Sun, a better model would show their orbits extending all the way around the Sun. Such a model would require an area measuring well over a kilometer (0.6 mile) on a side, equivalent to more than 300 football fields! Aside from the grapefruit-size Sun at the center, all we would find in the rest of this area would be the nine planets and their moons, plus scattered asteroids and comets—no object on this scale is larger than marble-size Jupiter, and most are far smaller than pinhead-size Earth.

**Table 1.1  Solar System Sizes and Distances, 1-to-10-Billion Scale**

| Object | Real Diameter | Real Distance from Sun (average) | Model Diameter | Model Distance from Sun |
|---|---|---|---|---|
| Sun | 1,392,500 km | — | 139 mm = 13.9 cm | — |
| Mercury | 4,880 km | 57.9 million km | 0.5 mm | 6 m |
| Venus | 12,100 km | 108.2 million km | 1.2 mm | 11 m |
| Earth | 12,760 km | 149.6 million km | 1.3 mm | 15 m |
| Mars | 6,790 km | 227.9 million km | 0.7 mm | 23 m |
| Jupiter | 143,000 km | 778.3 million km | 14.3 mm | 78 m |
| Saturn | 120,000 km | 1,427 million km | 12.0 mm | 143 m |
| Uranus | 52,000 km | 2,870 million km | 5.2 mm | 287 m |
| Neptune | 48,400 km | 4,497 million km | 4.8 mm | 450 m |
| Pluto | 2,260 km | 5,900 million km | 0.2 mm | 590 m |

If you are having difficulty visualizing the model, it's easy to make your own model. Use a grapefruit or similar-size object to represent the Sun and a pinhead to represent the Earth. In a long hallway or outdoors, place your Sun on a chair or table and place your tiny Earth about 15 meters from your Sun. Once you have these objects in place, you may find it easier to visualize the sizes and locations for the rest of the planets (using the information in Table 1.1).

**TIME OUT TO THINK** *Hold your pinhead-size model Earth in your hand and look toward your grapefruit-size model Sun 15 meters away. Aside from the tiny Earth that you hold, there is nowhere else in the solar system—and nowhere we yet know of in the universe—where humans can survive outside the artificial environment of a spacecraft or spacesuit. Does holding the model Earth affect your perspective on human existence in any way? Does it affect your perspective on the Earth? Explain.*

*(continued on p. 24, following the 12-page virtual tour)*

**FIGURE 1.6** The sizes of the Sun and the planets on the 1-to-10-billion scale.

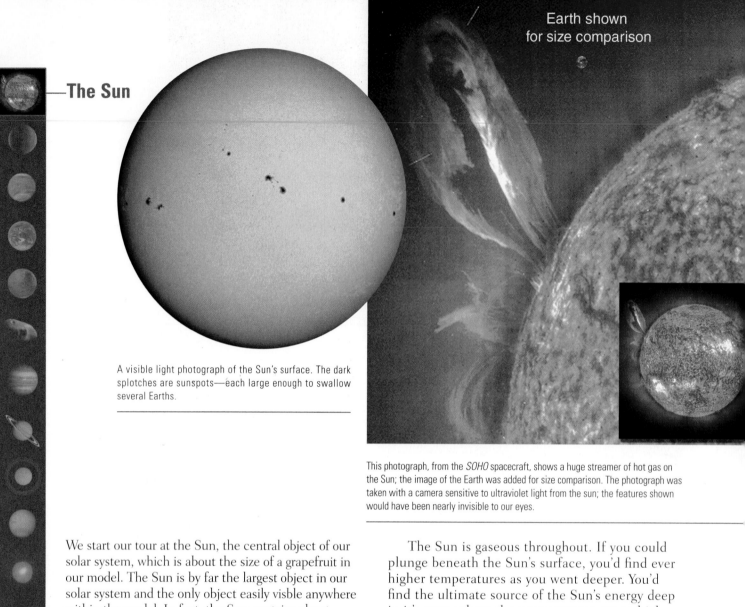

# The Sun

A visible light photograph of the Sun's surface. The dark splotches are sunspots—each large enough to swallow several Earths.

This photograph, from the *SOHO* spacecraft, shows a huge streamer of hot gas on the Sun; the image of the Earth was added for size comparison. The photograph was taken with a camera sensitive to ultraviolet light from the sun; the features shown would have been nearly invisible to our eyes.

We start our tour at the Sun, the central object of our solar system, which is about the size of a grapefruit in our model. The Sun is by far the largest object in our solar system and the only object easily visble anywhere within the model. In fact, the Sun contains about 99.9% of the solar system's total mass; that is, it out-weighs everything else in the solar system combined by a factor of one thousand.

Although the Sun's surface looks solid in photographs, it is a roiling sea of hot (about 6000°C, or 10,000°F) hydrogen and helium gas. The surface is speckled with sun spots that appear dark in photographs only because they are slightly cooler than their surroundings. Solar storms sometimes send streamers of hot gas soaring far above the surface and can disrupt radio communications on Earth and disable orbiting satellites.

The Sun is gaseous throughout. If you could plunge beneath the Sun's surface, you'd find ever higher temperatures as you went deeper. You'd find the ultimate source of the Sun's energy deep in it's core, where the temperatures are so high that the Sun becomes a natural nuclear-fusion power plant. Each second, fusion transforms about 600 million tons of the Sun's hydrogen into 596 million tons of helium; the "missing" 4 million tons becomes energy in accord with Einstein's famous equation $E = mc^2$, which we will discuss in Chapter 4. Despite losing 4 million tons of mass each second, the Sun contains so much hydrogen that it has shone steadily for almost 5 billion years already and will continue to shine for some 5 billion years to come.

This map shows the Sun's location in the Voyage scale model solar system on the National Mall in Washington, DC. The Sun itself is about the size of a grapefruit on this scale.

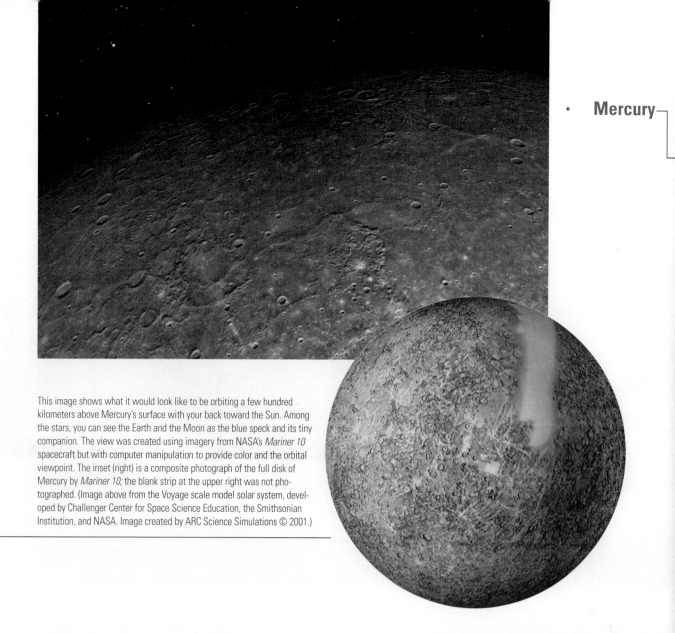

This image shows what it would look like to be orbiting a few hundred kilometers above Mercury's surface with your back toward the Sun. Among the stars, you can see the Earth and the Moon as the blue speck and its tiny companion. The view was created using imagery from NASA's *Mariner 10* spacecraft but with computer manipulation to provide color and the orbital viewpoint. The inset (right) is a composite photograph of the full disk of Mercury by *Mariner 10;* the blank strip at the upper right was not photographed. (Image above from the Voyage scale model solar system, developed by Challenger Center for Space Science Education, the Smithsonian Institution, and NASA. Image created by ARC Science Simulations © 2001.)

The innermost planet, Mercury, lies just a few steps from the model Sun. Mercury is the smallest planet except for Pluto, and in our model it is only about as big as the period at the end of this sentence. Mercury is a desolate, cratered world with no active volcanoes, no earthquakes, no wind, no rain, and no life. Because there is virtually no air to scatter sunlight or color the sky, you could see stars even in the daytime if you stood on Mercury with your back toward the Sun. You wouldn't want to stay long, however, because the ground on Mercury's day side is nearly as hot as hot coals (about 425°C). Nighttime would not be much more comfortable: With no atmosphere to retain heat during the long nights (which last about 3 months), temperatures plummet below −150°C (about −240°F)—far colder than Antartica in winter.

This map shows Mercury's location in the Voyage scale model solar system on the National Mall in Washington, DC. The dot at the top of the page (next to title) shows Mercury's size on the scale.

# Venus

This image shows a realistic picture of the surface of Venus. The surface topography is based on actual data from NASA's *Magellan* spacecraft, and the colors represent what scientists believe our eyes would see on Venus. The inset (left) shows the full disk of Venus as photographed by NASA's *Pioneer Venus Orbiter*. This photograph was taken with cameras sensitive to ultraviolet light; with visible light, cloud features cannot be distinguished from the general haze. (Image above from the Voyage scale model solar system, developed by Challenger Center for Space Science Education, the Smithsonian Institution, and NASA. Image by David P. Anderson, Southern Methodist University © 2001.)

We find the second planet from the Sun, Venus, just a few steps beyond Mercury in our model. Because Venus and the Earth are nearly identical in size—both pinheads in the model solar system—Venus is sometimes called our sister planet.

Venus is covered in dense clouds, and because it is not much closer to the Sun than the Earth science fiction writers once speculated that Venus might be a lush, tropical paradise. We now know that an extreme *greenhouse effect* bakes its surface to an incredible 450°C (about 850°F) and traps heat so effectively that nighttime offers no relief—day and night, Venus is hotter than a pizza oven. All the while, the thick atmosphere bears down on the surface with a pressure equivalent to that nearly a kilometer (0.6 mile) beneath the ocean surface on Earth. Besides the crushing pressure and searing temperature, a visitor to Venus would feel the corrosive effects of sulfuric acid and other toxic chemicals in its atmosphere. Far from being a beautiful sister planet to Earth, Venus resembles a traditional view of hell.

This map shows Venus's location in the Voyage scale model solar system on the National Mall in Washington, DC. The dot at the top of the page (next to title) shows Venus's size on the scale.

Earth—

This image, computer generated from satellite data, shows the striking contrast between the daylight and nighttime hemispheres of Earth. The day side reveals little evidence of human presence, but at night our presence is revealed by the lights of human activity (mostly from cities as well as from agricultural, oil, and gas fires). (From the Voyage scale model solar system, developed by Challenger Center for Space Science Education, the Smithsonian Institution, and NASA. Image created by ARC Science Simulations © 2001.)

This famous photograph shows astronaut Buzz Aldrin standing on the Moon in July 1969 during the Apollo 11 mission. The reflection in his visor shows Neil Armstrong and the lunar module (spacecraft), along with some scientific equipment. Aldrin and Armstrong were the first of 12 humans who walked on the Moon; Armstrong took the first step, saying, "That's one small step for [a] man, one giant leap for mankind."

Beyond Venus and only about 15 meters from the model Sun, we find our home planet. Its tiny size in a big solar system reminds us that Earth is a rare and precious oasis of life. It is the only planet with oxygen for us to breathe and ozone to shield us from deadly solar radiation. Only on Earth does water flow freely to nurture life. And temperatures are ideal for life because Earth's atmosphere contains just enough carbon dioxide and water vapor to maintain a moderate greenhouse effect.

Despite its small size, Earth is striking in it beauty. Blue oceans cover nearly three-fourths of the surface, broken by the continental land masses and scattered islands. The polar caps are white with snow and ice, and white clouds are scattered above the surface. At night, the glow of artificial lights clearly reveals the presence of an intelligent civilization.

Earth is the first planet on our tour with a moon. On our model scale, the Moon is barely visible speck that orbits the Earth at a distance of about 4 centimeters. Thus, your thumb could easily cover both the Earth and the Moon. The Moon is cratered and desolate, much like Mercury. though it has its own interesting history and geology. It is also the only world besides Earth on which humans have ever stepped. From July 1969 through December 1972, NASA's Apollo program successfully landed 12 people (six crews of two) on the lunar surface.

This map shows Earth's location in the Voyage scale model solar system on the National Mall in Washington, DC. The dot at the top of the page (next to title) shows Earth's size on the scale.

# Mars

A few more steps take us to the model Mars, which is about half the size (diameter) of Earth. Mars has two tiny moons, Phobos and Deimos, but they are so small as to be microscopic on our 1-to-10-billion scale.

Mars is a world of wonders, with extinct volcanoes that dwarf the largest mountains on Earth, a great canyon that runs nearly one-fifth of the way around the planet, and polar caps made of frozen carbon dioxide ("dry ice") and water ice. Although Mars is frozen today, the presence of dried-up riverbeds and rock-strewn floodplains offers clear evidence that Mars was warm and wet sometime in the distant past. Thus, Mars may once have been hospitable for life, though its wet era probably ended at least 3 billion years ago.

Mars looks almost Earth-like in photographs taken by spacecraft on its surface, but you wouldn't want to visit without a space suit. The air pressure is far less than that on top of Mount Everest, the temperature is usually well below freezing, the trace amounts of oxygen would not be nearly enough to breathe, and the lack of atmospheric ozone would leave you exposed to deadly ultraviolet radiation from the Sun.

Mars is the most studied planet besides Earth. More than a dozen spacecraft have flown past, orbited, or landed on Mars, and plans are in the works for many more. We may even send humans to Mars within our lifetime. Overturning rocks in ancient riverbeds or chipping away at ice in the polar caps, explorers will search for fossil evidence of past life—and perhaps even find a few places where microbes survive today.

The surface of Mars, photographed from NASA's *Pathfinder* lander in 1997; part of the lander is visible in the foreground. The little rover called *Sojourner* is in the upper right, studying a rock that scientists dubbed Yogi. The inset (right) shows the full disk of Mars; the "gash" going horizontally across the center is the giant canyon known as Valles Marineris.

This map shows Mars's location in the Voyage scale model solar system on the National Mall in Washington, DC. The dot at the top of the page (next to title) shows Mars's size on the scale.

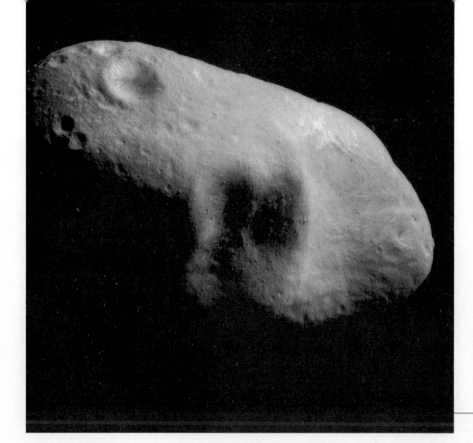

## The Asteroid Belt

The asteroid Eros, photographed by the *NEAR* spacecraft that orbited it during 2000. At the end of its mission in February 2001, NASA engineers guided *NEAR* to a soft landing on Eros.

As we pass by Mars, we notice one of the most important characteristics of our solar system. In contrast to the few steps separating the four inner planets in the model solar system, the walk from Mars to Jupiter covers more than 50 meters—over half the length of a football field. As we look ahead, we see that increasingly large distances separate the remaining planets. Thus, the solar system has two major regions: the **inner solar system**, where Mercury, Venus, Earth, and Mars orbit the Sun relatively closely, and the **outer solar system**, where the remaining planets are widely separated. In between we find the **asteroid belt**, where thousands of asteroids orbit the Sun.

Asteroids are chunks of rock and metal left over from the formation of our solar system—bits and pieces that never became part of a moon or a planet. The largest asteroid, Ceres, is about 1,000 kilometers (600 miles) across. But most asteroids are far smaller and would be microscopic on our 1-to-10-billion scale. Despite their large number, the total mass of the asteroids is less than that of any of the inner planets. The average distance between asteroids is millions of kilometers—so the real asteroid belt does not at all resemble the crowded rock fields depicted in many science fiction films.

Not all asteroids are confined to the asteroid belt, and those that orbit elsewhere in the solar system may collide with moons or planets; impact craters are the scars of such collisions. (Impact craters may also result from comet collisions.) Asteroid impacts may have played an important role in the development of life on Earth. For example, as we'll discuss in Chapter 12, an asteroid impact may have been responsible for the extinction of the dinosaurs some 65 million years ago. Smaller pieces of asteroids fall to the Earth quite often; we call these fragments *meteorites*.

This map shows the Asteroid Belt's location in the Voyage scale model solar system on the National Mall in Washington, DC. Individual asteroids are too small to see on this scale.

# Jupiter

This image shows a realistic view of what it would look like to be orbiting near Jupiter's moon Io as Jupiter comes into view displaying its Great Red Spot. The extraordinarily dark rings discovered in the Voyager missions are exaggerated to make them visible. This computer visualization was created using data from both NASA's Voyager and Galileo missions. (From the Voyage scale model solar system, developed by Challenger Center for Space Science Education, the Smithsonian Institution, and NASA. Image created by ARC Science Simulations © 2001.)

The model Jupiter is the size of a marble, making it a giant in comparison to the planets of the inner solar system. Indeed, Jupiter is so different from the planets of the inner solar system that we must create an entirely new mental image of the term *planet*. Its mass is more than 300 times that of the Earth, and its volume is more than 1,000 times that of the Earth. Its most famous feature—a long-lived storm called the Great Red Spot—is itself large enough to swallow two or three Earths. Like the Sun, Jupiter is made primarily of hydrogen and helium and has no solid surface. If you plunged deep into Jupiter, you would be crushed by the increasing gas pressure long before you ever reached its core.

Jupiter reigns over at least 28 moons and a thin set of rings (too faint to be seen in most photographs). The four largest moons—Io, Europa, Ganymede, and Callisto (often called the *Galilean moons* because they were discovered by Galileo)—are fascinating worlds in their own right and are easily visible on the scale of the model solar system. Io is the most volcanically active place in the solar system. Europa's icy crust probably hides a subsurface ocean of liquid water, making Europa a promising place to search for life. Indeed, as we'll discuss in Chapter 11, the moons of Jupiter and the other outer planets are at least as interesting as the planets themselves.

This map shows Jupiter's location in the Voyage scale model solar system on the National Mall in Washington, DC. The image at the top of the page (next to title) shows Jupiter's size on the scale.

**Saturn**

This computer simulation, built upon imagery from the *Voyager 1* mission, recreates the striking view from the space-craft at somewhat higher detail. We see the shadow of the rings on Saturn's sunlit face, and the rings become lost in Saturn's shadow on the night side. (From the Voyage scale model solar system, developed by Challenger Center for Space Science Education, the Smithsonian Institution, and NASA. Image created by ARC Science Simulations © 2001.)

The distance from Jupiter to Saturn is about 65 meters in our model, or nearly three-fourths the length of a football field; notice how much longer this walk takes than the few steps between the planets of the inner solar system. Saturn is only slightly smaller than Jupiter in size but is considerably less massive (about one-third Jupiter's mass) because it is less dense. Like Jupiter, Saturn is made mostly of hydrogen and helium and has no solid surface.

Saturn is famous for its spectacular rings. Although all four of the giant outer planets have rings, only Saturn's can be seen easily through a small telescope on Earth. The rings may look solid from a distance, but this appearance is deceiving. If you could wander into the rings, you'd find yourself surrounded by countless individual particles of rock and ice, rang-ing in size from dust grains to city blocks. Each parti-cle orbits Saturn like a tiny moon.

At least 30 moons orbit Saturn. Most are far too small to be visible in our model solar system (though they are still considerably larger than the ring parti-cles). But Saturn's largest moon, Titan, is bigger than the planet Mercury and is blanketed by a thick atmo-sphere. On Titan's surface, you'd find an atmospheric pressure slightly greater than that on Earth, and you would inhale air with roughly the same nitrogen con-tent as air on Earth. However, you'd need to bring your own oxygen, and you'd certainly want a warm spacesuit to protect yourself against frigid outside temperatures. NASA's *Cassini* spacecraft is currently on the way to Saturn; it will drop a probe to Titan's surface after it arrives in 2004.

This map shows the Saturn's location in the Voyage scale model solar system on the National Mall in Washington, DC. The image at the top of the page (next to title) shows Saturn's size on this scale.

19

# Uranus

To go from Saturn to Uranus in our model, we must walk as far as we've walked in our entire tour so far, again illustrating the vast distances that separate planets in the outer solar system. Uranus is much smaller than either Jupiter or Saturn, but it is still much larger than Earth. It is made largely of hydrogen, helium, and hydrogen compounds such as methane ($CH_4$); the latter gives Uranus its pale blue-green color. Like the other giants of the outer solar system, it lacks a solid surface. At least 21 moons orbit Uranus, along with a set of rings similar to those of Saturn but much darker and more difficult to see.

The entire Uranus system—planet, rings, and moon orbits—is tipped on its side compared to the rest of the planets. This unusual orientation may be the result of a cataclysmic collision suffered by Uranus as it was forming some 4.6 billion years ago. It also is responsible for the most extreme pattern of seasons on any planet. If you lived on a platform floating in Uranus's atmosphere near the north pole, you'd have continuous daylight for half of each orbit, or 42 years. Then, after a very gradual sunset, you'd be plunged into a 42-year-long night.

Uranus was the first "discovered" planet—all the planets closer to the Sun are easily visible to the naked eye and thus were known to all ancient cultures. English astronomer William Herschel discovered Uranus in 1781. He originally suggested naming the planet *Georgium Sidus,* Latin for "George's star," in honor of his patron, King George III. Fortunately, the idea of "Planet George" never caught on. Instead, many eighteenth- and nineteenth-century astronomers referred to the new planet as "Herschel." The modern name Uranus, after the mythological father of Saturn, was first suggested by one of Herschel's contemporaries, astronomer Johann Bode, and was generally accepted by the mid-nineteenth century.

This image shows a view from a vantage point high above Uranus's moon Ariel. Several other moons are visible in the image, and the thin vertical line is the ring system (actually too dark to see from this vantage point). Computer simulation based upon data from NASA's *Voyager 2* mission. (From the Voyage scale model solar system, developed by Challenger Center for Space Science Education, the Smithsonian Institution, and NASA. Image created by ARC Science Simulations © 2001.)

This map shows Uranus's location in the Voyage scale model solar system on the National Mall in Washington, DC. The image at the top of the page (next to title) shows Uranus's size on the scale.

From Uranus, we must cross a distance equivalent to more than one and a half football fields to reach Neptune in our model. Neptune looks nearly like a twin of Uranus, with very similar size and composition, although it is more strikingly blue. Neptune has rings and at least eight moons. Its largest moon, Triton, is unusual both in having a "backward" orbit around Neptune (orbiting in a direction opposite to Neptune's rotation) and in having active sites that spew plumes of gas into the sky. The backward orbit leads astronomers to believe that Triton originally may not have been a moon but instead was captured by Neptune sometime after it formed.

Neptune's discovery was a triumph for the theory of gravity, developed by Isaac Newton in the late 1600s. By the mid-nineteenth century, careful observations of Uranus had shown its orbit to be slightly inconsistent with that predicted by Newton's theory of gravity. In the early 1840s, Englishman John Couch Adams suggested that the inconsistency could be explained by a previously unseen "eighth planet" orbiting the Sun beyond Uranus. By making calculations based on Newton's theory, he even predicted the location of the planet and urged a telescopic search. Unfortunately, Adams was a student at the time and was unable to convince British astronomers to carry out the search.

In the summer of 1846, French astronomer Urbain Leverrier made similar calculations independently. He sent a letter to Johann Galle, of the Berlin Observatory, suggesting a search for the eighth planet. On the night of September 23, 1846, Galle pointed his telescope to the position suggested by Leverrier. There, within 1° of its predicted position, he saw the planet Neptune. Hence, Neptune's discovery truly was made by mathematics and physics and was merely confirmed with a telescope.

This map shows Neptune's location in the Voyage scale model solar system on the National Mall in Washington, DC. The image at the top of the page (next to title) shows Neptune's size on this scale.

21

# Pluto ·

Pluto and Charon, as photographed by the Hubble Space Telescope. Because no spacecraft has been to Pluto, we do not yet have clear pictures of this tiny planet or its moon.

At its average distance from the Sun, the model Pluto lies another 140 meters beyond Neptune. The grapefruit-size Sun, more than a half kilometer away, appears tiny from here. It is easy to imagine that the world of Pluto must be cold and dark.

One look at the model Pluto, along with its moon Charon, shows it to be out of character with the rest of the planets. Pluto is neither large and gaseous like the other planets of the outer solar system nor rocky like the planets of the inner solar system. Instead, it is very small—the smallest planet by far—and is made mostly of ices. Pluto's orbit is also unusual. Whereas all the other planets orbit the Sun along nearly circular paths and in nearly the same plane, Pluto's orbit is highly elongated and substantially inclined relative to the orbits of the other planets. Pluto actually comes closer to the Sun than Neptune for 20 years of each 284-year orbit. The last such period ended in 1999, so the next won't begin until 2263.

Although Pluto's characteristics make it a "misfit" among the planets, they give it much in common with the only other inhabitants of the outskirts of the solar system: the balls of ice and dust we call *comets*. In the past decade or so, astronomers have discovered many other Pluto-like objects, though none quite as large as Pluto. Indeed, it now seems likely that Pluto is merely the largest (or one of the largest) among thousands of "giant comets" that orbit the Sun beyond Neptune. Some astronomers have gone so far as to suggest demoting Pluto from its status as a planet, but most favor keeping its popular title as the ninth planet—a title it has held since its discovery in 1930 by Clyde Tombaugh.

This map shows Pluto's location in the Voyage scale model solar system on the National Mall in Washington, DC. The dot at the top of the page (next to title) shows Pluto's size on the scale.

22

## Realm of the Comets

Comet Hale–Bopp, photographed over Boulder, Colorado, during its appearance in 1997.

After Pluto's discovery, many people continued searching the skies in hopes of discovering a tenth planet, sometimes called "Planet X." Given the sensitivity with which our telescopes now scan the skies, it is unlikely that another large planet orbits our Sun (though other Pluto-size objects are possible). Thus, Pluto's orbit marks the end of the realm of the planets. However, the most numerous objects in the solar system still lie ahead: comets.

You are probably familiar with the occasional appearance of a comet in the inner solar system, where the heat of the Sun evaporates some of its ice and it grows a long, beautiful tail. But with very few exceptions, nearly all comets spend nearly their entire lifetime in the extreme outer reaches of the solar system. Our present technology does not allow us to detect comets when they are very far from the Sun. However, to account for the frequency with which we see comets in the inner solar system, astronomers have calculated that there must be something like a trillion ($10^{12}$) comets inhabiting the outskirts of our solar system.

As we will discuss in Chapter 12, the realm of the comets probably consists of two vast regions of space. The region containing the Pluto-like "giant comets"—called the *Kuiper belt*—begins near the orbit of Neptune and probably continues out to several times this distance. The comets in this region have orbits that lie close to the plane of planetary orbits and go around the Sun in the same direction as the planets. The second and much larger region—called the *Oort cloud*—may extend more than one-fourth of the way to the nearest stars. Comets in this region have orbits that are inclined at all angles to the plane of planetary orbits. Thus, the Oort cloud would look roughly spherical in shape if we could see it. But it is so vast that, even if it has a trillion comets, each comet would typically be separated from the next by more than a billion kilometers.

Comets and asteroids are discussed together in the Voyage scale model solar system on the National Mall in Washington, DC. Most comets actually reside well beyond the orbit of Pluto and are too small to see on this scale.

### Onward to the Stars

The nearest star system to our own, called Alpha Centauri, contains three stars (Figure 1.7). The largest is about the same size as our Sun—a grapefruit on the 1-to-10-billion scale. After completing the less than 1 kilometer walk from the Sun to Pluto, how much farther would we have to walk to reach Alpha Centauri?

**TIME OUT TO THINK** *Before reading further, make a guess. Look at the grapefruit-size model Sun that you placed nearby. Where do you think you'll find the next grapefruit-size star? Within a few blocks? Within your city? Farther away?*

To answer this question, recall that a light-year is about 10 trillion kilometers, which becomes 1,000 kilometers on the 1-to-10-billion scale (10 trillion ÷ 10 billion = 1,000). Alpha Centauri's real distance, about 4.4 light-years, therefore becomes about 4,400 kilometers (2,700 miles) on this scale—roughly equivalent to the distance from New York to Los Angeles. In other words, looking at the largest star of Alpha Centauri from the Earth is equivalent to looking from New York at a very bright grapefruit in Los Angeles (neglecting the problems introduced by the curvature of the Earth). All other stars in our night sky are even farther away. No wonder the stars appear as mere points of light in the sky even when viewed through powerful telescopes.

Now, consider the difficulty of seeing *planets* orbiting other stars. Imagine looking from New York and trying to see a pinhead-size model Earth orbiting a grapefruit-size model Sun in Los Angeles. You probably won't be surprised to learn that we have not yet discovered Earth-size planets around other stars. Indeed, the bigger surprise may be that we *have* discovered dozens of extra-solar planets (planets around other stars), though most are closer in size to Jupiter than to Earth [Section 8.7]. With planet-detecting technology improving rapidly, we will probably know whether Earth-size planets orbit nearby stars within a couple of decades.

Although telescopic technology allows us to learn much about the stars, travel to the stars is another story. Consider the *Voyager 2* spacecraft. Launched in 1977, *Voyager 2* flew by Jupiter in 1979, Saturn in 1981, Uranus in 1986, and Neptune in 1989. (*Voyager*'s trajectory did not take it near Pluto.) *Voyager 2* is now bound for the stars at a speed near 50,000 kilometers per hour—about as fast as anything ever built by humans. But even at this speed, *Voyager 2* would take about 100,000 years to reach Alpha Centauri if it were headed in that direction, which it's not. Clearly, convenient interstellar travel remains well beyond our present technology. (We discuss prospects for interstellar travel in Chapter S5.)

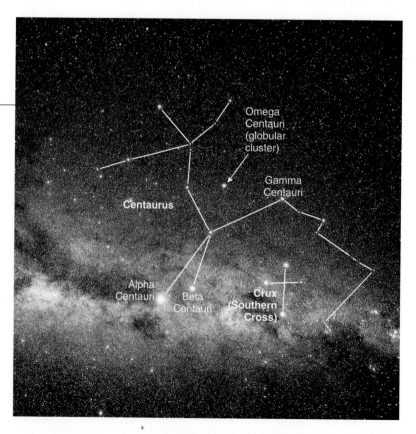

**FIGURE 1.7** Stars of the constellation Centaurus, including Alpha Centauri, which is visible only from tropical and southern latitudes. Stars are so far away that they should appear as mere points of light; photographs make them seem to have a measurable size only because of the limitations of cameras (brighter stars appear larger than dimmer stars because they are overexposed). In fact, despite being separated by about the distance between the Sun and Uranus, the two largest stars in the Alpha Centauri system look like a single point of light in this photograph. (The nearest of the three stars, Proxima Centauri, is too dim to see with the naked eye.)

## The Milky Way Galaxy

The vast separation between our solar system and Alpha Centauri is typical of the separations among star systems here in the outskirts of the Milky Way Galaxy. Thus, the 1-to-10-billion scale is useless for modeling even just a few dozen of the nearest stars, because they could not all be spaced properly on the surface of the Earth. Visualizing the entire galaxy requires a new scale.

Let's further reduce our solar system scale by a factor of 1 billion (making it a scale of 1 to $10^{19}$). On this new scale, each light-year becomes 1 millimeter. For example, the 4.4-light-year separation between the Sun and Alpha Centauri becomes just 4.4 millimeters on this scale—smaller than the width of your little finger. Aside from the fact that it makes the stars themselves become microscopic (about the size of individual atoms), this new scale makes it easy to visualize the Milky Way Galaxy. Its 100,000-light-year diameter becomes 100 meters on this scale, or about the length of a football field.

**TIME OUT TO THINK** *Visualize (or go to) a football field with our scale model of the galaxy centered over midfield. Standing on the 20-yard line puts you at about the correct location for our solar system. Hold your thumb and forefinger about 4 millimeters apart to represent the separation between the Sun and Alpha Centauri , and then remember what you learned about the separation between stars from the 1-to-10-billion solar system scale. How do these scale models affect your perspective on our place in the universe?*

Another way to put the galaxy into perspective is to consider its number of stars—more than 100 billion. Imagine that tonight you are having difficulty falling asleep (perhaps because you are contemplating the scale of the universe). Instead of counting sheep, you decide to count stars. If you are able to count about one star each second, on average, how long would it take you to count 100 billion stars in the Milky Way? Clearly, the answer is 100 billion ($10^{11}$) seconds. But how long is that? Amazingly, 100 billion seconds turns out to be more than 3,000 years. (You can confirm this by dividing 100 billion by the number of seconds in 1 year.) Thus, you would need thousands of years just to *count* the stars in the Milky Way Galaxy, and this assumes you never take a break—no sleeping, no eating, and absolutely no dying!

## Beyond the Milky Way

As incredible as the scale of our galaxy may seem, the Milky Way is only one of at least 100 billion galaxies in the observable universe. Just as it would take thousands of years to count the stars in the

Milky Way, it would also take thousands of years to count all the galaxies. Think for a moment about the total number of stars in all these galaxies. Assuming an average of 100 billion stars in each of these 100 billion galaxies, the total number of stars in the observable universe is roughly

$$100 \text{ billion} \times 100 \text{ billion} = 10^{11} \times 10^{11} = 10^{22}$$

This number, which we write out as

$$10,000,000,000,000,000,000,000$$

is so large that it does not even have a common name. How big is it?

Visit a beach. Run your hands through the fine-grained sand. Try to imagine counting every one of the tiny grains of sand as they slip through your fingers (Figure 1.8). Then imagine counting every grain of sand on the beach where you are sitting. Next think about counting *all* the grains of dry sand on *all* the beaches everywhere on Earth. The number you would count would be less than the number of stars in the observable universe.

## The Scale of Time

Now that we have developed some perspective on the scale of space, we can do the same for the scale of time. Imagine the entire history of the universe, from the Big Bang to the present, compressed into a single year. We can represent this history with a *cosmic calendar*, on which the Big Bang takes place at the first instant of January 1 and the present day is just before the stroke of midnight on December 31 (Figure 1.9). If we assume that the universe is about 12 billion years old (recall that we think the age is between 12 billion and 16 billion years), then each month on the cosmic calendar represents about 1 billion years.

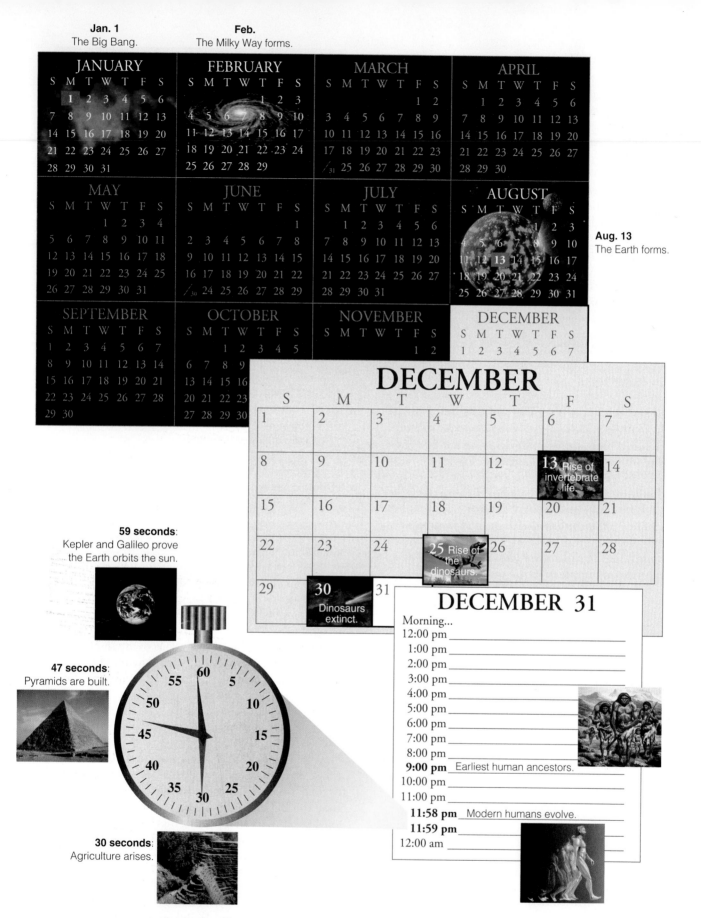

**Jan. 1**
The Big Bang.

**Feb.**
The Milky Way forms.

**Aug. 13**
The Earth forms.

## DECEMBER

| S | M | T | W | T | F | S |
|---|---|---|---|---|---|---|
| 1 | 2 | 3 | 4 | 5 | 6 | 7 |
| 8 | 9 | 10 | 11 | 12 | **13** Rise of invertebrate life. | 14 |
| 15 | 16 | 17 | 18 | 19 | 20 | 21 |
| 22 | 23 | 24 | **25** Rise of the dinosaurs. | 26 | 27 | 28 |
| 29 | **30** Dinosaurs extinct. | 31 | | | | |

**59 seconds**: Kepler and Galileo prove the Earth orbits the sun.

**47 seconds**: Pyramids are built.

**30 seconds**: Agriculture arises.

### DECEMBER 31

Morning...
12:00 pm _____
1:00 pm _____
2:00 pm _____
3:00 pm _____
4:00 pm _____
5:00 pm _____
6:00 pm _____
7:00 pm _____
8:00 pm _____
**9:00 pm** Earliest human ancestors.
10:00 pm _____
11:00 pm _____
**11:58 pm** Modern humans evolve.
**11:59 pm** _____
12:00 am _____

**FIGURE 1.9** The cosmic calendar compresses the history of the universe into 1 year; this version assumes that the universe is 12 billion years old, so that each month represents about 1 billion years. It is only within the last few seconds of the last day that human civilization has taken shape. (This version of the cosmic calendar is adapted from a version created by Carl Sagan.)

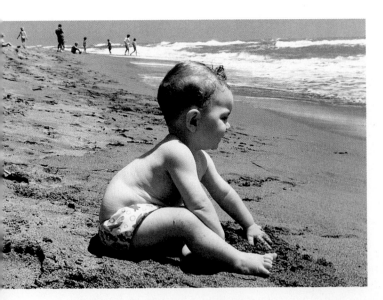

**FIGURE 1.8** The number of stars in the universe is larger than the total number of grains of sand on all the beaches on Earth.

On this scale, the Milky Way Galaxy may have formed sometime in February. Many generations of stars lived and died in the subsequent cosmic months, enriching the galaxy with the heavier elements from which we and the Earth are made. Not until about August 13, which represents a time 4.6 billion years ago, did our solar system form from a cloud of gas and dust in the Milky Way.

No one knows exactly when the earliest life arose on Earth, but it certainly was within the first billion years, or by mid-September on the cosmic calendar. For most of the Earth's history, living organisms remained relatively primitive and microscopic in size. Larger invertebrate life arose only about 600 million years ago, or about December 13 on the cosmic calendar. The age of the dinosaurs began shortly after midnight on Christmas (December 25) on the cosmic calendar. The dinosaurs vanished abruptly around 1:00 A.M. on December 30 (65 million years ago in real time), probably due to the impact of an asteroid or comet [Section 12.6].

With the dinosaurs gone, small furry mammals inherited the Earth. Some 60 million years later, or around 9:00 P.M. on December 31 of the cosmic calendar, the earliest hominids (human ancestors) walked upright. Most of the major events of human history took place within the final seconds of the final minute of the final day on the cosmic calendar. Agriculture arose about 30 seconds ago. The Egyptians built the pyramids about 13 seconds ago. It was only about 1 second ago on the cosmic calendar that Kepler and Galileo first proved that the Earth orbits the Sun. The average-age college student was born less than 0.1 second ago, around 11:59:59.9 P.M.

on December 31. On this scale of cosmic time, the human species is the youngest of infants, and a human lifetime is a mere blink of an eye.

**TIME OUT TO THINK** *Suppose the universe is 16 billion years old rather than the 12 billion years assumed in our cosmic calendar. How would this change the cosmic calendar? Would the changes affect the general point that human existence has been brief on the scale of cosmic time?*

## 1.3 Spaceship Earth

Now that we have discussed the scale of space and of time, the next step in our "big picture" overview is understanding motion in the universe. Wherever you are as you read this book, you probably have the feeling that you're "just sitting here." Nothing could be further from the truth. In fact, you are being spun in circles as the Earth rotates, you are racing around the Sun in the Earth's orbit, and you are careening through the cosmos in the Milky Way galaxy. In the words of noted inventor and philosopher R. Buckminster Fuller (1895–1983), you are a traveler on *spaceship Earth*.

### Rotation and Revolution

The Earth **rotates** on its axis once each day. (The axis is a line joining the North and South Poles and passing through the center of the Earth.) As a result, you are whirling around the Earth's axis at a speed of 1,000 kilometers per hour (600 miles per hour) or more—faster than most airplanes travel (Figure 1.10). It is this rotation that makes the Sun and the stars appear to make their daily circles around the sky. You see sunrise when the rotating Earth first allows you to glimpse the Sun in the east, noon when your location faces directly toward the Sun, and sunset just as your location rotates to the Earth's night side where the Sun is hidden from view. (Because the Earth orbits the Sun at the same time that it rotates, our 24-hour day is slightly longer—by about 4 minutes—than the Earth's actual rotation period [Section S1.1].)

The Earth **revolves** around the Sun once each year, following an orbit that is not quite circular (Figure 1.11). The *average* distance of the Earth from the Sun is called an **astronomical unit**, or **AU** (more technically, an astronomical unit is the *semimajor axis* of the Earth's orbit):

$$1 \text{ AU} \approx 150 \text{ million km (93 million miles)}$$

The Earth travels slightly faster in its orbit when it is nearer to the Sun and slightly slower when it is farther from the Sun. But at all times the Earth is carrying you around the Sun at a speed in excess of 100,000 kilometers per hour (60,000 miles per hour).

**FIGURE 1.10** As the Earth rotates, your speed around the Earth's axis depends on your latitude. Unless you live at very high latitude, your speed is over 1,000 km/hr. Notice that the Earth rotates counterclockwise as viewed from above the North Pole, so you are always rotating from west to east (which is why the Sun rises in the east and sets in the west).

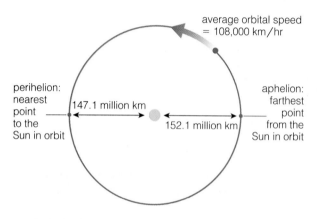

**FIGURE 1.11** Basic properties of the Earth's orbit. The orbit is not quite circular, so the Earth–Sun distance varies between 147.1 million and 152.1 million kilometers. The average distance, which defines 1 astronomical unit (AU), is 149.6 million kilometers.

**FIGURE 1.12** The Earth's axis is tilted by $23\frac{1}{2}°$ from a line *perpendicular* to the ecliptic plane. Note that, as viewed from above the North Pole, the Earth rotates *and* revolves counterclockwise.

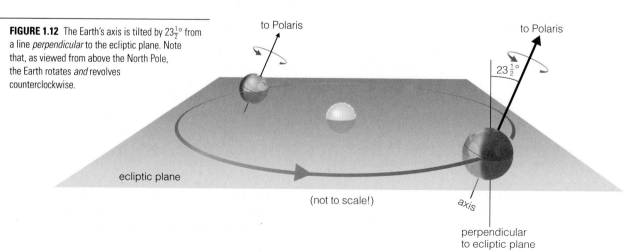

The plane of the Earth's orbit around the Sun is called the **ecliptic plane** (Figure 1.12). The Earth's rotation axis happens to be tilted by $23\frac{1}{2}°$ from a line perpendicular to the ecliptic plane, pointing nearly in the direction of Polaris, the North Star. Viewed from above the North Pole, the Earth both rotates and revolves counterclockwise.

*Seasons* The combination of the Earth's rotation and its revolution around the Sun explains why we have seasons. Because the Earth's rotation axis remains pointed in the same direction (toward Polaris) throughout the year, its orientation *relative to the Sun* changes as it orbits the Sun, as shown in Figure 1.13. The familiar seasonal changes—longer and warmer days in summer, and shorter and cooler days in winter—arise because of changes in how directly the Sun's rays strike a particular location on Earth. When the rays are fairly direct, the Sun's path through the sky is long and high and the days are warm. (By analogy, think of how you sunburn more easily on parts of your body that face the Sun more directly.) When the Sun's rays strike less directly, the Sun's path is short and low through the sky and the days are cool. Notice that the Sun's rays strike the Northern Hemisphere more directly on the side of the orbit near point 2 in Figure 1.13, while they strike the Southern Hemisphere more directly on the side of the orbit near point 4. That is why the seasons are opposite in the Northern and Southern Hemispheres.

The four labeled points in Figure 1.13 have special names related to the seasons. The Earth is at point 1 on about March 21 each year, which represents the **spring equinox** (or *vernal equinox*). Both hemispheres receive equal amounts of sunlight at this time; it is the beginning of spring for the Northern Hemisphere but the beginning of fall for the Southern Hemisphere. The Earth reaches point 2, which represents the **summer solstice**, around June 21. This is the day on which the Northern Hemisphere receives its most direct sunlight and has the

Sunlight striking the Northern Hemisphere is concentrated in a smaller area (note the smaller shadow) than the same amount of sunlight striking the Southern Hemisphere.

The situation is reversed from the summer solstice, with sunlight striking a smaller area in the Southern Hemisphere (note the smaller shadow) than in the Northern Hemisphere.

sunlight

sunlight

**1. Spring Equinox**
Spring begins in the Northern Hemisphere, fall in the Southern Hemisphere.

**2. Summer Solstice**
Summer begins in the Northern Hemisphere, winter in the Southern Hemisphere.

**4. Winter Solstice**
Winter begins in the Northern Hemisphere, summer in the Southern Hemisphere.

**3. Fall Equinox**
Fall begins in the Northern Hemisphere, spring in the Southern Hemisphere.

**FIGURE 1.13** Seasons occur because, even though the Earth's axis remains pointed toward Polaris throughout the year, the orientation of the axis *relative to the Sun* changes as the Earth orbits the Sun. Around the time of the summer solstice, the Northern Hemisphere has summer because it is tipped toward the Sun, and the Southern Hemisphere has winter because it is tipped away from the Sun. The situation is reversed around the time of the winter solstice, when the Northern Hemisphere has winter and the Southern Hemisphere has summer. At the equinoxes, both hemispheres receive equal amounts of light. (The solstices and equinoxes were named by people in the Northern Hemisphere, so the names of the four points reflect the Northern Hemisphere seasons.)

longest period of daylight of any day of the year; it is usually considered the first day of summer. Note that the Southern Hemisphere receives its least direct sunlight and has its shortest daylight period on the summer solstice, so this is the first day of winter for the Southern Hemisphere. Point 3 represents the **fall equinox** (or *autumnal equinox*), which occurs around September 21; both hemispheres again receive the same amount of sunlight, but it is the beginning of fall in the Northern Hemisphere and the beginning of spring in the Southern Hemisphere. Finally, point 4 represents the **winter solstice**, which occurs around December 21. The situation here is the reverse of that on the summer solstice; it is usually considered the first day of winter for the Northern Hemisphere and the first day of summer for the Southern Hemisphere.

**TIME OUT TO THINK** *After studying Figure 1.13, explain why regions near the Earth's equator do not experience seasons in the same way as mid-latitudes such as North America, Europe, and Australia. When is the Sun's path in the sky highest for equatorial regions?*

## Common Misconceptions: The Cause of Seasons

When asked the cause of the seasons, many people mistakenly answer that they are caused by variations in Earth's distance from the Sun. By knowing that the Northern and Southern Hemispheres experience opposite seasons, you'll realize that Earth's varying distance from the Sun *cannot* be the cause of the seasons; if it were, both hemispheres would have summer at the same time. Although Earth's distance from the Sun *does* vary slightly over the course of a year (Earth is closest to the Sun in January and farthest away in July), this factor is greatly overwhelmed by the way the tilt of the rotation axis causes the Northern and Southern Hemispheres to alternately receive more or less direct sunlight. Earth's varying distance from the Sun has no noticeable effect on our seasons. (This is not necessarily the case for other planets; seasons on Mars, for example, *are* affected by its varying distance from the Sun.)

*Precession* Although the Earth's axis will remain pointed toward Polaris throughout our lifetimes, it has not always been so and will not always remain so. The reason is a gradual motion called **precession**. Like the axis of a spinning top, the Earth's axis also sweeps out a circle (precesses)—but much more slowly (Figure 1.14). Note that the axis tilt remains close to $23\frac{1}{2}°$ throughout the cycle; only the axis *orientation* changes. Each cycle of the Earth's precession takes about 26,000 years. Today, the axis points toward Polaris, which is what makes it our North Star. In about 13,000 years, the axis will point nearly in the direction of the star Vega, making *it* our North Star. During most of the precession cycle, the axis does not point very near any bright star.

Precession also changes the locations in the Earth's orbit at which the equinoxes and solstices occur. For example, the spring equinox today occurs when the Sun appears in the direction of the constellation Pisces, but 2,000 years ago it occurred when the Sun appeared in Aries. (That is why the spring equinox is sometimes called "the first point of Aries.") In about 600 years, precession will move the spring equinox into the constellation Aquarius, marking what astrologers call "the age of Aquarius." (Astrologers disagree among themselves as to the starting date of this "age," with claims ranging from as early as the late-1700s to as late as the mid-2700s.)

### Traveling in the Milky Way Galaxy

Besides moving within our solar system, we are traveling with our solar system on a journey through the Milky Way Galaxy. For example, we are moving relative to nearby stars at an average speed of about

### Common Misconceptions: Sun Signs

You probably know your astrological "sign." When astrology began a few thousand years ago, your sign was supposed to represent the constellation in which the Sun appeared on your birth date. However, for most people, this is no longer the case. For example, if your birthday is the spring equinox, March 21, a newspaper horoscope will show that your sign is Aries, but the Sun appears in Pisces on that date. In fact, your astrological sign generally corresponds to the constellation in which the Sun *would have appeared* on your birth date if you had lived about 2,000 years ago. Why? Because the astrological signs are based on the positions of the Sun among the stars as described by the Greek scientist Ptolemy in his book *Tetrabiblios,* which was written in about A.D. 150 [Section 3.6].

70,000 kilometers per hour (40,000 miles per hour)—about three times as fast as the Space Shuttle orbits the Earth. In fact, all stars are in constant motion, and it is as valid to say that the stars are moving relative to us as it is to say that we are moving relative to them.

If nearby stars move at such high speeds, why don't we see them racing around the sky? The answer lies in their vast distances from us. You've probably noticed that a distant airplane appears to move through your sky more slowly than one flying close overhead. If we extend this idea to the stars, we find that even at speeds of 70,000 kilometers per hour

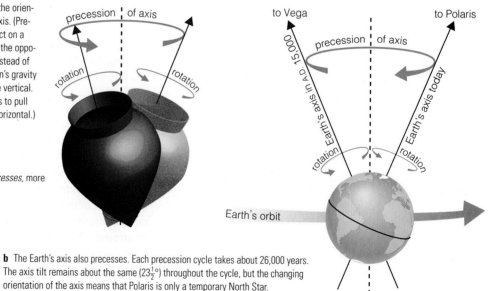

**FIGURE 1.14** Precession affects the orientation, but not the tilt, of Earth's axis. (Precession is caused by gravity's effect on a tilted axis. The Earth precesses in the opposite sense of the top [clockwise instead of counterclockwise] because the Sun's gravity tries to make the Earth's axis more vertical. In contrast, the Earth's gravity tries to pull a top's axis over, making it more horizontal.)

**a** A spinning top wobbles, or *precesses,* more slowly than it spins.

**b** The Earth's axis also precesses. Each precession cycle takes about 26,000 years. The axis tilt remains about the same ($23\frac{1}{2}°$) throughout the cycle, but the changing orientation of the axis means that Polaris is only a temporary North Star.

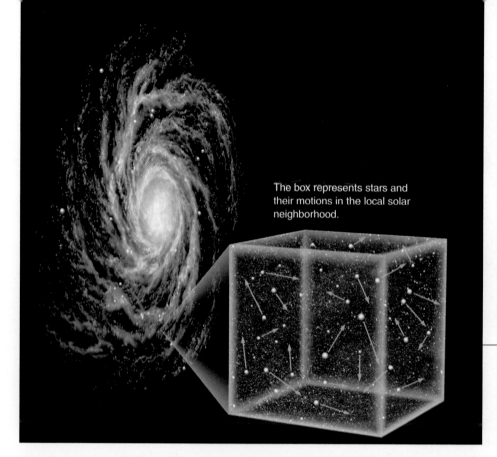

The box represents stars and their motions in the local solar neighborhood.

**FIGURE 1.15** As shown in this painting, the local solar neighborhood is only a tiny portion of the Milky Way Galaxy. The stars in the local solar neighborhood actually move quite fast relative to our solar system, but the enormous distances between stars make this motion barely detectable on human time scales. If you could watch a time-lapse movie made over a time period of millions of years, you would see the stars in the local solar neighborhood racing around in seemingly random directions.

stellar motions would be noticeable to the naked eye only if we watched for thousands of years. That is why the patterns in the constellations seem to remain fixed. Nevertheless, in 10,000 years the constellations will be noticeably different from those we see today. In 500,000 years they will be unrecognizable. If you could watch a time-lapse movie made over millions of years, you would see the stars of our *local solar neighborhood* (the Sun and nearby stars) racing around in seemingly random directions (Figure 1.15).

**TIME OUT TO THINK** *Despite the chaos of motion in the local solar neighborhood over millions of years, collisions between star systems are extremely rare. Explain why. (Hint: Consider the sizes of star systems, such as the solar system, relative to the distances between them.)*

If you look closely at leaves floating in a stream, their motions relative to one another might appear random, just like the motions of stars in the local solar neighborhood. As you widen your view, you see that all the leaves are being carried in the same general direction by the downstream current. In the same way, if you widened your view beyond the local

solar neighborhood, you would see that all the stars are moving in a simple and general way: The entire Milky Way Galaxy is rotating. Stars at different distances from the galactic center take different amounts of time to complete an orbit. Our solar system, located about 28,000 light-years from the galactic center, completes one orbit of the galaxy in about 230 million years (Figure 1.16). Even if you could watch from outside our galaxy, this motion would be unnoticeable to your naked eye. However, if you calculate the speed of our solar system as we orbit the center of the galaxy, you will find that it is close to 1 million kilometers per hour (600,000 miles per hour).

It is worth noting that the galactic rotation reveals one of the greatest mysteries in science—one that we will study in depth later in the book. The speeds at which stars orbit the galactic center depend on the strength of gravity, and the strength of gravity depends on how mass is distributed throughout the galaxy. Thus, careful study of the galactic rotation allows us to determine the distribution of mass in the galaxy. Remarkably, we find that the stars in the disk of the galaxy represent only the "tip of the iceberg" compared to the mass of the entire galaxy (Figure 1.17). That is, most of the mass of the galaxy is located outside the visible disk, in the galaxy's *halo*. We don't know the nature of this mass because we have

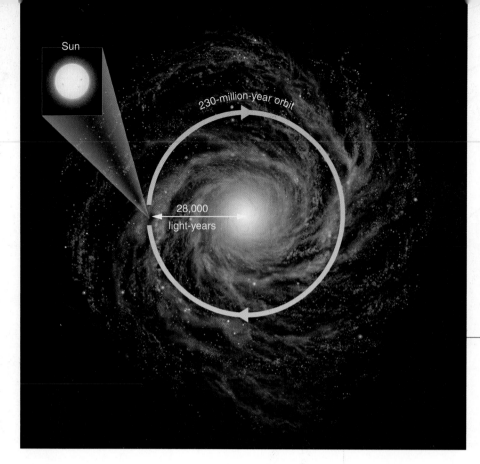

Sun

230-million-year orbit

28,000
light-years

**FIGURE 1.16** This painting shows how the entire Milky Way Galaxy rotates (in a direction that would tend to wind up the spiral arms). Our Sun and solar system are located about 28,000 light-years from the galactic center. At this distance, each orbit around the galactic center takes about 230 million years.

not detected any light coming from it, and we therefore call it **dark matter**. Studies of other galaxies show that they also are made mostly of dark matter. In fact, most of the mass in the universe appears to be made of this mysterious dark matter, but we do not yet know what it is.

### The Expanding Universe

The billions of galaxies in the universe also move relative to one another. Within the Local Group (see Figure 1.1), the motions are about as we might expect. Some of the galaxies move toward the Milky Way Galaxy, some move away, and some move in more complex ways. (For example, two small galaxies, known as the Large and Small Magellanic Clouds, apparently orbit the Milky Way.) Again, the speeds are enormous by earthly standards—the Milky Way is moving toward the Great Galaxy in Andromeda (M31) at about 300,000 kilometers per hour (180,000 miles per hour)—but are unnoticeable to our eyes. We needn't worry about a collision any time soon. Even if the Milky Way and Andromeda Galaxies are approaching each other head-on (which they might not be), it will be nearly 10 billion years before the collision begins.

When we look outside the Local Group, however, we find two astonishing facts that were first discov-

ered in the 1920s by Edwin Hubble, for whom the Hubble Space Telescope was named:

1. Virtually every galaxy outside the Local Group is moving *away* from us.

2. The more distant the galaxy, the faster it appears to be racing away from us.

Upon first becoming aware of these two facts, you might be tempted to conclude that our Local Group (which is held together by gravity) suffers a cosmic case of chicken pox. However, there is a much more natural explanation: *The entire universe is expanding.* We'll save details about this expansion for later in the book (Chapter 19), but you can understand the basic idea by thinking about a raisin cake baking in an oven.

Imagine that you make a raisin cake in which the distance between adjacent raisins is 1 centimeter. You place the cake in the oven, where it expands as it bakes. After 1 hour, you remove the cake, which has expanded so that the distance between adjacent raisins is 3 centimeters (Figure 1.18).

Pick any raisin (it doesn't matter which one), call it the Local Raisin, and identify it in the pictures of the cake both before and after baking; Figure 1.18 shows one possible choice for the Local Raisin, with several other nearby raisins labeled. Before baking,

Most of the galaxy's light comes from stars and gas in the galactic disk...

...but most of the galaxy's mass lies above and below the disk in the *halo.*

**FIGURE 1.17** This painting shows an edge-on view of the Milky Way Galaxy. Most visible stars reside within the galaxy's thin *disk,* which runs horizontally across the page in this figure. But careful study of galactic rotation shows that most of the mass lies in the galactic *halo*—a large, spherical region that surrounds and encompasses the disk. Because this mass emits no light that we have detected, we call it dark matter. (The dark matter may extend quite far out; see Figure 21.1.)

Raisin 1 is 1 centimeter away from the Local Raisin, Raisin 2 is 2 centimeters away, and Raisin 3 is 3 centimeters away. After baking, Raisin 1 is 3 centimeters away from the Local Raisin, Raisin 2 is 6 centimeters away, and Raisin 3 is 9 centimeters away. Nothing should seem surprising so far, because the new distances simply reflect the fact that the cake has expanded uniformly everywhere.

Now, suppose you live *inside* the Local Raisin. From your vantage point, the other raisins appear to move away from you as the cake expands. For example, Raisin 1 is 1 centimeter away before baking and 3 centimeters away after baking. It therefore appears to move 2 centimeters during the hour, so you'll see it moving away from you at a speed of 2 centimeters per hour. Raisin 2 is 2 centimeters away before baking and 6 centimeters away afterward; thus, it appears to move 4 centimeters during the hour of baking, giving it a speed of 4 centimeters per hour away from you. The following table lists the distances of other raisins before and after baking, along with their speeds as seen from the Local Raisin.

**FIGURE 1.18** An expanding raisin cake illustrates basic principles of the expansion of the universe.

**Distances and Speeds As Seen from the Local Raisin**

| Raisin Number | Distance Before Baking | Distance After Baking (1 hour later) | Speed |
|---|---|---|---|
| 1 | 1 cm | 3 cm | 2 cm/hr |
| 2 | 2 cm | 6 cm | 4 cm/hr |
| 3 | 3 cm | 9 cm | 6 cm/hr |
| 4 | 4 cm | 12 cm | 8 cm/hr |
| ⋮ | ⋮ | ⋮ | ⋮ |
| 10 | 10 cm | 30 cm | 20 cm/hr |
| ⋮ | ⋮ | ⋮ | ⋮ |

Note that, although the entire cake expanded uniformly, from the vantage point of the Local Raisin each subsequent raisin moved away at increasingly faster speeds. Also, because selection of the Local Raisin was arbitrary, you would find the same results no matter which raisin you chose to represent your Local Raisin.

If you now imagine the Local Raisin to represent our Local Group of galaxies and the other raisins to represent more distant galaxies or clusters of galaxies, you have a basic picture of the expansion of the universe. That is, *space* itself is growing, and more distant galaxies move away from us faster because they are carried along with this expansion like raisins in an expanding cake. And, just as the raisins themselves do not expand, the individual galaxies and clusters of galaxies do not expand (because they are bound together by gravity). The effects of expansion would appear basically the same viewed from any place in the universe.

### Summary of Motion

Let's summarize the motions we have covered. We spin around the Earth's axis as we revolve around the Sun. Our solar system moves among the stars of the local solar neighborhood, while this entire neighborhood orbits the center of the Milky Way Galaxy. Our galaxy, in turn, moves among the other galaxies of the Local Group, while the Local Group is carried along with the overall expansion of the universe. Table 1.2 lists the motions and their associated speeds. Spaceship Earth is indeed carrying us on a remarkable journey!

## 1.4 The Human Adventure of Astronomy

In a relatively few pages, we've laid out a fairly complete overview of our modern scientific view of the universe. But our goal in this book is not for you simply to be able to recite this view. Rather it is to help you understand the evidence supporting this view and the extraordinary story of how it developed. In many ways, this book is devoted to this goal.

Astronomy is a human adventure in the sense that it affects virtually everyone—even those who have

**Table 1.2  The Motions of Spaceship Earth**

| Motion | Typical Speed |
|---|---|
| rotation | 1,000 km/hr or more around axis |
| revolution | 100,000 km/hr around Sun |
| motion within local solar neighborhood | 70,000 km/hr relative to nearby stars |
| rotation of the Milky Way Galaxy | 1,000,000 km/hr around galactic center |
| motion within Local Group | 300,000 km/hr toward Andromeda Galaxy |
| universal expansion | more distant galaxies moving away faster, with the most distant moving at speeds close to the speed of light |

never looked at the sky—because the development of astronomy has been so deeply intertwined with the development of civilization as a whole. Revolutions in astronomy have gone hand in hand with the revolutions in science and technology that have shaped modern life. Witness the repercussions of the Copernican revolution, which changed our view of the Earth from the center of the universe to just one planet orbiting the Sun. This revolution, which we will discuss further in Chapter 5, began when Copernicus published his idea of a Sun-centered solar system in 1543. Three subsequent figures—Tycho Brahe, Johannes Kepler, and Galileo—provided the key evidence that eventually led to wide acceptance of the Copernican idea, and the revolution culminated with Isaac Newton's uncovering of the laws of motion and gravity. Newton's work, in turn, became the foundation of physics that helped fuel the industrial revolution.

More recently, the development of space travel and the computer revolution have helped fuel tremendous progress in astronomy. We've learned a lot about our solar system by sending probes to the planets, and many of our most powerful observatories, including the Hubble Space Telescope, reside in space. On the ground, computer design and control have led to tremendous growth in the size and power of telescopes, particularly in the past decade.

Many of these efforts, along with the achievements they spawned, have led to profound social change. The most famous example involved Galileo, whom the Vatican put under house arrest in 1633 for his claims that the Earth orbits the Sun. Although the Church soon recognized that Galileo was right, he was formally vindicated only with a statement by Pope John Paul II in 1992. In the meantime, his case spurred great debate in religious circles and had a profound influence on both theological and scientific thinking.

**FIGURE 1.19** This fanciful image, which is also the cover of this book, imagines hikers looking at a sky filled with galaxies; the galaxies are actually part of a photograph taken by the Hubble Space Telescope (see Figure 21.11). Although such a view could not really exist anywhere in the universe, the image shows how our minds can connect the deepest mysteries of the cosmos to our lives here on Earth. Indeed, a primary goal of this book is to help you understand the extraordinary story of how we have reached our current scientific understanding of the universe and to appreciate the many mysteries that still remain.

As you progress through this book and learn about astronomical discovery, try to keep in mind the context of the human adventure. You will then be learning not just about a science, but about one of the great forces that have helped shape our modern world. This context will also lead you to think about how the many astronomical mysteries that remain—such as the makeup of dark matter, the events of the first instant of the Big Bang, and the question of life beyond Earth—may influence our future. What would it mean to us if we were ever to learn the complete story of our cosmic origins? How would our view of the Earth be changed if we came to learn that Earth-like planets are common or exceedingly rare? Only time may answer these questions, but the chapters ahead give you the foundation you need to understand how we changed from primitive people looking at patterns in the night sky to a civilization capable of asking deep questions about our existence.

## THE BIG PICTURE

In this first chapter, we developed a broad overview of our place in the universe. It is not yet necessary for you to remember the details—everything presented in this chapter will be covered in greater depth later in the book. However, you should understand enough so that all the following "big picture" ideas are clear:

■ The Earth is not the center of the universe but instead is a planet orbiting a rather ordinary star in the Milky Way Galaxy. The Milky Way Galaxy, in turn, is one of billions of galaxies in our observable universe.

■ We are "star stuff." The atoms from which we are made began as hydrogen and helium in the Big Bang and were later fused into heavier elements in massive stars. When these stars died, they released these atoms into space, where our galaxy recycled them. Our solar system formed from such recycled matter some 4.6 billion years ago.

■ Cosmic distances are literally astronomical, but we can put them in perspective with the aid of scale models and other scaling techniques. When you think about these enormous scales, don't forget that every star is a sun and every planet is a unique world.

■ We are latecomers on the scale of cosmic time. The universe was more than halfway through its history by the time our solar system formed, and then it took billions of years more before humans arrived on the scene.

■ All of us are being carried through the cosmos on spaceship Earth. Although we cannot feel this motion in our everyday lives, the associated speeds are surprisingly high. Learning about the motions of spaceship Earth not only gives us a new perspective on the cosmos, but also helps us understand its nature and history.

■ Throughout history, the development of astronomy has gone hand in hand with social and technological development. In this sense, astronomy touches everyone, making it a human adventure to be enjoyed by all.

## Review Questions

1. What do we mean by a *geocentric* universe? In broad terms, contrast a geocentric universe with our modern view of the universe.

2. Describe the major levels of structure in the universe.

3. What do we mean when we say that the universe is *expanding*? Why does an expanding universe suggest a beginning in what we call the *Big Bang*?

4. Summarize our cosmic origins and explain what Carl Sagan meant when he said that we are "star stuff."

5. Explain the statement *The farther away we look in distance, the further back we look in time.*

6. What do we mean by the *observable universe*?

7. Describe key features of our solar system as they would appear on a scale of 1 to 10 billion.

8. How do the distances to the stars compare to distances within our solar system? Give a few examples to put the comparison in perspective.

9. Describe at least two ways to put the scale of the Milky Way Galaxy in perspective.

10. How many galaxies are in the observable universe? How many stars are in the observable universe? Put these numbers in perspective.

11. Imagine describing the cosmic calendar to friends. In your own words, give them a feel for how the human race fits into the scale of time.

12. Briefly summarize the major motions of the Earth through the universe.

13. What is an *astronomical unit*? What is the *ecliptic plane*?

14. Describe the cause of the Earth's seasons, and explain why the seasons are opposite in the Northern and Southern Hemispheres.

15. What is *precession,* and how does it affect the appearance of our sky?

16. Briefly describe the motion of the Sun relative to stars in the local solar neighborhood and to the entire Milky Way Galaxy. Given the relatively high speeds of stars relative to us, why don't we notice them racing around the sky?

17. Describe the raisin cake model of the universe, and explain how it shows that a uniform expansion would lead us to see more distant galaxies moving away from us at higher speeds.

18. Briefly describe how astronomy is interwoven with social and technological change.

## Discussion Questions

1. *Vast Orbs.* The chapter-opening quotation from Christiaan Huygens suggests that humans might be less inclined to wage war if everyone appreciated the Earth's place in the universe. Do you agree? Defend your opinion.

2. *Infant Species.* In the last few tenths of a second before midnight on December 31 of the cosmic calendar, we have developed an incredible civilization and learned a great deal about the universe, but we also have developed technology through which we could destroy ourselves. The midnight bell is striking, and the choice for the future is ours. How far into the next cosmic year do you think our civilization will survive? Defend your opinion.

3. *A Human Adventure.* How important do you think astronomical discoveries have been to our social development? Defend your opinion with examples drawn from your knowledge of history.

## Problems

(Quantitative problems are marked with an asterisk.)

*Sensible Statements?* For **problems 1–8**, decide whether the statement is sensible and explain why it is or is not.

*Example:* I walked east from our base camp at the North Pole.

*Solution:* The statement does not make sense because *east* has no meaning at the North Pole—all directions are south from the North Pole.

1. The universe is between 12 billion and 16 billion years old.

2. The universe is between 12 billion and 16 billion light-years old.

3. It will take me light-years to complete this homework assignment!

4. Someday we may build spaceships capable of traveling at a speed of 1 light-minute per hour.

5. Astronomers recently discovered a moon that does not orbit a planet.

6. NASA plans soon to launch a spaceship that will leave the Milky Way Galaxy to take a photograph of the galaxy from the outside.

7. The observable universe is the same size today as it was a few billion years ago.

8. Photographs of distant galaxies show them as they were when they were much younger than they are today.

9. *No Axis Tilt.* Suppose the Earth's axis had no tilt. Would we still have seasons? Why or why not?

10. *Tour Report.* A friend asks you the following questions concerning your tour of a scale-model solar system. Answer each question in one paragraph.

   a. Is the Sun really much bigger than the Earth?

   b. Is it true that the Sun uses nuclear energy?

   c. Would it be much harder to send humans to Mars than to the Moon?

   d. In elementary school, I heard that Neptune is farther from the Sun than Pluto. Is this true?

   e. I read that Pluto is not really a planet. What's the story?

   f. Why didn't they have any stars besides the Sun in the scale model?

   g. What was the most interesting thing you learned during your tour?

11. *Raisin Cake Universe.* Suppose that all the raisins in a cake are 1 centimeter apart before baking and after baking they are 4 centimeters apart.

   a. Draw diagrams to represent the cake before and after baking.

   b. Identify one raisin as the Local Raisin on your diagrams. Construct a table showing the distances and speeds of other raisins as seen from the Local Raisin.

   c. Briefly explain how your expanding cake is similar to the expansion of the universe.

12. *Scaling the Local Group of Galaxies.* Both the Milky Way Galaxy and the Great Galaxy in Andromeda (M31) have a diameter of about 100,000 light-years. The distance between the two galaxies is about 2.5 million light-years.

   a. Using a scale on which 1 centimeter represents 100,000 light-years, draw a sketch showing both galaxies and the distance between them to scale.

   b. How does the separation between galaxies compare to the separation between stars? Based on your answer, discuss the likelihood of galactic collisions in comparison to the likelihood of stellar collisions.

*13. *Distances by Light.* Just as a light-year is the distance that light can travel in 1 year, we define a light-second as the distance that light can travel in 1 second, a light-minute as the distance that light can travel in 1 minute, and so on. Following the method of Mathematical Insight 1.1, calculate the distance in kilometers represented by each of the following: 1 light-second; 1 light-minute; 1 light-hour; 1 light-day.

*14. *Driving to the Planets (and Stars).* Imagine that you could drive your car in space at a constant speed of 100 km/hr (62 mi/hr). (In reality, the law of gravity would make driving through space at a constant speed all but impossible.)

   a. How long would it take to circle the Earth in low orbit? (*Hint:* Use the Earth's circumference of approximately 40,000 km.)

   b. Suppose you started driving from the Sun. How long would it take to reach Earth? How long would it take to reach Pluto? Use the data in Table 1.1.

   c. How long would it take to drive the 4.4 light-years to Alpha Centauri? (*Hint:* You'll need to convert the distance to kilometers.)

   d. The *Voyager 2* spacecraft is traveling at about 50,000 km/hr. At this speed, how long would it take to reach Alpha Centauri (if it were headed in the right direction, which it is not)?

*15. *Speed Calculations.* Calculate each of the following speeds in both kilometers per hour and miles per hour. In each case, assume a circular orbit; recall that the formula for the circumference of a circle is $2 \times \pi \times$ radius. (*Hint:* Divide the distance traveled in the circular orbit by the time it takes to complete one orbit.)

   a. The speed of the Earth going around the Sun; use the average Earth–Sun distance of 149.6 million km.

   b. The speed of our solar system around the center of our galaxy; assume that we are located 28,000 light-years from the center and that each orbit takes 230 million years.

## Web Projects

Find useful links for Web projects on the text Web site.

1. *Astronomy on the Web.* The Web contains a vast amount of astronomical information. Starting from the links on the textbook Web site, spend at least an hour exploring astronomy on the Web. Write two or three paragraphs summarizing what you learned from your Web surfing. What was your favorite astronomical Web site, and why?

2. *Voyage.* Visit the Web site for the Voyage scale-model solar system on the National Mall. Write a one-page summary of what you learn from your virtual tour.

3. *NASA Missions.* Visit the NASA Web site to learn about upcoming missions that concern astronomy. Write a one-page summary of the mission you feel is most likely to give us new astronomical information during the time you are enrolled in your astronomy course.

*We had the sky, up there, all speckled with stars, and we used to lay on our backs and look up at them, and discuss about whether they was made, or only just happened.*

MARK TWAIN, *HUCKLEBERRY FINN*

# CHAPTER 2

# Discovering the Universe for Yourself

It is an exciting time in the history of astronomy. A new generation of telescopes is probing the depths of the universe. Increasingly sophisticated space probes are collecting new data about the planets and other objects in our solar system. Rapid advances in computing technology allow scientists to analyze the vast amount of new data and to model the processes that occur in planets, stars, galaxies, and the universe.

One of the goals of this book is to help *you* share in the ongoing adventure of astronomical discovery. One of the best ways to become a part of this adventure is to discover the universe for yourself by doing what other humans have done for thousands of generations: Go outside, observe the sky around you, and contemplate the awe-inspiring universe of which you are a part. In this chapter, we'll discuss a few key ideas that will help you understand what you see in the sky.

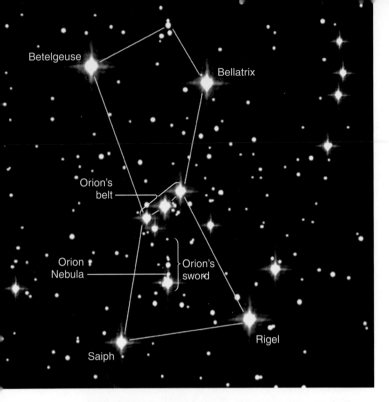

**FIGURE 2.1** This photograph shows stars in the constellation Orion. Stars are so far away that they have no visible size; brighter stars appear larger in photographs only because they are overexposed. The crosses on bright stars are an artifact of the telescope used to take the photograph.

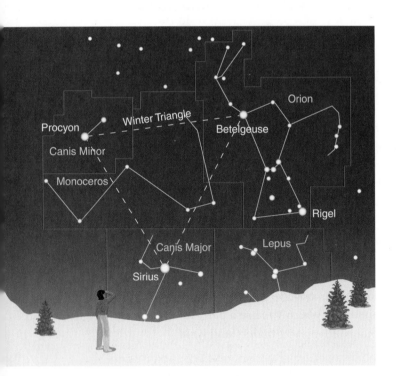

**FIGURE 2.2** Red lines mark official borders of several constellations near Orion. Yellow lines connect recognizable patterns of stars within constellations. Sirius, Procyon, and Betelgeuse form a pattern spanning several constellations and called the Winter Triangle; it is easy to find on clear winter evenings.

## 2.1 Patterns in the Sky

Shortly after sunset, as daylight fades to darkness, the sky appears to fill slowly with stars. On clear, moonless nights far from city lights, as many as 2,000–3,000 stars may be visible to your naked eye. As you look at the stars, your mind might group them into many different patterns. If you observe the sky night after night or year after year, you will recognize the same patterns of stars.

People of nearly every culture gave names to patterns in the sky. The pattern that the Greeks named Orion, the hunter (Figure 2.1), was seen by the ancient Chinese as a supreme warrior called *Shen.* Hindus in ancient India also saw a warrior, called *Skanda,* who as the general of a great celestial army rode a peacock. The three stars of Orion's belt were seen as three fishermen in a canoe by Aborigines of northern Australia. As seen from southern California, these three stars climb almost straight up into the sky as they rise in the east, which may explain why the Chemehuevi Indians of the California desert saw them as a line of three sure-footed mountain sheep.[1] These are but a few of the many names, each accompanied by a rich folklore, that have been given to the pattern of stars we call Orion.

### Constellations

The patterns of stars seen in the sky are usually called constellations. Astronomers, however, use the term **constellation** to refer to a specific *region* of the sky. Any place in the sky belongs to some constellation; familiar patterns of stars merely help locate particular constellations. For example, the constellation Orion includes all the stars in the familiar pattern of the hunter, along with the region of the sky in which these stars are found (Figure 2.2).

The official borders of the constellations were set in 1928 by members of the International Astronomical Union (IAU), an association of astronomers from around the world. The IAU divided the sky into 88 constellations whose borders correspond roughly to the star patterns recognized by Europeans. Thus, despite the wide variety of names given to patterns of stars by different cultures, the "official" names of constellations visible from the Northern Hemisphere can be traced back to the ancient Greeks and to other cultures of southern Europe, the Middle East, and northern Africa. No one knows exactly when these constellations were first named, although some names probably go back at least 5,000 years. The official names of the constellations visible from the Southern Hemisphere are primarily those given by seventeenth-century European explorers.

[1]These and other constellation stories are found in E. C. Krupp, *Beyond the Blue Horizon* (Oxford University Press, 1991).

**FIGURE 2.3** Our lack of depth perception when we look into space creates the illusion that the Earth is surrounded by a *celestial sphere*. However, stars that appear very close together in our sky may actually lie at very different distances from Earth.

**FIGURE 2.4** A model of the celestial sphere shows the patterns of the stars, the borders of the 88 official constellations, the ecliptic, and the celestial equator and poles. Because the celestial sphere shows the view from Earth, we imagine the Earth to reside in the center of the sphere. Thus, when we look into the sky, we see patterns of stars as they would appear from *inside* this imaginary sphere (which means the patterns appear left-right reversed compared to what we see when we look at the model from the outside).

Learning your way around the constellations is no more difficult than learning your way around your neighborhood, and recognizing the patterns of just 20–40 constellations is enough to make the entire sky seem familiar. The best way to learn the constellations is to go out and view them, guided by the help of a few visits to a planetarium and the star charts in the back of this book. The *Skygazer* software that comes with this book can also help you learn constellations.

### The Celestial Sphere

The stars in a particular constellation may appear to lie close to one another, but this is an illusion. All stars in a particular constellation lie in similar directions from Earth but not necessarily at similar distances (Figure 2.3). However, because we lack depth perception when we look into space, it looks like all the stars lie at the same distance. The ancient Greeks mistook this illusion for reality, imagining the Earth to be surrounded by a great **celestial sphere**.

Today, the concept of a celestial sphere is still useful for our learning about the sky, even though we know that the Earth does not really lie in the center of a giant ball. We give names to special locations on the imaginary celestial sphere. The point directly above the Earth's North Pole is called the **north celestial pole** (NCP), and the point directly above the Earth's South Pole is called the **south celestial pole**. The **celestial equator** represents an extension of the Earth's equator into space (see Figure 2.3).

The stars form the fixed patterns of the constellations on the celestial sphere, while the Sun, Moon, and planets slowly wander among the stars. As we'll discuss shortly, the apparent motion of the Moon

and the planets is fairly complex. The Sun, however, appears to slowly circle the celestial sphere on a simple annual path called the **ecliptic**; this apparent path is the projection of the ecliptic plane (see Figure 1.12) into space. A model of the celestial sphere typically shows the patterns of the stars, the borders of the 88 official constellations, the ecliptic, and the celestial equator and poles (Figure 2.4).

### Common Misconceptions: Stars in the Daytime

Because we don't see stars in the daytime, some people believe that the stars vanish in the daytime and "come out" at night. In fact, the stars are always present. The only reason you cannot see stars in the daytime is that their dim light is overwhelmed by the bright daytime sky. You *can* see bright stars in the daytime with the aid of a telescope, and you may see stars in the daytime if you are fortunate enough to observe a total eclipse of the Sun. Astronauts also see stars in the daytime—above the Earth's atmosphere, where no air is present to scatter sunlight through the sky, the Sun is a bright disk against a dark sky filled with stars. (However, because the Sun is so bright, astronauts must block its light and allow their eyes to adapt to darkness if they wish to *see* the stars.)

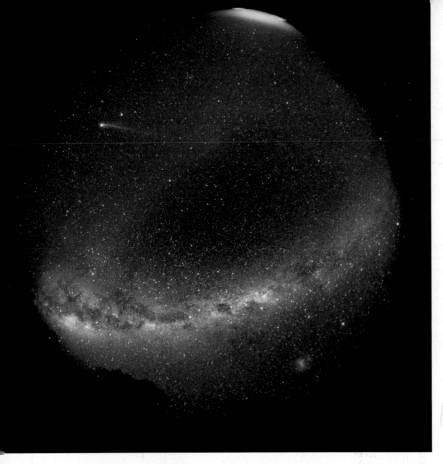

**FIGURE 2.5** A "fish-eye" photograph of the Milky Way in the Australian sky. Near the upper left, Comet Hale–Bopp is visible in this 1997 photo.

### The Milky Way

As your eyes adapt to darkness at a dark site, you'll begin to see the whitish band of light called the *Milky Way*. It is from this band of light that our Milky Way Galaxy gets its name. You can see only part of the Milky Way at any particular time, but it stretches all the way around the celestial sphere. If you look carefully, you will notice that the Milky Way varies in width and has dark fissures running through it. The widest and brightest parts of the Milky Way are most easily seen from the Southern Hemisphere (Figure 2.5), which probably explains why the Aborigines of Australia gave names to the patterns they saw within the Milky Way in the same way that other cultures gave names to patterns of stars.

The band of light called the Milky Way bears an important relationship to the Milky Way Galaxy: *It traces the galactic plane as it appears from our location in the outskirts of the galaxy* (Figure 2.6). Recall that the Milky Way Galaxy is shaped like a thin pancake with a bulge in the middle (see Figures 1.16 and 1.17). We view the universe from our location more than halfway outward from the center of this "pancake." When we look in any direction *within* the plane of the galaxy, we see countless stars, along with

interstellar gas and dust. These stars and glowing clouds of gas form the band of light we call the Milky Way. The dark fissures appear in regions where particularly dense interstellar clouds obscure our view of stars behind them. The central bulge of the galaxy makes the Milky Way wider in the direction of the galactic center, which is the direction of the constellation Sagittarius in our sky.

We see fewer stars when we look in directions pointing *away* from our location within the galactic plane, and there is relatively little gas and dust to obscure our view of more distant objects. Thus, we have a clear view to the far reaches of the universe, limited only by what our eyes or instruments allow. If you are fortunate enough to have a very dark sky, you may see a fuzzy patch in the constellation Andromeda (Figure 2.7). Although this patch may look like nothing more than a small cloud, you are actually seeing the Great Galaxy in Andromeda (M31)—some 2.5 million light-years away.

**TIME OUT TO THINK** *Contemplate the fact that light from M31 journeyed through space for some 2.5 million years to reach you and is the combined light of more than 100 billion stars. Do you think it possible that among some of those stars there are students like yourself gazing outward in amazement at the Milky Way Galaxy?*

## 2.2 The Circling Sky

If you spend a few hours out under a starry sky, you'll see stars (and the Moon and planets) rising and setting much like the Sun. In reality, it is we who are moving, not the stars. The Sun and stars appear to rise in the east and set in the west because the Earth rotates in the opposite direction, from west to east. In fact, the Earth's rotation makes the entire celestial sphere appear to rotate around us each day. If you could view the celestial sphere from outside, the daily circles of the stars would appear very simple (Figure 2.8).

However, because we live on the Earth, we see only *half* the celestial sphere at any one moment; the ground beneath us blocks our view of the other half. The particular half that we see depends on the time, the date, and our location on Earth. In this section, we'll discuss how to make sense of the sky as seen from Earth.

**FIGURE 2.6** Artist's conception of the Milky Way Galaxy from afar, showing how the galaxy's structure affects our view from Earth. When we look *into* the galactic plane in any direction, our view is blocked by stars, gas, and dust. Thus, we see the galactic plane as the band of light we call the Milky Way, stretching a full 360° around our sky (i.e., around the celestial sphere). We have a clear view to the distant universe only when we look away from the galactic plane.

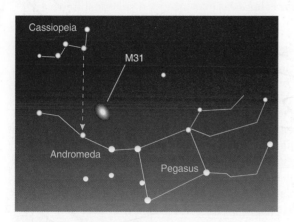

**FIGURE 2.7** Location of M31 in the night sky.

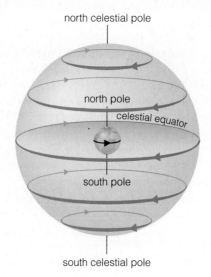

**FIGURE 2.8** The Earth rotates from west to east (black arrows), making the celestial sphere *appear* to rotate around us from east to west. Viewed from outside, the stars (and the Sun, Moon, and planets) therefore appear to make simple daily circles around us. The red circles represent the apparent daily paths of a few selected stars.

### The Dome of the Sky

Picture yourself standing in a flat, open field. The sky appears to take the shape of a dome, making it easy to understand why people of many ancient cultures believed we lived on a flat Earth lying under a great dome that encompassed the world. Today, we use the appearance of a dome to define the **local sky**—the sky as seen from wherever you happen to be standing (Figure 2.9). The boundary between Earth and sky is what we call the **horizon**. The point directly overhead is your **zenith**. Your **meridian** is an imaginary half-circle stretching from your horizon due south, through your zenith, to your horizon due north.

You can pinpoint the position of any object in your local sky by stating its **direction** along your horizon (more technically measured as *azimuth*[2]) and its **altitude** above your horizon. For example, Figure 2.9 shows a person pointing to a star located in a southeasterly direction at an altitude of 60°. (The zenith has an altitude of 90° but no direction, since it is straight overhead.)

Because of our lack of depth perception in the sky, we cannot tell the true sizes of objects or the true distances between objects just by looking at them. For example, the Sun and the Moon look about the same size in our sky, but the Sun is actually about 400 times larger than the Moon in diameter. We can, however, measure *angles* in the sky. The **angular size** of an object like the Sun or the Moon is the angle it appears to span in your field of view. The **angular distance** between a pair of objects is the angle that appears to separate them. For example, Figure 2.10 shows that the angular size of the Moon is about $\frac{1}{2}$° (about the same as that of the Sun), while the angular distance between the "pointer stars" at the end of the Big Dipper's bowl is about 5°. You can use your outstretched hand to make rough estimates of angles in the sky (Figure 2.10c).

For more precise astronomical measurements, we subdivide each degree into 60 **arcminutes** and subdivide each arcminute into 60 **arcseconds**. Thus, there are 60 arcseconds in 1 arcminute, 60 arcminutes in 1°, and 360° in a full circle. We abbreviate arcminutes with the symbol ′ and arcseconds with the symbol ″. For example, we read 35°27′15″ as "35 degrees, 27 arcminutes, 15 arcseconds."

### Variation with Latitude

If you stay in one place, you'll see the same set of stars following the same paths through your sky from one year to the next. But if you travel north or south,

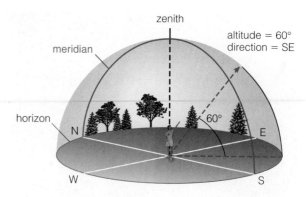

**FIGURE 2.9** Definitions in your local sky.

you'll notice somewhat different sets of stars moving through the sky on somewhat different paths. This observation convinced ancient scientists that the sky must be more than a simple dome.

According to historical records, the idea of the sky as a celestial sphere was first proposed by the Greek scientist Anaximander (c. 610–547 B.C.). Based on what he learned about how the sky changes with travel north or south, Anaximander also concluded that the Earth must not be flat. However, because *east–west* travel does *not* change the stars visible in the sky, he did not realize that the Earth is round and instead suggested that it might be a cylinder curved in the north–south direction. By about 500 B.C., the famous mathematician Pythagoras suggested that the Earth is a sphere. More than a century later, Aristotle (384–322 B.C.) cited observations of the Earth's curved shadow on the Moon during lunar eclipses as evidence for a spherical Earth.

---

### Common Misconceptions: A Flat Earth

A widespread myth holds that Columbus proved the Earth to be round rather than flat. In fact, knowledge of the round Earth predated Columbus by nearly 2,000 years. However, it is probably true that most people in Columbus's day believed the Earth to be flat, largely because of the poor state of education. The vast majority of the public was illiterate and unaware of the scholarly evidence for a spherical Earth. Interestingly, Columbus's primary argument with other scholars concerned the distance from Europe to Asia going westward—and it was Columbus who was wrong. He underestimated the true distance and as a result was woefully unprepared for the voyage to Asia that he thought he was undertaking. Indeed, his voyages would almost certainly have ended in disaster had it not been for the presence of the Americas, which offered a safe landing well to the east of Asia.

---

[2]Azimuth is usually measured clockwise around the horizon from due north. By this definition, the azimuth of due north is 0°, due east is 90°, due south is 180°, and due west is 270°.

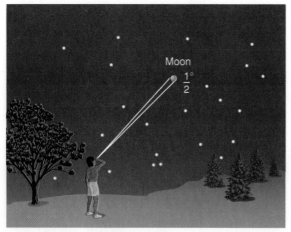

**a** The angular size of the Moon is about $\frac{1}{2}°$.

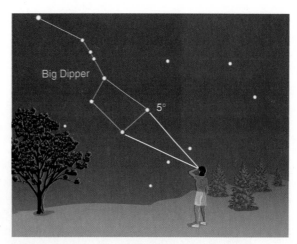

**b** The angular distance between the pointer stars of the Big Dipper is about 5°.

**c** You can estimate angular sizes or distances with your outstretched hand.

**FIGURE 2.10** We measure *angular sizes* or *angular distances*, rather than actual sizes or distances, when we look at objects in the sky.

Stretch out your arm as shown here.

To understand why the sky changes with north–south travel, we must first review how we locate points on the Earth (Figure 2.11a). **Latitude** measures positions north or south; it is defined to be 0° at the equator, so the North Pole and the South Pole have latitude 90°N and 90°S, respectively. Note that "lines of latitude" actually are circles running parallel to the equator. **Longitude** measures east–west position, so "lines of longitude" are semicircles extending from the North Pole to the South Pole. The line of longitude passing through Greenwich, England, is defined to be longitude 0° (Figure 2.11b). This line is sometimes called the **prime meridian**; the decision to denote the line of longitude passing through Greenwich as the prime meridian was made by international treaty in 1884. Stating a latitude and a longitude pinpoints a location. For example, Figure 2.11a shows that Rome lies at about 42°N latitude and 12°E longitude and that Miami lies at about 26°N latitude and 80°W longitude.

If we combine the idea of the sky's dome-shaped appearance when seen from the ground with the idea that stars make simple daily circles around the celestial sphere, we can see why the apparent paths of stars depend on *latitude*. Your latitude determines your orientation on Earth relative to the celestial sphere; "down" is toward the center of the Earth, and "up" (toward your zenith) is away from the center of the Earth. Figure 2.12 shows sample orientations relative to the celestial sphere for mid-latitudes in each hemisphere. If you study the diagrams carefully, you'll discover the following key features:

■ In the Northern Hemisphere, stars relatively near the north celestial pole remain constantly above the horizon. We say that such stars are **circumpolar**. They never rise or set but instead make daily counterclockwise circles around the north celestial pole. In the Southern Hemisphere,

**a** Latitude measures angular distance north or south of the equator. Longitude measures angular distance east or west of the prime meridian, which passes through Greenwich, England.

**b** The entrance to the Old Royal Greenwich Observatory, near London. The line emerging from the door marks the prime meridian.

**FIGURE 2.11** We can locate any place on Earth's surface by its latitude and longitude.

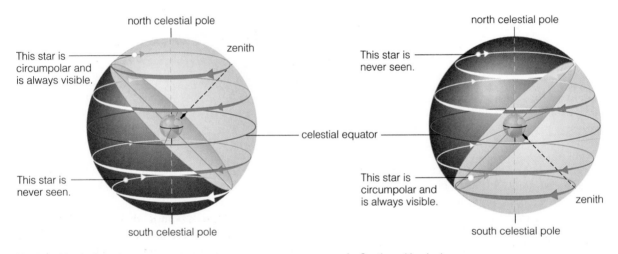

**a** Northern Hemisphere

**b** Southern Hemisphere

**FIGURE 2.12** Sample local skies for (**a**) the Northern Hemisphere and (**b**) the Southern Hemisphere. Compare to Figure 2.8; note that your latitude determines your orientation relative to the celestial sphere, and the daily rotation determines the paths of stars through your local sky. To view the local skies more clearly, rotate the page so the zenith points up.

circumpolar stars make daily clockwise circles around the south celestial pole. Figure 2.13 shows a beautiful photograph of the daily circles of stars.

■ In the Northern Hemisphere, stars relatively near the south celestial pole remain constantly below the horizon and are never seen. In the Southern Hemisphere, stars near the north celestial pole are never visible. Thus, different sets of constellations are visible in northern and southern skies.

Note that the set of constellations changes only with latitude, not with longitude.

■ All other stars (those that are neither circumpolar nor never visible) rise daily in the east and set daily in the west. Stars located north of the celestial equator on the celestial sphere rise north of due east and set north of due west, stars located on the celestial equator rise due east and set

**FIGURE 2.13** This time-exposure photograph, taken at Arches National Park in Utah, shows how the Earth's rotation causes stars to trace daily circles around the sky. The north celestial pole lies at the center of the circles. Over the course of a full day, circumpolar stars trace complete circles, and stars that rise in the east and set in the west trace partial circles. Here we see only a portion of the full daily paths, because the time exposure lasted only a couple of hours.

due west, and stars located south of the celestial equator rise south of due east and set south of due west.

■ If you study the geometry of the diagrams carefully, you'll see that in the Northern Hemisphere the altitude of the north celestial pole in your sky is equal to your latitude. For example, if the north celestial pole appears in your sky 40° above your horizon, your latitude is 40°N. Similarly, in the Southern Hemisphere the altitude of the south celestial pole in your sky is equal to your latitude.

The last feature listed above is very useful for navigation, since it allows you to determine your latitude just by finding the celestial pole in your sky. Finding the north celestial pole is fairly easy, because it lies very close to the star Polaris (Figure 2.14a). In the Southern Hemisphere, you can find the south celestial pole with the aid of the Southern Cross (Figure 2.14b). We'll discuss celestial navigation and

how the sky varies with latitude in more detail in Chapter S1.

**TIME OUT TO THINK** *Answer the following questions for your latitude: Where is the north (or south) celestial pole in your sky? Where should you*

**Common Misconceptions:
What Makes the North Star Special?**

Most people are aware that the North Star, Polaris, is a special star. Contrary to a relatively common belief, however, it is *not* the brightest star in the sky; more than 50 other stars are either considerably brighter or comparable in brightness. Polaris is special because it so closely marks the direction of due north and because its altitude in your sky is nearly equal to your latitude on Earth, making it very useful in navigation in the Northern Hemisphere.

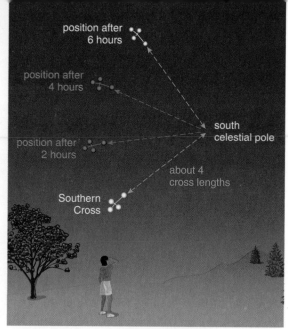

**a** In the Northern Hemisphere, the pointer stars of the Big Dipper point to Polaris, which lies within 1° of the north celestial pole. Note that the sky appears to turn *counterclockwise* around the north celestial pole.

**b** In the Southern Hemisphere, the Southern Cross points to the south celestial pole, which is not marked by any bright star. The sky appears to turn *clockwise* around the south celestial pole.

**FIGURE 2.14** The altitude of the celestial pole in your sky is equal to your latitude.

*look to see circumpolar stars? What portion of the celestial sphere is never visible in your sky?*

### Seasonal Changes in the Sky

The basic patterns of motion in the sky remain the same from one day to the next: The Sun, Moon, planets, and stars trace daily circles around the sky. However, if you observe the sky night after night, you will notice changes that cannot be seen over a single night. One pattern that becomes obvious after a few months is that the constellations visible at a particular time change with the seasons. For example, Orion is prominent in the evening sky in February, but by September it is visible only if you look shortly before dawn.

The nighttime constellations change with the seasons because of the Earth's orbit around the Sun. As shown in Figure 2.15, at different times of year we view the Sun from different places in our orbit. As a result, the Sun appears to move steadily *eastward* along a circular path through the constellations each year; we've already identified this path as the *ecliptic* (see Figure 2.4). The constellations along the ecliptic are called the constellations of the **zodiac**. (Tradition places 12 constellations along the zodiac, but the official borders include a wide swath of a thirteenth constellation, Ophiuchus.) The Sun's apparent location along the ecliptic determines which constellations you see at night. In late August, for example, the Sun appears to be in the constellation Leo, so you won't see the stars of Leo at all—they're

above your horizon only during the daytime. Aquarius, however, will be visible on your meridian at midnight because it is opposite Leo on the celestial sphere. Six months later, in February, it is Aquarius that cannot be seen and Leo that is on the meridian at midnight.

**TIME OUT TO THINK** *Based on Figure 2.15 and today's date, where among the zodiacal constellations does the Sun currently appear? What zodiacal constellation will be on your meridian at midnight? What zodiacal constellation will you see in the west shortly after sunset? Go outside at night to confirm your answers.*

The Sun's path through the daytime sky also changes with the seasons. Recall that the Earth's orientation *relative to the Sun* changes during the year because of the $23\frac{1}{2}°$ tilt of the Earth's axis (see Figure 1.13). This is also why the ecliptic crosses the celestial equator at angles of $23\frac{1}{2}°$ on the celestial sphere (see Figure 2.4). When the Sun appears north of the celestial equator, the Sun's daily path is long and high for the Northern Hemisphere (making the long, hot days of summer) but short and low for the Southern Hemisphere (making the short, cool days of winter). The situation for the two hemispheres is reversed when the Sun appears south of the celestial equator. At any particular location, you can notice this annual change by observing the Sun's position in your sky at the same time each day (Figure 2.16).

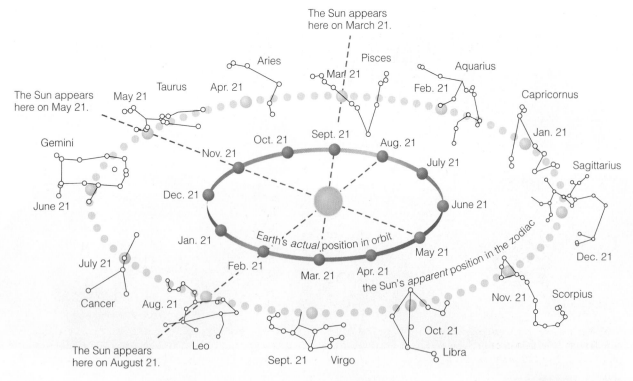

The Sun appears here on March 21.

Aries
Taurus
Apr. 21
Mar. 21
Pisces
Aquarius
Feb. 21
Capricornus

The Sun appears here on May 21.
May 21
Jan. 21

Gemini
Sagittarius

June 21

Oct. 21
Sept. 21
Aug. 21
July 21
June 21

Nov. 21
Dec. 21

Dec. 21

July 21
Jan. 21
Feb. 21
Mar. 21
Apr. 21
May 21

Earth's *actual* position in orbit

the Sun's apparent position in the zodiac

Nov. 21
Scorpius

Cancer
Aug. 21
Leo

Oct. 21
Libra

The Sun appears here on August 21.
Sept. 21   Virgo

**FIGURE 2.15** This diagram shows why the Sun appears to move steadily eastward along the ecliptic, through the constellations of the zodiac. As the Earth orbits the Sun, we see the Sun against the background of different zodiac constellations at different times of year. For example, on May 21, the Sun appears to be in Taurus, and on August 21, the Sun appears to be in Leo. Note that the zodiac constellations for particular dates are *not* the astrological sun signs (see "Common Misconceptions: Sun Signs" in Section 1.3).

**FIGURE 2.16** This composite photograph shows images of the Sun, always at the same time of day (mean solar time), snapped at 10-day intervals over an entire year. The three bright streaks show the path of the Sun's rise on three particular dates. This photograph looks east, so north is to the left and south is to the right; it was taken in the Northern Hemisphere. Notice that the Sun's altitude varies considerably: It is high in the summer and low in the winter. The sunrise position also changes: The Sun rises north of due east in the summer and south of due east in the winter. We'll discuss the reasons for the "figure 8" (called an *analemma*) in Chapter S1.

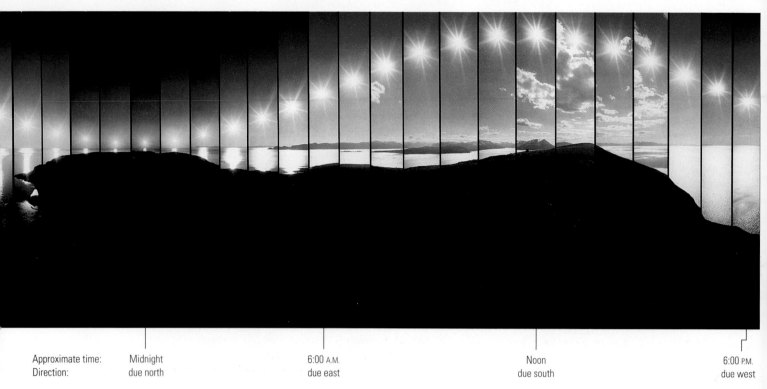

| Approximate time: | Midnight | 6:00 A.M. | Noon | 6:00 P.M. |
|---|---|---|---|---|
| Direction: | due north | due east | due south | due west |

**FIGURE 2.17** This sequence of photos shows the progression of the Sun around the horizon on the summer solstice at the Arctic Circle. Note that the Sun does not set but instead skims the northern horizon at midnight. It then gradually rises higher, reaching its highest point at noon, when it appears due south.

Moreover, just as the daily path of any star through your sky depends on your latitude, so does the daily path of the Sun at any time of year. During the summer, the Sun's daily path is longer at higher latitudes than at latitudes nearer the equator. The Sun's daily path is correspondingly shorter at higher latitudes in the winter. That is why higher latitudes have longer summer days and longer winter nights. In fact, the Sun becomes circumpolar at very high latitudes (within the *Arctic* or *Antarctic Circle*) in the summer. The Sun never sets during these summer days, giving these latitudes the name *land of the midnight Sun* (Figure 2.17). Of course, the name "land of noon darkness" is more appropriate in the winter, when the Sun never rises above the horizon at these high latitudes.

**Common Misconceptions: High Noon**

When is the Sun directly overhead in your sky? If you ask this question of friends and acquaintances, you'll probably find that many people answer "at noon." It's true that the Sun reaches its *highest* point each day when it crosses the meridian (hence the term "high noon," though the meridian crossing is rarely at precisely 12:00 [Section S1.3]), but unless you live in the Tropics (between latitudes 23.5°S and 23.5°N), the Sun is *never* directly overhead. In fact, any time you can see the Sun as you walk around, you can be sure it is *not* at your zenith; unless you are lying down, seeing objects at the zenith requires tilting your head back into a very uncomfortable position. (See Chapter S1 to learn how to determine the Sun's maximum altitude in your sky.)

## 2.3 The Moon, Our Constant Companion

Like all objects on the celestial sphere, each day the Moon rises in the east and sets in the west. Like the Sun, the Moon also moves gradually eastward through the constellations of the zodiac. However, it takes the Moon only about a month to make a complete circuit around the celestial sphere. If you carefully observe the Moon's position relative to bright stars over just a few hours, you can notice the Moon's drift among the constellations.

As the Moon moves through the sky, both its appearance and the time at which it rises and sets change with the cycle of **lunar phases**. Each com-

To Sun

**FIGURE 2.18** The phases demonstration. Your head represents the Earth and the ball represents the Moon. Hold the ball toward the Sun at arm's length. Then turn in a circle, always keeping the ball at arm's length and always looking directly at it. Be sure to swing the ball in a circle that carries it from being directly toward the Sun (when you are facing the Sun) to directly opposite the Sun (when you are facing away from the Sun). As you turn, you should see the ball go through phases just like the phases of the Moon.

plete cycle from one new moon to the next takes about $29\frac{1}{2}$ days—hence the origin of the word *month* (think of "moonth"). The easiest way to understand the lunar phases is with a simple demonstration. Use a small ball to represent the Moon while your head represents the Earth. If it's daytime and the Sun is shining, take your ball outside and watch how you see phases as you move the ball around your head (Figure 2.18); if it's dark or cloudy, you can place a flashlight a few meters away to represent the Sun. As you hold your ball at various places in its "orbit" around your head, you'll observe that phases result from just two basic facts:

1. At any particular time, half of the ball faces the Sun (or flashlight) and therefore is bright, while the other half faces away from the Sun and therefore is dark.

2. As you look at the ball, you see some combination of its bright and dark faces. This combination is the phase of the ball.

We see lunar phases for the same reason. Half of the Moon is always illuminated by the Sun, but the amount of this illuminated half that we see from Earth depends on the Moon's position in its orbit (Figure 2.19). The time of day during which the Moon is visible also depends on its phase. For example, full moon occurs when the Moon is opposite the Sun in the sky, so the full moon rises around sunset, reaches the meridian at midnight, and sets around sunrise.

## Common Misconceptions: Moon in the Daytime

In traditions and stories, night is so closely associated with the Moon that many people mistakenly believe that the Moon is visible only in the nighttime. In fact, the Moon is above the horizon as often in the daytime as at night, though it is easily visible only when its light is not drowned out by sunlight. For example, a first-quarter moon is easy to spot in the late afternoon as it rises through the eastern sky, and a third-quarter moon is visible in the morning as it heads toward the western horizon (see rise and set times in Figure 2.19). A related misconception appears in illustrations that show a star in the dark portion of the crescent moon (diagram below): A star in the dark portion appears to be in front of the Moon, which is impossible because the Moon is much closer to us than is any star.

This view, though common in art, can never occur because the star would have to be in front of the Moon.

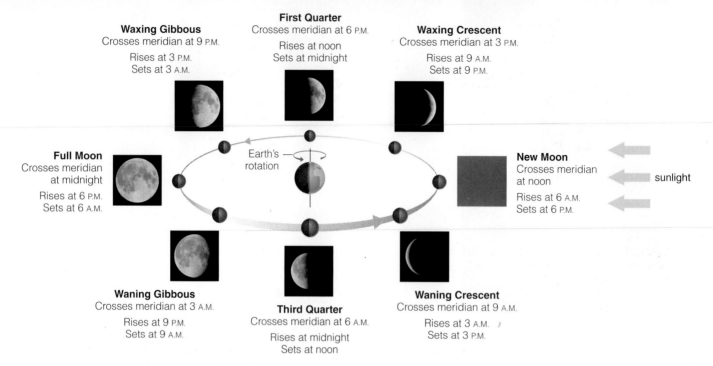

**Waxing Gibbous**
Crosses meridian at 9 P.M.
Rises at 3 P.M.
Sets at 3 A.M.

**First Quarter**
Crosses meridian at 6 P.M.
Rises at noon
Sets at midnight

**Waxing Crescent**
Crosses meridian at 3 P.M.
Rises at 9 A.M.
Sets at 9 P.M.

Earth's rotation

**Full Moon**
Crosses meridian at midnight
Rises at 6 P.M.
Sets at 6 A.M.

**New Moon**
Crosses meridian at noon
Rises at 6 A.M.
Sets at 6 P.M.

sunlight

**Waning Gibbous**
Crosses meridian at 3 A.M.
Rises at 9 P.M.
Sets at 9 A.M.

**Third Quarter**
Crosses meridian at 6 A.M.
Rises at midnight
Sets at noon

**Waning Crescent**
Crosses meridian at 9 A.M.
Rises at 3 A.M.
Sets at 3 P.M.

**FIGURE 2.19** The phases of the Moon depend on its location relative to the Sun in its orbit. To understand rise and set times, imagine yourself standing on the rotating Earth and looking at the Moon in a particular phase. (The times given are approximate; precise times depend on several factors including your latitude and the time of year. The photo for the new moon shows only a blue sky, because a new moon is above the horizon in daylight but cannot be seen because it is very close to the Sun in the sky.)

**TIME OUT TO THINK** *Suppose you go outside in the morning and notice that the visible face of the Moon is half light and half dark. Is this a first-quarter or third-quarter moon? How do you know?* (Hint: *Study Figure 2.19.*)

## Common Misconceptions: Moon on the Horizon

You've probably noticed that the full moon appears far larger when it is near the horizon than when it is high in your sky. However, this appearance is an illusion. If you measure the angular size of the full moon on a particular night, you'll find it is about the same whether it is near the horizon or high in the sky. (It actually appears slightly larger when overhead than when on the horizon, because you are viewing it from a position on Earth that is closer to the Moon by the radius of the Earth.) In fact, the Moon's angular size in the sky depends only on its distance from the Earth. Although this distance varies over the course of the Moon's monthly orbit, it does not change enough to cause a noticeable effect on a single night. (You can eliminate the illusion by viewing the Moon upside down between your legs when it is on the horizon.)

Although we see many *phases* of the Moon, we do not see many *faces*. In fact, from the Earth we always see (nearly) the same face of the Moon.[3] This tells us that the Moon must rotate once on its axis in the same time that it makes a single orbit of the Earth, as you can observe with another simple demonstration. Place a ball on a table to represent the Earth, while you represent the Moon. Start by facing the ball. If you do not rotate as you walk around the ball, you'll be looking away from it by the time you are halfway around your orbit (Figure 2.20a). The only way you can face the ball at all times is by completing exactly one rotation while you complete one orbit (Figure 2.20b). (We'll learn why the Moon's periods of rotation and orbit are the same in Chapter 5.)

The Moon's appearance is affected to a lesser degree by its varying distance from Earth. Just as the Earth's orbit around the Sun is not a perfect circle (see Figure 1.11), the Moon's orbit around the Earth is not perfectly circular. As a result, the Moon's distance from Earth varies during its orbit (from a minimum of about 356,000 kilometers to a maximum of

---

[3]Because the Moon's orbital speed varies while its rotation rate is steady, the Moon's visible face appears to wobble slightly back and forth as it orbits the Earth. This effect, called *libration*, allows us to see a total of about 59 percent of the Moon's surface by looking at different times of the month, even though we see only 50 percent of the Moon at any single time.

**a** If you do not rotate while walking around the model, you will not always face it.

**b** You will face the model at all times only if you rotate exactly once during each orbit.

**FIGURE 2.20** The fact that we always see the same face of the Moon means that the Moon must rotate once in the same amount of time that it takes to orbit the Earth once. You can see why by imagining that you are the Moon and walking around a model of the Earth.

about 407,000 kilometers, with an average distance of 380,000 kilometers). When the Moon happens to be closer to the Earth, it appears larger in angular size; when it is farther from Earth, it appears smaller in angular size.

### The View from the Moon

A good way to solidify your understanding of the lunar phases is to imagine that you live on the side of the Moon that faces the Earth. Look again at Figure 2.19. Note that at new moon you would be facing the day side of the Earth. Thus, you would see *full earth* when people on Earth see new moon. Similarly, at full moon you would be facing the night side of the Earth. Thus, you would see *new earth* when people on Earth see full moon. In general, you'd always see the Earth in a phase opposite the phase of the Moon that people on Earth see. Moreover, because the Moon always shows nearly the same face to Earth, the Earth would appear to hang nearly stationary in your sky. In addition, because the Moon takes about a month to rotate, your "day" would last about a month; that is, you'd have about 2 weeks of daylight followed by about 2 weeks of darkness as you watched the Earth hanging in your sky and going through its cycle of phases.

Thinking about the view from the Moon clarifies another interesting feature of the lunar phases: The dark portion of the lunar face is not *totally* dark. Imagine that you are standing on the Moon when it is in a crescent phase. Because it's nearly new moon as seen from Earth, you would see nearly full earth in your sky. Just as we can see at night by the light of the Moon, the light of the Earth would illuminate your night moonscape. (In fact, because the Earth

is much larger than the Moon, the full earth is much bigger and brighter in the lunar sky than the full moon is in Earth's sky.) This faint light illuminating the "dark" portion of the Moon's face is often called the *ashen light* or *earthshine*; it is the light that enables us to see the outline of the full face of the Moon even when the Moon is not full.

### Eclipses

Look once more at Figure 2.19. If this figure told the whole story of the lunar phases, a new moon would always block our view of the Sun, and the Earth would always prevent sunlight from reaching a full moon. More precisely, this figure makes it look as if the Moon's shadow should fall on Earth during new moon and that Earth's shadow should fall on the Moon during full moon. Any time one astronomical

---

**Common Misconceptions: The "Dark Side" of the Moon**

The term *dark side of the Moon* really should be used to mean the side facing away from the Sun. Unfortunately, *dark side* traditionally meant what would better be called the *far side*—the hemisphere that never can be seen from the Earth. Many people still refer to the far side as the "dark side," even though this side is not necessarily dark. For example, during new moon the far side faces the Sun and hence is completely sunlit; the only time the far side actually is completely dark is at full moon, when it faces away from both the Sun and the Earth.

**FIGURE 2.21** This painting represents the ecliptic plane as the surface of a pond. The Moon's orbit is slightly tilted to the ecliptic plane. Thus, in this illustration, the Moon spends half of each orbit above the pond surface and half below the surface; the points at which the orbit crosses the surface represent the *nodes* of the Moon's orbit. Eclipses occur only when the Moon both is at a node (splashing through the pond surface) *and* has a phase of either new moon or full moon—as is the case with the lower left and top right orbits shown. At all other times, new moons and full moons occur above or below the ecliptic plane, so no eclipse is possible.

object casts a shadow on another, we say that an **eclipse** is occurring. Thus, Figure 2.19 makes it look as if we should have an eclipse with every new moon and every full moon—but we don't.

The missing piece of the story in Figure 2.19 is that the Moon's orbit is inclined to the ecliptic plane by about 5°. An easy way to visualize this inclination is to imagine the ecliptic plane as the surface of a pond, as shown in Figure 2.21. Because of the inclination of its orbit, the Moon spends most of its time either above or below this surface. It crosses *through* this surface only twice during each orbit: once coming out and once going back in. The two points in each orbit at which the Moon crosses the surface are called the **nodes** of the Moon's orbit.

Figure 2.21 shows the position of the Moon's orbit at several different times of year. Note that the nodes are aligned the same way in each case (diag-

onally on the page). As a result, the nodes lie in a straight line with the Earth and the Sun only about twice each year. (For reasons we'll discuss shortly, it is not *exactly* twice each year.) Because an eclipse can occur only when the Earth, Moon, and Sun lie along a straight line, two conditions must be met simultaneously for an eclipse to occur:

1. The nodes of the Moon's orbit must be nearly aligned with the Earth and the Sun.

2. The phase of the Moon must be either new or full.

There are two basic types of eclipse. A **lunar eclipse** occurs when the Moon passes through the Earth's shadow and therefore can occur only at *full moon*. A **solar eclipse** occurs when the Moon's

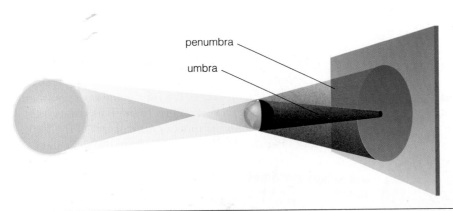

penumbra
umbra

**FIGURE 2.22** The shadow cast by an object in sunlight. Sunlight is fully blocked in the umbra and partially blocked in the penumbra.

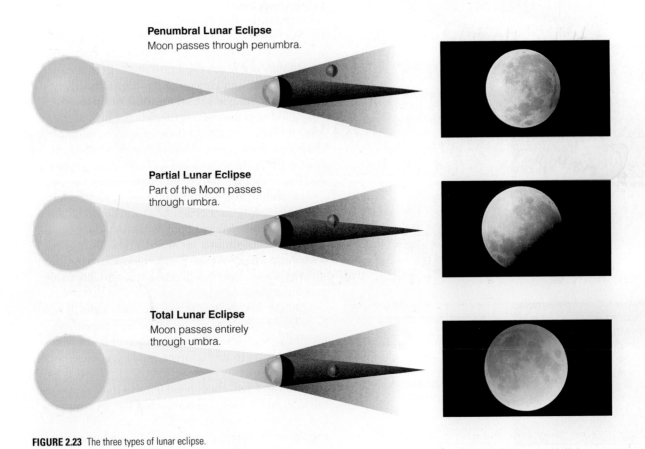

**Penumbral Lunar Eclipse**
Moon passes through penumbra.

**Partial Lunar Eclipse**
Part of the Moon passes through umbra.

**Total Lunar Eclipse**
Moon passes entirely through umbra.

**FIGURE 2.23** The three types of lunar eclipse.

shadow falls on the Earth and therefore can occur only at *new moon*. But the full story of eclipse types is more complex, because the shadow of the Moon or the Earth consists of two distinct regions: a central **umbra** where sunlight is completely blocked and a surrounding **penumbra** where sunlight is only partially blocked (Figure 2.22). Thus, an umbral shadow is totally dark, while a penumbral shadow is only slightly darker than no shadow.

*Lunar Eclipses* A lunar eclipse begins at the moment that the Moon's orbit first carries it into the Earth's penumbra. After that, we will see one of three types

of lunar eclipse (Figure 2.23). If the Sun, the Earth, and the Moon are nearly perfectly aligned, the Moon will pass through the Earth's umbra, and we will see a **total lunar eclipse**. If the alignment is somewhat less perfect, only part of the full moon will pass through the umbra (with the rest in the penumbra), and we will see a **partial lunar eclipse**. If the Moon passes *only* through the Earth's penumbra, we will see a **penumbral lunar eclipse**.

Penumbral eclipses are the most common type of lunar eclipse, but they are difficult to notice because the full moon darkens only slightly. Partial lunar

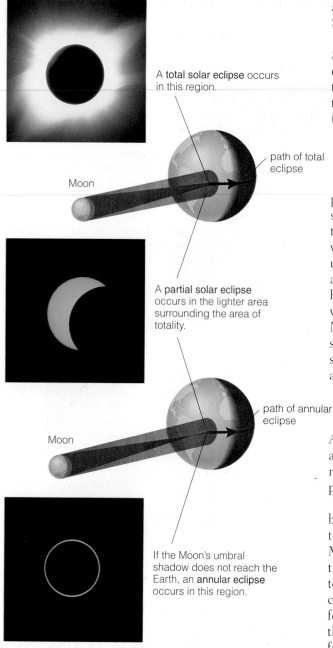

A **total solar eclipse** occurs in this region.

path of total eclipse

Moon

A **partial solar eclipse** occurs in the lighter area surrounding the area of totality.

path of annular eclipse

Moon

If the Moon's umbral shadow does not reach the Earth, an **annular eclipse** occurs in this region.

**FIGURE 2.24** The three types of solar eclipse. (The photographs on the left are, from top to bottom, a total solar eclipse, a partial solar eclipse, and an annular eclipse.)

eclipses are easier to see because the Earth's umbral shadow always clearly darkens part of the Moon's face. Note that the Earth's umbra always casts a curved shadow on the Moon, demonstrating that the Earth is round. A total lunar eclipse is particularly spectacular, because the Moon becomes dark and eerily red during **totality** (the time during which the Moon is entirely engulfed in the umbra)—dark because it is in shadow, and red because the Earth's

atmosphere bends some of the red light from the Sun around the Earth and toward the Moon.

*Solar Eclipses* We can also see three types of solar eclipse (Figure 2.24). If a solar eclipse occurs when the Moon is relatively close to the Earth in its orbit, the Moon's umbra touches a small area of the Earth (no more than about 270 kilometers in diameter). Anyone within this area will see a **total solar eclipse**. Surrounding this region of totality is a much larger area (typically about 7,000 kilometers in diameter) that falls within the Moon's penumbral shadow. Anyone within this region will see a **partial solar eclipse**, in which only part of the Sun is blocked from view. If the eclipse occurs when the Moon is relatively far from the Earth, the umbra may not reach the Earth at all. In that case, anyone in the small region of the Earth directly behind the umbra will see an **annular eclipse**, in which a ring of sunlight surrounds the disk of the Moon. (Again, anyone in the surrounding penumbral shadow will see a partial solar eclipse.) During any solar eclipse, the combination of the Earth's rotation and the orbital motion of the Moon causes the circular umbral and penumbral shadows to race across the face of the Earth at a typical speed of about 1,700 kilometers per hour (relative to the ground). As a result, the umbral (or annular) shadow traces a narrow path across the Earth, and totality (or annularity) never lasts more than a few minutes in any particular place.

A total solar eclipse is a spectacular sight. It begins when the disk of the Moon first appears to touch the Sun. Over the next couple of hours, the Moon appears to take a larger and larger "bite" out of the Sun. As totality approaches, the sky darkens and temperatures fall. Birds head back to their nests, and crickets begin their nighttime chirping. During the few minutes of totality, the Moon completely blocks the normally visible disk of the Sun, allowing the faint *corona* to be seen (Figure 2.25). The surrounding sky takes on a twilight glow, and planets and bright stars become visible in the daytime. As totality ends, the Sun slowly emerges from behind the Moon over the next couple of hours. However, because your eyes have adapted to the darkness, totality appears to end far more abruptly than it began.

*Predicting Eclipses* Few phenomena have so inspired and humbled humans throughout the ages as eclipses. For many cultures, eclipses were mystical events associated with fate or the gods, and countless stories and legends surround eclipses. One legend holds that the Greek philosopher Thales (c. 624–546 B.C.) successfully predicted the year (but presumably not the precise time) that a total eclipse of the Sun would be visible in the area where

## The Moon and Human Behavior

From myths of werewolves to stories of romance under the full moon, human culture is filled with claims that our behavior is influenced by the phase of the Moon. Can we say anything scientific about such claims?

The Moon clearly has important influences on Earth. The most noticeable influence is on the tides, for which the Moon is primarily responsible [Section 5.5]. However, tidal forces are felt only by relatively large objects, such as Earth, and we can rule out the possibility that tidal forces due to the Moon affect small objects such as people.

If a physical force from the Moon cannot affect human behavior, could we be influenced in other ways? Certainly, anyone who lives near the oceans is influenced by the rising and falling of the tides. For example, fishermen and boaters must follow the tides. Thus, although the Moon is not directly influencing their behavior, it is doing so indirectly through its effect on the oceans.

Many physiological patterns in many species appear to follow the lunar phases, and the human menstrual cycle is so close in length to a lunar month that it is difficult to believe the similarity is mere coincidence. Nevertheless, aside from the obvious physical cycles and the influence of tides on people who live near the oceans, claims that the lunar phase affects human behavior are difficult to verify scientifically. For example, although it is possible that the full moon brings out certain behaviors, it may also simply be that some behaviors are easier to exhibit when the sky is bright. Although a beautiful full moon may bring out your desire to walk on the beach under the moonlight, there is no scientific evidence that the full moon would affect you the same way if you lived in a cave and couldn't see it.

he lived, which is now part of Turkey. Coincidentally, the eclipse occurred as two opposing armies (the Medes and the Lydians) were massing for battle. The eclipse so frightened the armies that they put down their weapons, signed a treaty, and returned home. Because modern research shows that the only eclipse visible in that part of the world at about that time occurred on May 28, 585 B.C., we know the precise date on which the treaty was signed—the first historical event that can be dated precisely.

Much of the mystery of eclipses probably stems from the fact that they are relatively difficult to predict. Look again at Figure 2.21. The two periods each year when the nodes of the Moon's orbit are nearly aligned with the Sun are called **eclipse seasons**. Each eclipse season lasts a few weeks, so some type of lunar eclipse occurs during each eclipse season's full moon, and some type of solar eclipse occurs during its new moon. If Figure 2.21 told the whole story, eclipse seasons would occur every 6 months,

**FIGURE 2.25** This multiple-exposure photograph shows the progression of a total solar eclipse. Totality (central image) lasts only a few minutes, during which time we can see the faint corona around the outline of the Sun.

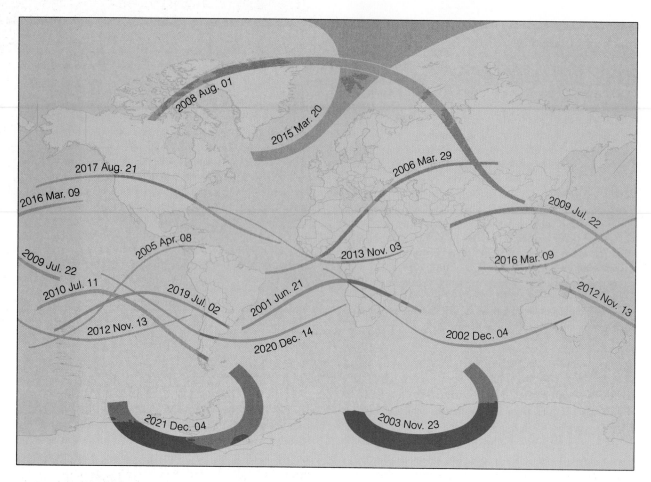

**FIGURE 2.26** This map shows the paths of totality for solar eclipses from 2001–2022. Paths of the same color represent eclipses occurring in successive saros cycles, separated by 18 years 11 days. For example, the 2019 eclipse occurs 18 years 11 days after the 2001 eclipse (both shown in green).

and predicting eclipses would be easy. For example, if eclipse seasons always occurred in January and July, eclipses would occur only on the dates of new and full moons in those months. But Figure 2.21 does not show one important fact about the Moon's orbit: The nodes slowly precess around the orbit. As a result, eclipse seasons actually occur slightly less than 6 months apart (about 173 days apart) and therefore do not recur in the same months year after year.

The combination of the changing dates of eclipse seasons and the $29\frac{1}{2}$-day cycle of lunar phases makes eclipses recur in a cycle of about 18 years $11\frac{1}{3}$ days. For example, if a solar eclipse were to occur today, another would occur 18 years $11\frac{1}{3}$ days from now. This roughly 18-year cycle is called the **saros cycle**.

Astronomers in many ancient cultures identified the saros cycle and therefore could predict *when* eclipses would occur. However, the saros cycle does not account for all the complications involved in predicting eclipses. If a solar eclipse occurred today,

the one that would occur 18 years $11\frac{1}{3}$ days from now would not be visible from the same places on the Earth and might not be of the same type (e.g., one might be total and the other only partial). As a result, no ancient culture achieved the ability to predict eclipses in every detail. Today, eclipses can be predicted because we know the precise details of the orbits of the Earth and the Moon; many astronomical software packages can do the necessary calculations. Table 2.1 lists upcoming total lunar eclipses, and Figure 2.26 shows paths of totality for upcoming total solar eclipses. It is well worth your while to plan a trip to see a total solar eclipse.

## 2.4 The Ancient Mystery of the Planets

Five planets are easy to find with the naked eye: Mercury, Venus, Mars, Jupiter, and Saturn. Mercury can be seen only infrequently, and then only just

### Table 2.1 Total Lunar Eclipses 2002–2010

| |
|---|
| May 16, 2003 |
| November 9, 2003 |
| May 4, 2004 |
| October 28, 2004 |
| March 3, 2007 |
| August 28, 2007 |
| February 21, 2008 |
| December 21, 2010 |

after sunset or before sunrise because it is so close to the Sun. Venus often shines brightly in the early evening in the west or before dawn in the east; if you see a very bright "star" in the early evening or early morning, it probably is Venus. Jupiter, when it is visible at night, is the brightest object in the sky besides the Moon and Venus. Mars is recognizable by its red color, but be careful not to confuse it with a bright red star. Saturn is easy to see with the naked eye, but because many stars are just as bright as Saturn, it helps to know where to look. (Also, planets tend not to twinkle as much as stars.) Sometimes several planets may appear close together in the sky, offering a particularly beautiful sight (Figure 2.27).

Like the Sun and the Moon, the planets appear to move slowly through the constellations of the zodiac. (The word *planet* comes from the Greek for "wandering star.") However, although the Sun and the Moon always appear to move eastward relative to the stars, the planets occasionally reverse course and appear to move *westward* through the zodiac. A period during which a planet appears to move westward relative to the stars is called a period of **apparent retrograde motion** (*retrograde* means "backward"). Figure 2.28 shows a period of apparent retrograde motion for Jupiter.

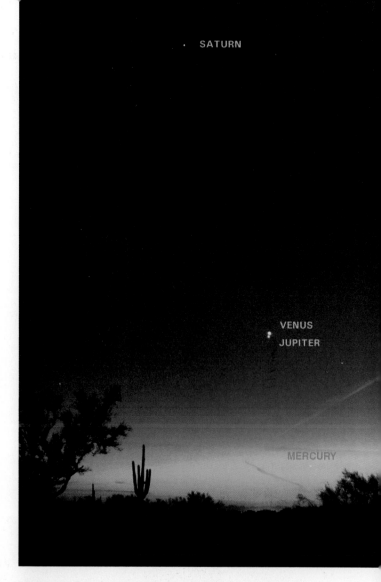

**FIGURE 2.27** This photograph shows Mercury, Venus, Jupiter, and Saturn appearing close together in the sky on February 23, 1999.

**FIGURE 2.28** This diagram shows Jupiter's approximate position among the stars in our sky during 2002–2003. Jupiter generally appears to drift eastward among the stars, but for about 4 months each year it turns back toward the west. Here, this apparent retrograde motion occurs between about December 2002 and April 2003. Note that Jupiter moves about one-twelfth of the way through the zodiac each year because it takes 12 years to complete one orbit of the Sun.

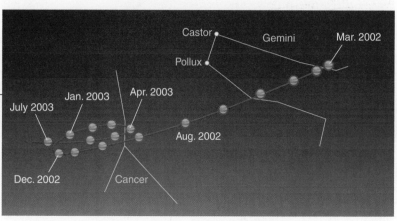

Dots represent Jupiter's approximate position at 1-month intervals.
(Jupiter not to scale.)

## Aristarchus

Until the early 1600s, nearly everyone believed that the Earth was the center of the universe. Yet Aristarchus (c. 310–230 B.C.) argued otherwise almost 2,000 years earlier.

Aristarchus proposed a Sun-centered system in about 260 B.C. Little of Aristarchus's work survives to the present day, so we cannot know why he made this proposal. It may have been an attempt to find a more natural explanation for the apparent retrograde motion of the planets. To account for the lack of detectable stellar parallax, Aristarchus suggested that the stars were extremely far away.

He further strengthened his argument by estimating the sizes of the Moon and the Sun. By observing the shadow of the Earth on the Moon during a lunar eclipse, Aristarchus estimated the Moon's diameter to be about one-third of the Earth's diameter—only slightly higher than the actual value. He then used a geometric argument, based on measuring the angle between the Moon and the Sun at first- and third-quarter phases, to conclude that the Sun must be larger than the Earth. (His measurements were imprecise, so he estimated the Sun's diameter to be about 7 times the Earth's, rather than the correct value of about 100 times.) His conclusion that the Sun is larger than the Earth may have been another reason why he felt that the Earth should orbit the Sun, rather than vice versa.

Like most scientific work, Aristarchus's work built upon the work of others. In particular, Heracleides (c. 388–315 B.C.) had suggested that the Earth rotates; Aristarchus may have drawn on this idea to explain the apparent daily rotation of the stars in our sky. Heracleides also was the first to suggest that not all heavenly bodies circle the Earth; based on the fact that Mercury and Venus always are close to the Sun in the sky, he argued that these two planets must orbit the Sun. Thus, in suggesting that all the planets orbit the Sun, Aristarchus was extending the ideas of Heracleides and others before him. Alas, Aristarchus's arguments were not widely accepted in ancient times and were revived only with the work of Copernicus some 1,800 years later.

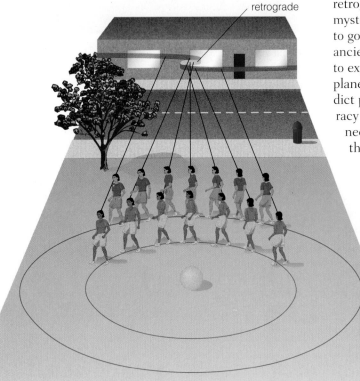

**FIGURE 2.29** The retrograde motion demonstration. Watch how your friend usually appears to you to move forward against the background of the building in the distance but appears to move backward as you catch up to and pass him or her in your "orbit."

Ancient astronomers could easily "explain" the daily paths of the stars through the sky by imagining that the celestial sphere was real and that it really rotated around the Earth each day. But the apparent retrograde motion of the planets posed a far greater mystery: What could cause the planets sometimes to go backward? As we'll discuss in Chapter 3, the ancient Greeks came up with some very clever ways to explain the occasional backward motion of the planets. But these ideas never allowed them to predict planetary positions in the sky with great accuracy (though the accuracy was sufficient for their needs at that time), because they were wedded to the incorrect idea of an Earth-centered universe.

In contrast, apparent retrograde motion has a simple explanation in a Sun-centered solar system. You can demonstrate it for yourself with the help of a friend (Figure 2.29). Pick a spot in an open field to represent the Sun. You can represent the Earth, walking counterclockwise around the Sun, while your friend represents a more distant planet (e.g., Mars, Jupiter, or Saturn) by walking counterclockwise around the Sun at a greater distance. Your friend should walk more slowly than you because more distant planets orbit the Sun more slowly. As you walk, watch how your friend appears to move relative to buildings or trees in the distance. Although both of you always walk the same way around the Sun, your friend will *appear* to move backward against the background during the part of your "orbit" at which you catch up to and pass him or her. (To understand the apparent retrograde motions of Mercury and Venus, which are closer to the Sun than is the Earth, simply switch places with your friend and repeat the demonstration.)

The apparent retrograde motion demonstration applies directly to the planets. For example, because Mars takes about 2 years to orbit the Sun (actually 1.88 years), it covers about half its orbit during the 1 year in which Earth makes a complete orbit. If you trace lines of sight from Earth to Mars from different points in their orbits, you will see that the line of sight usually moves eastward relative to the stars but moves westward during the time when Earth is passing Mars in its orbit (Figure 2.30). Like your friend in the demonstration, Mars never actually changes direction; it only *appears* to change direction from our perspective on Earth.

If the apparent retrograde motion of the planets is so readily explained by recognizing that the Earth is a planet, why wasn't this idea accepted in ancient times? In fact, the idea that the Earth goes around the Sun was suggested as early as 260 B.C. by the Greek astronomer Aristarchus and likely was debated many times thereafter. In a book published in 1440, the German scholar Nicholas of Cusa wrote that the Earth goes around the Sun. (Interestingly, although Galileo was punished by the Church for promoting the same belief two centuries later, Nicholas was ordained a priest in the year his book was published and later was elevated to cardinal.) The desire for a simple explanation for apparent retrograde motion was a primary motivation of Copernicus when he revived Aristarchus's idea in the early 1500s. (Copernicus was aware of the claim by Aristarchus but probably was not aware of the book by Nicholas of Cusa.)

Nevertheless, the idea that the Earth goes around the Sun did not gain wide acceptance among scientists until the work of Kepler and Galileo in the early 1600s [Section 5.3]. Although there were many reasons for the historic reluctance to abandon the idea of an Earth-centered universe, perhaps the most prominent involved the inability of ancient peoples to detect something called **stellar parallax**.

Extend your arm and hold up one finger. If you keep your finger still and alternately close your left eye and right eye, your finger will appear to jump back and forth against the background. This apparent shifting, called *parallax*, occurs simply because your two eyes view your finger from opposite sides of your nose. Note that if you move your finger closer to your face, the parallax increases. In con-

**FIGURE 2.30** The explanation for apparent retrograde motion. Follow the lines of sight from Earth to Mars in numerical order. The period during which the lines of sight shift *westward* relative to the distant stars is the period during which we observe apparent retrograde motion for Mars.

trast, if you look at a distant tree or flagpole instead of your finger, you probably cannot detect any parallax by alternately closing your left eye and right eye. Thus, parallax depends on distance, with nearer objects exhibiting greater parallax than more distant objects.

If you now imagine that your two eyes represent the Earth at opposite sides of its orbit around the Sun and that your finger represents a relatively nearby star, you have the idea of stellar parallax. That is, because we view the stars from different places in our orbit at different times of year, nearby stars should *appear* to shift back and forth against distant stars in the background during the course of the year (Figure 2.31). The Greeks actually expected stellar parallax in a slightly different way, because they believed that all stars lay on the same celestial sphere: They

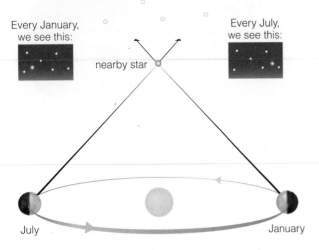

distant stars

Every January,
we see this:

nearby star

Every July,
we see this:

July

January

**FIGURE 2.31** Stellar parallax is an apparent shift in the position of a nearby star as we look at it from different places in the Earth's orbit. This figure is greatly exaggerated; in reality, the amount of shift is far too small to detect with the naked eye.

1. The Earth orbits the Sun but the stars are so far away that stellar parallax is undetectable to the naked eye.

2. There is no stellar parallax because the Earth doesn't move; it is the center of the universe.

Unfortunately, with notable exceptions such as Aristarchus, ancient astronomers rejected the correct answer (1) because they could not imagine that the stars could be *that* far away. Today, we can detect stellar parallax with the aid of telescopes, thereby providing direct proof that the Earth really does orbit the Sun. Careful measurements of stellar parallax also provide the most reliable means of measuring distances to nearby stars [Section 15.2].

**TIME OUT TO THINK** *How far apart are opposite sides of the Earth's orbit? How far away are the nearest stars? Describe the challenge of detecting stellar parallax. It may help to visualize the Earth's orbit and the distance to stars on the 1-to-10-billion scale used in Chapter 1.*

Thus, the ancient mystery of the planets drove much of the historical debate over the Earth's place in the universe. In many ways, the modern technological society that we take for granted today can be traced directly back to the scientific revolution that began because of the quest to explain the slow wandering of the planets among the stars in our sky.

assumed that (if Earth orbited the Sun) at different times of year we would be closer to different parts of the celestial sphere, which would change the angular separations of stars. However, no matter how hard they searched, ancient astronomers could find no sign of stellar parallax. They therefore concluded that one of the following must be true:

---

**THINKING ABOUT . . .**

### And Yet It Moves

On June 22, 1633, Galileo was brought before a Church inquisition in Rome and ordered to recant his heretical view that the Earth goes around the Sun rather than vice versa. Fearing for his life, Galileo recanted as ordered. However, legend has it that, as he rose from his knees following his renunciation, he whispered under his breath, *Eppur si muove*—Italian for "And yet it moves." (Given the likely consequences if church officials had heard him say this, most historians doubt the veracity of this legend.) The evidence supporting the idea that the Earth moves was quite strong by the mid-1600s, but it was still indirect. Today, we have much more direct proof.

French physicist Jean Foucault provided the first direct proof of *rotation* in 1851. Foucault built a large pendulum that he carefully started swinging. Because any pendulum tends to swing always in the same plane, the Earth's rotation made Foucault's pendulum appear to twist slowly in a circle. Today, *Foucault pendulums* are a popular attraction at many science centers and museums. A second direct proof that the Earth rotates is provided by the *Coriolis effect*, first described by French physicist

Gustave Coriolis (1792–1843). The Coriolis effect, which would not happen if the Earth were not rotating, is responsible for things such as the swirling of hurricanes and the fact that missiles that travel great distances on the Earth deviate from straight-line paths [Section 10.3].

Stellar parallax provides direct proof that the Earth orbits the Sun, and it was first measured by German astronomer Friedrich Bessel in 1838. However, another direct proof that the Earth orbits the Sun actually was found about a century earlier by English astronomer James Bradley (1693–1762). To understand Bradley's proof, imagine that starlight is like rain, falling straight down. If you are standing still you should hold your umbrella straight over your head, but if you are walking through the rain you should tilt your umbrella forward, because your motion makes the rain appear to be coming down at an angle. Bradley discovered that observing light from stars requires that telescopes be slightly tilted in the direction of Earth's motion—just like the umbrella; this effect is called the *aberration of starlight*.

## THE BIG PICTURE

In this chapter, we surveyed the phenomena of our sky. Keep the following "big picture" ideas in mind as you continue your study of astronomy:

- You can enhance your enjoyment of learning astronomy by spending time outside observing the sky. The more you learn about the appearance and apparent motions of the sky, the more you will appreciate what you can see in the universe.

- From our vantage point on Earth, it is convenient to imagine that we are at the center of a great celestial sphere—even though we really are on a planet orbiting a star in a vast universe. We can then understand what we see in the local sky by thinking about how the celestial sphere appears from our latitude.

- Most of the phenomena of the sky are relatively easy to observe and understand. But the more complex phenomena, particularly eclipses and apparent planetary motion, challenged our ancestors for thousands of years and helped drive the development of science and technology.

### Review Questions

1. What is a *constellation?* How is a constellation related to a pattern of stars in the sky?

2. What is the *celestial sphere?* Describe the major features shown on a model of the celestial sphere.

3. What is the *ecliptic,* and how is it related to the ecliptic plane?

4. What is the *Milky Way* in our sky, and how is it related to the Milky Way Galaxy?

5. Why does the local sky look like a dome? Define *horizon, zenith,* and *meridian.* Describe how you can locate an object in the local sky by its altitude and its direction along the horizon.

6. Explain why we can measure only *angular* sizes and distances for objects in the sky. What are *arcminutes* and *arcseconds?*

7. Briefly describe how and why the sky varies with latitude.

8. Briefly describe how and why the sky changes with the seasons.

9. Describe the Moon's cycle of *phases* and explain why we see phases of the Moon.

10. Why don't we see an eclipse at every new and full moon? Describe the conditions that must be met to see a solar or lunar eclipse.

11. Why are eclipses so difficult to predict? Explain the importance of *eclipse seasons* and the *saros cycle* to eclipse prediction.

12. What is the *apparent retrograde motion* of the planets? Why was it difficult for ancient astronomers to explain but easy for us to explain?

13. What is *stellar parallax?* Describe the role it played in making ancient astronomers believe in an Earth-centered universe.

### Discussion Questions

1. *Geocentric Language.* Many common phrases reflect the ancient Earth-centered view of our universe. For example, the phrase "the Sun rises each day" implies that the Sun is really moving over the Earth. In fact, the Sun only *appears* to rise as the rotation of the Earth carries us to a place where we can see the Sun in our sky. Identify other common phrases that imply an Earth-centered viewpoint.

2. *Flat Earth Society.* Believe it or not, there is an organization called the Flat Earth Society, whose members hold that the Earth is flat and that all indications to the contrary (such as pictures of the Earth from space) are fabrications made as part of a conspiracy to hide the truth from the public. Discuss the evidence for a round Earth and how you can check it for yourself. In light of the evidence, is it possible that the Flat Earth Society is correct? Defend your opinion.

### Problems

*Sensible Statements?* For **problems 1–8**, decide whether the statement is sensible and explain why it is or is not. (For an example, see Chapter 1 problems.)

1. If you had a very fast spaceship, you could travel to the celestial sphere in about a month.

2. The constellation Orion didn't exist when my grandfather was a child.

3. When I looked into the dark fissure of the Milky Way with my binoculars, I saw what must have been a cluster of distant galaxies.

4. Last night the Moon was so big that it stretched for a mile across the sky.

5. I live in the United States, and during my first trip to Argentina I saw many constellations that I'd never seen before.

6. Last night I saw Jupiter right in the middle of the Big Dipper. (*Hint:* Is the Big Dipper part of the zodiac?)

7. Last night I saw Mars move westward through the sky in its apparent retrograde motion. (*Hint:* How long does it take to notice apparent retrograde motion?)

8. Although all the known stars appear to rise in the east and set in the west, we might someday discover a star that will appear to rise in the west and set in the east.

9. *View from Afar.* Describe how the Milky Way Galaxy would look in the sky of someone observing from a planet around a star in M31.

10. *Your View.*

    a. Find your latitude and longitude, and state the source of your information.

    b. Describe the altitude and direction in your sky at which the north or south celestial pole appears.

    c. Is Polaris a circumpolar star in your sky? Explain.

    d. Describe the path of the meridian in your sky.

    e. Describe the path of the celestial equator in your sky. (*Hint:* Study Figure 2.12.)

11. *View from the Moon.* Suppose you lived on the Moon, near the center of the face that we see from Earth.

    a. During the phase of full moon, what phase would you see for Earth? Would it be daylight or dark where you live?

    b. On Earth, we see the Moon rise and set in our sky each day. If you lived on the Moon, would you see the Earth rise and set? Why or why not? (*Hint:* Remember that the Moon always keeps the same face toward Earth.)

    c. What would you see when people on Earth were experiencing an eclipse? Answer for both solar and lunar eclipses.

12. *A Farther Moon.* Suppose the distance to the Moon was twice its actual value. Would it still be possible to have a total solar eclipse? An annular eclipse? A total lunar eclipse? Explain.

13. *A Smaller Earth.* Suppose the Earth was smaller in size. Would solar eclipses be any different? If so, how? What about lunar eclipses? Explain.

14. *Observing Planetary Motion.* Find out what planets are currently visible in your evening sky. At least once a week, observe the planets and draw a diagram showing the position of each visible planet relative to stars in a zodiac constellation. From week to week, note how the planets are moving relative to the stars. Can you see any of the apparently "erratic" features of planetary motion? Explain.

15. *A Connecticut Yankee.* Find the book *A Connecticut Yankee in King Arthur's Court,* by Mark Twain. Read the portion that deals with the Connecticut Yankee's prediction of an eclipse (or read the entire book). In a one- to two-page essay, summarize the episode and how it helps the Connecticut Yankee gain power.

## Web Projects

Find useful links for Web projects on the text Web site.

1. *Sky Information.* Search the Web for sources of daily information about sky phenomena (such as lunar phases, times of sunrise and sunset, and unusual sky events). Identify and briefly describe your favorite source.

2. *Constellations.* Search the Web for information about the constellations and their mythology. Write a short report about one or more constellations.

3. *Upcoming Eclipse.* Find information about an upcoming solar or lunar eclipse that you might have a chance to witness. Write a short report about how you could best witness the eclipse, including any necessary travel to a viewing site, and what you can expect to see. Bonus: Describe how you could photograph the eclipse.

*Socrates: Shall we make astronomy the next study? What
do you say?*

*Glaucon: Certainly. A working knowledge of the seasons,
months, and years is beneficial to everyone, to commanders
as well as to farmers and sailors.*

*Socrates: You make me smile, Glaucon. You are so afraid that
the public will accuse you of recommending unprofitable studies.*

PLATO, REPUBLIC

# CHAPTER S1

# Celestial Timekeeping and Navigation

In ancient times, the practical need for timekeeping and navigation was one of the primary reasons for the study of astronomy. The celestial origins of timekeeping and navigation are still evident. The time of day comes from the location of the Sun in the local sky, the month comes from the Moon's cycle of phases, and the year comes from the Sun's annual path along the ecliptic. With regard to navigation, we've already learned how the position of the north or south celestial pole can tell us latitude (see Section 2.2).

Today, we can tell the time by glancing at an inexpensive electronic watch and navigate with hand-held devices that receive signals from satellites of the global positioning system (GPS). But knowing the celestial basis of timekeeping and navigation can still be useful, particularly for understanding the rich history of astronomical discovery. In this chapter, we will explore the apparent motions of Sun, Moon, and planets in greater detail than we have previously, enabling us to study the principles of celestial timekeeping and navigation.

## S1.1 Astronomical Time Periods

People began measuring time long before anyone knew that the Earth is round or that it is a planet that orbits the Sun. The only celestial motions that mattered were those that could be seen in the local sky. Many ancient cultures carefully tracked the motion of the Sun, Moon, planets, and stars through the sky. These ancient observations established astronomically based time periods such as the day, month, and year. Let's begin our study of timekeeping by examining several important astronomical time periods.

### Solar Versus Sidereal Day

We often think of our 24-hour day as the Earth's rotation period, but that's not quite true. The Earth's rotation period is the time it takes the Earth to complete one full rotation. Because the Earth's daily rotation makes the celestial sphere appear to rotate around us (see Figure 2.8), we can measure the rotation period by timing how long it takes the celestial sphere to make one full turn through the local sky. For example, we could start a stopwatch at the moment when a particular star is on our meridian (the semicircle stretching from due south, through the zenith, to due north [Section 2.2]), then stop the watch the next day when the same star again is on the meridian (Figure S1.1a). Measured in this way, the Earth's rotation period is about 23 hours 56 minutes (more precisely, $23^h 56^m 4.09^s$)—or about 4 minutes short of 24 hours. This time period is called a **sidereal day**, because it is measured relative to the apparent motion of stars in the local sky; *sidereal* (pronounced sy-dear-ee-al) means "related to the stars."

Our 24-hour day, which we call a **solar day**, is based on the time it takes for the *Sun* to make one circuit around our local sky. We could measure this time period by starting the stopwatch at the moment when the Sun is on our meridian one day and stopping it when the Sun reaches the meridian the next day (Figure S1.1b). The solar day is indeed 24 hours on average, although it varies slightly over the course of a year (see the Thinking About box on p. 71).

A simple demonstration shows why a solar day is slightly longer than a sidereal day. Set an object on a table to represent the Sun, and stand a few steps away from the object to represent the Earth. Point at the Sun and imagine that you also happen to be pointing toward some distant star. If you rotate (counterclockwise) while standing in place, you'll again be pointing at the Sun and the star after one full rotation (Figure S1.2a). But because the Earth orbits the Sun at the same time that it rotates, you can make the demonstration more realistic by taking a couple of steps around the Sun (counterclockwise) while you are rotating (Figure S1.2b). After one full rotation, you will again be pointing in the direction of the distant star; hence, this represents a sidereal day. However, because of your orbital motion, you'll need to rotate slightly more than once to be pointing again at the Sun; it is this "extra" bit of rotation that makes a solar day longer than a sidereal day.

The only problem with this demonstration is that it exaggerates the Earth's daily orbital motion. In reality, the Earth moves about 1° per day around its orbit (because it makes a full 360° orbit in 1 year, or about 365 days). Thus, if you recall that a single rotation means rotating 360°, the Earth must actually rotate about 361° with each solar day (Figure S1.2c).

**FIGURE S1.1** (**a**) A sidereal day is the time it takes any star to make a circuit of the local sky, that is, the time from its meridian crossing one day to its meridian crossing the next day. (**b**) A solar day is measured similarly, but by timing the Sun rather than a star.

a

b

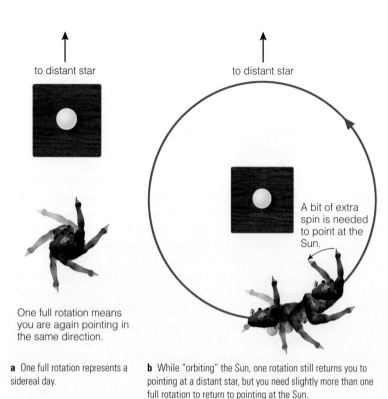

**a** One full rotation represents a sidereal day.

**b** While "orbiting" the Sun, one rotation still returns you to pointing at a distant star, but you need slightly more than one full rotation to return to pointing at the Sun.

**c** The Earth travels about 1° per day around its orbit, so a solar day requires about 361° of rotation.

**FIGURE S1.2** A demonstration showing why a solar day is slightly longer than a sidereal day.

The extra 1° rotation accounts for the extra 4 minutes by which the solar day is longer than the sidereal day. (To see why it takes 4 minutes to rotate 1°, note that the Earth rotates 360° in about 23 hours 56 minutes, or 1,436 minutes. Thus, 1° of rotation takes $\frac{1}{360} \times 1{,}436$ minutes $\approx 4$ minutes.)

### Synodic Versus Sidereal Month

As we discussed in Chapter 2, our month comes from the Moon's $29\frac{1}{2}$-day cycle of phases. More technically, the $29\frac{1}{2}$-day period required for each cycle of phases is called a **synodic month**. The word *synodic* comes from the Latin *synod*, which means "meeting," so a synodic month gets its name because the Sun and the Moon "meet" in the sky with every new moon.

Just as a solar day is not the Earth's true rotation period, a synodic month is not the Moon's true orbital period: the Earth's motion around the Sun means that the Moon must complete more than one full orbit of the Earth from one new moon to the next (Figure S1.3). The Moon's true orbital period, or **sidereal month**, is only about $27\frac{1}{3}$ days. Like the sidereal day, the sidereal month gets its name because it describes how long it takes the Moon to complete an orbit relative to the positions of distant stars.

### Tropical Versus Sidereal Year

A year is related to the Earth's orbital period, but again there are two slightly different definitions for the length of the year. The time it takes for the Earth to complete one orbit relative to the stars is called a **sidereal year**. But our calendar is based on the cycle of the seasons, which we can measure from the time of the spring equinox one year to the spring equinox the next year. This time period, called a **tropical year**, is about 20 minutes shorter than the sidereal year.

**FIGURE S1.3** The Moon completes one 360° orbit in about $27\frac{1}{3}$ days (a sidereal month), but the time from new moon to new moon is about $29\frac{1}{2}$ days (a synodic month).

Earth travels about 30° per month around the Sun, so the Moon must orbit around Earth about 360° + 30° = 390° from new moon to new moon.

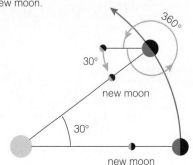

(A 20-minute difference might not seem like much, but it would make a calendar based on the sidereal year get out of sync with the seasons by 1 day every 72 years—a difference that would add up over centuries.)

The difference between the sidereal year and the tropical year arises from the Earth's 26,000-year cycle of axis precession [Section 1.3]. Recall that precession not only changes the orientation of the axis in space, but also changes the locations in the Earth's orbit at which the seasons occur. Each year, the location of the equinoxes and solstices among the stars shifts about $\frac{1}{26,000}$ of the way around the orbit. Note that $\frac{1}{26,000}$ of a year is about 20 minutes, which explains the 20-minute difference between the tropical and sidereal years.

### Planetary Periods (Synodic Versus Sidereal)

Planetary periods are not used in our modern time-keeping, but some ancient cultures used them. For example, the Mayan calendar was based in part on the apparent motions of Venus. Today, understanding planetary periods can help us make sense of what we see in the sky.

A planet's **sidereal period** is the time it takes to orbit the Sun; as usual, it has the name *sidereal* because it is measured relative to distant stars. For example, Jupiter's sidereal period is about 12 years (more precisely, 11.86 years), so it takes about 12 years for Jupiter to make a complete circuit around the constellations of the zodiac. Thus, Jupiter appears to move through roughly one zodiac constellation each year; if Jupiter is in Gemini this year (as it is in 2002), it will be in Cancer next year and Leo the following year, returning to Gemini in 12 years.

A planet's **synodic period** is the time between being lined up with the Sun in our sky one time and the next similar alignment; again, the term *synodic* refers to the planet's "meeting" the Sun in the sky. Figure S1.4 shows that the situation is somewhat different for planets nearer the Sun than Earth (that is, Mercury and Venus) and planets farther away (all the rest of the planets).

Look first at the situation for the more distant planet in Figure S1.4. As seen from Earth, this planet will sometimes line up with the Sun in what we call a **conjunction**. At other special times, it will appear exactly opposite the Sun in our sky, which we call **opposition**. We cannot see the planet during conjunction with the Sun, because it is hidden by the Sun's glare and rises and sets with the Sun in our sky. At opposition, the planet moves through the sky like the full moon, rising at sunset, reaching the meridian at midnight, and setting at dawn. Note that the planet is closest to Earth at opposition and hence appears brightest at this time.

Figure S1.4 shows that planets *nearer* than Earth to the Sun have two conjunctions—an "inferior conjunction" between the Earth and the Sun and a "superior conjunction" when the planet appears behind the Sun as seen from Earth—rather than one conjunction and one opposition. The planet is hidden by the Sun's glare at both conjunctions. Mercury and Venus usually appear slightly above or below the Sun at inferior conjunction, because they have slightly different orbital planes than the Earth. Occasionally, however, these planets appear to move across the disk of the Sun during inferior conjunction, creating a *transit* (Figure S1.5). Mercury transits occur an average of a dozen times per century, with the next two coming on May 7, 2003, and November 8, 2006. Venus transits typically come in pairs separated by a century or more. Its next pair of transits will occur on June 8, 2004, and June 6, 2012.

The inner planets are best viewed when they are near their points of greatest **elongation**, that is, when they are farthest from the Sun in our sky. At its greatest eastern elongation, Venus appears about 46° east of the Sun in our sky, which means it shines brightly in the evening sky. Similarly, at its greatest western elongation, Venus appears about 46° west of the Sun in our sky, shining brightly in the predawn

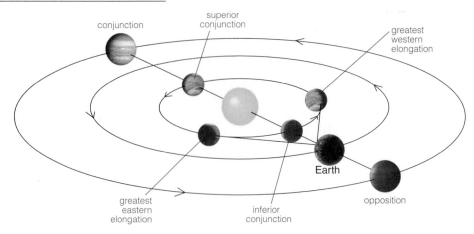

**FIGURE S1.4** This diagram shows important positions of planets relative to the Earth and the Sun. For a planet farther from the Sun than Earth (such as Mars, Jupiter, Saturn), conjunction is when it appears aligned with the Sun in the sky, and opposition is when it appears on our meridian at midnight. Planets nearer the Sun (Mercury and Venus) have two conjunctions and never get farther from the Sun in our sky than at their greatest elongations.

conjunction

superior conjunction

greatest western elongation

greatest eastern elongation

inferior conjunction

Earth

opposition

**FIGURE S1.5** NASA's *TRACE* satellite captured this image of a Mercury transit on November 15, 1999. The photograph was taken with ultraviolet light, so the colors are not real; the structures seen with ultraviolet light are patches of hot gas just above the Sun's visible surface.

sky. In between the times when Venus appears in the morning sky and the times when it appears in the evening sky, Venus disappears from view for a few weeks with each conjunction. Mercury's pattern is similar, but because it is closer to the Sun it never appears more than about 28° from the Sun in our sky. (Mercury's angular distance from the Sun at greatest elongation varies from about 18° to 28°, depending on where it is in its fairly eccentric orbit.) This makes it difficult to see Mercury, because it is almost always obscured by the glare of the Sun.

**TIME OUT TO THINK** *Based on Figure S1.4, explain why neither Mercury nor Venus can ever be on the meridian in the midnight sky.*

Measuring a planet's synodic period is fairly easy, because it requires simply observing its position relative to the Sun in the sky. In contrast, we must calculate a planet's sidereal period from the geometry of planetary orbits. Copernicus was the first to perform these calculations, and they revealed a simple pattern in which more distant planets had longer sidereal periods. The simplicity of this pattern helped convince him that his idea of a Sun-centered solar system was correct. (We'll discuss Copernicus further in Chapter 5.)

## S1.2 Daily Timekeeping

Now that we have discussed astronomical time periods, we can turn our attention to modern measures of time. Our clock is based on the 24-hour solar day. You are probably familiar with the basic principles. For example, we usually think of noon as the time when the Sun crosses the meridian and hence is highest in the local sky. However, several subtleties make this only an approximation. Let's investigate various ways of keeping daily time.

### Apparent Solar Time

If we base time on the Sun's *actual* position in the local sky, as is the case when we use a sundial (Figure S1.6), we are measuring **apparent solar time**. Noon is the precise moment when the Sun is on the meridian and the sundial casts its shortest shadow. Before noon, when the Sun is on its way toward the meridian, the apparent solar time is *ante meridian*, or *a.m.* (*ante* means "before"). For example, if the Sun will reach the meridian 2 hours from now, the apparent solar time is 10 A.M. After noon, the apparent solar time is *post meridian*, or *p.m.* (*post* means "after"). If the Sun crossed the meridian 3 hours ago, the

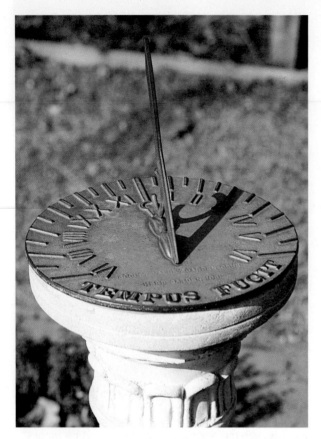

**FIGURE S1.6** A basic sundial consists of a stick, or *gnomon,* that casts a shadow, and a dial marked by numerals. Here, the shadow is on the Roman numeral III, indicating that the apparent solar time is 3:00 P.M. (The portion of the dial without numerals represents nighttime hours.) Because the Sun's path across the local sky depends on latitude, a particular sundial will be accurate only for a particular latitude.

apparent solar time is 3 P.M. Note that noon and midnight are *neither* a.m. nor p.m.; we must specify whether we mean 12:00 noon or 12:00 midnight. (Alternatively, we can use a 24-hour clock, in which case midnight is 0:00, noon is 12:00, 1 P.M. is 13:00, and so on.)

**TIME OUT TO THINK** *Is it daytime or night-time at 12:01 A.M.? 12:01 P.M.? Explain.*

### Mean Solar Time

Suppose you set your watch to read precisely 12:00 when a sundial reads noon today. If every solar day were precisely 24 hours, your watch would always remain synchronized with the sundial. However, while 24 hours is the *average* length of the solar day, the actual length of the solar day varies throughout the year. As a result, your watch will not remain per-fectly synchronized with the sundial. For example, your watch is likely to read a few seconds before or after 12:00 when the sundial reads noon tomorrow,

and over the course of the year your watch may read anywhere from 17 minutes before to 15 minutes after 12:00 when the sundial reads noon.

If you set your watch so it reads precisely 12:00 when the Sun is on the meridian on an "average" day, then your watch is set to read **mean solar time** (*mean* is another word for *average*). Mean solar time is more convenient than apparent solar time because, once set, a reliable mechanical or electronic clock can always tell you the mean solar time. In contrast, measuring apparent solar time requires a sundial, which is useless at night or when it is cloudy.

Note that, like apparent solar time, mean solar time is a *local* measure of time. That is, it varies with longitude because of the Earth's west-to-east rota-tion. You're probably familiar with this idea; for exam-ple, you probably know that clocks in New York are set 3 hours ahead of clocks in Los Angeles. When clocks are set precisely according to local mean solar time, they vary even over relatively short east–west distances. For example, mean solar clocks in central Los Angeles are about 2 minutes behind mean solar clocks in Pasadena, because Pasadena is slightly farther east.

### Standard, Daylight, and Universal Time

Clocks reading mean solar time were common dur-ing the early history of the United States. However, by the late 1800s, widespread railroad travel made the use of mean solar time increasingly problematic. Some states had dozens of different "official" times, usually corresponding to mean solar time in dozens of different cities, and each railroad company made schedules according to its own "railroad time." The many time systems made it difficult for passengers to follow the scheduling of trains. On November 18, 1883, the railroad companies agreed to a new system that divided the United States into four time zones, setting all clocks within each zone to the same time. That was the birth of **standard time**, which divides the world today into time zones (Figure S1.8). De-pending on where you live within a time zone, your standard time may vary by up to a half-hour or more from your mean solar time. (In principle, the stan-dard time in a particular time zone is the mean solar time in the *center* of the time zone. In that case, local mean solar time would always be within a half-hour of standard time. However, time zones often have unusual shapes to conform to social, economic, and political realities, so larger variations between stan-dard time and mean solar time sometimes occur.)

In most parts of the United States, clocks are set to standard time for only part of the year. Between the first Sunday in April and the last Sunday in Octo-ber, most of the United States changes to **daylight**

## Solar Days and the Analemma

The average length of a solar day is 24 hours, but the precise length varies over the course of the year. Two effects contribute to this variation.

The first effect is due to the Earth's varying orbital speed. Recall that the Earth moves slightly faster when it is closer to the Sun in its orbit and slightly slower when it is farther from the Sun [Section 1.3]. Thus, the Earth moves slightly farther along its orbit each day when it is closer to the Sun, which means that the solar day requires more than the average amount of "extra" rotation (see Figure S1.2) during these periods—making these solar days longer than average. Similarly, the solar day requires less than the average amount of "extra" rotation when it is in the portion of its orbit farther from the Sun—making these solar days shorter than average.

The second effect is due to the tilt of the Earth's axis, which causes the ecliptic to be inclined by $23\frac{1}{2}°$ to the celestial equator on the celestial sphere. Because the length of a solar day depends on the Sun's *eastward* motion along the ecliptic, the inclination would cause solar days to vary in length even if the Earth's orbit were perfectly circular. To see why, suppose the Sun appeared to move exactly 1° per day along the ecliptic. Around the times of the solstices, this motion would be entirely eastward, making the solar day slightly longer than average. Around the times of the equinoxes, when the motion along the ecliptic has a significant northward or southward component, the solar day would be slightly shorter than average.

Together, the two effects make the actual length of solar days vary by up to about 25 seconds (either way) from the 24-hour average. Moreover, because the effects accumulate at particular times of year, the apparent solar time can differ by as much as 17 minutes from the mean solar time. The net result is often depicted visually by an **analemma**, which is printed on many globes (Figure S1.7a; Figure 2.16 shows a photographic version).

By using the horizontal scale on the analemma in Figure S1.7a, you can convert between mean and apparent solar time for any date. (The vertical scale shows the declination of the Sun, which is discussed in Section S1.5.) For example, the dashed line shows that on November 10 a mean solar clock is about 17 minutes "behind the Sun," or behind apparent solar time; that is, if the apparent solar time is 6:00 P.M., the mean solar time is only 5:43 P.M. The discrepancy between mean and apparent solar time is called the **equation of time**; it is often plotted as a graph, which gives the same results as reading from the analemma (Figure S1.7b).

The discrepancy between mean and apparent solar time also explains why the times of sunrise and sunset don't follow seasonal patterns perfectly. For example, the winter solstice around December 21 has the shortest daylight hours (in the Northern Hemisphere), but the earliest sunset occurs around December 7, when the Sun is still well "behind" mean solar time.

---

**FIGURE S1.7** Two ways of illustrating discrepancies between mean and apparent solar time.

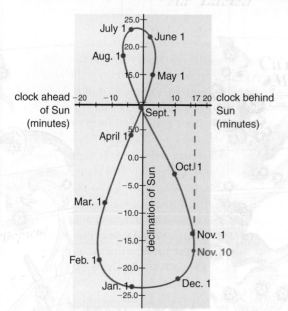

**a** The analemma shows the annual pattern of discrepancies between apparent and mean solar time. For example, the dashed line shows that on November 10, a mean solar clock reads 17 minutes behind (earlier than) apparent solar time.

**b** The discrepancies can also be plotted on a graph as the equation of time.

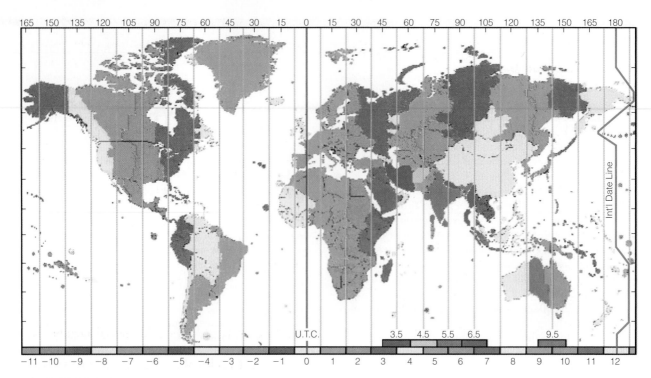

**FIGURE S1.8** Time zones around the world. The numerical scale at the bottom shows hours ahead of (positive numbers) or behind (negative numbers) the time in Greenwich, England; the scale at the top is longitude. The vertical lines show standard time zones as they would be in the absence of political considerations. The color-coded regions show the actual time zones. Note, for example, that all of China uses the same standard time, even though the country is wide enough to span several time zones. Note also that a few countries use time zones centered on a half-hour, rather than an hour, relative to Greenwich time.

saving time, which is 1 hour ahead of standard time. Because of the 1-hour advance on daylight saving time, clocks read around 1 P.M. (rather than around noon) when the Sun is on the meridian.

As we will see, for purposes of navigation and astronomy it is useful to have a single time for the entire Earth. For historical reasons, this "world" time was chosen to be the mean solar time in Greenwich, England—the place that also defines longitude 0° (see Figure 2.11). Today, this *Greenwich mean time* (*GMT*) is often called **universal time** (**UT**). (Outside astronomy, it is often called universal coordinated time (UTC); many airlines and weather services call it "Zulu time," because Greenwich's time zone is designated Z and "zulu" is a common way of phonetically identifying the letter Z.)

## S1.3 The Calendar

Our modern calendar is based on the length of the tropical year, which is the amount of time from one spring equinox to the next. The origins of our calendar go back to ancient Egypt: By 4200 B.C., the Egyptians were using a calendar that counted 365 days in a year.

Because the tropical year actually is closer to $365\frac{1}{4}$ days, the Egyptian calendar slowly drifted out of phase with the seasons by about 1 day every 4 years. For example, if the spring equinox occurred on March 21 one year, 4 years later it occurred on March 20, 4 years after that on March 19, and so on. Over many centuries, the spring equinox moved through many different months. To keep the seasons and the calendar in phase, in 46 B.C. Julius Caesar decreed the adoption of a new calendar. This **Julian calendar** introduced the concept of **leap year**: Every fourth year has 366 days, rather than 365, so that the average length of the calendar year is $365\frac{1}{4}$ days.

The Julian calendar originally had the spring equinox falling around March 24. If it had been perfectly synchronized with the tropical year, this calendar would have ensured that the spring equinox occurred on the same date every 4 years (that is, every leap-year cycle). It didn't work perfectly, however, because a tropical year is actually about 11 minutes short of $365\frac{1}{4}$ days. Thus, the moment of the spring equinox slowly advanced by an average of 11 minutes per year. By the late 1500s, the spring equinox was occurring on March 11.

In 1582, Pope Gregory XIII introduced a new calendar—the **Gregorian calendar**—designed to return the spring equinox to the same date after every

4-year cycle. The Gregorian calendar made two adjustments to the Julian calendar. First, Pope Gregory decreed that the day in 1582 following October 4 would be October 15. By eliminating the ten dates from October 5 through October 14, 1582, he pushed the date of the spring equinox in 1583 from March 11 to March 21. (He chose March 21 because it was the date of the spring equinox in A.D. 325, which was the time of the Council of Nicaea, the first ecumenical council of the Christian church.) Second, the Gregorian calendar added an exception to the rule of having leap year every 4 years: Leap year is skipped when a century changes (for example, in years 1700, 1800, 1900) *unless* the century year is divisible by 400. Thus, 2000 was a leap year because it is divisible by 400 (2000 ÷ 400 = 5), but 2100 will *not* be a leap year. These adjustments make the average length of the Gregorian calendar year almost exactly the same as the actual length of a tropical year, which ensures that the spring equinox will occur on March 21 every fourth year for thousands of years to come.

Today, the Gregorian calendar is used worldwide for international communication and commerce. (Many countries still use traditional calendars, such as the Chinese, Islamic, and Jewish calendars, for cultural purposes.) However, as you might guess, the Pope's decree was not immediately accepted in regions not bound to the Catholic Church. For example, the Gregorian calendar was not adopted in England or in the American colonies until 1752, and it was not adopted in China until 1912 or in Russia until 1919. In parts of the world that still used the Julian calendar, the dates October 5 through October 14 *did* occur in 1582, and the 10 days were removed from the calendar at some later time. Thus, a particular date, such as December 25, came at different times in different countries depending on whether a country had yet adopted the Gregorian calendar.

## S1.4 Locations in the Sky

We are now ready to turn our attention from time-keeping to navigation. The goal of celestial navigation is to use the Sun and the stars to find our position on Earth. Before we can do that, we need to become more familiar with the apparent motions of the sky. In this section, we'll discuss how we locate the Sun and stars on the celestial sphere; this will enable us to understand motions in the local sky, the topic of the next section. Then, in the final section, we'll use these ideas to explain the principles of celestial navigation.

### A Map of the Celestial Sphere

Recall that, for purposes of pinpointing objects in our sky, it's useful to think of the Earth as being in the center of a giant celestial sphere (see Figure 2.4). From our point of view on Earth, the celestial sphere appears to rotate around us each day (see Figure 2.8). We can use a model of the celestial sphere to locate stars or the Sun, much as we use a globe to locate places on Earth. The primary difference is that the celestial sphere models *apparent* positions in the sky, rather than true positions in space. As we discussed in Chapter 2, we can compare positions on the celestial sphere only by reference to the *angles* that separate them, not by actual distances. But aside from this important difference between a globe and the celestial sphere, we can use both as maps by identifying special locations (such as the equator and poles) and adding a system of coordinates (such as latitude and longitude).

We've already discussed the special locations we need for a map of the celestial sphere: the north and south celestial poles, the celestial equator, and the ecliptic. Figure S1.9 shows these locations on a schematic diagram; recall that the Earth is in the center because the celestial sphere represents the sky as we see it from Earth. The arrow along the ecliptic indicates the direction in which the Sun appears to move along it over the course of each year. It is much easier to visualize the celestial sphere if you make a model with a simple plastic ball. Use a felt-tip pen to mark the north and south celestial poles on your ball, then add the celestial equator and the ecliptic; note that the ecliptic crosses the celestial equator on

---

**FIGURE S1.9** This schematic diagram of the celestial sphere, shown without stars, helps us create a map of the celestial sphere by showing the north and south celestial poles, the celestial equator, the ecliptic, and the equinoxes and solstices. As a study aid, you should use a plastic ball as a model of the celestial sphere, marking it with the same special locations.

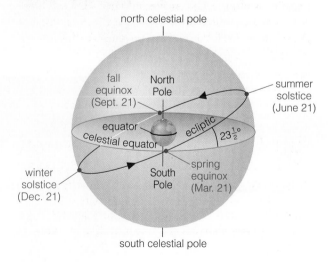

opposite sides of the celestial sphere at an angle of $23\frac{1}{2}°$ (because of the tilt of the Earth's axis).

### Equinoxes and Solstices

Recall that the equinoxes and solstices are special moments in the year that help define the seasons [Section 1.3]. For example, the *spring equinox,* which occurs around March 21 each year, is the moment when spring begins for the Northern Hemisphere and fall begins for the Southern Hemisphere. These moments correspond to positions in the Earth's orbit (see Figure 1.13) and hence to apparent locations of the Sun along the ecliptic. As shown in Figure S1.9, the spring equinox occurs when the Sun is on the ecliptic at the point where it crosses from south of the celestial equator to north of the celestial equator; this point is also called the spring equinox. Thus, the term *spring equinox* has a dual meaning: It is the *moment* when spring begins and also the *point* on the ecliptic at which the Sun appears to be located at that moment.

Figure S1.9 also shows the points marking the summer solstice, fall equinox, and winter solstice; labels indicate the dates on which the Sun appears to be located at each point. Remember that the dates are approximate. Because of the leap-year cycle and the fact that a tropical year is not exactly $365\frac{1}{4}$ days, the precise moments of the equinoxes and solstices may come anywhere between about the 20th and 23rd of the indicated months. (For example, the spring equinox may occur anytime between March 20 and March 23.)

Although no bright stars mark the locations of the equinoxes or solstices among the constellations, you can find them with the aid of nearby bright stars (Figure S1.10). For example, the spring equinox is located in the constellation Pisces and can be found with the aid of the four bright stars in the Great Square of Pegasus. Of course, when the Sun is located at this point around March 21, we cannot see Pisces or Pegasus because they are close to the Sun in our daytime sky.

**TIME OUT TO THINK** *Using your plastic ball as a model of the celestial sphere (which you have already marked with the celestial poles, equator, and ecliptic), mark the locations and approximate dates of the equinoxes and solstices. Based on the dates for these points, approximately where along the ecliptic is the Sun on April 21? On November 21? How do you know?*

### Celestial Coordinates

We can complete our map of the celestial sphere by adding a coordinate system similar to the coordinates that measure latitude and longitude on Earth. This

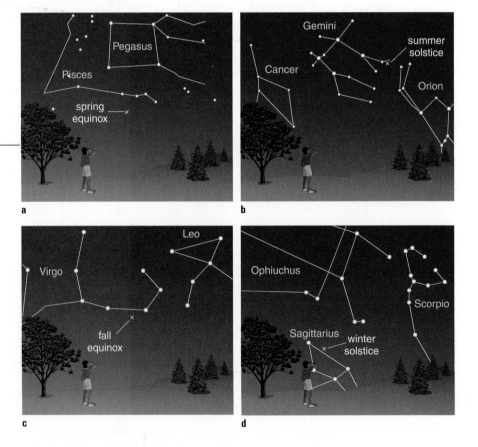

**FIGURE S1.10** These diagrams show the locations among the constellations of (**a**) the spring equinox, (**b**) the summer solstice, (**c**) the fall equinox, and (**d**) the winter solstice. No bright stars mark any of these points, so you must find them by studying their positions relative to recognizable patterns. The time of day and night at which each point is above the horizon depends on the time of year.

system will be the third coordinate system we've used in this book; Figure S1.11 reviews the three systems. Figure S1.11a shows the coordinates of *altitude* and *direction* (or *azimuth* [Section 2.2]) we use in the local sky. Figure S1.11b shows the coordinates of *latitude* and *longitude* we use on Earth's surface. Figure S1.11c shows the system of **celestial coordinates** we use to pinpoint locations on the celestial sphere; these coordinates are called **declination (dec)** and **right ascension (RA)**.

If you carefully compare Figures S1.11b and c, you'll see that declination on the celestial sphere is very similar to *latitude* on Earth:

■ Just as lines of latitude are parallel to the Earth's equator, lines of declination are parallel to the celestial equator.

■ Just as the Earth's equator has lat = 0°, the celestial equator has dec = 0°.

■ Whereas latitudes are labeled north or south relative to the equator, declinations are labeled *positive* or *negative*. For example, the North Pole has lat = 90°N, but the north celestial pole has dec = +90; the South Pole has lat = 90°S, but the south celestial pole has dec = −90°.

The diagrams in Figures S1.11b and c also show that right ascension on the celestial sphere is very similar to *longitude* on Earth:

■ Just as lines of longitude extend from the North Pole to the South Pole, lines of right ascension extend from the north celestial pole to the south celestial pole.

**FIGURE S1.11** Celestial coordinate systems.

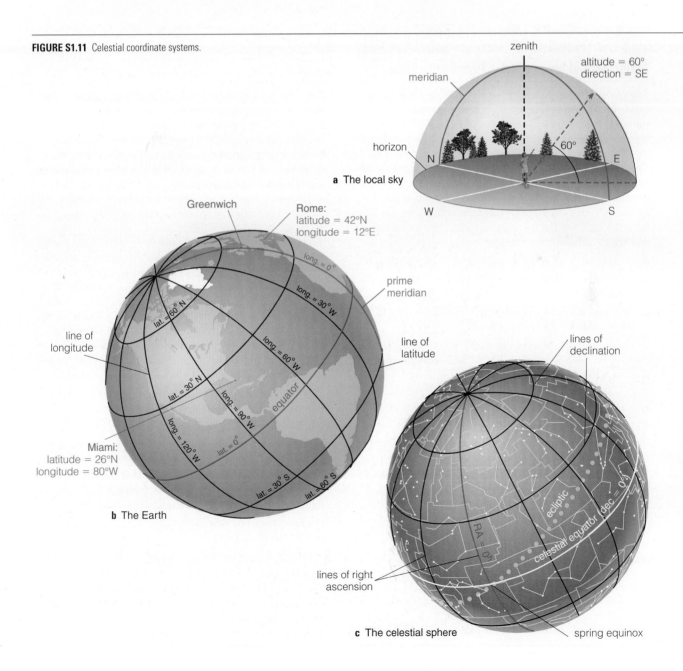

a The local sky

b The Earth

c The celestial sphere

- Just as there is no natural starting point for longitude, there is no natural starting point for right ascension. By international treaty, longitude zero (the prime meridian) is the line of longitude that runs through Greenwich, England. By convention, right ascension zero is the line of right ascension that runs through the spring equinox.

- Whereas longitudes are measured in degrees east or west of Greenwich, right ascensions are measured in hours (and minutes and seconds) east of the spring equinox. A full 360° circle around the celestial equator goes through 24 hours of right ascension, so each hour of right ascension represents an angle of $360° \div 24 = 15°$.

We can use celestial coordinates to describe the position of any object on the celestial sphere. For example, the bright star Vega has dec = +38°44′ and RA = $18^h 35^m$ (Figure S1.12). The positive declination tells us that Vega is 38°44′ *north* of the celestial equator. The right ascension tells us that Vega is 18 hours 35 minutes east of the spring equinox. Translating the right ascension from hours to angular degrees, we find that Vega is about 279° east of the spring equinox (because 18 hours represents $18 \times 15° = 270°$ and 35 minutes represents $\frac{35}{60} \times 15 \approx 9°$).

**TIME OUT TO THINK** *On your plastic ball model of the celestial sphere, add a scale for right ascension along the celestial equator and also add a few circles of declination, such as declination 0°, ±30°, ±60°, and ±90°. Locate Vega on your model.*

---

## Mathematical Insight S1.1     Time by the Stars

The clocks we use in daily life are set to solar time, ticking through 24 hours for each day of mean solar time. In astronomy, it is useful to have clocks that tell time by the stars, or **sidereal time**. Just as we define *solar time* according to the Sun's position relative to the meridian, *sidereal time* is based on the positions of stars relative to the meridian. We define the **hour angle** (**HA**) of any object on the celestial sphere to be the time since it last crossed the meridian. (For a circumpolar star, hour angle is measured from the *higher* of the two points at which it crosses the meridian each day.) For example:

- If a star is crossing the meridian now, its hour angle is $0^h$.

- If a star crossed the meridian 3 hours ago, its hour angle is $3^h$.

- If a star will cross the meridian 1 hour from now, its hour angle is $-1^h$ or, equivalently, $23^h$.

By convention, time by the stars is based on the hour angle of the spring equinox. That is, the **local sidereal time** (**LST**) is

$$LST = HA_{\text{spring equinox}}$$

For example, the local sidereal time is 00:00 when the spring equinox is *on* the meridian. Three hours later, when the spring equinox is 3 hours west of the meridian, the local sidereal time is 03:00.

Note that, because right ascension tells us how long after the spring equinox an object reaches the meridian, the local sidereal time is also equal to the right ascension (RA) of objects currently crossing your meridian. For example, if your local sidereal time is 04:30, stars with RA = $4^h 30^m$ are currently crossing your meridian. This idea leads to an important relationship between any object's current hour angle, the current local sidereal time, and the object's right ascension:

$$HA_{\text{object}} = LST - RA_{\text{object}}$$

This formula will make sense to you if you recognize that an object's right ascension tells us the time by which it trails the spring equinox on its daily trek through the sky. Because the local sidereal time tells us how long it has been since the spring equinox was on the meridian, the difference $LST - RA_{\text{object}}$ must tell us the position of the object relative to the meridian.

Sidereal time has one important subtlety: Because the stars (and the celestial sphere) appear to rotate around us in one sidereal day ($23^h 56^m$), sidereal clocks must tick through 24 hours of sidereal time in 23 hours 56 minutes of solar time. That is, a sidereal clock gains about 4 minutes per day over a solar clock. As a result, you cannot immediately infer the local sidereal time from the local solar time, or vice versa, without either doing some calculations or consulting an astronomical table. Of course, the easiest way to determine the local sidereal time is with a clock that ticks at the sidereal rate. Astronomical observatories always have sidereal clocks, and you can buy moderately priced telescopes that come with sidereal clocks.

*Example 1:* Suppose it is 9:00 P.M. on the spring equinox (March 21). What is the local sidereal time?

*Solution:* On the day of the spring equinox, the Sun is located at the point of the spring equinox in the sky. Thus, if the Sun is 9 hours past the meridian, so is the spring equinox. The local sidereal time is LST = 09:00.

*Example 2:* Suppose the local sidereal time is LST = 04:00. When will Vega cross your meridian?

*Solution:* Vega has RA = $18^h 35^m$. Thus, at LST = 04:00, Vega's hour angle is

$$HA_{\text{Vega}} = LST - RA_{\text{Vega}} = 4\!:\!00 - 18\!:\!35 = -14\!:\!35$$

Vega will cross your meridian in 14 hours 35 minutes, which also means it crossed your meridian 9 hours 25 minutes ago ($14^h 35^m + 9^h 25^m = 24^h$). (Note that these are intervals of sidereal time.)

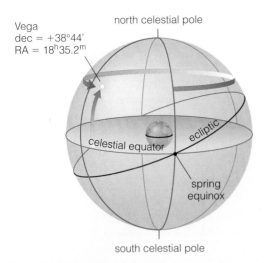

Vega
dec = +38°44'
RA = 18ʰ35.2ᵐ

north celestial pole

celestial equator

ecliptic

spring equinox

south celestial pole

**FIGURE S1.12** This diagram shows how we interpret the celestial coordinates of Vega. Its declination tells us that it is 38°44' north of the celestial equator. We can interpret its right ascension in two ways: As an angle, it means it is about 279° (the angular equivalent of 18ʰ 35ᵐ) east of the vernal equinox; as a time, it means that Vega crosses the meridian about 18 hours 35 minutes after the spring equinox.

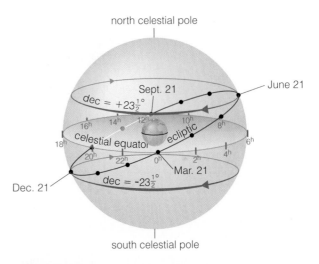

north celestial pole

Sept. 21

June 21

dec = $+23\frac{1}{2}°$

celestial equator

ecliptic

Dec. 21

Mar. 21

dec = $-23\frac{1}{2}°$

south celestial pole

**FIGURE S1.13** We can use this diagram of the celestial sphere to determine the Sun's right ascension and declination at monthly intervals.

You may be wondering why right ascension is measured in units of time. The answer is that time units are convenient for tracking the daily motion of objects through the local sky. All objects with a particular right ascension cross the meridian at the same time; for example, all stars with RA = 0ʰ cross the meridian at the same time that the spring equinox crosses the meridian. For any other object, the right ascension tells us when it crosses the meridian in hours *after* the spring equinox crosses the meridian. Thus, for example, Vega's right ascension, 18ʰ 35ᵐ, tells us that on any particular day it crosses the meridian about 18 hours 35 minutes after the spring equinox. (This is 18 hours 35 minutes of *sidereal time* later, which is not exactly the same as 18 hours 35 minutes of solar time; see Mathematical Insight S1.1.)

The celestial coordinates of stars are not quite constant; they change gradually with the Earth's 26,000-year precession cycle. The change occurs because celestial coordinates are tied to the celestial equator, which moves with precession relative to the constellations. (Precession does not affect the Earth's orbit, so it does not affect the location of the ecliptic among the constellations.) Thus, the celestial coordinates of stars change even while the stars themselves remain fixed in the patterns of the constellations. The coordinate changes are not noticeable to the eye on the time scale of a human lifetime, but precise astronomical work requires the updating of celestial coordinates almost constantly. Many astronomical software packages do these calculations automatically and can also give day-to-day celestial coordinates for the Sun, Moon, and planets as they wander among the constellations.

### Celestial Coordinates of the Sun

Unlike the Moon and the planets, which wander among the constellations in complex ways that require detailed calculations, the Sun moves through the zodiac constellations in a simple way: It moves roughly 1° per day along the ecliptic. In a month, the Sun moves approximately one-twelfth of the way around the ecliptic, meaning that its right ascension changes by about 24 ÷ 12 = 2 hours per month. Figure S1.13 shows the ecliptic marked with the Sun's monthly position and a scale of celestial coordinates. From this figure, we can create a table of the Sun's month-by-month celestial coordinates. Table S1.1 starts from the spring equinox, when the Sun has declination 0° and right ascension 0ʰ.

Note that, unlike its steady advance in right ascension, the Sun's declination changes much more rapidly around the equinoxes than around the solstices. For example, the Sun's declination changes from −12° on February 21 to +12° on April 21, a change of 24° in just two months. In contrast, between May 21 and July 21, the declination varies only between +20° and $+23\frac{1}{2}°$. This explains why the daylight hours increase rapidly in spring and decrease rapidly in fall but stay long for a couple of months around the summer solstice and short for a couple of months around the winter solstice.

**TIME OUT TO THINK** *On your plastic ball model of the celestial sphere, add dots along the ecliptic to show the Sun's monthly positions. Use your model to estimate the Sun's celestial coordinates on your birthday.*

**Table S1.1  The Sun's Approximate Celestial Coordinates at 1-Month Intervals**

| Approximate Date | RA | Dec | Approximate Date | RA | Dec |
|---|---|---|---|---|---|
| Mar. 21 (Spring equinox) | 0 hr | 0° | Sept. 21 (Fall equinox) | 12 hr | 0° |
| Apr. 21 | 2 hr | +12° | Oct. 21 | 14 hr | −12° |
| May 21 | 4 hr | +20° | Nov. 21 | 16 hr | −20° |
| June 21 (Summer solstice) | 6 hr | $+23\frac{1}{2}°$ | Dec. 21 (Winter solstice) | 18 hr | $-23\frac{1}{2}°$ |
| July 21 | 8 hr | +20° | Jan. 21 | 20 hr | −20° |
| Aug. 21 | 10 hr | +12° | Feb. 21 | 22 hr | −12° |

## S1.5  Understanding Local Skies

In Chapter 2, we briefly discussed how the daily circles of stars vary with latitude (see Figure 2.12). With our deeper understanding of the celestial sphere and celestial coordinates, we can now study local skies in more detail. We'll begin by focusing on star tracks through the local sky, which depend only on a star's declination. Then we'll discuss the daily path of the Sun, which varies with the Sun's declination and therefore with the time of year.

### Star Tracks

The apparent daily rotation of the celestial sphere makes star tracks seem simple when viewed from the outside (see Figure 2.8). Local skies seem complex only because the ground always blocks our view of half of the celestial sphere. The half that is blocked depends on latitude. Let's first consider the local sky at the Earth's North Pole, the easiest case to understand, and then look at the local sky at other latitudes.

*The North Pole*  Figure S1.14a shows the rotating celestial sphere and your orientation relative to it when you are standing at the North Pole. Your "up" points toward the north celestial pole, which therefore marks your zenith. The Earth blocks your view of anything south of the celestial equator, which therefore runs along your horizon. To make it easier for you to visualize the local sky, Figure S1.14b shows your horizon extending to the celestial sphere; note that the horizon is marked with directions and that all directions are south from the North Pole. (Because the meridian is defined as running from north to south in the local sky, there is no meridian at the North Pole.)

The daily circles of the stars keep them at constant altitudes above or below your horizon, and their

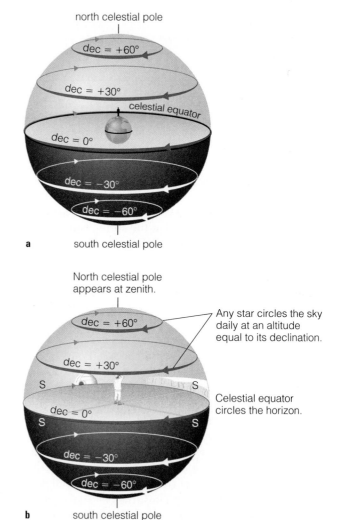

**FIGURE S1.14  (a)** The orientation of the local sky, relative to the celestial sphere, for the North Pole. **(b)** Extending the horizon to the celestial sphere makes it easier to visualize the local sky at the North Pole. (*Note:* To understand the extension, remember that the Earth should appear extremely small compared to the celestial sphere.)

altitudes are equal to their declinations. For example, a star with declination $+60°$ circles the sky at an altitude of $60°$, and a star with declination $-30°$ remains $30°$ below your horizon at all times. As a result, all stars north of the celestial equator are circumpolar at the North Pole, never falling below the horizon. Similarly, stars south of the celestial equator never appear in the sky as seen from the North Pole.

Note that right ascension does not affect a star's path at all; it affects only the time of day and year at which a star is found in a particular direction along your horizon. If you are having difficulty visualizing the star paths, it may help you to watch star paths as you rotate your plastic ball model of the celestial sphere.

*The Equator* Next imagine that you are standing somewhere on the Earth's equator (lat = $0°$), such as in Ecuador, in Kenya, or on the island of Borneo. Figure S1.15a shows that "up" points directly away from (perpendicular to) the Earth's rotation axis. Figure S1.15b shows the local sky more clearly by extending your horizon to the celestial sphere and rotating the diagram so your zenith is up. As everywhere except at the poles, the meridian extends from the horizon due south, through the zenith, to the horizon due north.

Look carefully at how the celestial sphere appears to rotate in the local sky. The north celestial pole remains stationary on your horizon due north; as we should expect, its altitude, $0°$, is equal to the equator's latitude [Section 2.2]. Similarly, the south celestial pole remains stationary on your horizon due south. At any particular time, half of the celestial equator is visible, extending from the horizon due east, through the zenith, to the horizon due west; the other half

lies below the horizon. As the equatorial sky appears to turn, all star paths rise straight out of the eastern horizon and set straight into the western horizon, with the following features:

- Stars with dec = $0°$ lie *on* the celestial equator and therefore rise due east, cross the meridian at the zenith, and set due west.

- Stars with dec > $0°$ rise north of due east, reach their highest point on the meridian in the north, and set north of due west. Their rise, set, and highest point depend on their declinations. For example, a star with dec = $+30°$ rises $30°$ north of due east, crosses the meridian $30°$ to the north of the zenith—that is, at an *altitude* of $90° - 30° = 60°$ in the north—and sets $30°$ north of due west.

- Stars with dec < $0°$ rise south of due east, reach their highest point on the meridian in the south, and set south of due west. For example, a star with dec = $-50°$ rises $50°$ south of due east, crosses the meridian $50°$ to the south of the zenith—that is, at an *altitude* of $90° - 50° = 40°$ in the south—and sets $50°$ south of due west.

Note that exactly half of any star's daily circle lies above the horizon. Thus, every star is above the horizon for exactly half of each sidereal day, or just under 12 hours, and below the horizon for the other half of the sidereal day.

**TIME OUT TO THINK** *Visualize the daily paths of stars as seen from the Earth's equator. Are any stars circumpolar? Are there stars that never rise above the horizon? Explain.*

**FIGURE S1.15** (**a**) The orientation of the local sky, relative to the celestial sphere, for the Earth's equator. (**b**) Extending the horizon and rotating the diagram make it easier to visualize the local sky at the equator.

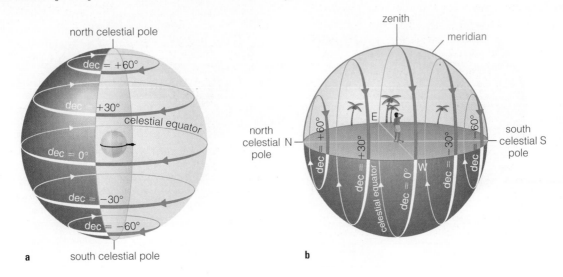

*Other Latitudes* We can use the same basic strategy to determine star tracks for other latitudes. Let's consider latitude 40°N, such as in Denver, Indianapolis, Philadelphia, or Beijing. First, as shown in Figure S1.16a, imagine standing at this latitude on a basic diagram of the rotating celestial sphere; note that "up" points to a location on the celestial sphere with declination +40°. To make it easier to visualize the local sky, we next extend the horizon and rotate the diagram so your zenith is up (Figure S1.16b).

As we would expect, the north celestial pole appears 40° above the horizon due north, since its altitude in the local sky is always equal to the latitude. Half of the celestial equator is visible; it extends from the horizon due east, to the meridian at an altitude of 50° in the south, to the horizon due west. By comparing this diagram to the local sky for the equator, you can probably notice a general rule for the celestial equator at any latitude: *Exactly half the celestial equator is always visible, extending from due east on the horizon to due west on the horizon and crossing the meridian at an altitude of 90° minus the latitude.* The celestial equator runs through the southern half of the sky at locations in the Northern Hemisphere and through the northern half of the sky at locations in the Southern Hemisphere. The diagram in Figure S1.16b also shows star tracks through the local sky for 40°N; it may be easier for you to visualize them if you rotate your plastic ball model of the celestial sphere while holding it in the orientation of Figure S1.16b. As you study the tracks, note the following key features:

- Stars with dec = 0° lie *on* the celestial equator and therefore follow the path of the celestial equator through the local sky. That is, for latitude 40°N, they rise due east, cross the meridian at 50° in the south, and set due west.

- Stars with dec > 0° follow paths parallel to the celestial equator but farther north. Thus, they rise north of due east, cross the meridian north of where the equator crosses it, and set north of due west. If they are within 40° of the north celestial pole on the celestial sphere (which means declinations greater than 90° − 40° = 50°), their entire circles are above the horizon, making them circumpolar. You can find the precise point at which a star crosses the meridian by adding its declination to the 50°S altitude at which the celestial equator crosses the meridian. For example, Figure S1.16b shows that a star with dec = +30° crosses the meridian at altitude 50° + 30° = 80° in the south and a star with dec = +60° crosses the meridian at altitude 70° in the north. (To calculate the latter result, note that the sum 50° + 60° = 110° goes 20° past the zenith altitude of 90°, making it equivalent to 90° − 20° = 70°.)

- Stars with dec < 0° follow paths parallel to the celestial equator but farther south. Thus, they rise south of due east, cross the meridian south of where the celestial equator crosses it, and set south of due west. If they are within 40° of the south celestial pole on the celestial sphere (which means declinations less than −90° + 40° =

---

**FIGURE S1.16** (**a**) The orientation of the local sky, relative to the celestial sphere, for latitude 40°N. Because latitude is the angle to the Earth's equator, "up" points to the circle on the celestial sphere with declination +40°. (**b**) Extending the horizon and rotating the diagram so the zenith is up make it easier to visualize the local sky. The blue scale along the meridian shows altitudes and directions in the local sky.

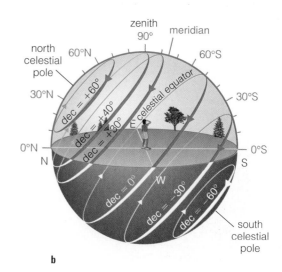

−50°), their entire circles are below the horizon and thus they are never visible.

Note that the fraction of any star's daily circle that is above the horizon—and hence the amount of time it is above the horizon each day—depends on its declination. Because exactly half the celestial equator is above the horizon, stars on the celestial equator (dec = 0°) are above the horizon for about 12 hours per day. Stars with positive declinations have more than half their daily circle above the horizon and hence are above the horizon for more than 12 hours each day (with the range extending to 24 hours a day for the circumpolar stars). Stars with negative declinations have less than half their daily circle above the horizon and hence are above the horizon for less than 12 hours each day (with the range going to zero for stars that are never above the horizon).

We can apply the same strategy we used in Figure S1.16 to find star paths for other latitudes. Figure S1.17 shows the process for latitude 30°S. Note that the south celestial pole is visible to the south and that the celestial equator passes through the northern half of the sky. If you study the diagram carefully, you can see how star tracks depend on declination.

**TIME OUT TO THINK** *Study Figure S1.17 for latitude 30°S. Describe the path of the celestial equator; explain how it obeys the 90° − latitude rule given above. Give a general description of how star tracks differ for stars with positive and negative declinations. What stars are circumpolar at this latitude?*

### *The Path of the Sun*

Just as a star's path through the sky depends only on its declination, the Sun's path through the sky on any particular day depends only on its declination for that day. For example, because the Sun's declination is $+23\frac{1}{2}°$ on the summer solstice, the Sun's path through the local sky on June 21 is the same as that of any star with declination $+23\frac{1}{2}°$. Thus, as long as we know the Sun's declination for a particular day, we can find the Sun's path at any latitude with the same local sky diagrams we used to find star tracks.

Figure S1.18 shows the Sun's path on the equinoxes and solstices for latitude 40°N. On the equinoxes, when the Sun is on the celestial equator (dec = 0°), the Sun's path follows the celestial equator: It rises due east, crosses the meridian at altitude 50° in the south, and sets due west; like any object on the celestial equator, it is above the horizon for 12 hours. On the summer solstice, the Sun rises well north of due east,[1] reaches an altitude of $73\frac{1}{2}°$ when it crosses the meridian in the south, and sets well

---

[1]Calculating exactly how far north of due east the Sun rises is beyond the scope of this book, but astronomical software packages will tell you exactly where—and at what time—the Sun rises and sets along the horizon for any location and any date.

**FIGURE S1.17** This pair of diagrams shows how we find star tracks for latitude 30°S. (**a**) The orientation of the local sky at latitude 30°S, relative to the celestial sphere; "up" points to the circle on the celestial sphere with declination −30°. (**b**) Extending the horizon and rotating the diagram so the zenith is up make it easier to visualize the local sky. Note that the south celestial pole is visible at altitude 30° in the south, while the celestial equator stretches across the northern half of the sky.

a

b

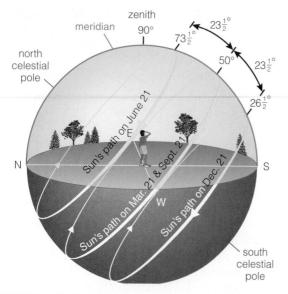

**FIGURE S1.18** The Sun's daily paths for the equinoxes and solstices at latitude 40°N.

*The North and South Poles* Recall that the celestial equator circles the horizon at the North Pole. Because the Sun appears *on* the celestial equator on the day of the spring equinox, the Sun circles the north polar sky *on the horizon* on March 21 (Figure S1.20); it completes a full circle of the horizon in 24 hours (1 solar day). Over the next 3 months, the Sun continues to circle the horizon, circling at gradually higher altitudes as its declination increases. It reaches its highest point on the summer solstice, when its declination of $+23\frac{1}{2}°$ means that it circles the north polar sky at an altitude of $23\frac{1}{2}°$. After the summer solstice, the daily circles gradually fall lower over the next 3 months, reaching the horizon on the fall equinox. Then, because the Sun's declination is negative for the next 6 months (until the following spring equinox), it remains below the north polar horizon. Thus, the North Pole essentially has 6 months of daylight and 6 months of darkness, with an extended twilight that lasts a few weeks beyond the fall equinox and an extended dawn that begins a few weeks before the spring equinox.

The situation is the opposite at the South Pole. Here the Sun's daily circles slowly rise above the horizon on the fall equinox to a maximum altitude of $23\frac{1}{2}°$ on the *winter* solstice, then slowly fall back to the horizon on the spring equinox. Thus, the South Pole has the Sun above the horizon during the 6 months it is below the north polar horizon.

There's an important caveat to this discussion: Although we've correctly described the Sun's true position in the polar skies over the course of the year, two effects complicate what we actually see at the poles around the times of the equinoxes. First, the atmosphere bends light enough so that the Sun *appears* to be above the horizon even when it is actually below it; near the horizon, this bending makes the

north of due west; the daylight hours are long, because much more than half of the Sun's path is above the horizon. On the winter solstice, the Sun rises well south of due east, reaches an altitude of only $26\frac{1}{2}°$ when it crosses the meridian in the south, and sets well south of due west; the daylight hours are short, because much less than half of the Sun's path is above the horizon.

We could make a similar diagram to show the Sun's path on various dates for any latitude. However, the $23\frac{1}{2}°$ tilt of the Earth's axis makes the Sun's path particularly interesting at the special latitudes shown in Figure S1.19. Let's investigate these latitudes.

**FIGURE S1.19** Special latitudes defined by the Sun's path through the sky.

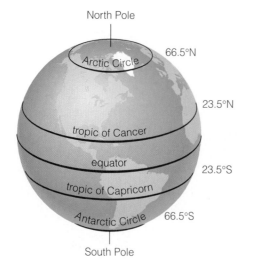

**FIGURE S1.20** Daily paths of the Sun for the equinoxes and solstices at the North Pole.

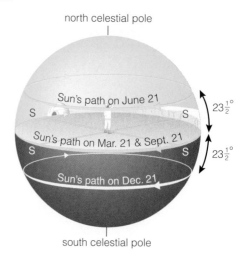

Sun appear about 1° higher than it would in the absence of an atmosphere. Second, the Sun's angular size of about $\frac{1}{2}$° means that it does not fall below the horizon at a single moment but instead sets gradually. Together, these effects mean that the Sun appears above the polar horizons for slightly longer (by several days) than 6 months each year.

*The Equator* Recall that, at the equator, the celestial equator extends from the horizon due east, through the zenith, to the horizon due west. The Sun therefore follows this path on each equinox, reaching the zenith at local noon (Figure S1.21). Following the spring equinox, the Sun's increasing declination means that it follows a daily track that takes it gradually northward in the sky. It is farthest north on the summer solstice, when it rises $23\frac{1}{2}$° north of due east, crosses the meridian at altitude $66\frac{1}{2}$° in the north, and sets $23\frac{1}{2}$° north of due west. Over the next 6 months, it gradually tracks southward until the winter solstice, when its path is the mirror image (across the celestial equator) of its summer solstice path.

Like all objects in the equatorial sky, the Sun is always above the horizon for half a day and below it for half a day. Moreover, the Sun's track is highest in the sky on the equinoxes and lowest on the summer and winter solstices. Thus, equatorial regions, unlike regions at temperate northern and southern latitudes, do not have four seasons. Instead, equatorial regions generally have a rainy season and a dry season, with the weather determined by wind patterns on Earth. (The Sun's path in the equatorial sky also makes it rise and set perpendicular to the horizon, making for a more rapid dawn and a briefer twilight than at other latitudes.)

*The Tropic Circles* We've seen that, while the Sun reaches the zenith twice a year at the equator (on the spring and fall equinoxes), it never reaches the zenith at mid-latitudes (such as 40°N). The boundaries of the regions on Earth where the Sun sometimes reaches the zenith are the circles of latitude 23.5°N and 23.5°S. These latitude circles are called the **tropic of Cancer** and the **tropic of Capricorn**, respectively. (The region between these two circles is generally called the *tropics*.)

Figure S1.22 shows why the tropic of Cancer is special. The celestial equator extends from due east on the horizon to due west on the horizon, crossing the meridian in the south at an altitude of 90° − $23\frac{1}{2}$° (the latitude) = $66\frac{1}{2}$°; this is the path the Sun follows on the equinoxes (March 21st and September 21st). As a result, the Sun's path on the summer solstice, when it crosses the meridian $25\frac{1}{2}$° northward of the celestial equator, takes it to the zenith at local noon. Because the Sun has its maximum declination on the summer solstice, the tropic of Cancer marks the northernmost latitude at which the Sun ever reaches the zenith. Similarly, at the tropic of Capricorn the Sun reaches the zenith at local noon on the winter solstice, making this the southernmost latitude at which the Sun ever reaches the zenith. Between the two tropic circles, the Sun passes through the zenith twice a year (the dates vary with latitude).

Incidentally, the names of the tropics of Cancer and Capricorn come from the locations of the summer and winter solstices along the ecliptic—as they were about 2,000 years ago. Recall that the summer solstice is currently in the constellation Gemini and the winter solstice is in the constellation Sagittarius (see Figure S1.10). However, these positions gradually change with the Earth's precession cycle. Some 2,000 years ago, the summer and winter solstices

---

**FIGURE S1.21** Daily paths of the Sun for the equinoxes and solstices at the equator.

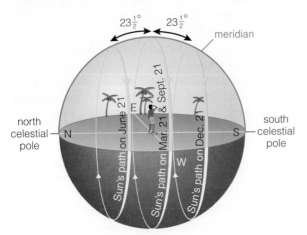

**FIGURE S1.22** Daily paths of the Sun for the equinoxes and solstices at the tropic of Cancer.

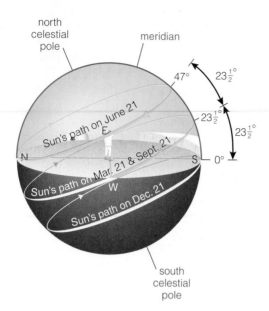

north
celestial
pole

meridian

47°

$23\frac{1}{2}°$

$23\frac{1}{2}°$

$23\frac{1}{2}°$

0°

E

N

S

Sun's path on June 21

Sun's path on Mar. 21 & Sept. 21

W

Sun's path on Dec. 21

south
celestial
pole

**FIGURE S1.23** Daily paths of the Sun for the equinoxes and solstices at the Arctic Circle.

were located in Cancer and Capricorn, respectively, which is how the tropic circles got their names.

*The Polar Circles* At the equator, the Sun is above the horizon for 12 hours each day year-round. At latitudes progressively farther from the equator, the daily time that the Sun is above the horizon varies progressively more with the seasons. The special latitudes at which the Sun remains continuously above the horizon for a full day each year mark the polar circles: the **Arctic Circle** at latitude 66.5°N and the **Antarctic Circle** at latitude 66.5°S. Poleward of these circles, the length of continuous daylight (or darkness) increases beyond 24 hours, reaching the extreme of 6 months at the North and South Poles.

Figure S1.23 shows why the Arctic Circle is special. The celestial equator extends from due east on the horizon to due west on the horizon, crossing the meridian in the south at an altitude of $90° - 66\frac{1}{2}°$ (the latitude) $= 23\frac{1}{2}°$. As a result, the Sun's path is circumpolar on the summer solstice: It skims the northern horizon at midnight, rises through the eastern sky to a noon maximum altitude of 47° in the south, and then gradually falls through the western sky until it is back on the horizon at midnight (see the photograph of this path in Figure 2.17). At the Antarctic Circle, the Sun follows the same basic pattern on the winter solstice, except that it skims the horizon in the south and rises to a noon maximum altitude of 47° in the north.

However, as at the North and South Poles, what we actually see at the polar circles is slightly different from this idealization. Again, the bending of light by the Earth's atmosphere and the Sun's angular size

of about $\frac{1}{2}°$ make the Sun *appear* to be above the horizon even when it is slightly below it. Thus, the Sun seems not to set for several days, rather than a single day, around the summer solstice at the Arctic Circle (or the winter solstice at the Antarctic Circle). Similarly, the Sun appears to peek above the horizon momentarily, rather than not at all, around the winter solstice at the Arctic Circle (or the summer solstice at the Antarctic Circle).

## S1.6 Principles of Celestial Navigation

Imagine that you're on a ship at sea, far from any landmarks. How can you figure out where you are? It's easy, at least in principle, if you understand the apparent motions of the sky discussed in this chapter.

### Latitude

Determining latitude is particularly easy if you can find the north or south celestial pole: Your latitude is equal to the altitude of the celestial pole in your sky. In the Northern Hemisphere at night, you can determine your approximate latitude by measuring the altitude of Polaris. Because Polaris has a declination within 1° of the north celestial pole, its altitude is within 1° of your latitude. For example, if Polaris has altitude 17°, your latitude is between 16°N and 18°N.

If you want to be more precise, you can determine your latitude from the altitude of *any* star as it crosses your meridian. For example, suppose Vega happens to be crossing your meridian at the moment and appears in your southern sky at altitude 78°44′. Because Vega has dec $= +38°44′$ (see Figure S1.12), it crosses your meridian 38°44′ north of the celestial equator. As shown in Figure S1.24a, you can conclude that the celestial equator crosses your meridian at an altitude of precisely 40° in the south. Your latitude must therefore be 50°N, because the celestial equator always crosses the meridian at an altitude of 90° minus the latitude; you know you are in the Northern Hemisphere because the celestial equator crosses the meridian in the south.

In the daytime, you can find your latitude from the Sun's altitude on your meridian, as long as you know the date and have a table that tells you the Sun's declination on that date. For example, suppose the date is March 21 and the Sun crosses your meridian at altitude 70° in the north (Figure S1.24b). Because the Sun has dec $= 0°$ on March 21, you can conclude that the celestial equator also crosses your meridian in the north at altitude 70°. You must be in the Southern Hemisphere, because the celestial equator crosses the meridian in the north. From the rule that the celestial equator crosses the meridian at

**FIGURE S1.24** (**a**) Because Vega has dec = +38°44′, it crosses the meridian 38°44′ north of the celestial equator. From Vega's meridian crossing at altitude 78°44′ in the south, the celestial equator must cross the meridian at altitude 40° in the south. Thus, the latitude must be 50°N. (**b**) To determine latitude from the Sun's meridian crossing, you must know the Sun's declination, which you can determine from the date. The case shown is for the spring equinox, when the Sun's declination is 0° and hence follows the path of the celestial equator through the local sky. From the celestial equator's meridian crossing at 70° in the north, the latitude must be 20°S.

an altitude of 90° minus the latitude, you can conclude that you are at latitude 20°S.

### Longitude

Determining longitude requires comparing the current positions of objects in your sky with their positions as seen from some known longitude. As a simple example, suppose you use a sundial to determine that the apparent solar time is 1:00 P.M. You immediately call a friend in England and learn that it is 3:00 P.M. in Greenwich. You now know that your local time is 2 hours earlier than the local time in Greenwich, which means you are 2 hours west of Greenwich. (An earlier time means you are *west* of Greenwich, because the Earth rotates from west to east.) Each hour corresponds to 15° of longitude, so "2 hours west of Greenwich" means longitude 30°W.

At night, you can find your longitude by comparing the positions of stars in your local sky and at some known longitude. For example, suppose Vega is on your meridian and a call to your friend reveals that it won't cross the meridian in Greenwich until 6 hours from now. In this case, your local time is 6 hours later than the local time in Greenwich. Thus, you are 6 hours east of Greenwich, or at longitude 90°E (because 6 × 15° = 90°).

### Celestial Navigation in Practice

Although celestial navigation is easy in principle, at least three practical considerations make it more difficult in practice. First, finding either latitude or longitude requires a tool for measuring angles in the sky. One such device, called an *astrolabe*, was invented by the ancient Greeks and significantly improved by Islamic scholars during the Middle Ages. The astrolabe's faceplate (Figure S1.25a) could be used to tell time, because it consisted of a rotating star map and horizon plates for specific latitudes; today you can buy similar rotatable star maps, called *planispheres*.

### Common Misconceptions: Compass Directions

Most people determine direction with the aid of a compass rather than the stars. However, to many people's surprise, a compass needle doesn't actually point to true geographic north. Instead, the compass needle responds to the Earth's magnetic field and points to *magnetic* north, which can be substantially different from true north. As a result, if you want to navigate precisely with a compass, you need a special map that shows local variations in the Earth's magnetic field. Such maps are available at most camping stores; however, they are not perfectly reliable because the magnetic field also varies with time. In general, celestial navigation is much more reliable than a compass for determining direction.

**a** The faceplate of an astrolabe; many astrolabes had sighting sticks on the back for measuring the positions of bright stars.

**b** A copper engraving of Italian explorer Amerigo Vespucci (for whom America was named) using an astrolabe to sight the Southern Cross. The engraving by Philip Galle, from the book *Nova Reperta,* was based on an original by Joannes Stradanus in the early 1580s.

**c** A woodcutting of Ptolemy holding a cross-staff (artist unknown).

**d** A sextant.

**FIGURE S1.25** Navigational instruments

In addition, the astrolabe contained a sighting stick, on the back, that allowed users to measure the altitudes of bright stars in the sky; these measurements could be correlated against special markings under the faceplate (Figure S1.25b). Astrolabes were effective but difficult and expensive to make. As a result, medieval sailors often measured angles with a simple pair of calibrated perpendicular sticks, called a *cross-staff* or *Jacob's staff* (Figure S1.25c). A more modern device called a *sextant* allows much more precise angle determinations by incorporating a small telescope for sightings (Figure S1.25d). Sextants are still used for celestial navigation on many ships. If you

want to practice celestial navigation yourself, you can buy an inexpensive plastic sextant at many science-oriented stores.

A second practical consideration is the need to know the celestial coordinates of stars and the Sun so that you can determine their paths through the local sky. At night, you can use a table listing the celestial coordinates of bright stars. In addition to knowing the celestial coordinates, you must either know the constellations and bright stars extremely well or carry star charts to help you identify them. For navigating by the Sun in the daytime, you'll need a table listing the Sun's celestial coordinates on each day of the year.

The third practical consideration is related to determining longitude: You need to know the current position of the Sun (or a particular star) in a known location, such as Greenwich, England. Although you could find this out by calling a friend who lives there, it's more practical to carry a clock set to universal time (that is, Greenwich mean time). In the daytime, the clock makes it easy to determine your longitude. If apparent solar time is 1:00 P.M. in your location and the clock tells you that it is 3:00 P.M. in Greenwich, then you are 2 hours west of Greenwich, or at longitude 30°W. The task is more difficult at night, because you must compare the position of a *star* in your sky to its current position in Greenwich. You can do this with the aid of detailed astronomical tables that allow you to determine the current position of any star in the Greenwich sky from the date and the universal time.

Historically, this third consideration created enormous problems for navigation. Before the invention of accurate clocks, sailors could easily determine their latitude but not their longitude. Indeed, most of the European voyages of discovery beginning in the 1400s relied on little more than guesswork about longitude, although some sailors learned complex mathematical techniques for estimating longitude through observations of the lunar phases. More accurate longitude determination, upon which the development of extensive ocean commerce and travel depended, required the invention of a clock that would remain accurate on a ship rocking in the ocean swells. By the early 1700s, solving this problem was considered so important that the British government offered a substantial monetary prize for the solution. The prize was claimed in 1761 by John Harrison, with a clock that lost only 5 seconds during a 9-week voyage to Jamaica.[2]

### The Global Positioning System

In the past decade, a new type of celestial navigation has supplanted traditional methods. It involves finding positions relative to a set of satellites in Earth orbit—the satellites of the **global positioning system (GPS)**. In essence, the GPS satellites function like artificial stars; the satellite positions at any moment are known precisely from their orbital characteristics. The GPS currently involves about two dozen satellites orbiting the Earth at an altitude of 20,000 kilometers. Each satellite transmits a radio signal that can be received by a small radio receiver—rain or shine, day or night. GPS receivers have a built-in computer that calculates your precise position on Earth by comparing the signals received from several GPS satellites.

The United States originally built the GPS in the late 1970s to give its military troops an advantage over adversaries, and the system was designed so that secret information would be needed to use the system to its fullest. Thus, while civilians (and adversaries) could use the GPS to determine their location on Earth to within about 100 meters, U.S. military personnel could pinpoint their location to within 1 meter. However, civilian scientists eventually found ways to measure position with far more precision than the designers of the GPS had imagined possible, even without the secret information. For example, the GPS has been used by geologists to measure *millimeter*-scale changes in the Earth's crust. Today, the many applications of the GPS include automobile navigation systems as well as systems for helping airplanes land safely, guiding the blind around town, and helping lost hikers find their way.

With the rapid growth in the use of GPS navigation, the ancient practice of celestial navigation is in danger of becoming a lost art. Fortunately, many amateur clubs and societies are keeping the art of celestial navigation alive.

## THE BIG PICTURE

In this chapter, we built upon concepts from Chapters 1 and 2 to form a more detailed understanding of celestial timekeeping and navigation. We also learned how to determine paths for the Sun and the stars in the local sky. As you look back at what you've learned, keep in mind the following "big picture" ideas:

- Our modern systems of timekeeping are rooted in the apparent motions of the Sun through the sky. Although it's easy to forget these roots when you look at a clock or a calendar, the sky was the only guide to time for most of human history.

- The term *celestial navigation* sounds a bit mysterious, but it involves simple principles that allow you to determine your location on Earth. Even if you're never lost at sea, you may find the basic techniques of celestial navigation useful to orient yourself at night (for example, on your next camping trip).

- If you understand the apparent motions of the sky discussed in this chapter and also learn the constellations and bright stars, you'll feel very much "at home" under the stars at night.

---

[2]The story of the difficulties surrounding the measurement of longitude at sea and how the problem was finally solved by Harrison is chronicled in Dava Sobel, *Longitude* (Walker and Company, 1995).

## Review Questions

1. Briefly explain the difference between a *solar day* and a *sidereal day*.

2. Briefly explain the difference between a *synodic month* and a *sidereal* month.

3. Why is the *tropical year* slightly shorter than the *sidereal year*?

4. What is the difference between a planet's *sidereal period* and its *synodic period*? Explain the meaning of *conjunction*, *opposition*, and *greatest elongation* for planetary orbits viewed from Earth.

5. What is *apparent solar time*? Why is it different from *mean solar time*?

6. Why did it become necessary to create time zones in the late 1800s? Explain how local mean solar time is related to *standard time* and *daylight saving time*.

7. What is *universal time (UT)*? Why is it useful?

8. Describe the origins of the *Julian* and *Gregorian calendars*. What is the rule for leap years on the Gregorian calendar?

9. Explain what we mean when we say that the equinoxes and solstices are both *moments* in time and *points* on the celestial sphere.

10. What are *declination* and *right ascension*? How are these *celestial coordinates* similar to latitude and longitude on Earth? How are they different?

11. Briefly describe how the Sun's celestial coordinates change over the course of each year.

12. Suppose you are standing at the North Pole. Where is the celestial equator in your sky? Where is the north celestial pole? Describe the daily motion of the sky.

13. Repeat question 12 for the equator.

14. Repeat question 12 for latitude 40°N.

15. Describe the Sun's paths through the local sky for latitude 40°N on the equinoxes and on the solstices.

16. Repeat question 15 for the North Pole.

17. Repeat question 15 for the Earth's equator.

18. Repeat question 15 for the *tropic of Cancer*. What makes the tropic circles special?

19. Repeat question 15 for the *Arctic Circle*. What makes the polar circles special?

20. Briefly describe how you can find your latitude by finding the north or south celestial pole.

21. Briefly describe how you can find your latitude from the meridian altitude of any star or the Sun.

22. Briefly describe how you can find your longitude from the position of the Sun and a clock set to universal time.

## Discussion Questions

1. *Northern Chauvinism*. Why is the solstice in June called the *summer solstice*, when it marks winter for places like Australia, New Zealand, and South Africa? Why is the writing on maps and globes usually oriented so that the Northern Hemisphere is at the top, even though there is no up or down in space? Discuss.

2. *When Do Seasons Begin?* It is usually said that the moments of the equinoxes and solstices mark the beginnings of the seasons. For example, it is said that the summer solstice marks the beginning of summer. Based on the annual progression of the Sun's celestial coordinates, do you think it is accurate to say that the equinoxes and solstices mark beginnings? Why or why not?

3. *Seasonal Weather*. The summer solstice occurs in June, but the months of July and August generally have warmer temperatures in the Northern Hemisphere. Similarly, the winter solstice occurs in December, but the months of January and February generally have cooler temperatures in the Northern Hemisphere. Why do you think this is the case? (*Hint*: Look at the distribution of land and oceans on a globe.)

## Problems

*Sensible Statements?* For **problems 1–12**, decide whether the statement is sensible and explain why it is or is not. (*Hint*: For statements that involve coordinates—such as altitude, longitude, or declination—check whether the correct coordinates are used for the situation; for example, it is not sensible to describe a location on Earth by an altitude, since altitude makes sense only for positions in the local sky.)

1. Last night I saw Venus shining brightly on the meridian at midnight.

2. The apparent solar time was noon, but the Sun was just setting.

3. My mean solar clock said it was 2:00 P.M., but my friend who lives east of here had a mean solar clock that said it was 2:11 P.M.

4. When the standard time is 3:00 P.M. in Baltimore, it is 3:15 P.M. in Washington, D.C.

5. The Julian calendar differed from the Gregorian calendar because it was based on the sidereal year.

6. Last night around 8:00 P.M. I saw Jupiter at an altitude of 45° in the south.

7. The latitude of the stars in Orion's belt is about 5°N.

8. Today the Sun is at an altitude of 10° on the celestial sphere.

9. Los Angeles is west of New York by about 3 hours of right ascension.

10. The summer solstice is east of the vernal equinox by 6 hours of right ascension.

11. If it were being named today, the tropic of Cancer would probably be called the tropic of Gemini.

12. Even though my UT clock had stopped, I was able to find my longitude by measuring the altitudes of 14 different stars in my local sky.

13. *Opposite Rotation.* Suppose the Earth rotated in the opposite direction from its revolution; that is, suppose it rotated clockwise (as seen from above the North Pole) every 24 hours while revolving counterclockwise around the Sun each year. Would the solar day still be longer than the sidereal day? Explain.

14. *Fundamentals of Your Local Sky.* Answer each of the following for *your* latitude.
    a. Where is the north (or south) celestial pole in your sky?
    b. Describe the location of the meridian in your sky; be sure to specify its shape and at least three distinct points along it (such as the points at which it meets your horizon and its highest point).
    c. Describe the location of the celestial equator in your sky; be sure to specify its shape and at least three distinct points along it (such as the points at which it meets your horizon and crosses your meridian).
    d. Does the Sun ever appear at your zenith? If so, when? If not, why not?
    e. What is the range of declinations that makes a star circumpolar in your sky? Explain.
    f. What is the range of declinations for stars that you can never see in your sky? Explain.

15. *Sydney Sky.* Repeat problem 14 for the local sky in Sydney, Australia (latitude 34°S).

16. *Path of the Sun in Your Sky.* Describe the path of the Sun through your local sky for each of the following days.
    a. The spring and fall equinoxes.
    b. The summer solstice.
    c. The winter solstice.
    d. Today. (*Hint:* Estimate the right ascension and declination of the Sun for today's date by using the data in Table S1.1.)

17. *Sydney Sun.* Repeat problem 16 for the local sky in Sydney, Australia (latitude 34°S).

18. *Lost at Sea I.* During an upcoming vacation, you decide to take a solo boat trip. While contemplating the universe, you lose track of your location. Fortunately, you have some astronomical tables and instruments, as well as a UT clock. You thereby put together the following description of your situation:
    ■ It is the spring equinox.
    ■ The Sun is on your meridian at altitude 75° in the south.
    ■ The UT clock reads 22:00.
    a. What is your latitude? How do you know?
    b. What is your longitude? How do you know?

c. Consult a map. Based on your position, where is the nearest land? Which way should you sail to reach it?

19. *Lost at Sea II.* Repeat problem 18, based on the following description of your situation:
    ■ It is the day of the summer solstice.
    ■ The Sun is on your meridian at altitude $67\frac{1}{2}°$ in the north.
    ■ The UT clock reads 06:00.

20. *Lost at Sea III.* Repeat problem 18, based on the following description of your situation:
    ■ Your local time is midnight.
    ■ Polaris appears at altitude 67° in the north.
    ■ The UT clock reads 01:00.

21. *Lost at Sea IV.* Repeat problem 18, based on the following description of your situation:
    ■ Your local time is 6 A.M.
    ■ From the position of the Southern Cross, you estimate that the south celestial pole is at altitude 33° in the south.
    ■ The UT clock reads 11:00.

*22. *Sidereal Time.*
    a. Suppose it is 4 P.M. on the spring equinox. What is the local sidereal time?
    b. Suppose the local sidereal time is 19:30. When will Vega cross your meridian?
    c. You observe a star that has an hour angle of +3 hours ($+3^h$) when the local sidereal time is 8:15. What is the star's right ascension?

## Web Projects

Find useful links for Web projects on the text Web site.

1. *Sundials.* Although they are no longer necessary for timekeeping, sundials remain popular for their cultural and artistic value. Search the Web for pictures and information about interesting sundials around the world. Write a short report about at least three sundials that you find particularly interesting.

2. *The Analemma.* Learn more about the analemma and its uses from information available on the Web. Write a short report on your findings.

3. *Calendar History.* Investigate the history of the Julian or Gregorian calendar in greater detail. Write a short summary of some interesting aspect of the history you learn from your Web research. (For example, why did Julius Caesar allow one year to have 445 days? How did our months end up with 28, 30, or 31 days?)

4. *Global Positioning System.* Learn more about the global positioning system and its uses. Write a short report summarizing how you think the GPS will affect our lives over the next 10 years.

# PART II
# Key Concepts for Astronomy

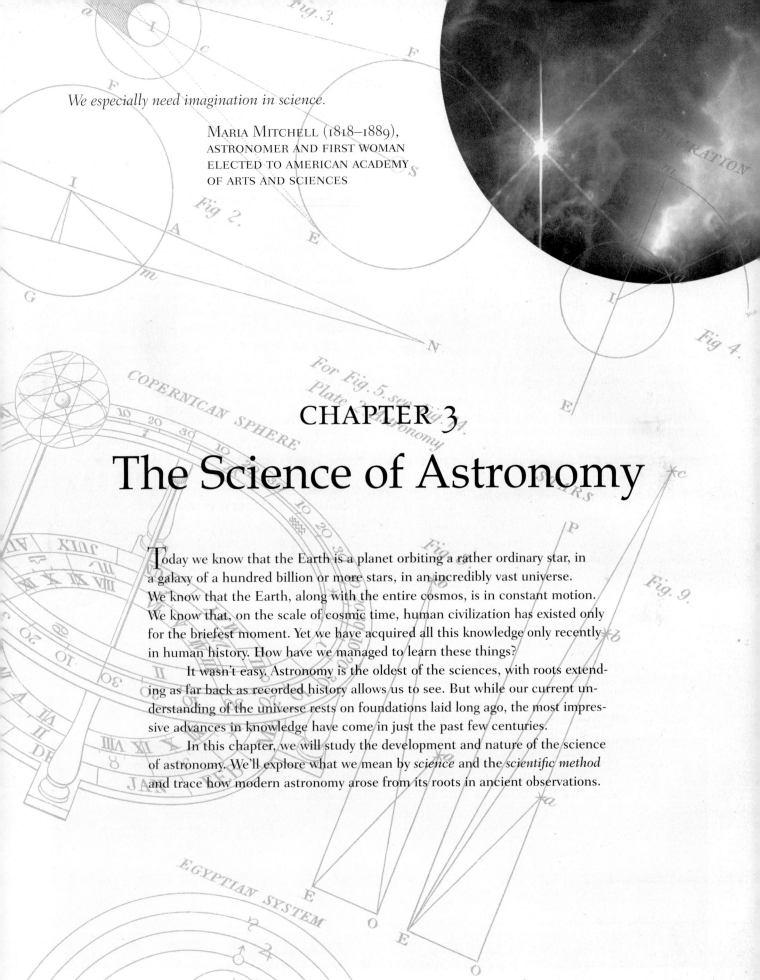

*We especially need imagination in science.*

MARIA MITCHELL (1818–1889),
ASTRONOMER AND FIRST WOMAN
ELECTED TO AMERICAN ACADEMY
OF ARTS AND SCIENCES

# CHAPTER 3
# The Science of Astronomy

Today we know that the Earth is a planet orbiting a rather ordinary star, in
a galaxy of a hundred billion or more stars, in an incredibly vast universe.
We know that the Earth, along with the entire cosmos, is in constant motion.
We know that, on the scale of cosmic time, human civilization has existed only
for the briefest moment. Yet we have acquired all this knowledge only recently
in human history. How have we managed to learn these things?

It wasn't easy. Astronomy is the oldest of the sciences, with roots extending as far back as recorded history allows us to see. But while our current understanding of the universe rests on foundations laid long ago, the most impressive advances in knowledge have come in just the past few centuries.

In this chapter, we will study the development and nature of the science
of astronomy. We'll explore what we mean by *science* and the *scientific method*
and trace how modern astronomy arose from its roots in ancient observations.

## 3.1 Everyday Science

A common stereotype holds that scientists are men and women in white lab coats who somehow think differently than other people. In reality, scientific thinking is a fundamental part of human nature.

Think about how a baby behaves. By about a year of age, she notices that objects fall to the ground when she drops them. She lets go of a ball; it falls. She pushes a plate of food from her high chair; it falls too. She continues to drop all kinds of objects, and they all plummet to Earth. Through powers of observation, the baby learns about the physical world: Things fall when they are unsupported. Eventually, she becomes so certain of this fact that, to her parents' delight, she no longer needs to test it continually.

One day somebody gives the baby a helium balloon. She releases it; to her surprise, it rises to the ceiling! Her rudimentary understanding of physics must be revised. She now knows that the principle "all things fall" does not represent the whole truth, although it still serves her quite well in most situations. It will be years before she learns enough about the atmosphere, the force of gravity, and the concept of density to understand *why* the balloon rises when most other objects fall. For now, she is delighted to observe something new and unexpected.

The baby's experience with falling objects and balloons exemplifies scientific thinking, which, in essence, is a way of learning about nature through careful observation and trial-and-error experiments. Rather than thinking differently than other people, modern scientists simply are trained to organize this everyday thinking in a way that makes it easier for them to share their discoveries and employ their col-

lective wisdom. This organizational scheme is what we call the *scientific method*; it is the method by which humanity has acquired its present physical knowledge of the universe.

**TIME OUT TO THINK** *When was the last time you used trial and error to learn something? Describe a few cases where you have learned by trial and error in cooking, participating in sports, fixing something, or any other situation.*

Just as it takes years for a child to learn to communicate through language, art, or music, it took humanity a long time to develop the principles of the scientific method. In its modern form, the scientific method requires painstaking attention to detail, relentless testing of each piece of information to ensure its reliability, and a willingness to give up old beliefs that are not consistent with observed facts about the physical world. For professional scientists, the demands of the scientific method are the "hard work" part of the job. At heart, professional scientists are like the baby with the balloon, delighted by the unexpected and motivated by those rare moments when they—and all of us—learn something new about the universe.

## 3.2 Ancient Observations

We will discuss the modern scientific method shortly, but first we will explore how it arose from the observations of ancient peoples. Our exploration begins in central Africa, where people of many indigenous societies predict the weather with reasonable accuracy

**FIGURE 3.1** This diagram shows how central Africans used the Moon to predict the weather. The graph depicts the annual rainfall pattern in central Nigeria, characterized by a wet season and a dry season. The Moon diagrams represent the orientation of a waxing crescent moon relative to the western horizon at different times of year. The angle of the crescent "horns" allows observers to determine the time of year and hence the expected rainfall. (The orientation is measured in degrees, where 0° means that the crescent horns are parallel to the horizon.)

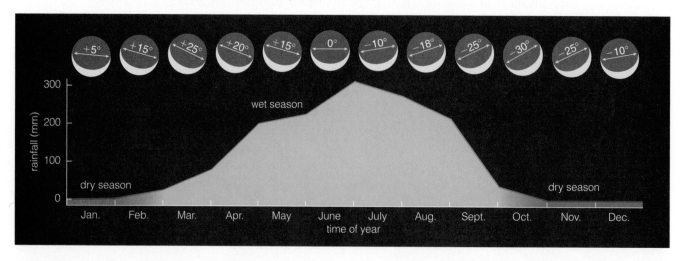

by making careful observations of the Moon. The Moon begins its monthly cycle as a crescent in the western sky just after sunset. Through long traditions of sky watching, central African societies learned that the orientation of the crescent "horns" relative to the horizon is closely tied to rainfall patterns (Figure 3.1).

No one knows when central Africans first developed the ability to predict weather using the lunar crescent. But the earliest-known written astronomical record comes from central Africa near the border of modern-day Congo and Uganda. It consists of an animal bone (known as the *Ishango* bone) etched with patterns that appear to be part of a lunar calendar, probably carved around 6500 B.C.

Why did ancient people bother to make such careful and detailed observations of the sky? In part, it was probably because they were just as curious and intelligent as we are today. In the daytime, they surely recognized the importance of the Sun to their lives. At night, without electric light, they were much more aware of the starry sky than we are today. Thus, it's not surprising that they paid attention to patterns of motion in the sky and developed ideas and stories to explain what they saw.

Astronomy played a practical role in ancient societies by enabling them to keep track of time and seasons, a crucial skill for people who depended on agriculture for survival. This ability may seem quaint today, when digital watches tell us the precise time and date, but it required considerable knowledge and skill in ancient times, when the only clocks and calendars were in the sky.

Modern measures of time still reflect their ancient astronomical roots. Our 24-hour day is the time it takes the Sun to circle our sky. The length of a month comes from the lunar cycle, and our calendar year is based on the cycle of the seasons. The days of the week are named after the seven naked-eye objects that appear to move among the constellations: the Sun, the Moon, and the five planets recognized in ancient times (Table 3.1).

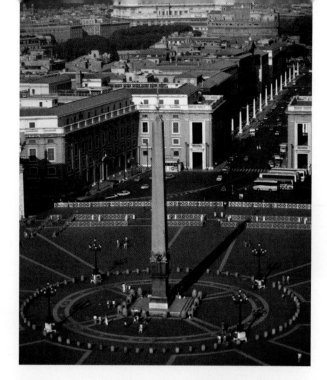

**FIGURE 3.2** This ancient Egyptian obelisk, which stands 83 feet tall and weighs 331 tons, resides in St. Peter's Square at the Vatican in Rome. It is one of 21 surviving obelisks from ancient Egypt, most of which are now scattered around the world. Shadows cast by the obelisks may have been used to tell time.

### Determining the Time of Day

In the daytime, ancient peoples could tell time by observing the Sun's path through the sky. Many cultures probably used the shadows cast by sticks as simple sundials [Section S1.2]. The ancient Egyptians built huge obelisks, often inscribed or decorated in homage to the Sun, that probably also served as simple clocks (Figure 3.2).

At night, the Moon's position and phase give an indication of the time (see Figure 2.19). For example, a first-quarter moon sets around midnight, so it is not yet midnight if the first-quarter moon is still above the western horizon. The positions of the stars also indicate the time if you know the approximate date. For example, in December the constellation Orion rises around sunset, reaches the meridian around midnight, and sets around sunrise. Hence, if it is winter and Orion is setting, dawn must be approaching. Most ancient peoples probably were adept at estimating the time of night, although written evidence is sparse.

Our modern system of dividing the day into 24 hours arose in ancient Egypt some 4,000 years ago. The Egyptians divided the daylight into 12 equal parts,

**Table 3.1  The Seven Days of the Week and the Astronomical Objects They Honor**
The correspondence between objects and days is easy to see in French and Spanish. In English, the correspondence becomes clear when we look at the names of the objects used by the Teutonic tribes who lived in the region of modern-day Germany.

| Object | Teutonic Name | English | French | Spanish |
|---|---|---|---|---|
| Sun | Sun | Sunday | dimanche | domingo |
| Moon | Moon | Monday | lundi | lunes |
| Mars | Tiw | Tuesday | mardi | martes |
| Mercury | Woden | Wednesday | mercredi | miércoles |
| Jupiter | Thor | Thursday | jeudi | jueves |
| Venus | Fria | Friday | vendredi | viernes |
| Saturn | Saturn | Saturday | samedi | sábado |

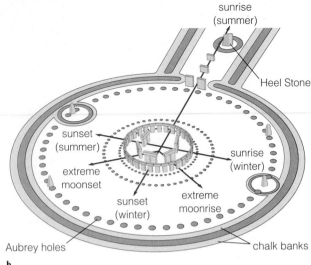

a b

**FIGURE 3.3** (**a**) Stonehenge today. (**b**) A sketch showing how archaeologists believe Stonehenge looked when construction was completed around 1550 B.C. Note, for example, that observers standing in the center would see the Sun rise directly over the Heel Stone on the summer solstice.

and we still break the 24-hour day into 12 hours each of a.m. and p.m.

The Egyptian "hours" were not a fixed amount of time because the amount of daylight varies during the year. For example, "summer hours" were longer than "winter hours," because one-twelfth of the daylight lasts longer in summer than in winter. Only much later in history did the hour become a fixed amount of time, subdivided into 60 equal minutes, each consisting of 60 equal seconds.

The Egyptians also divided the night into 12 equal parts, and early Egyptians used the stars to determine the time at night. Egyptian *star clocks,* often found painted on the coffin lids of Egyptian pharaohs, essentially cataloged where particular stars appear in the sky at particular times of night and particular times of year. By knowing the date from their calendar and observing the positions of particular stars in the sky, the Egyptians could use the star clocks to estimate the time of night.

By about 1500 B.C., Egyptians had abandoned star clocks in favor of clocks that measure time by the flow of water through an opening of a particular size, just as hourglasses measure time by the flow of sand through a narrow neck.[1] These *water clocks* had the advantage of being useful even when the sky was cloudy, and they eventually became the primary timekeeping instruments for many cultures, includ-

ing the Greeks, Romans, and Chinese. The water clocks, in turn, were replaced by mechanical clocks in the 1600s and by electronic clocks in the twentieth century. Despite the availability of other types of clocks, sundials remained in use throughout ancient times and are still popular today both for their decorative value and as reminders that the Sun and stars once were our only guides to time.

### Determining the Time of Year

Many cultures built structures to help them mark the seasons. One of the oldest standing human-made structures served such a purpose: Stonehenge in southern England, which was constructed in stages from about 2750 B.C. to about 1550 B.C. (Figure 3.3). Observers standing in its center see the Sun rise directly over the Heel Stone only on the summer solstice. Stonehenge also served as a social gathering place and probably as a religious site; no one knows whether its original purpose was social or astronomical. Perhaps it was built for both—in ancient times, social rituals and practical astronomy probably were deeply intertwined.

One of the most spectacular structures used to mark the seasons was the Templo Mayor in the Aztec city of Tenochtitlán, located on the site of modern-day Mexico City (Figure 3.4). Twin temples surmounted a flat-topped, 150-foot-high pyramid. From the location of a royal observer watching from the opposite side of the plaza, the Sun rose directly through the notch between the twin temples on the equinoxes. Like Stonehenge, the Templo Mayor served important social and religious functions in addition to its astronomical role. Before it was destroyed by the

---

[1]Hourglasses using sand were not invented until about the eighth century A.D., long after the advent of water clocks. Natural sand grains vary in size, so making accurate hourglasses required technology for getting uniform grains of sand.

**FIGURE 3.4** This scale model shows the Templo Mayor and the surrounding plaza as they are thought to have looked before Aztec civilization was destroyed by the Conquistadors.

Conquistadors, other Spanish visitors reported stories of elaborate rituals, sometimes including human sacrifice, that took place at the Templo Mayor at times determined by astronomical observations.

Many ancient cultures aligned their buildings with the cardinal directions (north, south, east, and west), enabling them to mark the rising and setting of the Sun relative to the building orientation. Some even created monuments that had a single special astronomical purpose. Perhaps in a practical form of ancient art, someone among the ancient Anasazi people carved a spiral known as the Sun Dagger on a vertical cliff face near the top of a butte in Chaco Canyon, New Mexico (Figure 3.5). The Sun's rays form a dagger of sunlight that pierces the center of the carved spiral only once each year—at noon on the summer solstice.

a

b

**FIGURE 3.5** (a) The Sun Dagger is an arrangement of rocks that shape the Sun's light into a dagger, with a spiral carved on a rock face behind them. The dagger pierces the center of the carved spiral each year at noon on the summer solstice. (b) The Sun Dagger is located on a vertical cliff face high on this butte in New Mexico.

## Lunar Cycles

Many ancient civilizations paid particular attention to the lunar cycle, often using it as the basis for lunar calendars. The months on lunar calendars generally have either 29 or 30 days, chosen to make the average agree with the approximately $29\frac{1}{2}$-day lunar cycle. A 12-month lunar calendar has only 354 or 355 days, or about 11 days fewer than a calendar based on the tropical year. Such a calendar is still used in the Muslim religion, which is why the month-long fast of Ramadan (the ninth month) begins about 11 days earlier with each subsequent year.

Other lunar calendars take advantage of the fact that 19 years is almost precisely 235 lunar months. That is, every 19 years we get the same lunar phases on about the same dates. Because this fact was discovered in 432 B.C. by the Greek astronomer Meton, the 19-year period is called the **Metonic cycle**. A lunar calendar can be synchronized to the Metonic cycle by adding a thirteenth month to 7 of every 19 years (making exactly 235 months in each 19-year period), thereby ensuring that "new year" comes on approximately the same date every nineteenth year. The Jewish calendar follows the Metonic cycle, adding a thirteenth month in the third, sixth, eighth, eleventh, fourteenth, seventeenth, and nineteenth years of each cycle. This also explains why the date of Easter changes each year: The New Testament ties the date of Easter to the Jewish festival of Passover, which has its date set by the Jewish lunar calendar. In a slight modification of the original scheme, most Western Christians now celebrate Easter on *the first Sunday after the first full moon after March 21;* if the full moon falls on Sunday, Easter is the following Sunday. (Eastern Orthodox churches calculate the date of Easter differently, because they base the date on the Julian rather than the Gregorian calendar [Section S1.3].)

Some ancient cultures learned to predict eclipses by recognizing the 18-year saros cycle [Section 2.3]. In the Middle East, the ancient Babylonians achieved remarkable success in predicting eclipses more than 2,500 years ago. Perhaps the most successful eclipse predictions prior to modern times were made by the Mayans in Central America. The Mayan calendar featured a sacred cycle that almost certainly was related to eclipses. This Mayan cycle, called the *sacred round,* lasted 260 days—almost exactly $1\frac{1}{2}$ times the 173.32 days between successive eclipse seasons [Section 2.3]. Unfortunately, we know little more about the extent of Mayan knowledge, because the Spanish Conquistadors burned most Mayan writings.

The complexity of the Moon's orbit leads to other long-term patterns in the Moon's appearance. For example, the full moon rises at its most southerly point along the eastern horizon only once every 18.6 years, a phenomenon that may have been observed from the 4,000-year-old sacred stone circle at Callanish, Scotland (Figure 3.6).

---

## Mathematical Insight 3.1    The Metonic Cycle

The Metonic cycle can be used to keep lunar calendars fairly closely synchronized with solar calendars, but only if the lunar calendar has 7 extra lunar months in every 19 years. To see why, recall that each cycle of lunar phases takes an average of 29.53 days (the synodic month [Section S1.1]). A 12-month lunar calendar has $12 \times 29.53 = 354.36$ days, or about 11 days less than our 365-day solar calendar. If the new year on a 12-month lunar calendar occurs this year on October 1, next year it will occur 11 days earlier, on September 20; the following year it will occur 11 days before that, on September 9; and so on. Without using the Metonic cycle, over many years the lunar new year would move all the way around the solar calendar.

The Metonic cycle is a period of 19 years on a solar calendar, which is almost precisely 235 months on a lunar calendar. To verify this fact, note that 19 solar years is equivalent to:

$$19 \, \cancel{yr} \times \frac{365.25 \text{ days}}{1 \, \cancel{yr}} = 6{,}939.75 \text{ days}$$

Similarly, 235 lunar months is:

$$235 \, \cancel{months} \times \frac{29.53 \text{ days}}{1 \, \cancel{month}} = 6{,}939.55 \text{ days}$$

Notice that the difference between 19 solar years and 235 lunar months is only about 0.2 day, or about 5 hours. This near equivalence means that the dates of lunar phases repeat with each Metonic cycle. For example, there was a new moon on October 1, 1998, and we will have a new moon on October 1, 2017. (In general, the dates may be off by 1 day because of the 5-hour "error" in the Metonic cycle and also because 19 years on our calendar may be either 6,939 days or 6,940 days, depending on the leap-year cycle.)

For a lunar calendar to remain roughly synchronized with a solar calendar, it must have exactly 235 months in each 19-year period. Because a 12-month lunar calendar has a total of only $19 \times 12 = 228$ months in 19 years, the lunar calendar needs 7 extra months to reach the required 235 months. One way to accomplish this is to have 7 years with a thirteenth lunar month in every 19-year cycle, as is the case for the Jewish calendar.

**FIGURE 3.6** The Moon rising between two stones of the 4,000-year-old sacred stone circle at Callanish, Scotland (on the Isle of Lewis in the Scottish Hebrides). The full moon rises in this position only once every 18.6 years.

### Observations of Planets and Stars

Many cultures also made careful observations of the planets and stars. Mayan observatories in Central America, such as the one still standing at Chichén Itzá (Figure 3.7), had windows strategically placed for observations of Venus.

More than 2,000 years ago, early Central American people marked the beginning of their year when the group of stars called the Pleiades first rose in the east after having been hidden from view for 40 days by the glare of the Sun. On the other side of the world, southern Greeks also used the Pleiades to time their planting and harvests, as described in this excerpt from an epic poem (*Works and Days*) composed by the Greek farmer Hesiod in about 800 B.C.:

> *When you notice the daughters of Atlas, the Pleiades, rising, start on your reaping, and on your sowing when they are setting. They are hidden from your view for a period of forty full days, both night and day, but then once again, as the year moves round, they reappear at the time for you to be sharpening your sickle.*

Observational aids could also mark the rising and setting of the stars. More than 800 lines, some stretching for miles, are etched in the dry desert sand of Peru between the Ingenio and Nazca Rivers. Many of these lines may simply have been well-traveled pathways, but others are aligned in directions that point to places where bright stars or the Sun rose at particular times of year. In addition to the many straight lines, the desert features many

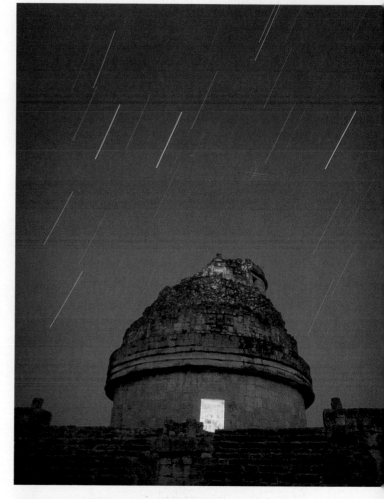

**FIGURE 3.7** The ruins of the Mayan observatory at Chichén Itzá.

large figures of animals, which may be representations of constellations made by the Incas who lived in the region (Figure 3.8).

**TIME OUT TO THINK** *The animal figures show up clearly only when seen from above. As a result, some UFO enthusiasts argue that the patterns must have been created by aliens. What do you think of this argument? Defend your opinion.*

The great Incan cities of South America clearly were built with astronomy in mind. Entire cities appear to have been designed so that particular arrangements of roads, buildings, or other human-made structures would point to places where bright stars rose or set, or where the Sun rose and set at particular times of year.[2]

Structures for astronomical observation also were popular in North America. Lodges built by the Pawnee people in Kansas featured strategically placed holes for observing the passage of constellations that figured prominently in their folklore. In the northern plains of the United States, Native American Medicine Wheels probably were designed for astronomical observations. The "spokes" of the Medicine Wheel at Big Horn, Wyoming, were aligned with the rising and setting of bright stars, as well as with the rising and setting of the Sun on the

**FIGURE 3.8** Hundreds of lines and patterns are etched in the sand of the Nazca desert in Peru. This aerial photo shows a large etched figure of a hummingbird.

equinoxes and solstices (Figure 3.9). The 28 spokes of the Medicine Wheel probably relate to the month of the Native Americans, which they measured as 28 days (rather than 29 or 30 days) because they did not count the day of the new moon.

Perhaps the people most dependent on knowledge of the stars were the Polynesians, who lived and

---

[2]For more details about the layout of Incan cities and other ancient astronomy discussed in this chapter, see Anthony F. Aveni, *Ancient Astronomers* (Smithsonian Books, St. Remy Press and Smithsonian Institution, 1993).

**FIGURE 3.9** Aerial and ground views of the Big Horn Medicine Wheel in Wyoming. Note the 28 "spokes" radiating out from the center. These spokes probably relate to the month of the Native Americans.

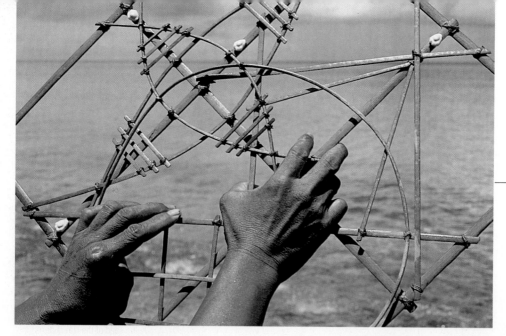

**FIGURE 3.10** A traditional Polynesian navigational instrument.

traveled among the many islands of the mid- and South Pacific. Because the next island in a journey usually was too distant to be seen, poor navigation meant becoming lost at sea. As a result, the most esteemed position in Polynesian culture was that of the Navigator, a person who had acquired the detailed knowledge necessary to navigate great distances among the islands. The Navigators employed a combination of detailed knowledge of astronomy and equally impressive knowledge of the patterns of waves and swells around different islands (Figure 3.10). The stars provided their broad navigational sense, pointing them in the correct direction of their intended destination. As they neared a destination, the wave and swell patterns guided them to their precise landing point. The Navigator memorized all his skills and passed them to the next generation through a well-developed program for training future Navigators. Unfortunately, with the advent of modern navigational technology, many of the skills of the Navigators have been lost.

### From Observation to Science

Before a structure such as Stonehenge could be built, careful observations had to be made and repeated over and over to ensure their validity. Careful, repeatable observations also underlie the modern scientific method. To this extent, elements of modern science were present in many early human cultures.

The degree to which scientific ideas developed in different societies depended on practical needs, social and political customs, and interactions with other cultures. Because all of these factors can change, it should not be surprising that different cultures were more scientifically or technologically advanced than others at different times in history. The ancient Chinese kept remarkably detailed records of astronomical observations beginning at least 5,000 years ago (Figure 3.11).

Yet, by the end of the 1600s, Chinese science and technology had fallen behind that of Europe. Some historians argue that a primary reason for this decline was that the Chinese tended to regard their science and technology as state secrets. This secrecy may have slowed Chinese scientific development

**FIGURE 3.11** This photo shows a model of the celestial sphere and other instruments on the roof of the ancient astronomical observatory in Beijing. The observatory was built in the 1400s; the instruments shown here were built later and show the influence of Jesuit missionaries.

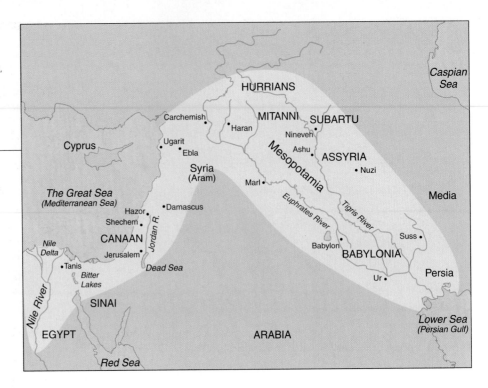

**FIGURE 3.12** Map of the Middle East in ancient times. Mesopotamia was the ancient Greek name for the region between the Tigris and Euphrates Rivers, but modern historians use the name for the entire region today occupied by Iraq. Three major cultures thrived at various times in ancient Mesopotamia: Sumer, Babylonia, and Assyria.

by preventing the broad-based collaborative science that fueled the European advance beginning in the Renaissance.

In Central America, the ancient Mayans also were ahead of their time in many ways. For example, their system of numbers and mathematics looks distinctly modern; their invention of the concept of zero preceded by some 500 years its introduction in the Eurasian world (by Hindu mathematicians, around A.D. 600). The Aztecs, Incas, Anasazi, and other ancient peoples of the Americas may have been quite advanced in many other areas as well, but few written records survive to tell the tale.

It appears that virtually all cultures employed scientific thinking to varying degrees. Had the circumstances of history been different, any one of these many cultures might have been the first to develop what we consider to be modern science. But, in the end, history takes only one of countless possible paths, and the path that led to modern science emerged from the ancient civilizations of the Mediterranean and the Middle East.

## 3.3 The Modern Lineage

By 3000 B.C., civilization was well established in two major regions of the Middle East: Egypt and Mesopotamia (Figure 3.12). Their geographical location placed these civilizations at a crossroads for travelers,

merchants, and armies of Europe, Asia, and Africa. This mixing of cultures fostered creativity, and the broad interactions among peoples ensured that new ideas spread throughout the region. Over the next 2,500 years, numerous great cultures arose. For example, the ancient Egyptians built the Great Pyramids between 2700 and 2100 B.C., using their astronomical knowledge to orient the Pyramids with the cardinal directions. They also invented papyrus scrolls and ink-based writing. The Babylonians invented methods of writing on clay tablets and developed arithmetic to serve in commerce and later in astronomical calculations. Many more of our modern principles of commerce, law, religion, and science originated with the cultures of Egypt and Mesopotamia.

The development of principles of modern science accelerated with the rise of Greece as a power in the Middle East, beginning around 500 B.C. In 330 B.C., Alexander the Great led the expansion of the Greek empire throughout the Middle East, absorbing all the former empires of Egypt and Mesopotamia. Alexander had a keen interest in science and education, perhaps fueled by his association with Aristotle [Section 5.3], who was his personal tutor. He encouraged the pursuit of knowledge and respect for foreign cultures. On the Nile delta in Egypt, he founded the city of Alexandria, which he hoped would become a center of world culture.

Although Alexander died at the age of 35, his dream came true. His successors continued to build Alexandria, including the construction of a great

### Eratosthenes Measures the Earth

In a remarkable ancient feat, the Greek astronomer and geographer Eratosthenes (c. 276–196 B.C.) estimated the size of the Earth in about 240 B.C. He did it by comparing the altitude of the Sun on the summer solstice in the Egyptian cities of Syene (modern-day Aswan) and Alexandria.

Eratosthenes knew that the Sun passed directly overhead in Syene on the summer solstice (it lies on the tropic of Cancer [Section S1.5]). He also knew that in the city of Alexandria to the north the Sun came within only 7° of the zenith on the summer solstice. He therefore concluded that Alexandria must be 7° of latitude to the north of Syene (Figure 3.13). Because 7° is $\frac{7}{360}$ of a circle, he concluded that the north-south distance between Alexandria and Syene must be $\frac{7}{360}$ of the circumference of the Earth.

Eratosthenes estimated the north-south distance between Syene and Alexandria to be 5,000 stadia (the *stadium* was a Greek unit of distance). Thus, he concluded that

$$\frac{7}{360} \times \text{circumference of Earth} = 5{,}000 \text{ stadia}$$

from which he found the Earth's circumference to be about 250,000 stadia.

Today, we don't know exactly what distance a stadium meant to Eratosthenes; however, based on the actual sizes of Greek stadiums, it must have been about $\frac{1}{6}$ kilometer. Thus, Eratosthenes estimated the circumference of the Earth to be about $\frac{250{,}000}{6} = 42{,}000$ kilometers—remarkably close to the modern value of just over 40,000 kilometers.

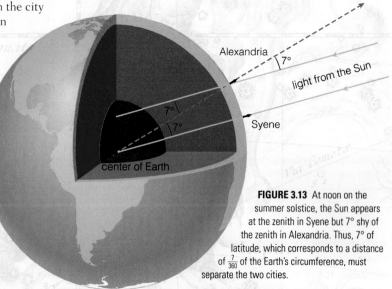

**FIGURE 3.13** At noon on the summer solstice, the Sun appears at the zenith in Syene but 7° shy of the zenith in Alexandria. Thus, 7° of latitude, which corresponds to a distance of $\frac{7}{360}$ of the Earth's circumference, must separate the two cities.

library and research center around 300 B.C. (Figure 3.14). The Library of Alexandria was the world's preeminent center of research for the next 700 years. Its end is associated with the death of Hypatia, perhaps the most prominent female scholar of the ancient world. Hypatia was a resident scholar of the Library of Alexandria, director of the observatory in Alexandria, and one of the leading mathematicians and astronomers of her time. Unfortunately, she lived during a time of rising sentiment against free inquiry and was murdered by anti-intellectual mobs in A.D. 415. The final destruction of the Library of Alexandria followed not long after her death.

At its peak, the Library of Alexandria held more than a half million books, handwritten on papyrus scrolls. As the invention of the printing press was far in the future, most of the scrolls probably were original manuscripts or the single copies of original manuscripts. When the library was destroyed, most of its storehouse of ancient wisdom was lost forever.

**TIME OUT TO THINK** *How old is the school that you attend? Compare its age to the 700 years that the Library of Alexandria survived. Estimate the number of books you've read in your life. Compare this number to the half million books once housed in the Library of Alexandria.*

### The Ptolemaic Model of the Universe

Perhaps the most important scientific idea developed by the ancient Greeks was that of creating **models** of nature. Just as a model airplane is a representation of a real airplane, a scientific model seeks to represent some aspect of nature. However, scientific models usually are conceptual models rather than miniature representations. The purpose of a scientific model is to explain and predict real phenomena, without any need to invoke myth, magic, or the supernatural. The ancient Greek idea of a celestial sphere is an example of a scientific model: The celestial sphere is the model, and it can be used to explain and predict the apparent motions of stars in our sky.

By combining the concept of modeling with advances in logic and mathematics, the ancient Greeks practiced a pursuit of knowledge very much like that of modern science. They used their models to make

a

b

**FIGURE 3.14** These renderings show an artist's reconstruction, based on scholarly research, of how (**a**) the Great Hall and (**b**) a scroll room of the Library of Alexandria might have looked.

predictions, such as predicting where the planets should appear among the constellations of the night sky. If the predictions proved inaccurate, they changed and refined their models. In this way, the Greeks soon learned that the simple idea of a celestial sphere could not explain all the phenomena they saw in the sky (particularly the apparent retrograde motion of the planets). They therefore added spheres for the Sun, the Moon, and each of the planets and continued to change their ideas of how the spheres moved in an ongoing attempt to make the model agree with reality (Figure 3.15).

The culmination of this ancient modeling came with the work of Claudius Ptolemy (c. A.D. 100–170), pronounced *tol-e-mee*. Ptolemy's model of the universe is a tribute to human ingenuity in that it made reasonably accurate predictions despite being built on the flawed premise of an Earth-centered universe. Following a Greek tradition dating back to Plato (428–348 B.C.), Ptolemy imagined that all heavenly motions must proceed in perfect circles. To explain the apparent retrograde motion of planets, Ptolemy used an idea first suggested by Apollonius (c. 240–190 B.C.) and further developed by Hipparchus (c. 190–120 B.C.). This idea held that each planet moved along a small circle that, in turn, moved around a larger circle (Figure 3.16). As seen from Earth, this "circle upon circle" motion meant that a planet usually moved eastward relative to the stars but sometimes moved westward in apparent retrograde motion.

Ptolemy selected the sizes of the circles and the rates of motion of the planets along the circles

**FIGURE 3.15** This diagram depicts the heavenly spheres, an ancient Greek model of the universe (c. 200 B.C.).

so that his model reproduced the apparent retrograde motion of all the known planets. He also incorporated more complex ideas into his model, such as allowing the Earth to be slightly off-center from the circles of a particular planet, so that it could forecast future planetary positions to within a few degrees—which was considered quite accurate at that time.

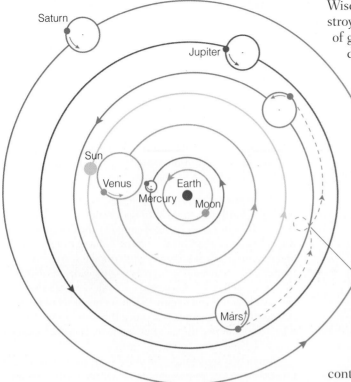

**FIGURE 3.16** This diagram shows several key features of Ptolemy's model of the motions of the Sun, Moon, and planets around the Earth. The planets move around the small circles at the same time that these circles move around the Earth. By careful selection of the sizes of the circles and the rates at which planets moved, along with a few other adjustments, this model made reasonably accurate predictions of planetary positions and showed their apparent retrograde motions. In order to show the circle-upon-circle idea clearly, this diagram exaggerates several features of the true Ptolemaic model; for example, for each retrograde loop, Mars moves much farther in the actual model than shown here.

Ptolemy's model remained the standard until the time of the Copernican revolution, some 1,400 years later.

### *The Islamic Role*

Most of the great scholarly work of the ancient Greeks was lost with the fall of the Roman Empire and the destruction of the Library of Alexandria in the fifth century A.D. Much more would have been lost had it not been for the rise of a new center of intellectual achievement in Baghdad (present-day Iraq). While European civilization fell into the period of intellectual decline known as the Dark Ages, scholars of the new religion of Islam sought knowledge of mathematics and astronomy in hopes of better understanding the wisdom of Allah. During the eighth and ninth centuries A.D., scholars working in the Muslim empire centered in Baghdad translated and thereby saved many of the ancient Greek works.

Around A.D. 800, an Islamic leader named Al-Mamun (A.D. 786–833) established a "House of

Wisdom" in Baghdad comparable in scope to the destroyed Library of Alexandria. Founded in a spirit of great openness and tolerance, the House of Wisdom employed Jews, Christians, and Muslims, all working together in scholarly pursuits. Using the translated Greek scientific manuscripts as building blocks, these scholars developed algebra and many new instruments and techniques for astronomical observation. Most of the official names of constellations and stars come from Arabic because of the work of the scholars at Baghdad. If you look at a star chart, you will see that the names of many bright stars begin with *al* (e.g., Aldebaran, Algol), which simply means "the" in Arabic. Ptolemy's book describing his astronomical system is also known by its Arabic name *Almagest,* from Arabic words meaning "the greatest compilation."

The Islamic world of the Middle Ages was in frequent contact with Hindu scholars from India, who in turn brought knowledge of ideas and discoveries from China. Hence, the intellectual center in Baghdad achieved a synthesis of the surviving work of the ancient Greeks and that of the Indians and the Chinese. The accumulated knowledge of the Arabs spread throughout the Byzantine Empire (the eastern part of the former Roman Empire). When the Byzantine capital of Constantinople (modern-day Istanbul) fell to the Turks in 1453, many Eastern scholars headed west to Europe, carrying with them the knowledge that helped ignite the European Renaissance.

## 3.4 Modern Science and the Scientific Method

As we have seen, many different cultures developed scientific modes of thinking, and the ancient Greeks developed principles of modeling very similar to those underlying the modern scientific method. But there are important differences between these ancient ideas and modern science. For example, Ptolemy's writings suggest that he designed his model to aid in calculations, with little concern for whether it reflected reality. While modern scientists also employ purely computational models when necessary, understanding the underlying reality of nature is an important goal of modern science.

The principles that govern modern science coalesced during the European Renaissance. Within 100 years after the fall of Constantinople, Copernicus began the process of overturning the Earth-centered,

## Logic and the Scientific Method

In science, we attempt to learn new knowledge through logical reasoning. The process of reasoning is carried out by constructing arguments in which we begin with a set of premises and try to draw appropriate conclusions. Note that this concept of a logical argument differs somewhat from the definition of *argument* in everyday life; in particular, a logical argument need not imply any animosity or dissension. There are two basic types of argument: *deductive* and *inductive*. Both are important in the scientific method.

The following is a simple example of a *deductive argument*:

> PREMISE:  All planets orbit the Sun in ellipses with the Sun at one focus.
> PREMISE:  Earth is a planet.
> CONCLUSION:  Earth orbits the Sun in an ellipse with the Sun at one focus.

Note that, as long as the two premises are true, the conclusion must also be true; this is the essence of deduction. In addition, note that the first premise is a general statement that applies to all planets, whereas the conclusion is a specific statement that applies only to Earth. As this example suggests, deduction is often used to *deduce* a specific prediction from a more general theory. If the specific prediction proves to be false, then something must be wrong with the theoretical premises from which it was deduced. If it proves true, then we've acquired a piece of evidence in support of the theory.

Contrast the deductive argument above with the following example of an *inductive argument*:

> PREMISE:  Birds fly up into the air but eventually come back down.
> PREMISE:  People who jump into the air fall back down.
> PREMISE:  Rocks thrown into the air come back down.
> PREMISE:  Balls thrown into the air come back down.
> CONCLUSION:  What goes up must come down.

Imagine that you lived in the time of ancient Greece, when the Earth was thought to be a realm distinct from the sky. Because each premise supports the conclusion, you might agree that this is a strong inductive argument and that its conclusion probably is true. However, no matter how many more examples you consider of objects that go up and come down, you could never *prove* that the conclusion is true—only that it seems likely to be true. A single counterexample can prove the conclusion to be false—for example, the fact that some rockets are launched into space and never return to Earth.

Inductive arguments *generalize* from specific facts to a broader model or theory and hence are the arguments used to build scientific theories. That is why theories can never be proved true beyond all doubt—they can only be shown to be consistent with ever larger bodies of evidence. Theories can be proved false, however, if they fail to account for observed or experimental facts.

Ptolemaic model, setting into motion a burst of scientific discovery that continues to this day. Before we can fully appreciate the Copernican revolution, which we'll discuss in Chapter 5, we must investigate a more basic question: What is modern science?

The word **science** comes from the Latin *scientia*, meaning "knowledge"; it is also the root of the words *conscience* (related to the idea of self-knowledge or self-awareness) and *omniscience* (the quality of being all-knowing). Today, science connotes a special kind of knowledge: the kind that makes predictions that can be confirmed by rigorous observations and experiments. In brief, the modern **scientific method** is an organized approach to explaining observed facts with a model of nature, subject to the constraint that any proposed model must be testable and the provision that the model must be modified or discarded if it fails these tests.

In its most idealized form, the scientific method begins with a set of observed facts. A fact is supposed to be a statement that is objectively true. For exam-

ple, we consider it a fact that the Sun rises each morning, that the planet Mars appeared in a particular place in our sky last night, and that the Earth rotates. Facts are not always obvious, as illustrated by the case of the Earth's rotation—for most of human history, the Earth was assumed to be stationary at the center of the universe. In addition, our interpretations of facts often are based on beliefs about the world that others might not share. For example, when we say that the Sun rises each morning, we assume that it is the *same* Sun day after day—an idea that might not have been accepted by ancient Egyptians, whose mythology held that the Sun died with every sunset and was reborn with every sunrise. Nevertheless, facts are the raw material that scientific models seek to explain, so it is important that scientists agree on the facts. In the context of science, a fact must therefore be something that anyone can verify for himself or herself, at least in principle.

Once the facts have been collected, a model can be proposed to explain them. A useful model must also make predictions that can be tested through further observations or experiments. Ptolemy's model of the universe was useful because it predicted future locations of the Sun, Moon, and planets in the sky. However, although the Ptolemaic model remained in use for nearly 1,500 years, eventually it became clear that its predictions didn't quite match actual observations—a key reason why the Earth-centered model of the universe finally was discarded.

In summary, the idealized scientific method proceeds as follows:

- *Observation:* The scientific method begins with the collection of a set of observed facts.

- *Hypothesis:* A model is proposed to explain the observed facts and to make new predictions. A proposed model is often called a **hypothesis**, which essentially means an *educated guess.*

- *Further observations/experiments:* The model's predictions are tested through further observations or experiments. When a prediction is verified, we gain confidence that the model truly represents nature. When a prediction fails, we recognize that the model is flawed, and we therefore must refine or discard the model.

- *Theory:* A model must be continually challenged with new observations or experiments by many different scientists. A model achieves the status of a **scientific theory** only after a broad range of its predictions has been repeatedly verified. Note that, while we can have great confidence that a scientific theory truly represents nature, we can never prove a theory to be true *beyond all doubt.* Therefore, even well-established theories must be subject to continuing challenges through further observations and experiments.

In reality, scientific discoveries rarely are made by a process as mechanical as the idealized scientific method described here. For example, Johannes Kepler, who discovered the laws of planetary motion in the early 1600s, tested his model against observations that had been made previously, rather than verifying new predictions based on his model [Section 5.3]. Moreover, like most scientific work, Kepler's work involved intuition, collaboration with others, moments of insight, and luck. Nevertheless, with hindsight we can look back at Kepler's theory and see that other scientists eventually made plenty of observations to verify the planetary positions predicted by his model. In that sense, the scientific method represents an ideal prescription for judging objectively whether a proposed model of nature is close to the truth.

**TIME OUT TO THINK** *Look up* theory *in a dictionary. How does its definition differ from that given here for* scientific theory?

### Science, Pseudoscience, and Nonscience

People often seek knowledge in ways that do not follow the basic tenets of the scientific method and therefore are not science. When we leave the realm of science, claims of knowledge become far more subjective and difficult to verify. Nevertheless, it can be useful to categorize such claims of knowledge as either *pseudoscience* or *nonscience.*

By **pseudoscience** we mean attempts to search for knowledge in ways that may at first seem scientific but do not adhere to the testing and verification requirements of the scientific method; the prefix *pseudo* means "false." For example, at the beginning of each year you can find tabloid newspapers offering predictions made by people who claim to be able to "see" the future. Because they make specific predictions, we can test their claims by checking whether their predictions come true, and numerous studies have shown that their predictions come true no more often than would be expected by pure chance. But these seers seem unconcerned with the results of such studies. The fact that they make testable claims but then ignore the results of the tests marks their claimed ability to see the future as pseudoscience.

By **nonscience** we mean knowledge sought through pure intuition, societal traditions, ancient scriptures, and other processes that make no claim

---

#### Common Misconceptions: Eggs on the Equinox

A central principle of science is that you needn't take scientific claims on faith; in principle, at least, you can always test them for yourself. Consider the claim, repeated in news reports every year, that the spring equinox is the only day on which you can balance an egg on its end. Many people believe this claim, but you'll be immediately skeptical if you think about the nature of the spring equinox. The equinox is merely a point in the Earth's orbit at which sunlight strikes both hemispheres equally (see Figure 1.13), and it's difficult to see how sunlight could affect an attempt to balance eggs (especially if the eggs are indoors). More important, you can test this claim directly. It's not easy to balance an egg on its end, but with practice you'll find that you can do it on *any* day of the year, not just on the spring equinox. Not all scientific claims are so easy to test for yourself, but the basic lesson should be clear: Before you accept any scientific claim, you should demand at least a reasonable explanation of the evidence that backs it up.

to adhere to the scientific method. In nonscience, experimental testing is irrelevant because nonscientific beliefs are based on things such as faith, political conviction, and tradition. Because nonscience makes no pretense of following the scientific method, science can say nothing about the validity of nonscience.

**TIME OUT TO THINK** *Can the scientific method be applied in any way to questions of faith, prayer, emotion, or values? Defend your view.*

### Is Science Objective?

The boundaries between science, nonscience, and pseudoscience are sometimes blurry. In particular, because science is practiced by human beings, individual scientists carry their personal biases and beliefs with them in their scientific work. These biases can influence how a scientist proposes or tests a model, and in some cases scientists have been known to cheat—either deliberately or subconsciously—to obtain the results they desire. For example, in the late nineteenth and early twentieth centuries, some astronomers claimed to see networks of "canals" in their blurry telescopic images of Mars, and they hypothesized that Mars was home to a dying civilization that used the canals to transport water to thirsty cities [Section 9.5]. Because no such canals actually exist, these astronomers apparently were allowing their beliefs to influence how they interpreted blurry images. It was, in essence, a form of cheating—even though it certainly was not intentional.

Sometimes, bias can show up even in the thinking of the scientific community as a whole. Thus, some valid ideas may not be considered by any scientist because the ideas fall too far outside the general patterns of thought, or the **paradigm**, of the time. Einstein's theory of relativity provides an example. Many other scientists had gleaned hints of this theory in the decades before Einstein but did not investigate them, at least in part because they seemed too outlandish.

The beauty of the scientific method is that it encourages continued testing by many people. Even if personal biases affect some results, tests by others eventually will uncover the mistakes. Similarly, even when a new idea falls outside the accepted paradigm, sufficient testing and verification of the idea eventually will force a change in the paradigm. Thus, although individual scientists rarely follow the scientific method in its idealized form, the collective action of many scientists over many years generally *does* follow the basic tenets of the scientific method. That is why, despite the biases of individual scientists, science as a whole is usually objective.

## 3.5 Astronomy Today

The modern scientific method has fueled a dramatic rise in human knowledge. It took humanity some 6,000 years to progress from the early lunar astronomy recorded in Africa to the ancient Greek idea of creating models of the universe, and another 2,000 years to finally recognize that the Earth orbits the Sun. In contrast, the past 400 years have seen discovery upon discovery, and we have come to know that the universe is filled with wonders far beyond the wildest imagination of our ancestors.

Today, the science of astronomy continues to develop at an ever-growing rate. New telescopes are fueling a renaissance in astronomy. In the past decade alone, we made the first discoveries of planets around other stars, witnessed the birth of galaxies near the edge of the observable universe, and discovered tantalizing hints of an accelerating universal expansion. If we measure information as a computer does, in *bytes* (where 1 byte represents the information content of one typed character and 1 megabyte represents the information in a 500-page book), then the information recorded at a single major observatory in a single night exceeds the total amount of astronomical information recorded by all ancient peoples combined.

The abundance of new data is disseminated worldwide via the Internet, and new data are collected at international observatories in many different countries and in space. The result is that, after a few centuries during which advances in astronomy were made primarily in Europe and the United States, astronomy is once again a worldwide endeavor. Just as the ancient civilizations of Egypt and Mesopotamia benefited from the cross-fertilization of ideas brought by people of many different cultures, astronomy today is benefiting from the great variety of perspectives of scientists from all over the world.

## 3.6 Astrology

Although the terms *astrology* and *astronomy* sound very similar, today they describe very different practices. In ancient times, however, astrology and astronomy often went hand in hand, and astrology played an important role in the historical development of astronomy.

In brief, the basic tenet of astrology is that human events are influenced by the apparent positions of the Sun, Moon, and planets among the stars in our sky. The origins of this idea are easy to understand. After all, there is no doubt that the position of the Sun in the sky influences our lives—it determines the seasons and hence the times of planting and harvesting, of warmth and cold, and of daylight and darkness. Similarly, the Moon determines the tides, and the cycle of lunar phases coincides with many biological cycles. Because the planets also appear to move among the stars, it seemed reasonable that planets also influence our lives, even if these influences were much more difficult to discover.

Ancient astrologers hoped that they might learn *how* the positions of the Sun, Moon, and planets influence our lives. They charted the skies, seeking correlations with events on Earth. For example, if an earthquake occurred when Saturn was entering the constellation Leo, might Saturn's position have been the cause of the earthquake? If the king became ill when Mars appeared in the constellation Gemini and the first-quarter moon appeared in Scorpio, might it mean another tragedy for the king when this particular alignment of the Moon and Mars next recurred? Surely, the ancient astrologers thought, the patterns of influence eventually would become clear. Thus, the astrologers hoped that they might someday learn to forecast human events with the same reliability with which astronomical observations of the Sun could forecast the coming of spring.

Ptolemy
(c. A.D. 85–165)

### Astrology's Role in Astronomical History

Because forecasts of the seasons and forecasts of human events were imagined to be closely related, astrologers and astronomers usually were one and the same in the ancient world. For example, in addition to his books on astronomy, Ptolemy published a treatise on astrology called *Tetrabiblios* that remains the foundation for much of astrology today. Interestingly, Ptolemy himself recognized that astrology stood upon a far shakier foundation than astronomy. In the introduction to *Tetrabiblios*, Ptolemy compared astronomical and astrological predictions:

> [Astronomy], which is first both in order and effectiveness, is that whereby we apprehend the aspects of the movements of sun, moon, and stars in relation to each other and to the earth. . . . I shall now give an account of the second and less sufficient method [of prediction (astrology)] in a proper philosophical way, so that one whose aim is the truth might never compare its perceptions with the sureness of the first, unvarying science. . . .

Other ancient scientists probably likewise recognized that their astrological predictions were far less reliable than their astronomical ones. Nevertheless, if there was even a slight possibility that astrologers could forecast the future, no king or political leader would dare to be without one. Astrologers therefore held esteemed positions as political advisers in the ancient world and were provided with the resources they needed to continue charting the heavens and

history. Much of the development of ancient astronomy was made possible through wealthy political leaders' support of astrology.

Throughout the Middle Ages and into the Renaissance, many astronomers continued to practice astrology. For example, Kepler cast numerous **horoscopes**—the predictive charts of astrology—even as he was discovering the laws of planetary motion. However, given Kepler's later description of astrology as "the foolish stepdaughter of astronomy" and "a dreadful superstition," he may have cast the horoscopes solely as a source of much-needed income. Modern-day astrologers also claim Galileo as one of their own, in part for his having cast a horoscope for the Grand Duke of Tuscany. However, whereas his astronomical discoveries changed human history, the horoscope he cast was just plain wrong: It predicted a long and fruitful life for the duke, who died just a few weeks later.

The scientific triumph of Kepler and Galileo in showing the Earth to be a planet orbiting the Sun heralded the end of the linkage between astronomy and astrology. Nevertheless, astrology remains popular today. More people earn income by casting horoscopes than through astronomical research, and books and articles on astrology often outsell all but the most popular books on astronomy.

### Scientific Tests of Astrology

Today, different astrologers follow different practices, which makes it difficult even to define *astrology*. Some astrologers no longer claim any ability to make testable predictions and therefore are practicing a form of *nonscience*—which modern science can say nothing about. However, for most astrologers the business of astrology is casting horoscopes. Horoscopes often are cast for individuals and either predict future events in the person's life or describe characteristics of the person's personality and life. If the horoscope predicts future events, it can be evaluated by whether the predictions come true. If it describes the person's personality and life, the description can be checked for accuracy.

A *scientific* test of astrology requires evaluating many horoscopes and comparing their accuracy to what would be expected by pure chance. For example, suppose a horoscope states that a person's best friend is female. Because that is true of roughly half the population in the United States, an astrologer who casts 100 such horoscopes would be expected by pure chance to be right about 50 times. Thus, we would be impressed with the predictive ability of the astrologer only if he or she were right much more often than 50 times out of 100. In hundreds of scientific tests, astrological predictions have never proved to be accurate by a substantially greater margin than expected from pure chance.[3] Similarly, in tests in which astrologers are asked to cast horoscopes for people they have never met, the horoscopes fail to correctly match personalities any more often than expected by chance. The verdict is clear: The methods of astrology are useless for predicting the past, the present, or the future.

What about newspaper horoscopes, which often appear to ring true? If you read them carefully, you will find that these horoscopes generally are so vague as to be untestable. For example, a horoscope that says "It is a good day to spend time with your friends" doesn't offer much for testing. Indeed, if you read the horoscopes for all 12 astrological signs, you'll probably find that several of them apply equally well to you.

**TIME OUT TO THINK** *Look in a local newspaper for today's weather forecast and for your horoscope. Contrast the nature of their predictions. By the end of the day, you will know if the weather forecast was accurate. Will you know whether your horoscope was accurate? Explain.*

### Does It Make Sense?

In science, observations and experiments are the ultimate judge of any idea. No matter how outlandish an idea might appear, it cannot be dismissed if it successfully meets observational or experimental tests. The idea that the Earth rotates and orbits the Sun at one time seemed outlandish, yet today it is so strongly supported by the evidence that we con-

sider it a fact. The idea that the positions of the Sun, Moon, and planets among the stars influence our lives might sound outlandish today, but if astrology were to make predictions that came true, adherence to the scientific method would force us to take it seriously. However, given that scientific tests of astrology have never found any evidence that its predictive methods work, it is worth looking back at its premises to see whether they make sense. Might there be a few kernels of wisdom buried within the lore of astrology?

Let's begin with one of the key premises of astrology: There is special meaning in the patterns of the stars in the constellations. This idea may have seemed quite reasonable in ancient times, when the stars were assumed to be fixed on an unchanging celestial sphere. But today we know that the patterns of the stars in the constellations are accidents of the moment; long ago the constellations did not look the same, and they will look still different far in the future [Section 1.3]. Moreover, the stars in a constellation don't necessarily have any *physical* association. Because stars vary in distance, two stars that appear on opposite sides of our sky might well be closer together than two stars in the same constellation. Thus, constellations are only *apparent* associations of stars, with no more physical reality than the water in a desert mirage.

Astrology also places great importance on the positions of the planets among the constellations. Again, this idea might have seemed quite reasonable in ancient times, when it was thought that the planets truly wandered among the stars. But today we know that the planets only *appear* to wander among the stars. In reality, the planets are in our own solar system, while the stars are vastly farther away. It is difficult to see how mere appearances could have profound effects on our lives.

Many other ideas at the heart of astrology are equally suspect. For example, most astrologers claim that a proper horoscope must account for the positions of *all* the planets. Does that mean that all horoscopes cast before the discovery of Pluto in 1930 were invalid? If so, why didn't astrologers notice that something was wrong with their horoscopes and thereby predict Pluto's existence? Given that several moons in the solar system are larger than Pluto, with two larger than Mercury, should astrologers also be tracking the positions of these moons? What about asteroids, which orbit the Sun like planets? What about planets orbiting other stars? Given seemingly unanswerable questions like these, there seems little hope that astrology will ever meet its ancient goal of being able to forecast human events.

---

[3]An excellent summary of scientific tests of astrology can be found in Roger B. Culver and Philip A. Ianna, *Astrology: True or False?* (Buffalo, New York: Prometheus Books, 1988).

## THE BIG PICTURE

In this chapter, we focused on the scientific principles through which we have learned so much about the universe. Key "big picture" concepts from this chapter include the following:

■ The basic ingredients of scientific thinking—careful observation and trial-and-error testing—are a part of everyone's experience. The modern scientific method simply provides a way of organizing this everyday thinking to facilitate the learning and sharing of new knowledge.

■ Although knowledge about the universe is growing rapidly today, each new piece rests upon foundations of older discoveries. The foundations of astronomy reach far back into history and are intertwined with the general development of human culture and civilization.

■ The concept of making models of nature lies at the heart of modern science. Models are created by generalizing from many specific facts. They then yield further predictions that allow the models to be tested. Models that withstand repeated testing rise to the status of scientific theories, while models that fail must be modified or discarded.

■ Although astronomy and astrology once developed hand in hand, today they represent very different things. The predictions of astrology either fail rigorous testing or are so vague as to be untestable. Astronomy is a science and is the primary means by which humans learn about the physical universe.

### Review Questions

1. In what ways is scientific thinking a fundamental part of human nature? What characteristics does the modern scientific method possess that go beyond this everyday type of thinking?

2. Explain how the people of central Africa predicted the weather by observing the Moon.

3. How are the names of the seven days of the week related to astronomical objects?

4. Briefly explain how the ancient Egyptians determined the time of day or night.

5. Briefly describe the astronomical uses of each of the following: Stonehenge, the Templo Mayor, the Sun Dagger, the Mayan observatory at Chichén Itzá, lines in the Nazca desert, Pawnee lodges, the Big Horn Medicine Wheel.

6. Explain why the Muslim fast of Ramadan occurs earlier with each subsequent year.

7. What is the *Metonic cycle*? How does the Jewish calendar follow the Metonic cycle? How does this influence the date of Easter?

8. What role did the Navigator play in Polynesian society?

9. What was the Library of Alexandria? What role did it play in the ancient empires of Greece and Rome?

10. What do we mean by a *model* of nature? Explain how the celestial sphere represents such a model.

11. Who was Ptolemy? Briefly describe how the Ptolemaic model of the universe explains apparent retrograde motion while preserving the idea of an Earth-centered universe.

12. Briefly describe the role played by Islamic scholars of the Middle Ages in the development of modern science.

13. Describe the basic process of the *scientific method*. What is the role of a *model* in this method? What do we mean by *facts* when discussing science?

14. Briefly describe how science differs from *pseudoscience* and *nonscience*.

15. Briefly explain how science as a whole can be objective even while individual scientists have personal biases and beliefs.

16. Briefly describe the international character of modern astronomy.

17. What is the basic tenet of *astrology*? Why might this idea have seemed quite reasonable in ancient times? What role did astrology play in the development of astronomy?

18. How do we make scientific tests of astrology? What have such tests found?

### Discussion Questions

1. *The Impact of Science.* The modern world is filled with ideas, knowledge, and technology that developed through science and application of the scientific method. Discuss some of these things and how they affect our lives. Which of these impacts do you think are positive? Which are negative? Overall, do you think science has benefited the human race? Defend your opinion.

2. *The Importance of Ancient Astronomy.* Why was astronomy important to people in ancient times? Discuss both the practical importance of astronomy and the importance it may have had for religious or other traditions. Which do you think was more important in the development of ancient astronomy, its practical or its philosophical role? Defend your opinion.

3. *Secrecy and Science.* The text mentions that some historians believe that Chinese science and technology fell behind that of Europe because of the Chinese culture of secrecy. Do you agree that secrecy can hold back the advance of science? Why or why not? For the past 200 years, the United States has allowed a greater degree of free speech than most other countries in the world. How great a role do you think this has played in making the United States the world leader in science and technology? Defend your opinion.

4. *Lunar Cycles.* We have now discussed four distinct lunar cycles: the $29\frac{1}{2}$-day cycle of phases, the 18-year-$11\frac{1}{3}$-day saros cycle, the 19-year Metonic cycle, and the 18.6-year cycle over which a full moon rises at its most southerly place along the horizon. Discuss how each of these cycles can be observed and the role each cycle has played in human history.

5. *Astronomy and Astrology.* Why do you think astrology remains so popular around the world even though it has failed all scientific tests of its validity? Do you think the popularity of astrology has any positive or negative social consequences? Defend your opinions.

## Problems

*True Statements?* For **problems 1–6**, decide whether the statements are true or false and clearly explain how you know.

1. If we defined hours as the ancient Egyptians did, we'd have the longest hours on the summer solstice and the shortest hours on the winter solstice.

2. The date of Christmas (December 25) is set each year according to a lunar calendar.

3. When navigating in the South Pacific, the Polynesians found their latitude with the aid of the pointer stars of the Big Dipper.

4. The Ptolemaic model reproduced apparent retrograde motion by having planets move sometimes counterclockwise and sometimes clockwise in their circles.

5. In science, saying that something is a theory means that it is really just a guess.

6. Ancient astronomers were convinced of the validity of astrology as a tool for predicting the future.

7. *Cultural Astronomy.* Choose a particular culture of interest to you, and research the astronomical knowledge and accomplishments of that culture. Write a two- to three-page summary of your findings.

8. *Astronomical Structures.* Choose an ancient astronomical structure of interest to you (e.g., Stonehenge, Nazca lines, Pawnee lodges) and research its history. Write a two- to three-page summary of your findings. If possible, also build a scale model of the structure or create detailed diagrams to illustrate how the structure was used.

9. *Venus and the Mayans.* The planet Venus apparently played a particularly important role in Mayan society. Research the evidence and write a one- to two-page summary of current knowledge about the role of Venus in Mayan society.

10. *Scientific Test of Astrology.* Find out about at least one scientific test that has been conducted to test the validity of astrology. Write a short summary of how the test was conducted and what conclusions were reached.

11. *Your Own Astrological Test.* Devise your own scientific test of astrology. Clearly define the methods you will use in your test and how you will evaluate the results. Then carry out the test.

## Web Projects

Find useful links for Web projects on the text Web site.

1. *Easter.* Find out when Easter is celebrated by different sects of Christianity. Then research how and why different sects set different dates for Easter. Summarize your findings in a one- to two-page report.

2. *Greek Astronomers.* Many ancient Greek scientists had ideas that, in retrospect, seem well ahead of their time. Choose one or more of the following ancient Greek scientists, and learn enough about their work in science and astronomy to write a one- to two-page "scientific biography."

| | | |
|---|---|---|
| Thales | Anaximander | Pythagoras |
| Anaxagoras | Empedocles | Democritus |
| Meton | Plato | Eudoxus |
| Aristotle | Callipus | Aristarchus |
| Archimedes | Eratosthenes | Apollonius |
| Hipparchus | Seleucus | Ptolemy |
| Hypatia | | |

3. *The Ptolemaic Model.* This chapter gives only a very brief description of Ptolemy's model of the universe. Investigate the model in greater depth. Using diagrams and text as needed, give a two- to three-page description of the model.

*The eternal mystery of the world is its comprehensibility.*
*The fact that it is comprehensible is a miracle.*

ALBERT EINSTEIN

# CHAPTER 4
# A Universe of Matter and Energy

In this and the next three chapters, we turn our attention to the scientific concepts that lie at the heart of modern astronomy. We begin by investigating the nature of matter and energy, the fundamental stuff from which the universe is made.

The history of the universe essentially is a story about the interplay between matter and energy since the beginning of time. Interactions between matter and energy govern everything from the creation of hydrogen and helium in the Big Bang to the processes that make Earth a habitable planet. Understanding the universe therefore depends on familiarity with how matter responds to the ebb and flow of energy.

The concepts of matter and energy presented in this chapter will enable you to understand most of the topics in this book. Some of the concepts and terminology may already be familiar to you. If not, don't worry. We will go over them again as they arise in various contexts, and you can refer back to this chapter as needed during the remainder of your studies.

## 4.1 Matter and Energy in Everyday Life

The meaning of **matter** is obvious to most people, at least on a practical level. Matter is simply material, such as rocks, water, or air. You can hold matter in your hand or put it in a box. The meaning of **energy** is not quite as obvious, although we certainly talk a lot about it. We pay energy bills to the power companies, we use energy from gasoline to run our cars, and we argue about whether nuclear energy is a sensible alternative to fossil fuels. On a personal level, we often talk about how energetic we feel on a particular day. But what *is* energy?

Broadly speaking, energy is what makes matter move. For Americans, the most familiar way of measuring energy is in Calories, which we use to describe how much energy our bodies can draw from food. A typical adult uses about 2,500 Calories of energy each day. Among other things, this energy keeps our hearts beating and our lungs breathing, generates the heat that maintains our 37°C (98.6°F) body temperature, and allows us to walk and run.

Just as there are many different units for measuring height, such as inches, feet, and meters, there are many alternatives to Calories for measuring energy. If you look closely at an electric bill, you'll probably find that the power company charges you for electrical energy in units called *kilowatt-hours*. If you purchase a gas appliance, its energy requirements may be labeled in *British thermal units,* or *BTUs.* In science and internationally, the favored unit of energy is the **joule**, which is equivalent to $\frac{1}{4,184}$ of a Calorie. Thus, the 2,500 Calories used daily by a typical adult are equivalent to about 10 million joules. For purposes of comparison, some energies given in joules are listed in Table 4.1.

Although energy can always be measured in joules, it has many different forms. Already we have talked about food energy, electrical energy, the energy of a beating heart, the energy represented by our body temperature, and more. Fortunately, the many forms of energy can be grouped into three basic categories.

First, whenever matter is moving, it has energy of motion, or **kinetic energy** (*kinetic* comes from a Greek word meaning "motion"). Falling rocks, the moving blades on an electric mixer, a car driving down the highway, and the molecules moving in the air around us are all examples of objects with kinetic energy.

The second basic category of energy is **potential energy**, or energy being stored for later conversion

### Table 4.1  Energy Comparisons

| Item | Energy (joules) |
| --- | --- |
| Average daytime solar energy striking Earth, per m² per second | $1.3 \times 10^3$ |
| Energy released by metabolism of one average candy bar | $1 \times 10^6$ |
| Energy needed for 1 hour of walking (adult) | $1 \times 10^6$ |
| Kinetic energy of average car traveling at 60 mi/hr | $1 \times 10^6$ |
| Daily energy needs of average adult | $1 \times 10^7$ |
| Energy released by burning 1 liter of oil | $1.2 \times 10^7$ |
| Energy released by fission of 1 kg of uranium-235 | $5.6 \times 10^{13}$ |
| Energy released by fusion of hydrogen in 1 liter of water | $7 \times 10^{13}$ |
| Energy released by 1-megaton H-bomb | $5 \times 10^{15}$ |
| Energy released by major earthquake (magnitude 8.0) | $2.5 \times 10^{16}$ |
| U.S. annual energy consumption | $10^{20}$ |
| Annual energy generation of Sun | $10^{34}$ |
| Energy released by supernova (explosion of a star) | $10^{44}$–$10^{46}$ |

into kinetic energy. A rock perched on a ledge has *gravitational* potential energy because it will fall if it slips off the edge. Gasoline contains *chemical* potential energy, which a car engine converts to the kinetic energy of the moving car. Power companies supply *electrical* potential energy, which we use to run dishwashers and other appliances.

The third basic category is energy carried by light, or **radiative energy** (the word *radiation* is often used as a synonym for *light*). Plants directly convert the radiative energy of sunlight into chemical potential energy through the process of *photosynthesis.* Radiative energy is fundamental to astronomy, because telescopes collect the radiative energy of light from distant stars.

**TIME OUT TO THINK** *We buy energy in many different forms. For example, we buy chemical potential energy in the form of food to fuel our bodies. Describe several other forms of energy that you commonly buy.*

Understanding how energy changes from one form to another helps us understand many common phenomena. For example, a diver standing on a 10-meter platform has gravitational potential energy owing to her height above the water and chemical potential energy stored in her body tissues. She uses the chemical potential energy to flex her muscles in such a way as to initiate her dive and then to help her execute graceful twists and spins (Figure 4.1). Meanwhile, her gravitational potential energy becomes kinetic energy of motion as she falls toward the water.

Following how energy changes from one form to another also helps us understand the universe. For example, the particles in a collapsing cloud of interstellar gas convert gravitational potential energy into kinetic energy as they fall inward, and their motion generates heat that can eventually ignite a star. But before we study astronomical phenomena, we need ways to describe energy quantitatively.

## 4.2 A Scientific View of Energy

In this section, we discuss a few ways to quantify kinetic and potential energy; we'll discuss radiative energy in Chapter 6, in which we study properties of light.

### Kinetic Energy

We can calculate the kinetic energy of any moving object with a very simple formula:

$$\text{kinetic energy} = \tfrac{1}{2}mv^2$$

where $m$ is the mass of the object and $v$ is its speed ($v$ for *velocity*). If we measure the mass in kilograms and the speed in meters per second, the resulting

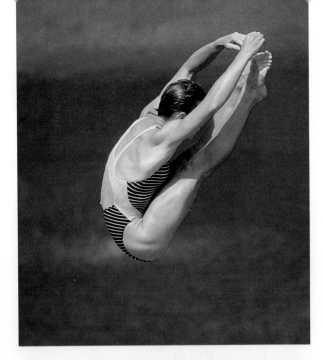

**FIGURE 4.1** Understanding energy can help us understand both the graceful movements of a diver and the story of the universe.

---

### Mathematical Insight 4.1 Temperature Scales

Three temperature scales are commonly used today (Figure 4.2). In the United States, we usually use the **Fahrenheit** scale, defined so that water freezes at 32°F and boils at 212°F. Internationally, temperature is usually measured on the **Celsius** scale, which places the freezing point of water at 0°C and the boiling point at 100°C.

Scientists measure temperature on the **Kelvin** scale, which is the same as the Celsius scale except for its zero point. A temperature of 0 K is the coldest possible temperature, known as **absolute zero**; it is equivalent to −273.15°C. (The degree symbol ° is not used when writing temperatures on the Kelvin scale.) Thus, any particular temperature has a Kelvin value that is numerically 273.15 larger than its Celsius value. Using T to stand for temperature and a subscript to indicate the temperature scale, we can write the conversions between Celsius and Kelvin as follows:

$$T_{\text{Kelvin}} = T_{\text{Celsius}} + 273.15$$
$$T_{\text{Celsius}} = T_{\text{Kelvin}} - 273.15$$

To find the conversion between Fahrenheit and Celsius, note that the Fahrenheit scale has 180° (212°F − 32°F = 180°F) between the freezing and boiling points of water, whereas the Celsius scale has only 100° between these points. A temperature change of 1 Celsius degree therefore is equivalent to a temperature change of 1.8 Fahrenheit degrees. Furthermore, the freezing point of water is numerically 32 larger on the Fahrenheit scale than on the Celsius scale. Combining these two facts we find the conversions between Fahrenheit and Celsius:

$$T_{\text{Celsius}} = \frac{T_{\text{Fahrenheit}} - 32}{1.8}$$
$$T_{\text{Fahrenheit}} = 32 + (1.8 \times T_{\text{Celsius}})$$

*Example:* Convert human body temperature of 98.6°F into Celsius and Kelvin.

*Solution:* First, we convert 98.6°F to Celsius:

$$T_{\text{Celsius}} = \frac{T_{\text{Fahrenheit}} - 32}{1.8} = \frac{98.6 - 32}{1.8} = 37.0°C$$

Next, we convert Celsius to Kelvin:

$$T_{\text{Kelvin}} = T_{\text{Celsius}} + 273.15 = 37.0 + 273.15 = 310.15 \text{ K}$$

Thus, human body temperature of 98.6°F is 37.0°C or 310.15 K.

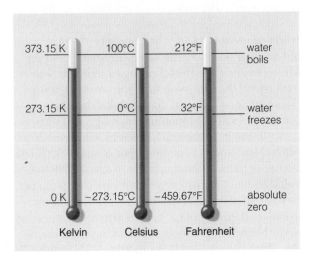

**FIGURE 4.2** Three common temperature scales: Kelvin, Celsius, and Fahrenheit.

answer will be in joules. (That is, energy has units of a mass times a velocity squared, so 1 joule = 1 (kg × m²)/s².) The kinetic energy formula is easy to interpret. The *m* in the formula tells us that kinetic energy is proportional to mass: A 5-ton truck has 5 times the kinetic energy of a 1-ton car moving at the same speed. The $v^2$ tells us that kinetic energy increases with the *square* of the velocity: If you double your speed (e.g., from 30 km/hr to 60 km/hr), your kinetic energy becomes $2^2 = 4$ times greater.

*Thermal Energy* Suppose we want to know about the kinetic energy of the countless tiny particles (atoms and molecules) inside a rock or of the countless particles in the air or in a distant star. Each of these tiny particles has its own motion relative to surrounding particles, and these motions constantly change as the particles jostle one another. The result is that the particles inside a substance appear to move randomly: Any individual particle may be moving in any direction with any of a wide range of speeds. Despite the seemingly random motion of particles within a substance, it's easy to measure the *average* kinetic energy of the particles—**temperature** is a measure of this average. A higher temperature simply means that, on average, the particles have more kinetic energy and hence are moving faster (Figure 4.3). (Kinetic energy depends on both mass and speed, but for a particular set of particles, greater kinetic energy means higher speeds.) The speeds of particles within a substance can be surprisingly fast. For example, the air molecules around you move at typical speeds of about 500 meters per second (about 1,000 miles per hour).

The energy contained *within* a substance as measured by its temperature is often called **thermal energy**. Thus, thermal energy represents the collective kinetic energy of the many individual particles moving within a substance.

*Temperature and Heat* The concepts of *temperature* and *heat* are not quite the same. To understand the difference, imagine the following experiment (but don't try it!). Suppose you heat your oven to 500°F. Then you open the oven door, quickly thrust your arm inside (without touching anything), and immediately remove it. What will happen to your arm? Not much. Now suppose you boil a pot of water. Although the temperature of boiling water is only 212°F, you would be badly burned if you put your arm in the pot, even for an instant. Thus, the water in the pot transfers more thermal energy to your arm than does the air in the oven, even though it has a lower temperature. That is, your arm heats more quickly in the water. This is because thermal energy content depends on both the temperature and the total number

Longer arrows mean higher average speed.

**FIGURE 4.3** The particles in the box on the right have a higher temperature because their average speeds are higher (assuming that both boxes contain particles of the same mass).

**FIGURE 4.4** Both boxes have the same temperature, but the box on the right contains more *thermal energy* because it contains more particles.

of particles, which is much larger in a pot of water (Figure 4.4).

Let's look at what is happening on the molecular level. If air or water is hotter than your body, molecules striking your skin transfer some of their thermal energy to your arm. The high temperature in a 500°F oven means that the air molecules strike your skin harder, on average, than the molecules in a 212°F pot of boiling water. However, because the *density* is so much higher in the pot of water, many more molecules strike your skin each second. Thus, while each individual molecular collision transfers a little less thermal energy in the boiling water than in the oven, the sheer number of collisions in the water transfers so much thermal energy that your skin burns rapidly.

**TIME OUT TO THINK** *In air or water that is colder than your body temperature, thermal energy transfers from you to the surrounding cold air or water. Use this fact to explain why falling into a 32°F (0°C) lake is much more dangerous than standing naked outside on a 32°F day.*

The environment in space provides another example of the difference between temperature and heat. Surprisingly, the temperature in low Earth orbit is several thousand degrees. However, astronauts working in Earth orbit (e.g., outside the Space Shuttle) tend to get very cold and therefore use heated space suits and gloves. The astronauts feel cold despite the high temperature because the extremely low density of space means that relatively few particles are available to transfer thermal energy to an astronaut. (You may wonder how the astronauts become cold given that the low density also means the astronauts cannot transfer much of their own thermal energy to the particles in space. It turns out that they lose their body heat by emitting *thermal radiation,* which we will discuss in Chapter 6.)

### Potential Energy

Potential energy can be stored in many different forms and is not always easy to quantify. Fortunately, it is easy to describe two types of potential energy that we use frequently in astronomy.

*Gravitational Potential Energy* Gravitational potential energy is extremely important in astronomy. The conversion of gravitational potential energy into kinetic (or thermal) energy helps explain everything from the speed at which an object falls to the ground to the formation processes of stars and planets. The mathematical formula for gravitational potential energy can take a variety of forms, but in words the idea is simple: *The amount of gravitational potential energy released as an object falls depends on its mass, the strength of gravity, and the distance it falls.*

This statement explains the obvious fact that falling from a 10-story building hurts more than falling out of a chair. Your gravitational potential energy is much greater on top of the 10-story building than in your chair because you can fall much farther. Because your gravitational potential energy will be converted to kinetic energy as you fall, you'll have a lot more kinetic energy by the time you hit the ground after falling from the building than after falling from the chair, which means you'll hit the ground much harder.

Gravitational potential energy also helps us understand how the Sun became hot enough to sustain nuclear fusion. Before the Sun formed, its matter was contained in a large, cold, diffuse cloud of gas. Most of the individual gas particles were far from the center of this large cloud and therefore had considerable amounts of gravitational potential energy. As the cloud collapsed under its own gravity, the gravitational potential energy of these particles was converted to thermal energy, eventually making the center of the cloud hot enough to ignite nuclear fusion.

*Mass-Energy* Although matter and energy seem very different in daily life, they are intimately connected. Einstein showed that mass itself is a form of potential energy, often called **mass-energy**. The mass-energy of any piece of matter is given by the formula

$$E = mc^2$$

where $E$ is the amount of potential energy, $m$ is the mass of the object, and $c$ is the speed of light. If the mass is measured in kilograms and the speed of light in meters per second, the resulting mass-energy has units of joules. Note that the speed of light is a large number ($c = 3 \times 10^8$ m/s) and the speed of light squared is much larger still ($c^2 = 9 \times 10^{16}$ m$^2$/s$^2$). Thus, Einstein's formula implies that a relatively small amount of mass represents a huge amount of mass-energy.

Mass-energy can be converted to other forms of energy, but noticeable amounts of mass become other forms of energy only under special but important circumstances. The process of nuclear fusion in the core of the Sun converts some of the Sun's mass into energy, ultimately generating the sunlight that sustains most life on Earth. On Earth, nuclear reactors and nuclear bombs also work in accord with Einstein's formula. In nuclear reactors, the splitting (fission) of elements such as uranium or plutonium converts some of the mass-energy of these materials into heat, which is then used to generate electrical

### Mathematical Insight 4.2   Density

The term *density* usually refers to *mass density,* which quantifies how much mass is packed into each unit of volume. The more tightly matter is packed, the higher its density. In science, the most common unit of density is grams per cubic centimeter (a cubic centimeter is about the size of a sugar cube):

$$density = \frac{mass\ (in\ g)}{volume\ (in\ cm^3)}$$

For example, if a 30-gram rock has a volume of 10 cubic centimeters, we calculate its density as follows:

$$density\ of\ rock = \frac{mass\ of\ rock}{volume\ of\ rock} = \frac{30\ g}{10\ cm^3} = 3\ \frac{g}{cm^3}$$

A useful guide for putting densities in perspective is the density of water, which is 1 gram per cubic centimeter; this isn't a coincidence—it's how the gram was defined. Rocks, like the one with a density of 3 grams per cubic centimeter, are denser than water and therefore sink in water. Wood floats in water because it is less dense than water.

The concept of density is sometimes applied to things other than mass. For example, an average of about 25,000 people live on each square kilometer of Manhattan, so we say that Manhattan has a *population density* of 25,000 people per square kilometer. As another example, 1 liter of oil releases about 12 million joules of energy when burned, so we say that the *chemical energy density* of oil is about 12 million joules per liter.

power. In an H-bomb, nuclear fusion similar to that in the Sun uses a small amount of the mass-energy in hydrogen to devastating effect. Incredibly, a 1-megaton H-bomb that could destroy a major city requires the conversion of only about 0.1 kilogram of mass (about 3 ounces) into energy (Figure 4.5).

Just as $E = mc^2$ tells us that mass can be converted into other forms of energy, it also tells us that energy can be transformed into mass. In *particle accelerators*, scientists accelerate subatomic particles to extremely high speeds. When these particles collide with one another or with a barrier, some of the energy released in the collision spontaneously turns into mass, appearing as a shower of subatomic particles. These showers of particles allow scientists to test theories about how matter behaves at extremely high temperatures such as those that prevailed in the universe during the first fraction of a second after the Big Bang. Among the most powerful particle accelerators in the world are Fermilab in Illinois, the Stanford Linear Accelerator in California, and CERN in Switzerland.

**TIME OUT TO THINK** *Einstein's formula $E = mc^2$ is probably the most famous physics equation of all time. Considering its role as described in the preceding paragraphs, do you think its fame is well deserved?*

### Conservation of Energy

A fundamental principle in science is that, regardless of how we change the *form* of energy, the total *quantity* of energy never changes. This principle is called the **law of conservation of energy**. It has been carefully tested in many experiments, and it

**FIGURE 4.5** The energy from this H-bomb comes from converting only about 0.1 kg of mass into energy in accordance with $E = mc^2$.

is a pillar upon which modern theories of the universe are built. Because of this law, the story of the universe is a story of the interplay of energy and matter: All actions in the universe involve exchanges of energy or the conversion of energy from one form to another.

For example, imagine that you've thrown a baseball so that it is moving and hence has kinetic energy. Where did this kinetic energy come from? The baseball got its kinetic energy from the motion of your

---

## Mathematical Insight 4.3    Mass-Energy

It's easy to calculate mass-energies with Einstein's formula $E = mc^2$. Once we calculate an energy, we can compare it to other known energies.

*Example:* Suppose a 1-kilogram rock were completely converted into energy. How much energy would it release? Compare this to the energy released by burning 1 liter of oil.

*Solution:* The total mass-energy of the rock is $E = mc^2$, where $m$ is the 1-kg mass and $c = 3 \times 10^8$ m/s:

$$E = mc^2 = 1 \text{ kg} \times \left(3 \times 10^8 \frac{\text{m}}{\text{s}}\right)^2$$

$$= 1 \text{ kg} \times \left(9 \times 10^{16} \frac{\text{m}^2}{\text{s}^2}\right)$$

$$= 9 \times 10^{16} \frac{\text{kg} \times \text{m}^2}{\text{s}^2}$$

$$= 9 \times 10^{16} \text{ joules}$$

Burning 1 liter of oil releases 12 million joules (see Table 4.1). Dividing the mass-energy of the rock by the energy released by burning 1 liter of oil, we find:

$$\frac{9 \times 10^{16} \text{ joules}}{1.2 \times 10^7 \text{ joules}} = 7.5 \times 10^9$$

That is, if the rock could be converted completely to energy, its mass would supply as much energy as 7.5 billion liters of oil—roughly the amount of oil used by *all* cars in the United States in a week. Unfortunately, no technology available now or in the foreseeable future can release all the mass-energy of a rock.

arm as you threw it; that is, some of the kinetic energy of your moving arm was transferred to the baseball. Your arm, in turn, got its kinetic energy from the release of chemical potential energy stored in your muscle tissues. Your muscles got this energy from the chemical potential energy stored in the foods you ate. The energy stored in the foods came from sunlight, which plants convert into chemical potential energy through photosynthesis. The radiative energy of the Sun was generated through the process of nuclear fusion, which releases some of the mass-energy stored in the Sun's supply of hydrogen. Thus, the ultimate source of the energy of the moving baseball is the mass-energy stored in hydrogen—which was created in the Big Bang.

We have described where the baseball got its kinetic energy. Where will this energy go? As the baseball moves through the air, some of its energy is transferred to molecules in the air, generating heat or sound. If someone catches the baseball, its energy will cause his or her hand to recoil and perhaps will also generate some heat and sound. Ultimately, the energy of the moving baseball will be converted to a barely noticeable amount of heat (thermal energy) in the air, the ground, or a person's hand, making it extremely difficult to track. Nevertheless, the energy will never disappear. According to present understanding, the total energy content of the universe was determined in the Big Bang. It remains the same today and will stay the same forever into the future.

## 4.3 The Material World

Now that we have seen how energy animates the matter in the universe, it's time to consider matter itself in greater detail. You are familiar with two basic properties of matter on Earth from everyday experience. First, matter can exist in different **phases**: as a **solid**, such as ice or a rock; as a **liquid**, such as flowing water or oil; or as a **gas**, such as air. Second, even in a particular phase, matter exists in a great variety of different substances.

What is matter, and why does it have so many different forms? Let's follow the lead of the ancient Greek philosopher Democritus (c. 470–380 B.C.), who wondered what would happen if we broke a piece of matter, such as a rock, into ever smaller pieces. Democritus believed that the rock would eventually break into particles so small that nothing smaller could be possible. He called these particles *atoms,* a Greek term meaning "indivisible." (By modern definition, atoms are *not* indivisible because they are composed of smaller particles.) Building upon the beliefs of earlier Greek scientists, Democritus thought that all materials were composed of just four

Democritus

basic *elements:* fire, water, earth, and air. He proposed that the different properties of the elements could be explained by the physical characteristics of their atoms. Democritus suggested that atoms of water were smooth and round, so water flowed and had no fixed shape, while burns were painful because atoms of fire were thorny. He imagined atoms of earth to be rough and jagged, like pieces of a three-dimensional jigsaw puzzle, so that they could stick together to form a solid substance. He even explained the creation of the world with an idea that sounds uncannily modern, suggesting that the universe began as a chaotic mix of atoms that slowly clumped together to form the Earth.

Although Democritus was wrong about there being only four types of atoms and about their specific properties, his general idea was right. Today, we know that all ordinary matter is composed of **atoms** and that each different type of atom corresponds to a different chemical **element**. Among the most familiar chemical elements are hydrogen, helium, carbon, oxygen, silicon, iron, gold, silver, lead, and uranium. (Appendix D gives the periodic table of all the elements.)

The number of different material substances is far greater than the number of chemical elements because atoms can combine to form **molecules**.

Some molecules consist of two or more atoms of the same element. For example, we breathe $O_2$, oxygen molecules made of two oxygen atoms. Other molecules, such as water ($H_2O$) and sulfuric acid ($H_2SO_4$), are made up of atoms of two or more different elements; such molecules are called **compounds**. The chemical properties of a molecule are different from those of its individual atoms. For example, water behaves very differently than pure hydrogen or pure oxygen, even though each water molecule is composed of two hydrogen atoms and one oxygen atom, as indicated by the familiar symbol $H_2O$.

### Atomic Structure

Atoms are incredibly small: Millions could fit end to end across the period at the end of this sentence, and the number in a single drop of water ($10^{22}$ to $10^{23}$ atoms) may exceed the number of stars in the observable universe. Yet atoms are composed of even smaller particles. A small, dense **nucleus** lies at the center of an atom; atomic nuclei (plural of nucleus) are made of particles called **protons** and **neutrons**. The nucleus is surrounded by particles called **electrons**.

The properties of an atom depend mainly on the amount of **electrical charge** in its nucleus. Electrical charge is a fundamental physical property that is always conserved, just as energy is always conserved. Electrons carry a negative electrical charge of $-1$, protons carry a positive electrical charge of $+1$, and neutrons are electrically neutral. Oppositely charged particles attract one another, and similarly charged particles repel one another. The attraction between the positively charged protons in the nucleus and the negatively charged electrons that surround it is what holds an atom together. Ordinary atoms have identical numbers of electrons and protons, making them electrically neutral overall. (You may wonder why electrical repulsion doesn't cause the positively charged protons in a nucleus to fly apart from one another. It tries, but it is overcome by an even stronger force that holds nuclei together, called the *strong nuclear force,* which we will discuss in Chapter S4.)

Although electrons can be thought of as tiny particles, they are not quite like tiny grains of sand, and they don't really orbit the nucleus as planets orbit the Sun. Instead, the electrons in an atom are "smeared out," forming a kind of cloud that surrounds the nucleus and gives the atom its apparent size. The electrons aren't really cloudy; it's just that it is impossible to pinpoint their positions. An atomic nucleus is very tiny, even compared to the atom itself: If we imagine an atom on a scale on which its nucleus is the size of your fist, its electron cloud would be many miles wide. Nearly all the atom's mass resides in its nucleus, because protons and neutrons are each about 2,000 times more massive than an electron. Figure 4.6 shows the structure of a typical atom.

Each different chemical element contains a different number of protons in its nucleus called its **atomic number**. For example, a hydrogen nucleus contains just one proton, so its atomic number is 1; a helium nucleus contains two protons, so its atomic number is 2.

The *combined* number of protons and neutrons in an atom is called its **atomic mass** (or *atomic weight*). The atomic mass of ordinary hydrogen is 1 because its nucleus is just a single proton. Helium usually has two neutrons in addition to its two protons, giving it an atomic mass of 4. Carbon usually has six protons and six neutrons, giving it an atomic mass of 12.

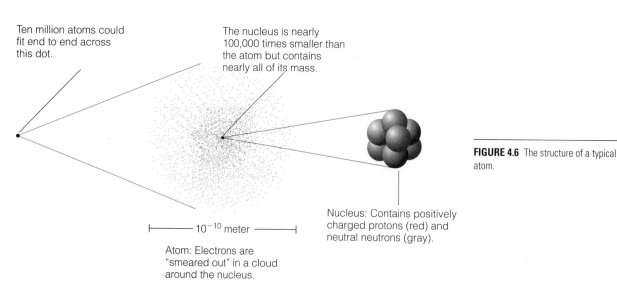

Ten million atoms could fit end to end across this dot.

The nucleus is nearly 100,000 times smaller than the atom but contains nearly all of its mass.

|— $10^{-10}$ meter —|

Atom: Electrons are "smeared out" in a cloud around the nucleus.

Nucleus: Contains positively charged protons (red) and neutral neutrons (gray).

**FIGURE 4.6** The structure of a typical atom.

Sometimes, the same element can have varying numbers of neutrons. For example, in rare cases a hydrogen nucleus contains a neutron in addition to its proton, making its atomic mass 2; hydrogen with atomic mass 2 is often called *deuterium*. The different forms of hydrogen are called **isotopes** of one another. A third isotope of hydrogen, tritium ($^3$H), contains two neutrons in addition to its one proton. Each isotope of an element has the same number of protons but a different number of neutrons.

We usually denote different isotopes by showing the atomic mass to the upper left of the chemical symbol. For example, most carbon atoms contain six neutrons in addition to their six protons, making their atomic mass $6 + 6 = 12$; we write this isotope of carbon as $^{12}$C and read it as carbon-12. The symbol $^{14}$C (carbon-14) represents a rarer isotope of carbon with atomic mass 14 and hence eight neutrons rather than six. Figure 4.7 illustrates some atomic terminology.

**TIME OUT TO THINK** *The symbol $^4$He represents helium with an atomic mass of 4; this is the most common form, containing two protons and two neutrons. What does the symbol $^3$He represent?*

### Phases of Matter

Everyday experience tells us that, depending on the temperature, the same substance exists in different phases. The main difference between phases is how tightly neighboring particles are bound together. As a substance is heated, the average kinetic energy of its particles increases, enabling the particles to break the bonds holding them to their neighbors. Each change in phase corresponds to the breaking of a different kind of bond. Phase changes occur in all substances; let's consider what happens when we heat water, starting from its solid phase, ice (Figure 4.8):

■ Below 0°C (32°F), water molecules have a relatively low average kinetic energy, and each mole-

---

**Common Misconceptions: One Phase at a Time?**

In daily life, we usually think of $H_2O$ as being in the phase of either solid ice, liquid water, or water vapor, with the phase depending on the temperature. In reality, two or even all three phases can exist at the same time. In particular, some sublimation *always* occurs over solid ice, and some evaporation *always* occurs over liquid water. Thus, the phases of solid ice and liquid water never occur alone but instead occur in conjunction with water vapor. The *amount* of water vapor increases with the temperature, which is why more and more steam rises from a kettle as you heat it.

cule is bound tightly to its neighbors, making the *solid* structure of ice.

■ As the temperature increases (but remains below freezing), the rigid arrangement of the molecules in ice vibrates more and more. At 0°C, the molecules have enough energy to break the solid bonds of ice. The molecules can then move relatively freely among one another, allowing the water to flow as a *liquid*. Even in liquid water, a type of bond between adjacent molecules still keeps them close together.

■ When a water molecule breaks free of all bonds with its neighbors, we call it a molecule of water vapor, which is a *gas*. Molecules in the gas phase move independently of other molecules. Even at temperatures at which water is a solid or liquid, a few molecules will have enough energy to enter the gas phase. We call the process **evaporation** when molecules escape from a liquid and **sublimation** when they escape from a solid. As temperatures rise, the rates of sublimation and

---

**FIGURE 4.7** Terminology of atoms.

atomic number = number of protons
atomic mass = number of protons + neutrons

**Hydrogen ($^1$H)**
atomic number = 1
atomic mass = 1
(1 electron)

**Helium ($^4$He)**
atomic number = 2
atomic mass = 4
(2 electrons)

**Carbon ($^{12}$C)**
atomic number = 6
atomic mass = 12
(6 electrons)

The number of electrons in a neutral atom equals its atomic number.

**Isotopes of Hydrogen**
hydrogen
$^1$H
(1 proton)

deuterium
$^2$H
(1 proton + 1 neutron)

**Isotopes of Carbon**
carbon 12
$^{12}$C
(6 protons + 6 neutrons)

carbon 14
$^{14}$C
(6 protons + 8 neutrons)

evaporation increase, eventually changing all the solid and liquid water into water vapor.

What happens if we continue to raise the temperature of water vapor? As the temperature rises, the molecules move faster, making collisions among them more violent. These collisions eventually split the water molecules into their component atoms of hydrogen and oxygen. The process by which the bonds that hold the atoms of a molecule together are broken is called **molecular dissociation**. At still higher temperatures, collisions can break the bonds holding electrons around the nuclei of individual atoms, allowing the electrons to go free. The loss of one or more negatively charged electrons leaves a remaining atom with a net positive charge. Such charged atoms are called **ions**, and the process of stripping electrons from atoms is called **ionization**. Thus, at high temperatures, what once was water becomes a hot gas consisting of freely moving electrons and positively charged ions of hydrogen and oxygen. This type of hot gas, in which atoms have become ionized, is called a **plasma**, sometimes referred to as "the fourth phase of matter." Other chemical substances go through similar phase changes, but the temperatures at which phase changes occur depend on the types of atom or molecules involved.

Note that neutral hydrogen contains only one electron, which balances the single positive charge of the one proton in its nucleus. Thus, hydrogen can be ionized only once, and the remaining hydrogen ion, designated $H^+$, is simply a proton. Oxygen, with atomic number 8, has eight electrons when it is neutral, so it can be ionized multiple times. *Singly ionized* oxygen is missing one electron, so it has a charge of $+1$ and is designated $O^+$. *Doubly ionized* oxygen, or $O^{++}$, is missing two electrons; *triply ionized* oxygen, or $O^{+3}$, is missing three electrons; and so on. At extremely high temperatures, oxygen can be *fully ionized,* in which case all eight electrons are stripped away and the remaining ion has a charge of $+8$.

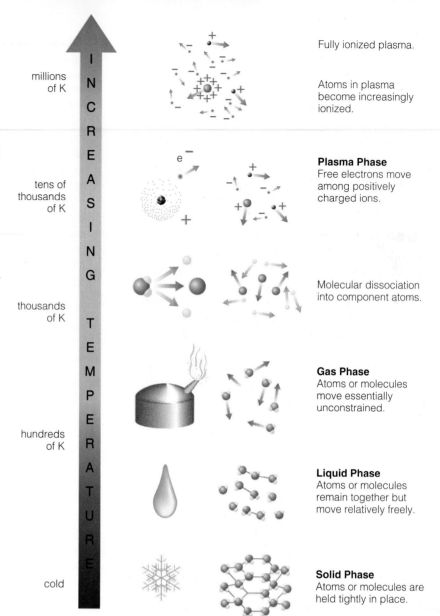

Fully ionized plasma.

Atoms in plasma become increasingly ionized.

**Plasma Phase**
Free electrons move among positively charged ions.

Molecular dissociation into component atoms.

**Gas Phase**
Atoms or molecules move essentially unconstrained.

**Liquid Phase**
Atoms or molecules remain together but move relatively freely.

**Solid Phase**
Atoms or molecules are held tightly in place.

**FIGURE 4.8** The general progression of phase changes.

## 4.4 Energy in Atoms

So far, we've seen two different ways in which atoms have energy. First, by virtue of their mass, they possess mass-energy in the amount $mc^2$. Second, they possess kinetic energy by virtue of their motion. Atoms also contain energy in a third way: as *electric potential energy* in the distribution of their electrons around their nuclei. The simplest case is that of hydrogen, which has only one electron. Remember that an electron tends to be "smeared out" into a cloud around the nucleus. When the electron is "smeared out" to the minimum extent that nature allows, the atom contains its smallest possible amount of electric potential energy; we say that the atom is in its **ground state** (Figure 4.9). If the electron somehow gains energy, then it becomes "smeared out" over a ground state       excited state       ionization

**FIGURE 4.9** In its ground state, an electron is "smeared out" to the minimum extent allowed by nature. Adding energy can raise the electron to an excited state that occupies a larger volume. Adding enough energy can ionize the atom.

greater volume, and we say that the atom is in an **excited state**. If the electron gains enough energy, it can escape the atom completely, in which case the atom has been *ionized*.

Perhaps the most surprising aspect of atoms was discovered in the 1910s, when scientists realized that electrons in atoms can have only *particular* energies (which correspond to particular sizes and shapes of the electron cloud). As a simple analogy, suppose you're washing windows on a building. If you use an adjustable platform to reach high windows, you can stop the platform at any height above the ground (Figure 4.10a). But if you use a ladder, you can stand only at *particular* heights—the heights of the rungs of the ladder—and not at any height in between (Figure 4.10b). The possible energies of electrons in atoms are like the possible heights on a ladder. Only a few particular energies are possible, and energies between these special few are not possible.

The possible energy levels of the electron in hydrogen are represented like the steps of a ladder in Figure 4.11. The ground state, or level 1, is the bottom rung of the ladder; its energy is labeled zero because the atom has no excess electrical potential energy to lose. Each subsequent rung of the ladder represents a possible excited state for the electron. Each level is labeled with the electron's energy above the ground state in units of **electron-volts**, or **eV** ($1 \text{ eV} = 1.60 \times 10^{-19}$ joule). For example, the energy of an electron in energy level 2 is 10.2 eV greater than that of an electron in the ground state. That is, an electron must gain 10.2 eV of energy to "jump" from level 1 to level 2. Similarly, jumping from level 1 to level 3 requires gaining 12.1 eV of energy.

Note that, unlike a ladder built for climbing, the rungs on the electron's energy ladder are closer together near the top. The top itself represents the energy of ionization—if the electron gains this much energy, 13.6 eV above the ground state in the case of hydrogen, the electron breaks free from the atom. (Any excess energy beyond that needed for ionization becomes kinetic energy of the free-moving electron.)

Because energy is always conserved, an electron cannot jump to a higher energy level unless its atom

**FIGURE 4.10** (**a**) A window washer on an adjustable platform can be at any height. (**b**) A window washer on a ladder can be at only the particular heights of the steps. Similarly, electrons in an atom can have only particular energy levels.

| | |
|---|---|
| ionization level | 13.6 eV |
| level 4 | 12.8 eV |
| level 3 | 12.1 eV |
| level 2 | 10.2 eV |
| level 1 (ground state) | 0 eV |

**FIGURE 4.11** Energy levels for the electron in a hydrogen atom. There are many more closely spaced energy levels between level 4 and the ionization level.

gains the energy from somewhere else. Generally, the atom gains this energy either from the kinetic energy of another particle colliding with it or from the absorption of energy carried by light. Similarly, when an electron falls to a *lower* energy level, it either transfers its energy to another particle through a collision or emits light that carries the energy away. The key point is this: *Electron jumps can occur only with the particular amounts of energy representing differences between possible energy levels.*

The result is that electrons in atoms can absorb or emit only particular amounts of energy and not other amounts in between. For example, if you attempt to provide a hydrogen atom in the ground state with 11.1 eV of energy, the atom won't accept it because it is too high to boost the electron to level 2 but not high enough to boost it to level 3.

**TIME OUT TO THINK** *We will see in Chapter 6 that light comes in "pieces" called photons that carry specific amounts of energy. Can a hydrogen atom absorb a photon with 11.1 eV of energy? Why or why not? Can it absorb a photon with 10.2 eV of energy? Explain.*

If you think about it, the idea that electrons in atoms can jump only between particular energy levels is quite bizarre. It is as if you had a car that could go only particular speeds and not other speeds in between. How strange it would seem if your car suddenly jumped from 5 miles per hour to 20 miles per hour without gradually passing through a speed of 10 miles per hour! In scientific terminology, the electron's energy levels are said to be *quantized*, and the study of the energy levels of electrons (and other particles) is called *quantum mechanics*.

Electrons have quantized energy levels in all atoms, not just in hydrogen. Moreover, the allowed energy levels differ from element to element and even from one ion of an element to another ion of the same element. This fact holds the key to the study of distant objects in the universe. As we will see in Chapter 6 when we study light, the different energy levels of different elements allow light to carry "fingerprints" that can tell us the chemical composition of distant objects.

## Common Misconceptions: Orbiting Electrons?

Most people have been taught to think of electrons in atoms as "orbiting" the nucleus like tiny planets orbiting a tiny sun. But this representation is simply not true. Electrons and other subatomic particles do not behave at all like baseballs, rocks, or planets. In fact, the behavior of subatomic particles is so strange that human minds may be incapable of visualizing it. Nevertheless, the *effects* of electrons are easy to observe, and one of the most important effects is that electrons give atoms their size. Thus, we say that electrons in atoms are "smeared out" into an "electron cloud" around the nucleus. This description is rather vague, but it is far more accurate than the misleading picture of electrons circling like tiny planets.

## THE BIG PICTURE

In this chapter, we discussed the concepts of energy and matter in some detail. Key "big picture" ideas to draw from this chapter include the following:

- Energy and matter are the two basic ingredients of the universe. Therefore, understanding energy and matter, and the interplay between them, is crucial to understanding the universe.

- Energy is always conserved, and we can understand many processes in the universe by following how energy changes from one form to another in its interactions with matter. Don't forget that mass itself is a form of potential energy, called mass-energy.

- The strange laws of quantum mechanics govern the interactions of matter and energy on the atomic level. Electrons in atoms can have only particular energies and not energies in between, and each element has a different set of allowed energy levels.

## Review Questions

1. Briefly describe and differentiate between *kinetic energy*, *potential energy*, and *radiative energy*.

2. What is the formula for the kinetic energy of an object? Based on this formula, explain why (a) a 4-ton truck moving at 100 km/hr has 4 times as much kinetic energy as a 1-ton car moving at 100 km/hr; (b) a 1-ton car moving at 100 km/hr has the *same* kinetic energy as a 4-ton truck moving at 50 km/hr.

3. What does *temperature* measure? How is it related to kinetic energy? What is *thermal energy*?

4. Briefly describe how a 500°F oven and a pot of boiling water illustrate the difference between *temperature* and *heat*. How is this difference important to astronauts in Earth orbit?

5. What is *gravitational potential energy*? How does an object's gravitational potential energy depend on its mass, the distance it has to fall, and the strength of gravity?

6. What do we mean by *mass-energy*? Explain the meaning of the formula $E = mc^2$ and what it has to do with the Sun, nuclear bombs, and particle accelerators.

7. What is the *law of conservation of energy*? Your body is using energy right now to keep you alive. Where does this energy come from? Where does it go?

8. Briefly define *atom*, *element*, and *molecule*. How was Democritus's idea of atoms similar to the modern concept of atoms? How was it different?

9. What is *electrical charge?* What type of electrical charge is carried by *protons, neutrons,* and *electrons?* Under what circumstances do electrical charges attract? Under what circumstances do they repel?

10. Briefly describe the structure of an atom. How big is an atom? How big is the *nucleus* in comparison to the entire atom?

11. Define and distinguish between *atomic number* and *atomic mass.* Under what conditions are two atoms different *isotopes* of the same element?

12. What do we mean by a *phase* of matter? Briefly describe how the idea of *bonds* between atoms (or molecules) explains the difference between the *solid, liquid,* and *gas* phases.

13. Briefly explain why a few atoms (or molecules) are always in gas phase around any solid or liquid. Then explain how *sublimation* and *evaporation* are similar and how they are different.

14. Explain why, at sufficiently high temperatures, molecules undergo *molecular dissociation* and atoms undergo *ionization.*

15. What is a *plasma?* Explain why, at very high temperatures, all matter is in this "fourth phase of matter."

16. Describe the three basic ways in which atoms can contain energy. In what way does an atom in an *excited state* contain more energy than an atom in the *ground state?*

17. How are the possible energy levels of electrons in atoms similar to the possible gravitational potential energies of a person on a ladder? How are they different?

## Discussion Questions

1. *Knowledge of Mass-Energy.* Einstein's discovery that energy and mass are equivalent has led to technological developments both beneficial and dangerous. Discuss some of these developments. Overall, do you think the human race would be better or worse off if we had never discovered that mass is a form of energy? Defend your opinion.

2. *Perpetual Motion Machines.* Every so often, someone claims to have built a machine that can generate energy perpetually from nothing. Why isn't this possible according to the known laws of nature? Why do you think claims of perpetual motion machines sometimes receive substantial media attention?

3. *Indoor Pollution.* Given that sublimation and evaporation are very similar processes, why is sublimation generally much more difficult to notice? Discuss how sublimation, particularly from plastics and other human-made materials, can cause "indoor pollution."

4. *Democritus and the Path of History.* Besides his belief in atoms, Democritus held several other strikingly modern notions. For example, he maintained that the Moon was a world with mountains and valleys and that the Milky Way was composed of countless individual stars—ideas that weren't generally accepted until the time of Galileo, more than 2,000 years later. Unfortunately, we know of Democritus's work only secondhand because none of the 72 books he is said to have written survived the destruction of the Library of Alexandria. How do you think history might have been different if the work of Democritus had not been lost?

## Problems

*Sensible Statements?* For **problems 1–4**, decide whether the statement is sensible and explain why it is or is not.

1. The sugar in my soda will provide my body with about a million joules of energy.

2. When I drive my car at 30 miles per hour, it has three times as much kinetic energy as it does at 10 miles per hour.

3. If you put an ice cube outside the Space Station, it would take a very long time to melt, even though the temperature in Earth orbit is several thousand degrees (Celsius).

4. Someday soon, scientists are likely to build an engine that produces more energy than it consumes.

5. *Gravitational Potential Energy.*
   a. Why does a bowling ball perched on a cliff ledge have more gravitational potential energy than a baseball perched on the same ledge?
   b. Why does a diver on a 10-meter platform have more gravitational potential energy than a diver on a 3-meter diving board?
   c. Why does a 100-kg satellite orbiting Jupiter have more gravitational potential energy than a 100-kg satellite orbiting the Earth, assuming both satellites orbit at the same distance from the planet centers?

6. *Einstein's Famous Formula.*
   a. What is the meaning of the formula $E = mc^2$? Be sure to define each variable.
   b. How does this formula explain the generation of energy by the Sun?
   c. How does this formula explain the destructive power of nuclear bombs?

7. *Atomic Terminology Practice.*
   a. The most common form of iron has 26 protons and 30 neutrons in its nucleus. State its atomic number, atomic mass, and number of electrons if it is electrically neutral.
   b. Consider the following three atoms: Atom 1 has 7 protons and 8 neutrons; atom 2 has 8 protons and 7 neutrons; atom 3 has 8 protons and 8 neutrons. Which two are *isotopes* of the same element?

c. Oxygen has atomic number 8. How many times must an oxygen atom be ionized to create an $O^{+5}$ ion? How many electrons are in an $O^{+5}$ ion?

d. Consider fluorine atoms with 9 protons and 10 neutrons. What are the atomic number and atomic mass of this fluorine? Suppose we could add a proton to this fluorine nucleus. Would the result still be fluorine? Explain. What if we added a neutron to the fluorine nucleus?

e. The most common isotope of gold has atomic number 79 and atomic mass 197. How many protons and neutrons does the gold nucleus contain? If it is electrically neutral, how many electrons does it have? If it is triply ionized, how many electrons does it have?

f. The most common isotope of uranium is $^{238}$U, but the form used in nuclear bombs and nuclear power plants is $^{235}$U. Given that uranium has atomic number 92, how many neutrons are in each of these two isotopes of uranium?

8. *The Fourth Phase of Matter.*

a. Explain why nearly all the matter in the Sun is in the plasma phase.

b. Based on your answer to part (a), explain why plasma is the most common phase of matter in the universe.

c. Given that plasma is the most common phase of matter in the universe, why is it so rare on Earth?

9. *Energy Level Transitions.* The labeled transitions below represent an electron moving between energy levels in hydrogen. Answer each of the following questions and explain your answers.

a. Which transition could represent an electron that *gains* 10.2 eV of energy?

b. Which transition represents an electron that *loses* 10.2 eV of energy?

c. Which transition represents an electron that is breaking free of the atom?

d. Which transition, as shown, is *not* possible?

e. Describe the process taking place in transition A.

*10. *Energy Comparisons.* Use the data in Table 4.1 to answer each of the following questions.

a. Compare the energy of a 1-megaton hydrogen bomb to the energy released by a major earthquake.

b. If the United States obtained all its energy from oil, how much oil would be needed each year?

c. Compare the Sun's annual energy output to the energy released by a supernova.

*11. *Moving Candy Bar.* Metabolizing a candy bar releases about $10^6$ joules. How fast must the candy bar travel to have the same $10^6$ joules in the form of kinetic energy? (Assume the candy bar's mass is 0.2 kg.) Is your answer faster or slower than you expected?

*12. *Calculating Densities.* Find the average density of the following objects in grams per cubic centimeter.

a. A rock with volume 15 cm$^3$ and mass 50 g.

b. Earth, with its mass of $6 \times 10^{24}$ kg and radius of about 6,400 km. (*Hint:* The formula for the volume of a sphere is $\frac{4}{3} \times \pi \times$ radius$^3$.)

c. The Sun, with its mass of $2 \times 10^{30}$ kg and radius of about 700,000 km.

*13. *Spontaneous Human Combustion.* Suppose that, through a horrific act of an angry god (or a very powerful alien, if you prefer), all the mass in your body was suddenly converted into energy according to the formula $E = mc^2$. How much energy would be produced? Compare this to the energy released by a 1-megaton hydrogen bomb (see Table 4.1). What effect would your disappearance have on the surrounding region? (*Hint:* Multiply your mass in kilograms by $c^2$.)

*14. *Fusion Power.* No one has yet succeeded in creating a commercially viable way to produce energy through nuclear fusion. However, suppose we could build fusion power plants using the hydrogen in water as a fuel. Based on the data in Table 4.1, how much water would we need each minute in order to meet U.S. energy needs? Could such a reactor power the entire United States with the water flowing from your kitchen sink? Explain. (*Hint:* Use the annual U.S. energy consumption to find the energy consumption per minute; then divide by the energy yield from fusing 1 liter of water to figure out how many liters would be needed each minute.)

## Web Projects

Find useful links for Web projects on the text Web site.

1. *Energy Comparisons.* Using information from the Energy Information Administration Web site, choose some aspect of U.S. or world energy use that interests you. Write a short report on this issue.

2. *Nuclear Power.* There are two basic ways to generate energy from atomic nuclei: through nuclear fission (splitting nuclei) and through nuclear fusion (combining nuclei). All current nuclear reactors are based on fission, but fusion would have many advantages if we could develop the technology. Research some of the advantages of fusion and some of the obstacles to developing fusion power. Do you think fusion power will be a reality in your lifetime? Explain.

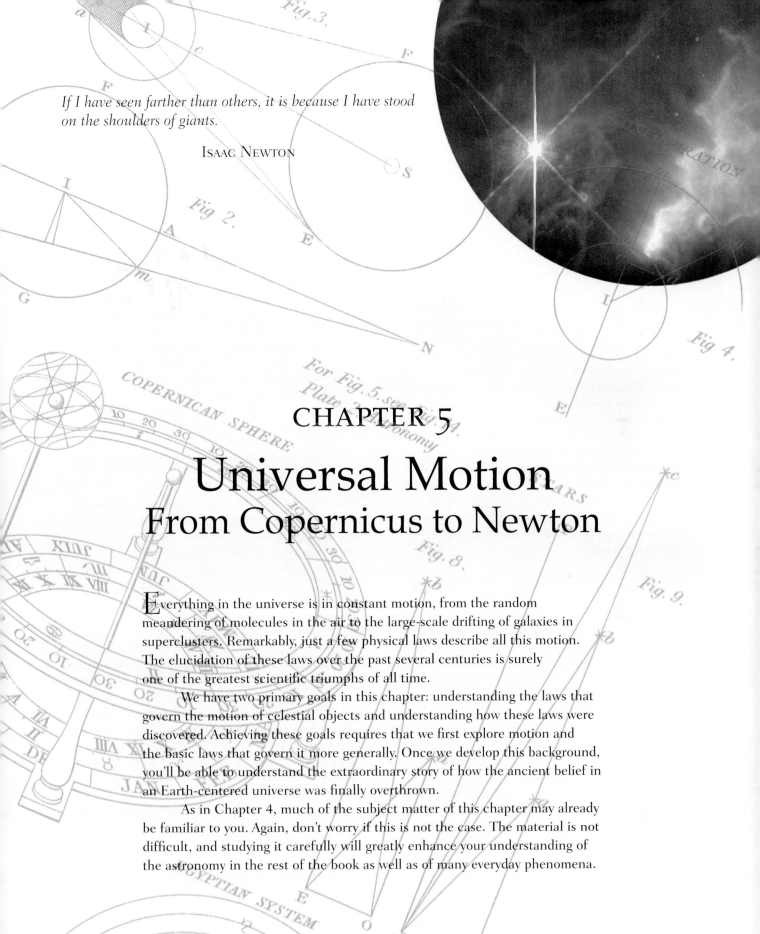

*If I have seen farther than others, it is because I have stood
on the shoulders of giants.*

Isaac Newton

# CHAPTER 5

# Universal Motion
## From Copernicus to Newton

Everything in the universe is in constant motion, from the random
meandering of molecules in the air to the large-scale drifting of galaxies in
superclusters. Remarkably, just a few physical laws describe all this motion.
The elucidation of these laws over the past several centuries is surely
one of the greatest scientific triumphs of all time.

We have two primary goals in this chapter: understanding the laws that
govern the motion of celestial objects and understanding how these laws were
discovered. Achieving these goals requires that we first explore motion and
the basic laws that govern it more generally. Once we develop this background,
you'll be able to understand the extraordinary story of how the ancient belief in
an Earth-centered universe was finally overthrown.

As in Chapter 4, much of the subject matter of this chapter may already
be familiar to you. Again, don't worry if this is not the case. The material is not
difficult, and studying it carefully will greatly enhance your understanding of
the astronomy in the rest of the book as well as of many everyday phenomena.

## 5.1 Describing Motion: Examples from Daily Life

Think about what happens when you throw a ball to a dog: The dog runs and catches it. Now think about the complexity of this trick. The ball leaves your hand traveling in some particular direction with some particular amount of kinetic energy. As the ball rises, gravity converts some of its kinetic energy into potential energy, slowing the ball's rise until it reaches the top of its trajectory. Then gravity transforms the potential energy of the ball back into kinetic energy, bringing it back toward the ground. Meanwhile, the ball may lose some of its kinetic energy to air resistance or may be pushed by gusts of wind. Despite this complexity, the dog still catches the ball.

We humans can perform an even better trick: We have learned how to figure out where the ball will land even before throwing it, and we can perform this trick with extraordinary precision. Understanding how we perform this trick and applying it to problems of motion throughout the universe require understanding the laws that govern motion. We'll study these laws shortly, but first we need to discuss the scientific concepts used to describe motion.

We all have a great deal of experience with motion and natural intuition as to how motion works, so we begin our discussion with some familiar examples. Indeed, you probably are familiar with all the terms defined in this section, but their scientific definitions may differ subtly from those you use in casual conversation.

### Speed, Velocity, and Acceleration

The concepts we use to determine the trajectory of a ball, a rocket, or a planet are familiar to you from driving a car. The speedometer indicates your **speed**, usually in units of both miles per hour (mi/hr) and kilometers per hour (km/hr); for example, 100 km/hr is a speed. Your **velocity** is your speed in a certain direction; "100 km/hr going due north" describes a velocity. It is possible to change your velocity without changing your speed, for example, by maintaining a steady 60 km/hr as you drive around a curve. Because your direction is changing as you round the curve, your *velocity* is also changing—even though your *speed* is constant.

Whenever your velocity is changing, you are experiencing **acceleration**. You are undoubtedly familiar with the term *acceleration* as it applies to increasing speed, such as when you accelerate away from a stop sign while driving your car. In science, we also say that you are accelerating when you slow down or turn. Slowing occurs when your acceleration is in a direction opposite to your motion; we say that your acceleration is negative, causing your velocity to decrease. Turning changes your direction, which

means a change in velocity and thus involves acceleration even if your speed remains constant.

Note that you don't feel anything when you are traveling at *constant velocity*, which is why you don't feel any sensation of motion when you're traveling in an airplane on a smooth flight. In contrast, you can often feel acceleration: As you speed up in a car you feel yourself being pushed back into your seat, as you slow down you feel yourself being pulled forward from the seat, and as you drive around a curve you lean outward because of your acceleration.

### The Acceleration of Gravity

One of the most important types of acceleration is that caused by gravity, which makes objects accelerate as they fall. In a famous (though probably apocryphal) experiment that involved dropping weights from the Leaning Tower of Pisa, Galileo demonstrated that gravity accelerates all objects by the same amount, regardless of their mass. This fact may be surprising because it seems to contradict everyday experience: A feather floats gently to the ground, while a rock plummets. However, this difference is caused by air resistance. If you dropped a feather and a rock on the Moon, where there is no air, both would fall at exactly the same rate.

**TIME OUT TO THINK** *Find a piece of paper and a small rock. Hold both at the same height, one in each hand, and let them go at the same instant. The rock, of course, hits the ground first. Next crumple the paper into a small ball and repeat the experiment. What happens? Explain how this experiment suggests that gravity accelerates all objects by the same amount.*

The acceleration of a falling object is called the **acceleration of gravity**, abbreviated $g$. On Earth, the acceleration of gravity causes falling objects to fall faster by 9.8 meters per second (m/s), or about 10 m/s, with each passing second. For example, suppose you drop a rock from a tall building. At the moment you let it go, its speed is 0 m/s. After 1 second, the rock will be falling downward at about 10 m/s. After 2 seconds, it will be falling at about 20 m/s. In the absence of air resistance, its speed will continue to increase by about 10 m/s each second until it hits the ground (Figure 5.1).

We therefore say that the acceleration of gravity is about 10 *meters per second per second*, or 10 *meters per second squared*, which we write as 10 m/s². (More precisely, $g = 9.8$ m/s².)

### Momentum and Force

Imagine that you're innocently stopped in your car at a red light when a bug flying at a velocity of 30 km/hr

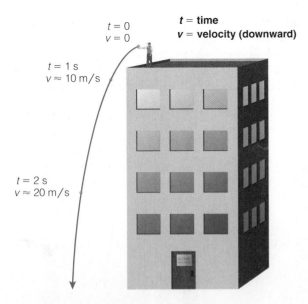

$t = 0$
$v = 0$

$t = \mathbf{time}$
$v = \mathbf{velocity}$ (downward)

$t = 1\ \mathrm{s}$
$v \approx 10\ \mathrm{m/s}$

$t = 2\ \mathrm{s}$
$v \approx 20\ \mathrm{m/s}$

**FIGURE 5.1** On Earth, gravity causes falling objects to accelerate downward at about 10 m/s². That is, a falling object's downward velocity increases by about 10 m/s with each passing second. (Gravity does not affect horizontal velocity.) More precisely, $g = 9.8\ \mathrm{m/s^2}$.

due south slams into your windshield. What will happen to your car? Not much, except perhaps a bit of a mess on your windshield. Next imagine that a 2-ton truck runs the red light and hits you head-on with the same velocity as the bug. Clearly, the truck will cause far more damage.

Scientifically, we say that the truck imparts a much larger jolt than the bug because it transfers more **momentum** to you. Momentum describes a combination of mass and velocity. We can describe the momentum of the truck before the collision as "2 tons moving due south at 30 km/hr," while the momentum of the bug is perhaps "1 gram moving due south at 30 km/hr." Mathematically, momentum is defined as mass × velocity.

In transferring some of its momentum to your car, the truck (or bug) exerts a **force** on your car. More generally, a force is anything that can cause a change in momentum. You are familiar with many types of force besides collisional force. For example, if you shift into neutral while driving along a flat stretch of road, the forces of air resistance and road friction will continually sap your car's momentum (transferring it to molecules in the air and the pavement), slowing your velocity until you come to a stop. You probably are also familiar with forces arising from gravity, electricity, and magnetism.

The mere presence of a force does not always cause a change in momentum. For example, if the engine works hard enough, a car can maintain constant velocity—and hence constant momentum—despite air resistance and road friction. In this case, the force generated by the engine to turn the wheels

precisely offsets the forces of air resistance and road friction that act to slow the car, and we say that no **net force** is acting on the car.

As long as an object is not shedding (or gaining) mass, a change in momentum means a change in velocity (because momentum = mass × velocity), which means an acceleration. Hence, any net force will cause acceleration, and all accelerations must be caused by a force. That is why you feel forces when you accelerate in your car.

### Mass and Weight

Up until now, we've been glossing over one key term: *mass*. Your **mass** refers to the amount of matter in your body, which is different from your *weight*. Imagine standing on a scale in an elevator (Figure 5.2). When the elevator is stationary or moving at constant velocity, the scale reads your "normal" weight. When the elevator is accelerating upward, the floor exerts an additional force that makes you feel heavier, and the scale verifies your greater apparent weight.[1] Note that your weight is greater than its "normal" value only while the elevator is *accelerating,* not while it is moving at constant velocity. When the elevator accelerates downward, the floor and the scale are dropping away, so your weight is reduced. Thus, your weight varies with the elevator's motion, but your mass remains the same. (You can verify these facts by taking a small bathroom scale with you on an elevator.)

More precisely, your (apparent) **weight** describes the *force* that acts on your mass, and it depends on the strength of gravity and other forces acting on you (such as the force due to the elevator's acceleration). Thus, while your mass is the same anywhere, your weight can vary. For example, your mass would be the same on the Earth and on the Moon, but you would weigh less on the Moon because of its weaker gravity.

### Free-Fall, Weightlessness, and Orbit

If the cable breaks so that the elevator is in **free-fall**, the floor drops away at the same rate that you fall. You lose contact with the scale, so your apparent weight is zero and you feel **weightless**. In fact, you are in free-fall whenever nothing is *preventing* you from falling. For example, you are in free-fall when you jump off a chair or spring from a diving board or trampoline. Surprising as it may seem, you have therefore experienced weightlessness many times in your life and can experience it right now simply by jumping

---

[1]Many physics texts distinguish between *true weight* that is due only to the effects of gravity on mass and the *apparent weight* that a scale reads when other forces (such as in an accelerating elevator) also act. In this book, you may assume that "weight" refers to apparent weight, except when stated otherwise.

**FIGURE 5.2** Mass is not the same as weight. The man's mass never changes, but his apparent weight does.

Within the figure:

elevator stationary or moving at constant velocity — Normal weight

elevator accelerating upward — Heavier-than-normal weight

elevator accelerating downward — Lighter-than-normal weight

elevator in free-fall — Weightless

## Common Misconceptions: No Gravity in Space?

Most people are familiar with pictures of astronauts floating weightlessly in Earth orbit. Unfortunately, because we usually associate weight with gravity, many people assume that the astronauts' weightlessness implies a lack of gravity in space. Actually, there's plenty of gravity in space; even at the distance of the Moon, the Earth's gravity is strong enough to hold the Moon in orbit. In fact, in the low-Earth orbit of the Space Station, the acceleration of gravity is scarcely less than it is on the Earth's surface. Why, then, are the astronauts weightless? Because the Space Station and all other orbiting objects are in a constant state of *free-fall*, and any time you are in free-fall you are weightless. Imagine being an astronaut. You'd have the sensation of free-fall—just as when falling from a diving board—the entire time you were in orbit. This constantly falling sensation makes most astronauts sick to their stomach when they first experience weightlessness. Fortunately, they quickly get used to the sensation, which allows them to work hard and enjoy the view.

off your chair. Of course, your weightlessness lasts for only the very short time until you hit the ground.

Astronauts are weightless for much longer periods because orbiting spacecraft are in a constant state of free-fall. To understand why, imagine a cannon that shoots a ball horizontally from a tall mountain. Once launched, the ball falls solely because of gravity and hence is in free-fall. Thus, the faster the cannon shoots the ball, the farther it goes (Figure 5.3). If the cannonball could go fast enough, its motion would keep it constantly "falling around" the Earth and it would never hit the ground (as long as we neglect air resistance). This is precisely what spacecraft such as the Space Shuttle and the Space Station do as they orbit the Earth. Their constant state of free-fall makes the spacecraft and everything in them weightless.

If an orbiting object travels at the **escape velocity** or faster, it can completely escape from the Earth, never to return. (It will still be weightless as long as it does not fire any engines, because it is still in free-fall—only now "falling" in response to the gravity of the Sun, planets, and other objects.) The escape velocity from the Earth's surface is about 40,000 km/hr (25,000 mi/hr). We'll discuss escape velocity in more detail in Section 5.6.

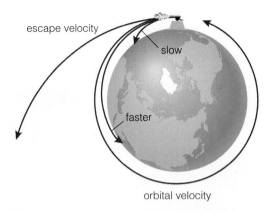

FIGURE 5.3 The faster the cannonball is shot, the farther it goes before hitting the ground. If it goes fast enough, it will continually "fall around," or orbit, the Earth. With an even faster speed, it may escape the Earth's gravity altogether.

**TIME OUT TO THINK** *In the* Hitchhiker's Guide to the Galaxy *books, author Douglas Adams says that the trick to flying is to throw yourself at the ground and miss. Although this phrase does not really explain flying, which involves lift from air, it does describe an orbit fairly well. Explain.*

## 5.2 Understanding Motion: Newton's Laws

The human "trick" of being able to figure out where a ball will land before it is thrown or to predict how other motions will unfold requires understanding precisely how forces affect objects in motion. At first, the complexity of motion in daily life might lead you to guess that the laws governing how forces affect motion are quite complex. For example, if you watch a piece of paper fall to the ground, you'll see it waft lazily back and forth in a seemingly unpredictable pattern. However, the complexity of this motion arises because the paper is affected by a variety of forces, including gravity and the changing forces caused by air currents. If you could analyze the forces individually, you'd find that each force affects the paper's motion in a simple, predictable way. Three simple laws, known as **Newton's laws of motion**, describe how forces affect motion. Let's investigate them, again using examples from everyday life. (Credit for discovering these laws really should go jointly to Galileo and Newton. They are called Newton's laws because he enumerated them in his book *Principia.*)

### Newton's First Law of Motion

Newton's first law of motion deals with situations in which no net force is acting on an object. It states:

*In the absence of a net force, an object moves with constant velocity.*

Thus, objects at rest (velocity = 0) tend to remain at rest, and objects in motion tend to remain in motion with no change in either their speed or their direction.

The idea that an object at rest should remain at rest is rather obvious; after all, if a car is parked on a flat street, it won't suddenly start moving for no reason. But what if the car is traveling along a flat, straight road? Newton's first law says that the car should keep going forever *unless* a force acts on it. You know that the car eventually will come to a stop if you take your foot off the gas pedal, so we must conclude that some forces are stopping the car—in this case forces arising from friction and air resistance.[2] If the car were in space, and therefore unaffected by friction or air, it would keep moving forever (though gravity would eventually alter its speed and direction). That is why interplanetary spacecraft, once launched into space, need no fuel to keep going.

Although friction cannot be eliminated on Earth, it can sometimes be minimized enough so that Newton's first law becomes more evident. For example, friction is low on ice, so a single push-off allows an ice skater to glide for a long time. Popular arcade games like *air hockey* also minimize friction so that a puck can travel for a long time before friction finally stops it.

Newton's first law also explains why you don't feel any sensation of motion when you're traveling in an airplane on a smooth flight. As long as the plane is traveling at constant velocity, no net force is acting on it or on you. Therefore, you feel no different from how you would feel at rest. You can walk around the cabin, play catch with a person a few rows forward, or relax and go to sleep just as though you were "at rest" on the ground.

### Newton's Second Law of Motion

Newton's second law of motion tells us what happens to an object when a net force *is* present. We have already said that a net force changes an object's momentum, accelerating it in the direction of the force. Newton's second law quantifies this relationship, which can be stated in two equivalent ways:

**force = rate of change in momentum**

**force = mass × acceleration (or $F = ma$)**

This law explains why you can throw a baseball farther than you can throw a shot-put. For both the

---

[2]Some readers might wonder why gravity does not help stop the car. A force can affect motion only if it is acting along the direction of motion. Because gravity acts downward, it cannot affect the motion of a car traveling along a flat (level) road.

**FIGURE 5.4 (a)** When you swing a ball on a string, the ball moves in a circle because the string exerts a force that pulls the ball inward. The acceleration must also be inward. **(b)** If the string breaks, the force disappears and the ball flies off in a straight line with velocity *v*.

$F = ma$

*v*

string breaks

**a**

**b**

baseball and the shot-put, the force delivered by your arm equals the product of mass and acceleration. Because the mass of the shot-put is greater than that of the baseball, the same force from your arm gives the shot-put a smaller acceleration. Due to its smaller acceleration, the shot-put leaves your hand with less speed than the baseball and thus travels a shorter distance before hitting the ground.

We can also use Newton's second law of motion to understand acceleration around curves. Suppose you swing a ball on a string around your head (Figure 5.4a). The ball is accelerating even if it has a steady speed, because it is constantly changing direction. What makes it accelerate? From Newton's second law, the taut string must be applying a force to the ball. We can understand this force by considering what would happen if it disappeared, such as if the string were to break (Figure 5.4b). In that case, the ball would simply fly off in a straight line. Thus, when the string is intact, the force must be pulling the ball *inward* to keep it from flying off. Because

acceleration must be in the same direction as the force, we conclude that the ball has an inward acceleration as it moves around the circle.

The same idea helps us understand the force on a car moving around a curve or a planet orbiting around the Sun. In the case of a car, the force comes from friction between the tires and the road. The tighter the curve or the faster the car is going, the greater the force needed to keep the car moving around it. If the force is not great enough, the car skids outward. For a planet moving around the Sun, the force pulling inward is gravity, as we'll discuss shortly. Thus, an orbiting planet is always accelerating toward the Sun. Indeed, it was Newton's discovery of the precise nature of this acceleration that helped him deduce the law of gravity.

### Newton's Third Law of Motion

Think for a moment about standing still on the ground. The force of gravity acts downward on you,

---

## Mathematical Insight 5.1    Units of Force, Mass, and Weight

Newton's second law, $F = ma$, shows that the units of force are equal to a unit of mass multiplied by a unit of acceleration. For example, if a mass of 1 kg accelerates at 10 m/s$^2$, the magnitude of the responsible force is

$$\text{force} = \text{mass} \times \text{acceleration}$$

$$= 1 \text{ kg} \times 10 \ \frac{\text{m}}{\text{s}^2} = 10 \ \frac{\text{kg} \times \text{m}}{\text{s}^2}$$

$$= 10 \text{ newtons}$$

The standard unit of force is the *kilogram-meter per second squared,* called the **newton** for short.

We can now further clarify the difference between mass and weight. When you stand on a scale, it records the downward force that you exert on it, which is equal and opposite to the upward force it exerts on you. If the scale were suddenly pulled out from under your feet, you would

begin accelerating downward with the acceleration of gravity. Thus, when you are standing still, the scale must support you with a force equal to your mass times the acceleration of gravity. Your weight must also equal this force (but in an opposite direction):

$$\text{weight} = \text{mass} \times \text{acceleration of gravity}$$

Your apparent weight may differ from this value if forces besides gravity are affecting you.

Like any force, weight has units of mass times acceleration. Thus, although we commonly speak of weights in *kilograms,* this usage is not technically correct: Kilograms are a unit of mass, not of force. You may safely ignore this technicality as long as you are dealing with objects on the Earth that are not accelerating. In space or on other planets, the distinction between mass and weight is important and cannot be ignored.

**FIGURE 5.5** Momentum conservation as demonstrated on a pool table.

before collision

first ball
momentum = $m \times v$

second ball
momentum = 0

**The collision transfers momentum
from the first ball to the second ball.**

after collision

first ball
momentum = 0

second ball
momentum = $m \times v$

so if this force were acting alone Newton's second law would demand that you be accelerating downward. The fact that you are not falling means that the ground must be pushing back up on you with exactly the right amount of force to offset gravity. This fact is embodied in Newton's third law of motion:

*For any force, there always
is an equal and opposite reaction force.*

According to this law, your body exerts a gravitational force on the Earth identical to the one the Earth exerts on you, except that it acts in the opposite direction. In this mutual pull, the ground just happens to be caught in the middle. Because other forces (between atoms and molecules in the Earth) keep the ground stationary with respect to the center of the Earth, the opposite, upward force is transmitted to you by the ground, holding you in place. Newton's third law also explains how rockets work: Engines generate an explosive force driving hot gas out the back, which creates an equal and opposite force propelling the rocket forward.

### Conservation of Momentum

If you look more closely at Newton's laws, you will see that they all reflect aspects of a deeper principle: the *conservation of momentum.* Like the amount of energy, the total amount of momentum in the universe is conserved—that is, it does not change. Newton's first law says that an individual object's momentum will not change at all if the object is left alone. Newton's second law says that a force can change the object's momentum, but Newton's third law says that another equal and opposite force simultaneously changes some other object's momentum by a precisely opposite amount. Total momentum always remains unchanged.

### Common Misconceptions:
### What Makes a Rocket Launch?

If you've ever watched a rocket launch, it's easy to see why many people believe that the rocket "pushes off" the ground. In fact, the ground has nothing to do with the rocket launch. The rocket takes off because of momentum conservation. Rocket engines are designed to expel hot gas with an enormous amount of momentum. To balance the explosive force driving gas out the back of the rocket, an equal and opposite force must propel the rocket forward, keeping the total momentum—gas plus rocket—unchanged. Thus, rockets can be launched horizontally as well as vertically, and a rocket can be "launched" in space (e.g., from a space station) with no need for any nearby solid ground.

On a pool table, momentum conservation is rather obvious. When one ball hits another ball "dead on," the first ball stops and the second one takes off with the speed of the first (Figure 5.5). Sometimes, momentum conservation is less apparent. When you jump into the air, how do you get your upward momentum? As your legs propel you skyward, they are actually pushing the Earth in the other direction,

FIGURE 5.6 The angular momentum of an object moving in a circle is $m \times v \times r$.

angular momentum = $m \times v \times r$

or orbiting has angular momentum. We can write a simple formula for the angular momentum of an object moving in a circle:

$$\text{angular momentum} = m \times v \times r$$

where $m$ is the object's mass, $v$ is its speed around the circle, and $r$ is the radius of the circle (Figure 5.6).

Just as momentum can be changed only by a force, the angular momentum of any object can be changed only by a twisting force, or **torque**. For example, opening a door requires rotating the door on its hinges. Making it rotate means giving it some angular momentum, which you can do by applying a torque (Figure 5.7). Note that the torque depends not only on how much force you use to push on the door, but also on *where* you push. The farther out from the hinges you push, the more torque you can apply and the easier it is to open the door.

**TIME OUT TO THINK** *Use the idea of torque to explain why it is easier to change a tire with a long wrench than with a short wrench.*

When no net torque is present, a law very similar to Newton's first law applies—the **law of conservation of angular momentum**:

*In the absence of net torque (twisting force), the total angular momentum of a system remains constant.*

A spinning ice skater illustrates this law. Because there is so little friction on ice, the ice skater essentially keeps a constant angular momentum. When she pulls in her extended arms, she effectively decreases her radius. Therefore, for the product $m \times v \times r$ to remain unchanged, her velocity of rotation must increase (Figure 5.8).

The law of conservation of angular momentum arises frequently in astronomy, because gravity is often the only significant force and gravity rarely acts

giving the Earth's momentum an equal and opposite kick. However, the Earth's huge mass renders its acceleration undetectable. During your brief flight, the gravitational forces between you and the Earth return your upward momentum to the Earth. Again, the total momentum remains the same at all times.

### Conservation of Angular Momentum

In astronomy, a special kind of momentum is particularly important. Consider an ice skater spinning in place. She certainly has some kind of momentum, but it is a little different from the momentum we've discussed previously because she's not actually going anywhere. Technically, her "spinning momentum" is called **angular momentum**. (The term *angular* arises because each spin involves turning through an *angle* of 360°.) In fact, any object that is spinning

FIGURE 5.7 Opening a door requires applying a torque. Given the same amount of force, the torque on the door is greater if you push farther from the hinges (the door's rotation axis).

low torque

moderate torque

most torque

In the product $m \times v \times r$, extended arms mean larger radius and smaller velocity of rotation.

Bringing in her arms decreases her radius and therefore increases her rotational velocity.

**FIGURE 5.8** A spinning skater conserves angular momentum.

as a twisting force.[3] For example, angular momentum is generally conserved for rotating planets, planets orbiting a star, and rotating galaxies. Indeed, conservation of angular momentum explains why the Earth doesn't need any fuel to make it rotate: In the absence of any torque to stop the rotation, the Earth would keep rotating forever. (In Section 5.5, we'll see that Earth's rotation gradually slows, due to a torque caused by tides.)

## 5.3 Planetary Motion: The Copernican Revolution

Now that we have described motion in general terms, we can turn to the important issue of planetary motion in our solar system. Although planetary motion is among the simplest motions found in nature, it remained mysterious for most of human history because of its *apparent* complexity in our sky [Section 2.4]. The prevailing view of European scholars at the dawn of the Renaissance remained that of Ptolemy, whose complex model had planets spinning on circles upon circles around the Earth [Section 3.3]. The dramatic change in human understanding of planetary motion, one of the most remarkable stories in the history of science, began early in the sixteenth century, with the work of Nicholas Copernicus.

### Nicholas Copernicus: The Revolution Begins

Copernicus was born in Toruń, Poland, on February 19, 1473. His family was wealthy, and he received a first-class education, studying mathematics, medicine, and law. He began studying astronomy in his late teens. By that time, tables of planetary motion based on the Ptolemaic model of the universe were

noticeably inaccurate.[4] Copernicus concluded that planetary motion could be explained more simply in a Sun-centered solar system, as had been suggested by Aristarchus some 1,800 years earlier [Section 2.4], and he began developing a Sun-centered system for predicting planetary positions.

Copernicus was hesitant to publish his work for fear that his suggestion that the Earth moved would be considered absurd. Nevertheless, he discussed his system with other scholars and generated great interest in his work. At the urging of some of these scholars, including some high-ranking officials of the Catholic Church, he finally agreed to publish a book describing his system. The book, *De Revolutionibus Orbium Caelestium*, or "Concerning the Revolutions of the Heavenly Spheres," was published in 1543. Copernicus saw the first printed copy on the day he died—May 24, 1543.

In addition to its aesthetic advantages, the Sun-centered system of Copernicus allowed him to discover a mathematical relationship between a planet's true orbital period around the Sun and the time between successive appearances of the planet

---

[3]Gravity exerts a torque only when it acts on an object with a non-spherical mass distribution and a rotation axis tilted (i.e., not perpendicular) to the direction of the gravitational force; this torque causes the axis to precess. This type of torque, created by the gravitational attraction of the Sun and the Moon acting on the Earth's tilted rotation axis, is the cause of the Earth's 26,000-year precession cycle.

[4]The best set of tables, known as the *Alfonsine Tables,* was compiled in 1252 under the guidance of the Spanish monarch Alfonso X (1221–1284). Commenting on the tedious nature of the calculations required by the Ptolemaic model, Alfonso X supposedly said that if he had been present at the creation, he would have recommended a simpler design for the universe.

Copernicus (1473–1543)

at opposition in the sky [Section S1.1]. He was also able to use geometrical techniques to estimate the distances of the planets from the Sun in terms of the Earth–Sun distance (i.e., distances in astronomical units). However, the model published by Copernicus did not predict planetary positions substantially more accurately than did the old Ptolemaic model. Moreover, it remained complex because Copernicus held to the ancient Greek belief that all heavenly motions must follow perfect circles. Because the true orbits of the planets are *not* circles, Copernicus found it necessary to add circles upon circles to his system, just as in the Ptolemaic system. As a result, the Copernican system won relatively few converts in the 50 years after it was published. After all, why throw out thousands of years of tradition for a new system that predicted planetary motion equally poorly?

### Tycho Brahe: The Greatest Naked-Eye Observer of All Time

Part of the difficulty faced by astronomers who sought to improve either the Ptolemaic or the Copernican system was a lack of quality data. The telescope had not yet been invented, and existing naked-eye observations were not very accurate. In the late 1500s, a Danish nobleman named Tycho Brahe (1546–1601) set about correcting this problem.

When Tycho was a young boy, his family discouraged his interest in astronomy. He therefore hid his passion, learning the constellations from a miniature model of a celestial sphere that he kept hidden. As he grew older, Tycho was often arrogant about both his noble birth and his learned abilities. At age 20, he fought a duel with another student over which of them was the better mathematician. Part of his nose was cut off, so he designed a replacement piece made of silver and gold.

In 1563, Tycho decided to observe a widely anticipated conjunction of Jupiter and Saturn. To his

surprise, the conjunction occurred nearly two days later than Copernicus had predicted. He resolved to improve the state of astronomical prediction and set about compiling careful observations of stellar and planetary positions in the sky.

Tycho's fame grew after he observed what he called a *nova,* meaning "new star," in 1572 and proved that it was at a distance much farther away than the Moon. (He compared observations made by other astronomers at other locations on Earth to his own, proving that the nova had no observable parallax and must be more distant than the Moon.) Today, we know that Tycho saw a *supernova*—the explosion of a distant star. In 1577, Tycho observed a comet and proved that it too lay in the realm of the heavens; others, notably Aristotle, had argued that comets were phenomena of the Earth's atmosphere. King Frederick II of Denmark then decided to sponsor Tycho's ongoing work, providing him with money to build an unparalleled observatory for naked-eye observations. (After Frederick II died in 1588, Tycho moved to Prague, where his work was supported by German emperor Rudolf II.)

Over a period of three decades, Tycho and his assistants compiled naked-eye observations accurate to within less than 1 arcminute. Because the telescope was invented shortly after his death, Tycho's data remain the best set of naked-eye observations ever made.

Despite the quality of his observations, Tycho never succeeded in coming up with a satisfying explanation for planetary motion. He did, however, succeed in finding someone who could: In 1600, he hired a young German astronomer named Johannes Kepler (1571–1630). Kepler and Tycho had a strained relationship while Tycho was living.[5] But in 1601, as

---

[5]For a particularly moving version of the story of Tycho and Kepler, see episode 3 of Carl Sagan's *Cosmos* video series.

Tycho Brahe (1546–1601)

Tycho's naked-eye observatory

Kepler
(1571–1630)

one model for the east-west positions and another for the north-south positions. He attempted to find a unified model with a circular orbit, but in doing so he found that some of his predictions differed from Tycho's observations by as much as 8 arcminutes.

Kepler surely was tempted to ignore these discrepancies and attribute them to errors by Tycho. After all, 8 arcminutes is barely one-fourth the angular diameter of the full moon. But Kepler trusted Tycho's careful work, and the misses by 8 arcminutes finally led him to abandon the idea of circular orbits—and to find the correct solution to the ancient riddle of planetary motion. About this event, Kepler wrote:

> If I had believed that we could ignore these eight minutes [of arc], I would have patched up my hypothesis accordingly. But, since it was not permissible to ignore, those eight minutes pointed the road to a complete reformation in astronomy.

**TIME OUT TO THINK** *Some historians assert that Kepler's discovery represented the true birth of modern science because, for the first time, a scientist was willing to cast off long-held beliefs in a quest to match theory to observation. How did Kepler's work meet the criteria for the modern scientific method?*

Kepler summarized his discoveries with three simple laws that we now call **Kepler's laws of planetary motion**. He published the first two laws in 1610 and the third in 1618. (Be careful not to confuse Kepler's three laws of *planetary* motion with Newton's three laws that apply generally to *all* motion.)

Tycho lay on his deathbed, he begged Kepler to find a system that would make sense of the observations so "that it may not appear I have lived in vain."

### Kepler's Reformation: The Laws of Planetary Motion

Kepler was deeply religious and believed that understanding the geometry of the heavens would bring him closer to God. Kepler, like Copernicus, believed that Earth and the other planets traveled around the Sun in circular orbits, and he worked diligently to match circular motions to Tycho's data.

Kepler worked with particular intensity to find an orbit for Mars, which posed the greatest difficulties in matching the data to a circular orbit. After years of calculation, Kepler found a circular orbit that matched all of Tycho's observations of Mars' position along the ecliptic (east-west) to within 2 arcminutes. However, the same model did not correctly predict Mars' positions north or south of the ecliptic. Because Kepler sought a physically realistic orbit for Mars, he could not (as Ptolemy and Copernicus had done) tolerate

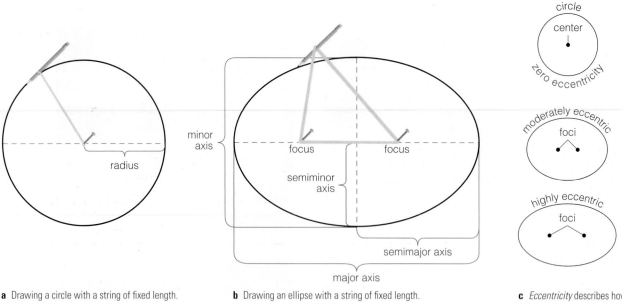

minor axis

radius

focus    focus

semiminor axis

semimajor axis

major axis

circle

center

zero eccentricity

moderately eccentric

foci

highly eccentric

foci

**a** Drawing a circle with a string of fixed length.

**b** Drawing an ellipse with a string of fixed length.

**c** *Eccentricity* describes how much an ellipse deviates from a perfect circle.

**FIGURE 5.9** Basic characteristics of circles and ellipses.

Kepler's key discovery was that planetary orbits are not circles but instead are a special type of oval called an **ellipse**. You probably know how to draw a circle by putting a pencil on the end of a string, tacking the string to a board, and pulling the pencil around (Figure 5.9a). Drawing an ellipse is similar, except that you must stretch the string around *two* tacks (Figure 5.9b). The locations of the two tacks are called the **foci** (singular, **focus**) of the ellipse. By altering the distance between the two foci while keeping the same length of string, you can draw ellipses of varying **eccentricity**, a quantity that describes how much an ellipse deviates from a perfect circle (Figure 5.9c): A circle has zero eccentricity, and greater eccentricity means a more elongated ellipse. (Mathematically, eccentricity is the center-to-focus distance divided by the length of the semimajor axis.)

**Kepler's first law** states that *the orbit of each planet about the Sun is an ellipse with the Sun at one focus* (Figure 5.10). (There is nothing at the other focus.) This law tells us that a planet's distance from the Sun varies during its orbit: It is closest at the point called **perihelion**, and farthest at the point called **aphelion**. (*Helios* is Greek for the Sun, the prefix *peri* means "near," and the prefix *ap* (or *apo*) means "away." Thus, *perihelion* means "near the Sun" and *aphelion* means "away from the Sun.") The *average* of a planet's perihelion and aphelion distances is called its **semimajor axis**; we will refer to this simply as the planet's average distance from the Sun.

**Kepler's second law** states that *as a planet moves around its orbit, it sweeps out equal areas in equal times.*

As shown in Figure 5.11, this means that the planet moves a greater distance when it is near perihelion than it does in the same amount of time near aphelion; that is, the planet travels faster when it is nearer to the Sun and slower when it is farther from the Sun.

**Kepler's third law** describes how a planet's *orbital period* (the time it takes to complete one orbit of the Sun), measured in years, is related to its average distance from the Sun in astronomical units (1 AU ≈ 150 million km):

(orbital period in years)$^2$ = (average distance in AU)$^3$

This formula is often written more simply as $p^2 = a^3$, where $p$ is the orbital period measured in years and $a$ is the average distance measured in AU (Figure 5.12a). The formula also tells us that *more distant planets move at slower speeds* in their orbits about the Sun, which we can see by graphing planetary periods against average distances from the Sun (Figure 5.12b). For example, Saturn is slightly less than twice as far as Jupiter from the Sun but takes almost three times as long to orbit the Sun; thus, Saturn must be moving along its orbit at a slower average speed than Jupiter.

Note that a planet's period does not depend on the eccentricity of its orbit: All orbits with the same semimajor axis have the same period. Nor does the period depend on the mass of the planet: Any object located an average of 1 AU from the Sun would orbit the Sun in a year (as long as the object's mass was small compared to the Sun's mass).

## Galileo: The Death of the Earth-Centered Universe

The success of Kepler's laws in matching Tycho's data provided strong evidence in favor of Copernicus's placement of the Sun, rather than the Earth, at the center of the solar system. Nevertheless, many scientists still voiced reasonable objections to the Copernican view. There were three basic objections, all rooted in the 2,000-year-old beliefs of Aristotle (384–322 B.C.) and other ancient Greeks. First, Aristotle had held that the Earth could not be moving because, if it were, objects such as birds, falling stones, and clouds would be left behind as the Earth moved along its way. Second, the idea of noncircular orbits contradicted the ancient Greek belief that the heavens—the realm of the Sun, Moon, planets, and stars—must be perfect and unchanging. The third objection was the ancient argument that stellar parallax ought to be detectable if the Earth orbits the Sun [Section 2.4]. Galileo (1564–1642), a contemporary and correspondent of Kepler, answered all three objections.

Galileo defused the first objection with experiments that almost single-handedly overturned the Aristotelian view of physics. His demonstration that gravity accelerates all objects by the same amount directly contradicted Aristotle's claim that heavier objects would fall to the ground faster. Aristotle also had taught that the natural tendency of any object was to come to rest. Galileo demonstrated that a moving object remains in motion *unless* a force acts to stop it, an idea now codified in Newton's first law of motion. Thus, he concluded that objects such as birds, falling stones, and clouds that are moving with the Earth should *stay* with the Earth unless some force knocks them away. This same idea explains why passengers in an airplane stay with the moving airplane even when they leave their seats.

Tycho's supernova and comet observations already had shown that the heavens could change, and Galileo shattered the idea of heavenly perfection after he built a telescope in late 1609. (Galileo did *not* invent the telescope; it was invented in 1608 by Hans Lippershey. However, Galileo took what was little more than a toy and turned it into a scientific instrument.) Through his telescope, Galileo saw sunspots on the Sun, which were considered "imperfections" at the time. He also used his telescope to prove that the Moon has mountains and valleys like the "imperfect" Earth by noticing the shadows cast near the dividing line between the light and dark portions of the lunar face (Figure 5.13). If the heavens were not perfect, then the idea of elliptical (rather than circular) orbits was not so objectionable.

The absence of observable stellar parallax had been of particular concern to Tycho. Based on his estimates of the distances of stars, Tycho believed that his naked-eye observations were sufficiently

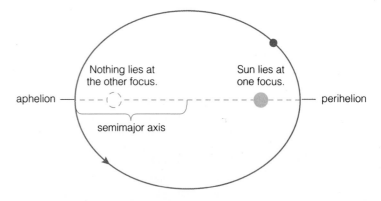

**FIGURE 5.10** Kepler's first law: The orbit of each planet about the Sun is an ellipse with the Sun at one focus. (The eccentricity shown here is exaggerated compared to the actual eccentricities of the planets.)

The areas swept out in 30-day periods are all equal.

**FIGURE 5.11** Kepler's second law: As a planet moves around its orbit, it sweeps out equal areas in equal times.

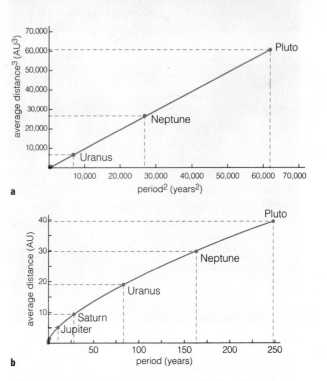

**FIGURE 5.12** (a) Kepler's third law states that the period of a planet squared is equal to its average orbital distance cubed. (b) A plot of average distance against orbital period. We can use this plot to find that planets nearer the Sun orbit faster than more distant planets.

## Aristotle

Aristotle (384–322 B.C.) is among the best-known philosophers of the ancient world. Both his parents died when he was a child, and he was raised by a family friend. In his 20s and 30s, he studied under Plato (427–347 B.C.) at Plato's Academy. He later founded his own school, called the Lyceum, where he studied and lectured on virtually every subject. Historical records tell us that his lectures were collected and published in 150 volumes. About 50 of these volumes survive to the present day.

Many of Aristotle's scientific discoveries involved the nature of plants and animals. He studied more than 500 animal species in detail, including dissecting specimens of nearly 50 species, and came up with a strikingly modern classification system. For example, he was the first person to recognize that dolphins should be classified with land mammals rather than with fish. In mathematics, he is known for laying the foundations of mathematical logic. Unfortunately, he was far less successful in physics and astronomy, areas in which many of his claims turned out to be wrong.

Interestingly, Aristotle's philosophies were not particularly influential until many centuries after his death. His books were preserved and valued by Islamic scholars, but they were unknown in Europe until they were translated into Latin in the twelfth and thirteenth centuries. Aristotle achieved his near-reverential status only after St. Thomas Aquinas (1225–1274) integrated Aristotle's philosophy into Christian theology. In the ancient world, Aristotle's greatest influence came indirectly, through his role as the tutor of Alexander the Great [Section 3.3].

Galileo (1564–1642)

**FIGURE 5.13** The shadows cast by mountains and crater rims near the dividing line between the light and dark portions of the lunar face prove that the Moon's surface is not perfectly smooth.

precise to detect stellar parallax if the Earth did in fact orbit the Sun.[6] (His planetary observations convinced him that the *planets* must orbit the Sun, so he advocated a model in which the Sun orbits the Earth while all other planets orbit the Sun. Few people took this model seriously, and Kepler's work soon made it a mere historical curiosity.) Refuting Tycho's argument required showing that the stars were more distant than Tycho had thought and therefore too distant for him to have observed stellar parallax. Although Galileo didn't actually prove this fact, he provided strong evidence in its favor. In particular, he saw with his telescope that the Milky Way resolved into countless individual stars, which helped

---

[6]Tycho based his estimates of stellar distances on what he *thought* were their angular sizes, but he was really measuring effects of atmospheric refraction.

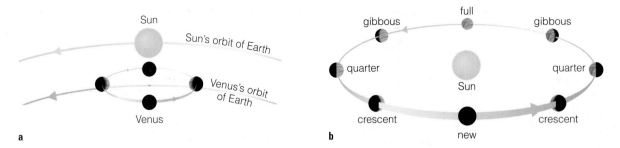

a

b

**FIGURE 5.14** (**a**) In the Ptolemaic system, Venus follows a circle upon a circle that keeps it close to the Sun in our sky. Therefore, its phases would range only from new to crescent. (**b**) Galileo observed Venus go through a complete set of phases and therefore proved that it orbits the Sun.

him argue that the stars were far more numerous and more distant than Tycho had imagined.

The true death knell for an Earth-centered universe came with two of Galileo's earliest discoveries through the telescope. First, he observed four moons clearly orbiting Jupiter, *not* the Earth. (By itself, this observation still did not rule out a stationary, central Earth. However, it showed that moons can orbit a moving planet like Jupiter, which overcame some critics' complaints that the Moon could not stay with a moving Earth.) Soon thereafter, he observed that Venus goes through phases like the Moon, proving that Venus must orbit the Sun and not the Earth (Figure 5.14). With Earth clearly removed from its position at the center of the universe, the scientific debate turned to the question of whether Kepler's laws were the correct model for our solar system. The most convincing evidence came in 1631, when astronomers observed a transit of Mercury across the Sun's face [Section S1.1]; Kepler's laws had predicted the transit with overwhelmingly better success than any competing model.

At last, the Copernican revolution was complete. Thanks in large part to Galileo, by the mid-1600s most astronomers accepted Kepler's model of planetary motion. Note that it took roughly a century from the time Copernicus published his ideas in 1543 to the time that a Sun-centered system became widely accepted. The dramatic shift in thought that occurred during this period offers an excellent example of the process of science. Prior to the start of this revolution, Ptolemy's model seemed an adequate way of explaining planetary motions in the sky. But as more and better observations were gathered, it became apparent that Ptolemy's model did not agree with the data. Copernicus offered an alternative model that had the right geneal idea in displacing the Earth from the center of the universe, but he still did not make predictions that agreed sufficiently with observations. As a result, the idea of an Earth that orbits the Sun remained controversial until Kepler created a model that successfully matched the observations and Galileo defused the objections raised on other grounds. The agreement between theory and observation became so strong that the debate finally turned away from how planets move to the question of *why* Kepler's laws hold true.

## 5.4 The Force of Gravity

The Aristotelian view of the world, held in Europe as near-gospel truth, was in tatters. The Earth was not the center of the universe, and the laws of physics were not what Aristotle had believed. But the final blow was still to come. Aristotle had maintained that the heavens were totally distinct from Earth and that the physical laws on Earth could not be applied to understanding heavenly motion.

In 1666, Isaac Newton saw an apple fall to the ground. (The story of the apple may or may not be true, but Newton himself told the story.) He suddenly realized that the force that brought the apple to the ground and the force that held the Moon in orbit were the same. That insight brought the Earth and the heavens together in one *universe*. It also heralded the birth of the modern science of *astrophysics* (although the term wasn't coined until much later), in which physical laws discovered on Earth are applied to phenomena throughout the cosmos.

Newton (1642–1727)

**FIGURE 5.15** The universal law of gravitation.

### Newton and the Universal Law of Gravitation

Newton was born prematurely in Lincolnshire, England, on Christmas Day in 1642. His father, a farmer who had never learned to read or write, died 3 months before he was born. Newton had a difficult childhood and showed few signs of unusual talent. He attended Trinity College at Cambridge, where he earned his keep by performing menial labor, such as cleaning the boots and bathrooms of wealthier students and waiting on their tables.

Shortly after he graduated, the plague hit Cambridge, and Newton returned home. It was there that he saw the apple fall and began his detailed investigations of gravity, light, optics, and mathematics. Over the next 20 years, Newton's work completely revolutionized mathematics and science. In addition to his work on motion and gravity, he conducted crucial experiments regarding the nature of light, built the first reflecting telescopes, and invented the branch of mathematics called *calculus*. The compendium of Newton's discoveries is so tremendous that it would take a complete book just to describe them, and many more books to describe their influence on civilization. When Newton died in 1727, at age 84, the English poet Alexander Pope composed the following epitaph:

> *Nature, and Nature's laws lay hid in the Night.*
> *God said,* Let Newton be! *and all was Light.*

In 1687, Newton published *Philosophiae Naturalis Principia Mathematica* ("Mathematical Principles of Natural Philosophy"), usually referred to as *Principia*. In this book, Newton stated his three laws of motion and another law, called the **universal law of gravitation**, that describes the force of gravity.

Three simple statements summarize the universal law of gravitation:

- Every mass attracts every other mass through the force called *gravity*.

- The force of attraction between any two objects is *directly proportional* to the product of their masses. For example, doubling the mass of *one* object doubles the force of gravity between the two objects.

- The force of attraction between two objects decreases with the *square* of the distance between their centers. That is, the force follows an **inverse square law** with distance. For example, doubling the distance between two objects weakens the force of gravity by a factor of $2^2$, or 4.

**TIME OUT TO THINK** *How does the gravitational force between two objects change if the distance between them triples? If the distance between them drops in half?*

Mathematically, Newton's law of universal gravitation is written:

$$F_g = G\frac{M_1 M_2}{d^2}$$

where $F_g$ is the force of gravitational attraction, $M_1$ and $M_2$ are the masses of the two objects, and $d$ is the distance between their *centers* (Figure 5.15). The symbol $G$ is a constant called the **gravitational constant**. Its numerical value was not known to Newton but has since been measured by experiments to be $G = 6.67 \times 10^{-11}$ m³/(kg × s²).

### The "Why" of Kepler's Laws, and More

For some 70 years after Kepler published his laws of planetary motion, the outstanding unsolved problem in science was what caused Kepler's laws to hold true. Kepler himself speculated that his laws might be explained by a force holding the planets in their orbits about the Sun. He incorrectly guessed that this force might be related to magnetism, an idea shared by Galileo. (This idea was first suggested by William Gilbert [1544–1603], an early believer in the Copernican system.) In *Principia*, Newton showed this force to be gravity.

Newton explained Kepler's laws by *solving* the law of universal gravitation together with the laws of motion. The solution is a bit like solving a pair of algebraic equations, but it requires the use of calculus. Newton found that the elliptical orbits with varying speeds described by Kepler's first two laws represent one possible solution. The easiest way to understand the varying speeds is to think of them in terms of conservation of angular momentum. A planet's orbital angular momentum is the product $m \times v \times r$, where $m$ is the mass of the planet, $v$ is its orbital speed, and $r$ is its distance ("radius") from the Sun. To keep this product constant, the planet's orbital speed ($v$) must go up when its distance from the Sun ($r$) goes down, and vice versa.

Newton's work showed that Kepler's first two laws apply not just to planets but to *any* object going around another object under the force of gravity. (More technically, pairs of objects orbit each other in ellipses with their *center of mass* at one focus. If one object is much more massive than the other, the center of mass is very close to the massive object's center.) The orbits of satellites around the Earth, of moons around planets, of asteroids around the Sun, and of binary stars around each other are all ellipses in which orbital speeds vary so that angular momentum is conserved. Moreover, Newton found that elliptical orbits are not the only possible solution to the equations involving the law of gravity. Orbits in the shape of *parabolas* or *hyperbolas* are also allowed (Figure 5.16). Elliptical orbits are **bound orbits** because gravity creates a bond that makes one object go around and around the other. In contrast, parabolas and hyperbolas are **unbound orbits**, in which gravity governs the orbital path but cannot prevent the orbiting object from escaping. A comet with an unbound orbit comes in toward the Sun just once, looping around the Sun and never returning.

Kepler's third law also follows naturally from the law of gravity: The force is stronger nearer the Sun, so inner planets must move faster than outer planets to avoid falling toward the Sun. However, in solving the equations involving gravity, Newton showed that Kepler's statement $p^2 = a^3$ is only one special case of a more general law. Newton's generalization of Kepler's third law is:

$$p^2 = \frac{4\pi^2}{G(M_1 + M_2)} a^3$$

In this form, the law applies to any pair of orbiting objects with bound orbits, and it is not necessary to measure the period ($p$) in years and the average distance ($a$) in astronomical units; you can use any units, as long as you properly match them to the units you use for the gravitational constant, $G$. In addition, the general law includes the *masses* of the orbiting objects, which has important implications.

Suppose the two objects are the Sun and a planet. Because the Sun is much more massive than any planet, the sum $M_{Sun} + M_{planet}$ is pretty much just $M_{Sun}$. In that case, we can rewrite Newton's version of Kepler's third law as:

$$p^2_{planet} \approx \frac{4\pi^2}{G \times M_{Sun}} a^3_{planet}$$

We now find two remarkable results. First, note that the only characteristic of a planet that affects its orbital period is its average distance from the Sun. Generalizing this result, we find that the orbital period of any object orbiting a much more massive object depends only on its average distance. For example, the period of any satellite orbiting the Earth depends only on its average distance from the center of the Earth. All satellites orbiting 42,000 kilometers from the center of the Earth take 1 day to complete an orbit, and all satellites in the low-Earth orbit of the Space Shuttle (or Space Station) orbit the Earth in about 90 minutes. Thus, an astronaut on a space walk remains close to the Space Shuttle because the astronaut and the shuttle both orbit the Earth in the same amount of time (Figure 5.17).

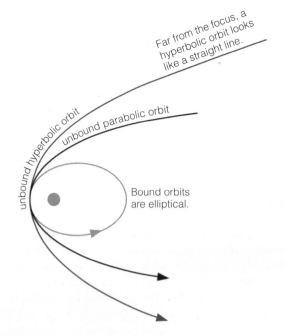

Far from the focus, a hyperbolic orbit looks like a straight line.

unbound hyperbolic orbit

unbound parabolic orbit

Bound orbits are elliptical.

**FIGURE 5.16** Orbits allowed by the law of gravity.

Second, by knowing the period $p$ and the average distance $a$ of any planet, we can calculate the mass of the Sun. More generally, we can calculate the mass of any massive object by measuring the period $p$ and the average distance $a$ of something that orbits it. By measuring the period and average distance of any one of Jupiter's moons, we can calculate the mass of Jupiter. By measuring the period and distance of a small star orbiting a more massive star, we can calculate (approximately) the larger star's mass. In fact, Newton's version of Kepler's third law provides

**FIGURE 5.17** Newton's version of Kepler's third law shows that, when one object orbits a much more massive object, the orbital period depends only on its average orbital distance. Thus, the astronaut and the Space Shuttle share the same orbit despite their different masses—even as both orbit the Earth at a speed of some 25,000 km/hr.

the primary means by which we determine masses throughout the universe.

Newton's law of gravitation has applications that go far beyond explaining Kepler's laws. In the rest of this chapter, we'll explore three important concepts that we can understand with the help of the law of gravitation: tides, orbital energy and escape velocity, and the acceleration of gravity.

## 5.5 Tides

If you've spent time near an ocean, you're probably aware of the rising and falling of the tide twice each day. What causes the tides, and why are there two each day?

We can understand the basic idea by examining the gravitational attraction between the Earth and the Moon. Gravity attracts the Earth and the Moon toward each other (with the Moon staying in orbit as it "falls around" the Earth), but it affects different parts of the Earth slightly differently: Because the strength of gravity declines with distance, the side of the Earth facing the Moon feels a slightly stronger gravi-

*Not to scale!* The real tidal bulge raises the oceans by only about 2 meters.

**FIGURE 5.18** Tidal bulges face toward and away from the Moon because of the difference in the strength of the gravitational attraction in parts of the Earth at different distances from the Moon. (Arrows represent the strength and direction of the gravitational attraction toward the Moon.) There are two daily high tides as any location on Earth rotates through the two tidal bulges.

tational attraction than the side facing away from the Moon. As shown in Figure 5.18, this creates two tidal bulges, one facing the Moon and one opposite the Moon. The Earth's rotation carries your location through each of the two bulges each day, creating two high tides; low tides occur when your location is at the points halfway between the two tidal bulges.

## Mathematical Insight 5.2    Using Newton's Version of Kepler's Third Law

The following examples show the remarkable power of Newton's version of Kepler's third law.

*Example 1:* Use the fact that the Earth orbits the Sun in 1 year at an average distance of 150 million km (1 AU) to calculate the mass of the Sun.

*Solution:* The Earth is much less massive than the Sun, so the sum of their masses is approximately the mass of the Sun alone; that is, $M_{Sun} + M_{Earth} \approx M_{Sun}$. We can therefore use Newton's version of Kepler's third law in the form:

$$(p_{Earth})^2 \approx \frac{4\pi^2}{G \times M_{Sun}} (a_{Earth})^3$$

We solve this equation for the mass of the Sun by multiplying both sides by $M_{Sun}$ and dividing both sides by $(p_{Earth})^2$:

$$M_{Sun} \approx \frac{4\pi^2}{G} \frac{(a_{Earth})^3}{(p_{Earth})^2}$$

The Earth's orbital period is $p_{Earth} = 1$ year, which is the same as $3.15 \times 10^7$ seconds. Its average distance from the Sun is $a_{Earth} \approx 150$ million km, or $1.5 \times 10^{11}$ m. Using these values and the experimentally measured value $G = 6.67 \times 10^{-11}$ m³/(kg × s²), we find:

$$M_{Sun} \approx \frac{4\pi^2}{G} \frac{(a_{Earth})^3}{(p_{Earth})^2}$$

$$= \frac{4\pi^2 (1.5 \times 10^{11} \text{ m})^3}{\left(6.67 \times 10^{-11} \dfrac{\text{m}^3}{\text{kg} \times \text{s}^2}\right)\left(3.15 \times 10^7 \text{ s}\right)^2}$$

$$= 2 \times 10^{30} \text{ kg}$$

The mass of the Sun is about $2 \times 10^{30}$ kg. Simply by knowing the Earth's orbital period and distance from the Sun, and the gravitational constant G, we have used Newton's version of Kepler's third law to "weigh" the Sun.

*Example 2.* A *geosynchronous satellite* orbits the Earth in the same amount of time that Earth rotates: 1 sidereal day. If a geosynchronous satellite is also in an equatorial orbit, it is said to be *geostationary* because it remains fixed in the sky (i.e., it maintains a constant altitude and direction) as seen from the ground (see problem 11). Calculate the orbital distance of a geosynchronous satellite.

*Solution:* A satellite is much less massive than the Earth, so $M_{Earth} + M_{satellite} \approx M_{Earth}$ and we can use Newton's version of Kepler's third law in the form:

$$(p_{satellite})^2 \approx \frac{4\pi^2}{G \times M_{Earth}} (a_{satellite})^3$$

Because we want to know the satellite's distance, we solve for $a_{satellite}$ by multiplying both sides of the equation by $(G \times M_{Earth})$, dividing both sides by $4\pi^2$, and then taking the cube root of both sides:

$$a_{satellite} \approx \sqrt[3]{\frac{G \times M_{Earth}}{4\pi^2} (p_{satellite})^2}$$

We know that $p_{satellite} = 1$ sidereal day $\approx 86,164$ seconds. You should confirm that substituting this value and the mass of the Earth yields $a_{satellite} \approx 42,000$ km. Thus, a geosynchronous satellite orbits at a distance of 42,000 km above the *center* of the Earth.

**FIGURE 5.19** Photographs of high and low tide at the abbey at Mont-Saint-Michel, France, one of the world's most popular tourist destinations. Here the tide rushes in much faster than a person can swim. Before a causeway was built, the Mont was accessible by land only at low tide; at high tide, it became an island.

In a simple sense, the reason there are *two* daily high tides is that the oceans facing the Moon bulge because they are being pulled out from the Earth, while the oceans opposite the Moon bulge because the Earth is being pulled out from under them. However, a better way to look at tides is to recognize that the attraction toward the Moon gets progressively weaker with distance throughout the Earth. This varying attraction creates a "stretching force," or **tidal force**, that stretches the *entire Earth*—land and ocean—along the Earth–Moon line. The tidal bulges are more noticeable for the oceans than for the land only because liquids flow more readily than solids.

The two "daily" high tides actually come slightly more than 12 hours apart. Because the Moon orbits the Earth while the Earth rotates, the Moon is at its highest point (i.e., on the meridian) at any location about every 24 hours 50 minutes, rather than every 24 hours. Thus, the tidal cycle of two high tides and two low tides actually takes about 24 hours 50 minutes, with each high tide occurring about 12 hours 25 minutes after the previous one.

In addition, the height and timing of tides can vary considerably from place to place around the Earth, depending on factors such as latitude, the orientation of the coastline (e.g., north-facing or west-facing), and the depth and shape of any channel through which the rising tide must flow. For example, while the tide rises gradually in most locations, the incoming tide near the famous abbey on Mont-Saint-Michel, France, moves much faster than a person can swim (Figure 5.19). In centuries past, the Mont was an island twice a day at high tide but was connected to the mainland at low tide. (Today, a man-made land bridge connects the island to the mainland.) Many

pilgrims drowned when they were caught unprepared by the inrushing tide. Another unusual tidal pattern occurs in coastal states along the northern shore of the Gulf of Mexico, where the topography and other factors combine to make only one noticeable high tide and low tide each day.

## Common Misconceptions: The Origin of Tides

Many people believe that tides arise because the Moon pulls the Earth's oceans toward it. But if that were the whole story, there would be a bulge only on the side of Earth facing the Moon, and hence only one high tide each day. The correct explanation for tides must account for why the Earth has *two* tidal bulges. If you think about it, you'll realize there's only one simple way to explain this fact: The Earth must be stretching from its center in both directions (toward and away from the Moon). Once you see this, it becomes clear that tides must come from the difference between the force of gravity on one side of the Earth and that on the other, since a difference makes the Earth stretch. In fact, stretching due to tides affects many objects, not just the Earth. Many moons are stretched into oblong shapes by tidal forces caused by their parent planets, and mutual tidal forces stretch close binary stars into teardrop shapes. In regions where gravity is extremely strong, such as near a black hole, tides could even stretch spaceships or people [Section 17.4].

## Spring and Neap Tides

The Sun also exerts a tidal force on the Earth, causing the Earth to stretch along the Sun–Earth line. You might at first guess that the Sun's tidal force would be substantial, since the Sun's mass is more than a million times the mass of the Moon. Indeed, the *gravitational* force between the Earth and the Sun is much greater than that between the Earth and the Moon, which is why the Earth orbits the Sun. However, the much greater distance to the Sun (than to the Moon) means that the *difference* in the Sun's pull on the near and far sides of the Earth is relatively small, and the overall tidal force caused by the Sun is only about one-third that caused by the Moon (Figure 5.20). When the tidal forces of the Sun and the Moon work together, as is the case at both new moon and full moon, we get the especially pronounced *spring tides* (so named because the water tends to "spring up" from the Earth). When the tidal forces of the Sun and the Moon oppose each other, as is the case at first- and third-quarter moon, we get the relatively small tides known as *neap tides*.

**FIGURE 5.20** Tides also depend on tidal force from the Sun, which is about one-third as strong as that from the Moon. In these diagrams, yellow arrows represent tidal force due to the Sun, which causes the Earth to stretch along the Sun–Earth line, and black arrows represent tidal force due to the Moon, which causes the Earth to stretch along the Earth–Moon line.

**spring tides**

new
moon

full
moon

to Sun

**a** At new moon and full moon, the tidal forces from both the Moon and the Sun stretch the Earth along the same line, leading to enhanced *spring tides*.

**neap tides**

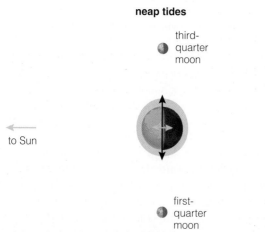

third-
quarter
moon

to Sun

first-
quarter
moon

**b** At first- and third-quarter moon, the Sun's tidal force stretches the Earth along a line perpendicular to the Moon's tidal force. The tides still follow the Moon, because the Moon's tidal force is greater, but they are reduced in size, making *neap tides*.

**TIME OUT TO THINK** *Explain why any tidal effects (on Earth) caused by the other planets would be extremely small (in fact, so small as to be unnoticeable).*

## Tidal Friction

So far, we have talked as if the Earth slides smoothly through the tidal bulges as it rotates. But because it is the Earth itself that stretches, this process involves some friction, called **tidal friction**. In essence, the friction arises because the tidal bulges try to stay on the Earth–Moon line, while the Earth's rotation tries to pull the bulges around with it. The resulting "compromise" puts the bulges just ahead of the Earth–Moon line at all times (Figure 5.21), ensuring that the Earth feels continuous friction as it rotates through the tidal bulges.

This tidal friction has two important effects. First, it causes the Earth's rotation to slow gradually, so that the length of a day gradually gets longer. Second, it makes the Moon move gradually farther from the Earth, because the tidal bulge is always slightly ahead of the Earth–Moon line and thus exerts a gravitational attraction that tends to pull the Moon slightly ahead in its orbit. This makes it harder for the Earth's overall gravity to hold on to the Moon, and as a result the Moon moves slightly farther from the Earth.

These two effects are barely noticeable on human time scales. For example, tidal friction increases the length of a day by only about 1 second every 50,000 years. (On shorter time scales, the length of the day fluctuates by up to a second or more per year due to slight changes in the Earth's internal mass distribution; this is why you may hear of "leap seconds" occasionally being added to or subtracted from the year.) But the effects add up over billions of years; early in the Earth's history, a day may have been only 5 or 6 hours long and the Moon may have been one-tenth or less its current distance from Earth. The changes in the Earth's rotation and the Moon's orbit also provide a remarkable example of conservation of angular momentum: The amount of angular momentum the Earth loses as its rotation slows is precisely the same as the amount the Moon gains through its growing orbit.

## Synchronous Rotation

Tidal friction has had even more dramatic effects on the Moon. Recall that the Moon always shows (nearly) the same face to the Earth [Section 2.3]. This trait is called **synchronous rotation**, because it means that the Moon's rotation period and orbital period are the same (see Figure 2.20). Synchronous rotation may seem like an extraordinary coincidence, but it is a natural consequence of tidal friction.

The Moon probably once rotated much faster than it does today. But just as the Moon exerts a tidal

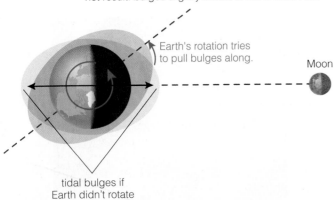

net result: bulges slightly ahead of Earth-Moon line

Earth's rotation tries
to pull bulges along.

Moon

tidal bulges if
Earth didn't rotate

**FIGURE 5.21** If the Earth always kept the same face to the Moon, the tidal bulges would stay fixed on the Earth–Moon line. But the Earth's rotation tries to pull them along with it. The result is that the bulges stay nearly fixed relative to the Moon but in a position slightly ahead of the Earth–Moon line. (The effect is exaggerated here for clarity.)

force on the Earth, the Earth exerts a tidal force on the Moon. In fact, because of its larger mass, the Earth exerts a greater tidal force on the Moon than vice versa. This tidal force stretches the Moon along the Earth–Moon line, creating two tidal bulges similar to those on Earth. As long as the Moon rotated through these bulges, the motion created tidal friction that slowed the Moon's rotation. But once the Moon's rotation slowed to the point at which the Moon and its bulges rotated at the same rate—that is, synchronously with the orbital period—there was

**FIGURE 5.22** Pluto and Charon rotate synchronously with each other, so that each always shows the same face to the other. If you stood on Pluto, Charon would remain stationary in your sky, always showing the same face (but going through phases like the phases of our Moon). Similarly, if you stood on Charon, Pluto would remain stationary in your sky, always showing the same face (and going through phases). Tidal bulges are exaggerated in this figure.

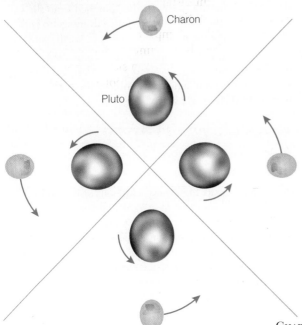

Charon

Pluto

no further source for tidal friction. The Moon has stayed in synchronous rotation ever since, with its two tidal bulges permanently fixed along the Earth–Moon line. (Interestingly, the Moon's tidal bulges cannot be seen outwardly because the Moon's diameter is not greater on this line; however, as we would expect, the Moon does have mass concentrations along the line of the tidal bulges.)

Tidal friction has led to synchronous rotation in many other cases. Most of the moons of the jovian planets rotate synchronously; for example, Jupiter's four large moons (Io, Europa, Ganymede, and Callisto) keep nearly the same face toward Jupiter at all times. Pluto and Charon *both* rotate synchronously: Like two dancers, they always keep the same face toward each other (Figure 5.22). If the Earth and the Moon were to stay together, tidal friction would eventually (in a few hundred billion years) create a similar situation: The Earth would always show the same face to the Moon.

Some moons and planets exhibit variations on synchronous rotation. For example, Mercury rotates exactly three times for every two orbits of the Sun (Figure 5.23). This pattern ensures that Mercury's tidal bulge always aligns with the Sun at perihelion, where the Sun exerts its strongest tidal force. As you study astronomy, you will encounter many more cases where tides and tidal friction play important roles.

## 5.6 Orbital Energy and Escape Velocity

Consider a satellite in an elliptical orbit around the Earth. Its gravitational potential energy is greatest when it is farthest from the Earth, and smallest

**FIGURE 5.23** These "snapshots" of Mercury, in which Mercury's exaggerated shape represents its tidal bulges, show that it rotates exactly one and a half times per orbit, or three times for every two orbits. The rotation pattern ensures that the tidal bulges are always aligned with the Sun at perihelion, when the tidal forces are strongest. The orbital eccentricity is also exaggerated.

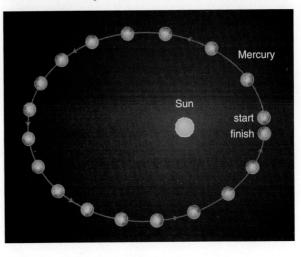

Mercury

Sun

start
finish

when it is nearest the Earth. Conversely, its kinetic energy is greatest when it is nearest the Earth and moving fastest in its orbit, and smallest when it is farthest from the Earth and moving slowest in its orbit. Throughout its orbit, its total *orbital energy*—the sum of its kinetic and gravitational potential energies—must be conserved.

Because any change in its orbit would mean a change in its total orbital energy, a satellite's orbit around the Earth cannot change if it is left completely undisturbed. If the satellite's orbit *does* change, it must somehow have gained or lost energy. For a satellite in low-Earth orbit, the Earth's thin upper atmosphere exerts a bit of drag that can cause the satellite to lose energy and eventually plummet back to Earth. The satellite's lost orbital energy is converted to thermal energy in the atmosphere, which is why a falling satellite usually burns up. Raising a satellite to a higher orbit requires that it gain energy by firing one of its rockets. The chemical potential energy of the rocket fuel is converted to gravitational potential energy as the satellite moves to a higher orbit.

Generalizing from the satellite example shows that conservation of energy has a very important implication for motion throughout the cosmos: *Orbits cannot change spontaneously.* For example, an asteroid or a comet passing near a planet cannot spontaneously be "sucked in" to crash on the planet. It can hit the planet only if its current orbit already intersects the planet's surface or if it somehow gains or loses orbital energy so that its new orbit intersects

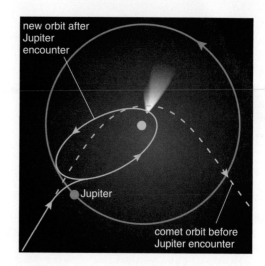

**FIGURE 5.24** Depiction of a comet in an unbound orbit of the Sun that happens to pass near Jupiter. The comet loses orbital energy to Jupiter, thereby changing to a bound orbit around the sun.

the planet's surface. Of course, if the asteroid or comet *gains* energy, something else must *lose* exactly the same amount of energy, and vice versa.

One way two objects can exchange orbital energy is through a **gravitational encounter**, in which they pass near enough so that each can feel the effects of the other's gravity. For example, Figure 5.24 shows a gravitational encounter between Jupiter and a comet headed toward the Sun on an unbound orbit. The comet's close passage by Jupiter allows the

## Mathematical Insight 5.3    Calculating the Escape Velocity

A simple formula allows us to calculate the escape velocity from any planet, moon, or star:

$$v_{escape} = \sqrt{\frac{2 \times G \times M}{R}}$$

where $M$ is the object's mass, $R$ is the starting distance above the object's center, and $G$ is the gravitational constant. If you use this formula to calculate the escape velocity from an object's surface, replace $R$ with the object's radius.

*Example 1:* Calculate the escape velocity from the Moon. Compare it to that from the Earth.

*Solution:* The mass and radius of the Moon are, respectively, $M = 7.4 \times 10^{22}$ kg and $R = 1.7 \times 10^6$ m. Plugging these numbers into the escape-velocity formula, we find:

$$v_{escape} = \sqrt{\frac{2 \times \left(6.67 \times 10^{-11} \frac{m^3}{kg \times s^2}\right) \times \left(7.4 \times 10^{22} \text{ kg}\right)}{1.7 \times 10^6 \text{ m}}}$$

$$\approx 2,400 \text{ m/s} = 2.4 \text{ km/s}$$

The escape velocity from the Moon is 2.4 km/s, or less than one-fourth the 11-km/s escape velocity from the Earth.

*Example 2:* Suppose a future space station orbits the Earth in geosynchronous orbit, which is 42,000 km above the center of the Earth (see Mathematical Insight 5.2). At what velocity must a spacecraft be launched from the station to escape the Earth? Is there any advantage to launching from the space station instead of from Earth's surface?

*Solution:* We use the escape-velocity formula with the mass of the Earth ($M_{Earth} = 6.0 \times 10^{24}$ kg) and the distance of the orbit above the center of the Earth ($R = 42,000$ km $= 4.2 \times 10^7$ m):

$$v_{escape} = \sqrt{\frac{2 \times \left(6.67 \times 10^{-11} \frac{m^3}{kg \times s^2}\right) \times \left(6.0 \times 10^{24} \text{ kg}\right)}{4.2 \times 10^7 \text{ m}}}$$

$$= 4,400 \text{ m/s} = 4.4 \text{ km/s}$$

The escape velocity from geosynchronous orbit is 4.4 km/s—considerably lower than the 11-km/s escape velocity from the Earth's surface. Thus, it requires substantially less fuel to launch the spacecraft from the space station than from the Earth. (In addition, the spacecraft would already have the orbital velocity of the space station.) Of course, this assumes that the space station is already in place and that the spacecraft is assembled at the space station.

comet and Jupiter to exchange energy: The comet loses orbital energy and changes to a bound, elliptical orbit; Jupiter must gain the energy the comet loses. However, because Jupiter is so much more massive than the comet, the effect on Jupiter is unnoticeable.

More generally, when two objects exchange orbital energy, we expect one to lose energy and fall to a lower orbit while the other gains energy and is thrown to a higher orbit. If an object gains enough energy, it may end up on an unbound orbit that allows it to *escape* from the gravitational influence of the object it is orbiting. For example, if we want to send a space probe to Mars, we must use a large rocket that gives the probe enough energy to achieve an unbound orbit (relative to Earth) and ultimately escape the Earth's gravitational influence. Although it would probably make more sense to say that the probe achieves "escape energy," we instead say that it achieves *escape velocity* (see Figure 5.3). For example, the escape velocity from the Earth's surface is about 40,000 km/hr, or 11 km/s, meaning that this is the *minimum* velocity required to escape the Earth's

gravity if you start near the surface. The escape velocity does not depend on the mass of the escaping object; *any* object must travel at a velocity of 11 km/s to escape from the Earth, whether it is an individual atom or molecule escaping from the atmosphere, a spacecraft being launched into deep space, or a rock blasted into the sky by a large impact. But escape velocity does depend on whether you start from the surface or from someplace high above the surface. Because gravity weakens with distance, it takes less energy—and hence a lower escape velocity—to escape from a point high above the Earth than from the Earth's surface.

## 5.7 The Acceleration of Gravity

Throughout the remainder of the text, we will see many more applications of the universal law of gravitation. For the moment, let's look at just one more: Galileo's discovery that the acceleration of a falling object is independent of its mass.

---

### Mathematical Insight 5.4    The Acceleration of Gravity

The text on page 148 shows that the acceleration of a falling rock near the surface of the Earth is:

$$a_{rock} = G \times \frac{M_{Earth}}{(R_{Earth})^2}$$

Because this formula applies to *any* falling object, it is the *acceleration of gravity, g*. Calculating $g$ is easy. Simply look up the Earth's mass ($6.0 \times 10^{24}$ kg) and radius ($6.4 \times 10^6$ m), and then "plug in":

$$g = G \times \frac{M_{Earth}}{(R_{Earth})^2}$$

$$= \left( 6.67 \times 10^{-11} \frac{m^3}{kg \times s^2} \right) \times \frac{6.0 \times 10^{24} \text{ kg}}{(6.4 \times 10^6 \text{ m})^2}$$

$$= 9.8 \frac{m}{s^2}$$

We can find the acceleration of gravity on the surface of any other world by using the same formula, using the other world's mass and radius instead of Earth's.

*Example 1:*  What is the acceleration of gravity on the surface of the Moon?

*Solution:*  We use the Moon's mass ($7.4 \times 10^{22}$ kg) and radius ($1.7 \times 10^6$ m) to find:

$$g_{Moon} = G \times \frac{M_{Moon}}{(R_{Moon})^2}$$

$$= \left( 6.67 \times 10^{-11} \frac{m^3}{kg \times s^2} \right) \times \frac{7.4 \times 10^{22} \text{ kg}}{(1.7 \times 10^6 \text{ m})^2}$$

$$= 1.7 \frac{m}{s^2}$$

The acceleration of gravity on the Moon is 1.7 m/s², or about one-sixth that on the Earth. Thus, objects on the

Moon weigh about one-sixth of what they would weigh on Earth. If you can lift a 50-kilogram barbell on Earth, you'll be able to lift a 300-kilogram barbell on the Moon.

*Example 2:*  The Space Station orbits at an altitude roughly 300 kilometers above the Earth's surface. What is the acceleration of gravity at this altitude?

*Solution:*  Because the Space Station is significantly above the Earth's surface, we cannot use the approximation $d \approx R_{Earth}$ that we used in the text. Instead, we must go back to Newton's second law, set the gravitational force on the Space Station equal to its mass times acceleration, and then solve for its acceleration:

$$G \times \frac{M_{Earth} M_{station}}{d^2} = M_{station} \times a_{station}$$

$$\Rightarrow a_{station} = G \times \frac{M_{Earth}}{d^2}$$

In this case, the distance $d$ is the 6,400-km radius of the Earth *plus* the 300-km altitude of the station, or $d = 6,700$ km $= 6.7 \times 10^6$ m. Thus, the gravitational acceleration of the Space Station when orbiting the Earth is:

$$a_{station} = G \times \frac{M_{Earth}}{d^2}$$

$$= \left( 6.67 \times 10^{-11} \frac{m^3}{kg \times s^2} \right) \times \frac{6.0 \times 10^{24} \text{ kg}}{(6.7 \times 10^6 \text{ m})^2}$$

$$= 8.9 \frac{m}{s^2}$$

The acceleration of gravity in low-Earth orbit is 8.9 m/s², or only slightly less than the 9.8 m/s² acceleration of gravity at the Earth's surface.

If you drop a rock, the force acting on the rock is the force of gravity. The two masses involved are the mass of the Earth and the mass of the rock, denoted $M_{Earth}$ and $M_{rock}$, respectively. The distance between their *centers* is the distance from the *center of the Earth* to the center of the rock. If the rock isn't too far above the Earth's surface, this distance is approximately the radius of the Earth, $R_{Earth}$ (about 6,400 km); that is, $d \approx R_{Earth}$. Thus, the force of gravity acting on the rock is

$$F_g = G \frac{M_{Earth} M_{rock}}{d^2} \approx G \frac{M_{Earth} M_{rock}}{(R_{Earth})^2}$$

According to Newton's second law of motion, this force is equal to the product of the mass and the acceleration of the rock; that is,

$$G \frac{M_{Earth} \cancel{M_{rock}}}{(R_{Earth})^2} = \cancel{M_{rock}} a_{rock}$$

Note that $M_{rock}$ "cancels" because it appears on both sides of the equation (as a multiplier), giving Galileo's result that the acceleration of the rock—or of any falling object—does not depend on the object's mass.

The fact that objects of different mass fall with the same acceleration struck Newton as an astounding coincidence, even though his own equations showed it to be so. For the next 240 years, this seemingly odd coincidence remained just that—a coincidence—in the minds of scientists. However, in 1915 Einstein discovered that it is not a coincidence at all. Rather, it reveals something deeper about the nature of gravity and of the universe; the new insights were described by Einstein in his *general theory of relativity* (the topic of Chapter S3).

## THE BIG PICTURE

We've covered a lot of ground in this chapter, from the scientific terminology of motion to the story of how universal motion was understood by Newton. Be sure you understand the following "big picture" ideas:

- Understanding the universe requires understanding motion. Although the terminology of the laws of motion may be new to you, the *concepts* are familiar from everyday experience. Think about these experiences so that you'll better understand the less familiar astronomical applications of the laws of motion.

- The Copernican revolution, which overthrew the ancient belief in an Earth-centered universe, did not occur instantaneously. It unfolded over a period of more than a century and involved careful observational, experimental, and theoretical work by many different people—especially Copernicus, Tycho Brahe, Kepler, and Galileo.

- Newton's discovery of the universal law of gravitation allowed him to explain *how* gravity holds planets in their orbits. Perhaps even more important, it showed that the same physical laws we observe on Earth apply throughout the universe. This universality of physics opens up the entire universe as a possible realm of human study.

## Review Questions

1. How does *speed* differ from *velocity*? Give an example in which you can be traveling at constant speed but not at constant velocity.

2. What do we mean by *acceleration*? Explain the units of acceleration.

3. What is the *acceleration of gravity* on Earth? If you drop a rock from very high, how fast will it be falling after 4 seconds (neglecting air resistance)?

4. What is *momentum*? How can momentum be affected by a *force*? What do we mean when we say that momentum will be changed only by a *net force*?

5. What is the difference between *mass* and *weight*?

6. What is *free-fall*, and why does it make you *weightless*? Briefly describe why astronauts are weightless in the Space Station.

7. Why does a spaceship require a high speed to achieve orbit? What would happen if it were launched with a speed greater than the Earth's *escape velocity*?

8. State each of Newton's three laws of motion. For each law, give an example of its application.

9. What is *angular momentum*? What kind of force can cause a change in angular momentum? Explain.

10. What is the *law of conservation of angular momentum*? How can a skater use this principle to vary his or her rate of spin?

11. Was Copernicus the first person to suggest a Sun-centered solar system? What advantages did his model have over the Ptolemaic model? In what ways did it fail to improve on the Ptolemaic model?

12. How were Tycho Brahe's observations important to the development of modern astronomy?

13. State Kepler's three laws of motion, and explain the meaning of each law.

14. Describe how Galileo helped spur acceptance of Kepler's Sun-centered model of the solar system.

15. What is the *universal law of gravitation*? Summarize what this law says in words, and then state the law mathematically. Define each variable in the formula.

16. Describe how Newton's laws of motion and law of universal gravitation explain why each of Kepler's three laws is true.

17. What do we mean by *bound* and *unbound* orbits?

18. Why is Newton's version of Kepler's third law so important to our understanding of the universe?

19. Explain how the Moon creates tides on the Earth. How do tides vary with the phase of the Moon? Why?

20. What is *tidal friction*? Briefly describe how tidal friction has affected the Earth and the Moon.

21. What is *synchronous rotation*, and what causes it? Describe the synchronous rotation of Pluto and Charon. Describe the variation on synchronous rotation that applies to Mercury.

22. Explain why orbits cannot change spontaneously. How can atmospheric drag cause an orbit to change? How can a *gravitational encounter* cause an orbit to change?

## Discussion Questions

1. *Kepler's Choice.* Casting aside the idea that orbits must be perfect circles meant going against deeply entrenched beliefs, and Kepler said that it shook his deep religious faith. Given that only two of Tycho's observations disagreed with a perfectly circular orbit—and only by 8 arcminutes—do you think that most other people would have made the choice Kepler made to abandon perfect circles? Have you ever performed an experiment that disagreed with theory? Which did you question, the theory or your experiment? Why?

2. *Aristotle and Modern English.* Aristotle believed that the Earth was made from the four elements fire, water, earth, and air, while the heavens were made from *ether* (literally, "upper air"). The literal meaning of *quintessence* is "fifth element," and the literal meaning of *ethereal* is "made of ether." Look up these words in the dictionary. Discuss how their modern meanings are related to Aristotle's ancient beliefs.

3. *Tidal Complications.* The ocean tides on Earth are much more complicated than they might at first seem from the simple physics that underlies tides. Discuss some of the factors that make the real tides so complicated and how these factors affect the tides. Some factors to consider: the distribution of land and oceans; the Moon's varying distance from Earth in its orbit; the fact that the Moon's orbital plane is not perfectly aligned with the ecliptic and neither the Moon's orbit nor the ecliptic is aligned with the Earth's equator.

## Problems

*Sensible Statements?* For **problems 1–4**, decide whether the statement is sensible and explain why it is or is not.

1. If you could go shopping on the Moon to buy a pound of chocolate, you'd get a lot more chocolate than if you bought a pound on Earth.

2. Upon its publication in 1543, the Copernican model was immediately accepted by most scientists because its predictions of planetary positions were essentially perfect.

3. Newton's version of Kepler's third law allows us to calculate the mass of Saturn from orbital characteristics of its moon Titan.

4. If an asteroid passed by Earth at just the right distance, it would be captured by the Earth's gravity and become our second moon.

5. *Understanding Acceleration.*

   a. Some schools have an annual ritual that involves dropping a watermelon from a tall building. Suppose it takes 6 seconds for the watermelon to fall to the ground (which would mean it's dropped from about a 60-story building). If there were no air resistance so that the watermelon would fall with the acceleration of gravity, how fast would it be going when it hit the ground? Give your answer in m/s, km/hr, and mi/hr.

   b. As you sled down a steep, slick street, you accelerate at a rate of 4 m/s². How fast will you be going after 5 seconds? Give your answer in m/s, km/hr, and mi/hr.

   c. You are driving along the highway at a speed of 70 miles per hour when you slam on the brakes. If your acceleration is at an average rate of −20 miles per hour per second, how long will it take to come to a stop?

6. *Spinning Skater.* Suppose an ice skater wants to *start* spinning. Explain why she won't start spinning if she simply stomps her foot straight down on the ice. How should she push off on the ice to start spinning? Why? What should she do when she wants to stop spinning?

7. *New Comet.* Imagine that a new comet is discovered and studies of its motion indicate that it orbits the Sun with a period of 1,000 years. What is the comet's average distance (semimajor axis) from the Sun? (*Hint:* Use Kepler's third law in its original form.)

8. *The Gravitational Law.* Use the universal law of gravitation to answer each of the following questions.

   a. How does tripling the distance between two objects affect the gravitational force between them?

   b. Compare the gravitational force between the Earth and the Sun to that between Jupiter and the Sun. The mass of Jupiter is about 318 times the mass of the Earth.

   c. Suppose the Sun were magically replaced by a star with twice as much mass. What would happen to the gravitational force between the Earth and the Sun?

9. *Head-to-Foot Tides.* You and the Earth attract each other gravitationally, so you should also be subject to a tidal force resulting from the difference between the gravitational attraction felt by your feet and that felt by your head (at least when you are standing). Explain why you can't feel this tidal force.

10. *Eclipse Frequency in the Past.* Over billions of years, the Moon has gradually been moving farther from the Earth. Thus, the Moon used to be substantially nearer the Earth than it is today.

    a. How would the Moon's past angular size in our sky compare to its present angular size? Why?

    b. How would the length of a lunar month in the past compare to the length of a lunar month today? Why? (*Hint:* Think about Kepler's third law as it would apply to the Moon orbiting the Earth.)

    c. Based on your answers to parts (a) and (b), would eclipses (both solar and lunar) have been more or less common in the past? Why?

11. *Geostationary Orbit.* A satellite in geostationary orbit appears to remain stationary in the sky as seen from any particular location on Earth.

    a. Briefly explain why a geostationary satellite must orbit the Earth in 1 *sidereal* day, rather than 1 solar day.

    b. Communications satellites, such as those used for television broadcasts, are often placed in geostationary orbit. The transmissions from such satellites are received with satellite dishes, such as those that can be purchased for home use. In one or two paragraphs, explain why geostationary orbit is a convenient orbit for communications satellites.

12. *Elevator to Orbit.* Suppose that someday we build a giant elevator from the Earth's surface to geosynchronous orbit. The top of the elevator would then have the same orbital distance and period as any satellite in geosynchronous orbit.

    a. Suppose you were to drop an object out of the elevator at its top. Explain why the object would appear to float right next to the elevator rather than falling.

    b. Briefly explain why (not counting the huge costs for construction) the elevator would make it much cheaper and easier to put satellites in orbit or to launch spacecraft into deep space.

13. *Understanding Kepler's Third Law.* Use Newton's version of Kepler's third law to answer the following questions. (*Hint:* The calculations for this problem are so simple that you will not need a calculator.)

    a. Imagine another solar system, with a star of the same mass as the Sun. Suppose there is a planet in that solar system with a mass twice that of Earth orbiting at a distance of 1 AU from the star. What is the orbital period of this planet? Explain.

    b. Suppose a solar system has a star that is four times as massive as our Sun. If that solar system has a planet the same size as Earth orbiting at a distance of 1 AU, what is the orbital period of the planet? Explain.

*14. *Gees.* Acceleration is sometimes measured in *gees*, or multiples of the acceleration of gravity: 1 gee (1g) means 1 × g, or 9.8 m/s²; 2 gees (2g) means 2 × g, or 2 × 9.8 m/s² = 19.6 m/s²; and so on. Suppose you experience 6 gees of acceleration in a rocket.

a. What is your acceleration in meters per second squared?

b. You will feel a compression force from the acceleration. How does this force compare to your normal weight?

c. Do you think you could survive this acceleration for long? Explain.

*15. *Measuring Masses.* Use Newton's version of Kepler's third law to answer each of the following questions.

a. The Moon orbits the Earth in an average of 27.3 days at an average distance of 384,000 kilometers. Use these facts to determine the mass of the Earth. You may neglect the mass of the Moon and assume $M_{Earth} + M_{Moon} \approx M_{Earth}$. (The Moon's mass is about $\frac{1}{80}$ of Earth's.)

b. Jupiter's moon Io orbits Jupiter every 42.5 hours at an average distance of 422,000 kilometers from the center of Jupiter. Calculate the mass of Jupiter. (Io's mass is very small compared to Jupiter's.)

c. Calculate the orbital period of the Space Shuttle in an orbit 300 kilometers above the Earth's surface.

d. Pluto's moon Charon orbits Pluto every 6.4 days with a semimajor axis of 19,700 kilometers. Calculate the *combined* mass of Pluto and Charon. Compare this combined mass to the mass of the Earth.

*16. *Weights on Other Worlds.* Calculate the acceleration of gravity on the surface of each of the following worlds. How much would *you* weigh, in pounds, on each of these worlds?

a. Mars (mass = $0.11M_{Earth}$, radius = $0.53R_{Earth}$).

b. Venus (mass = $0.82M_{Earth}$, radius = $0.95R_{Earth}$).

c. Jupiter (mass = $317.8M_{Earth}$, radius = $11.2R_{Earth}$). Bonus: Given that Jupiter has no solid surface, how could you weigh yourself on Jupiter?

d. Jupiter's moon Europa (mass = $0.008M_{Earth}$, radius = $0.25R_{Earth}$).

e. Mars's moon Phobos (mass = $1.1 \times 10^{16}$ kg, radius = 12 km).

*17. Calculate the escape velocity from each of the following. (Masses and radii are listed in problem 16.)

a. The surface of Mars.

b. The surface of Phobos.

c. The cloud tops of Jupiter.

d. Our solar system, starting from the Earth's orbit. (*Hint:* Most of the mass of our solar system is in the Sun; $M_{Sun} = 2.0 \times 10^{30}$ kg.)

e. Our solar system, starting from Saturn's orbit.

## Web Projects

Find useful links for Web projects on the text Web site.

1. *Players in the Copernican Revolution.* A number of interesting personalities played important roles in the Copernican revolution besides Copernicus, Tycho, Kepler, and Galileo. Research one or more of these people and write a short biography of their scientific lives and their contributions to the Copernican revolution. Among the people you might consider: Nicholas of Cusa (1401–1464), who argued for a Sun-centered solar system and believed that other stars might be circled by their own planets; Leonardo da Vinci (1452–1519), who made many contributions to science, engineering, and art and also believed the Earth *not* to be the center of the universe; Rheticus (1514–1574), a student of Copernicus who persuaded him to publish his work; William Gilbert (1540–1603), who studied the Earth's magnetism and influenced the thinking of Kepler; Giordano Bruno (1548–1600), who was burned at the stake for his beliefs in the Copernican system and the atomism of Democritus; and Francis Bacon (1561–1626), whose writings contributed to the acceptance of experimental methods in science.

2. *Tide Tables.* Find a tide table or tide chart for a beach town that you'd like to visit. Briefly explain how to read the table or chart, and discuss any differences between the actual tidal pattern and the idealized tidal pattern described in this chapter.

3. *Space Elevator.* Read more about space elevators (see problem 12) and how they might make it easier and cheaper to get to Earth orbit or beyond. Write a short report about the feasibility of building a space elevator, and briefly discuss the pros and cons of such a project.

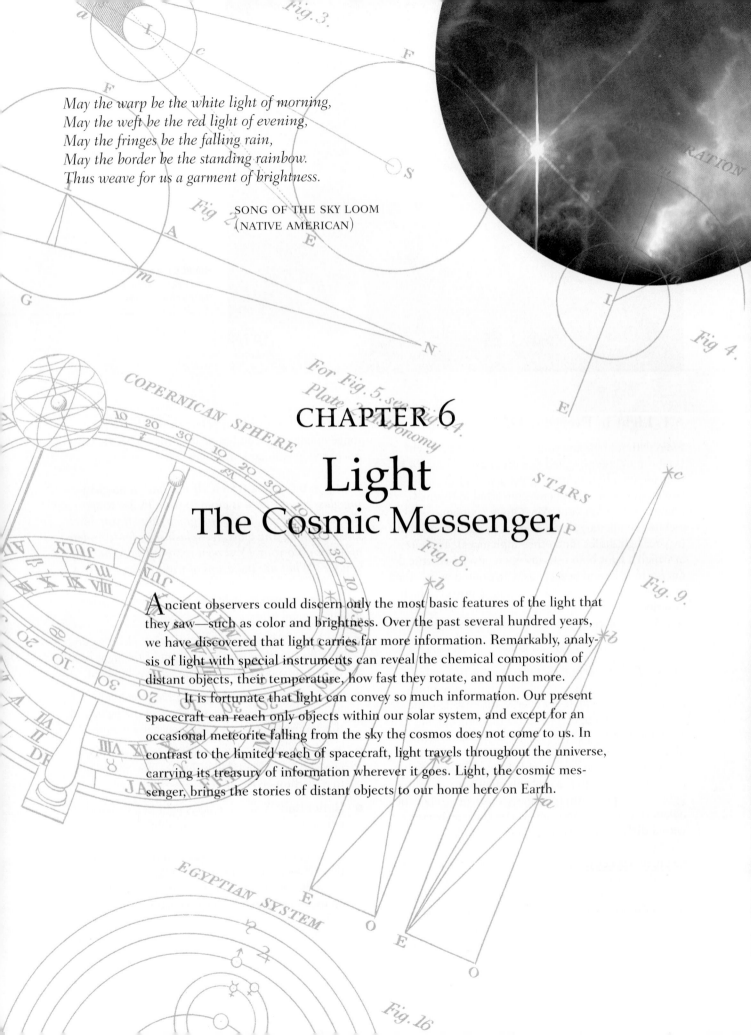

*May the warp be the white light of morning,*
*May the weft be the red light of evening,*
*May the fringes be the falling rain,*
*May the border be the standing rainbow.*
*Thus weave for us a garment of brightness.*

SONG OF THE SKY LOOM
(NATIVE AMERICAN)

# CHAPTER 6

# Light
# The Cosmic Messenger

Ancient observers could discern only the most basic features of the light that they saw—such as color and brightness. Over the past several hundred years, we have discovered that light carries far more information. Remarkably, analysis of light with special instruments can reveal the chemical composition of distant objects, their temperature, how fast they rotate, and much more.

It is fortunate that light can convey so much information. Our present spacecraft can reach only objects within our solar system, and except for an occasional meteorite falling from the sky the cosmos does not come to us. In contrast to the limited reach of spacecraft, light travels throughout the universe, carrying its treasury of information wherever it goes. Light, the cosmic messenger, brings the stories of distant objects to our home here on Earth.

**FIGURE 6.1** A prism reveals that white light contains a spectrum of colors from red to violet.

## 6.1 Light in Everyday Life

Even without opening your eyes, it's clear that light is a form of energy, called *radiative energy* [Section 4.1]. Outside on a hot, sunny day, you can feel the radiative energy of sunlight being converted to thermal energy as it strikes your skin. On an economic level, electric companies charge you for the energy needed by your light bulbs (and other appliances). The rate at which a light bulb uses energy (converts electrical energy to light and heat) is usually printed on it—for example "100 watts." A watt is a unit of **power**, which describes the *rate* of energy use; 1 watt of power means that 1 joule of energy is being used each second:

$$1 \text{ watt} = 1 \text{ joule/s}$$

Thus, for every second that you leave a 100-watt light bulb turned on, you will have to pay the utility company for 100 joules of energy. Interestingly, the power requirement of an average human—about 10 million joules per day—is about the same as that of a 100-watt light bulb.

Another basic property of light is what our eyes perceive as *color*. You've probably seen a prism split light into a **spectrum** (plural, spectra), or rainbow of colors (Figure 6.1). You can also produce a spectrum with a **diffraction grating**—a piece of plastic or glass etched with many closely spaced lines. The colors in a spectrum are pure forms of the basic colors red, orange, yellow, green, blue, and violet. The wide variety of all possible colors comes from mixtures of these basic colors in varying proportions; *white* is simply what we see when the basic colors are mixed in roughly equal proportions. Your television takes advantage of this fact to simulate a huge range of colors by combining only three specific colors of red, green, and blue light.

**TIME OUT TO THINK** *If you have a magnifying glass handy, hold it close to your TV set to see the individual red, blue, and green dots. If you don't have a magnifying glass, try splashing a few droplets of water onto your TV screen (carefully!). What do you see? What are the drops of water doing?*

Energy carried by light can interact with matter in four general ways:

- **Emission**: When you turn on a lamp, electric current flowing through the filament of the light bulb heats it to a point at which it *emits* visible light.

- **Absorption**: If you place your hand near a lit light bulb, your hand *absorbs* some of the light, and this absorbed energy makes your hand warmer.

- **Transmission**: Some forms of matter, such as glass or air, *transmit* light; that is, they allow light to pass through them.

- **Reflection**: A mirror *reflects* light in a very specific way, similar to the way a rubber ball bounces off a hard surface, so that the direction of a reflected beam of light depends on the direction of the incident (incoming) beam of light (Figure 6.2a). Sometimes, reflection is more random, so that an incident beam of light is **scattered** in many different directions. The screen in a movie theater, for example, scatters a narrow beam of light from the projector into an array of beams that reach every member of the audience (Figure 6.2b).

Materials that transmit light are said to be **transparent**, and materials that absorb light are called **opaque**. Many materials are neither perfectly transparent nor perfectly opaque, and the technical term that describes *how much* light they transmit and absorb is **opacity**. For example, dark sunglasses have a higher opacity than clear glasses because they absorb more light.

Particular materials can affect different colors of light differently. For example, red glass transmits red light but absorbs other colors. A green lawn reflects green light but absorbs all other colors.

Now let's put all these ideas together and think about what happens when you walk into a dark room and turn on the light switch. The light bulb begins to emit white light, which is a mix of all the colors in the spectrum. Some of this light exits the room, transmitted through the windows. The rest of the light strikes the surfaces of objects inside the room, and each object's material properties determine the colors absorbed or reflected. The light coming from each object therefore carries an enormous amount of information about the object's location, shape and structure, and material makeup. You acquire this information when light enters your eyes, where it is absorbed by special cells (called *cones* and *rods*) that use the energy of the absorbed light to send signals to your brain. Your brain interprets the messages carried by the light, recognizing materials and objects in the process we call *vision*.

In fact, light carries even more information than your ordinary vision can recognize. Just as a microscope can reveal structure that is invisible to the naked eye, modern instruments can reveal otherwise invisible details in the spectrum of light. Learning to interpret these details is the key to unlocking the vast amount of information carried by light.

## 6.2 Properties of Light

Despite our familiarity with light, its nature remained a mystery for most of human history. The first real insights into the nature of light came with experiments performed by Isaac Newton in the 1660s. It was already well known that light passed through a prism separates into the rainbow of colors, but the most common belief held that the colors were a property of the prism rather than of the light itself. Newton dispelled this belief by placing a second prism in front of the light of just one color, such as red, from the first prism. He found that the color did not change any further, thereby proving that the colors were not a property of the prism but must be part of the white light itself.

Newton guessed that light, with all its colors, is made up of countless tiny particles. However, later experiments by other scientists demonstrated that light behaves like waves. Thus began one of the most important debates in scientific history: Is light a wave or a particle? We must address this question if we hope to understand the messages conveyed by light; first let's consider the difference between a wave and a particle.

### Particles and Waves

Marbles, baseballs, and individual atoms are all examples of *particles*. A particle of matter can sit still or it can move from one place to another. If you throw

angle of incidence = angle of reflection

30°       30°

a

screen

projection booth

b

**FIGURE 6.2** (**a**) A mirror reflects light along a path determined by the angle at which the light strikes the mirror. (**b**) A movie screen scatters light into an array of beams that reach every member of the audience.

a baseball at a wall, it moves from your hand to the wall. In contrast, imagine tossing a pebble into a pond (Figure 6.3). The ripples moving out from the place where the pebble lands are *waves*, consisting of *peaks* where the water is higher than average and *troughs* where the water is lower than average. If you watch as the waves pass by a floating leaf, you'll see the leaf rise up with the peak and drop down with the trough, but the leaf itself does *not* move across the pond's surface with the wave; this tells us that the water is moving up and down, but not outward. That is, the wave carries *energy* outward from the place where the pebble landed but does not carry matter along with it. In a sense, a particle is a *thing*, while a wave is a *pattern* revealed by its interaction with particles.

peak
trough

Leaf bobs up and down with *frequency* of wave.

pebble thrown into pond

wavelength

speed of wave moving outward

**FIGURE 6.3** Tossing a pebble into a pond generates waves traveling outward.

**TIME OUT TO THINK** *Hold a piece of rope with one end in each hand. Make waves moving along the rope by shaking one end up and down. Watch the motion of the peaks and troughs. As a peak moves along the rope, does any material move with it? Explain.*

Three basic properties characterize the waves moving outward through the pond. Their **wavelength** is the distance between adjacent peaks. Their **frequency** is the number of peaks passing by any point each second. If a passing wave causes the leaf to bob up and down twice per second, then its frequency is 2 **cycles per second** (referring to the up and down "cycles" of the passing waves). Cycles per second often are called **hertz** (**Hz**), so we can also describe this frequency as 2 Hz. The third basic characteristic of the waves is the **speed** at which any peak travels across the pond. (A fourth characteristic of a wave is its amplitude, or height from trough to peak, but this will not be important to our study of light in this book.)

The wavelength, frequency, and speed of a wave are related by a simple formula, which we can understand with the help of an example. Suppose a wave has a wavelength of 1 centimeter and a frequency of 2 hertz. The wavelength tells us that each time a peak passes by, the wave peak has traveled 1 centimeter. The frequency tells us that two peaks pass by each second. Thus, the speed of the wave must be 2 centimeters per second. If you try a few more similar examples, you'll find that the general rule is

$$\text{wavelength} \times \text{frequency} = \text{speed}$$

## Photons and Electromagnetic Waves

In our everyday lives, waves and particles appear to be very different. After all, no one would confuse the ripples on a pond with a baseball. However, light behaves as *both* a particle and a wave. Like particles, light comes in individual "pieces," called **photons**, that can hit a wall one at a time. Like ripples on a pond, light can make (charged) particles bob up and down. We will discuss the implications of this "wave–particle duality" in Chapter S4. Here we need only discuss how we measure the wave and particle properties of light.

First, let's ignore the particle properties of light and look at its wave nature. Although waves don't carry material along with them, something must vibrate to transmit energy along a wave. For example, water waves are the up-and-down vibrations of the water surface, and sound waves are back-and-forth vibrations of the air as it responds to changing pressure. In the case of light, it is electric and magnetic *fields* that vibrate.

The concept of a **field** is a bit abstract. Fields associated with forces, such as electric and magnetic fields, describe how these forces affect a particle placed at any point in space. For example, we say that the Earth has a *gravitational field* because if you place an object above the Earth's surface, the force of gravity pulls the object to the ground. That is, any object placed in a gravitational field feels the force of gravity. In a similar way, a charged particle (such as an electron) placed in an *electric field* or a *magnetic field* feels electric or magnetic forces.

Light is an **electromagnetic wave**—a wave in which electric and magnetic fields vibrate. Like a leaf on a rippling pond, an electron will bob up and down when an electromagnetic wave passes by. If you could set up a row of electrons, they would wriggle like a snake (Figure 6.4a). The wavelength is the distance between adjacent peaks of the electric or magnetic field, and the frequency is the number of peaks that pass by any point each second (Figure 6.4b). All light travels at the same speed (in a vacuum)—about 300,000 kilometers per second, or $3 \times 10^8$ m/s—regardless of its wavelength or frequency. Therefore, light with a shorter wavelength must have a higher frequency, and vice versa.

Measuring the particle properties of light requires thinking of each photon as a distinct entity. Just as a baseball carries a specific amount of kinetic energy, each photon of light carries a specific amount of radiative energy. The shorter the wavelength of the light (or, equivalently, the higher its frequency), the higher the energy of the photons. For example, a photon with a wavelength of 100 nanometers (nm) has more energy than a photon with a 120-nm wave-

a

Wavelength is the distance between adjacent peaks of the electric field.

Frequency is the number of waves (cycles) passing any point each second.

wavelength

All light travels with speed c = 300,000 km/s.

b

**FIGURE 6.4** **(a)** A row of electrons would wriggle up and down as light passes by, showing that light carries a vibrating electric field. It also carries a magnetic field (not shown) that vibrates perpendicular to the direction of the electric field vibrations. **(b)** Characteristics of light waves. Because all light travels at the same speed, light of longer wavelength must have lower frequency.

## Mathematical Insight 6.1 Wavelength, Frequency, and Energy

As described in the text, the speed of any wave is the product of its wavelength and its frequency. Because all forms of light travel at the same speed (in a vacuum), $c = 3 \times 10^8$ m/s, we can write:

$$\lambda \times f = c$$

where $\lambda$ (the Greek letter *lambda*) stands for wavelength and $f$ stands for frequency. Solving this formula allows us to find the wavelength of light if we know the frequency, or vice versa:

$$\lambda = \frac{c}{f} \quad \text{or} \quad f = \frac{c}{\lambda}$$

The formula for the radiative energy carried by a photon of light is:

$$E = h \times f$$

where $h$ is a number called *Planck's constant* ($h = 6.626 \times 10^{-34}$ joule $\times$ s). Thus, energy increases in proportion to the frequency of the photon. Because $f = c/\lambda$, we can also write this formula as:

$$E = \frac{hc}{\lambda}$$

showing that the energy decreases in proportion to the wavelength of the photon.

*Example 1:* The numbers on a radio dial for FM radio stations are their frequencies in megahertz (MHz), or millions of hertz. If your favorite radio station is "93.3 on your dial," it broadcasts radio waves with a frequency of 93.3 million cycles per second. What is the wavelength of these radio waves?

*Solution:* We know the speed of light and the frequency, so the wavelength is:

$$\lambda = \frac{c}{f} = \frac{3 \times 10^8 \frac{m}{s}}{93.3 \times 10^6 \frac{1}{s}} = 3.2 \text{ m}$$

Note that, when we work with frequency in equations, the "cycles" do not show up as a unit; that is, the units of frequency are simply 1/s, or "per second."

*Example 2:* The average wavelength of visible light is about 550 nanometers (1 nm = $10^{-9}$ m). What is the frequency of this light?

*Solution:* This time we know the wavelength, so the frequency of the light is:

$$f = \frac{c}{\lambda} = \frac{3 \times 10^8 \frac{m}{s}}{550 \times 10^{-9} \text{ m}} = 5.45 \times 10^{14} \frac{1}{s}$$

The frequency of visible light is about $5.5 \times 10^{14}$ cycles per second, or about 550 trillion Hz.

*Example 3:* What is the energy of a visible light photon with wavelength 550 nm?

*Solution:* We know the wavelength, so the energy is:

$$E = \frac{hc}{\lambda}$$

$$= \frac{(6.626 \times 10^{-34} \text{ joule} \times s) \times (3 \times 10^8 \frac{m}{s})}{550 \times 10^{-9} \text{ m}}$$

$$= 3.6 \times 10^{-19} \text{ joule}$$

Note that this energy for a single photon is extremely small compared to, say, the energy of 100 joules used each second by a 100-watt light bulb.

length. (A nanometer (nm) is a billionth of a meter: $1\ \text{nm} = 10^{-9}$ m. Many astronomers work with a unit called the Angstrom (Å): $1\ \text{nm} = 10\text{Å}$.)

## 6.3 The Many Forms of Light

Because light consists of electromagnetic waves, light is often called *electromagnetic radiation* and the spectrum of light is called the **electromagnetic spectrum**. Photons of light can have *any* wavelength or frequency, so in principle the complete electromagnetic spectrum extends from a wavelength of zero to infinity. For convenience, we refer to different portions of the electromagnetic spectrum by different names (Figure 6.5).

The **visible light** that we see with our eyes has wavelengths ranging from about 400 nm at the blue end of the rainbow to about 700 nm at the red end. Light with wavelengths somewhat longer than red light is called **infrared**, because it lies beyond the red end of the rainbow. Light with very long wavelengths is called **radio** (or *radio waves*)—thus, radio is a form of light, *not* a form of sound.

At the other end of the spectrum, light with wavelengths somewhat shorter than blue light is called **ultraviolet**, because it lies beyond the blue (or violet) end of the rainbow. Light with even shorter wavelengths is called **X rays**, and the shortest-wavelength light is called **gamma rays**. Note that visible light is an extremely small part of the entire electromagnetic spectrum: The reddest red that our eyes can see has only about twice the wavelength of the bluest blue, but the radio waves from your favorite radio station are a billion times longer than the X rays used in a doctor's office.

Because wavelengths decrease as we move from the radio end toward the gamma-ray end of the spectrum, the frequencies and energies must increase. Visible photons happen to have enough energy to

activate the molecular receptors in our eyes. Ultraviolet photons, with a shorter wavelength than visible light, carry more energy—enough to harm our skin cells, causing sunburn or skin cancer. X-ray photons have enough energy to transmit easily through skin and muscle but not so easily through bones or teeth. That is why photographs taken with X-ray light allow doctors and dentists to see our underlying bone structures.

Interactions between light and matter depend on the types of light and matter involved. A brick wall is opaque to visible light but transmits radio waves, and glass that is transparent to visible light can be

**FIGURE 6.5** The electromagnetic spectrum. The unit of frequency, hertz, is equivalent to waves (or cycles) per second. For example, $10^3$ hertz means that $10^3 = 1,000$ wave peaks pass by a point each second.

opaque to ultraviolet light. In general, certain types of matter tend to interact more strongly with certain types of light, so each type of light carries different information about distant objects in the universe. Astronomers therefore seek to observe light of all wavelengths, using telescopes adapted to detecting each different form of light, from radio to gamma rays.

## 6.4 Light and Matter

Whenever matter and light interact, matter leaves its fingerprints. Examining the color of an object is a crude way of studying the clues left by the matter it contains. For example, a red shirt absorbs all visible photons except those in the red part of the spectrum, so we know that it must contain a dye with these special light-absorbing characteristics. If we take

light and disperse it into a spectrum, we can see the spectral fingerprints in more detail.

Figure 6.6 shows a schematic spectrum of light from a celestial body such as a planet. The spectrum is a graph that shows the amount of radiation, or **intensity**, at different wavelengths. At wavelengths where a lot of light is coming from the celestial body, the intensity is high; at wavelengths where there is little light, the intensity is low. Our goal is to see how the bumps and wiggles in this graph convey a wealth of information about the celestial body in question. Let's begin by going through a short list of ways that matter interacts with light and showing the spectra that result from these interactions.

**FIGURE 6.6** A schematic spectrum obtained from the light of a distant object. The "rainbow" at bottom shows how the light would appear when viewed through a prism or diffraction grating. The graph shows the corresponding intensity of the light at each wavelength. Note that the intensity is high where the rainbow is bright and low where it is dim (such as in places where the rainbow shows dark lines).

**FIGURE 6.7** (**a**) Photons emitted by various energy level transitions in hydrogen. (**b**) The visible emission line spectrum from heated hydrogen gas. These lines come from transitions in which electrons fall from higher energy levels to level 2. (**c**) If we pass white light through a cloud of cool hydrogen gas, we get this absorption line spectrum. These lines come from transitions in which electrons jump from energy level 2 to higher levels.

### Absorption and Emission by Thin Gases

You know that gases can absorb light; for example, ozone in the Earth's atmosphere absorbs ultraviolet light from space, preventing it from reaching the ground. Gases can also emit light, which is what makes neon lights and interstellar clouds glow so beautifully. But *how* do gases absorb or emit light?

Recall that the electrons in atoms can have only specific energies, somewhat like the specific heights of the rungs on a ladder [Section 4.4]. If an electron in an atom is bumped from a lower energy level to a higher one—by a collision with another atom, for example—it will eventually fall back to the lower level. The energy that the atom loses when the electron falls back down must go somewhere, and often it goes to *emitting* a photon of light. The emitted photon must have exactly the same amount of energy that the electron loses, which means that it has a specific wavelength (and frequency).

Figure 6.7a shows the allowed energy levels in hydrogen, along with the wavelengths of the photons emitted by various downward *transitions* of an electron from a higher energy level to a lower one. For

example, transitions from level 2 to level 1 emit an ultraviolet photon of wavelength 121.6 nm, and transitions from level 3 to level 2 emit a red visible light photon of wavelength 656.3 nm.[1] If you heat some hydrogen gas so that collisions are continually bumping electrons to higher energy levels, you'll get an **emission line spectrum** consisting of the photons emitted as each electron falls back to lower levels (Figure 6.7b).

**TIME OUT TO THINK** *If nothing continues to heat the hydrogen gas, all the electrons eventually will end up in the lowest energy level (the ground state, or level 1). Use this fact to explain why we should* not *expect to see an emission line spectrum from a very cold cloud of hydrogen gas.*

---

[1]Astronomers call transitions between level 1 and other levels the *Lyman* series of transitions. The transition between level 1 and level 2 is Lyman $\alpha$, between level 1 and level 3 Lyman $\beta$, and so on. Similarly, transitions between level 2 and higher levels are called *Balmer* transitions. Other sets of transitions also have names, but they are less commonly used.

helium

sodium

neon

**FIGURE 6.8** Emission line spectra for helium, sodium, and neon. The patterns and wavelengths of lines are different for each element, giving each a unique spectral fingerprint.

He  He  He  O⁺  He  Ne⁺⁺

hydrogen lines

**FIGURE 6.9** The emission line spectrum of the Orion Nebula. The lines are identified with the chemical elements or ions that produce them (He = helium; O = oxygen; Ne = neon).

Photons of light can also be absorbed, causing electrons to jump *up* in energy—but only if an incoming photon happens to have precisely the right amount of energy. For example, just as an electron moving downward from level 2 to level 1 in hydrogen emits a photon of wavelength 121.6 nm, absorbing a photon with this wavelength will cause an electron in level 1 to jump up to level 2.

Suppose a lamp emitting white light illuminates a cloud of hydrogen gas from behind. The cloud will absorb photons with the precise energies needed to bump electrons from a low energy level to a higher one, while all other photons pass right through the cloud. The result is an **absorption line spectrum** that looks like a rainbow with light missing at particular wavelengths (Figure 6.7c).

If you compare the bright emission lines in Figure 6.7b to the dark absorption lines in Figure 6.7c, you will see that the lines occur at the same wavelengths regardless of whether the hydrogen is absorbing or emitting light. Absorption lines simply correspond to upward jumps of the electrons between energy levels, while emission lines correspond to downward jumps.

The energy levels of electrons in each chemical element are unique [Section 4.4]. As a result, each element produces its own distinct set of spectral lines, giving it a unique "spectral fingerprint." For example, Figure 6.8 shows emission line spectra for helium, sodium, and neon. Note that the spectra of atoms such as neon are more complex than the spectra of hydrogen and helium because they have many electrons and therefore many allowed energy levels.

**TIME OUT TO THINK** *Three common examples of objects with emission line spectra are storefront neon signs, fluorescent light bulbs, and the yellow sodium lights used in many cities at night. When you look at objects of different colors under such lights, do you see their normal colors? Why or why not?*

The fact that each chemical element has a unique spectral fingerprint makes spectral analysis extremely useful: When you see the fingerprint of a particular element, you immediately know that the gas producing the spectrum contains this element. For example, Figure 6.9 shows the spectral fingerprints of hydrogen, helium, oxygen, and neon in an emission line spectrum from the Orion Nebula. Not only does each chemical element produce a unique spectral fingerprint, but *ions* of a particular element (atoms that are missing one or more electrons) produce fingerprints different from those of neutral atoms [Section 4.3]. For example, the spectrum of doubly ionized neon ($Ne^{++}$) is different from that of singly ionized neon ($Ne^+$), which in turn is different from that of neutral neon (Ne). This fact can help us determine the temperature of a hot gas or plasma. At higher temperatures, more highly charged ions will be present, so we can estimate the temperature by identifying the ions that are creating spectral lines.

Just as atoms and ions can absorb or emit light at particular wavelengths, so can *molecules*. Like electrons in atoms, the electrons in molecules can have only particular energies, and therefore molecules produce spectral lines when electrons change energy levels. However, because molecules are made of two

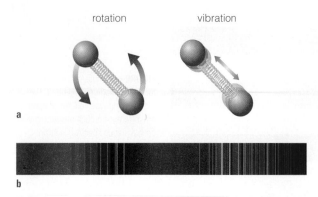

rotation          vibration

a

b

**FIGURE 6.10** (**a**) We can think of a two-atom molecule as two balls connected by a spring. Although this model is overly simplistic, it illustrates how molecules can rotate and vibrate. (**b**) This spectrum of molecular hydrogen ($H_2$) shows that molecular spectra consist of lines bunched into broad *molecular bands*.

or more atoms bound together, they can also have energy due to vibration or rotation (Figure 6.10a). It turns out that, just as its electrons can be in only specific energy levels, a molecule can rotate or vibrate only with particular amounts of energy. Thus, a molecule can absorb or emit a photon when it changes its rate of vibration or rotation. Because molecules can change energy in three different ways, their spectra look very different from the spectra of individual atoms. Molecules produce a spectrum with many sets of tightly bunched lines, called **molecular bands** (Figure 6.10b). The energy jumps in molecules are usually smaller than those in atoms—and therefore produce lower-energy photons—so most molecular bands lie in the infrared rather than in the visible or ultraviolet. That is one reason why infrared telescopes and instruments are so important to astronomers.

### Thermal Radiation: Every Body Does It

In a low-density gas, individual atoms or molecules are essentially independent of one another [Section 4.3]. That is why thin, low-density clouds of gas produce relatively simple emission or absorption spectra, with lines (or bands) in locations determined by the energy levels of their constituent atoms (or molecules). But what happens in an opaque object, such as a star, a planet, or you? (Although saying that a star is opaque may sound strange, it is true because we cannot see *through* a star.) Because photons of light cannot pass through an opaque object, they bounce randomly around among the atoms or molecules inside it, constantly exchanging energy. Recall that the "bouncing around" of atoms and molecules tends to randomize their kinetic energies, giving them an average kinetic energy that characterizes the object's *temperature*. In a similar way, the "bouncing around" of the photons inside an opaque object randomizes their radiative energies in a way that also depends only on the object's temperature. These photons can escape only when they happen to reach the surface of the object (where no more material is "in the way" to block their escape). Thus, the radiation coming from an opaque object depends only on its temperature and is called **thermal radiation** (sometimes called *blackbody* radiation).

No real object is "perfectly" opaque (absorbing and reemitting *all* radiation that strikes it), but many objects make close approximations. For example, almost all familiar objects—including the Sun, the planets, and even you—glow with light that approximates thermal radiation.

Two simple rules describe how a thermal radiation spectrum depends on the temperature of the emitting object:

## Mathematical Insight 6.2    Laws of Thermal Radiation

The two rules of thermal radiation have simple mathematical formulas. Rule 1, called the *Stefan–Boltzmann law* (named after its discoverers), is expressed as:

$$\text{emitted power per square meter} = \sigma T^4$$

where $\sigma$ (Greek letter *sigma*) is a constant ($\sigma = 5.7 \times 10^{-8}$ watt/($m^2 \times $ Kelvin$^4$).

Rule 2, called *Wien's law*, is expressed approximately as:

$$\lambda_{max} \approx \frac{2,900,000}{T \text{ (Kelvin)}} \text{ nm}$$

where $\lambda_{max}$ (*lambda-max*) is the wavelength (in nanometers) of maximum intensity, which is the peak of the hump in a thermal radiation spectrum.

*Example:* Consider a perfectly opaque object with a temperature of 15,000 K. How much power does it emit per square meter? What is its wavelength of peak intensity?

*Solution:* The emitted power per square meter from a 15,000-K object is:

$$\sigma T^4 = 5.7 \times 10^{-8} \frac{\text{watt}}{m^2 \times K^4} \times (15,000 \text{ K})^4$$

$$= 2.9 \times 10^9 \frac{\text{watt}}{m^2}$$

Its wavelength of maximum intensity is:

$$\lambda_{max} \approx \frac{2,900,000}{15,000 \text{ (Kelvin)}} \text{ nm} \approx 190 \text{ nm}$$

This wavelength is in the ultraviolet portion of the electromagnetic spectrum.

1. *Hotter objects emit more total radiation per unit surface area.* The radiated energy is proportional to the *fourth* power of the temperature expressed in Kelvin (*not* in Celsius or Fahrenheit). For example, a 600 K object has twice the temperature of a 300 K object and therefore radiates $2^4 = 16$ times as much total energy per unit surface area.

2. *Hotter objects emit photons with a higher average energy,* which means a shorter average wavelength.

You can see the first rule in action by playing with a light that has a dimmer switch: When you turn the switch up, the filament in the light bulb gets hotter and the light brightens; when you turn it down, the filament gets cooler and the light dims. (You can verify the changing temperature by placing your hand near the bulb.) You can see the second rule in action by observing a fireplace poker (Figure 6.11). When the poker is relatively cool, it emits only infrared radiation, which we cannot see. As it gets hot, it begins to glow red ("red hot"). If the poker continues to heat up, the average wavelength of the emitted photons gets shorter, moving toward the blue end of the visible spectrum. By the time it gets very hot, the mix of colors emitted by the poker looks white ("white hot").

Figure 6.12 shows how these two rules affect the idealized thermal radiation spectra. The spectra of hotter objects show bigger "humps" because they emit more total radiation per unit area (rule 1). Hotter objects also have the peaks of their humps at shorter wavelengths because of the higher average energy of their photons (rule 2). Note that hotter objects emit more light at *all* wavelengths but the biggest difference appears at the shortest wavelengths. An object with a temperature of 310 K, which is about human body temperature, emits mostly in the infrared and emits no visible light at all—that explains why we don't glow in the dark! A relatively cool star, with a 3,000-K surface temperature, emits mostly red light; that is why some bright stars in our sky appear reddish, such as Betelgeuse (in Orion) and Antares (in Scorpius). The Sun's 5,800-K surface emits most strongly in green light (around 500 nm), but the Sun looks yellow or white to our eyes because it also emits other colors throughout the visible spectrum. Hotter stars emit mostly in the ultraviolet, but because our eyes cannot see ultraviolet they appear blue-white in color. If an object were heated to a temperature of millions of degrees, it would radiate mostly X rays. Some astronomical objects are indeed hot enough to emit X rays, such as disks of gas encircling exotic objects like neutron stars and black holes (see Chapter 17).

### Summary of Spectral Formation

We can now summarize the circumstances under which objects produce thermal, absorption line, or emission line spectra. (These rules are often called *Kirchhoff's laws.*)

- Any opaque object produces thermal radiation over a broad range of wavelengths. If the object

**FIGURE 6.11** A fireplace poker gets brighter as it is heated, demonstrating rule 1 for thermal radiation (hotter objects emit more total radiation per unit surface area). In addition, its "color" moves from infrared to red to white as it is heated, demonstrating rule 2 (hotter objects emit photons with higher average energy).

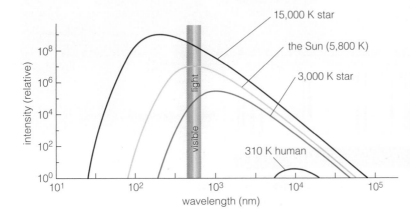

**FIGURE 6.12** Graphs of idealized thermal radiation spectra. Note that, per unit surface area, hotter objects emit more radiation at every wavelength, demonstrating rule 1 for thermal radiation. The peaks of the spectra occur at shorter wavelengths (higher energies) for hotter objects, demonstrating rule 2 for thermal radiation.

is hot enough to produce visible light, as is the case with the filament of a light bulb, we see a smooth, *continuous* rainbow when we disperse the light through a prism or a diffraction grating (Figure 6.13a). On a graph of intensity versus wavelength, the rainbow becomes the characteristic hump of a thermal radiation spectrum.

■ When thermal radiation passes through a thin cloud of gas, the cloud leaves fingerprints that may be either absorption lines or emission lines, depending on its temperature. If the background source of thermal radiation is hotter than the cloud, the balance between emission and absorption in the cloud's spectral lines tips toward absorption. We then see absorption lines cutting into the thermal spectrum. This is the case when the light from the hot light bulb passes through a cool gas cloud (Figure 6.13b). On the graph of intensity versus wavelength, these absorption lines create dips in the thermal radiation spectrum; the width and depth of each dip depend on

how much light is absorbed by the chemical responsible for the line.

■ If the background source is colder than the cloud or if there is no background source at all, the spectrum is dominated by bright emission lines produced by the cloud's atoms and molecules (Figure 6.13c). These lines create narrow peaks on a graph of intensity versus wavelength.

### *Reflected Light*

We've now covered enough material to understand spectra emitted by objects generating their own light, such as stars and clouds of interstellar gas. But most of our daily experience involves *reflected* (or *scattered*) light. The source of the light is thermal radiation from the Sun or a lamp. After this light strikes the ground, clouds, people, or other objects, we see only the wavelengths of light that are reflected. For example, a red sweatshirt absorbs blue light and reflects red light, so its visible spectrum looks like the ther-

**FIGURE 6.13** (**a**) An opaque object, such as a light bulb filament, produces a continuous spectrum of thermal radiation. (**b**) If thermal radiation passes through a thin gas that is cooler than the emitting object, dark absorption lines are superimposed on the continuous spectrum. (**c**) Viewed against a cold, dark background, the same gas produces an emission line spectrum.

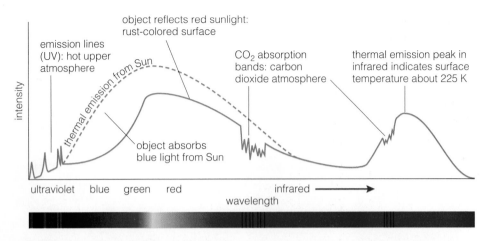

**FIGURE 6.14** The spectrum of Figure 6.6, with interpretation. We can conclude that the object looks red in color because it absorbs more blue light than red light from the Sun. The absorption lines tell us that the object has a carbon dioxide atmosphere, and the emission lines tell us that its upper atmosphere is hot. The hump in the infrared (near the right of the diagram) tells us that the object has a surface temperature of about 225 K. It is a spectrum of the planet Mars.

mal radiation spectrum of its light source—the Sun—but with blue light missing.

In the same way that we distinguish lemons from limes, we can use color information in reflected light to learn about celestial objects. Different fruits, different rocks, and even different atmospheric gases reflect and absorb light at different wavelengths. Although the absorption features that show up in spectra of reflected light are not as distinct as the emission and absorption lines for thin gases, they still provide useful information. For example, the surface materials of a planet determine how much light of different colors is reflected or absorbed. The reflected light gives the planet its color, while the absorbed light heats the surface and helps determine its temperature.

### *Putting It All Together*

Figure 6.14 again shows the complicated spectrum we began with in Figure 6.6, but this time with labels indicating the processes responsible for its various features. What can we say about this object from its spectrum? The hump of thermal emission shows that this object has a surface temperature of about 225 K, well below the freezing point of water. The absorption bands in the infrared come mainly from carbon dioxide, which tells us that the object has a carbon dioxide atmosphere. The emission lines in the ultraviolet come from hot gas in a high, thin layer of the object's atmosphere. The reflected light looks like the Sun's 5,800 K thermal radiation except that the blue light is missing, so the object must be reflecting sunlight and must look red in color. Perhaps by now you have guessed that this figure represents the spectrum of the planet Mars.

## 6.5 The Doppler Shift

The volume of information about temperature and composition that light contains is truly amazing, but we can learn even more once we identify the various lines in a spectrum. Among the most important pieces of information contained in light is information about motion. In particular, we can determine the radial motion (toward or away from us) of a distant object from changes in its spectrum caused by the **Doppler effect**.

You've probably noticed the Doppler effect on *sound;* it is especially easy to notice when you stand near train tracks and listen to the whistle of a train (Figure 6.15). As the train approaches, its whistle is relatively high pitched; as it recedes, the sound is relatively low pitched. Just as the train passes by, you hear the dramatic change from high to low pitch—a sort of "weeeeeeee–ooooooooooh" sound. You can visualize the Doppler effect by imagining that the train's sound waves are bunched up ahead of it, resulting in shorter wavelengths and thus the high pitch you hear as the train approaches. Behind the train, the sound waves are stretched out to longer wavelengths, resulting in the low pitch you hear as the train recedes.

The Doppler effect causes similar shifts in the wavelengths of light. If an object is moving toward us, then its entire spectrum is shifted to shorter wavelengths. Because shorter wavelengths are bluer when we are dealing with visible light, the Doppler shift of an object coming toward us is called a **blueshift**. If an object is moving away from us, its light is shifted to longer wavelengths; we call this a **redshift** because longer wavelengths are redder when we are

true wavelength;
normal pitch
for sound

true wavelength;
normal pitch
for sound

a

longer wavelength;
sound lower pitched

shorter wavelength;
sound higher pitched

b

c

**FIGURE 6.15** The Doppler effect. (**a**) Each circle represents the crests of sound waves going in all directions from the train whistle. The circles represent wave crests coming from the train at different times, say, 1/10 second apart. (**b**) If the train is moving, each set of waves comes from a different location. Thus, the waves appear bunched up in the direction of motion and stretched out in the opposite direction. (**c**) We get the same basic effect from a moving light source.

Laboratory spectrum
Lines at rest wavelengths.

Object 1
Lines redshifted: Object is moving away from us.

Object 2
Greater redshift: Object is moving away faster than Object 1.

Object 3
Lines blueshifted: Object is moving toward us.

Object 4
Greater blueshift: Object is moving toward us faster than Object 3.

**FIGURE 6.16** Spectral lines provide the crucial reference points for measuring Doppler shifts.

dealing with visible light. Note that the terms *blue-shift* and *redshift* are used even when we are not dealing with visible light.

Spectral lines provide the reference points we use to identify and measure Doppler shifts (Figure 6.16). For example, suppose we recognize the pattern of hydrogen lines in the spectrum of a distant object. We know the **rest wavelengths** of the hydrogen lines—that is, their wavelengths in stationary clouds of hydrogen gas—from laboratory experiments in which a tube of hydrogen gas is heated so the wavelengths of the spectral lines can be measured. If the hydrogen lines from the object appear at longer wavelengths, then we know that they are redshifted and the object is moving away from us; the larger the shift, the faster the object is moving. If the lines appear at shorter wavelengths, then we know that they are blueshifted and the object is moving toward us. Note that the Doppler shift tells us only the component of an object's velocity that is directly toward or away from us (that is, the *radial* component); it does not give us any information about the component of velocity across our line of sight.

**TIME OUT TO THINK** *Suppose the hydrogen emission line with a rest wavelength of 121.6 nm (the transition from level 2 to level 1) appears at a wavelength of 120.5 nm in the spectrum of a particular star. Given that these wavelengths are in the ultraviolet, is the shifted wavelength closer to or farther from blue visible light in the spectrum? Why then, do we say that this spectral line is blueshifted?*

The Doppler effect not only tells us how fast a distant object is moving toward or away from us but also can reveal information about motion *within* the object. For example, suppose we look at spectral lines of a planet or star that happens to be rotating (Figure 6.17). As the object rotates, light from the part of the object rotating toward us will be blueshifted, light from the part rotating away from us will be redshifted, and light from the center of the object won't be shifted at all. The net effect, if we look at the whole object at once, is to make each spectral line appear *wider* than it would if the object were not rotating. The faster the object is rotating, the broader in wavelength the spectral lines become. Thus, we can determine the rotation rate of distant objects by measuring the width of their spectral lines. As we will see later, this is only a small part of the information revealed through the Doppler effect on the spectra of celestial objects.

## Mathematical Insight 6.3    The Doppler Shift

As long as an object's radial velocity is small compared to the speed of light (i.e., less than a few percent of $c$), we can use a simple formula to calculate the radial velocity (toward or away from us) of an object from its Doppler shift:

$$\frac{\text{radial velocity}}{\text{speed of light}} = \frac{\text{shifted wavelength} - \text{rest wavelength}}{\text{rest wavelength}}$$

If the result is positive, the object has a redshift and is moving away from us; a negative result means that the object has a blueshift and is moving toward us. The formula can also be written symbolically as:

$$\frac{v}{c} = \frac{\Delta\lambda}{\lambda_0} \quad \text{or} \quad v = \frac{\Delta\lambda}{\lambda_0} \times c$$

where $v$ is the object's radial velocity, $c$ is the speed of light, $\lambda_0$ is the rest wavelength of a particular spectral line, and $\Delta\lambda$ is its wavelength shift (positive for a redshift and negative for a blueshift).

*Example:* The rest wavelength of one of the visible lines of hydrogen is 656.285 nm. This line is easily identifiable in the spectrum of the bright star Vega, but it appears at a wavelength of 656.255 nm. What is the radial velocity of Vega?

*Solution:* The line's wavelength in Vega's spectrum is slightly shorter than its rest wavelength, so the line is blueshifted and Vega's radial motion is *toward* us. Vega's radial velocity is:

$$\frac{656.255 \text{ nm} - 656.285 \text{ nm}}{656.285 \text{ nm}} \times 300{,}000 \, \frac{\text{km}}{\text{s}}$$

$$= (-4.57 \times 10^{-5}) \times (3 \times 10^5) \, \frac{\text{km}}{\text{s}}$$

$$= -13.7 \, \frac{\text{km}}{\text{s}}$$

The negative answer confirms that Vega is moving *toward* us at 13.7 km/s.

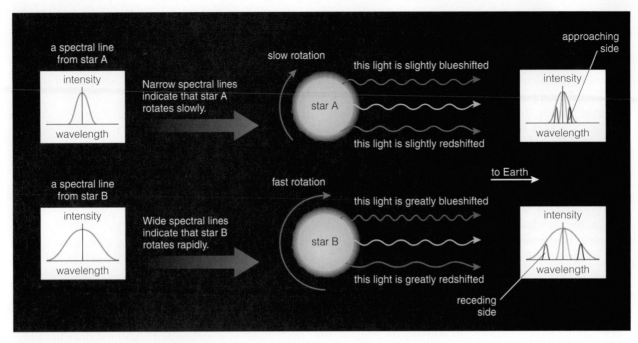

**FIGURE 6.17** The Doppler effect broadens the widths of the spectral lines of rotating objects. One side of a rotating object is moving toward us, creating a blueshift, while the other side is rotating away from us, creating a redshift. The faster the rotation, the greater the spread in wavelength between the light from the two sides. When we look at a spectral line for the object as a whole, we see light from all parts of the object—that is, the parts with blueshifts as well as the parts with redshifts—at the same time. Thus, the greater Doppler shifts in a fast-rotating object make the overall spectral line wider, since the light is spread over a greater range of wavelengths.

## THE BIG PICTURE

This chapter was devoted to one essential purpose: understanding how to read the messages contained in the spectra of distant objects. "Big picture" ideas that will help you keep your understanding in perspective include the following:

■ There is far more to light than meets the eye. By dispersing light into a spectrum with a prism or a diffraction grating, we discover a wealth of information about the object from which the light has come. Most of what we know about the universe comes from information that we receive in the form of light.

■ The visible light that our eyes can see is only a small portion of the complete electromagnetic spectrum. Different portions of the spectrum may contain different pieces of the story of a distant object, so it is important to study spectra at many wavelengths.

■ The spectrum of any object is determined by interactions of light and matter. These interactions can produce *emission lines, absorption lines,* or *thermal radiation;* the spectra of most objects contain some degree of all three of these. Some spectra also include transmitted light (from a light source behind the object) and reflected light.

■ By studying the spectra of a distant object, we can determine its composition, surface temperature, motion toward or away from us, rotation rate, and more.

## Review Questions

1. What is the difference between *energy* and *power*, and what units do we use to measure each?

2. What do we mean when we speak of a *spectrum* produced by a prism or *diffraction grating*?

3. Describe each of the four basic ways that light can interact with matter: *emission*, *absorption*, *transmission*, and *reflection*. How is *scattering* related to reflection?

4. What does it mean for a material to be *transparent*? To be *opaque*? What is *opacity*?

5. How does a particle differ from a wave? Define each of the following terms as it applies to waves: *wavelength*, *frequency*, *cycles per second*, *hertz*, *speed*.

6. What is a *photon*? In what way is a photon like a particle? In what way is it like a wave?

7. Briefly describe the concept of a *field*, and use it to explain why we say that light is an *electromagnetic wave*.

8. Explain why light with a shorter wavelength must have a higher frequency, and vice versa.

9. Describe the *electromagnetic spectrum*. In terms of frequency, wavelength, and energy, distinguish among *radio*, *infrared*, *visible light*, *ultraviolet*, *X rays*, and *gamma rays*.

10. Explain how transitions between energy levels can cause atoms to emit or absorb photons.

11. Explain how spectral lines can be used to determine the composition and temperature of their source.

12. What is *thermal radiation*? Describe the two laws of thermal radiation. Explain how the effects of both laws can be seen in Figure 6.12.

13. Summarize the circumstances under which objects produce *thermal*, *emission line*, or *absorption line* spectra as shown in Figure 6.13.

14. Study Figure 6.14 carefully, and explain each feature in the spectrum.

15. Describe the *Doppler effect* for light. Explain why light from objects moving toward us shows a *blueshift*, while light from objects moving away from us shows a *redshift*. What can we say about an object with a large Doppler shift, compared to an object with a small Doppler shift?

16. Describe how the Doppler effect allows us to determine the rotation rates of distant stars.

## Discussion Questions

1. *The Changing Limitations of Science.* In 1835, French philosopher Auguste Comte stated that the composition of stars could never be known by science. Although spectral lines had been seen in the Sun's spectrum by that time, not until the mid-1800s did scientists recognize that spectral lines give clear information about chemical composition (primarily through the work of Foucault and Kirchhoff). Why might our present knowledge have seemed unattainable in 1835? Discuss how new discoveries can change the apparent limitations of science. Today, other questions seem beyond the reach of science, such as the question of how life began on Earth. Do you think such questions will ever be answerable by science? Defend your opinion.

2. *Your Microwave Oven. Microwaves* is a name sometimes given to light near the long-wavelength end of the infrared portion of the spectrum. A *microwave oven* emits microwaves that happen to have just the right wavelength needed to cause energy level jumps in water molecules. Use this fact to explain how a microwave oven cooks your food. Why doesn't a microwave oven make a plastic or ceramic dish get hot?

## Problems

*Sensible Statements?* For **problems 1–4**, decide whether the statement is sensible and explain why it is or is not.

1. If you could view a spectrum of light reflecting off a blue sweatshirt, you'd find the entire rainbow of color.

2. Because of their higher frequency, X rays must travel through space faster than radio waves.

3. If the Sun's surface became much hotter (while the Sun's size remained the same), the Sun would emit more ultraviolet light but less visible light than it currently emits.

4. If a distant galaxy has a substantial redshift (as viewed from our galaxy), then anyone living in that galaxy would see a substantial redshift in a spectrum of the Milky Way Galaxy.

5. *Spectral Summary.* Clearly explain how studying an object's spectrum can allow us to determine each of the following properties of the object.
   a. The object's surface chemical composition.
   b. The object's surface temperature.
   c. Whether the object is a thin cloud of gas or something more substantial.
   d. Whether the object has a hot upper atmosphere.
   e. The speed at which the object is moving toward or away from us.
   f. The object's rotation rate.

6. *Planetary Spectrum.* Suppose you take a spectrum of light coming from a planet that looks blue to the eye. Do you expect to see any visible light in the planet's spectrum? Is the visible light emitted by the planet, reflected by the planet, or both? Which (if any) portions of the visible spectrum do you expect to find "missing" in the planet's spectrum? Explain your answers clearly.

7. *Hotter Sun.* Suppose the surface temperature of the Sun were about 12,000 K, rather than 6,000 K.

   a. How much more thermal radiation would the Sun emit?

   b. How would the thermal radiation spectrum of the Sun be different?

   c. Do you think it would still be possible to have life on Earth? Explain.

8. *The Doppler Effect.* In hydrogen, the transition from level 2 to level 1 has a rest wavelength of 121.6 nm. Suppose you see this line at a wavelength of 120.5 nm in Star A, at 121.2 nm in Star B, at 121.9 nm in Star C, and at 122.9 nm in Star D. Which stars are coming toward us? Which are moving away? Which star is moving fastest relative to us (either toward or away)? Explain your answers without doing any calculations.

9. *The Expanding Universe.* Recall from Chapter 1 that we know the universe is expanding because (1) all galaxies outside our Local Group are moving away from us and (2) more distant galaxies are moving faster. Explain how Doppler shift measurements allow us to know these two facts.

*10. *Human Wattage.* A typical adult uses about 2,500 Calories of energy each day.

   a. Using the fact that 1 Calorie is about 4,000 joules, convert the typical adult energy usage to units of joules per day.

   b. Use your answer from part (a) to calculate a typical adult's average *power* requirement, in watts. Compare this to that of a light bulb.

*11. *Wavelength, Frequency, and Energy.*

   a. What is the frequency of a visible light photon with wavelength 550 nm?

   b. What is the wavelength of a radio photon from an "AM" radio station that broadcasts at 1,120 kilohertz? What is its energy?

   c. What is the energy (in joules) of an ultraviolet photon with wavelength 120 nm? What is its frequency?

   d. What is the wavelength of an X-ray photon with energy 10 keV (10,000 eV)? What is its frequency? (*Hint:* Recall that 1 eV $= 1.60 \times 10^{-19}$ joule.)

*12. *How Many Photons?* Suppose that all the energy from a 100-watt light bulb came in the form of photons with wavelength 600 nm. (This is not quite realistic; see problem 15.)

   a. Calculate the energy of a *single* photon with wavelength 600 nm.

   b. How many 600-nm photons must be emitted each second to account for all the light from this 100-watt light bulb? Based on your answer, explain why we don't notice the particle nature of light in our everyday lives.

*13. *Taking the Sun's Temperature.* The Sun radiates a total power of about $4 \times 10^{26}$ watts into space. The Sun's radius is about $7 \times 10^8$ meters.

   a. Calculate the average power radiated by each square meter of the Sun's surface. (*Hint:* The formula for the surface area of a sphere is $A = 4\pi r^2$.)

   b. Using your answer from part (a) and the Stefan–Boltzmann law (see Mathematical Insight 6.2), calculate the average surface temperature of the Sun. (*Note:* The temperature calculated this way is called the Sun's *effective temperature.*)

*14. *Doppler Calculations.* Calculate the speeds of each of the stars described in problem 8. Be sure to state whether each star is moving toward or away from us.

*15. *Understanding Light Bulbs.* A standard (incandescent) light bulb uses a hot tungsten coil to produce a thermal radiation spectrum. The temperature of this coil is typically about 3,000 K.

   a. What is the wavelength of maximum intensity for a standard light bulb? Compare this to the 500-nm wavelength of maximum intensity for the Sun. Also explain why standard light bulbs must emit a substantial portion of their radiation as invisible, infrared light.

   b. Overall, do you expect the light from a standard bulb to be the same as, redder than, or bluer than light from the Sun? Why? Use your answer to explain why professional photographers use a different type of film for indoor photography than for outdoor photography.

   c. *Fluorescent* light bulbs primarily produce emission line spectra rather than thermal radiation spectra. Explain why, if the emission lines are in the visible part of the spectrum, a fluorescent bulb can emit more light than a standard bulb of the same wattage.

   d. Today, *compact fluorescent* light bulbs are designed to produce so many emission lines in the visible part of the spectrum that their light looks very similar to the light of standard bulbs. However, they are much more energy-efficient: A 15-watt compact fluorescent bulb typically emits as much visible light as a standard 75-watt bulb. Although compact fluorescent bulbs generally cost more than standard bulbs, is it possible that they could save you money? Besides initial cost and energy efficiency, what other factors must be considered?

## Web Projects

1. *Kids and Light.* Visit one of the many Web sites designed to teach middle and high school students about light. Read the content and try the activities. If you were a teacher, would you find the site useful for your students? Why or why not? Write a one-page summary of your conclusions.

2. *Light Bulbs.* Learn about alternatives to standard incandescent lightbulbs, such as fluorescent lights, compact fluorescent lights, and halogen lights. Write a short report summarizing some of the advantages and disadvantages of each technology.

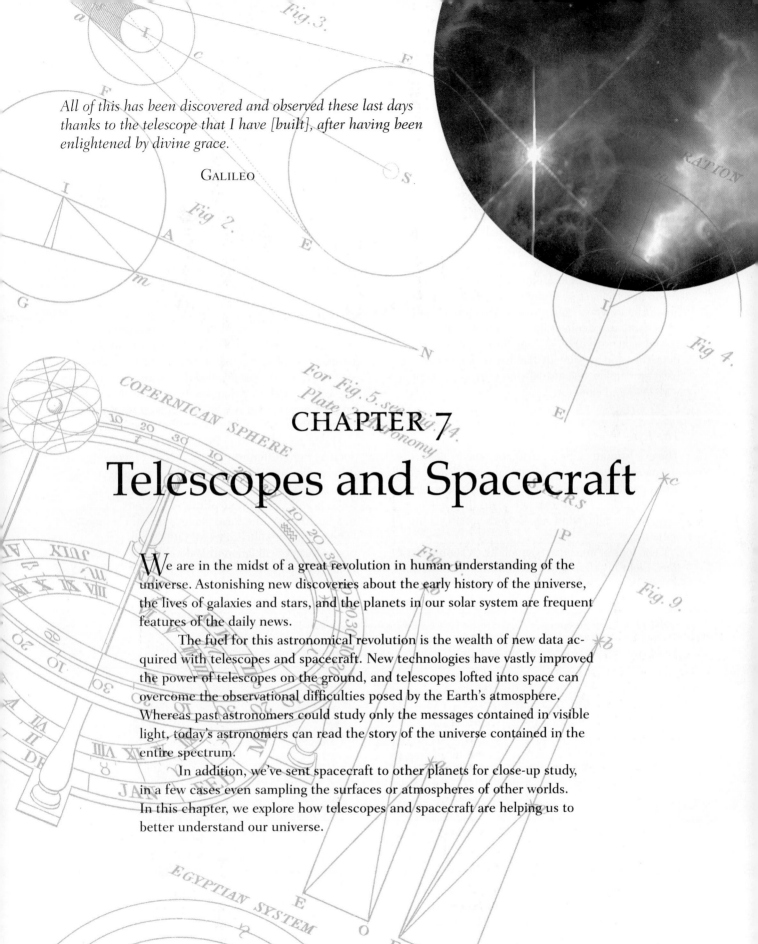

*All of this has been discovered and observed these last days thanks to the telescope that I have [built], after having been enlightened by divine grace.*

GALILEO

# CHAPTER 7
# Telescopes and Spacecraft

We are in the midst of a great revolution in human understanding of the universe. Astonishing new discoveries about the early history of the universe, the lives of galaxies and stars, and the planets in our solar system are frequent features of the daily news.

The fuel for this astronomical revolution is the wealth of new data acquired with telescopes and spacecraft. New technologies have vastly improved the power of telescopes on the ground, and telescopes lofted into space can overcome the observational difficulties posed by the Earth's atmosphere. Whereas past astronomers could study only the messages contained in visible light, today's astronomers can read the story of the universe contained in the entire spectrum.

In addition, we've sent spacecraft to other planets for close-up study, in a few cases even sampling the surfaces or atmospheres of other worlds. In this chapter, we explore how telescopes and spacecraft are helping us to better understand our universe.

## 7.1 Eyes and Cameras: Everyday Light Sensors

We observe the world around us with the five basic senses: touch, taste, smell, hearing, and sight. We learn about the world by using our brains to analyze and interpret the data recorded by our senses. The science of astronomy progresses similarly. We collect data about the universe, and then we analyze and interpret the data to develop theories about how the universe works. Within our solar system, we can analyze some matter directly, by collecting samples from the Earth's surface or from meteorites that fall to Earth, or by occasionally sending spacecraft to sample the surfaces or atmospheres of other worlds. Aside from these few samples, nearly all other data about the universe come to us in the form of light.

Astronomers collect light with telescopes and record light with photographic film or electronic detectors. You are already familiar with many of the basic principles, because of your everyday experience with eyes and cameras.

### The Eye

The eye is more complex than any human-made instrument, but its basic components are a *lens,* a *pupil,* and a *retina* (Figure 7.1). The retina contains light-sensitive cells (called *cones* and *rods*) that, when triggered by light, send signals to the brain via the optic nerve.

The lens of an eye acts much like a simple glass lens. Light rays that enter the lens farther from the

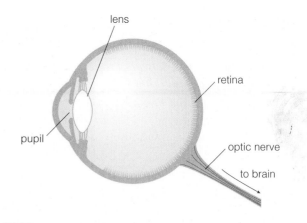

**FIGURE 7.1** A simplified diagram of the human eye.

center are bent more, and rays that pass directly through the center are not bent at all. In this way, parallel rays of light, such as the light from a distant star, converge to a point called the **focus** (Figure 7.2a). If you have perfect vision, the focus of your lens is on your retina. That is why distant stars appear as *points* of light to our eyes or on photographs.

Light rays that come from different directions, such as from different parts of an object, converge at different points to form an **image** of the object (Figure 7.2b). The place where the image appears in focus is called the **focal plane** of the lens. Again, in a healthy eye, the focal plane is on your retina. (The retina actually is curved, rather than a flat plane, but we will ignore this detail.) Note that the image formed by a lens is upside down. It is flipped

**FIGURE 7.2** (**a**) A glass lens bends parallel rays of light to a point called the focus of the lens. In a healthy eye, the lens focuses light on the retina. (**b**) Light from different parts of an object focuses at different points to make an image of the object. Note that the image formed on the retina is upside-down. The world does not look upside-down because your brain flips the image.

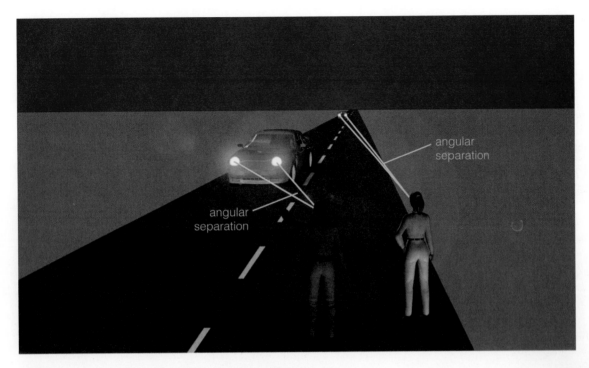

**FIGURE 7.3** The angular separation of the headlights increases as the car comes closer.

right side up by your brain, where the true miracle of vision occurs.

The pupil controls the amount of light that enters the eye by adjusting the size of its opening. The pupil dilates (opens wider) in low light levels, allowing your eye to gather as many photons as possible. It constricts in bright light, so that your eye is not overloaded with light.

**TIME OUT TO THINK** *Cover one eye and look toward a bright light. Then look immediately into a mirror and compare the openings of your two pupils. Which one is wider, and why? Why do eye doctors dilate your pupils during eye exams?*

One way to quantify your visual acuity is to measure the smallest angle over which your eyes can tell that two dots—or two stars—are distinct. Imagine looking at a car heading toward you on a long, straight road. When the car is very far away, your eyes cannot distinguish the headlights individually, and they look like one light. But as the car comes closer, the angular separation of the two headlights gets bigger, and you eventually see two distinct headlights (Figure 7.3). The smallest angular separation at which you can tell that the headlights are distinct is the **angular resolution** of your eyes.

The human eye has an angular resolution of about 1 arcminute ($\frac{1}{60}°$), meaning that two stars will appear distinct if they lie farther than 1 arcminute

apart in the sky. Two stars separated by *less* than 1 arcminute therefore appear as a single point of light. Most stars are actually members of binary or multiple-star systems, but, because they are so far away, the angular separation of the individual stars is far below the angular resolution of our eyes.

### Cameras and Film

The basic operation of a camera is quite similar to that of an eye (Figure 7.4). The camera lens plays the role of the lens of the eye, and film plays the role of the retina. The camera is "in focus" when the film lies in the focal plane of the lens. Fancier cameras even have an adjustable circular opening, called the camera's *aperture*, that controls the amount of light entering the camera just as the pupil controls the amount of light entering the eye.

The chemicals in photographic film darken or change color in response to light, thereby recording an image. Recording images on film offers at least two important advantages over simply looking at them or drawing them. First, an image on film is much more reliable and detailed than a drawing. Second, whereas the eye continually and automatically sends images to the brain, we can use a camera's *shutter* to control the amount of time, called the **exposure time**, over which light collects on a single piece of film. A longer exposure time means that more photons reach the film, allowing more opportunities for the light-sensitive chemicals to change in

**FIGURE 7.4** **(a)** A camera works much like an eye. When the shutter is open, light passes through the lens to form an image on the film or electronic detector. **(b)** Basic components of a camera.

## Mathematical Insight 7.1    Angular Separation

The angular separation of two points is related to their actual separation and distance. Figure 7.5 shows two points with an actual separation *s* between them. The angle $\alpha$ is the angular separation between the two points when viewed from a distance *d*.

As long as *d* is much larger than *s*, we can think of *s* as a small portion of an imaginary circle with radius *d*. Recall that the circumference of a circle is $2 \times \pi \times$ radius, so the circumference of the dotted circle in the figure is $2\pi d$. Thus, the separation *s* represents a fraction $s/(2\pi d)$ of this circumference. We find the angle $\alpha$ by multiplying this fraction by the 360° in a full circle:

$$\alpha = \frac{s}{2\pi d} \times 360°$$

*Example 1:*  Suppose the two headlights on a car are separated by 1.5 meters and you are looking at the car from a distance of 500 meters. What is the angular separation of the headlights? Can your eyes resolve the two headlights?

*Solution:*  The separation of the headlights is $s = 1.5$ m, and their distance is $d = 500$ m. Thus, their angular separation is

$$\alpha = \frac{1.5 \text{ m}}{2\pi \times 500 \text{ m}} \times 360° = 0.17°$$

The angular resolution of the human eye is about $\frac{1}{60}° \approx 0.017°$, or 10 times smaller than the angular separation of the two headlights. Thus, your eyes can easily resolve the two headlights at a distance of 500 meters.

*Example 2:*  The angular diameter of the Moon is about 0.5°, and the Moon is about 380,000 km away. Estimate the diameter of the Moon.

*Solution:*  We are given $\alpha = 0.5°$ and $d = 380,000$. We are looking for *s*—the diameter of the Moon in this case—so we first solve the angular separation equation for *s*:

$$\alpha = \frac{s}{2\pi d} \times 360° \quad \Rightarrow \quad s = \frac{2\pi d}{360°} \times \alpha$$

Now we substitute the given values:

$$s = \frac{2\pi \times 380,000 \text{ km}}{360°} \times 0.5° \approx 3,300 \text{ km}$$

This estimate is fairly close to the Moon's actual diameter (3,476 km), which we could find by using more precise values for the Moon's angular diameter and distance.

**FIGURE 7.5** As long as the angle $\alpha$ is small, the lengths *s* and *d* are related to $\alpha$ by the formula $\alpha = (s/2\pi d) \times 360°$.

response to light. As a result, long-exposure photographs can reveal images of objects far too faint for our eyes to see.

### CCDs

Thanks to the advantages of film over the human eye, the advent of photography in the mid-1800s spurred a leap in astronomical data collection. However, photographic film is far from ideal for recording light. Most photons striking film have no effect at all: Fewer than 10% of the visible photons reaching the film cause a change in the light-sensitive chemicals.[1] Thus, your film may record nothing if too little light reaches it. At the other extreme, a long exposure time can *overexpose* (or *saturate*) your film, darkening so large a fraction of the light-sensitive chemicals that details of the image are lost.

Today, many cameras and camcorders come equipped to record images with electronic detectors called *charge-coupled devices,* or **CCDs**, that can accurately record 90% or more of the photons that strike them. A CCD is a chip of silicon carefully engineered to be extraordinarily sensitive to photons (Figure 7.6). The chip is physically divided into a grid of squares called *picture elements,* or **pixels** for short. When a photon strikes a pixel, it causes a bit of electric charge to accumulate. Each subsequent photon striking the same pixel adds to this accumulated electric charge. After an exposure is complete, a computer measures the total electric charge in each pixel, thus determining how many photons have struck each one. The overall image is stored in the computer as an array of numbers representing the results from each pixel. At this point, the image can be manipulated through techniques of *image processing* to bring out details that otherwise might be missed in analyzing an image.

## 7.2 Telescopes: Giant Eyes

Our naked eyes allow us to admire the beauty of the night sky, but for most astronomical purposes they are completely inadequate. Their small size limits their angular resolution and the amount of light they can collect. They are sensitive only to visible light. And they are attached to bodies that require a pleasantly warm atmosphere for survival, an atmosphere that distorts light and prevents much of the electromagnetic spectrum from reaching the ground.

---

[1]The probability that an individual photon will be detected is called the *quantum efficiency.* It is about 1% for the human eye, up to about 10% for film, and 90% or more for CCDs.

**FIGURE 7.6** This photograph shows a CCD (charge-coupled device) on a circuit board. The quarter is included for size comparison.

Telescopes solve all these problems. We can design telescopes to compensate for the distorting effects of our atmosphere or launch them into space aboard spacecraft. We can build telescopes and detectors that are sensitive to light our eyes cannot see, such as radio waves or X rays. Most important, telescopes function as giant eyes, collecting far more light with far better angular resolution than our naked eyes.

### Basic Telescope Design

Telescopes come in two basic designs: *refracting* and *reflecting*. A **refracting telescope** operates much like an eye, using transparent glass lenses to focus the light from distant objects (Figure 7.7a). The earliest telescopes, including those built by Galileo, were refracting telescopes. The world's largest refracting telescope, completed in 1897, has a lens that is 1 meter (40 inches) in diameter and a telescope tube that is 19.5 meters (64 feet) long (Figure 7.7b).

A **reflecting telescope** uses a precisely curved **primary mirror** to gather and focus light (Figure 7.8a). Note that the mirror focuses light at the **prime focus**, which lies *in front of* the mirror. Thus, if we place a camera at the prime focus, it blocks some of the light entering the telescope. This does not create a serious problem as long as the camera is small compared to the primary mirror. If the telescope is large enough, a "cage" in which an astronomer can work can be suspended over the prme focus (Figure 7.8b).

An alternative and more common arrangement for reflecting telescopes is to place a **secondary mirror** just below the prime focus. The secondary mirror reflects the light to a location that is more

**FIGURE 7.7** (**a**) The basic design of a refracting telescope. The eyepiece contains a small lens that brings the collected light to a focus for an observer looking through it. (**b**) The 1-meter refractor at the University of Chicago's Yerkes Observatory is the world's largest refracting telescope.

lens

starlight

focus

eyepiece

a

to eye

b

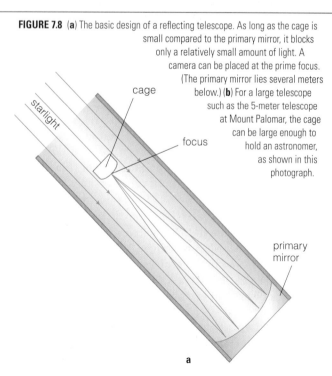

**FIGURE 7.8** (**a**) The basic design of a reflecting telescope. As long as the cage is small compared to the primary mirror, it blocks only a relatively small amount of light. A camera can be placed at the prime focus. (The primary mirror lies several meters below.) (**b**) For a large telescope such as the 5-meter telescope at Mount Palomar, the cage can be large enough to hold an astronomer, as shown in this photograph.

cage

starlight

focus

primary
mirror

a

b

Labels in figure:

secondary mirror

starlight

focus

primary mirror

Cassegrain focus

secondary mirror

focus

starlight

primary mirror

Newtonian focus

secondary mirror

starlight

focus

primary mirror

coudé focus

**FIGURE 7.9** Alternative designs for reflecting telescopes. Each of these designs incorporates a small, secondary mirror just below the prime focus. The secondary mirror reflects the light to a location that is more convenient for viewing or for attaching instruments.

convenient for viewing or for attaching instruments (Figure 7.9): through a hole in the primary mirror (a *Cassegrain focus*), to a hole in the side (a *Newtonian focus*, particularly common in smaller telescopes), or to a third mirror that deflects light toward instruments that are not attached to the telescope (a *coudé focus* or a *Nasmyth focus*).

Today, most astronomical research involves reflecting telescopes, mainly for two practical reasons. First, because light passes *through* the lens of a refracting telescope, lenses must be made from clear, high-quality glass with precision-shaped surfaces on both sides. In contrast, only the reflecting surface of a mirror must be precisely shaped, and the quality of the underlying glass is not a factor. Second, large glass lenses are extremely heavy and can be held in place only by their edges, making it difficult to stabilize refracting telescopes, in which lenses are positioned at the top. The primary mirror of a reflecting telescope is mounted at the bottom, where its weight is a far less serious problem. (A third problematic feature of lenses, called *chromatic aberration,* occurs because a lens brings different colors of light into focus at slightly different places. This problem also plagues camera lenses, but it can be minimized by using combinations of lenses and special optical coatings.)

### Fundamental Properties of Telescopes

The power of any telescope, whether refracting or reflecting, is characterized by two fundamental properties: its **light-collecting area**, which describes

### Common Misconceptions: Magnification and Telescopes

You are probably familiar with how binoculars, magnifying glasses, and telephoto lenses for cameras make objects appear larger in size—the phenomenon we call magnification. Many people assume that astronomical telescopes are also characterized by their magnification. In fact, astronomers are much more interested in a telescope's light-collecting area and angular resolution. The magnification of most telescopes is set to achieve the maximum amount of detail given the telescope's resolution—no more, no less. After all, there's little point in magnifying an image if doing so doesn't show any more detail.

the telescope's size in terms of how much light it can collect, and its **angular resolution**, which tells us how much detail we can see in the telescope's images. Let's examine each property in a bit more detail.

*Light-Collecting Area* The "size" of a telescope is usually described by the diameter of its primary mirror (or lens). For example, a "5-meter telescope" is a telescope with a primary mirror measuring 5 meters in diameter. The light-collecting area is proportional to the *square* of the mirror diameter. (More specifically,

**Table 7.1  Largest Optical Telescopes**

| Size | Telescope Name | Sponsor | Location | Operational Date | Special Features |
|------|----------------|---------|----------|------------------|------------------|
| 10 m | Keck I | Cal Tech, U. California, NASA | Mauna Kea, HI | 1993 | Primary mirror consists of 36 1.8-m hexagonal segments. |
| 10 m | Keck II | Cal Tech, U. California, NASA | Mauna Kea, HI | 1996 | Twin of Keck I; future plans for interferometry with Keck I. |
| 9.2 m | Hobby–Eberly | U. Texas, Penn State, Stanford, Germany | Mt. Locke, TX | 1997 | Consists of 91 1-m segments, for a total diameter of 11 m, but only 9.2 m can be used at a time; designed primarily for spectroscopy. |
| 2 × 8.4 m | Large Binocular Telescope | U. Arizona, Arcetri Astrophysical Observatory (Italy) | Mt. Graham, AZ | 2004* | Two 8.4-m mirrors on a common mount give light-collecting area of 11.8-m telescope. |
| 4 × 8 m | Very Large Telescope | European Southern Observatory | Cerro Paranal, Chile | 2000 | Four separate 8-m telescopes can work individually or together as the equivalent of a 16-m telescope. |
| 8.3 m | Subaru | National Observatory of Japan | Mauna Kea, HI | 1999 | Japan's first large telescope project. |
| 8 m | Gemini North | U.S., U.K., Canada, Chile, Brazil, Argentina | Mauna Kea, HI | 1999 | Identical to Gemini South so similar observations can be made from each hemisphere. |
| 8 m | Gemini South | U.S., U.K., Canada, Chile, Brazil, Argentina | Cerro Pachon, Chile | 2000 | Identical to Gemini North. |
| 6.5 m | Magellan | Carnegie Institute, Harvard, U. Michigan, MIT | Las Campanas, Chile | 2000 | A second 6.5-m telescope is planned at a later date. |
| 6.5 m | MMT | Smithsonian Institution, U. Arizona | Mt. Hopkins, AZ | 2000 | Replaced an older telescope in same observatory. |

*Scheduled completion date.

for a round mirror surface, we can use the formula for the area of a circle: area = $\pi \times$ (radius)$^2$.) Thus, a 2-meter telescope has $2^2 = 4$ times the light-collecting area of a 1-meter telescope.

For more than 40 years after its opening in 1947, the 5-meter Hale telescope on Mount Palomar outside San Diego remained the world's most powerful. (A Russian telescope built in 1976 was larger, but it suffered optical quality problems that made it far less useful.) Building larger telescopes posed a technological challenge, because large mirrors tend to sag under their own weight. Recent technological innovations have made it possible to build very large, low-weight mirrors, fueling a boom in large telescope construction (Table 7.1). For example, each of the twin 10-meter Keck telescopes in Hawaii has a primary mirror consisting of 36 smaller mirrors that

function together (Figure 7.10). When you realize that each Keck telescope has more than a million times the light-collecting area of the human eye, it is no wonder that modern telescopes have so dramatically enhanced our ability to observe the universe.

**TIME OUT TO THINK** *What is the population of your hometown? Suppose everyone in your hometown looked at the dark sky at the same time. How would the total amount of light entering everyone's eyes compare with the light collected by a 10-meter telescope? Explain.*

*Angular Resolution* Large telescopes can have remarkable angular resolution. For example, the Hubble Space Telescope has an angular resolution of about 0.05 arcsecond (for visible light), which would allow you to read this book from a distance of about 800 meters (a half mile).

a

b

FIGURE 7.10 (a) The two Keck telescopes sit atop Mauna Kea in Hawaii. (b) The Keck telescopes use 36 hexagonal mirrors to function as a single 10-meter primary mirror. These mirrors make the honeycomb pattern that surrounds the hole enclosing the man in this photo.

In principle, larger telescopes have better angular resolution; that is, they can distinguish finer details. However, the angular resolution may be degraded if a telescope is poorly made, and, as we'll discuss shortly, turbulence in the Earth's atmosphere can limit the angular resolution of ground-based telescopes.

The ultimate limit to a telescope's resolving power comes from the properties of light. Because light is an electromagnetic wave [Section 6.2], beams of light can interfere with one another like overlapping sets of ripples on a pond (Figure 7.11). This *interference* causes a blurring of images that limits a telescope's angular resolution even when all other conditions are perfect. That is why even a high-quality telescope in space, such as the Hubble Space Telescope, cannot have perfect angular resolution[2] (Figure 7.12).

The angular resolution that a telescope could achieve if it were limited only by the interference of light waves is called its **diffraction limit**. (*Diffraction* is a technical term for the specific effects of interference that limit telescope resolution.) It depends on both the diameter of the primary mirror and the wavelength of the light being observed. Larger telescopes have smaller diffraction limits for any

FIGURE 7.11 This computer-generated image shows how overlapping sets of ripples on a pond interfere with one another. The effects of the two sets of ripples add in some places, making the water rise extra high or fall extra low, and cancel in other places, making the water surface flat. Light waves also exhibit interference. (The colors in this image are for visual effect only.)

---

[2]In fact, the Hubble Space Telescope's primary mirror was made with the wrong shape, which further limited its angular resolution until corrective optics were installed in 1993. The corrective optics consist of small mirrors that essentially undo the blurring created by the primary mirror.

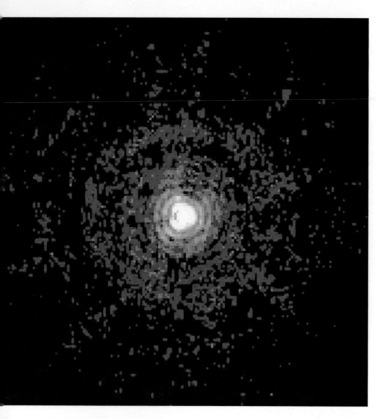

**FIGURE 7.12** When examined in detail, a Hubble Space Telescope image of a star has rings resulting from the wave properties of light. With higher angular resolution, the rings would be smaller.

particular wavelength of light. However, achieving a particular angular resolution requires a larger telescope for longer-wavelength light. That is why, for example, a radio telescope must be far larger than an optical telescope to achieve the same angular resolution.

## 7.3 Uses of Telescopes

Astronomers use many different kinds of instruments and detectors to extract the information contained in the light collected by a telescope. Every astronomical observation is unique, but most observations fall into one of three basic categories:

- **Imaging** yields pictures of astronomical objects. At its most basic, an imaging instrument is simply a camera. Astronomers sometimes place *filters* in front of the camera that allow only particular colors or wavelengths of light to pass through. Most of the richly hued images in this and other astronomy books are made by combining images recorded through different filters (Figure 7.13).

- **Spectroscopy** involves spreading light into a spectrum. Instruments called *spectrographs* use diffraction gratings (or other devices) to disperse light into spectra, which are then recorded with a detector such as a CCD (Figure 7.14).

- **Timing** tracks how an object's brightness varies with time. For a slowly varying object, a timing experiment may be as simple as comparing a set

## Mathematical Insight 7.2 The Diffraction Limit

A simple formula gives the diffraction limit of a telescope in arcseconds.

$$\text{diffraction limit} \approx 2.5 \times 10^5 \times \left( \frac{\text{wavelength of light}}{\text{diameter of telescope}} \right)$$
$$\text{\small (arcseconds)}$$

The wavelength of light and the diameter of the telescope must be in the same units.

*Example 1:* What is the diffraction limit of the 2.4-m Hubble Space Telescope for visible light with a wavelength of 500 nm?

*Solution:* For light with a wavelength of 500 nm ($500 \times 10^{-9}$ m), the diffraction limit of the Hubble Space Telescope is approximately:

$$\begin{aligned} \text{diffraction limit} &= 2.5 \times 10^5 \times \left( \frac{\text{wavelength}}{\text{telescope diameter}} \right) \\ &= 2.5 \times 10^5 \times \frac{500 \times 10^{-9} \text{ m}}{2.4 \text{ m}} \\ &= 0.05 \text{ arcsecond} \end{aligned}$$

*Example 2:* Suppose you wanted to achieve a diffraction limit of 0.001 arcsecond for visible light of wavelength 500 nm. How large a telescope would you need?

*Solution:* First we solve the diffraction limit equation for telescope diameter:

$$\text{diffraction limit} \approx 2.5 \times 10^5 \times \left( \frac{\text{wavelength}}{\text{telescope diameter}} \right)$$
$$\Downarrow$$
$$\text{telescope diameter} \approx 2.5 \times 10^5 \times \left( \frac{\text{wavelength}}{\text{diffraction limit}} \right)$$

Now we substitute the given values for the wavelength and diffraction limit:

$$\begin{aligned} \text{telescope diameter} &= 2.5 \times 10^5 \times \frac{500 \times 10^{-9} \text{ m}}{0.001 \text{ arcsecond}} \\ &= 125 \text{ m} \end{aligned}$$

An optical telescope would need a mirror diameter of 125 meters—longer than a football field—to achieve an angular resolution of 0.001 arcsecond.

actual light collected

blue filter

green filter

red filter

Images are combined to show true colors.

**FIGURE 7.13** In astronomy, color images are usually constructed by combining several images taken through different filters.

focused starlight

primary mirror

3. Diffraction grating: Disperses reflected light into a spectrum.

1. Slit: Allows only the light from the object of interest to pass through.

5. CCD: Records an image of the spectrum.

2. Collimating mirror: Makes all the reflected rays parallel.

4. Camera mirror: Focuses the spectrum onto the CCD.

**FIGURE 7.14** The basic design of a spectrograph. In this diagram, the spectrograph is attached to the bottom of a reflecting telescope, with light entering the spectrograph through a hole in the primary mirror. A narrow slit (or small hole) at the entrance to the spectrograph allows only light from the object of interest to pass through. This light bounces from the collimating mirror to the diffraction grating, which disperses the light into a spectrum. The dispersed light is then focused by the camera mirror and recorded by a CCD, giving an image of the spectrum.

of images or spectra obtained on different nights. For more rapidly varying sources, specially designed instruments essentially make rapid multiple exposures, in some cases recording the arrival time of every individual photon.

Major observatories typically have several different instruments capable of each of these tasks, and some instruments can perform all three basic tasks. (Note that some astronomers include a fourth general category called *photometry*, which is the accurate measurement of light intensity from a particular object at a particular time. We do not call this out as a separate category because today's detectors can do photometry at the same time that they are being used for imaging, spectroscopy, or timing.)

### Images of Nonvisible Light

Many astronomical images show nonvisible light; for example, Figure 7.15 is an "X-ray image." But what exactly does this mean, given that X rays are invisible to the eye? The easiest way to understand the idea is to think about X rays at a doctor's office [Section 6.3]. When the doctor makes an "X ray of your arm," he or she actually uses a machine that sends X rays through your arm; those that pass through are recorded on a piece of X-ray-sensitive film. We cannot see the X rays themselves, but we can see the image left behind on

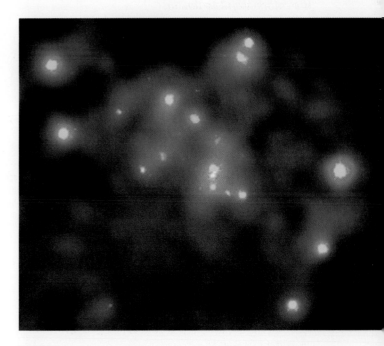

**FIGURE 7.15** X rays are invisible, but we can color-code the information recorded by an X-ray detector to make an image of the object as it would appear in X rays. This image, from NASA's Chandra X-Ray Observatory, shows the region (roughly 700 light-years on a side) in the center of the Andromeda Galaxy. The blue dot in the center marks what astronomers believe to be a supermassive black hole [Section 20.5]. The rest of the image is color-coded, with yellow indicating the most intense X rays. Most of the other bright X-ray sources are probably X-ray binaries [Section 17.3], star systems in which a neutron star or black hole orbits a normal star.

the film. Astronomical images work the same way; whether a detector records visible or nonvisible light, it makes an image showing the intensity of the light.

The simplest way to display a nonvisible image is in black and white, with brighter regions of the image corresponding to brighter light coming from the object. (A doctor's X ray is actually a negative, making bones look bright because few X rays pass through them.) However, it is much easier for the human eye to perceive color differences than shades of gray. That is why nonvisible images are often color-coded. In Figure 7.15, for example, the colors (except for the blue dot) correspond to the intensity of the recorded X rays: The brightest regions are yellow, while the violet and black represent regions that emit few, if any, X rays. All images recorded in nonvisible light must necessarily use some kind of color or gray-scale coding. Because the colors in these images do not represent what our eyes actually see, they are often called **false-color** images.

**TIME OUT TO THINK** *False-color images are common even outside astronomy. For example, medical images from CAT scans and MRIs are usually displayed in color, even though neither type of imaging uses visible light. What do you think the colors mean in CAT scans and MRIs? How are the colors useful to doctors?*

### Spectral Resolution

As we discussed in Chapter 6, a spectrum can reveal a wealth of information about an object, including its chemical composition, temperature, and rotation rate. However, just as the amount of information we can glean from an image depends on the angular resolution, the information we can glean from a spectrum depends on the **spectral resolution**: The higher the spectral resolution, the more detail we can see (Figure 7.16).

In principle, astronomers would always like the highest possible spectral resolution. However, higher spectral resolution comes at a price. A telescope collects only so much light in a given amount of time, and the spectral resolution depends on how widely this light is spread out by the spectrograph. If the spectrograph spreads out the light too much, the spectrum may become so dim that nothing can be recorded without a very long exposure time. Thus, for a particular telescope, making a spectrum of an object requires a longer exposure time than making an image of the same object, and high-resolution spectra take longer than low-resolution spectra.

## 7.4 Atmospheric Effects on Observations

A telescope on the ground does not look directly into space but rather looks through the Earth's sometimes murky atmosphere. In fact, the Earth's atmosphere creates several problems for astronomical observations. The most obvious problem is weather—an optical telescope is useless under cloudy skies. Another problem is that our atmosphere scatters the bright lights of cities, creating what astronomers call **light pollution**, which can obscure the view even for the best telescopes. For example, the 2.5-meter telescope at Mount Wilson, the world's largest when it was built in 1917, would still be very useful today

**FIGURE 7.16** Higher spectral resolution means we can see more details in the spectrum. Both (**a**) and (**b**) show spectra of the same object for the same wavelength band, but the higher spectral resolution in (**b**) enables us to see individual spectral lines that appear merged together in (**a**). (The spectrum shows interstellar absorption lines.)

if it weren't located so close to the lights of what was once the small town of Los Angeles. Similar but less serious light pollution hinders many other telescopes, including the Mount Palomar telescopes near San Diego and the telescopes of the National Optical Astronomy Observatory on Kitt Peak near Tucson. Fortunately, many communities are working to reduce light pollution. Placing reflective covers on the tops of streetlights directs more light toward the ground, rather than toward the sky. Using "low pressure" (sodium) lights also helps. Because these lights shine most brightly in just a few wavelengths of light, special filters can be used to absorb these wavelengths while transmitting most of the light from the astronomical objects under study. It's worth noting that both reflective covers and low-pressure lights also offer significant energy savings to communities that use them.

A somewhat less obvious problem is the fact that the atmosphere distorts light. The ever-changing motion, or **turbulence**, of air in the atmosphere bends light in constantly shifting patterns. This turbulence causes the familiar twinkling of stars and blurs astronomical images.

**TIME OUT TO THINK** *If you look down a long, paved street on a hot day, you'll notice the images of distant cars and buildings rippling and distorting. How are these distortions similar to the twinkling of stars? Why do you think these distortions are more noticeable on hot days than on cooler days?*

Many of these atmospheric effects can be mitigated by choosing appropriate sites for observatories. The key criteria are that the sites be dark (limiting light pollution), dry (limiting rain and clouds), calm (limiting turbulence), and high (placing them above at least part of the atmosphere). Islands are often ideal, and the 4,300-meter (14,000-foot) summit of Mauna Kea on the Big Island of Hawaii is home to many of the world's best observatories (Figure 7.17).

## Common Misconceptions: Twinkle, Twinkle Little Star

Twinkling, or apparent variation in the brightness and color of stars, is *not* intrinsic to the stars. Instead, just as light is bent by water in a swimming pool, starlight is bent by the Earth's atmosphere. Air turbulence causes twinkling because it constantly changes how the starlight is bent. Hence, stars tend to twinkle more on windy nights and at times when they are near the horizon (and therefore are viewed through a thicker layer of atmosphere). Planets also twinkle, but not nearly as much as stars: Because planets have a measurable angular size, the effects of turbulence on any one ray of light are compensated for by the effects of turbulence on others, reducing the twinkling seen by the naked eye (but making planets shimmer noticeably in telescopes). While twinkling may be beautiful, it blurs telescopic images. Avoiding the effects of twinkling is one of the primary reasons for putting telescopes in space. There, above the atmosphere, astronauts and telescopes do not see any twinkling.

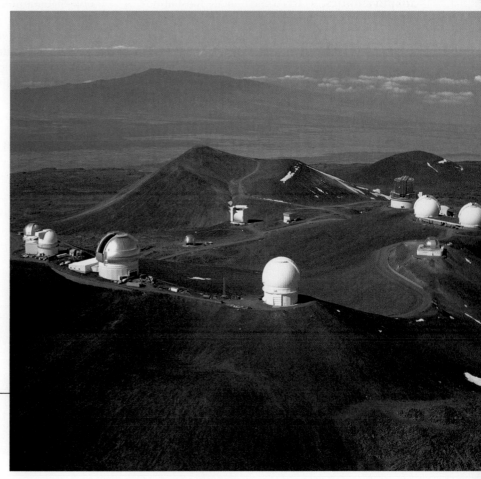

**FIGURE 7.17** Observatories on the summit of Mauna Kea in Hawaii.

**FIGURE 7.18** This photograph shows the airplane for NASA's airborne observatory, SOFIA, during a test flight. The 2.5-meter telescope will be located in the fuselage behind the painted black rectangle, which will open so the telescope can view the heavens. SOFIA is scheduled to begin observations in late 2004.

Modern technology also provides solutions to some of the problems caused by the atmosphere. Putting a telescope on an airplane takes it above much of the atmosphere, allowing many infrared observations not possible from the ground. NASA's new airborne observatory, called SOFIA (Stratospheric Observatory for Infrared Astronomy), will have a 2.5-meter infrared telescope looking out through a large hole cut in the fuselage of a Boeing 747 airplane (Figure 7.18). Advanced technologies make it possible for the airplane to fly smoothly despite its large hole and to keep the telescope pointed accurately at observing targets during flight.

Perhaps the most amazing new technology is **adaptive optics**, which can eliminate most atmospheric distortion. Atmospheric turbulence causes a stellar image to dance around in the focal plane of a telescope. Adaptive optics essentially make the telescope's mirrors do an opposite dance, canceling out the atmospheric distortions (Figure 7.19). The mirror shape (usually the secondary mirror) must change slightly many times each second to compensate for the rapidly changing atmospheric distortions. A computer calculates the necessary changes by monitoring the distortions of a bright star near the object under study. In some cases, if there is no bright star near the object of interest, the observatory shines a laser into the sky to create an *artificial star* (a point of light in the Earth's atmosphere) that can be monitored for distortions.

Of course, the ultimate solution to atmospheric distortion is to put telescopes in space. That is the primary reason why the Hubble Space Telescope (Figure 7.20) was built, and it is why it is so successful even though its 2.4-meter primary mirror is much smaller than the mirrors of many ground-based telescopes.

## 7.5 Telescopes Across the Spectrum

If we studied only visible light, we'd be missing much of the picture. Planets are relatively cool and emit primarily infrared light. The hot upper layers of stars like the Sun emit ultraviolet and X-ray light. Many objects emit radio waves, including some of the most exotic objects in the cosmos—*quasars*, which may contain black holes buried in their centers [Section 20.5]. Some violent events even produce gamma rays that travel through space to the Earth. Indeed, most objects emit light over a broad range of wavelengths.

Unfortunately, the atmosphere poses a major problem that no Earth-bound technology can overcome: It prevents most forms of light from reaching the ground at all. Figure 7.21 shows the depth to which different forms of light penetrate the Earth's atmosphere. Only radio waves, visible light, parts of the infrared spectrum, and the longest wavelengths of ultraviolet light reach the ground. Observing other wavelengths requires placing telescopes in space (or,

**FIGURE 7.19** (a) Atmospheric distortion makes this ground-based image of a double star look like a single star. (b) Using the same telescope, but with adaptive optics, the two stars are clearly distinguishable. The angular separation between the two stars is 0.38 arcsecond. (Both images were taken in near-infrared light with the Canada-France-Hawaii telescope and are shown in false color.)

a

b

light enters

telescope cover

solar panels

secondary mirror

primary mirror

scientific instruments

b

**FIGURE 7.20** The Hubble Space Telescope orbits the Earth. Although it orbits at a relatively low altitude, it is high enough to be above the distorting effects of the Earth's atmosphere and to observe infrared and ultraviolet light. (**a**) This photograph shows astronauts working on the telescope in the Space Shuttle cargo bay during a servicing mission in 1997. (**b**) This diagram shows the basic components of the Hubble Space Telescope.

a

**FIGURE 7.21** Diagram showing the approximate depths to which different wavelengths of light penetrate the Earth's atmosphere. Note that most of the electromagnetic spectrum—except for visible light, a small portion of the infrared, and radio—can be observed only from very high altitudes or from space.

gamma ray    X ray    ultraviolet   visible   infrared    radio

500 km

100 km

10 km

sea level

in a few cases, very high in the atmosphere on airplanes or balloons).

Today, astronomers study light across the entire spectrum. With the exception of telescopes for radio, some infrared, and visible-light observations, most of these telescopes are in space. Indeed, while the Hubble Space Telescope is the only major visible-light observatory in space (it is also used for infrared and ultraviolet observations), many less famous observatories are in Earth orbit for the purpose of making observations in nonvisible wavelengths. Table 7.2 lists some of the most important existing and planned telescopes in space.

## Infrared and Ultraviolet Telescopes

Telescopes for nonvisible wavelengths often require very different designs than optical telescopes. However, light from much of the infrared and ultraviolet portions of the spectrum behaves enough like visible light to eliminate the need for significant telescope modifications. That is, an optical telescope can record infrared or ultraviolet light as long as it is equipped with appropriate detectors and mirror coatings. Of course, the telescope must be in space to receive significant ultraviolet light.

Near the extreme-wavelength ends of the infrared or ultraviolet, telescopes need special technology. Extreme ultraviolet light (the shortest wavelengths of ultraviolet) behaves like X rays, which we'll discuss shortly. Extreme infrared light (the longest wavelengths of infrared) poses observing difficulties, because ordinary telescopes are warm enough to emit significant amounts of long-wavelength infrared light and this telescope emission would interfere with any attempt to observe these wavelengths from the cosmos. One solution to this problem is to make the telescope so cold that it emits very little infrared radiation. NASA's planned Space Infrared Telescope Facility (SIRTF), scheduled for launch in 2002 or 2003, will be cooled with liquid helium to just a few degrees above absolute zero.

## X-Ray and Gamma-Ray Telescopes

X rays have sufficient energy to penetrate many materials, including living tissue and ordinary mirrors. While this property makes X rays very useful to med-

## Table 7.2  Selected Major Observatories in Space

| Name | Launch Year | Lead Space Agency | Special Features |
|---|---|---|---|
| Hubble Space Telescope | 1990 | NASA | Optical, infrared, and ultraviolet imaging and spectroscopy |
| Rossi X-Ray Timing Experiment (RXTE) | 1995 | NASA | X-ray timing and spectroscopy |
| Far Ultraviolet Spectroscopic Explorer (FUSE) | 1999 | NASA | Ultraviolet spectroscopy |
| Chandra X-Ray Observatory | 1999 | NASA | X-ray imaging and spectroscopy |
| X-Ray Multi-Mirror Mission (XMM) | 1999 | ESA[*] | European-led mission for X-ray spectroscopy |
| High Energy Transient Explorer (HETE-2) | 2000 | NASA | Study of gamma-ray bursts |
| Microwave Anisotropy Probe (MAP) | 2001[**] | NASA | Study of the cosmic microwave background |
| Space Infrared Telescope Facility (SIRTF) | 2002[**] | NASA | Infrared observations of the cosmos |
| Space Interferometry Mission (SIM) | 2006[**] | NASA | First mission for optical interferometry in space |
| Next Generation Space Telescope (NGST) | 2009[**] | NASA | Follow-on to Hubble Space Telescope |
| Terrestrial Planet Finder (TPF) | 2011[**] | NASA | Search for Earth-like planets |

[*]European Space Agency
[**]Scheduled launch year

ical doctors, it gives astronomers headaches. Trying to focus X rays is somewhat like trying to focus a stream of bullets. If the bullets are fired directly at a metal sheet, they will puncture or damage the sheet. However, if the metal sheet is angled so that the bullets barely graze its surface, it will slightly deflect the bullets. Specially designed mirrors can deflect X rays in much the same way. Such mirrors are called **grazing incidence** mirrors because X rays merely graze their surfaces as they are deflected toward the focal plane. X-ray telescopes, such as NASA's Chandra X-ray Observatory, generally consist of several nested grazing incidence mirrors (Figure 7.22).

**TIME OUT TO THINK** *If you look straight down at your desktop, you probably cannot see your reflection. But if you glance along the desktop surface (or another smooth surface, such as that of a book), you should see reflections of objects in front of you. Explain how these reflections represent* grazing incidence *for visible light.*

Gamma rays can penetrate even grazing incidence mirrors and therefore cannot be focused in the tradi-tional sense. Capturing such high-energy light at all requires detectors so massive that the photons can-not simply pass through them. The largest gamma-ray observatory to date was the 17-ton Compton Gamma Ray Observatory (Figure 7.23), which was launched in 1991 and destroyed in a controlled crash to Earth in 2000.

### Radio Telescopes and Interferometry

**Radio telescopes** use large metal dishes as "mir-rors" to reflect radio waves. However, the long wave-lengths of radio waves mean that very large telescopes are necessary to achieve reasonable angular resolu-tion. The largest radio dish in the world, the Arecibo telescope, stretches 305 meters (1,000 feet) across a natural valley in Puerto Rico (Figure 7.24). Despite its large size, Arecibo's angular resolution is only about 1 arcminute at commonly observed radio wave-lengths (e.g., 21 cm [Section 18.2])—a few hundred times worse than the visible-light resolution of the Hubble Space Telescope.

In the 1950s, radio astronomers developed an in-genious technique for improving the angular resolution

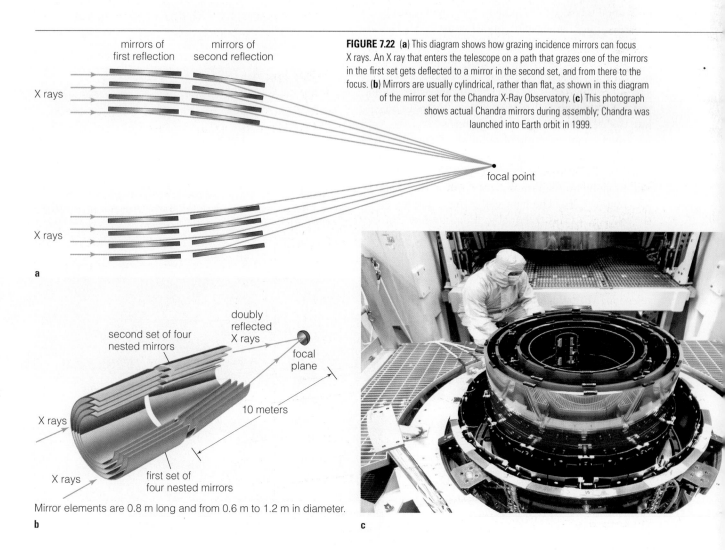

**FIGURE 7.22** (**a**) This diagram shows how grazing incidence mirrors can focus X rays. An X ray that enters the telescope on a path that grazes one of the mirrors in the first set gets deflected to a mirror in the second set, and from there to the focus. (**b**) Mirrors are usually cylindrical, rather than flat, as shown in this diagram of the mirror set for the Chandra X-Ray Observatory. (**c**) This photograph shows actual Chandra mirrors during assembly; Chandra was launched into Earth orbit in 1999.

mirrors of first reflection

mirrors of second reflection

X rays

X rays

focal point

a

second set of four nested mirrors

doubly reflected X rays

focal plane

10 meters

X rays

X rays

first set of four nested mirrors

Mirror elements are 0.8 m long and from 0.6 m to 1.2 m in diameter.

b

c

FIGURE 7.23 This photograph shows the Compton Gamma Ray Observatory being deployed from the Space Shuttle in 1991. Compton revolutionized our understanding of the gamma-ray universe before it was destroyed in 2000. Its demise came about after a gyroscope failure raised the prospect that atmospheric drag would eventually lead to an uncontrolled crash; NASA therefore used the spacecraft's on-board fuel for a controlled crash in the ocean, eliminating the possibility of major damage from the 17-ton observatory hitting the ground.

FIGURE 7.24 The Arecibo radio telescope stretches across a natural valley in Puerto Rico. At 305 meters across, it is the world's largest single radio dish.

of radio telescopes: They learned to link two or more individual telescopes to achieve the angular resolution of a much larger telescope (Figure 7.25). This technique is often called **interferometry** because it works by taking advantage of the wavelike properties of light that cause interference (see Figure 7.11). The procedure relies on precisely timing when radio waves reach each dish and supercomputers to analyze the resulting interference patterns.

One famous example of radio interferometry, the Very Large Array (VLA) near Socorro, New Mexico, consists of 27 individual radio dishes that can be moved along railroad tracks laid down in the shape of a Y (Figure 7.26). The light-gathering capability of the VLA's 27 dishes is equal to their combined area, equivalent to that of a single telescope 130 meters across. But the VLA's angular resolution, achieved by spacing the individual dishes as widely as possible, is equivalent to that of a single radio telescope with a diameter of almost 40 kilometers. Today, astronomers can achieve even higher angular resolution by linking radio telescopes around the world.

In principle, interferometry can improve angular resolution not only for radio waves but also for any other form of light. In practice,

FIGURE 7.25 Interferometry gives two (or more) small radio dishes the angular resolution of a much larger dish. However, their total light-collecting area is only the sum of the light-collecting areas of the individual dishes.

FIGURE 7.26 The Very Large Array (VLA) in New Mexico consists of 27 telescopes that can be moved along train tracks. The telescopes work together through interferometry and can achieve an angular resolution equivalent to that of a single radio telescope almost 40 kilometers across.

interferometry becomes increasingly difficult for light with shorter wavelengths, and astronomers are only beginning to succeed at infrared and visible interferometry. Nevertheless, one reason why *two* Keck telescopes were built on Mauna Kea is so that they can be used for infrared interferometry and someday for optical interferometry. The potential value of such interferometers is enormous. In the future, infrared interferometers may be able to obtain spectra from individual planets around other stars, allowing spectroscopy that could determine the compositions of their atmospheres and help determine whether they harbor life.

## 7.6 Spacecraft

The space age began in earnest with the launch of the Soviet Union's *Sputnik* satellite in 1957. Within the first decade after *Sputnik*, astronomers were already using spacecraft to carry telescopes into orbit and to make the first close-up studies of the Moon, Venus, and Mars. Today, orbiting spacecraft carry telescopes that allow us to collect light from nearly every region of the electromagnetic spectrum, while other spacecraft have visited all the planets in our solar system except Pluto. Spacecraft are even used to study the Earth. In fact, we can study many facets of our planet much more easily from space than from the ground. Because spacecraft are so important to astronomy, let's briefly investigate what they do and how they work.

### *Spacecraft Basics*

With a few exceptions, such as the Space Shuttle, the Space Station, and the Apollo missions to the Moon, nearly all spacecraft are *robotic,* meaning that no humans are aboard. Their operations are partly automatic and partly controlled by

scientists who send instructions via radio signals from Earth. Broadly speaking, most robotic spacecraft fall into four main categories:

1. **Earth-orbiters**. Simply being in space is enough to overcome the observational problems presented by Earth's atmosphere, so most space-based astronomical observatories orbit the Earth. Earth orbit is also the obvious place for spacecraft that study the Earth itself.

2. **Flybys**. Close-up study of other planets requires sending spacecraft to them. Flybys follow unbound orbits past their destinations; that is, they fly past a world just once and then continue on their way. For example, *Voyager 2*'s orbit allowed it to make flybys of Jupiter, Saturn, Uranus, and Neptune (Figure 7.27).

3. **Orbiters** (of other worlds). A flyby can study a planet or moon close up—but only once. For more detailed or longer-term studies, we need a spacecraft that goes into orbit around another world.

4. **Probes and landers**. The most "up close and personal" study of other worlds comes from spacecraft that send probes into their atmospheres or landers to their surfaces.

Table 7.3 lists a few of the most significant robotic missions to other worlds.

**FIGURE 7.27** The trajectory of *Voyager 2,* which made flybys of each of the four jovian planets in our solar system.

Earth
Aug. 20, 1977

Jupiter
July 9, 1979

Saturn
Aug. 25, 1981

Uranus
Jan. 24, 1986

Neptune
Aug. 25, 1989

**Table 7.3  Selected Robotic Missions to Other Worlds**

| Name | Type | Destination | Lead Space Agency | Arrival Year | Mission Highlights |
|---|---|---|---|---|---|
| Cassini | Orbiter | Saturn | NASA | 2004* | Includes lander (called Huygens) for Titan |
| Mars Exploration Rovers | Lander | Mars | NASA | 2004* | Twin rovers to study the surface in two locations |
| Mars Express | Orbiter and lander | Mars | ESA** | 2004* | Climate and surface studies of Mars |
| Nozomi | Orbiter | Mars | Japan | 2004* | Japanese-led mission to study Martian atmosphere |
| Contour | Flyby | 3 comets | NASA | 2003*, 2006*, 2008* | Detailed study of three comet nuclei |
| Mars Odyssey 2001 | Orbiter | Mars | NASA | 2001 | Detailed study of Martian surface features and composition |
| Near Earth Asteroid Rendezvous (NEAR) | Orbiter | Eros (asteroid) | NASA | 2000 | First spacecraft dedicated to in-depth study of an asteroid |
| Mars Global Surveyor | Orbiter | Mars | NASA | 1997 | Detailed imaging of surface from orbit |
| Mars Pathfinder | Lander | Mars | NASA | 1997 | Carried *Sojourner*, the first robotic rover on Mars |
| Galileo | Orbiter | Jupiter | NASA | 1995 | Dropped probe into Jupiter; close-up study of moons |
| Magellan | Orbiter | Venus | NASA | 1990 | Detailed radar mapping of surface of Venus |
| Voyager 1 | Flyby | Jupiter, Saturn | NASA | 1979, 1980 | Unprecedented views of Jupiter and Saturn; continuing out of solar system |
| Voyager 2 | Flyby | Jupiter, Saturn, Uranus, Neptune | NASA | 1979, 1981, 1986, 1989 | Only mission to Uranus and Neptune; continuing out of solar system |
| Vikings 1 and 2 | Orbiter and lander | Mars | NASA | 1976 | First landers on Mars |

*Scheduled arrival year.    **European Space Agency

### Orbital Considerations and Cost

Because spacecraft require very high speeds to leave the Earth, spacecraft must be launched atop large rockets. The heavier the spacecraft, the larger and more expensive the rocket required. The most obvious way to reduce the weight and launch cost of a spacecraft is to make it smaller. Just as powerful computers today are smaller than ever, new technologies are reducing the size of many scientific instruments.

Once a spacecraft is on its way, it requires no more fuel unless it needs to *change* its orbit [Section 5.6]. Thus, because a spacecraft headed toward another world approaches on an unbound orbit (relative to the target world), it is destined for a flyby unless it carries rocket engines and fuel to change its orbit to a bound one (elliptical or circular). The weight of these engines and fuel tends to make orbiters heavier and more expensive to launch than flybys.

Two 1997 Mars missions used imaginative techniques to reduce the amount of fuel they needed to carry. The *Pathfinder* lander used parachutes to slow its descent through the thin Martian atmosphere. Before hitting the surface at about 50 km/hr, it deployed air bags around itself for protection (Figure 7.28). The air bags made the lander bounce several times along the surface before it settled at its landing site. The *Mars Global Surveyor*, an orbiter, saved on weight by carrying only enough fuel to change its flyby trajectory to a highly eccentric orbit around Mars. To settle into a smaller and more circular orbit, it skimmed the Martian atmosphere at the low point

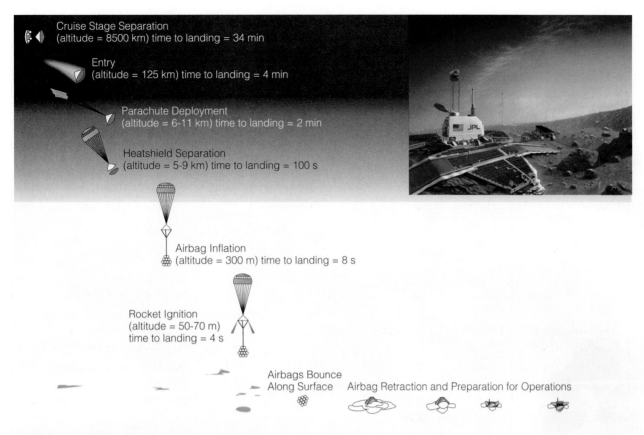

Cruise Stage Separation
(altitude = 8500 km) time to landing = 34 min

Entry
(altitude = 125 km) time to landing = 4 min

Parachute Deployment
(altitude = 6-11 km) time to landing = 2 min

Heatshield Separation
(altitude = 5-9 km) time to landing = 100 s

Airbag Inflation
(altitude = 300 m) time to landing = 8 s

Rocket Ignition
(altitude = 50-70 m)
time to landing = 4 s

Airbags Bounce
Along Surface    Airbag Retraction and Preparation for Operations

**FIGURE 7.28** The *Pathfinder* lander used parachutes and air bags to land safely on Mars. The inset shows an artist's conception of the lander on Mars.

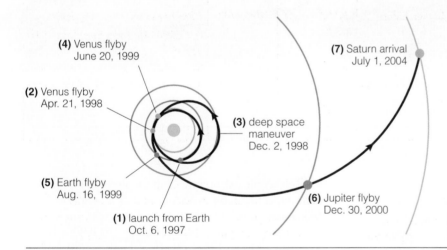

**(4)** Venus flyby
June 20, 1999

**(7)** Saturn arrival
July 1, 2004

**(2)** Venus flyby
Apr. 21, 1998

**(3)** deep space
maneuver
Dec. 2, 1998

**(5)** Earth flyby
Aug. 16, 1999

**(1)** launch from Earth
Oct. 6, 1997

**(6)** Jupiter flyby
Dec. 30, 2000

**FIGURE 7.29** The trajectory of *Cassini* from Earth to Saturn.

of each elliptical orbit. Atmospheric drag slowed the spacecraft, removing its unwanted orbital energy.

Spacecraft headed to the outer solar system present another problem: The farther we wish to send a spacecraft from the Sun, the more energy it requires. To date, we've never launched a spacecraft to the outer solar system with enough energy to reach its final destination directly. Instead, we've given it only enough energy to make it to at least one planet and then have taken advantage of that planet's gravity to

"slingshot" the spacecraft to higher speeds. In effect, a spacecraft gains energy by stealing a little bit of the planet's orbital energy around the Sun; because spacecraft are so small compared to planets, the effect on the planet's orbit is negligible. The Cassini mission used this slingshot technique four times: twice at Venus, then with a close flyby of Earth, and finally with a flyby of Jupiter in December, 2000. Cassini is scheduled to arrive at Saturn in 2004 (Figure 7.29).

**FIGURE 7.30** An artist's conception of a lunar observatory.

### The Future of Astronomy in Space

It will always be cheaper and easier to do astronomy from ground-based observatories, but space is likely to play an ever-increasing role in astronomy. NASA is considering future missions to every planet, as well as to some moons, asteroids, and comets. Mars is targeted for a particularly ambitious set of missions, with at least one mission scheduled about every 2 years (when Mars is located at the position in its orbit that makes it easiest to reach from Earth). A sample return mission, bringing Mars rocks back to Earth, may occur as early as 2005. Some scientists hope to launch a human mission to Mars within the next couple of decades.

Telescopic astronomy in space also should advance spectacularly. NASA is already at work on follow-ons to the Hubble Space Telescope, such as the *Next Generation Space Telescope* (NGST), which may launch as early as 2009. For the more distant future, many astronomers dream of an observatory on the far side of the Moon (Figure 7.30). Because the Moon has no atmosphere, it offers all the advantages of telescopes in space while also offering the ease of operating on a solid surface.

## THE BIG PICTURE

In this chapter, we've focused on the technological side of astronomy: the telescopes and spacecraft that we use to learn about the universe. Keep in mind the following "big picture" ideas as you continue to learn about astronomy:

■ Technology drives astronomical discovery. Every time we build a bigger telescope or a more sensitive detector, open up a new wavelength region to study, or send a spacecraft to another world, we learn more about the universe than was possible before.

■ Telescopes work much like giant eyes, enabling us to see the universe in great detail. New technologies for making larger telescopes, along with advances in adaptive optics and interferometry, are making ground-based telescopes more powerful than ever.

■ For the ultimate in observing the universe, space is the place! Telescopes in space allow us to detect light from across the entire spectrum while also avoiding the distortion caused by Earth's atmosphere. Flybys, orbiters, and landers allow us to make detailed studies of other worlds in our solar system that are not possible from Earth.

### Review Questions

1. Briefly describe how the eye collects light. How is a camera lens similar to the eye?

2. What is the *focus* of a lens? What is the *focal plane?*

3. What is *angular resolution?* Suppose you look at two stars with an angular resolution smaller than that of your eye. What will you see?

4. Briefly describe how a camera collects and records light. How do we control the *exposure time* with a camera?

5. What is a *CCD?* Briefly describe the advantages of using CCDs over using photographic film.

6. Briefly distinguish between a *refracting telescope* and a *reflecting telescope.*

7. Define and distinguish between a telescope's *light-collecting area* and its *angular resolution.* Why are these properties the two most important properties of a telescope?

8. What is the *diffraction limit* of a telescope, and how does it depend on the telescope's size and the particular wavelength of light being observed?

9. Define and differentiate between the three basic categories of astronomical observation: *imaging, spectroscopy,* and *timing.*

10. What is a *false-color* image? Why are false-color images useful?

11. What do we mean by *spectral resolution?* Explain why high spectral resolution is desirable but more difficult to achieve than lower spectral resolution.

12. Explain how *light pollution* and atmospheric *turbulence* affect astronomical observations made from the Earth's surface.

13. What is *adaptive optics?* What problems caused by the Earth's atmosphere can it solve?

14. Study Figure 7.21 in detail, and describe how deeply each portion of the electromagnetic spectrum penetrates the Earth's atmosphere.

15. Briefly describe the advantages of putting telescopes in space. Are there any disadvantages? Explain.

16. Why is it useful to study light from across the spectrum? Briefly describe the characteristics of telescopes used to observe different portions of the spectrum.

17. Briefly explain the purpose of using two or more telescopes together through *interferometry.*

18. Describe each of the four main categories of spacecraft and their uses.

19. Briefly explain the trade-offs between orbital considerations and cost involved in planning a spacecraft mission. How were costs reduced in the Mars Pathfinder mission, the Mars Global Surveyor mission, and the Cassini mission?

### Discussion Questions

1. *Science and Technology Funding.* Technological innovation clearly drives scientific discovery in astronomy, but the reverse is also true. For example, Newton's discoveries were made in part to explain the motions of the planets, but they have had far-reaching effects on our civilization. Congress often must make decisions between funding programs with purely scientific purposes ("basic research") and programs designed to develop new technologies. If you were a member of Congress, how would you try to allocate spending between basic research and technology? Why?

2. *A Lunar Observatory.* Do the potential benefits of building an astronomical observatory on the Moon justify its costs at the present time? If it were up to you, would you recommend that Congress begin funding such an observatory? Defend your opinions.

## Problems

*Sensible Statements?* For **problems 1–8**, decide whether the statement is sensible and explain why it is or is not.

1. The image was blurry because the photographic film was not placed at the focal plane.

2. By using a CCD, I can photograph the Andromeda Galaxy with a shorter exposure time than I would need with photographic film.

3. Thanks to adaptive optics, the telescope on Mount Wilson can now make ultraviolet images of the cosmos.

4. New technologies will soon allow astronomers to use X-ray telescopes on the Earth's surface.

5. Thanks to interferometry, a properly spaced set of 10-meter radio telescopes can achieve the angular resolution of a single, 100-kilometer radio telescope.

6. Thanks to interferometry, a properly spaced set of 10-meter radio telescopes can achieve the light-collecting area of a single, 100-kilometer radio telescope.

7. Scientists are planning a flyby of Uranus in order to do long-term monitoring of the planet's weather.

8. An observatory on the Moon's surface could have telescopes monitoring light from all regions of the electromagnetic spectrum.

9. *Angular Resolution.*

   a. Briefly describe why smaller is better when it comes to angular resolution.

   b. Suppose that two stars are separated in the sky by 0.1 arcsecond. What will you see if you look at them with a telescope that has an angular resolution of 0.01 arcsecond? What will you see if you look at them with a telescope that has an angular resolution of 0.5 arcsecond?

10. *Light-Collecting Area.*

   a. How much greater is the light-collecting area of one of the 10-meter Keck telescopes than that of the 5-meter Hale telescope?

   b. Suppose astronomers built a 100-meter telescope. How much greater would its light-collecting area be than that of the 10-meter Keck telescope?

11. *Project: Twinkling Stars.* Using a star chart, identify 5 to 10 bright stars that should be visible in the early evening. On a clear night, observe each of these stars for a few minutes. Note the date and time, and for each star record the following information: approximate altitude and direction in your sky, brightness compared to other stars, color, how much the star twinkles compared to other stars. Study your record. Can you draw any conclusions about how brightness and position in your sky affect twinkling? Explain.

*12. *Angular Separation Calculations.*

   a. Two light bulbs are separated by 0.2 meter and you look at them from a distance of 2 kilometers. What is the angular separation of the lights? Can your eyes resolve them? Explain.

   b. The diameter of a dime is about 1.8 centimeters. What is its angular diameter if you view it from across a 100-meter-long football field?

*13. *Calculating the Sun's Size.* The angular diameter of the Sun is about the same as that of the Moon (0.5°). Use this fact and the Sun's average distance of about 150 million km to estimate the diameter of the Sun. Compare your result to the Sun's actual diameter of 1.392 million km.

*14. *Viewing a Dime with the HST.* The Hubble Space Telescope (HST) has an angular resolution of about 0.05 arcsecond. How far away would you have to place a dime (diameter = 1.8 cm) for its angular diameter to be 0.05 arcsecond? (*Hint:* Start by converting an angular diameter of 0.05 arcsecond into degrees.)

*15. *Close Binary System.* Suppose that two stars in a binary star system are separated by a distance of 100 million km and are located at a distance of 100 light-years from Earth. What is the angular separation of the two stars? Give your answer in both degrees and arcseconds. Can the Hubble Space Telescope resolve the two stars?

*16. *Diffraction Limit of the Eye.* Calculate the diffraction limit of the human eye, assuming a lens size of 0.8 cm, for visible light of 500-nm wavelength. How does this compare to the diffraction limit of a 10-meter telescope?

*17. *The Size of Radio Telescopes.* What is the diffraction limit of a 100-meter radio telescope observing radio waves with a wavelength of 21 cm? Compare this to the diffraction limit of the 2.4-meter Hubble Space Telescope for visible light. Use your results to explain why radio telescopes must be much larger than optical telescopes to be useful.

*18. *Hubble's Field of View.* Large telescopes often have small fields of view. For example, the Hubble Space Telescope's (HST) "wide field" camera has a field of view that is roughly square and about 0.04° on a side.

   a. Calculate the angular area of the HST's field of view in square degrees.

   b. The angular area of the entire sky is about 41,250 square degrees. How many pictures would the HST have to take with its wide field camera to obtain a complete picture of the entire sky?

   c. Assuming that it requires an average of 1 hour to take each picture, how long would it take to acquire the number of pictures you calculated in part (b)? Use your answer to explain why astronomers would like to have more than one large telescope in space.

## Web Projects

Find useful links for Web projects on the text Web site.

1. *Planetary Mission.* Choose a current mission to a planet and find as much information as you can about the mission. Write a two- to three-page summary of the mission, including discussion of its purpose, design, and cost.

2. *Major Observatories.* Take a virtual tour of one of the world's major astronomical observatories. Write a short report on why the observatory is useful to astronomy.

3. *Earth-Observing Satellites.* Research one or more satellites that are designed to study the Earth. Briefly explain the purpose of each satellite and why it is able to collect data from space that would be more difficult to collect on the ground.

# PART III
# Learning from Other Worlds

*The evolution of the world may be compared to a display of fireworks that has just ended: some few red wisps, ashes and smoke. Standing on a cooled cinder, we see the slow fading of the suns, and we try to recall the vanished brilliance of the origin of the worlds.*

G. Lemaître (1894–1966),
Astronomer and Catholic Priest

# CHAPTER 8

# Formation of the Solar System

How old is the Earth, and how did it come to be? Is it unique? Our ancestors could do little more than guess, but today we can answer with reasonable confidence: The Earth and the rest of our solar system formed from a great cloud of gas and dust about 4.6 billion years ago. Whereas ancient astronomers believed the Earth to be fundamentally different from objects in the heavens, we now see the Earth as just one of many worlds.

As we examine the evidence that helped shape the modern scientific view of the formation of our solar system, we'll highlight one common technique of scientific research: sifting through seemingly unrelated facts to find the most important trends, patterns, and characteristics and then attempting to explain them. The explanation must be based on known physical laws, and the success or failure of a theory depends on how well it matches the facts. As we discover more and more planets around other stars, we hope to test our theories further and modify them as necessary.

## 8.1 Comparative Planetology

Galileo's telescopic observations began a new era in astronomy in which the Sun, the Moon, and the planets could be studied for the first time as *worlds*, rather than merely as lights in the sky. During the early part of this new era, astronomers studied each world independently, but in recent decades we have discovered that the similarities among worlds are often more profound than the differences.

Today, we know that the Sun, planets, moons, and other bodies in our solar system all formed at about the same time from the same cloud of interstellar gas and dust (*interstellar* means "between the stars") and in accord with the same physical laws. Thus, the differences between these worlds must be attributable to physical processes that we can study and understand by comparing the worlds to one another. This approach is called **comparative planetology**; the term *planetology* is used broadly to include moons, asteroids, and comets as well as planets. The idea is that we can learn more about the Earth, or any other world, by studying it in the context of other objects in our solar system—rather like learning about a person by studying his or her family, friends, and culture.

Before beginning the comparative study of worlds, we must be sure that the comparison will provide valid lessons. The basic premise of comparative planetology—that the similarities and differences among worlds in our solar system can be traced to common physical processes—assumes that the planets share a common origin. Thus, we begin our study of comparative planetology by seeking clues to our origins from the current state of our solar system; then we will examine the modern theory of solar system formation that explains much of what we see.

## 8.2 The Origin of the Solar System: Four Challenges

Learning about the origin of the solar system is easiest if we begin by looking at our solar system with a "big picture" view, rather than focusing on individual worlds. Imagine that we have the perspective of an alien spacecraft making its first scientific survey of our solar system. What would we see?

First, as we learned from our tour of a scale model of our solar system in Chapter 1, we'd find that our solar system is mostly empty. Interplanetary space is a near-vacuum containing only very low density gas and tiny, solid grains of dust. But we'd soon focus on the widely spaced planets, mapping their orbits, measuring their sizes, compositions, and densities, and taking inventory of their moons and ring systems. Figure 8.1 shows the resulting schematic maps, and

Table 8.1 summarizes the planetary properties. Note that asteroids and comets are also listed in the table because these objects orbit the Sun, though with orbital properties somewhat different from those of the planets.

Careful study of the maps and the table reveals several general features of our solar system. Let's investigate by grouping our observations into four major challenges that must be met by any theory claiming to explain how our solar system formed.

### Challenge 1: Patterns of Motion

The maps in Figure 8.1 show several striking patterns:

■ All planets orbit the Sun in the same direction—counterclockwise as seen from high above the Earth's North Pole.

■ All planetary orbits lie nearly in the same plane.

■ Almost all planets travel on nearly circular orbits, and the spacing between planetary orbits increases with distance from the Sun according to a fairly regular trend. The most notable exception to this trend is an extra-wide gap between Mars and Jupiter that is populated with asteroids.

■ Most planets rotate in the same direction in which they orbit—counterclockwise as seen from above the Earth's North Pole—with fairly small axis tilts (i.e., less than about 25°).

■ Almost all moons orbit their planet in the same direction as the planet's rotation and near the planet's equatorial plane.

■ The Sun rotates in the same direction in which the planets orbit.

These patterns show that motion in the solar system is generally quite organized. If each planet had come into existence independently, we might expect planetary motions to be much more random. (Note that the motions of asteroids are slightly more random, and those of comets even more so, as we will discuss shortly.)

*The first challenge for any theory of solar system formation is to explain why motions in the solar system are generally so orderly.*

### Challenge 2: Categorizing Planets

Before reading any further, study the properties of the planets in Table 8.1. Can you categorize the planets into groups? How many categories do you need? What characteristics do planets within a category share?

Astronomers classify most of the planets in two distinct groups: the rocky **terrestrial planets** and the gas-rich **jovian planets**. The word *terrestrial*

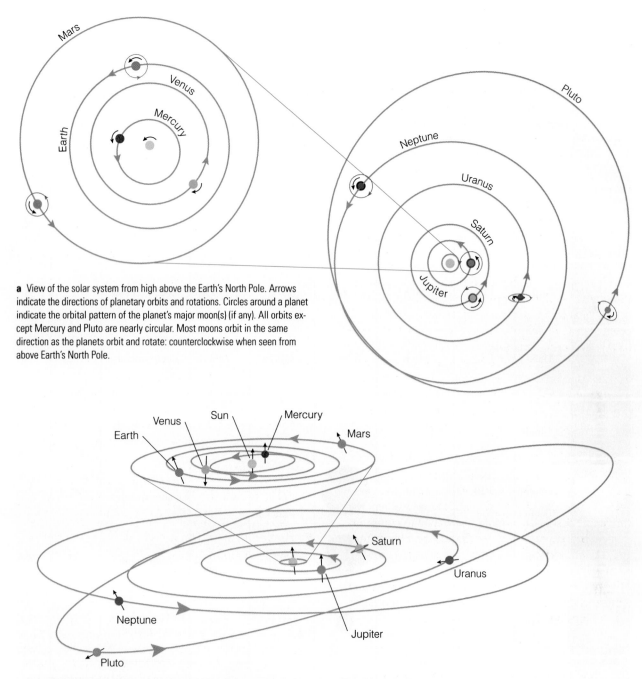

**a** View of the solar system from high above the Earth's North Pole. Arrows indicate the directions of planetary orbits and rotations. Circles around a planet indicate the orbital pattern of the planet's major moon(s) (if any). All orbits except Mercury and Pluto are nearly circular. Most moons orbit in the same direction as the planets orbit and rotate: counterclockwise when seen from above Earth's North Pole.

**b** Side view of the solar system. Arrows indicate the orientation of the rotation axes of the planets and their orbital motion. (Planetary tilts in this diagram are aligned in the same plane for easier comparison. Planets not to scale.)

**FIGURE 8.1** The layout of the solar system.

---

means "Earth-like" (*terra* is the Latin word for Earth), and the terrestrial planets are the four planets of the inner solar system—Mercury, Venus, Earth, and Mars. These are the worlds most like our own. They are relatively small, close to the Sun, and close together. They have solid, rocky surfaces and an abundance of metals deep in their interiors. They have few moons, if any, and none have rings. Note that many scientists count our Moon as a fifth terrestrial world because it shares these general characteristics, although it's not technically a planet.

The word *jovian* means "Jupiter-like," and the four jovian planets are Jupiter, Saturn, Uranus, and Neptune. The jovian planets are much larger than the terrestrial planets, farther from the Sun, and widely separated from each other. These huge planets have little in common with Earth. They are made mostly of hydrogen, helium, and **hydrogen compounds** such as water, ammonia, and methane. They contain small amounts of rocky material only deep in their cores. (Here we mean small in a relative

## Table 8.1  Planetary Facts*

| Photo | Planet | Average Distance from Sun (AU) | Temperature[†] | Relative Size | Average Equatorial Radius (km) | Average Density (g/cm³) | Composition | Known Moons | Rings? |
|-------|--------|-------------------------------|----------------|---------------|-------------------------------|-------------------------|-------------|-------------|--------|
| | Mercury | 0.387 | 700 K | · | 2,440 | 5.43 | Rocks, metals | 0 | No |
| | Venus | 0.723 | 740 K | • | 6,051 | 5.24 | Rocks, metals | 0 | No |
| | Earth | 1.00 | 290 K | • | 6,378 | 5.52 | Rocks, metals | 1 | No |
| | Mars | 1.52 | 240 K | · | 3,397 | 3.93 | Rocks, metals | 2 (tiny) | No |
| | Most asteroids | 2–3 | 170 K | | ≤500 | 1.5–3 | Rocks, metals | ? | No |
| | Jupiter | 5.20 | 125 K | ● | 71,492 | 1.33 | H, He, hydrogen compounds[‡] | 28 | Yes |
| | Saturn | 9.53 | 95 K | ● | 60,268 | 0.70 | H, He, hydrogen compounds[‡] | 30 | Yes |
| | Uranus | 19.2 | 60 K | ● | 25,559 | 1.32 | H, He, hydrogen compounds[‡] | 21 | Yes |
| | Neptune | 30.1 | 60 K | ● | 24,764 | 1.64 | H, He, hydrogen compounds[‡] | 8 | Yes |
| | Pluto | 39.5 | 40 K | · | 1,160 | 2.0 | Ices, rock | 1 | No |
| | Most comets | 10–50,000 | A few K[§] | · | A few km? | <1? | Ices, dust | ? | No |

*Appendix C gives a more complete list of planetary properties.

[†]Surface temperatures for all objects except Jupiter, Saturn, Uranus, and Neptune, for which cloud-top temperatures are listed.

[‡]Includes water ($H_2O$), methane ($CH_4$), and ammonia ($NH_3$).

[§]Comets passing close to the Sun warm considerably, especially their outer layers.

**Table 8.2  Comparison of Terrestrial and Jovian Planets**

| Terrestrial Planets | Jovian Planets |
| --- | --- |
| Smaller size and mass | Larger size and mass |
| Higher density (rocks, metals) | Lower density (light gases, hydrogen compounds) |
| Solid surface | No solid surface |
| Closer to the Sun (and closer together) | Farther from the Sun (and farther apart) |
| Warmer | Cooler |
| Few (if any) moons and no rings | Rings and many moons |

sense: The cores are still probably 10 Earth masses or more.) Jovian planets do not have solid surfaces; if you plunged into the atmosphere of a jovian planet, you would sink deeper and deeper until you were crushed by overwhelming pressure. The jovian planets are sometimes said to be made mostly of gas, but in fact the intense pressures and temperatures of the jovian planet interiors transform familiar gases (and solids) to phases unlike anything we see on Earth. Each jovian planet has rings and an extensive system of moons. These solid satellites are made mostly of low-density ices and rocks. Table 8.2 contrasts the general traits of the terrestrial and jovian planets.

*The second challenge for any theory of solar system formation is to explain why the inner and outer solar system planets divide so neatly into two classes.*

**TIME OUT TO THINK** *Are the distinctions in Table 8.2 clear-cut? Examine Table 8.1 to compare, for example, the radii of the largest terrestrial planet and the smallest jovian planet.*

Note that Pluto is left out in the cold, both literally and figuratively. On one hand, it is small and solid like the terrestrial planets. On the other hand, Pluto is far from the Sun, cold, and made of low-density ices. Pluto also has an unusual orbit, more eccentric than the orbit of any other planet and substantially inclined to the plane in which the other planets orbit the Sun. For a long time, scientists considered Pluto to be a lone misfit. However, some scientists now classify Pluto with other icy bodies in the outer solar system: comets [Section 12.5].

### Challenge 3: Asteroids and Comets

No formation theory is complete without an explanation for the most numerous objects in the solar system: asteroids and comets. **Asteroids** are small, rocky bodies that orbit the Sun primarily in the **asteroid belt** between the orbits of Mars and Jupiter (Figure 8.2). (Another large population of asteroids—the Trojan asteroids—shares Jupiter's orbit, falling into two clumps leading and trailing Jupiter by 60° [Section 12.2].) Asteroids orbit the Sun in the same

**FIGURE 8.2** Most asteroids orbit the Sun between Mars and Jupiter. Their orbits are noticeably tilted and eccentric.

**FIGURE 8.3** Small, icy comets orbit the Sun in two regions: the Kuiper belt just outside Neptune's orbit, and the Oort cloud beyond. (Diagram not to scale.)

Kuiper belt
about 30–100 AU

Neptune's orbit

typical Kuiper belt
comet orbit

typical Oort cloud comet orbit

Oort cloud extends out
to about 50,000 AU

direction as the planets. Their orbits generally lie close to the plane of planetary orbits, although they are usually a bit tilted. Some asteroids have elliptical orbits that are quite eccentric compared to the nearly circular orbits of the planets. More than 10,000 asteroids have been identified and cataloged, but these are probably only the largest among a much greater number of small asteroids. The very largest asteroids are a few hundred kilometers in radius—much less than half the Moon's radius.

**Comets** are small, icy bodies that spend most of their lives well beyond the orbit of Pluto; we generally recognize them only on the rare occasions when one dives into the inner solar system and grows a spectacular tail. Based on the orbits of the relatively few comets that reach the inner solar system, astronomers have determined that many billions of comets must be orbiting the Sun, primarily in two broad regions (Figure 8.3). The first region, called the **Kuiper belt** (pronounced koy-per), begins somewhere in the vicinity of the orbit of Neptune (about 30 AU from the Sun) and extends to perhaps 100 AU from the Sun. Comets in the Kuiper belt have orbits that lie fairly close to the plane of planetary orbits, and they travel around the Sun in the same direction as the planets. The second region populated by comets, called the **Oort cloud**, is a huge, spherical region centered on the Sun and extending perhaps halfway to the nearest stars. The orbits of comets in the Oort cloud are completely random, with no pattern to their inclinations, orbital directions, or eccentricities.

*The third challenge for any theory of solar system formation is to explain the existence and general properties of the large numbers of asteroids and comets.*

### Challenge 4: Exceptions to the Rules

The first three challenges involve explaining general patterns in our solar system. But some objects don't fit these patterns. For example, Mercury and Pluto have larger orbital eccentricities and inclinations than the other planets. The rotational axes of Uranus and Pluto are substantially tilted, and Venus rotates "backward"—clockwise, rather than counterclockwise, as viewed from high above Earth's North Pole. Unlike the other terrestrial planets, Earth has a large moon. Pluto has a moon almost as big as itself. While most moons of the jovian planets orbit in the planet's equatorial plane with the same orientation as their planet's rotation, a few orbit in the opposite direction or on tilted or eccentric orbits.

*Allowing for these and other exceptions to the general patterns is the fourth challenge for any theory of solar system formation.*

## Summarizing the Challenges

Table 8.3 summarizes the major characteristics of our solar system embodied in the four challenges. In the remainder of this chapter, we will examine the leading theory of solar system formation and put it to the test to see whether it can meet these four challenges. In this sense, we will be following the idealized scientific method by starting with the facts, putting forward a theory, and putting the theory to the test. In doing so, we have the benefit of hindsight. The historical path to our modern theory of the solar system was actually quite complex, with many competing theories being proposed and eventually discarded because they were unable to meet the challenges we have laid out.

The process of identifying the most important facts to explain is an essential first step in scientific analysis, followed by the development of a theory to explain these facts. We might tackle an environmental problem with a similar approach—for example, determining which pollutants are damaging an ecosystem and then developing a logical explanation for how these pollutants get there. A correct explanation of the facts is the first step in finding a solution.

## 8.3 The Nebular Theory of Solar System Formation

Over the past three centuries, several models have been put forth in attempts to meet the four challenges for a solar system formation theory. In the past few decades, a tremendous amount of evidence has accumulated in support of one model. This model, called the **nebular theory**, holds that our solar system formed from a giant, swirling **interstellar cloud** of gas and dust; such a cloud is also called a **nebula** (the Latin word for "cloud"). (We use the term *nebular theory* to encompass the entire formation process described in this chapter; some texts use this term more narrowly.) More generally, we now have evidence that all star systems (e.g., a star and its planets or a binary star system) form similarly from interstellar clouds (Figure 8.4).

Our galaxy, like the entire universe, originally contained only hydrogen and helium (and trace amounts of lithium) [Section 1.1]. All the heavier elements are produced in stars. The galactic recycling process (see Figure 8.5) gradually enriches the galaxy with heavier elements so that later generations of stars are born with a greater proportion of heavier elements than earlier generations.

**Table 8.3 Four Major Characteristics of the Solar System**

**Large bodies in the solar system have orderly motions.** All planets and most satellites have nearly circular orbits going in the same direction in nearly the same plane. The Sun and most of the planets rotate in this same direction as well.

**Planets fall into two main categories:** small, rocky terrestrial planets near the Sun and large, hydrogen-rich jovian planets farther out. The jovian planets have many moons and rings made of rock and ice.

**Swarms of asteroids and comets populate the solar system.** Asteroids are concentrated in the asteroid belt, and comets populate the regions known as the Kuiper belt and the Oort cloud.

**Several notable exceptions to these general trends stand out,** such as planets with unusual axis tilts or surprisingly large moons, and moons with unusual orbits.

**FIGURE 8.4** This photograph shows the central region of the Orion Nebula, an interstellar cloud in which star systems—possibly including planets—are forming. The photo is actually a composite of more than a dozen separate images taken with the Hubble Space Telescope. (See Figure 18.14 for a complete view of the Orion Nebula.)

interstellar gas

increase in density

stellar winds, explosions

star-forming clouds

star systems

gravitational collapse

**FIGURE 8.5** The galactic recycling process: Interstellar gas contracts under gravity to star-forming clouds. These clouds fragment into smaller clouds, like the solar nebula, that give birth to individual star systems. Stellar winds and explosions return gas from stars to interstellar space; some of this returned gas consists of heavy elements produced in the stars.

By the time our solar system formed, 4.6 billion years ago, about 2% of the original hydrogen and helium in the galaxy had been converted into heavier elements. Although 2% sounds like a small amount, it was more than enough to form the rocky terrestrial planets—and us. Nevertheless, hydrogen and helium remain the most abundant elements by far and make up the bulk of the Sun and the jovian planets.

**TIME OUT TO THINK** *Could a solar system like ours have formed with the first generation of stars after the Big Bang? Explain.*

### Collapse of the Solar Nebula

An individual star system forms from just a small part of a giant interstellar cloud. We refer to the collapsed piece of cloud that formed our own solar system as the **solar nebula**. The solar nebula collapsed under its own gravity; the collapse may have been triggered by a cataclysmic event such as the impact of a shock wave from a nearby exploding star. Before the collapse, the low-density gas may have spanned a few light-years in diameter. As it collapsed to a diameter of about 200 AU, roughly twice the present-day diameter of Pluto's orbit, three important processes gave form to our solar system (Figure 8.6).

First, the temperature of the solar nebula increased as it collapsed. Such heating represents energy conservation in action [Section 4.2]. As the cloud shrank, its gravitational potential energy was con-

verted to the kinetic energy of individual gas particles falling inward. These particles crashed into one another, converting the kinetic energy of their inward fall into the random motions of thermal energy. Some of this energy was radiated away as thermal radiation. The solar nebula became hottest near its center, where much of the mass collected to form the **protosun** (the prefix *proto* comes from a Greek word meaning "earliest form of"). The protosun eventually became so hot that nuclear fusion ignited in its core—at which point our Sun became a full-fledged star.

Second, like an ice skater pulling in her arms as she spins, the solar nebula rotated faster and faster as it shrank in radius. This increase in rotation rate represents the conservation of angular momentum in action [Section 5.2]. The rotation helped ensure that not all of the material in the solar nebula collapsed onto the protosun: The greater the angular momentum of a rotating cloud, the more spread out it will be.

Third, the solar nebula flattened into a disk—the **protoplanetary disk** from which the planets eventually formed. This flattening is a natural consequence of collisions between particles, which explains why flat disks are so common in the universe (e.g., the disks of spiral galaxies like the Milky Way, ring systems around planets, and *accretion disks* around neutron stars or black holes [Section 17.3]). A cloud may start with any size or shape, and different clumps of gas within the cloud may be moving in random directions at random speeds. When the cloud collapses,

**a** The original cloud is large and diffuse, and its rotation is almost imperceptibly slow.

**b** The cloud heats up and spins faster as it contracts.

**c** The result is a spinning, flattened disk, with mass concentrated near the center.

**FIGURE 8.6** This sequence of paintings shows the collapse of an interstellar cloud. In our solar nebula, the hot, dense central bulge became the Sun, and the planets formed in the disk.

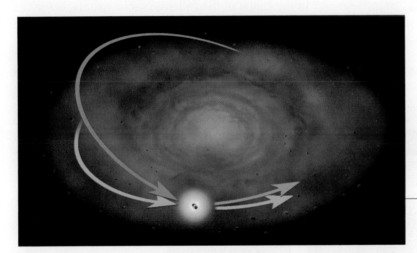

**FIGURE 8.7** As shown in this painting, collisions between particles in the solar nebula average out their random motions and flatten the cloud into a disk. The green arrow represents the path of a particle that originally had a tilted orbit. After the collision, its orbit lies closer to the plane of the other particles. If the particles had started on an eccentric orbit, collisions would have made its orbit more circular. (Particle sizes are highly exaggerated.)

these different clumps collide and merge, giving the new clumps the average of their differing velocities (Figure 8.7). The result is that the random motions of the clumps in the original cloud become more orderly as the cloud collapses, changing the cloud's original lumpy shape into a rotating, flattened disk. Similarly, collisions between clumps of material in highly elliptical orbits reduce their ellipticities, making their orbits more circular. You can see a similar effect if you shake some pepper into a bowl of water and quickly stir it in a random way. Because the water molecules are always colliding with one another, the motion of the pepper grains will settle down into a slow rotation representing the average of the original, random velocities.

**TIME OUT TO THINK** *Try the experiment with the pepper and bowl of water. Note that, no matter how you stir the water, it almost always settles down into a slow rotation in one direction or the other. How is this process similar to what took place in the solar nebula? How is it different?*

These three processes—heating, spinning, and flattening—explain the tidy layout of our solar system. The flattening of the protoplanetary disk explains why all planets orbit in nearly the same plane. The spinning explains why all planets orbit in the same direction and also plays a role in making most planets rotate in this same direction. The fact that collisions in the protoplanetary disk tend to make highly elliptical orbits more circular explains why most planets in our solar system have nearly circular orbits today.

## Evidence Concerning Nebular Collapse

The theory that our solar system formed from interstellar gas may sound reasonable, but we cannot accept it without hard evidence. Fortunately, we have strong observational evidence that the same processes are occurring elsewhere in our galaxy. A collapsing nebula emits thermal radiation [Section 6.4], primarily in the infrared. We've detected such infrared radiation from many other nebulae where star systems appear to be forming. We've even seen structures around other stars that look similar to protoplanetary disks (Figure 8.8).

Other support for the nebular theory comes from sophisticated computer models that simulate formation processes. A simulation begins with a set of data representing the conditions that we observe in interstellar clouds. Then, with the aid of a computer, we apply the laws of physics to these data to simulate how the conditions in a real cloud would change with time. These computer simulations successfully reproduce most of the general characteristics of motion in our solar system, suggesting that the nebular theory is on the right track. To date, however, the simulations do not explain the observed patterns of spacing between planets; much work lies ahead before we will fully understand the early history of our solar system. All in all, though, the nebular theory

meets the challenge of explaining most of the orderly motions of the planets and satellites. Now let's turn to our second challenge: explaining the strikingly different characteristics of the terrestrial and jovian planets.

## 8.4 Building the Planets

The churning and mixing of the gas in the solar nebula ensured that its composition was about the same throughout: roughly 98% hydrogen and helium, and 2% heavier elements such as carbon, nitrogen, oxygen, silicon, and iron. How did the planets and other bodies in our solar system end up with such a wide variety of compositions when they came from such uniform material? To answer this question, we must investigate how the material in the protoplanetary disk came together to form the planets.

### Condensation: Sowing the Seeds of Planets

In the center of the collapsing solar nebula, gravity drew much of the material together into the protosun. In the rest of the spinning protoplanetary disk, however, the gaseous material was so spread out that, at first, gravity was not strong enough to pull it to-

Central star blocked out

200 AU

**a** (Left) A dust disk around the star Beta Pictoris taken by the Hubble Space Telescope at optical wavelengths. (Right) Twin dust disks around binary stars, taken by the VLA at radio wavelengths.

Central star blocked out

500 AU

**b** Protoplanetary disks around stars in the constellation Auriga (left) and in the Orion Nebula (right). Hubble Space Telescope images.

**FIGURE 8.8** Evidence for disks around other stars.

| Materials in the Solar Nebula | | | | |
|---|---|---|---|---|
| | **Metals** | **Rocks** | **Hydrogen Compounds** | **Light Gases** |
| Examples | iron, nickel, aluminum | silicates | water ($H_2O$) methane ($CH_4$) ammonia ($NH_3$) | hydrogen, helium |
| Typical Condensation Temperature | 1,000–1,600 K | 500–1,300 K | <150 K | (do not condense in nebula) |
| Relative Abundance (by mass) | . (0.2%) | ■ (0.4%) | ■ (1.4%) | ■ (98%) |

FIGURE 8.9 A summary of the four types of materials present in the solar nebula, along with examples of each type and their typical condensation temperatures. The squares represent the relative proportions of each type (by mass).

gether to form planets. The formation of planets therefore required "seeds"—solid chunks of matter that gravity could eventually draw together. Understanding these seeds is the key to explaining the differing compositions of the planets.

The vast majority of the material in the solar nebula was gaseous: High temperatures kept virtually all the ingredients of the solar nebula vaporized near the protosun. Farther out the nebula was still primarily gaseous because hydrogen and helium are gases at nearly all temperatures. But the 2% of material consisting of heavier elements could form solid seeds where temperatures were low enough. The formation of solid or liquid particles from a cloud of gas is called **condensation**. Pressures in the solar nebula were so low that liquid droplets rarely formed, but solid particles could condense in the same way that snowflakes condense from water vapor in our atmosphere. We refer to such solid particles as **condensates**. The different kinds of planets and satellites formed out of the different kinds of condensates present at different locations in the solar nebula.

The ingredients of the solar nebula fell into four categories based on their condensation temperatures (Figure 8.9):

- **Metals** include iron, nickel, aluminum, and other materials that are familiar on Earth but less common on the surface than ordinary rock. Most metals condense into solid form at temperatures between 1,000 K and 1,600 K. Metals made up less than 0.2% of the solar nebula's mass.

- **Rocks** are materials common on the surface of the Earth, primarily silicon-based minerals (sili-

cates). Rocks are solid at temperatures and pressures found on Earth but typically melt or vaporize at temperatures of 500–1,300 K depending on their type. Rocky materials made up about 0.4% of the nebula by mass.

- **Hydrogen compounds** are molecules such as methane ($CH_4$), ammonia ($NH_3$), and water ($H_2O$) that solidify into **ices** below about 150 K. These compounds were significantly more abundant than rocks and metals, making up 1.4% of the nebula's mass.

- **Light gases** (hydrogen and helium) never condense under solar nebula conditions. These gases made up the remaining 98% of the nebula's mass.

The order of condensation temperatures is easy to remember: It's the same as the order of densities.

Temperature differences between the hot inner regions and the cool outer regions of the solar nebula determined what kinds of condensates were available to form planets (Figure 8.10). Very near the protosun, where the nebula temperature was above 1,600 K, there were no condensates—everything remained gaseous. Slightly farther out, where the temperature was slightly lower, metal flakes appeared. Near the distance of Mercury's orbit, flakes of rock joined the mix. Moving outward past the orbits of Venus and Earth, more varieties of rock minerals condensed. Near the location of the future asteroid belt, temperatures were low enough to allow minerals containing small amounts of water to condense as well. Dark, carbon-rich materials also condensed here.

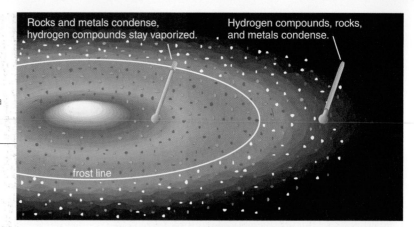

Rocks and metals condense, hydrogen compounds stay vaporized.

Hydrogen compounds, rocks, and metals condense.

frost line

**FIGURE 8.10** Temperature differences in the solar nebula led to different kinds of condensed materials, sowing the seeds for two different kinds of planets.

Only beyond the **frost line**, which lay between the present-day orbits of Mars and Jupiter, were temperatures low enough (150 K ≈ −123°C) for hydrogen compounds to condense into ices. (Water ice did not form at the familiar 0°C because the pressures in the nebula were 10,000 times lower than on Earth.) Thus, the outer solar system contained condensates of all kinds: rocks, metals, and ices. However, ice flakes were nearly three times more abundant than flakes of rock and metal because of the greater abundance of hydrogen compounds in the solar nebula.

### Accretion: Assembling the Planetesimals

The first solid flakes that condensed from the solar nebula were microscopic in size. They orbited the protosun in the same orderly, circular paths as the gas from which they condensed. Individual flakes therefore moved with nearly the same speed as their neighboring flakes, allowing them to collide very gently. At this point, the flakes were far too small to attract one another by gravity, but they were able to stick together through electrostatic forces—the same "static electricity" that makes hair stick to a comb. Thus, the flakes grew slowly into larger particles. As the particles grew in mass, gravity began to aid the process of their sticking together, accelerating their growth. This process of growing by colliding and sticking is called **accretion**. The growing objects formed by accretion are called **planetesimals**, which essentially means "pieces of planets." Small planetesimals probably came in a variety of shapes, such as we see in many small asteroids today. Larger planetesimals (i.e., those several hundred kilometers across) became spherical because the force of gravity was strong enough to overcome the strength of rock and pull everything toward the center (Figure 8.11).

The growth of planetesimals was rapid at first: As planetesimals grew larger, they had both more surface area with which to collide and more gravity to attract other planetesimals. Some probably grew to

## Common Misconceptions: Solar Gravity and the Density of Planets

You might think that the dense rocky and metallic materials were simply pulled to the inner part of the solar nebula by the Sun's gravity or that light gases simply escaped from the inner nebula because gravity couldn't hold them. But this is not the case; all the ingredients were orbiting the Sun together under the influence of the Sun's gravity. The orbit of a particle or a planet does *not* depend on its size or density, so the Sun's gravity is *not* the cause of the different kinds of planets. Rather, the different temperatures in the solar nebula are the cause.

**FIGURE 8.11** Gravity is not strong enough to alter the irregular shapes of small objects. A larger object with the same shape will eventually be compressed to a sphere by the greater strength of gravity.

Weak gravity is unable to deform small objects.

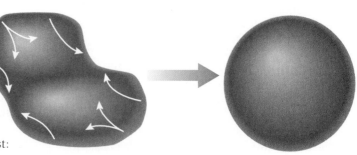

Stronger gravity makes larger objects spherical.

**FIGURE 8.12** These diagrams show how planetesimals gradually accrete into the terrestrial planets. Early in the accretion process, there are many Moon-size planetesimals on crisscrossing orbits (left). As time passes, a few planetesimals grow larger by accreting smaller ones, while others shatter in collisions (center). Ultimately, only the largest planetesimals avoid shattering and grow into full-fledged planets (right). Diagram not to scale.

hundreds of kilometers in size in only a few million years. (This might sound like a long time, but it is only about 1/1,000 the age of the solar system.) However, once the planetesimals reached these relatively large sizes, further growth became more difficult. Gravitational encounters between planetesimals tended to alter their orbits, particularly those of the smaller planetesimals [Section 5.6]. With different orbits crossing each other, collisions between planetesimals tended to occur at higher velocities and hence were more destructive. Collisions started to produce fragmentation more often than accretion. Only the largest planetesimals avoided such shattering and continued to grow into full-fledged planets (Figure 8.12).

The sizes and compositions of the planetesimals depended on the temperature of the surrounding solar nebula. In the inner solar system, where only rocky and metallic flakes condensed, planetesimals were made of rock and metal. That is why the terrestrial planets ended up being composed of rocks and metals. Moreover, because rocky and metallic elements made up only about 0.6% of the material in the solar nebula, the planetesimals in the inner solar system could not grow very large, which explains why the terrestrial planets are relatively small.

Beyond the frost line between the orbits of Mars and Jupiter, where temperatures were cold enough for ices to condense, planetesimals were built from ice flakes in addition to flakes of rock and metal. Because ice flakes were much more abundant, these planetesimals were made mostly of ices and could grow to much larger sizes than could planetesimals in the inner solar system. The largest icy planetesimals of the outer solar system became the cores of the jovian planets.

The densities of various objects in the solar system support this theory. The high density of planets

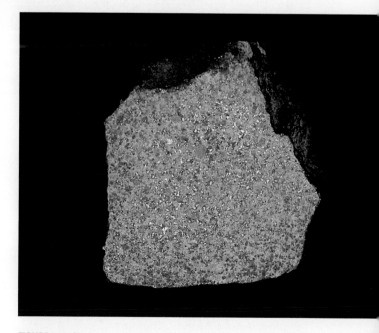

**FIGURE 8.13** Shiny flakes of metal are clearly visible in this meteorite, mixed in among the rocky material. Such metallic flakes are just what we would expect to find if condensation really occurred in the solar nebula as described by the nebular theory.

near the Sun (4–5 g/cm$^3$) shows that they are made of rock and metal. In the outer solar system, solid objects such as moons and comets have much lower densities (1–3 g/cm$^3$), revealing a high proportion of ices and a lower proportion of rocks and metals.

Further evidence of accretion comes from study of *meteorites*—pieces of our solar system that have fallen to Earth. Many meteorites contain metallic grains embedded in a variety of rocky minerals (Figure 8.13). Meteorites thought to come from greater

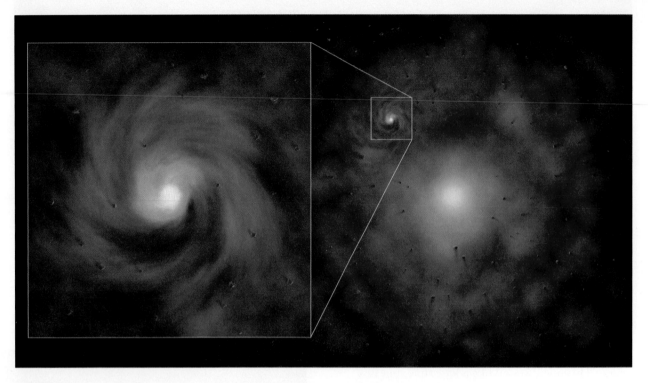

**FIGURE 8.14** Large icy planetesimals in the cold outer regions of the solar nebula captured significant amounts of hydrogen and helium gas. This process of nebular capture created jovian nebulae, resembling the solar nebula in miniature, in which the jovian planets and satellites formed. This painting shows a jovian nebula (enlarged at left) located within the entire solar nebula.

distances contain abundant carbon-rich materials, and some contain water [Section 12.3].

### Nebular Capture: Making the Jovian Planets

Accretion proceeded rapidly in the outer solar system, because the presence of ices meant much more material in solid form. Some of the icy planetesimals of the outer solar system quickly grew to sizes many times larger than the Earth. At these large sizes, their gravity was strong enough to capture the far more abundant hydrogen and helium gas from the surrounding nebula. As they accumulated substantial amounts of gas, the gravity of these growing planets grew larger still—allowing them to capture even more gas. The process by which icy planetesimals act as seeds for capturing far larger amounts of hydrogen and helium gas, called **nebular capture**, led directly to the formation of the jovian worlds (Figure 8.14). It explains their huge sizes and the large abundance of hydrogen and helium reflected in their low average densities.

Nebular capture also explains the formation of the diverse satellite systems of the jovian planets. As the early jovian planets captured large amounts of gas from the solar nebula, the same processes that formed the protoplanetary disk—heating, spinning, and flattening—formed similar but smaller disks of material around these planets. Condensation (of

metals, rocks, and a lot of ice) and accretion took place within these **jovian nebulae**, essentially creating a miniature solar system around each jovian planet. The spinning disks of the jovian nebulae explain why most of the jovian planet satellites orbit in nearly circular paths lying close to the equatorial plane of their parent planet and also why they orbit in the same direction in which their planet rotates. The composition of the jovian nebulae explains why the jovian planets possess systems of large, icy satellites. Their densities of $1–3$ g/cm$^3$ reflect their mixtures of icy and rocky condensates. Temperature differences within the jovian nebulae may have led to density differences between satellites analogous to the density differences between planets.

Our theory of condensation, accretion, and nebular capture meets the second challenge for our solar system formation theory: It explains the general differences between terrestrial and jovian planets. (Our theory can also explain the presence of planetary rings, but we postpone this interesting discussion until Chapter 11.) However, our theory does not yet explain why the spacing between the planets increases with distance from the Sun, although we can come up with some reasonable hypotheses. For example, the rapid accretion in the outer solar system may have allowed a few protoplanets to gobble up all their neighbors, leaving the jovian planets widely spaced.

**FIGURE 8.15** The magnetic braking process: Charged particles in the solar nebula tend to move with the Sun's magnetic field (represented by the purple loops). As the magnetic field rotates with the Sun, these charged particles are dragged through the disk. Friction between the charged particles and the rest of the disk slows the Sun's rotation (and also slightly speeds up the disk). The Sun's relatively slow rotation probably resulted from this process. (Particle sizes are highly exaggerated.)

### The Solar Wind: Clearing Away the Nebula

What happened to the remaining gas of the solar nebula? Apparently, this gas was blown into interstellar space by the **solar wind**, a flow of energetic particles ejected by the Sun in all directions. Although the solar wind is fairly weak today, we have evidence that it was much stronger when the Sun was young— strong enough to have swept huge quantities of gas out of our solar system. The clearing of the gas interrupted the cooling process in the nebula. Had the cooling continued longer, ices might have condensed in the inner solar system. Instead, the solar wind swept the still-vaporized hydrogen compounds away from the inner solar system, along with the remaining hydrogen and helium throughout the solar system. When the gas cleared, the compositions of objects in the early solar system were essentially set.

We've seen that the nebular theory accounts quite well for the motions of the planets and moons and the compositional trends in the solar system. However, the nebular theory also makes one prediction that at first seems to contradict our observations: Conservation of angular momentum in the collapsing solar nebula means that the young Sun should have been rotating very fast, but the Sun actually rotates quite slowly, with each full rotation taking about a month.

Fortunately, this apparent contradiction between theory and observation has a simple resolution. Angular momentum cannot simply disappear, but it is possible to transfer angular momentum from one object to another—and then get rid of the second

object. A spinning skater can slow her spin by grabbing her partner and then pushing him away. Beginning in the 1950s, scientists realized that the young Sun's rapid rotation would have generated a magnetic field far stronger than that of the Sun today. It made the Sun highly *active* (e.g., more and larger sunspots on its surface), a circumstance under which the Sun emits larger amounts of ultraviolet and X-ray light [Section 14.5]. This high-energy radiation ionized gas in the solar nebula, creating many charged particles.

As we will discuss in more detail in Chapter 14, charged particles and magnetic fields tend to stick together. As the sun rotated, its magnetic field dragged the charged particles along and added to their angular momentum. Because the particles were gaining angular momentum, the Sun was losing it. The strong solar wind then blew these particles into interstellar space, leaving the Sun with greatly diminished angular momentum and hence the much slower rotation that we see today. The process by which the Sun's magnetic field helped slow its rotation is called **magnetic braking**, because it effectively "applied the brakes" to the Sun's rapid rotation (Figure 8.15).

Although we cannot look into the past to see if magnetic braking really did slow the Sun's rotation, we can look for evidence of the magnetic braking process in other star systems. When we look at young stars that have recently formed in interstellar clouds, we find that nearly all of them rotate rapidly and have strong magnetic fields and strong stellar winds [Section 16.2]. In contrast, older stars almost invariably rotate slowly, just like our Sun. This fact suggests that nearly all stars have their original rapid rotations slowed by magnetic braking, just as we should expect from the nebular theory.

## 8.5 Leftover Planetesimals

We are now ready to turn to our third and fourth challenges: explaining the existence of asteroids and comets and explaining the various exceptions to general trends. Both challenges involve the planetesimals that remained between the forming planets in the early solar system.

### Origin of Asteroids and Comets

The strong wind from the young Sun cleared excess gas from the solar nebula, but many planetesimals remained scattered between the newly formed planets. These "leftovers" became comets and asteroids. Like the planetesimals that formed the planets, they formed from condensation and accretion in the solar nebula. Thus, their compositions followed the pattern determined by condensation: planetesimals of rock and metal in the inner solar system, and icy planetesimals in the outer solar system.

Leftover planetesimals originally must have had nearly circular orbits in the same plane as the orbits of the planets. But gravitational encounters with the newly formed planets soon made their orbits more random [Section 5.6]. When small planetesimals passed near a large planet, the planet was hardly affected, but the planetesimals were flung off at high speed in random directions. The strong gravity of the jovian planets, in particular, tugged and nudged the orbits of leftover planetesimals, even at great distances. The result was that the remaining planetesimals ended up with more highly elliptical orbits than the planets, and sometimes with large tilts relative to the plane of planetary orbits. Most of these planetesimals eventually either crashed into one of the planets or were flung out of the solar system, but many others still survive today.

Asteroids are the rocky, leftover planetesimals of the inner solar system. Some asteroids are scattered throughout the inner solar system, but most are concentrated in the "extra-wide" gap between Mars and Jupiter that contains the *asteroid belt*. This region probably once contained enough rocky planetesimals to form another terrestrial planet. However, the gravity of Jupiter (the largest and closest jovian planet) tended to nudge the orbits of these planetesimals, sending most of them on collision courses with the planets or with one another. The present-day asteroid belt contains the remaining planetesimals from this "frustrated planet formation." Although thousands of asteroids remain in the asteroid belt, their *combined* mass is less than 1/1,000 of Earth's mass. Jupiter's gravity continues to nudge these asteroids, changing their orbits and sometimes leading to violent, shattering collisions. Debris from these collisions often crashes to Earth in the form of meteorites.

Comets are the icy, leftover planetesimals of the outer solar system. The icy planetesimals that cruised the space between Jupiter and Neptune couldn't grow to more than a few kilometers in size before suffering either a collision or a gravitational encounter with one of the jovian planets. Many were flung into distant, randomly oriented orbits, becoming the comets of the spherical *Oort cloud* (see Figure 8.3). Beyond the orbit of Neptune, the icy planetesimals were much less likely to be destroyed by collisions or cast off by gravitational encounters. Instead, they remained in orbits going in the same direction as planetary orbits and concentrated near the plane of planetary orbits (but with somewhat more randomness than the orbits of the planets). They were also able to continue their accretion, and many may have grown to hundreds or even thousands of kilometers in diameter. These are the comets of the *Kuiper belt* (see Figure 8.3); Pluto is probably the largest member of this class. (Important discoveries often lead to confusion in nomenclature. The Kuiper belt is sometimes called the Kuiper disk, and its residents are sometimes called comets, Kuiper belt objects [KBOs], Kuiperoids, iceteroids, or Plutinos. To astronomers, they are technically just distant asteroids, even though they are icy instead of rocky.)

Evidence that asteroids and comets really are leftover planetesimals comes from analysis of meteorites, spacecraft visits to comets and asteroids, and computer simulations of solar system formation. Note also that our theory predicts the existence of comets in both the Oort cloud and the Kuiper belt— a prediction first made in the 1950s. Not until the early 1990s did astronomers verify the existence of objects orbiting within the Kuiper belt. The nebular theory has thus met our third challenge: explaining the existence of asteroids and comets. Moreover, it has suggested an explanation for the seemingly anomalous planet Pluto. Now we turn to our fourth and final challenge: explaining the exceptions to the general trends in our solar system.

### The Early Bombardment: A Rain of Rock and Ice

The collision of a leftover planetesimal with a planet is called an **impact**, and the responsible planetesimal is called the **impactor**. On planets with solid surfaces, impacts leave the scars we call **impact craters**. Impacts were extremely common in the young solar system; in fact, impacts were part of the accretion process in the late stages of planetary formation. The vast majority of impacts occurred in the first few hundred million years of our solar system's history.

The heavy bombardment of planetary surfaces in the early solar system would have resembled a rain of rock and ice from space (Figure 8.16). The surface of the Earth was once scarred like the Moon's surface, but most impact craters on Earth were erased long ago by erosion and other geological processes. Only the outlines of a few large craters are recognizable on Earth. But vast numbers of craters remain on worlds that experience less erosion, such as the Moon and Mercury. Indeed, one way of estimating the age of a planetary surface (the time since the surface last changed in a substantial way) is to count the number of craters: If there are many craters, the surface must still look much as it did when the early bombardment ended, about 4 billion years ago.

The early rain of rock and ice did more than just scar planetary surfaces. It also brought the materials from which atmospheres, oceans, and polar caps eventually formed. Remember that the terrestrial planets were built from planetesimals of metal and rock. But Earth's oceans, the polar caps of Earth and Mars, and the atmospheres of Venus, Earth, and Mars are all derived from hydrogen compounds that remained gaseous in the inner solar nebula. These materials must have arrived on the terrestrial planets after their initial formation, most likely brought by impacts of planetesimals formed farther out in the solar system. We don't yet know whether the impactors came from the asteroid belt, where rocky planetesimals contained small amounts of water and other hydrogen compounds that had condensed as ices, or whether they were comets containing huge amounts of ice. Either way, the water we drink and the air we breathe probably once were part of planetesimals floating beyond the orbit of Mars.

**TIME OUT TO THINK** *What was Jupiter's role in bringing water (and other materials that could not condense in the inner solar nebula) to Earth? How might Earth be different if Jupiter had never formed?*

**FIGURE 8.16** Around 4 billion years ago, Earth, its Moon, and the other planets were heavily bombarded by leftover planetesimals. This painting shows the young Earth and Moon glowing with the heat of accretion, and an impact in progress on the Earth.

### Captured Moons

We can easily explain the orbits of most jovian planet satellites by their formation in a jovian nebula that swirled around the forming planet. But our fourth challenge reminds us that some moons have unusual orbits—orbits in the "wrong" direction (opposite the rotation of their planet) or with large inclinations to the planet's equator. These unusual moons are probably leftover planetesimals that were *captured* into orbit around a planet.

It's not easy for a planet to capture a moon. An object cannot switch from an unbound orbit (e.g., an asteroid whizzing by Jupiter) to a bound orbit (e.g., a moon orbiting Jupiter) unless it somehow loses orbital energy [Section 5.6]. Captures probably occurred when the capturing planet had a very extended atmosphere or, in the case of the jovian planets, its own miniature solar nebula. Passing planetesimals could be slowed by friction with the gas, just as artificial satellites are slowed by drag with the Earth's atmosphere. If friction reduced a planetesimal's orbital energy enough, it could have become an orbiting moon. Because of the random nature of the capture process, the captured moons would not necessarily orbit in the same direction as their planet or in its equatorial plane.

a Phobos                      b Deimos

**FIGURE 8.17** The two moons of Mars, shown here in photos taken by the Viking spacecraft, are probably captured asteroids. Phobos is only about 13 km across and Deimos is only about 8 km across—making each of these two moons small enough to fit within the boundaries of a typical large city.

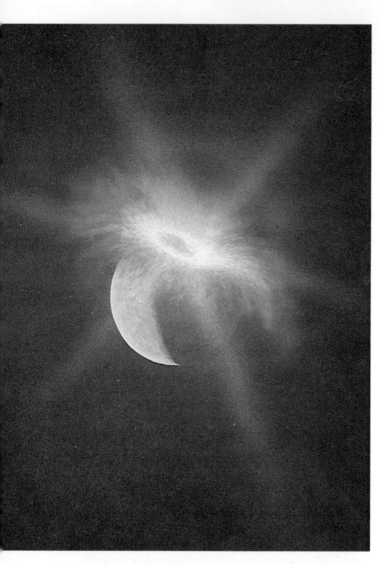

**FIGURE 8.18** Artist's conception of the impact of a Mars-size object with Earth, as may have occurred soon after Earth's formation. The ejected material comes mostly from the outer rocky layers and accretes to form the Moon, which is poor in metal.

The two small moons of Mars—Phobos and Deimos—probably were asteroids captured by this process (Figure 8.17). They resemble asteroids seen in the asteroid belt and are much darker and lower in density than Mars. Jupiter probably also captured several of its moons. Two groups of four satellites circle Jupiter in unusual orbits: All are noticeably eccentric and tilted, and one of the two groups orbits Jupiter in the "wrong" direction. Astronomers speculate that two asteroids may have been captured by Jupiter and that each broke into several pieces in the process. Other jovian planets may also have captured moons, including one that is particularly large—Triton, the largest moon of Neptune. Triton is considerably larger than Pluto and orbits Neptune in a direction opposite to Neptune's rotation. It may be a captured object from the Kuiper belt [Section 11.5]. The one unusual moon that cannot be explained by this process is our own. Our Moon is much too large to have been captured by Earth.

### Giant Impacts and the Formation of Our Moon

The largest planetesimals remaining as the planets formed may have been huge; some may have been the size of Mars. When one of these planet-size planetesimals collided with a planet, the spectacle would have been awesome. Such a **giant impact** could have significantly altered the planet's fate and may explain some of the remaining mysteries in our fourth challenge.

What if an object the size of Mars had collided with Earth? Computer simulations address this interesting question. The Earth would have shattered from the impact, and material from the outer layers would have ended up in orbit around the Earth (Figure 8.18). There this material could have reaccreted to form a large satellite. Depending on exactly where and how fast the giant impactor struck the Earth, the blow might also have tilted the Earth's axis, changed its rotation rate, or completely torn it apart. Today, such a giant impact is the leading hypothesis for explaining the origin of our Moon. The Moon's composition is similar to that of the Earth's outer layers, exactly what we would predict for the kind of collision shown in Figure 8.18. The Moon is also depleted in easily vaporized ingredients, as would be expected from the tremendous heating that would have occurred during the collision. Moreover, we can rule out the idea of the Moon forming simultaneously with Earth. In that case, Earth and the Moon would have formed from the same material and therefore should have the same density, but the Moon's density is considerably lower than the Earth's.

In fact, many of the unusual properties of specific planets—properties that defy the general trends expected by the nebular theory—may be the results of giant impacts. Mercury may have lost much of its outer, rocky layer in a giant impact, leaving it with a huge metallic core. A giant impact might even have contributed to the slow, backward rotation of Venus, which may have had a "normal" rotation until the arrival of the giant impactor. Giant impacts probably also were responsible for the axis tilts of many planets (including Earth) and for tipping Uranus on its side. Pluto's moon Charon may have formed in a giant-impact process similar to the one that formed our Moon.

Unfortunately, we can do little to test whether a particular giant impact really occurred billions of years ago. The difficulty in proving the giant-impact hypothesis makes the idea controversial, and most planetary scientists didn't take such ideas seriously when they were first proposed. But no other idea so effectively explains the formation of our Moon and other "oddities" that we've discussed. Moreover, giant impacts certainly should have occurred, given the number of large, leftover planetesimals predicted by the nebular theory. Random giant impacts are the most promising explanation for the many exceptional circumstances noted in the fourth challenge.

### Summary: Meeting the Challenges

The nebular theory explains the great majority of important facts contained in our four challenges. But you should not be left with the impression that competing theories were never put forth or that solar system formation is now a "solved problem." Theories have evolved hand-in-hand with the discovery of the nature of our solar system, and what we have presented here is the culmination of that endeavor to date. Planetary scientists are still struggling with more quantitative aspects, seeking reasons for the

exact sizes, locations, and compositions of the planets. Perhaps as we study other planetary systems and examine their properties, we will be able to improve our understanding of solar system formation.

Assuming that the nebular theory is correct, it is interesting to ask whether our solar nebula was "destined" to form the solar system we see today. The first stages of planet formation were orderly and inevitable according to the nebular theory. Nebular collapse, condensation, and the first stages of accretion were relatively gradual processes that probably would happen all over again if we turned back the clock. But the final stages of accretion, and giant impacts in particular, are inherently random in nature and probably would not happen again in just the same way. A larger or smaller planet might form at Earth's location and might suffer from a larger giant impact or from no impact at all. We don't yet know whether these differences would fundamentally alter the solar system or simply change a few "minor" details—such as the possibility of life on Earth.

## 8.6 The Age of the Solar System

The nebular theory accounts for the major physical properties of our solar system, supporting the idea that all the planets formed at about the same time from the same cloud of gas. But *when* did it all happen, and how do we know? The answer is that the solar system began forming about 4.6 billion years ago, a fact we learned by determining the age of the oldest rocks in the solar system.

The concept of a rock's age is tricky: The rock's atoms were forged in stars and are therefore much older than the Earth. Atoms are not stamped with any date of manufacture, and old atoms are truly indistinguishable from young ones. By the age of a rock, we mean the time since those atoms became locked together, that is, *the time since the rock last solidified.*

### Radioactive Dating

Most rocks contain minute amounts of **radioactive elements**—atoms whose nuclei have a tendency to break apart. (The term *radioactive* has nothing to do with radio waves, though both terms come from the concept of particles or waves radiating away from a source.) A radioactive element starts with a certain number of protons and neutrons in its nucleus. When that nucleus breaks apart, or **decays**, it ejects some subatomic particles and leaves behind a **decay product**—a different element or isotope with a different number of protons and/or neutrons [Section 4.3]. Over time, the amount of the original radioactive material (the *parent*) in the rock decreases, and the amount of the decay product (the *daughter*) increases.

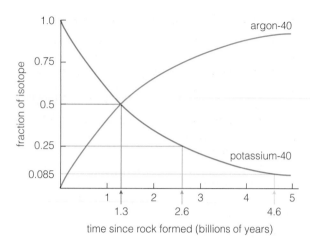

**FIGURE 8.19** Radioactive decay of potassium-40 to argon-40. The red line shows the decreasing amount of potassium-40, and the blue line shows the increasing amount of argon-40. The half-life for this reaction is 1.3 billion years. At 2.6 billion years, only a quarter of the original potassium-40 remains. After 4.6 billion years, only 0.085 of the original amount remains.

Most nuclei are stable, but certain combinations of neutrons and protons in a nucleus are unstable and prone to break apart sooner or later. One kind of radioactive decay is called *nuclear fission*. The ejected particles are very energetic; this is the energy that drives nuclear power plants and that generates much of the Earth's internal heat.

The rate at which a particular radioactive substance decays is characterized by its **half-life**, the time it takes for half of the parent nuclei to decay. Each isotope of each element has its own half-life, ranging from a fraction of a second to billions of years. For example, potassium-40 (i.e., potassium with atomic weight 40) has a half-life of about 1.3 billion years. If a rock begins with a certain amount of potassium-40, half this amount will remain after 1.3 billion years, one-fourth the original amount will remain after 2.6 billion years, one-eighth the original amount will remain after 3.9 billion years, and so on (Figure 8.19). As the potassium-40 decays, it leaves behind its decay product, argon-40. Thus, by comparing the amounts of potassium-40 and argon-40 in the rock, we can determine its age. This process of determining the age of an object by studying the results of radioactive decay is called **radioactive dating**.

## Mathematical Insight 8.1   Radioactive Decay

The amount of a radioactive substance decays by a factor of 2 with each half-life, so radioactivity is an example of *exponential decay*. We can express this decay process with a simple formula relating the current amount of a radioactive substance in a rock to the original amount:

$$\frac{\text{current amount}}{\text{original amount}} = \left(\frac{1}{2}\right)^{t/T_{\text{half}}}$$

where $t$ is the time since the rock formed and $T_{\text{half}}$ is the half-life of the radioactive material. This equation is graphed in Figure 8.19 for the decay of potassium-40 into argon-40. Note that the steady decline in the amount of potassium-40 with time is matched by a steady rise in the amount of argon-40. If you examine the graph over any 1.3-billion-year period (the half-life of potassium-40), you'll see that the amount of potassium declines by half.

*Example:* The famous Allende meteorite lit up the skies of Mexico as it shattered during its fall to Earth on February 8, 1969. Scientists collected pieces of the meteorite for study. To determine the age of the meteorite, they heated and chemically analyzed a small bit of meteorite. They found both potassium-40 and argon-40 present in a ratio of approximately 0.85 unit of potassium-40 atoms to 9.15 units of gaseous argon-40 atoms. (The units are unimportant, since only the relative amounts of the parent and daughter materials matter.) How old is the Allende meteorite?

*Solution:* Since no argon gas should have been present in the meteorite when it formed, the 9.15 units of argon must originally have been potassium. Thus, the sample started with $0.85 + 9.15 = 10$ units of potassium-40, of which 0.85 unit remains. Thus, the *current amount* of potassium-40 is 0.85 unit, and the *original amount* is 10 units. With these values, the radioactive decay equation becomes:

$$\left(\frac{1}{2}\right)^{t/T_{\text{half}}} = \frac{\text{current amount}}{\text{original amount}} = \frac{0.85}{10} = 0.085$$

You can get a fairly accurate estimate of the age $t$ by reading the graph in Figure 8.19 or by testing some guesses in the equation above using your calculator. The most accurate method is to solve the equation for the age $t$ by using logarithms:

$$t = T_{\text{half}} \times \frac{\log_{10}\left(\dfrac{\text{current amount}}{\text{original amount}}\right)}{\log_{10}\left(\dfrac{1}{2}\right)}$$

$$= 1.3 \text{ billion yr} \times \frac{\log_{10}(0.085)}{\log_{10}\left(\dfrac{1}{2}\right)} = 4.6 \text{ billion yr}$$

Thus, from the ratio of potassium-40 to argon-40, we conclude that the Allende meteorite solidified from the solar nebula about 4.6 billion years ago.

Radioactive dating is simple in principle, but in practice it requires careful laboratory work and a good understanding of "rock chemistry." For example, suppose you find a rock that contains equal numbers of atoms of potassium-40 and argon-40. If you assume that all the argon came from potassium decay, then the rock must be 1.3 billion years old (because half the original potassium atoms must have decayed to yield equal numbers of potassium and argon atoms). But this age is correct only if the assumption is valid; that is, the rock must not have contained any argon-40 when it formed. In this case, knowing a bit of chemistry helps. Potassium-40 is a natural ingredient of many minerals in rocks, but argon-40 is a gas that never combines with other elements and did not condense in the solar nebula. Therefore, if you find argon-40 gas trapped inside minerals, you can be sure that it came from the radioactive decay of potassium-40. Another assumption is that none of the argon-40 gas has escaped from the rock. Rock chemistry tells us that as long as the rock has not been significantly heated, even atoms of gases will remain trapped within it.

As another example, consider rocks from the ancient lunar highlands [Section 9.5]. These rocks contain minerals with a very small amount of uranium-238, which decays (in several steps) to lead-206 with a half-life of about 4.5 billion years. Lead and uranium have very different chemical behaviors, and some minerals start with virtually no lead. Laboratory analysis of such minerals in lunar rocks shows that they now contain almost equal proportions of uranium-238 and lead-206. We conclude that half the original uranium-238 has decayed, turning into the same number of lead-206 atoms. The lunar rock must be about one half-life old, or almost 4.5 billion years. (More precisely, the oldest lunar rocks are about 4.4 billion years old.)

**TIME OUT TO THINK** *If future scientists examine the lunar rocks 4.5 billion years from now, what proportions of uranium-238 and lead-206 will they find?*

Radioactive dating is possible with many other materials having a variety of different half-lives. In some cases it can be very difficult, particularly if some of the daughter material may have been present when the rock first formed. In that case, sophisticated chemistry may be needed to determine how much material is original and how much is the product of decay. Fortunately, rocks often contain several different radioactive materials, so scientists can date a rock by analyzing several different parent–daughter ratios. If the ages found from analyzing the different materials agree, we can be very confident that we know the true age of the rock.

### Earth Rocks, Moon Rocks, and Meteorites

How on Earth can we measure the age of the solar system? In fact, nothing on Earth's surface remains from the formation era. Geological activity, such as plate tectonics and volcanoes, has ensured that virtually all the rocks present on the early Earth have since melted and resolidified. Because dating tells us only how long it has been since a rock last solidified, we cannot determine the age of our planet from its rocks, let alone the age of the solar system. Nevertheless, Earth rocks tell us that the solar system is old: The oldest rocks on the Earth date back about 4 billion years, although most of the Earth is covered in rocks only hundreds of millions of years old.

**TIME OUT TO THINK** *Suppose you do radioactive dating on a chunk of lava recently spewed out of Kilauea, an active volcano on the island of Hawaii. How old would it be? Explain.*

Determining the age of the solar system requires finding rocks from beyond the Earth—rocks that might not have melted or vaporized since the birth of the solar system. But how do we get rocks from space? Astronauts brought back numerous rocks from the Moon, and the oldest of these date to about 4.4 billion years ago. But this still is not the age of the solar system, because the Moon's surface melted and resolidified as a result of the early bombardment. Our other main source of rocks from space is meteorites that have fallen to Earth.

Many meteorites appear to be unchanged since their formation and are therefore samples of the condensation and accretion processes in the early solar system. Careful analysis of radioactive elements in meteorites shows that the oldest ones formed about 4.6 billion years ago, marking the beginning of accretion from the solar nebula. (Museums and specialty catalogs sell meteorite samples. For a few dollars, you can buy a small, solidified piece of the solar nebula. It will be the oldest object you'll ever touch.) Calculations show that accretion probably lasted only about 0.1 billion years (100 million years), so Earth and the other planets formed about 4.5 billion years ago.

The age of 4.6 billion years means our solar system is less than half as old as the universe. Ours is a middle-aged solar system in an old universe.

### A Trigger for the Collapse?

The very existence of radioactive elements in meteorites is profoundly important, quite apart from the age information those elements provide. Radioactive elements are made only deep inside stars or in violent stellar explosions (supernovae). Thus, the presence of these elements in meteorites and on Earth underscores the fact that our solar system is made from the remnants of past generations of stars.

The discovery of daughter elements of short-lived radioactive elements has further implications. The rare isotope xenon-129 is found in some meteorites. Xenon is gaseous even at extremely low temperatures, so it could not have condensed and become trapped in planetesimals forming in the solar nebula. Thus, any xenon present in meteorites must be a product of radioactive decay. In fact, xenon-129 is a decay product of iodine-129. But iodine-129 has a half-life of just 17 million years, so this iodine must have traveled from the star in which it was produced to our solar nebula fairly quickly. (If the supernova had occurred a billion years earlier, the iodine would have decayed entirely into xenon, which would not have condensed or accreted.) This suggests that a nearby star exploded only a few million years (or less) before our solar system formed. The shock wave emanating from the exploding star may even have triggered the collapse of the solar nebula by giving gravity a little extra push. Once gravity got started, the rest of the collapse was inevitable.

## 8.7 Other Planetary Systems

How common are planetary systems? What are the odds of another Earth-like planet? Are habitable planets as common in the real universe as they are in science fiction? We cannot yet answer these questions definitively, but we've made great progress in our understanding of planetary systems.

As we've discussed, observations have confirmed that protoplanetary disks are common, as predicted by our theory of solar system formation. Even binary and multiple star systems, which many astronomers once thought unlikely to harbor planets, now seem to be reasonable candidates for planets. Observations show protoplanetary disks around at least some binary star systems (see Figure 8.8a), and recent calculations show that planets can safely orbit in such systems either by being close to one star or by being in a large orbit around both stars.

More importantly, rapid advances in observational technology now allow us to search for actual planets, not just for protoplanetary disks. At the beginning of the 1990s, we had no conclusive proof that planets existed around any star besides our Sun. By 2001, dozens of planetlike objects had been detected around other stars. We cannot always determine precise masses for these objects, and some may turn out to be more like small stars than the planets of our solar system. In addition, our current technology is not yet capable of detecting planets as small as Earth, so we still have no observational evidence concerning the existence of Earth-like planets. Nevertheless, we can now be quite sure that our solar system is not the only planetary system, and we know of many more planets outside our solar system than within it.

### Detecting Extrasolar Planets

You might think that the easiest way to discover **extrasolar planets**, or planets around other stars, would be simply to photograph them through powerful telescopes. Unfortunately, current observational technology cannot produce such images. The primary problem arises from the fact that any light from an orbiting planet would be overwhelmed by light from the star it orbits. For example, a Sun-like star would be a *billion times* brighter than the reflected light from an Earth-like planet. Because even the best telescopes blur the light from stars at least a little, finding the small blip of planetary light amid the glare of scattered starlight would be very difficult. Astronomers are working on technologies that may overcome this problem, but for now we rely primarily on techniques that observe the star itself to find indirect evidence of planets.

To date, the most commonly used strategy involves searching for a planet by watching for the small gravitational tug it exerts on its star. In most cases, the easiest way to find this tug is to identify small Doppler shifts in the star's spectrum [Section 5.5]. An orbiting planet causes its star to alternately move slightly toward and away from us, which makes the star's spectral lines alternately shift toward the blue and toward the red (Figure 8.20). Remarkably, current techniques can measure a star's velocity to better than 3 m/s—jogging speed—which is good enough to find gravitational tugs caused by planets the size of Jupiter, and in some cases even smaller. For example, the data in Figure 8.20b reveal a planet with roughly 60% of the mass of Jupiter orbiting the star called 51 Pegasi. This planet lies so close to its star that its "year" lasts only four of our days and its temperature is probably over 1000 K.

By 2001, the Doppler-shift method had been used to identify more than 50 planets around other stars (Figure 8.21), and discoveries are coming so rapidly that the number may be far greater by the time you read this. Highlights of recent discoveries include a bona fide "planetary system" of three planets orbiting the star Upsilon Andromedae, a handful of planets as small as Saturn around various stars (see Figure 8.21), and a dust disk plus a planet orbiting the star Epsilon Eridani.

Interestingly, astronomers have recently discovered some planet-sized objects that appear to be floating freely between stars. These objects seem to

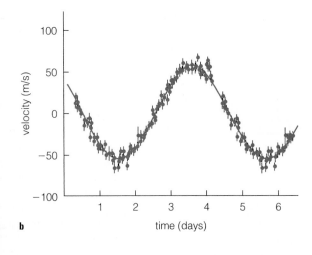

**b**

**FIGURE 8.20** (**a**) Doppler shifts allow us to detect the slight motion of a star caused by an orbiting planet. (**b**) A periodic Doppler shift in the spectrum of 51 Pegasi shows the presence of a large planet with an orbital period of about 4 days. Dots are actual data points; bars through dots represent measurement uncertainty.

be Jupiter-like in mass; because they do not orbit stars, astronomers are still debating whether or not they should be called planets. The first such objects were found in 2000 in the Orion Nebula. We see these objects not in reflected sunlight (since they have no suns), but in the afterglow of the heat of their formation. These objects probably did not form in planetary systems as we have discussed throughout this chapter. Instead, they probably formed in much the same way that stars form in interstellar clouds but ended up much smaller in size.

### The Nature of Extrasolar Planets

Although the Doppler-shift technique allows us to discover orbiting objects, by itself it cannot tell us the nature of the orbiting bodies. The first problem is that the amount of a Doppler shift depends both on the mass of the orbiting object and on the tilt of its orbit: Orbits seen edge-on (from our vantage point on Earth) produce the largest Doppler shifts, while face-on orbits produce no Doppler shift at all. Therefore, an observed Doppler shift could be produced either by a low-mass planet in an edge-on orbit or by a more massive planet (or even a *brown dwarf* [Section 16.2] or small star) in a more tilted orbit. The masses listed in Figure 8.21 are therefore underestimates in some cases, but probably by no more than a factor of 2. The second problem is that, even with precise mass estimates, we still would not know the size of the planet or whether the planet is more terrestrial or jovian in nature.

For the planet orbiting HD209548, the uncertainties in mass and size vanished in fall 1999 when meticulous observations by two teams of astronomers revealed a 1.7% drop in the brightness of the star (Figure 8.22). The drop occurred at exactly the time that a newly discovered planet was expected to pass on the side of the orbit nearest Earth. The planet must have passed directly on the line of sight between the Earth and the star, temporarily blocking some of the star's light from reaching the Earth. At that moment, we learned that the orbit was truly edge-on and therefore that the mass estimate was correct. We also learned that the planet's disk covers about 1.7% of the star's disk which allowed us to estimate the planet's radius and confirm that it is a jovian planet.

### Lessons for Solar System Formation

The discovery of extrasolar planets presents us with opportunities to test our theory of solar system formation. Can our existing theory explain other planetary systems, or will we have to go back to the drawing board? So far, the discoveries have presented at least one significant challenge.

The new challenge arises from the fact that most of the recently discovered planets are quite different from those of our solar system. Many have highly elliptical orbits rather than the nearly circular orbits of planets in our solar system, and most of the planets are more massive than Jupiter. Most intriguing is the fact that many of these large planets lie quite close to their stars—a very different situation from

## Planets Around Sun-like Stars

| Star | Mass / orbital position |
|---|---|
| inner solar system | ·Mercury  ·Venus  ·Earth  ·Mars |
| HD 83443 | $0.35M_{Jup}$ |
| HD 46375 | $0.25M_{Jup}$ |
| HD 187123 | $0.54M_{Jup}$ |
| HD 179949 | $0.86M_{Jup}$ |
| BD-103166 | $0.48M_{Jup}$ |
| Tau Boo | $4.14M_{Jup}$ |
| HD 75289 | $0.46M_{Jup}$ |
| HD 209458 | $0.63M_{Jup}$ |
| 51 Peg | $0.46M_{Jup}$ |
| UpsAnd | $0.68M_{Jup}$   $2.05M_{Jup}$   $4.29M_{Jup}$ |
| HD 168746 | $0.24M_{Jup}$ |
| HD 217107 | $1.29M_{Jup}$ |
| HD 162020 | $13.73M_{Jup}$ |
| HD 130322 | $1.15M_{Jup}$ |
| HD 108147 | $0.35M_{Jup}$ |
| GJ 86 | $4.23M_{Jup}$ |
| 55 Cnc | $0.93M_{Jup}$ |
| HD 38529 | $0.77M_{Jup}$ |
| GJ 876 | $0.56M_{Jup}$   $1.9M_{Jup}$ |
| HD 195019 | $3.55M_{Jup}$ |
| HD 6434 | $0.48M_{Jup}$ |
| HD 192263 | $0.81M_{Jup}$ |
| HD 83443c | $0.16M_{Jup}$ |
| RhoCrB | $0.99M_{Jup}$ |
| HD 168443 | $7.73M_{Jup}$   $17.1M_{Jup}$ |
| HD 121504 | $0.89M_{Jup}$ |
| HD 16141 | $0.22M_{Jup}$ |
| HD 114762 | $10.96M_{Jup}$ |
| 70 Vir | $7.42M_{Jup}$ |
| HD 52265 | $1.14M_{Jup}$ |
| HD 1237 | $1.14M_{Jup}$ |
| HD 37124 | $1.14M_{Jup}$ |
| HD 202206 | $14.68M_{Jup}$ |
| HD 12661 | $2.83M_{Jup}$ |
| HD 134987 | $1.58M_{Jup}$ |
| HD 169830 | $2.95M_{Jup}$ |
| HD 89744 | $7.17M_{Jup}$ |
| IotaHor | $2.98M_{Jup}$ |
| HD 92788 | $3.86M_{Jup}$ |
| HD 177830 | $1.24M_{Jup}$ |
| HD 210277 | $1.29M_{Jup}$ |
| HD 27442 | $1.13M_{Jup}$ |
| HD 82943 | $2.3M_{Jup}$ |
| HD 222582 | $5.18M_{Jup}$ |
| HD 160691 | $1.87M_{Jup}$ |
| 16CygB | $1.68M_{Jup}$ |
| 47UMa | $2.60M_{Jup}$ |
| HD 10697 | $6.08M_{Jup}$ |
| HD 190228 | $5.0M_{Jup}$ |
| 14 Her | $5.55M_{Jup}$ |

0          1          2          3

orbital semimajor axis (AU)

**FIGURE 8.21** This diagram shows the orbital distances and approximate masses of the first 55 planets discovered around other stars. Most of the planets found so far are closer to their stars and more massive than the planets in our solar system. (Planet sizes are not to scale.)

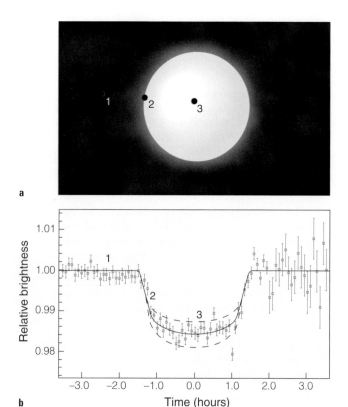

**FIGURE 8.22** Careful measurements of the brightness of the star called HD209548 revealed that an orbiting planet passes directly in front of it as seen from Earth, which means that the planet's orbit must be edge-on as seen from Earth. (**a**) Artist's conception of the planet as it passes directly in front of its star as seen from Earth. (**b**) These data show the 1.7% drop in the star's brightness that proved the planet is passing in front of the star as seen from Earth.

Second, the extrasolar planets discovered to date may turn out to be relatively rare exceptions to general rules. Astronomers have succeeded in detecting planets around only a few percent of the stars they've studied so far. It's possible that planets also circle most of the other stars but have eluded detection because they are more like the planets in our own solar system. The Doppler technique makes it much easier to find large planets with close-in orbits, because such planets exert greater gravitational tugs on their stars than smaller or more distant planets. Thus, our early discoveries of extrasolar planets may be like glancing at animals in the rain forest: The jungle appears full of brightly colored parrots and frogs, but far more animals fail to catch our eye. In the same way, we may have discovered the rare exceptions but so far missed the more common cases that are like our own solar system.

As we discover more planets, we should gain a better understanding of how well our theory of solar system formation holds up. The discoveries should come rapidly, thanks to new technologies and planned space missions. In particular, NASA has placed a high priority on building ambitious orbital telescopes for the detection and study of extrasolar planets. Within a couple of decades, NASA hopes to launch high-resolution interferometers [Section 7.5] that will enable us to obtain images and spectra of planets in other solar systems. Then, at last, we will know whether solar systems like ours—and planets like Earth—are rare or common.

that in our solar system, where the large planets are found in the outer solar system. Moreover, as we discussed in Section 8.4, our theory has a good explanation for why large planets should form only in the outer solar system: That is the only place where the solar nebula was cool enough for ices to condense and grow into the large seeds needed for jovian planets. Thus, the existence of dozens of systems with large, close-in planets seems to contradict our theory.

Fortunately, there are at least two reasonable ways out of this dilemma. First, recent theoretical work has shown that the gas in a forming solar system can exert drag on young jovian planets, tending to make them migrate closer to their stars. Thus, if a star's wind does not sweep the remaining nebular gas into space soon enough, the jovian planets may end up close to their stars—which could explain the large, close-in planets we've detected. In some cases, the planets may even end up being consumed by their parent stars! If this idea proves correct, the layout of our solar system suggests that the solar wind blew out the remaining gas of the solar nebula relatively early compared to other star systems.

## THE BIG PICTURE

We've seen that the nebular theory accounts for the major characteristics of our solar system. As you continue your study of the solar system, keep in mind the following "big picture" ideas.

- Close examination of the solar system unveils a wealth of patterns, trends, and groupings, leading us to the conclusion that all the planets formed from the same cloud of gas at about the same time.

- Chance events may have played a large role in determining how individual planets turned out. No one knows how different the solar system might be if it started over.

- Planet-forming processes are apparently universal. The discovery of protoplanetary disks and full-fledged planets around other stars has brought planetary science to the brink of an exciting new era.

## Review Questions

1. What is *comparative planetology*? What is its basic premise? What are its primary goals?

2. Briefly summarize the observed patterns of motion in our solar system.

3. Summarize the differences between *terrestrial planets* and *jovian planets*. Why is the Moon grouped with the terrestrial planets? Where does Pluto fit in?

4. What are *asteroids*? Where are they found? What are *comets*, and how do those of the *Oort cloud* and the *Kuiper belt* differ in terms of their orbits?

5. Summarize the four challenges that any theory of the solar system must explain.

6. What is the *nebular theory*? How does it get its name? What do we mean by the *solar nebula*?

7. Describe the processes that led the solar nebula to collapse into a spinning disk. Also describe the evidence supporting the idea that our solar system had a *protosun* and a *protoplanetary disk* early in its history.

8. Distinguish among *metals*, *rocks*, *hydrogen compounds*, and *light gases*. What were their relative abundances in the solar nebula?

9. Explain how temperature differences in the solar nebula led to the condensation of different materials at different distances from the protosun. What do we mean by the *frost line* in the solar nebula?

10. What is *accretion*? What are *planetesimals*? Explain the role of electrostatic forces in getting accretion started and the role of gravity in accelerating accretion as planetesimals grow larger.

11. Briefly explain why accretion was able to produce much larger planetesimals in the outer solar system than in the inner solar system.

12. Describe the process of *nebular capture* that allowed the jovian planets to grow to large sizes. How does this process explain the satellite systems of jovian planets?

13. What is the *solar wind*? How did its strength in the past differ from its strength today? What role did it play in ending the growth of the planets?

14. Why does the Sun's slow rotation rate seem, at least at first, to contradict the nebular theory? Explain how the process of *magnetic braking* accounts for this apparent contradiction.

15. Why do we think that asteroids and comets are leftover planetesimals? Briefly describe how gravitational encounters affected their orbits.

16. What was the early bombardment? How can we use *impact crators* to estimate the age of a planetary surface?

17. What clues suggest that a moon was captured instead of forming with its planet? How do we think such captures occurred? Give a few examples of moons thought to have been captured.

18. Describe the process by which a giant impact may have led to the formation of our Moon. What other oddities of our solar system might be explained by giant impacts?

19. Summarize how the nebular theory meets the four challenges laid out in this chapter. Describe a few of the remaining unanswered questions.

20. Briefly describe the process of *radioactive dating* and how we use it to establish the age of our solar system. Why can't we determine the age of our solar system by dating Earth rocks? What kinds of rocks can we use?

21. What evidence suggests that a nearby stellar explosion may have triggered the collapse of the solar nebula?

22. Describe how we can detect *extrasolar planets* today, and summarize the current evidence concerning planets in other solar systems.

23. What have we learned about solar system formation from discoveries of extrasolar planets?

## Discussion Questions

1. *Theory and Observation.* Discuss the interplay between theory and observation that has led to our modern theory of the formation of the solar system. What role does technology play in allowing us to test this theory?

2. *Random Events in Solar System History.* According to our theory of solar system formation, numerous random events, such as giant impacts, had important consequences for the way our solar system turned out. Can you think of other random events that might have caused the planets to form very differently? If there had been a different set of random events, what important properties of our solar system would have turned out the same and what ones might be different? Discuss.

3. *Lucky to Be Here?* In considering the overall process of solar system formation, do you think it was very likely for a planet like Earth to have formed? Could random events in the early history of the solar system have prevented us from even being here today? Defend your opinion. Do your opinions on these questions have any implications for your belief in the possibility of Earth-like planets around other stars?

## Problems

*Surprising Discoveries?* For **problems 1–8**, suppose we found a solar system with the property described. (These are *not* real discoveries.) In light of our theory of solar system formation, decide whether the discovery should be considered reasonable or surprising. Explain.

1. A solar system has five terrestrial planets in its inner solar system and three jovian planets in its outer solar system.

2. A solar system has four large jovian planets in its inner solar system and seven small planets made of rock and metal in its outer solar system.

3. A solar system has ten planets that all orbit the star in approximately the same plane. However, five planets orbit in one direction (e.g., counterclockwise), while the other five orbit in the opposite direction (e.g., clockwise).

4. A solar system has 12 planets that all orbit the star in the same direction and in nearly the same plane. The 15 largest moons in this solar system orbit their planets in nearly the same direction and plane as well. However, several smaller moons have highly inclined orbits around their planets.

5. A solar system has six terrestrial planets and four jovian planets. Each of the six terrestrial planets has at least five moons, while the jovian planets have no moons at all.

6. A solar system has four Earth-size terrestrial planets. Each of the four planets has a single moon nearly identical in size to Earth's Moon.

7. A solar system has many rocky asteroids and many icy comets. However, most of the comets orbit the star in a belt much like the asteroid belt of our solar system, while the asteroids inhabit regions much like the Kuiper belt and Oort cloud of our solar system.

8. A solar system has several planets similar in composition to our jovian planets but similar in mass to our terrestrial planets.

9. *Two Classes of Planets.* Explain in terms a friend or roommate would understand why the jovian planets are lower in density than the terrestrial planets even though they all formed from the same cloud.

10. *A Cold Solar Nebula.* Suppose the entire solar nebula had cooled to 50 K before the solar wind cleared it away. How would the composition and sizes of the terrestrial planets be different from what we see today? Explain your answer in a few sentences.

11. *No Nebular Capture.* Suppose the solar wind had cleared away the solar nebula before the process of nebular capture was completed in the outer solar system. How would the jovian planets be different? Would they still have satellites? Explain your answer in a few sentences.

12. *Angular Momentum.* Suppose our solar nebula had begun with much more angular momentum than it did. Do you think planets could still have formed? Why or why not? What if the solar nebula had started with zero angular momentum? Explain your answers in one or two paragraphs.

13. *Jupiter's Action.* Suppose that, for some reason, the planet Jupiter had never formed. How do you think the distribution of asteroids and comets in our solar system would be different? How would these differences have affected Earth? Explain your answer in a few sentences.

14. *Satellite Systems as Mini–Solar Systems.* The nebula surrounding the forming jovian planets was hotter near its center, so satellites forming from the nebula could be built from different types of condensates, just as the planets were. Would satellite densities increase or decrease with increasing distance from the planet? According to Appendix C, which jovian planet satellite system best matches this prediction? Explain your answers in a few sentences.

*15. *Dating Lunar Rocks.* Suppose you are analyzing Moon rocks that contain small amounts of uranium-238, which decays into lead with a half-life of 4.5 billion years.
   a. In one rock from the "lunar highlands," you determine that 55% of the original uranium-238 remains; the other 45% has decayed into lead. How old is the rock?
   b. In a rock from the "lunar maria," you find that 63% of its original uranium-238 remains; the other 37% has decayed into lead. Is this rock older or younger than the highlands rock? By how much? (The significance of these ages will become clear in the next chapter.)

*16. *Radioactive Dating with Carbon-14.* The half-life of carbon-14 is about 5,700 years.
   a. You find a piece of cloth painted with organic dyes. By analyzing the dye in the cloth, you find that only 77% of the carbon-14 originally in the dye remains. When was the cloth painted?
   b. A well-preserved piece of wood found at an archaeological site has 6.2% of the carbon-14 that it must have had when it was alive. Estimate when the wood was cut.
   c. Is carbon-14 useful for establishing the age of the Earth? Why or why not?

*17. *Unusual Meteorites.* Some unusual meteorites thought to be chips from Mars [Section 12.3] contain small amounts of the radioactive element thorium-232 and its decay product lead-208. The half-life for this decay process is 14 billion years. A detailed analysis shows that 94% of the original thorium remains. How old are these meteorites? Compare your answer to the age of the solar system and comment briefly.

*18. *51 Pegasi.* The star 51 Pegasi has about the same mass as our Sun, and the planet discovered around it has an orbital period of 4.23 days. The mass of the planet is estimated to be 0.6 times the mass of Jupiter.

   a. Use Kepler's third law to find the planet's average distance (semimajor axis) from its star. (*Hint:* Because the mass of 51 Pegasi is about the same as the mass of our Sun, you can use Kepler's third law in its original form, $p^2 = a^3$ [see Chapter 5]; be sure to convert the period into years.)

   b. Briefly explain why, according to our theory of solar system formation, it is surprising to find a planet the size of the 51 Pegasi planet orbiting at this distance.

   c. Hypothesize as to how the 51 Pegasi planet might have come to exist. Explain your hypothesis in a few sentences.

*19. *Transiting Planets.* The star HD209548 is about the same size as our Sun, and the planet discovered around it blocks 1.7% of the star's area when it passes in front of the star. (Appendix E contains useful data for this problem.)

   a. How large a planet is required to block the observed fraction of the star's area? Give your answer in kilometers. (*Hint:* Remember that the brightness drop tells us that the planet blocked 1.7% of the star's visible *area.*)

   b. The mass of the planet is estimated to be 0.6 times the mass of Jupiter. What is the density of the planet?

   c. Compare the density of this planet to that of planets in our solar system, and comment on whether this density makes the planet terrestrial or jovian in nature.

## Web Projects

Find useful links for Web projects on the text Web site.

1. *New Planets.* Find up-to-date information about discoveries of planets in other solar systems. Create a personal "Web journal," complete with pictures from the Web, describing at least three recent discoveries of new planets. For each case, write one or two paragraphs in your journal describing the method used in the discovery, comparing the discovered planet to the planets of our own solar system, and summarizing whether the discovery poses any new challenges to our theory of solar system formation.

2. *Missions to Search for Planets.* Learn about one proposed space mission to search for planets around other stars, such as Kepler, SIM, or Terrestrial Planet Finder. Write a short report about the plans for the mission and its current status.

*Nothing is rich but the inexhaustible wealth of nature. She shows us only surfaces, but she is a million fathoms deep.*

RALPH WALDO EMERSON

# CHAPTER 9

# Planetary Geology
## Earth and the Other
## Terrestrial Worlds

Think back to a time when you went for a walk or a drive through the open countryside. Did you see a valley? If so, the creek or river that carved it probably still flows at the bottom. Were the valley walls composed of lava, telling of an earlier time when molten rock gushed from volcanoes? Or were they made of neatly layered sedimentary rocks that formed when ancient seas covered the area? Were the rock layers tilted? That's a sign that movements of the Earth's crust have pushed the rocks around.

Since the beginning of the space age, we've been able to make similar observations and ask similar questions about geological features on other worlds. As a result, we can now make detailed geological comparisons among the different planets. We've learned that, even though all the terrestrial worlds are similar in composition and formed at about the same time, their geological histories have differed because of a few basic properties of each world. Thus, by comparing the geologies of the terrestrial worlds, we can learn much more about the Earth.

Venus

Mercury

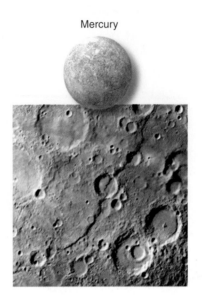

**FIGURE 9.1** Global views of the terrestrial planets to scale and representative surface close-ups, each a few hundred kilometers across. The global view of Venus shows its surface without its atmosphere, based on radar data from the Magellan spacecraft; all other images are photos (or composite photos) taken from spacecraft.

## 9.1 Comparative Planetary Geology

The five terrestrial worlds—Mercury, Venus, Earth, the Moon, and Mars—share a common ancestry in their birth from the solar nebula, but their present-day surfaces show vast differences (Figure 9.1). Mercury and the Moon are battered worlds densely covered by craters except in areas that appear to be volcanic plains. Venus has volcanic plains that appear to have been twisted and torn by internal stresses, leaving bizarre bulges and odd volcanoes that dot the surface. Mars, despite its middling size, has the solar system's largest volcanoes and is the only planet other than Earth where running water played a major role in shaping the surface. Earth has surface features similar to all those on other terrestrial worlds and more—including a unique layer of living organisms that covers almost the entire surface of the planet. Our purpose in this chapter is to understand how the profound differences among the terrestrial surfaces came to be.

The study of surface features and the processes that create them is called **geology**. The root *geo* means "Earth," and *geology* originally referred only to the study of the Earth. Today, however, we speak of *planetary geology,* the extension of geology to include all the solid bodies in the solar system, whether rocky or icy.

Geology is relatively easy to study on Earth, where we can examine the surface in great detail. People have scrambled over much of the Earth's surface, identifying rock types and mapping geological features. We've pierced the Earth's surface with 10-kilometer-deep drill shafts and learned about the deeper interior by studying *seismic waves* generated by earthquakes. Thanks to these efforts, today we have a fairly good understanding of the history of our planet's surface and the processes that shaped it.

Studying the geology of other planets is much more challenging. The Moon is the only alien world from which we've collected rocks, some gathered by the Apollo astronauts and others by Russian robotic landers in the 1970s. We can also study the dozen or so meteorites from Mars that have landed on Earth. Aside from these few rocks, we have little more than images taken from spacecraft from which to decode the history of the other planets over the past 4.6 billion years. It's like studying people's facial expressions to understand what they're feeling inside—and what their childhood was like! Fortunately, this decoding is considerably easier for planets than for people.

Spacecraft have visited and photographed all the terrestrial worlds. Patterns of sunlight and shadow on photographs taken from orbit reveal features such as cliffs, craters, and mountains. Besides ordinary, visible-light photographs, we also have spacecraft images

Earth

Earth's Moon

Mars

taken with infrared and ultraviolet cameras, spectroscopic data, and in some cases three-dimensional data compiled with the aid of radar. Finally, we have close-up photographs of selected locations on all the terrestrial worlds but Mercury, taken by spacecraft that have landed on their surfaces (Figure 9.2). The result is that we now understand the geology of the terrestrial worlds well enough to make detailed and meaningful comparisons among them.

Comparative planetary geology (one part of comparative planetology) hinges on the principle that a planet's surface features can be traced back to its fundamental properties. For example, we saw in Chapter 8 that a planet's composition depends primarily on how far from the Sun it formed. In the rest of this chapter, we will look for relationships between surface features and the fundamental properties and processes of the planets. But because surface geology depends largely on a planet's interior, we must first look inside the terrestrial worlds.

## 9.2 Inside the Terrestrial Worlds

Planets are all approximately spherical and quite smooth relative to their size. For example, compared to the Earth's radius of 6,378 km, the tallest mountains could be represented by grains of sand on a typical globe.

**TIME OUT TO THINK** *Find a globe of the Earth that shows mountains in raised relief (i.e., you can feel the mountains as bumps on the globe). Are the heights of the mountains correctly scaled relative to the Earth's size? Explain.*

It's easy to understand why the gaseous jovian planets ended up nearly spherical: Gravity always acts to pull material together, and a sphere is the most compact shape possible. It's a bit subtler when we deal with the rocky terrestrial worlds, because rock can resist the pull of gravity. Indeed, many small moons and asteroids are "potato-shaped" precisely because their weak gravity is unable to overcome the rigidity of their rocky material. Before we can understand why the terrestrial worlds ended up smooth and spherical and why they all have similar internal structures, we must first investigate the behavior of rock.

### Solid as a Rock?

We often think of rocks as the very definition of strength, but rocks are not always as solid as they may seem. Most rocks are a hodgepodge of different minerals, each characterized by its chemical compo-

**a** Mercury

**FIGURE 9.2** Surface views of the terrestrial worlds. No spacecraft have landed on Mercury, so an artist's conception is shown; all other images are photos. The Venus photo shows only a small patch of surface at the base of the Russian Venera lander, visible in the lower right.

**b** Venus

**c** Earth

**d** Moon

**e** Mars

sition. For example, *granite* is a common rock composed of crystals of quartz ($SiO_2$), feldspar ($NaAlSi_3O_8$ is one of several varieties), and other minerals. Rocks are solid because of electrical bonds between the mineral molecules. But when these bonds are subjected to sustained stress over millions or billions of years, they can break and re-form, gradually allowing rocky material to deform and flow. In fact, the long-term behavior of rock is much like that of Silly Putty™, which stretches when you pull it slowly but breaks if you pull it sharply (Figure 9.3).

The strength of a rock depends on its composition, its temperature, and the surrounding pressure. Rocks of different composition are held together by molecular bonds of different strength. Even two very similar rocks may differ in strength if one contains traces of water: The water can act as a lubricant to reduce the rock's strength. Higher temperatures also make rocks weaker: Just as Silly Putty becomes more pliable if you heat it, warm rocks are weaker and more deformable than cooler rocks of the same type. Pressure can increase rock strength: The very high pressures found deep in planetary interiors can compress rocks so much that they stay solid even at temperatures high enough to melt them under ordinary conditions. (Most substances are denser as solids than as liquids, so the compression caused by high pressure tends to make things solid. Water is a rare exception, becoming *less* dense when it freezes—which is why ice floats in water.)

At high enough temperatures (usually over 1,000 K), some or all of the minerals in a rock may melt, making it *molten* (or partially molten, if only some minerals have melted). Just as different types of solid rock are more deformable than others, different types of rock behave differently when molten. Some molten rocks are runny like water, while others flow slowly like honey or molasses. We describe the "thickness" of a liquid with the technical term **viscosity**: Water has a low viscosity because it flows easily, while honey and molasses have much higher viscosities because they flow slowly. As we'll soon see, molten rock viscosities are very important to understanding volcanoes.

### Terrestrial-World Layering

The rocky terrestrial worlds became spherical because of rock's ability to flow. Even when rock is solid, the strength of gravity in a moderately large world (over about 500 km in diameter) can overcome the strength of solid rock and make the world spherical in less than a billion years. If the world is molten, as was the case with the terrestrial worlds in their early histories, it can become spherical much more quickly. (For similar reasons, Earth's ocean surface is smoother and more spherical than its rocky surface.)

**FIGURE 9.3** Silly Putty stretches when pulled slowly but breaks cleanly when pulled rapidly. Rock behaves just the same, but on a longer time scale.

Gravity also gave the terrestrial worlds layered interiors. You know that in a mixture of oil and water, the less dense oil rises to the top while the denser water sinks to the bottom. This process in which gravity separates materials by density is called **differentiation** (because it results in layers made of *different* materials). The terrestrial worlds underwent differentiation early in their histories, when they were molten throughout their interiors. As a result, each terrestrial world now has three interior layers of differing composition (Figure 9.4). Dense metals such as iron and nickel sank through molten rocky material to form a **core**. Rocky material composed of *silicates*—minerals that contain silicon and oxygen (and other elements)—came to rest above the core, forming a thick **mantle**. A low-density "scum" of rocks composed of the lightest silicates rose to form a **crust**.

The terms *core, mantle,* and *crust* are defined by the composition within each layer. But characterizing the layers by *rock strength* rather than composition

rocky crust
(lower density)

mantle
(medium density)

rigid lithosphere
(crust and part of mantle)

metal core
(highest density)

**FIGURE 9.4** Interior structure of a generic terrestrial world. The thicknesses of the crust and lithosphere are enlarged for clarity.

will lead to volcanoes and other geological activity on a planet with a relatively thin lithosphere. In contrast, a thick, strong lithosphere inhibits geological activity. The most important factor determining lithospheric thickness is internal temperature: Higher internal temperature makes rocks softer, leading to a thinner rigid lithosphere.

Figure 9.5 compares the interior structures of the terrestrial worlds. Note that the smaller worlds have thicker lithospheres, indicating that they have cooler interiors. The cores and mantles also differ in their relative sizes: Because cores are made from metals and mantles are made from rock, their relative sizes depend on the proportions of metal and rock in a planet. These proportions were determined primarily by condensation in the solar nebula, but they may also have been affected by giant impacts [Section 8.5]. Planetary cores may be partially or completely molten, depending on the particular combination of internal temperature and pressure.

You may be wondering how we know what the interiors of the terrestrial worlds look like. After all, even on Earth our deepest drill shafts barely prick the lithosphere. Fortunately, several techniques allow us to study planetary interiors without actually having to drill into them. First, we can measure a planet's size from telescopic or spacecraft images, and its mass by applying Newton's version of Kepler's third law to the orbital properties of a natural or artificial satellite [Section 5.4]. Together, these measurements tell us the average density of the planet, which gives clues about its composition. Second, the strength of gravity on a planet may differ slightly from place to place depending on the underlying interior structure, so we can learn about that structure through gravity measurements made from orbiting satellites. Third, a planet's magnetic field is generated in its interior, so measurements of the magnetic-field strength also

turns out to be more useful for understanding geological activity. From this point of view, we speak of an outer layer of relatively rigid rock called the **lithosphere** (*lithos* means "stone" in Greek). The lithosphere generally encompasses the crust and the uppermost portion of the mantle. Beneath the lithosphere, the higher temperatures allow rock to deform and flow much more easily. Thus, the lithosphere is essentially a layer of rigid rock that "floats" on the softer rock below. (The underlying layer of softer rock is called the *asthenosphere* (literally, the "weak-o-sphere"). Although rock in the asthenosphere deforms more easily, it is not actually molten.) On the Earth, the lithosphere is broken into *plates* that move as the underlying rock flows gradually, creating the phenomenon called *continental drift* [Section 13.2].

The thickness of the lithosphere plays an important role in surface geology. Interior heat and motion

**FIGURE 9.5** Interior structures of the terrestrial worlds, in order of size. The crust and lithosphere are enlarged on Venus and Earth for greater visibility.

Key

crust

mantle

core

Earth

Venus

Mars

Mercury

Moon

lithosphere

lithosphere

lithosphere

lithosphere

lithosphere

### Seismic Waves

Earthquakes (or "planet-quakes") generate vibrations, or **seismic waves**, that propagate through a planet's interior. The word *seismic* comes from the Greek word for "shake," and seismic waves shake the surface when they arrive—even if they've traveled all the way through the interior from the location where a quake originated.

On Earth, *seismographs* located in many places around the world record the shaking of the surface as seismic waves arrive after an earthquake. By comparing the recordings from many different places, we can reconstruct the paths that the seismic waves took through the Earth's interior. Seismic waves generally travel through the Earth at speeds of thousands of kilometers per hour, but the precise speeds and directions of the waves depend on the composition, density, pressure, temperature, and phase (solid or liquid) of the material they pass through. Thus, we can deduce all of these internal conditions through careful study of seismic waves.

Seismic waves come in two basic types, and the difference between the two types helps us study Earth's interior. We can demonstrate the two wave types by imagining that the bonds holding rocks together are like Slinkys (Figure 9.6a). Pushing and pulling on one end of a Slinky generates a wave in which the Slinky is bunched up in some places and stretched out in others. Waves like this in rock are called P waves. (The *P* stands for *primary,* because these waves travel fastest and therefore are the first to arrive, but is more easily remembered as *pressure* or *pushing.*) P waves are essentially a type of sound wave and therefore can travel through liquid or gas as well as through solid rock. In the second type of wave, shaking one end of the Slinky side-to-side or up and down sends a wave down its length. Such waves are called S waves in rock, and they travel through rock a bit more slowly than P waves. (The S stands for *secondary* but is easier to remember as *shear* or *shake.*) Unlike P waves, S waves cannot travel through liquids (or gases): Molecules in liquid are not connected by strong bonds like those that hold Slinkys together, so they cannot exert sideways forces on their neighbors. Thus, the fact that S waves do not reach the side of the world opposite an earthquake tells us that the Earth's interior must have a liquid layer in the outer region of the core (Figure 9.6b).

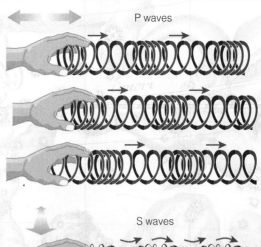

P waves

S waves

**a** Slinky examples demonstrating P and S waves.

Molten outer core stops S waves, bends P waves.

**b** Since S waves do not reach the side of the Earth opposite the earthquake, we infer that part of Earth's core is molten.

**FIGURE 9.6** Seismic waves provide a probe of a planet's interior.

provide information about interior structure. Fourth, lava brought up from deep inside a planet can tell us something about the interior composition. Finally, planetary vibrations (*seismic waves* from "planet-quakes") tell us about interior structure in much the same way that shaking a present offers a few hints on what's inside. These diverse types of measurements are combined with computer models based on known laws of physics to calculate a planet's interior structure. Our measurements are much more extensive for Earth than for any other world, so we know the most about Earth's interior. But scientists have applied some of the same techniques in more limited ways to other worlds, giving us confidence that the general pictures shown in Figure 9.5 are correct.

## 9.3  How Interiors Work

Geological activity depends on a planet's interior structure, and interior structure depends on internal temperature. In this section, we investigate how heat (thermal energy) is deposited in the planetary interior and how it leaks outward over time.

### How Interiors Get Hot

It's often said that the Sun is the ultimate source of all our energy. On the surface, this statement is true: Sunlight bathes the Earth's surface with a power of roughly 1,000 watts per square meter (in the daytime), while the heat leaking outward from the Earth's interior contributes only about 0.05 watt per square meter. Thus, the Earth's surface receives more than 10,000 times as much energy from the Sun as from its own interior. In general, the energy a world receives from sunlight depends on its distance from the Sun. This energy, along with properties of the planet's atmosphere, determines the surface temperature [Section 10.2].

In contrast, the Sun contributes very little to a planet's *internal* temperature. In fact, the Sun's only role is in helping to determine the starting point for the interior temperature structure: A terrestrial world is coolest at its surface and gets warmer as you go into its interior. The three most important sources of internal heat are *accretion, differentiation,* and *radioactivity* (Figure 9.7). (A fourth process, called *tidal heating,* is not important for the terrestrial worlds but is for some of the jovian moons, particularly Io [Section 11.5].)

Accretion was the earliest major source of internal heat for the terrestrial worlds. The many violent impacts that occurred during the latter stages of accretion deposited so much energy that planet-wide melting occurred. Imagine the entire Earth engulfed in molten rock! This melting enabled the process of differentiation, in which the densest materials (metals) settled to the planet's core, while lighter rocks rose to the surface.

Both accretion and differentiation yield heat by converting *gravitational potential energy* into thermal energy [Section 4.2]. An object that hits an accreting world starts with a lot of gravitational potential energy when it is far away. This gravitational potential energy is converted to kinetic energy as gravity makes the object accelerate toward the planet's surface. Upon impact, the kinetic energy is converted to sound

Gravitational potential energy is converted into kinetic energy.

Kinetic energy is converted into thermal energy.

accretion

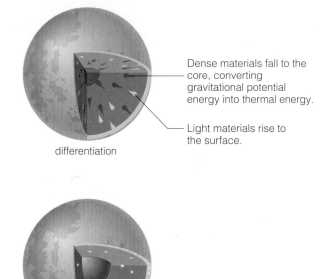

Dense materials fall to the core, converting gravitational potential energy into thermal energy.

Light materials rise to the surface.

differentiation

Nuclear energy is converted into thermal energy.

radioactivity

**FIGURE 9.7** The three main internal energy sources in terrestrial planets. Only radioactivity is a major heat source today.

and heat, thus adding to the thermal energy of the planet. Differentiation converts gravitational potential energy to thermal energy just like a brick falling to the bottom of a swimming pool. The brick loses gravitational potential energy as it falls, and this energy ultimately appears as thermal energy in the water.

The third internal heat source is the decay of radioactive elements such as uranium, potassium, thorium, and others. When radioactive nuclei decay, subatomic particles fly off at high speeds, colliding with neighboring atoms and heating them. In essence, this transfers some of the mass-energy of the radioactive element ($E = mc^2$ [Section 4.2]) to the thermal energy of the planetary interior. Most radioactive elements are locked in minerals that make up the

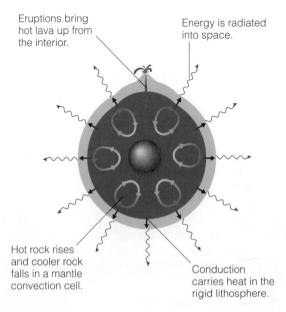

Eruptions bring hot lava up from the interior.

Energy is radiated into space.

Hot rock rises and cooler rock falls in a mantle convection cell.

Conduction carries heat in the rigid lithosphere.

**FIGURE 9.8** Heat escapes a planet's interior through conduction, convection, and eruption.

## Common Misconceptions: Pressure and Temperature

You might think that Earth's interior is hot just because the pressures are high. After all, if we compress a gas from low pressure to high pressure, it heats up. But the same is not necessarily true of rock. High pressure hardly compresses rock, so the compression causes little increase in temperature. Thus, while high pressures and temperatures sometimes go together in planets, they don't have to. In fact, after all the radioactive elements decay (billions of years from now), Earth's deep interior will become quite cool even though the pressure will be the same as it is today. The temperatures inside Earth and the other planets can remain high only if there is an internal source of heat, such as accretion, differentiation, or radioactivity.

crust and mantle, but some end up in the core as well. Note that accretion and differentiation deposited heat in planetary interiors billions of years ago, but radioactivity continues to heat the terrestrial planets to this very day.

### How Interiors Cool Off

Some of a planet's internal heat, or thermal energy, is always escaping. Heat flows outward from the hot interior toward the cooler surface through three main processes: *conduction, convection,* and *eruption* (Figure 9.8). **Conduction** is the process that makes heat flow from your hand to a glass of ice water. It occurs because the microscopic jiggling of molecules is more energetic (faster) at higher temperatures. Some of the thermal energy of this motion is transferred from a warm rock to its cooler neighbors. Conduction is the main process by which heat flows upward through the lithosphere.

Some planetary interiors also lose heat through **convection,** in which hot material expands and rises, while cooler material contracts and falls. Convection can occur any time a substance is strongly heated from underneath; you can see convection whenever you heat a pot of soup on the stove, and you're probably also familiar with it in the context of weather, in which warm air rises, while cool air falls in our atmosphere. A planet's hot interior also convects, but much more slowly. The rising hot material transfers heat from deep in the planetary interior toward the surface. When the material fully cools, it begins to descend back down until the heating from below heats

it enough to make it rise upward again. Convection is an ongoing process, and each small region of rising and falling material is called a **convection cell.**

The third major process by which heat can escape a planet's interior is volcanic **eruption.** An eruption directly transfers heat outward by depositing hot lava on the surface.

Regardless of whether heat reaches the surface through the slow leakage of convection and conduction or through the sudden burst of an eruption, this heat eventually radiates away into space. Recall that all objects emit *thermal radiation* characteristic of their temperatures [Section 6.4]. Because of their relatively low surface temperatures, planets radiate almost entirely in the infrared portion of the spectrum.

The interiors of the terrestrial planets are slowly cooling as their heat escapes. By now, 4.6 billion years after their formation, much of the original heat from accretion and differentiation has leaked away. Most of the heat today comes from radioactive decay, and even the rate of radioactive decay declines as a planet ages (because a particular nucleus can decay only once). Meanwhile, interior cooling gradually thickens the lithosphere and leaves any molten rock lying deeper inside.

Ultimately, a planet's size is the single most important factor in determining how long its interior remains hot: Larger planets stay hot longer, just as larger baked potatoes stay hot longer than small ones. You can see why size is the critical factor by picturing a large planet as a smaller planet wrapped in extra layers of rock. The extra rock acts as insulation, so heat from the center takes longer to reach the surface on the larger planet than it would on the smaller one. Because of their relatively large sizes, Earth and Venus have scarcely cooled off since their births and therefore have thin lithospheres and substantial geological activity. The smallest terrestrial worlds—Mercury and the Moon—have mostly cooled off and therefore have very thick lithospheres that essentially make them geologically "dead." Mars, intermediate in size, has cooled significantly, resulting in an intermediate interior temperature.

**TIME OUT TO THINK** *Give an example from everyday life of a small object cooling off faster than a large one and of a smaller object warming up more quickly than a large one. How do these examples relate to the issue of geological activity on the terrestrial worlds?*

### Planetary Cores and Magnetic Fields

Interior structure also determines whether a planet has a **magnetic field** through which it can influence charged particles or magnetic materials. You are probably familiar with the general pattern of a bar magnet's magnetic field, which we can see by placing it among small iron filings (Figure 9.9a). A planet's magnetic field is generated by a process more similar to that of an *electromagnet,* in which the magnetic field arises as a battery forces charged particles (elec-

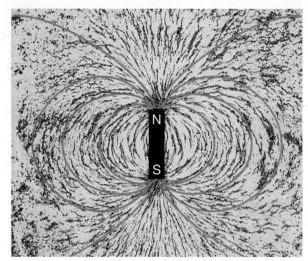

**a** This photo shows how a bar magnet influences iron filings (small black specks) around it. The *magnetic field lines* (red) represent this influence graphically.

**FIGURE 9.9** Sources of magnetic fields.

trons) to move along a coiled wire (Figure 9.9b). Planets do not have batteries, but they may have charged particles in motion in their metallic cores (Figure 9.9c). Deep within an electrically conducting core, molten metals rise and fall in convection cells. At the same time, the molten material spins with the planet's rotation. If this combination of convection and rotation is strong enough, it moves electrons in the same way they move in an electromagnet. The

---

### Mathematical Insight 9.1    The Surface Area–to–Volume Ratio

We can see why large planets cool more slowly than smaller ones by thinking about their relative surface areas and volumes. Consider the Earth and the Moon. Both started out hot inside but continually radiate heat away from their surfaces to space. As heat escapes from the surface, more heat flows upward from the interior to replace it. This process will continue until the interior is no hotter than the surface. Because all the heat escapes from the surface, the key factor in a world's heat-loss rate is its *surface area.* The surface area of a sphere is given by the formula $4\pi \times (\text{radius})^2$, so the ratio of Earth's surface area to that of the Moon is:

$$\frac{\text{Earth surface area}}{\text{Moon surface area}} = \frac{4\pi \times (r_{\text{Earth}})^2}{4\pi \times (r_{\text{Moon}})^2}$$

$$= \left(\frac{r_{\text{Earth}}}{r_{\text{Moon}}}\right)^2 = \left(\frac{6,378 \text{ km}}{1,738 \text{ km}}\right)^2 \approx 13$$

Thus, at a given temperature, Earth has about 13 times more area from which to radiate its heat away.

However, the total amount of heat deposited inside a world by radioactivity roughly depends on its mass or, if we assume that we're dealing with worlds of similar density, its volume. The formula for the volume of a sphere is

$\frac{4}{3}\pi \times (\text{radius})^3$, so the volume ratio for Earth and the Moon is:

$$\frac{\text{Earth volume}}{\text{Moon volume}} = \frac{\frac{4}{3}\pi \times (r_{\text{Earth}})^3}{\frac{4}{3}\pi \times (r_{\text{Moon}})^3}$$

$$= \left(\frac{r_{\text{Earth}}}{r_{\text{Moon}}}\right)^3 = \left(\frac{6,378 \text{ km}}{1,738 \text{ km}}\right)^3 \approx 50$$

Thus, Earth's interior contains some 50 times more heat than the Moon's interior. This larger amount of internal heat more than offsets the larger radiating area. That is why the Earth is still hot inside while the Moon has mostly cooled off.

The general idea that larger objects cool more slowly than smaller ones is described by the mathematical idea of the *surface area–to–volume ratio.* As the Earth–Moon example shows, larger objects have relatively smaller surface areas compared to their volumes. Thus, they lose internal heat more slowly and also take longer to be heated from the outside. This principle explains many everyday phenomena. For example, crushing a cube of ice into smaller pieces increases the total amount of surface area, while the total volume of ice remains the same. Thus, the crushed ice will cool a drink more quickly than would the original ice cube.

**b** A similar magnetic field is created by an electromagnet, which is essentially just a coiled wire attached to a battery. The field is created by the battery-forced motion of charged particles (electrons) along the wire.

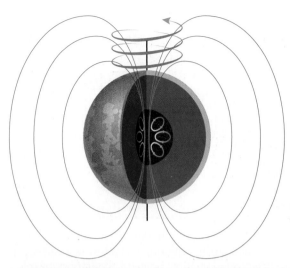

**c** A planet's magnetic field also arises from motion of charged particles. For a terrestrial planet, the charged particles are in a molten metallic core, and their motion arises from the planet's rotation and interior convection.

result is a planetary magnetic field. Similar combinations of convection and rotation of conducting materials (such as metallic hydrogen or ionized plasma) give rise to magnetic fields in the jovian planets and in stars.

This simple analysis explains why Earth has the strongest magnetic field of the terrestrial worlds: It is the only one that has both a partially molten metallic core (which can convect) and reasonably rapid rotation. The Moon may lack a metallic core; even if it has one, it has certainly solidified and ceased convecting. In either case, it generates no magnetic field. Mars also has virtually no magnetic field, probably because of similar core solidification. In contrast, Venus probably has a molten metal layer in its core, but either its convection or its 243-day rotation period is too slow to generate a magnetic field. Mercury remains an enigma: It possesses a measurable magnetic field despite its small size and slow, 59-day rotation. The solution to this enigma may lie in Mercury's high density, which tells us that it has a huge metal core—a larger core than that of Mars, even though it is a smaller planet overall. Perhaps Mercury's core is still partly molten and convecting.

Although convection and rotation of electrically conducting material basically explain why planetary magnetic fields exist, many details remain mysterious. For example, we don't know why the Earth's magnetic axis intersects the surface in northern Canada, 11° away from the rotation axis at the North Pole. Nor do we know why Earth's magnetic field varies in strength over time. Even more mysterious is the fact, discovered from geological evidence, that Earth's entire magnetic field completely reverses its orientation (magnetic north becomes magnetic south, and vice versa) every half-million years or so.

Magnetic fields can be very useful. On Earth, they help us navigate. Their presence or absence and their strength on any planet provide important information about the planetary interior. But aside from this utility, magnetic fields have virtually no effect on the structure of a planet itself. They can, however, form a protective *magnetosphere* that surrounds a planet, with potentially profound effects on a planet's atmosphere and any inhabitants [Section 10.3].

## 9.4 Shaping Planetary Surfaces

When we look around the Earth, we find an apparently endless variety of geological surface features. The diversity increases when we survey the other planets. But on closer examination, geologists have found that almost all the features observed result from just four major **geological processes** that affect planetary surfaces:

 **Impact cratering**: the excavation of bowl-shaped depressions (*impact craters*) by asteroids or comets striking a planet's surface.

 **Volcanism**: the eruption of molten rock, or *lava*, from a planet's interior onto its surface.

 **Tectonics**: the disruption of a planet's surface by internal stresses.

 **Erosion**: the wearing down or building up of geological features by wind, water, ice, and other phenomena of planetary weather.

Planetary geology once consisted largely of cataloging the number and kinds of geological features found on the planets. The field has advanced remarkably in recent decades, however, and it is now possible to describe how planets work in general and what geological features we expect to find on different planets. This progress has been made possible by a detailed examination of the geological processes and the determination of what factors affect and control them.

### Understanding Geological Relationships

We can understand the fundamental ideas of comparative geology by exploring just a few key cause-and-effect relationships. Some of the important relationships are fairly easy to see. For example, a planet can have active volcanoes only if it has a sufficiently hot interior; and water, a major agent of erosion, remains liquid only if the planet has a temperature in the proper range and an atmosphere with sufficient pressure. Other relationships are subtler, such as that between the presence of an atmosphere and the planetary surface temperature. We can use flowcharts (or "concept maps") to help us keep track of the most important geological relationships.

Figure 9.10 shows one such planetary flowchart. The first row lists four **formation properties** with which each planet was endowed at birth: *size (mass and radius)*, *distance from the Sun*, *chemical composition*, and *rotation rate*. These properties generally remain unchanged throughout a planet's history, unless the planet suffers a giant impact. The second row lists four **geological controlling factors** that drive a planet's geological activity: *surface gravity, internal temperature, surface temperature,* and the characteristics of the planet's *atmosphere*. Before we move on, let's briefly discuss how to interpret blocks and arrows on the flowchart:

- Each block represents a particular property, controlling factor, or process.

- Each arrow represents a cause-and-effect relationship between one block and another. (There may be other connections besides those shown; the figure includes only those that have substantial effects on geology.)

Arrows from the first row to the second row show how a planet's formation properties help determine the geological controlling factors. The single arrow pointing from *mass and radius* to *surface gravity* shows that the strength of gravity at the surface is determined solely by size, in accord with Newton's law of gravity. Two arrows point to *internal temperature*, indicating that the formation properties of *size* and

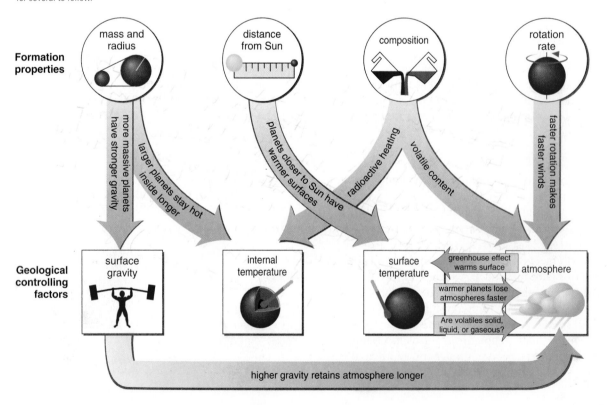

**FIGURE 9.10** Major cause-and-effect relationships between a planet's formation properties and its geological controlling factors. Each block represents a particular formation property, controlling factor, or geological process. Each arrow represents a cause-and-effect relationship between one block and another. This diagram forms the foundation for several to follow.

*composition* both affect it: Size is the most important factor in determining how rapidly a planet loses its internal heat, and composition—particularly the amount of radioactive elements—determines how much new heat is released in the interior. Other arrows from the first to the second row in Figure 9.10 show that a planet's *surface temperature* depends in part on its *distance from the Sun* and that its *atmosphere* is affected by both its *composition* and its *rotation rate*.

Arrows between the geological controlling factors show how they affect one another. Both *surface gravity* and *surface temperature* have arrows pointing to *atmosphere*, because a planet's ability to hold atmospheric gases depends on both how fast the gas molecules move (which depends on temperature) and the strength of the planet's gravity [Section 10.5]. A second arrow from *surface temperature* to *atmosphere* shows that the temperature also influences what substances exist as gases (versus solid or liquid). The *atmosphere*, in turn, points back to *surface temperature* because a thick atmosphere can make a planet's surface warmer than it would be otherwise (through the *greenhouse effect* [Section 10.2]).

**TIME OUT TO THINK** *To make sure you understand the planetary flowchart, answer the following questions: (1) What planetary formation properties determine whether a planet's interior is hot, and why? (2) How does surface gravity affect a planet's atmosphere, and why?*

The planetary flowcharts in this chapter contain all the information needed for a conceptual model of how planetary geology works—a model that allows us to answer questions about why different planets have different geological features. Figure 9.10 represents the beginning of this model. In the sections that follow, we will add each of the four geological processes (impact cratering, volcanism, tectonics, and erosion) to the set of relationships we have just covered, ending up with a fairly complete model for planetary geology. You do not need to memorize the model in this graphical form; instead, use it to help you understand planetary geology. You should also think about how you could adapt this technique of developing a conceptual model to any other problem that interests you.

### Impact Cratering

Impact cratering occurs when a leftover planetesimal (such as a comet or an asteroid) crashes into the surface of a terrestrial world. Impacts can have devastating effects on planetary surfaces, which we can see both from the impact craters left behind and from laboratory experiments that reproduce the impact process (Figure 9.11). Impactors typically hit planets at speeds between 30,000 and 250,000 km/hr (10–70 km/s) and pack enough energy to vaporize solid rock and excavate a *crater* (the Greek word for "cup"). Craters are generally circular because the impact blasts out material in all directions, no matter

**FIGURE 9.11** Artist's conception of the impact process. The last frame shows how, in a larger crater, the center can rebound just as water does after you drop a pebble into it.

Lunar maria are huge impact basins that were flooded by lava. Only a few small craters appear on the maria.

Lunar highlands are ancient and heavily cratered.

**a** The Moon's surface, as seen in this Apollo photograph, shows both heavily and lightly cratered areas.

**b** This map of the entire lunar surface shows the differences between the lightly cratered maria (dark areas) and the heavily cratered highlands. At the lower left is a multi-ring basin on the far side of the moon known as Mare Orientale. The mare in the center and right portions of the map make the "man-in-the-moon" face we see from Earth.

**FIGURE 9.12** Geology of the Moon.

which direction the impactor came from. A typical crater is about 10 times wider than the impactor that created it, with a depth about 10–20% of the crater width. Thus, for example, a 1-kilometer-wide impactor creates a crater about 10 kilometers wide and 1–2 kilometers deep. Debris from the blast, called **ejecta**, shoots high into the atmosphere and then rains down over a large area. If the impact is large enough, some of the atmosphere may be blasted away into space, and some of the rocky ejecta may completely escape from the planet.

Craters come in all sizes, but small craters far outnumber large ones because there are far more small objects orbiting the Sun than large ones. Very large impacts can form **impact basins**. The **lunar maria**, easily visible with binoculars, are impact basins up to 1,100 kilometers across (Figure 9.12a). (*Maria* is the Latin word for "seas"; they got their name because their smooth appearance reminded early observers of oceans.) These large impacts violently fractured the Moon's lithosphere, making cracks through which molten lava later escaped to flood the impact basins; when the lava cooled and solidified, it left a smooth surface in the region of the lava flood. The impacts that made the largest basins were so violent they sent out ripples that left tremendous *multi-ring basins* shaped like bull's-eyes (Figure 9.12b).

The present-day abundance of craters on a planet's surface tells us a great deal about its geological his-

tory. Even though impacts still occur today, the vast majority of craters formed during the "rain of rock and ice" that ended around 3.8 billion years ago [Section 8.5]. At that time, the terrestrial worlds were saturated (completely covered) with impact craters. A surface region that is still saturated with craters, such as the *lunar highlands,* must have remained essentially undisturbed for the last 3.8 billion years (Figure 9.12a). In contrast, the original craters must have been somehow "erased" in regions that now have few craters, such as the lunar maria. The flood of lava that formed the lunar maria covered any craters that had formed inside the impact basin, and the few craters that exist today within the maria must have formed from impacts occurring after the lava flows solidified. These craters tell us that the impact rate since the end of heavy bombardment has been quite small: Radioactive dating of moon rocks shows that the maria are 3–3.5 billion years old, but they have only 3% as many craters as the lunar highlands.

**TIME OUT TO THINK** *Earth must also have been saturated with impact craters early in its history, but we see relatively few impact craters on Earth today. What processes erase impact craters on Earth?*

Craters with unusual shapes provide additional clues about surface conditions, as we can see by comparing craters on Mars. Craters in rocky surfaces usually have a simple bowl shape (Figure 9.13a).

**a** Many craters are bowl-shaped.

**b** Impacts into icy ground may form muddy ejecta.

**c** Ancient Martian rains apparently eroded this crater. (See Figure 9.27d for a stunning close-up view of the floor of this crater.)

**FIGURE 9.13** Crater shapes on Mars tell us about Martian geology. These photos were taken from orbit by the Viking spacecraft.

However, some Martian craters look as if they were formed in mud (Figure 9.13b), suggesting that underground water or ice vaporized upon impact and lubricated the flow of ejecta away from the crater. Other craters lack a sharp rim and bowl-shaped floor, suggesting that geological processes such as erosion have altered their shape over time (Figure 9.13c). Planetary geologists must be cautious in interpreting unusually shaped craters, because impacts are not the only process that can form craters. Fortunately, craters created by other processes, such as volcanism, tend to have distinctly different shapes than impact craters (see Figure 9.17b).

The most common impactors are sand-size particles called *micrometeorites* when they impact a surface. Such tiny particles burn up as meteors in the atmospheres of Venus, Earth, and Mars. But on worlds that lack significant atmospheres, such as Mercury and the Moon, the countless impacts of micrometeorites gradually pulverize the surface rock to create a layer of powdery "soil." On the Moon, the Apollo astronauts and their rovers left marks in this powdery surface (Figure 9.14). Because of the lack of wind and rain, the footprints and tire tracks will last millions of years, but they will eventually be erased by micrometeorite impacts. In fact, over millions and billions of years, these tiny impacts smooth out rough crater rims much as erosion processes do more rapidly on Earth.

**FIGURE 9.14** Reminders of the Apollo missions to the Moon, including this footprint, will last for millions of years.

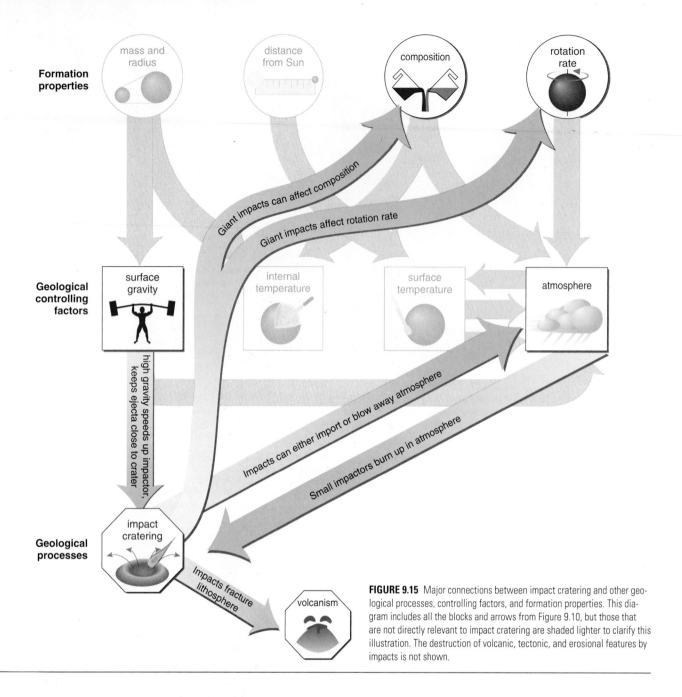

**Formation properties**

mass and radius

distance from Sun

composition

rotation rate

Giant impacts can affect composition

Giant impacts affect rotation rate

**Geological controlling factors**

surface gravity

internal temperature

surface temperature

atmosphere

high gravity speeds up impactor, keeps ejecta close to crater

Impacts can either import or blow away atmosphere

Small impactors burn up in atmosphere

**Geological processes**

impact cratering

Impacts fracture lithosphere

volcanism

**FIGURE 9.15** Major connections between impact cratering and other geological processes, controlling factors, and formation properties. This diagram includes all the blocks and arrows from Figure 9.10, but those that are not directly relevant to impact cratering are shaded lighter to clarify this illustration. The destruction of volcanic, tectonic, and erosional features by impacts is not shown.

Figure 9.15 summarizes the important cause-and-effect relationships linking impact cratering with other geological processes, controlling factors, and formation properties. Note that the planet's formation properties do not greatly affect impact cratering, because the impactors do not come from the planet itself. Craters formed on all the terrestrial worlds, especially early in their histories. But giant impacts can affect formation properties by altering a planet's composition or rotation rate. In addition, impacts affect features made by other geological processes. Apart from simply obliterating volcanoes, cliffs, or riverbeds, impacts can fracture the lithosphere, creating a path for volcanic lava to reach the surface (as

occurred in the lunar maria). The relationships between impacts and the atmosphere are particularly interesting: Not only can an atmosphere burn up small impactors, but the impactors themselves can either bring in atmospheric ingredients or blast away some of the atmosphere. Before you read on, take a bit of time to analyze the remaining arrows and make sure all the connections make sense to you.

### Volcanism

We find evidence for volcanoes and lava flows on all the terrestrial planets, as well as on a few of the

**a** Hot magma erupts to the surface.

magma

**b** Eruption of an active volcano on the flanks of Kilauea on the Big Island in Hawaii.

**FIGURE 9.16** Volcanism.

moons of the outer solar system. (The moons may have "lavas" of water or other normally icy materials.) Volcanic surface features differ from one world to another, but some general principles apply.

Volcanoes erupt when underground molten rock, or **magma**, finds a path through the lithosphere to the surface (Figure 9.16). Magma rises for two main reasons: First, molten rock is generally less dense than solid rock, so it has a natural tendency to rise. Second, a *magma chamber* may be squeezed by tectonic forces, driving the magma upward under pressure. Any trapped gases expand as magma rises, sometimes leading to dramatic eruptions.

The structure of a volcanic flow depends on the viscosity of the lava that erupts onto the surface. The rock type known as **basalt** makes relatively low-viscosity lava when molten because it is made of relatively short molecular chains that don't tangle with one another. Temperature affects lava viscosity as well: The hotter the lava, the more easily the chains

can jiggle and slide along one another and the lower the viscosity. The amount of water or gases trapped in the lava also affects viscosity. Such materials can act as a lubricant, decreasing the viscosity of subsurface magma. But when lavas erupt, materials such as water may form gas bubbles that *increase* the viscosity. (You can understand why bubbles increase viscosity by thinking about how much higher a "mountain" you can build with bubble-bath foam than you can with soapy water.)

The runniest basalt lavas flow far and flatten out before solidifying, creating vast *volcanic plains* such as the lunar maria (Figure 9.17a). Somewhat more viscous basalt lavas solidify before they can completely spread out, resulting in **shield volcanoes** (so-named because they are shield-shaped). Shield volcanoes can be very tall, but they are not very steep; most have slopes of only 5°–10° (Figure 9.17b). The mountains of the Hawaiian Islands are shield vol-

**a** Low-viscosity lava makes flat lava plains.

Lava plains (maria) on the Moon

**b** Medium-viscosity lava makes shallow-sloped shield volcanoes.

Olympus Mons (Mars)

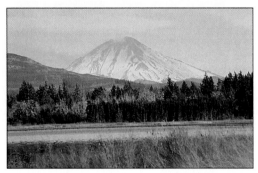

Mount St. Helens

**c** High-viscosity lava makes steep-sloped stratovolcanoes.

**FIGURE 9.17** Volcanoes produce different types of features depending primarily on the viscosity of the lava erupted.

canoes; measured from the ocean floor to their summits, the Hawaiian mountains are the tallest (and widest) on Earth. Tall, steep **stratovolcanoes** such as Mount St. Helens are made from much more viscous lavas that can't flow very far before solidifying (Figure 9.17c).

Figure 9.18 summarizes the geological relationships that involve volcanism. The main point to keep in mind is that internal temperature exerts the greatest control over volcanism: A hotter interior means that lava lies closer to the surface and can erupt more easily. The formation property of composition is also very important, because it determines the melting temperatures and viscosities of lavas that erupt and

therefore what types of volcanoes form. Volcanism is connected to other geological processes in several ways beyond the simple fact that lava flows can cover up or fill in previous geological features. Tectonics and volcanism often go together: Tectonic stresses can force lava to the surface or cut off eruptions. Another connection reveals far-reaching effects: Volcanism affects erosion indirectly, because volcanoes are the primary source of gases in the current terrestrial planet atmospheres [Section 10.5]. Before continuing, be sure you understand all the relationships shown in Figure 9.18.

## Tectonics

We are now ready to discuss tectonics, the third major geological process in our model. The root of the word *tectonics* comes from Greek legend, in which Tecton was a carpenter. In geology, *tectonics* refers to the processes that do "carpentry" on planetary surfaces—that is, to the internal forces and stresses that act on the lithosphere to create surface features.

Several types of internal stress can drive tectonic activity. On planets with internal convection, the strongest type of stress often comes from the circu- lation of the convection cells themselves. The tops of convection cells can drag against the lithosphere, sometimes forcing sections of the lithosphere to- gether or apart. On Earth, these forces have broken the lithosphere into *plates* that move over, under, and around each other in what we call *plate tectonics*; we'll discuss plate tectonics further in Chapter 13. Even if the crust does not break into plates, stresses from underlying convection cells may create vast mountain ranges, cliffs, and valleys. A second type of stress associated with convection comes from indi- vidual rising *plumes* of hot mantle material that push

**FIGURE 9.18** Major connections between volcanism and other geological processes, controlling factors, and formation properties. This diagram includes all the blocks and arrows from Figure 9.10, but those that are not directly relevant to volcanism are shaded lighter to clarify this illustration. Volcanoes also cover up impact, tectonic, and erosional features, but these connections are not shown.

Appalachian Mountains in eastern United States

Guinevere Plains on Venus

Compression in crust can make mountains.

Extension can make cracks and valleys.

**FIGURE 9.19** Tectonic forces can produce a wide variety of features. Mountains and fractured plains are among the most common.

up on the lithosphere. (The Hawaiian Islands result from such a plume [Section 13.2].) Internal stress can also arise from temperature changes in the planetary interior. For example, the crust may be forced to expand and stretch if the planetary interior heats up from radioactive decay. Conversely, the mantle and lithosphere must respond when a planetary core cools and contracts, leading to planet-wide compression forces. Tectonic stresses can even occur on more local scales; for example, the weight of a newly formed volcano can bend or crack the lithosphere beneath it.

Tectonic features take an incredible variety of forms (Figure 9.19). Mountains may rise where the crust is compressed. Such crustal compression helped create the Appalachian Mountains of the eastern United States. Huge valleys and cliffs may result where the crust is pulled apart; examples include the Guinevere Plains on Venus and New Mexico's Rio

Grande Valley. (The river named Rio Grande came *after* the valley formed from tectonic processes.) Tectonic forces may bend or break rocks, and tectonic activity on Earth is always accompanied by earthquakes. Other worlds undoubtedly experience "planet-quakes," and planetary geologists are eager to plant seismometers on them to probe their interiors.

Figure 9.20 summarizes the connections between tectonics and other geological processes and properties. Like volcanism, tectonics is most likely on larger worlds that remain hot inside. Tectonics may also have been important in the past on smaller worlds that underwent major shrinking or expansion.

### Erosion

The last of the four major geological processes to be added to our model is erosion, which encompasses a

**Formation properties**

mass and radius    distance from Sun    composition    rotation rate

**Geological controlling factors**

surface gravity    internal temperature    surface temperature    atmosphere

**Geological processes**

Internal temperature changes disrupt crust

Warm interior causes convection

Affects thickness, strength of lithosphere

tectonics

Tectonic stresses start or stop eruptions

volcanism

**FIGURE 9.20** Connections between tectonics and other geological processes, controlling factors, and formation properties. This diagram includes all the blocks and arrows from Figure 9.10, but those that are not directly relevant to tectonics are shaded lighter to clarify this illustration. Tectonics can also destroy impact, volcanic, and erosional features, but these connections are not shown.

variety of processes connected by a single theme: the breakdown and transport of rocks by **volatiles**. The term *volatile* means "evaporates easily" and refers to substances—such as water, carbon dioxide, and methane—that are usually found as gases, liquids, or surface ices on the terrestrial worlds. Wind, rain, rivers, flash floods, and glaciers are just a few examples of processes that contribute to erosion on Earth. Erosion not only breaks down existing geological features (wearing down mountains and forming gullies, riverbeds, and deep valleys), but also builds new

ones (such as sand dunes, river deltas, and lakebed deposits). If enough material is deposited over time, the layers can compact to form **sedimentary rocks**.

Virtually no erosion takes place on worlds without a significant atmosphere, such as Mercury and the Moon. But planets with atmospheres can have significant erosional activity. Larger planets are better able to generate atmospheres by releasing gases trapped in their interiors; their stronger gravity also tends to prevent their atmospheres from escaping to space

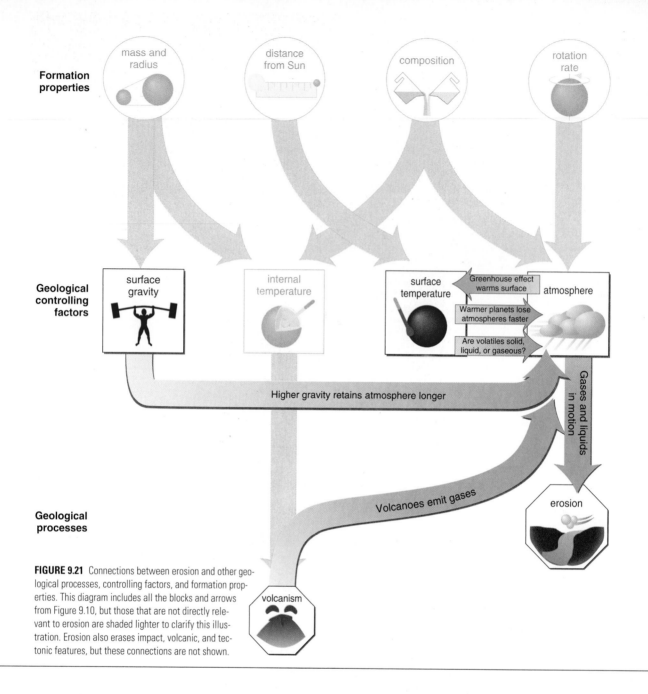

**Formation properties**

mass and radius

distance from Sun

composition

rotation rate

**Geological controlling factors**

surface gravity

internal temperature

surface temperature

Greenhouse effect warms surface

atmosphere

Warmer planets lose atmospheres faster

Are volatiles solid, liquid, or gaseous?

Higher gravity retains atmosphere longer

Gases and liquids in motion

**Geological processes**

Volcanoes emit gases

erosion

volcanism

**FIGURE 9.21** Connections between erosion and other geological processes, controlling factors, and formation properties. This diagram includes all the blocks and arrows from Figure 9.10, but those that are not directly relevant to erosion are shaded lighter to clarify this illustration. Erosion also erases impact, volcanic, and tectonic features, but these connections are not shown.

[Section 10.5]. In general, a thick atmosphere is more capable of driving erosion than a thin atmosphere, but a planet's rotation rate is also important. Slowly rotating planets like Venus have correspondingly slow winds and therefore weak or nonexistent wind erosion. Surface temperature also matters: Erosion isn't very effective if most of the volatiles stay frozen on the surface, but it can be very powerful when volatiles are able to evaporate and then recondense as rain or snow. Figure 9.21 summarizes the connections between erosion and other geological processes and properties.

## 9.5 A Geological Tour of the Terrestrial Worlds

Now that we've examined the processes and properties that shape the geology of the terrestrial worlds, we're ready to return to the issue of why the terrestrial worlds ended up so geologically different from one another. We'll take a brief "tour" of the terrestrial worlds. We could organize the tour by distance from the Sun, by density, or even by alphabetical order. But we'll choose the planetary property that has the strongest effect on geology: size, which controls a planet's internal heat. We'll start with our Moon, the smallest terrestrial world.

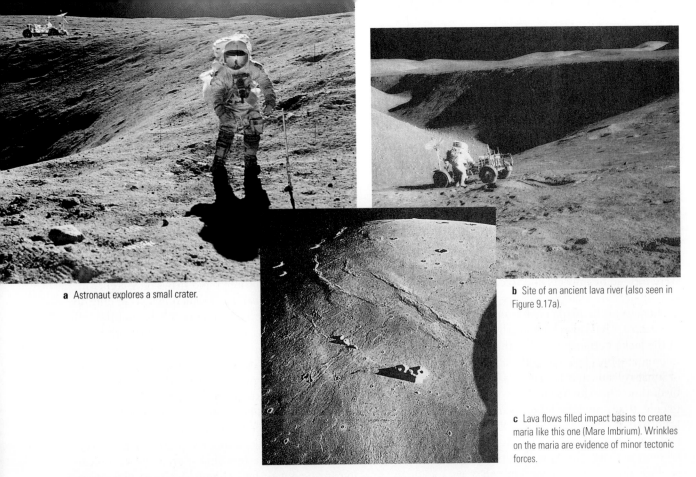

a Astronaut explores a small crater.

b Site of an ancient lava river (also seen in Figure 9.17a).

c Lava flows filled impact basins to create maria like this one (Mare Imbrium). Wrinkles on the maria are evidence of minor tectonic forces.

FIGURE 9.22 Impact cratering and volcanism are the most important geological processes on the Moon.

### The Moon (1,731-km radius, 1.0 AU from Sun)

On a clear night, you can see much of the Moon's global geological history with your naked eye. The Moon is unique in this respect; other planets are too far away for us to see any surface details, and Earth is so close that we see only the local geological history. Twelve Apollo astronauts visited the lunar surface between 1969 and 1972, taking photographs, making measurements, and collecting rocks. Thanks to these visits and more recent observations of the Moon from other spacecraft, we know more about the Moon's geology than that of any other object, with the possible exception of the Earth.

The Moon's composition differs somewhat from the Earth's. According to the leading theory, our Moon formed early in the history of our solar system when a giant impact blasted away some of Earth's rocky outer layers [Section 8.5]. The impact did not dredge up metallic core material, which explains why the Moon has a lower metal content than Earth and a smaller metal core. In addition, lunar rocks collected by astronauts contain a much smaller proportion of volatiles (such as water) than Earth rocks, presumably because heat from the giant impact evaporated the volatiles and allowed them to escape into space before the Moon formed from the debris.

As the Moon accreted following the giant impact, the heat of accretion melted its outer layers. The lowest-density molten rock rose upward through the process of differentiation, forming what is sometimes called a *magma ocean*. This magma ocean cooled and solidified during the heavy bombardment that took place early in the history of the solar system, leaving the Moon's surface crowded with craters. We still see this ancient, heavily cratered landscape in the lunar highlands (Figure 9.22a). Lunar samples confirm that the highlands are composed of low-density rocks. As the bombardment tailed off, around 3.8 billion years ago, a few larger impactors struck the surface and formed impact basins.

Even as the heat of accretion leaked away, radioactive decay kept the Moon's interior molten long enough for volcanism to reshape parts of its surface. Between about 3 and 4 billion years ago, molten rock welled up through cracks in the deepest impact basins, forming the lunar maria. Because the lava that filled the maria rose up from the Moon's mantle, the maria contain dense, iron-rich rock that is darker in color than the rock of the lunar highlands. The contrasts between the light-colored rock of the highlands and the dark rock of the maria make the "man-in-the-Moon" pattern that some people imagine when they look at the full moon.

The lunar lavas must have been among the least viscous (runniest) in the solar system, perhaps because the lack of volatiles meant a lack of bubbles (which increase viscosity) in the erupting lava. The lava plains of the maria cover a large fraction of the lunar surface. Only a few small shield volcanoes exist on the Moon, and no steeper-sided stratovolcanoes have been found. Low-viscosity lavas also carved out long, winding channels. These channels must once have been rivers of molten rock that helped fill the lunar maria (Figure 9.22b).

Almost all the geological features of the Moon were formed by impacts and volcanism, although a few small-scale tectonic stresses wrinkled the surface as the lava of the maria cooled and contracted (Figure 9.22c). The Moon has virtually no erosion because of the lack of atmosphere, but the continual rain of micrometeorites has rounded crater rims. The heyday of lunar volcanism is long gone—3 billion years gone. Over time, the Moon's small size allowed its interior to cool, thickening the lithosphere. Today, the Moon's lithosphere probably extends to a depth of 1,000 km, making it far too thick to allow further volcanic or tectonic activity. The Moon has probably been in this geologically "dead" state for 3 billion years.

Despite its geological inactivity, the Moon is of prime interest to those hoping to build colonies in space. The *Lunar Prospector* arrived at the Moon in early 1998 and began mapping the surface in search of promising locations for a permanent human base. Although no concrete plans are yet in place, several nations are exploring the possibility of building a human outpost on the Moon within the next couple of decades.

### Mercury (2,439-km radius, 0.39 AU from Sun)

Mercury (Figure 9.23) is the least studied of the terrestrial worlds. Its proximity to the Sun makes it difficult to study through telescopes, and it has been visited by only one spacecraft: *Mariner 10,* which collected data during three rapid flybys of Mercury in 1974–1975. *Mariner 10* obtained images of only one hemisphere of Mercury (Figure 9.23b), but the influence of Mercury's gravity on *Mariner 10*'s orbit allowed planetary scientists to determine Mercury's mass and average density. Based on its relatively high density, Mercury must be about 61% iron by mass, with a core that extends to perhaps 75% of its radius. Mercury's high metal content is due to its formation close to the Sun, possibly enhanced by a giant impact that blasted away its outer, rocky layers [Section 8.6].

Mercury has craters almost everywhere, indicating an ancient surface (Figure 9.23c). A huge impact basin, called the *Caloris Basin* (Figure 9.23a), covers a large portion of one hemisphere. Like the large

a  Edge of Caloris Basin

b  Mercury

**FIGURE 9.23** Mercury, like the Moon, is a heavily cratered object with evidence of volcanism.

c  Close up view showing small lava plains that have covered up craters lunar basins, the Caloris Basin has few craters within it, indicating that it must have been formed toward the end of the solar system's early period of heavy bombardment.

Despite the superficial similarity between their cratered surfaces, Mercury and the Moon also exhibit significant differences. Mercury has noticeably fewer craters than the lunar highlands (compare Figure 9.12a to Figure 9.23b). Smooth patches between many of the craters tell us that volcanic lava once flowed, covering up small craters. Mercury has no vast maria but has smaller lava plains almost everywhere, suggesting that Mercury had at least as much volcanism as the Moon.

**TIME OUT TO THINK** *Geologists have discovered that the ejecta didn't travel quite as far away from craters on Mercury as it did on the Moon. Why not? (Hint: What planetary formation properties affect impact craters?)*

Tectonic processes played a more significant role on Mercury than on the Moon, as evidenced by tremendous cliffs. The cliff shown in Figure 9.24a is several hundred kilometers long and up to 3 kilometers high in places; the central crater apparently crumpled during the cliff's formation. This cliff, and many others on Mercury, probably formed when tectonic forces compressed the crust (Figure 9.24b).

**a**

**FIGURE 9.24** (a) The tall cliff (indicated by the arrow) on Mercury is several hundred kilometers long. (b) Cliffs formed from tectonic stresses (indicated by arrows) caused by Mercury's contraction.

However, nowhere on Mercury do we find evidence of extension (stretching) to match this crustal compression. Can it be that the whole planet simply shrank? Apparently so. Early in its history, Mercury gained much more internal heat from accretion and differentiation than did the Moon, owing to its larger proportion of iron and stronger gravity. Then, as the core cooled, it contracted by perhaps as much as 20 kilometers in radius. This contraction crumpled and compressed the crust, forming the many cliffs. The contraction probably also closed off volcanic vents, ending Mercury's period of volcanism.

Mercury lost its internal heat relatively quickly because of its small size. Its days of volcanism and tectonic shrinking probably ended within its first billion years. Mercury, like the Moon, has been geologically dead for most of its existence.

### Mars (3,396-km radius, 1.52 AU from Sun)

Early telescopic observations of Mars revealed several uncanny resemblances to Earth. A Martian day is just over 24 hours, and the Martian rotation axis is tilted about the same amount as Earth's. Mars also has polar caps, which we now know to be composed primarily of frozen carbon dioxide, with smaller amounts of water ice. Telescopic observations also showed seasonal variations in surface coloration over the course of the Martian year (about 1.9 Earth years). All these discoveries led to the perception that Mars and Earth were at least cousins, if not twins. By the early 1900s, many astronomers—as well as the public—envisioned Mars as nearly Earth-like, possessing water, vegetation that changed with the seasons, and possibly intelligent life.

In 1877, Italian astronomer Giovanni Schiaparelli reported seeing linear features across the surface of Mars through his telescope. He named these features *canali*, the Italian word for "channels." (It's not clear whether he really thought the channels contained water or was merely continuing the tradition, started with the Moon, of naming dark features after bodies of water.) This report inspired the American astronomer Percival Lowell to build an observatory in Flagstaff, Arizona, for the study of Mars. In 1895, Lowell claimed the *canali* were *canals* being used by intelligent Martians to route water around their planet. He suggested that Mars was falling victim to unfavorable climate changes and that water was a precious resource that had to be managed carefully. Lowell's studies drove rampant speculation about the nature of the Martians, fueling science fiction fantasies. The public mania drowned out the skepticism of astronomers who saw

**FIGURE 9.25** Can you see how the markings on Mars in the telescopic photo on the left might have resembled the geometrical features in the drawing by Percival Lowell on the right? Try blurring your eyes.

no canals through their telescopes or in their photographs (Figure 9.25).

The debate about Martian canals and cities was finally put to rest in 1965 with photos of the barren, cratered surface taken during the *Mariner 4* flyby. Schiaparelli's *canali* turned out to be nothing more than dark dust deposits redistributed by seasonal winds. Several other spacecraft studied Mars in the 1960s and 1970s, culminating with the impressive Viking missions in 1976. Each of the two Viking spacecraft deployed an orbiter that mapped the Martian surface from above and landers that returned surface images and regular weather reports for almost 5 years. More than 20 years passed before the next successful missions to Mars, the Mars Pathfinder mission and Mars Global Surveyor mission in 1997 [Section 7.6].

*Martian Geology* The Viking and Mars Global Surveyor images show a much wider variety of geological features than seen on the Moon or Mercury. Some areas of the southern hemisphere are heavily cratered (Figure 9.26a), while the northern hemisphere is covered by huge volcanoes surrounded by extensive volcanic plains. Volcanism was expected on Mars—40% larger than Mercury, it should have retained a hot interior much longer. But no one knows why volcanism affected the northern hemisphere so much more than the southern hemisphere, or why the northern hemisphere on average is lower in altitude than the southern hemisphere.

Mars has a long, deep system of valleys called *Valles Marineris* running along its equator (Figure 9.26b). Named for the *Mariner 9* spacecraft that first imaged it, Valles Marineris is as long as the United States is wide and almost four times deeper than the Grand Canyon. No one knows exactly how it formed; parts of the canyon are completely enclosed by high cliffs on all sides, so neither flowing lava nor water could have been responsible. Nevertheless, the linear "stretch marks" around the valley are evidence of tectonic stresses on a very large scale.

More cracks are visible on the nearby *Tharsis Bulge,* a continent-size region that rises well above the surrounding Martian surface (Figure 9.26c). Tharsis was probably created by a long-lived plume of rising mantle material that bulged the surface upward while stretching and cracking the crust. The plume was also responsible for releasing vast amounts of basaltic lava that built up several gigantic shield volcanoes, including *Olympus Mons,* the largest shield volcano in the solar system (Figure 9.26d). Olympus Mons has roughly the same shallow slope as the volcanic island of Hawaii, but it is three times larger in every dimension. Its base is some 600 kilometers across, making it large enough to cover an area the size of Arizona; it stands 26 kilometers high—some three times higher than Mount Everest.

How old are the volcanoes? Are they still active? In the absence of red-hot lava (none has been seen so far), the abundance of impact craters provides the best evidence. The Martian volcanoes are almost devoid of craters, but not quite. Planetary geologists

**a** The southern hemisphere of Mars is heavily cratered. The image spans several hundred kilometers.

**b** Valles Marineris is a huge valley created in part by tectonic stresses.

**c** A mantle plume below the Tharsis Bulge region was probably responsible for the volcanoes near the bottom of the image and the network of valleys near the top.

**d** Olympus Mons—the largest shield volcano in the solar system—covers an area the size of Arizona and rises higher than Mt. Everest.

**FIGURE 9.26** These photos of the Martian surface, taken from orbiting spacecraft, show that impact cratering has been an important process on Mars, but volcanism and tectonics have been even more important in shaping the current Martian surface.

therefore estimate that the volcanoes went dormant about a billion years ago. Geologically speaking, a billion years is not that long, and it remains possible that the Martian volcanoes will someday come back to life. However, the Martian interior is presumably cooling and its lithosphere thickening. At best, it's only a matter of a few billion more years before Mars becomes as geologically dead as the Moon and Mercury.

*Martian Water* The Martian robotic explorers have also revealed geological features unlike any seen on the Moon or Mercury—features caused by erosion. Figure 9.27a no doubt reminds you of a dry riverbed on Earth seen from above. The eroded craters visible on some of the oldest terrain suggest that rain fell on the Martian surface billions of years ago (see Fig-

ure 9.13c). In some places, erosion has even acted below the surface, where underground water and ice have broken up or dissolved the rocks. When the water and ice disappeared, a wide variety of odd pits and troughs were left behind. This process may have contributed to the formation of parts of Valles Marineris.

Underground ice may be the key to one of the biggest floods in the history of the solar system. Figure 9.27b shows a landscape hundreds of kilometers across that was apparently scoured by rushing water. Geologists theorize that heat from a volcano melted great quantities of underground ice, unleashing a catastrophic flood that created winding channels and large sandbars along its way.

The *Mars Pathfinder* spacecraft went to this interesting region to see the flood damage close up.

**a** This Viking photo (from orbit) shows ancient riverbeds that were probably created billions of years ago.

**FIGURE 9.27** Unlike Mercury and the Moon, Mars shows unmistakable evidence of widespread erosion. The latest results point to the action of liquid water.

**b** This photo shows winding channels and sandbars that were probably created by catastrophic floods.

**c** View from the floodplain (see **b** above) from the *Mars Pathfinder;* the *Pathfinder* landing site is now known as Carl Sagan Memorial Station. The *Sojourner* rover is visible near the large rock.

**d** Close-up view of the floor of the eroded crater shown in Figure 9.13c. Billions of years ago, the crater was apparently a pond, and layer upon layer of sediment was deposited on the bottom. The water is long gone, and winds have since sculpted the layers into the astonishing patterns captured in this photograph from the *Mars Global Surveyor.*

400 m
437 yd

**e** Topographic map of Mars with low-lying regions in blue and higher elevations in red, brown, and white. The white patches are tall volcanoes; Valles Marineris cuts through the terrain to their right. Some planetary geologists believe that an ocean once filled the smooth, low-lying northern regions shown in dark blue.

400 m
437 yd

**f** This photograph from *Mars Global Surveyor* shows gullies on a crater wall; scientists suspect they were formed by water seeping out from the ground during episodic flash floods. The gullies are geologically young, but no one yet knows whether similar gullies may still be forming today.

The lander released the *Sojourner* rover, named after Sojourner Truth, an African-American heroine of the Civil War era who traveled the nation advocating equal rights for women and blacks. The six-wheeled rover, no larger than a microwave oven, carried cameras and instruments to measure the chemical composition of nearby rocks. Together the lander and rover confirmed the flood hypothesis: Gentle, dry, winding channels were visible in stereo images; rocks of many different types had been jumbled together in the flood; and the departing waters had left rocks stacked against each other in just the same manner that floods do here on Earth (Figure 9.27c).

In the decades since we first learned of past water on Mars, scientists have debated when water last flowed. Recent images from the *Mars Global Surveyor* have only deepened the mystery. Figure 9.27d shows a close-up view of the floor of a crater (the same crater shown in Figure 9.13c). The sculpted patterns in this picture were probably created as erosion exposed layer upon layer of sedimentary rock, much like the sedimentary layers visible in Earth's Grand Canyon. This suggests that ancient rains once filled the crater like a pond, with the sedimentary layers built up by material that settled to the bottom. Figure 9.27e, made from the spacecraft's precise topographic measurements, shows evidence of even more widespread water, suggesting that much of Mars's northern hemisphere was once covered by an ocean. Perhaps the most surprising finding is the presence of small gullies on the walls of many craters and valleys (Figure 9.27f). The gullies probably formed when underground water broke out in episodic flash floods, carrying boulders and soil into a broad fan at the bottom of the slope. Moreover, the gullies must be geologically young, because they have not been covered over by ongoing dust storms, nor have small craters formed on their surfaces. Unfortunately, "young" can be quite ambiguous in a geological sense: No one knows if these gullies formed "just" millions of years ago or if some might still be forming today.

Even if water still flows on occasion, it seems clear that Mars was much wetter in the past than it is today. Ironically, Percival Lowell's supposition that Mars was drying up has turned out to be basically correct, even though he did not have real evidence to support it. We'll discuss reasons for Mars's dramatic climate change in Chapter 10.

The Mars Global Surveyor and Pathfinder missions are paving the way for more adventurous missions. *Mars Global Surveyor* is searching for optimal landing sites for future rovers—one will search for evidence of life past and present, and another will gather rock samples for return to Earth. For the latest news on Mars missions, check the book Web site and Web sites listed in Appendix H.

### Venus (6,051-km radius, 0.72 AU from Sun)

Venus is a big step up in size from Mars—it is almost as big as Earth. Thus, we would expect it to have had an early geological history much like Earth's, with impact cratering, volcanism, and tectonics.

Venus's thick cloud cover prevents us from seeing through to its surface, but we can study its geological features with radar. *Radar mapping* involves bouncing radio waves off the surface from a spacecraft and using the reflections to create three-dimensional images of the surface. From 1990 to 1993, the *Magellan* spacecraft used radar to map the surface of Venus, discerning features as small as 100 meters across. During its 4 years of observations, *Magellan* returned more data than all previous planetary missions combined. Scientists have named almost all the geological features for female goddesses and famous women.

*Venusian Impacts and Volcanism* Most of Venus is covered by relatively smooth, rolling plains with few mountain ranges. The surface has some impact craters (Figure 9.28a), but very few compared to the Moon or even Mars. Venus lacks very small craters, because small impactors burn up in its dense atmosphere. But large craters are also rare, indicating that they must be erased by other geological processes. Volcanism is clearly at work on Venus, as evidenced by an abundance of volcanoes and lava flows. Some are shield volcanoes, indicating familiar basaltic eruptions (Figure 9.28b). Some volcanoes have steeper sides, probably indicating eruptions of a higher-viscosity lava (Figure 9.28c).

*Venusian Tectonics* The most remarkable features on Venus are tectonic in origin. Its crust is quite contorted; in some regions, the surface appears to be fractured in a regular pattern (Figure 9.28d; see also Figure 9.19). Many of the tectonic features are associated with volcanic features, suggesting a strong linkage between volcanism and tectonics on Venus. One striking example of this linkage is a type of roughly circular feature called a *corona* (Latin for "crown") that probably resulted from a hot, rising plume in the mantle (Figure 9.28e). The plume pushed up on the crust, forming rings of tectonic stretch marks on the surface. The plume also forced lava to the surface, dotting the area with volcanoes.

Does Venus, like Earth, have plate tectonics that moves pieces of its lithosphere around? Convincing evidence for plate tectonics might include deep trenches and linear mountain ranges like those we see on Earth, but *Magellan* found no such evidence on Venus. The apparent lack of plate tectonics suggests that Venus's lithosphere is quite different from Earth's. Some geologists theorize that Venus's lithosphere is thicker and stronger, preventing its surface

**a** Impact craters like these are rare on Venus.

**b** Shield volcanoes like this one are common on Venus.

**c** These volcanoes were made from viscous lava.

**d** Tectonic forces have fractured and twisted the crust in this region.

**FIGURE 9.28** The surface of Venus is covered with abundant lava flows and tectonic features, along with a few large impact craters. Because these images were taken by the Magellan spacecraft radar, dark and light areas correspond to how well radio waves are reflected, not visible light. Nonetheless, geological features stand out well. All images are several hundred kilometers across.

**e** A mantle plume probably created the round corona, which is surrounded by tectonic stress marks.

from fracturing into plates. Another possibility is that plate tectonics happens only occasionally on Venus. The uniform but low abundance of craters suggests that most of the surface formed around a billion years ago. Plate tectonics is one candidate for the process that wiped out older surface features and created a fresh surface at that time. For the last billion years, only volcanism, a bit of impact cratering, and small-scale tectonics have occurred.

*Venusian Erosion?* One might expect Venus's thick atmosphere to drive strong erosion, but the view both from orbit and from the surface suggests otherwise. The Soviet Union landed two probes on the surface of Venus in 1975. Before being destroyed by the 700 K

heat, they returned images of a bleak, volcanic landscape with little evidence of erosion (see Figure 9.2). Venus apparently lacks the rains and winds that drive erosion, probably because of its high surface temperature and slow rotation rate.

The lack of strong erosion on Venus leaves the tectonic contortions of its surface exposed to view, even though some probably approach a billion years in age. Earth's terrain might look equally stark and rugged from space if not for the softening influences of wind, rain, and life. Like Earth, Venus probably has ongoing tectonic and volcanic activity, although we have no direct proof of it.

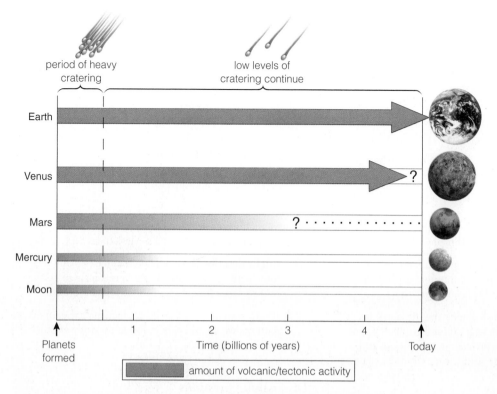

**FIGURE 9.29** Volcanic/tectonic histories of the ancient worlds. This diagram summarizes the relationship between planetary size and volcanic/tectonic activity for the terrestrial worlds. The length of the red arrow shows the duration of activity: Earth is the only terrestrial world that we know to be active today, but we expect that Venus is still active as well. Most ancient craters have been erased on both. Mars may still have low levels of volcanism, and some ancient craters still remain. The narrower width of the arrows for Mercury and the Moon indicates that their volcanic and tectonic activity was never strong enough to wipe out all their heavily cratered surfaces. The diagram also shows the period of heavy cratering in the early history of the solar system. Erosion is not shown; it is negligible everywhere except Earth (where it is significant) and Mars (where it was once significant and endures to the present day at low levels).

### Earth (6,378-km radius, 1.0 AU from Sun)

We've toured our neighboring terrestrial worlds and found a clear relationship between size and volcanic and tectonic activity. Thus, it should come as no surprise that Earth, the largest of the terrestrial worlds, has a high level of ongoing volcanism and tectonics. We've already discussed some of the volcanic and tectonic features on Earth, and we'll explore others in Chapter 13, where we'll also see how plate tectonics has affected Earth's climate and hence its biology.

Figure 9.29 summarizes the trends among the terrestrial worlds for volcanism and tectonics. It shows one of the key rules in planetary geology: Larger planets stay volcanically and tectonically active much longer than smaller planets. The situation for erosion is somewhat more complex. Earth has far more erosion than any other terrestrial world, but the most similar erosion is found on Mars, whose surface is sculpted by flowing water despite its small size. To understand erosion, we must look more closely at planetary atmospheres—the topic of our next chapter.

**TIME OUT TO THINK** *Suppose another star system has a rocky terrestrial planet that is much larger than Earth. What kind of geology would you expect it to have: a surface saturated with craters, or widespread volcanic and tectonic activity? Explain.*

## THE BIG PICTURE

In this chapter, we have seen how the images returned from our robotic explorers have helped decipher the histories of the terrestrial worlds and have yielded clues to what their interiors must be like. As you continue your study of the solar system, keep the following "big picture" ideas in mind:

■ Much of planetary geology can be distilled down to a few basic geological processes that depend on a handful of planetary properties.

■ Every terrestrial world was once as heavily cratered as the Moon is today, but craters have been erased on the other worlds to varying degrees—mainly depending on each planet's size.

■ Volcanism and tectonics depend primarily on a world's size, but erosion depends on characteristics of planetary atmospheres.

■ Our model of planetary geology explains much of what we see on terrestrial worlds in our solar system and therefore might help us learn what happens on planets in other solar systems.

## Review Questions

1. Briefly explain how the terrestrial planets ended up spherical in shape. Would you also expect small asteroids to be spherical? Why or why not?

2. What is *viscosity*? Give examples of substances with low viscosity and substances with high viscosity.

3. How does *differentiation* occur, and under what circumstances? Explain how differentiation led to the *core–mantle–crust* structure of the terrestrial worlds.

4. What is a *lithosphere?* What determines the strength and thickness of a planet's lithosphere?

5. Describe and distinguish among the three major processes by which planetary interiors get hot: *accretion, differentiation,* and *radioactivity.*

6. Describe and distinguish among the three major processes by which planetary interiors transfer heat to planetary surfaces: *conduction, convection,* and *eruption.* How does the heat escape from the planet's surface into space?

7. What is the primary factor in determining how long a planetary interior remains hot? Why?

8. What is a *magnetic field?* Contrast the magnetic fields of terrestrial planets.

9. Briefly describe the four major geological processes: *impact cratering, volcanism, tectonics,* and *erosion.*

10. Describe and distinguish between what we call *formation properties* and *geological controlling factors* in the context of planetary geology. Summarize in your own words the relationships shown in Figure 9.10.

11. Briefly describe how impacts affect planetary surfaces, and explain how we can estimate the geological age of a planetary surface from its number of impact craters.

12. What created the "soil" on the lunar surface? Explain why the footprints of the astronauts on the Moon will last a long time, but not forever.

13. Explain how differences in lava viscosity lead to *volcanic plains, shield volcanoes,* or *stratovolcanoes.*

14. Describe several types of internal stress that can drive tectonic activity. Under what conditions does a lithosphere break into *plates* and show *plate tectonics?*

15. What are *volatiles,* and how are they important to erosion? Briefly explain why Mercury and the Moon have virtually no erosion.

16. Briefly summarize the geological history of the Moon. How and when did the maria form? Why is the Moon geologically "dead" today?

17. Briefly summarize the geological history of Mercury. What is the Caloris Basin? How did Mercury get its many huge cliffs?

18. Briefly discuss the superficial similarities between Mars and Earth that led many people in the early 1900s to believe that Mars must harbor life. What were the *canali* that some astronomers reported on Mars? Do they really exist?

19. Briefly describe major geological features on Mars and their possible origins.

20. Describe the evidence for past water flow on Mars, including catastrophic floods and rainfall. Is it possible that water still flows on Mars today? Explain.

21. Briefly describe the evidence for volcanic and tectonic activity on Venus. Does Venus have plate tectonics? Does it show signs of significant erosion?

22. Briefly explain how Earth's geology fits the general patterns we should expect based on study of other terrestrial worlds.

## Discussion Questions

1. *Making Models.* In this chapter, we developed a relatively simple conceptual model to describe the complex interactions that govern planetary geology. Use a similar approach to make a model for a complex problem of interest to you. The problem need not be astronomical; for example, you might consider global warming, changes in the stock market, or ways that class size could be reduced at your college or university. Your model need not use flowcharts, but it should include (1) some phenomenon you wish to understand, (2) the processes that affect it, and (3) the various factors those processes depend on.

2. *Geological Connections.* Consider the four geological processes: impact cratering, volcanism, tectonics, and erosion. Which two do you think are most closely connected to each other? Explain your answer, giving several ways in which the processes are connected.

3. *Testing the Model.* Our theories of planetary geology seem to explain the terrestrial worlds fairly well, but do they work elsewhere in the solar system?

   a. According to the model based on the terrestrial worlds, which of the four geological processes would you predict to be most important on Jupiter's moon Io (1,815-km radius) and Uranus's moon Miranda (243-km radius)?

   b. Based on the photos of these moons (Figure 11.17 and Figure 11.25), are your predictions correct?

   c. In a strictly logical sense, what would you conclude about our model of planetary geology based on your answer to part (b)? Explain.

## Problems

*Surprising Discoveries?* For **problems 1–4,** suppose a spacecraft were to make the observations described. (These are *not* real discoveries.) In light of your understanding of planetary geology, decide whether the discovery should be considered reasonable or surprising. Explain your answer, tracing your logic back to the planet's formation properties. Explain.

1. The next mission to Mercury photographs part of the surface never seen before and detects vast fields of sand dunes.

2. A radar mapper in orbit around Venus detects a new volcano larger than any other on Venus but not seen by the Magellan spacecraft.

3. A Venus radar mapper discovers extensive regions of layered sedimentary rocks similar to those found on Earth and Mars.

4. Clear-cutting in the Amazon rain forest exposes vast regions of ancient terrain that is as heavily cratered as the lunar highlands.

5. *Earth vs. Moon.* Why is the Moon heavily cratered, but not Earth? Explain in a paragraph or two, relating your answer to their planetary formation properties.

6. *Erosion.* Consider erosion on Mercury, Venus, the Moon, and Mars. Which of these four worlds shows the greatest erosion? Why? Write a paragraph for each world explaining why the other three worlds do not have significant erosion and relating erosional activity to the four planetary formation properties.

7. *Miniature Mars.* Suppose Mars had turned out to be significantly smaller than its current size—say, the size of our Moon. How would this have affected the number of geological features due to each of the four major geological processes (impact cratering, volcanism, tectonics, and erosion)? Do you think Mars would still be a good candidate for harboring extraterrestrial life? Why or why not? Summarize your answers in two or three paragraphs.

8. *Mystery Planet.* It's the year 2098, and you are designing a robotic mission to a newly discovered planet around a star that is nearly identical to our Sun. The planet is as large in radius as Venus, rotates with the same daily period as Mars, and lies 1.2 AU from its star. Your spacecraft will orbit but not land.

   a. Some of your colleagues believe that the planet has no metallic core. How could you support or refute their hypothesis? (*Hint:* Remember that metal is dense and electrically conducting.)

   b. Other colleagues believe that the planet formed with few if any radioactive elements. How could images of the surface support or refute their hypothesis?

   c. Others suspect it has no atmosphere, but the instruments designed to study the planet's atmosphere fail due to a software error. How could you use the spacecraft's photos of geological features to determine whether a significant atmosphere is (or was) present on this planet?

9. *Dating Planetary Surfaces.* We have discussed two basic techniques for determining the age of a planetary surface: studying the abundance of impact craters, and radioactive dating of surface rocks [Section 8.6].

   a. Which technique seems more reliable? Why?

   b. Which technique is easier to use for planets besides Earth? Why?

*10. *Impact Energies.* A relatively small impact crater 10 km in radius could be made by a comet 1 km in radius traveling at 30 km/s.

   a. Assume the comet has a density of 1 g/cm³ (1,000 kg/m³), and calculate its total kinetic energy. *Hints:* First find the volume of the comet in m³, then find its mass by multiplying its volume by its density, and finally calculate its kinetic energy. You'll need the following formulas; if you use mass in kg and velocity in m/s, the answer for kinetic energy will have units of joules:

   $$\text{volume of sphere} = \tfrac{4}{3}\pi \times (\text{radius})^3$$
   $$\text{kinetic energy} = \tfrac{1}{2} \times \text{mass} \times (\text{velocity})^2$$

   b. Convert your answer from part (a) to megatons of TNT, the unit used for nuclear bombs. Comment on the degree of devastation that the impact of such a comet could cause if it struck a populated region on Earth. (*Hint:* One megaton of TNT releases $4.2 \times 10^{15}$ joules of energy.)

11. *Project: Geological Properties of Silly Putty.*

   a. Roll room-temperature Silly Putty into a ball and measure its diameter. Place the ball on a table and gently place one end of a heavy book on it. After 5 seconds, measure the height of the squashed ball.

   b. Warm the Silly Putty in hot water and repeat the experiment in part (a). Then chill the Silly Putty in ice water and repeat. How did the different temperatures affect the rate of "squashing"?

   c. Did heating and cooling have a small or large effect on the rate of "squashing"? How does this experiment relate to planetary geology?

12. *Project: Planetary Cooling in a Freezer.* To simulate the cooling of planetary bodies of different sizes, use a freezer and two small *plastic* containers of similar shape but different size. Fill them with cold water and place them in the freezer. Checking every hour or so, record the time and your estimate of the thickness of the "lithosphere" (the frozen layer) in the two tubs.

*(continued)*

a. On a graph, plot the lithospheric thickness versus time for each tub. In which tub does the lithosphere thicken faster?

b. How long does it take each tub to freeze completely? What is the ratio of the two freezing times?

c. Describe in a few sentences the relevance of your experiment to planetary geology.

13. *Amateur Astronomy: Observing the Moon.* Any amateur telescope is adequate to identify geological features on the Moon. The light highlands and dark maria should be evident, and the shading of topography will be seen in the region near the terminator (the line between night and day). Try to observe near first- or third-quarter phase. Sketch the Moon at low magnification, and then zoom in on a region of interest, noting its location on your sketch. Sketch your field of view, label its features, and identify the geological process that created them. Look for craters, volcanic plains, and tectonic features. Estimate the horizontal size of the features by comparing them to the size of the whole Moon (radius = 1,738 km).

## Web Projects

Find useful links for Web projects on the text Web site.

1. *Current Mars Exploration.* Find the latest results from current Mars missions and briefly explain how the latest results have changed or improved our understanding of Mars.

2. *Future Planetary Missions.* Learn about at least one upcoming mission designed to study a terrestrial world. Write a short summary of the mission and what it is designed to accomplish.

*For the first time in my life I saw the horizon as a curved line. It was accentuated by a thin seam of dark blue light—our atmosphere. Obviously this was not the ocean of air I had been told it was so many times in my life. I was terrified by its fragile appearance.*

ULF MERBOLD, ASTRONAUT (GERMANY)

# CHAPTER 10

# Planetary Atmospheres
## Earth and the Other Terrestrial Worlds

Life as we know it would be impossible on Earth without our atmosphere. In addition to supplying the oxygen we breathe, it shields us from harmful ultraviolet and X-ray radiation coming from the Sun, protects us from continual bombardment by micrometeorites, generates rain-giving clouds, and traps just enough heat to keep Earth habitable. We couldn't have designed a better atmosphere if we'd tried.

Despite forming under similar conditions, our neighboring planets ended up with atmospheres utterly inhospitable to us. No other planet in our solar system has air that we could breathe, or temperature and pressure conditions in which we could survive without a spacesuit. Mars, only slightly farther from the Sun than Earth, has an atmosphere that leaves its surface cold, dry, and barren. Venus, only slightly closer to the Sun, has an atmosphere that makes its surface conditions resemble a classical view of hell.

How did Earth end up with such fortunate conditions? To fully appreciate what happened on Earth, we must understand what happened on all the terrestrial worlds.

Mercury

Venus

**FIGURE 10.1** Views of the terrestrial worlds and their atmospheres from orbit and from the surface. The surface views for Mercury and Venus are artist's conceptions; the others are photos. The global views are photos taken from spacecraft—although the Venus image shows the clouds as they appear in ultraviolet light rather than visible light.

## 10.1 Planetary Atmospheres

All the planets of our solar system have atmospheres to varying degrees, as do several of the solar system's larger moons. The jovian planets are essentially atmosphere throughout—they are largely made of gaseous material. In contrast, the atmospheres of solid bodies—terrestrial worlds, jovian moons with atmospheres, and Pluto—are relatively thin layers of gas that contain only a minuscule fraction of a world's mass. Although we will concentrate on understanding the atmospheres of the terrestrial worlds, similar principles apply to the atmospheres of all the planets and satellites.

The terrestrial atmospheres are even more varied than the terrestrial geologies. The Moon and Mercury have very little atmosphere at all—even in broad daylight you would seem to be facing the blackness of space when standing on their surfaces. What little atmosphere they possess probably comes from materials vaporized as the surface is bombarded by micrometeorites, the solar wind, or energetic solar photons. These materials consist mostly of individual atoms of potassium, sodium, and oxygen, among others. If you could condense the entire atmosphere of the Moon into solid form, you would have so little material that you could store it in a basement.

At the other extreme, Venus is completely enshrouded by a thick atmosphere. If you stood on the surface of Venus, you'd feel a crushing pressure

90 times greater than that on Earth and a searing temperature higher than that in the hottest ovens used for cooking. Moving through the air on Venus would feel something like a cross between swimming and flying, because its density at the surface is nearly 10% of the density of liquid water. You couldn't breathe the air, because it consists almost entirely of carbon dioxide and does not contain any of the molecular oxygen ($O_2$) on which we depend. The surface views are perpetually overcast as weak sunlight filters though the thick clouds above. Violent storms on Venus's surface are virtually nonexistent, and corrosive chemicals that rain downward from high in the atmosphere evaporate before ever hitting the ground.

The atmosphere of Mars is also made mostly of carbon dioxide, but much less of it than on Venus. The result is very thin air with a pressure so low that your body tissues would bulge painfully if you stood on the surface without wearing a full space suit. In fact, the pressure and temperature are both so low that liquid water would rapidly disappear, some evaporating and some freezing into ice. Thus, the fact that we see dried-up riverbeds on Mars tells us that its atmosphere must have been very different in the past [Section 9.5]. Mars has seasons like Earth because of its similar axis tilt, and it is occasionally engulfed in planet-wide dust storms.

Earth's atmosphere of nitrogen and oxygen is the only one under which human life is possible, at least without the creation of an artificial environment.

Earth

Earth's Moon

Mars

What makes Earth's atmosphere so special? The best way to answer this question is to compare planetary atmospheres. Each atmosphere is unique, but, as we saw with geology in Chapter 9, similar properties and processes determine the characteristics of all atmospheres. Table 10.1 summarizes the properties of the terrestrial atmospheres, and Figure 10.1 shows representative views from above the worlds and from their surfaces. We'll spend the rest of this chapter learning how and why the terrestrial atmospheres came to differ so profoundly. Before we begin our comparative study, however, we need to discuss a few basic properties of atmospheres. Let's begin with the most basic question: What is an atmosphere?

## Table 10.1 Atmospheres of the Terrestrial Worlds

| World | Composition | Surface Pressure* | Winds, Weather Patterns | Clouds, Hazes |
|-------|-------------|-------------------|-------------------------|---------------|
| Mercury | helium, sodium, oxygen | $10^{-14}$ bar | None: too little atmosphere | None |
| Venus | 96% $CO_2$ 3.5% $N_2$ | 90 bars | Slow winds, no violent storms, acid rain | Sulfuric acid clouds |
| Earth | 77% $N_2$ 21% $O_2$ 1% argon $H_2O$ (variable) | 1 bar | Winds, hurricanes | $H_2O$ clouds, pollution |
| Moon | helium, sodium, argon | $10^{-14}$ bar | None: too little atmosphere | None |
| Mars | 95% $CO_2$ 2.7% $N_2$ 1.6% argon | 0.007 bar | Winds, dust storms | $H_2O$ and $CO_2$ clouds, dust |

*1 bar ≈ the pressure at sea level on Earth.

## What Is an Atmosphere?

An *atmosphere* is a layer of gases that surrounds a world. The air that makes up any atmosphere is a mixture of many different gases that may consist either of individual atoms or of molecules. At the relatively low temperatures found throughout most planetary atmospheres, most atoms in gases combine to form molecules. For example, the air that we breathe consists of *molecular* nitrogen ($N_2$) and oxygen ($O_2$), as opposed to individual atoms (N or O). The wide variety of gases in planetary atmospheres falls into the category called *volatiles* [Section 9.4], materials that are usually gaseous or liquid at temperatures of a few hundred Kelvin. Common volatiles include nitrogen ($N_2$), oxygen ($O_2$), and water ($H_2O$) on Earth; carbon dioxide ($CO_2$) on Venus and Mars; and hydrogen ($H_2$), helium (He), methane ($CH_4$), and ammonia ($NH_3$) on the jovian planets.

Even at moderate temperatures, individual air molecules whiz around at high speeds and frequently collide with one another. On Earth, the nitrogen and oxygen molecules fly around at average speeds of about 500 meters per second—fast enough to cross your bedroom a hundred times in a second. Given that a single breath of air contains some $10^{22}$ molecules, you can imagine how frequently molecules collide. In fact, each molecule in the air around you will suffer a million collisions in the time it takes to read this paragraph.

All these collisions in a gas create the **gas pressure**. An easy way to understand pressure is to think about a balloon. The air molecules inside a balloon are constantly colliding with the balloon walls, exerting a pressure that tends to make the balloon expand. Because the particles in a gas move every which way, the pressure acts equally in all directions. At the same time, air molecules outside the balloon collide with the walls from the other side, tending to make the balloon contract. A sealed balloon remains stable when the inward pressure and the outward pressure are balanced. (We are neglecting any tension in the balloon material.) Now imagine that you blow more air into the balloon. The extra molecules inside mean more collisions with the balloon wall, momentarily making the pressure inside greater than the pressure outside. The balloon therefore expands until the inward and outward pressures are again in balance. If you heat the balloon, the gas molecules begin moving faster and therefore collide harder with the walls. Thus, heating a balloon also makes the inside pressure momentarily greater than the outside pressure, causing the balloon to expand. Conversely, cooling a balloon makes it contract, because the outside pressure momentarily exceeds the inside pressure.

We can understand *atmospheric pressure* using similar principles. Gas in an atmosphere is held down by gravity. The atmosphere over any area has some weight that presses downward, tending to compress the atmosphere beneath it. At the same time, gas pressure pushes in all directions, including upward, which tends to make the atmosphere expand. Planetary atmospheres exist in a perpetual balance between the downward weight of their gases and the upward push of their gas pressure. (We call this balance *gravitational equilibrium* [or *hydrostatic equilibrium*]; it is also very important in stars [Section 14.1].) The higher you go in an atmosphere, the less the weight of the gas above you. Thus, the pressure must also become less as you go upward, which explains why the pressure decreases as you climb a mountain or ascend in an airplane. You can visualize what happens by imagining the atmosphere as a very big stack of pillows. The pillows at the bottom are very compressed because of the weight of all the pillows above. As you go upward, the pillows are less and less compressed because less weight lies on top of them. The standard unit of pressure is the **bar** (as in *barometer*) and is roughly equal to Earth's atmospheric pressure at sea level.[1]

**TIME OUT TO THINK** *There is pressure under water just as there is pressure under air. Use this fact to explain why the pressure increases dramatically with depth in the oceans. How does this pressure affect deep-sea divers and submarines?*

## Where Does an Atmosphere End?

The higher you go in an atmosphere, the lower the pressure becomes. Atmospheres therefore do not have clear upper boundaries but instead gradually fade away with increasing altitude. Nevertheless, there are a number of ways to characterize the thickness of an atmosphere surrounding a planet. One simple way is to ask when you would seem to have left the atmosphere and entered "space." Atmospheres scatter sunlight, which is what prevents us from seeing stars in the daytime. Thus, you might say that you had reached "space" when you had risen high enough that you could see stars in the daytime. The terrestrial atmospheres are remarkably thin when viewed in this way. For example, stars become visible in the daytime at an altitude of a few tens of kilometers above the Earth—less than 1% of the Earth's radius (Figure 10.2a). But even the Space Shuttle, orbiting hundreds of kilometers above the Earth's surface, runs into the upper vestiges of Earth's atmosphere (Figure 10.2b). So the question of where an atmosphere ends is more one of semantics than of science.

---

[1] 1 bar $\approx$ 14.7 pounds/inch$^2$ ($\approx$ 100,000 newtons/m$^2$). That is, if you gathered up all the air directly above 1 square inch of the Earth's surface, it would weigh 14.7 pounds. You don't feel this weight on your shoulders because the pressure is also pushing up under your arms, inward against your sides, and so on in all directions. Also, the fluids in your body push outward with the same pressure.

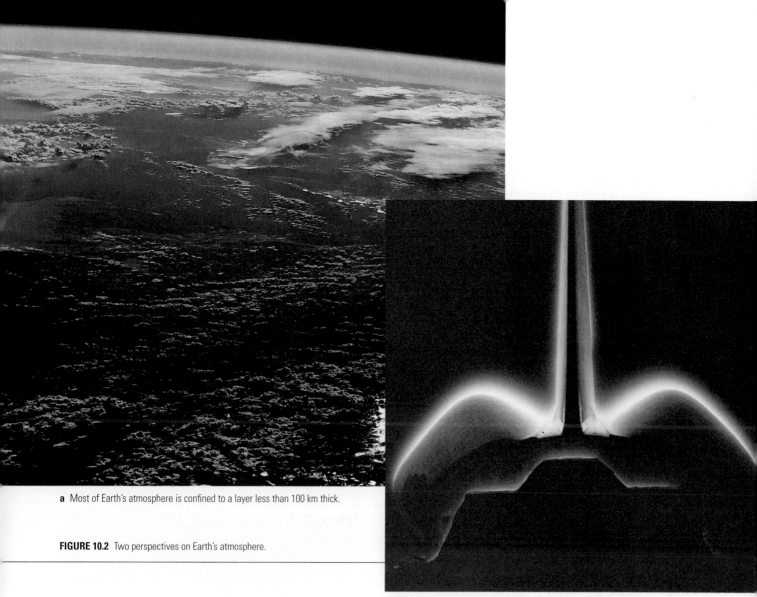

**a** Most of Earth's atmosphere is confined to a layer less than 100 km thick.

**FIGURE 10.2** Two perspectives on Earth's atmosphere.

**b** The atmosphere does not end suddenly; some gas is present even at altitudes of hundreds of kilometers, causing the glow visible around the tail of the Space Shuttle as it orbits.

## 10.2 Atmospheric Structure

If you've ever driven up a mountain, you know that the atmosphere changes with altitude. Your popping ears and shortness of breath prove that the pressure is lower as you go higher, and the chill tells you that temperature also decreases with altitude. On airplane flights, you may have noticed that the ride generally becomes smoother at high altitudes, indicating that air becomes less turbulent up high. In this section, we discuss how atmospheric structure—that is, the variation in atmospheric properties with altitude—depends on the effects of sunlight on a planet's surface and on its atmospheric gases.

### What If Planets Had No Atmospheres?

You may already know that an atmosphere can greatly affect a planet's temperature through the *greenhouse*

*effect,* which we'll discuss in detail shortly. But first we need to look at how sunlight would heat a planet without an atmosphere—or at least without any of the gases that contribute to the greenhouse effect. In that case, the surface temperature of any planet would be determined by only three basic properties:

1. How far is the planet from the Sun? The closer it is to the Sun, the more energy the planet receives from sunlight on each square meter of its surface.

2. How much sunlight does the surface absorb, and how much does it reflect? The darker the surface, the more light it absorbs and the less it reflects. The term **albedo** describes the fraction of sunlight reflected by the planet. A higher albedo means more reflection and less absorption: albedo = 0 means no reflection at all (a per-

fectly black surface); albedo = 1 means all light is reflected (a perfectly white surface). Clouds, snow, and ice have albedos of 0.7 or more, meaning that they reflect 70% or more of the light that hits them. Rocks have low albedos, usually between 0.1 and 0.25.

3. How fast does the planet rotate? A planet with a very long day will be very hot on the dayside and very cold on the nightside, but a planet with a short day will have similar temperatures both day and night. (A planet's atmosphere can also transport heat from dayside to nightside.)

**TIME OUT TO THINK** *On a hot summer day, you can gain a brief respite from walking barefoot across blacktop by stepping on a surface that is painted white. Use the idea of how albedo affects temperature to explain why.*

These three factors determine how much sunlight is actually absorbed by a planet and whether the energy is distributed over one or both sides of the planet. Any absorbed sunlight heats the planetary surface, which causes the planet to emit its own thermal radiation back into space (Figure 10.3). The energy absorbed from sunlight must be precisely balanced by the energy radiated away by the planet—otherwise the planet would rapidly heat up (if it absorbed more energy than it emitted) or cool down (if it emitted more energy than it absorbed).

We can use these simple ideas to calculate the temperature a planet would have in the absence of any extra retention of heat by the greenhouse effect in the atmosphere. Table 10.2 shows the results, giving both the "no greenhouse" temperatures and the actual surface temperatures for the terrestrial worlds. Note that the "no greenhouse" temperatures for Mercury and the Moon lie between their actual day and night temperatures—just as we should expect on worlds with very little atmosphere. The "no greenhouse" temperature for Mars is just 5 K lower than

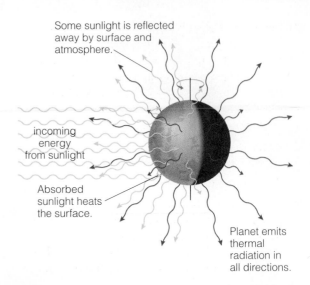

**FIGURE 10.3** To maintain a steady temperature, a planet must emit precisely as much energy as it absorbs from sunlight.

the actual value, but the "no greenhouse" temperature for Earth is almost 40 K lower than the actual surface temperature. If Earth were really this cold, our oceans would freeze (250 K = −23°C ≈ −9°F). The "no greenhouse" temperature for Venus is even farther from its actual temperature—about 500 K lower.

### A Generic Planetary Atmosphere

Clearly, the presence of an atmosphere can make a planet much warmer than it would be otherwise. But how? The solution lies with how gases interact with the radiative energy of light.

Gases can *absorb, transmit,* or *scatter* light, and they can also *emit* their own radiation [Section 6.1]. Whether a particular gas absorbs, transmits, or scatters light depends on its composition and the wavelength of the light. Fortunately, we can make a few general observations about the common gases in atmospheres (Figure 10.4):

### Table 10.2 Temperatures of the Terrestrial Worlds

| World | Distance to Sun (AU) | Albedo (0 = black, 1 = white) | Length of Day (Earth days) | "No Greenhouse" Temperature* | Observed Average Surface Temperature |
|---|---|---|---|---|---|
| Mercury | 0.38 | 0.11 | 176 | 440 K | 700 K (day), 100 K (night) |
| Venus | 0.72 | 0.72 | 117 | 230 K | 740 K |
| Earth | 1.00 | 0.36 | 1 | 250 K | 288 K |
| Moon | 1.00 | 0.07 | 28 | 273 K | 400 K (day), 100 K (night) |
| Mars | 1.52 | 0.25 | ≈1 | 218 K | 223 K |

*Assumes rapid rotation, in which case day and night temperatures would be the same.

- Some gases absorb infrared light, which causes the gas molecules to begin "wiggling" (i.e., vibrating and rotating). These added random motions mean the gases are warmer. Molecules that are particularly good at absorbing infrared light—such as carbon dioxide, methane, and water vapor—are called **greenhouse gases**.

- Atmospheric gases are generally transparent to visible light, but they can also *scatter* (change the direction of) some of the visible light.

- Ultraviolet photons can break molecules apart, particularly weakly bonded molecules such as **ozone** ($O_3$). This process of *molecular dissociation* [Section 4.3] produces atoms that may then react with other atoms or molecules or even escape from the planet.

- X rays have enough energy to knock electrons free from atoms, thereby ionizing gases. (We are neglecting radio waves and gamma rays because the Sun emits very little of these forms of radiation.)

Different wavelengths of sunlight are absorbed in different layers of the atmosphere, causing the variation of temperature with altitude. Figure 10.5 shows the structure of a "generic" planetary atmosphere; it shows how and why the temperature varies with

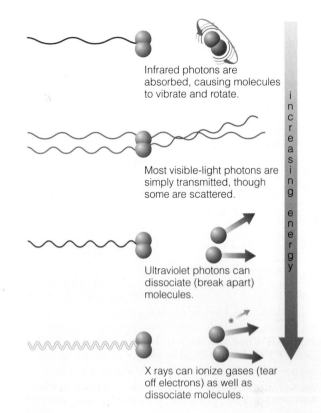

Infrared photons are absorbed, causing molecules to vibrate and rotate.

Most visible-light photons are simply transmitted, though some are scattered.

Ultraviolet photons can dissociate (break apart) molecules.

X rays can ionize gases (tear off electrons) as well as dissociate molecules.

increasing energy

**FIGURE 10.4** Light of different energies has different effects on atmospheric gases.

**FIGURE 10.5** The structure of a generic planetary atmosphere: Solar X rays are absorbed in the thermosphere, ultraviolet light is absorbed in the stratosphere, and visible light reaches the ground. Planets that lack ultraviolet-absorbing molecules will lack a stratosphere, and planets with very little gas will have only an exosphere.

X ray    UV    visible

**Exosphere**
heated by solar UV and X rays; region of greatest escape

**Thermosphere and Ionosphere**
X rays heat and ionize gases

**Stratosphere**
heated by UV light; no convection

**Troposphere**
greenhouse gases trap infrared radiation; convection important

infrared

altitude

temperature

ground

## Mathematical Insight 10.1 "No Greenhouse" Temperatures

The average temperature of a planet without any greenhouse gases depends on only three things: the planet's distance from the Sun, its albedo, and its rotation rate. As discussed in the text, the total energy the planet absorbs from sunlight must precisely balance the total energy the planet emits back into space. If we assume that a planet is rotating fast enough so that its dayside and nightside have the same temperature, we can write a simple formula for the "no greenhouse" temperature by equating the total amounts of incoming and outgoing power (energy per unit time; e.g., watts):

$$\text{total power absorbed from sunlight} = \text{total power emitted by thermal radiation}$$

Now we need to find mathematical expressions for each term. Let's start with the total power absorbed. At Earth's distance from the Sun of 1 AU, the power per unit area contained in sunlight is 1,360 watts/m$^2$. The power per unit area of light follows an inverse square law with distance. For example, the power per unit area at a distance of 2 AU from the Sun is $(\frac{1}{2})^2 = \frac{1}{4}$ as great as at the distance of Earth, and the power per unit area at a distance of 0.5 AU is $(\frac{1}{0.5})^2 = 4$ times greater than at Earth [Section 15.2]. Thus, in general, the power per unit area contained in sunlight is:

$$1{,}360 \, \frac{\text{watt}}{\text{m}^2} \times \frac{1}{d^2}$$

where $d$ is the distance from the Sun in AU. The *total* amount of power striking a planet is this power per unit area times the total area the planet has facing the Sun. As shown in Figure 10.6, this area is simply the area of a circle with the same radius as the planet, or $\pi \times (R_{planet})^2$. However, a planet does not absorb all the power that reaches it from the Sun. It reflects the fraction that we call the *albedo* and therefore absorbs a fraction of *1 minus the albedo*. Putting these facts together, we can calculate the total amount of power that a planet absorbs from sunlight:

total power absorbed =

$$\underbrace{\left(1{,}360 \, \frac{\text{watt}}{\text{m}^2} \times \frac{1}{d^2}\right)}_{\substack{\text{power per unit area} \\ \text{at distance } d \text{ (AU)}}} \times \underbrace{\pi \times (R_{planet})^2}_{\substack{\text{total area of planet} \\ \text{facing the Sun}}} \times \underbrace{(1 - \text{albedo})}_{\substack{\text{fraction of sunlight} \\ \text{absorbed by surface}}}$$

Next, we need a formula for the total power emitted by the planet. As discussed in Mathematical Insight 6.2, the power per unit area emitted by thermal radiation is $\sigma T^4$, where $T$ is the average surface temperature of the planet and $\sigma = 5.7 \times 10^{-8} \frac{\text{watt}}{\text{m}^2 \times \text{Kelvin}^4}$. As shown in Figure 10.3, the planet radiates this power from its entire surface (assuming the temperature is the same everywhere). Because the surface area of a planet is $4\pi \times (R_{planet})^2$, the total amount of power that a planet emits by thermal radiation is:

$$\text{total power emitted} = \underbrace{\sigma T^4}_{\substack{\text{emitted power} \\ \text{per unit area}}} \times \underbrace{4\pi \times (R_{planet})^2}_{\substack{\text{total surface area} \\ \text{of planet}}}$$

**FIGURE 10.6** A planet intercepts a circular area of sunlight.

We can now equate the formulas we've found for the total power absorbed and the total power emitted:

$$\underbrace{1{,}360 \, \frac{\text{watt}}{\text{m}^2} \times \frac{1}{d^2} \times \pi \times (R_{planet})^2 \times (1 - \text{albedo})}_{\text{total power absorbed}}$$
$$= \underbrace{\sigma T^4 \times 4\pi \times (R_{planet})^2}_{\text{total power emitted}}$$

You should confirm that solving this equation for the temperature $T$ yields:

$$T = \sqrt[4]{\frac{1{,}360 \, \frac{\text{watt}}{\text{m}^2} \times (1 - \text{albedo})}{4\sigma \times d^2}}$$

(Recall that the symbol $\sqrt[4]{\phantom{x}}$ means the fourth root, or the square root of the square root.) You should also confirm that, by substituting the value $\sigma = 5.7 \times 10^{-8} \frac{\text{watt}}{\text{m}^2 \times \text{Kelvin}^4}$, this formula becomes:

$$T = 280 \text{ K} \times \sqrt[4]{\frac{(1 - \text{albedo})}{d^2}}$$

This is our formula for the "no greenhouse" temperature of a planet, where $d$ must be measured in AU. (You might pause for a moment to consider why the planet's size does not affect its temperature.)

*Example:* Calculate the "no greenhouse" temperature of Mercury, assuming that it rotates rapidly enough to make its temperature the same on its dayside and nightside.

*Solution:* Table 10.2 shows that Mercury's distance from the Sun is $d = 0.38$ AU and its albedo is 0.11. Plugging these numbers into our formula for the temperature, we find:

$$T = 280 \text{ K} \times \sqrt[4]{\frac{(1 - \text{albedo})}{d^2}}$$
$$= 280 \text{ K} \times \sqrt[4]{\frac{(1 - 0.11)}{0.38^2}} = 440 \text{ K}$$

Note that this value for Mercury's temperature agrees with the value shown in Table 10.2.

altitude. The uppermost portion of the atmosphere is called the **exosphere**. The exosphere is the region where the atmosphere "fades away" into space; it is hot because the gases absorb X rays from the Sun. The remaining X rays are absorbed in the next layer down, called the **thermosphere**. These X rays ionize atoms in the part of the thermosphere that we call the **ionosphere**. Ultraviolet photons are absorbed by certain gases in the **stratosphere**.[2] Visible photons penetrate the entire atmosphere, and some are absorbed by the ground. The ground radiates away this energy as infrared light, which is trapped in the lowest atmospheric layer, called the **troposphere**. In the rest of this section, we will investigate in more detail the processes that make these basic atmospheric layers, from the ground up.

**TIME OUT TO THINK** *As we will discuss shortly, some planetary atmospheres lack ultraviolet-absorbing gases and therefore lack stratospheres. How would the structure of such a planetary atmosphere differ from that of the generic atmosphere shown in Figure 10.6?*

### Visible Light: Warming the Surface and Coloring the Sky

The Sun emits most of its energy in the form of visible light, and atmospheres are generally transparent to visible light. Thus, it is primarily visible light from the Sun that reaches and warms a planetary surface.

Although most visible light passes directly through the atmosphere, some is scattered by molecules in the atmosphere. This scattering of sunlight prevents us from seeing stars in the daytime. If our atmosphere did not scatter light, you'd be able to block out the light of the Sun simply by holding your hand in front of it, and then you'd have no trouble seeing other stars. Scattering of light also prevents shadows from being pitch black. On the Moon, where there is no air to scatter light, you can see stars in the daytime, and shadowed regions are extremely dark.

The scattering of light by the atmosphere also explains why the sky is blue. It turns out that molecules scatter blue light (higher frequencies) much more effectively than red light (lower frequencies). Thus, although the Sun illuminates the atmosphere with all colors of light, effectively only the blue light gets scattered. When the Sun is overhead, this scattered blue light reaches your eyes from all directions, explaining why the sky appears blue (Figure 10.7). At sunset (or sunrise), the sunlight must pass through

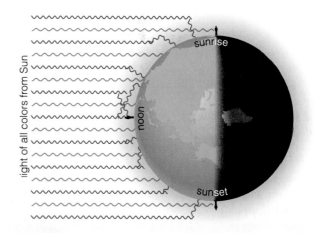

**FIGURE 10.7** Atmospheric gases scatter blue light more than they scatter red light. During most of the day, you therefore see blue photons coming from most directions in the sky, making the sky look blue. But only the red photons reach your eyes at sunrise or sunset, when the light must travel a longer path through the atmosphere to reach you.

a greater amount of atmosphere on its way to you. Thus, most of the blue light is scattered away from you altogether (making someone else's sky blue), leaving only red light to color your sunset.

**TIME OUT TO THINK** *Suppose atmospheric molecules didn't scatter light at all. In that case, what color would the sky be? Explain.*

### Infrared Light, the Greenhouse Effect, and the Troposphere

The relatively small amount of sunlight emitted farther in the infrared is mostly absorbed in our generic atmosphere before it reaches the ground. But the planet itself emits significant amounts of infrared radiation, because the planet must radiate exactly as much energy as it absorbs from the Sun to maintain a constant temperature. Herein lies the key to how atmospheres make planetary surfaces warmer than they would be otherwise.

Figure 10.8 shows how the **greenhouse effect** works.[3] Carbon dioxide, water vapor, and other *greenhouse gases* in the atmosphere absorb some of the infrared radiation emitted upward from the planet's surface. These gases therefore warm up and emit infrared thermal radiation themselves—but in all directions. Some of this radiation is directed back

---

[2]Technically, the stratosphere is only the region where the temperature rises with altitude above the troposphere. The region where the temperature falls again is called the *mesosphere*. We will not make this distinction in this book.

[3]The name *greenhouse effect* comes from botanical greenhouses, usually built mostly of glass, which keep the air inside them warmer than it would be otherwise. But it turns out that greenhouses trap heat simply by not letting hot air rise, a very different way of trapping heat than the infrared absorption that leads to the "greenhouse effect" in planetary atmospheres.

down toward the surface, making the surface warmer than it would be from absorbing visible sunlight alone. The more greenhouse gases present, the greater the degree of greenhouse warming.

**TIME OUT TO THINK** *Clouds on Earth are made of water, and $H_2O$ is a very effective greenhouse gas—even when the water vapor condenses into droplets in clouds. Use this fact to explain why clear nights tend to be colder than cloudy nights. (Hint: Sunlight warms the surface only in the daytime, but the surface radiates its heat away both day and night.)*

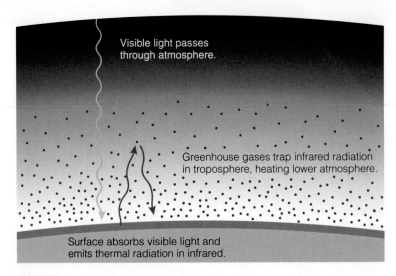

Visible light passes through atmosphere.

Greenhouse gases trap infrared radiation in troposphere, heating lower atmosphere.

Surface absorbs visible light and emits thermal radiation in infrared.

**FIGURE 10.8** The greenhouse effect: The troposphere becomes warmer than it would be if it had no greenhouse gases. Note that the surface emits thermal radiation at longer wavelengths than the visible light that heated it. (See Section 7.2.)

Air is denser at lower altitudes, so the greenhouse effect primarily affects temperatures in the troposphere. Above the troposphere, there is so little air that greenhouse gases cannot effectively trap infrared radiation. The fact that the greenhouse effect makes air warmer near the ground drives *convection* [Section 9.3] in the troposphere. The warm air near the ground expands and rises, while cooler air near the top of the troposphere contracts and falls. The descending cooler air gets heated, and the cycle repeats. The troposphere gets its name from this convection: *Tropos* is Greek for "turning." The process of convection carries heat upward and continually churns the air in the troposphere, causing the ever-changing conditions that we call the weather.

Local weather patterns called *inversions* occasionally make the air colder near the surface than higher up in the troposphere—the opposite of the usual condition, in which the troposphere is warmer at the bottom. Over cities on Earth, inversions often lead to smog problems by inhibiting the convection that normally carries pollution away to higher altitudes.

### Ultraviolet Light and the Stratosphere

The primary source of heat in the troposphere—the absorption of infrared radiation from the ground—is not important in higher layers of the atmosphere. Once infrared radiation from the ground reaches the top of the troposphere, it travels essentially unhindered to space. Thus, we need to consider only the effects of sunlight in investigating atmospheric structure above the troposphere. As we move upward through the stratosphere, the primary source of atmospheric heating is absorption of ultraviolet light from the Sun. This heating tends to be stronger at higher altitudes because the ultraviolet light gets absorbed before it reaches lower altitudes.

As a result, the stratosphere gets warmer with increasing altitude—the opposite of the situation in the troposphere. Convection therefore cannot occur in the stratosphere: Heat cannot rise if the air is even hotter higher up. (Convection lessens even in the upper troposphere, where temperature changes slowly with altitude. Thus, airplane rides become smoother at high altitudes because less convection means less turbulence.) The stratosphere gets its name because the lack of convection makes its air relatively stagnant and *stratified* (layered), rather like a sitting jar of oil and water. The lack of convection also means that the stratosphere essentially has no weather and no rain. That is why pollutants that reach the stratosphere—such as ozone-destroying chlorofluorocarbons (CFCs) [Section 13.5]—remain there for decades.

Note that a planet can have a stratosphere *only* if its atmosphere contains molecules that are particularly good at absorbing ultraviolet photons. Ozone plays this role on Earth. In fact, Earth is the only terrestrial planet with such an ultraviolet-absorbing layer and hence the only terrestrial planet with a stratosphere—at least in our solar system. (We'll discuss why Earth is unique in this way in Chapter 13.) The jovian planets also have stratospheres, as we'll discuss in the next chapter.

### X Rays and the Thermosphere and Ionosphere

Virtually all gases are good X-ray absorbers, because X rays have sufficient energy to ionize almost any atom and more than enough to dissociate almost any molecule. Solar X rays are absorbed by the first gases they encounter as they enter the atmosphere. This

X-ray absorption strongly heats the upper atmosphere in the daytime, usually to much higher temperatures than those on the surface. That is why this upper region of the atmosphere is called the *thermo*sphere. Despite its high temperatures, the gas in the thermosphere would not feel hot to your skin because its density and pressure are so low [Section 4.2].

The thermosphere contains a small but important fraction of its gas as charged ions and free electrons—the result of ionization. The layer within the thermosphere that contains most of these ions is called the *ionosphere*. The ionosphere is very important for radio communications on Earth. Most radio broadcasts are completely reflected back to Earth's surface by the ionosphere, almost as though the Earth were wrapped in aluminum foil. Without this reflection by the ionosphere, radio communication would work only between locations in sight of each other.

### The Exosphere

The exosphere is the region that marks the fuzzy "boundary" between the atmosphere and space. (The prefix *exo* means "outermost" or "outside.") The gas density in the exosphere is so low that collisions between atoms or molecules are very rare. The high temperatures in the exosphere give the individual atoms or molecules high speeds, sometimes allowing them to escape from the planet. The Space Station and many satellites actually orbit the Earth within its exosphere, and the small amount of gas in the exosphere can exert a bit of atmospheric drag. That is why satellites in low-Earth orbit eventually spiral deeper into the atmosphere and burn up [Section 5.4].

### Comparative Structure of the Terrestrial Atmospheres

Now that we understand the structure of our generic atmosphere, let's see how it corresponds to actual terrestrial atmospheres. The atmospheres of the Moon

and Mercury have so little gas that they essentially possess only the top layer, the exosphere. Venus, Earth, and Mars have denser atmospheres and are more comparable (Figure 10.9). The similarities and differences among these three planetary atmospheres make sense in light of our study of the generic atmosphere. All three have a warm troposphere at the bottom, created by the greenhouse effect, and a warm thermosphere at the top, where solar X rays are absorbed. The greatest difference is the extra "bump" of Earth's stratosphere, where ultraviolet light is absorbed. Without the warming in our unique layer of stratospheric ozone, Earth's middle altitudes would be almost as cold as those on Mars.

Although the structures of the tropospheres are similar on Venus, Earth, and Mars, the tropospheric temperatures on the three planets are dramatically different. On Venus, the thick $CO_2$ atmosphere causes a greenhouse effect that raises the surface temperature about 500 K above what it would be without greenhouse gases. The thin $CO_2$ atmosphere of Mars creates only a weak greenhouse effect, making its surface temperature only 5 K warmer than its "no greenhouse" temperature. Earth has a moderate greenhouse effect that increases its temperature about 40 K, making it comfortable for life. The greenhouse effect on Earth is almost entirely due to gases that make up less than 2% of our atmosphere: mainly carbon dioxide, water vapor, and methane. The major constituents of Earth's atmosphere, $N_2$ and $O_2$, have no effect on infrared light and do not contribute to the greenhouse effect. (Molecules with only two atoms—and especially molecules with two of the

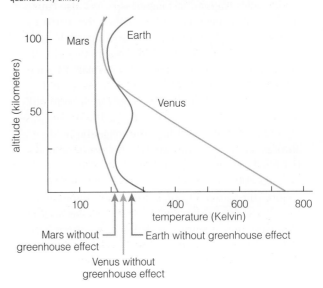

**FIGURE 10.9** Temperature profiles for Venus, Earth, and Mars. Note that Venus and Earth are considerably warmer than they would be without the greenhouse effect. (The thermospheres and exospheres, not shown, are qualitatively alike.)

same kind of atom—are poor infrared absorbers because they have very few ways to vibrate and rotate.) If they did contribute to the greenhouse effect, Earth might be too warm for life.

## 10.3 Magnetospheres and the Solar Wind

One more type of energy that we haven't yet considered comes from the Sun: the low-density breeze of charged particles that we call the *solar wind* [Section 8.4]. Although the solar wind does not significantly affect atmospheric structure, it can have other important influences. Among the terrestrial planets, only Earth has a strong enough magnetic field to divert the charged particles of the solar wind. Thus, solar wind particles can impact the exospheres of Venus and Mars—and the surfaces of Mercury and the Moon. In contrast, Earth's strong magnetic field creates a **magnetosphere** that acts like a protective bubble surrounding the planet (Figure 10.10). (Jovian planets also have magnetospheres [Section 11.4].) Charged particles cannot easily pass through a magnetic field, so a magnetosphere diverts most of the solar wind around a planet.

Some solar wind particles manage to infiltrate Earth's magnetosphere at its most vulnerable points, near the magnetic poles. Once inside, they have a difficult time escaping. Charged particles are restricted by magnetic forces to following magnetic field lines (Figure 10.10a). In many magnetospheres, the ions and electrons accumulate to make **charged particle belts** encircling the planet. (The charged particle belts around the Earth are called the *Van Allen belts* after their discoverer.) The high energies of the particles in charged particle belts can be very hazardous to spacecraft and astronauts passing through them.

Particles trapped in magnetospheres also cause the beautiful spectacle of light called the **aurora** (Figure 10.10b). If a trapped charged particle has enough energy, it can follow the magnetic field all the way down to the upper parts of a planet's atmosphere. The charged particles collide with atmospheric atoms and molecules, causing them to radiate and produce auroras (Figure 10.10c,d). Because the charged particles follow the magnetic field, auroras are most common near the magnetic poles. On Earth, auroras therefore are best viewed from Canada, Alaska, and Russia in the Northern Hemisphere (the *aurora borealis,* or northern lights) and from Australia, Chile, and Argentina in the Southern Hemisphere (the *aurora australis,* or southern lights).

---

**Common Misconceptions:
The Greenhouse Effect Is Bad**

The greenhouse effect is often in the news, usually in discussions about environmental problems. But the greenhouse effect itself is not a bad thing. In fact, we could not exist without it. Remember that the "no greenhouse" temperature of the Earth is well below freezing. Thus, the greenhouse effect is the only reason why our planet is not frozen over. Why, then, is the greenhouse effect discussed as an environmental problem? [Section 13.5] It is because human activity is adding more greenhouse gases to the atmosphere—which might change the Earth's climate. After all, while the greenhouse effect makes the Earth livable, it is also responsible for the searing 740 K temperature of Venus—proving that it's possible to have too much of a good thing.

## 10.4 Weather and Climate

So far, we've mostly talked about a planet's atmosphere as if it were the same at all locations and at all times. The atmospheric structure profiles show only *average* temperatures at different altitudes in the atmosphere. But we know from experience on Earth that surface and atmospheric conditions constantly change. In any particular location, some days may be hotter or cooler than others, some may be clearer or cloudier, some may be calmer or stormier. This ever-varying combination of winds, clouds, temperature, and pressure is what we call **weather**.

Local weather can vary dramatically from one day to the next, or even from hour to hour. The weather can also vary greatly between places just a short distance apart. For example, temperatures on a warm day may be several degrees hotter just a few kilometers inland from a coastal city. The complexity of weather makes it difficult to predict, although modern-day *meteorologists*[4] (people who study weather) often can predict weather quite accurately a few days in advance. On longer time scales, local weather is fundamentally unpredictable, at least on Earth.

**Climate** is the long-term average of weather and is generally stabler than weather. Deserts remain deserts and rain forests remain rain forests over periods of hundreds or thousands of years, while the day-to-day and even year-to-year weather may vary dramatically. Weather and climate can be hard to distinguish on a human time scale: Do a few hot sum-

---

[4]The word *meteor* comes from a Greek word meaning "a thing in the air," which explains why the very different concepts of *meteorology* and *meteors* have the same word origin.

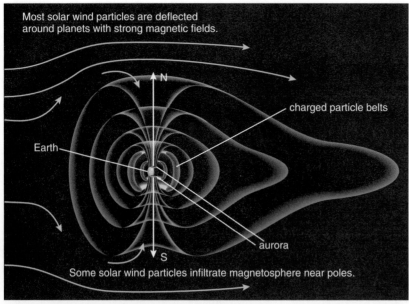

Most solar wind particles are deflected around planets with strong magnetic fields.

N

charged particle belts

Earth

aurora

S

Some solar wind particles infiltrate magnetosphere near poles.

**a** Earth's magnetosphere and its interaction with the solar wind.

Collisions of charged particles with the atmosphere cause auroral glows.

Particles in polar regions spiral into atmosphere

**c** Origin of the aurora.

**FIGURE 10.10** A planet's magnetosphere acts like a protective bubble that shields the surface from charged particles coming from the solar wind. Among the terrestrial planets, only the Earth has a strong enough magnetic field to create a magnetosphere. The Earth's magnetosphere allows charged particles to strike the atmosphere only near the poles, thereby creating the phenomena of the aurora borealis and aurora australis.

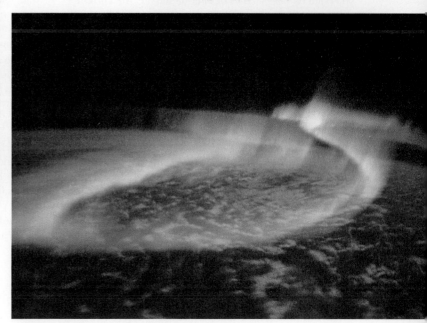

**b** Aurora along the coast of Norway.

**d** Earth's aurora as seen from the Space Shuttle.

mers in a row imply a change in climate, or are they merely coincidence? We'll return to this question when we study the issue of global warming on Earth in Chapter 13. For now, let's concentrate on understanding what drives planetary weather.

### Seasonal Weather Patterns

The most obvious weather pattern on a planet is the change in the seasons. In general, a planet has seasons only if it has a significant axis tilt, so that over the course of its orbit around the Sun, first one hemisphere and then the other receives more direct sunlight [Section 1.3]. Otherwise, both hemispheres receive the same amount of sunlight year-round. For example, Venus has no seasons because its axis is nearly perpendicular to the ecliptic. Mars has seasonal changes like Earth because its 25° axis tilt is comparable to Earth's $23\frac{1}{2}°$ tilt. Thus, when one Martian hemisphere is in summer, the other is in winter, and vice versa. However, Martian seasons last almost

### Weather and Chaos

Scientists today have a very good understanding of the physical laws and mathematical equations that govern the behavior and motion of atoms in the air, oceans, and land. Why, then, do we have so much trouble predicting the weather? For a long time, most scientists assumed that the difficulty of weather prediction would go away once we had enough weather stations to collect data from around the world and sufficiently powerful computers to deal with all the data. However, we now know that weather is fundamentally unpredictable on time scales longer than a few weeks. To understand why, we must look at the nature of scientific prediction.

Suppose you want to predict the location of a car on a road 1 minute from now. You need two basic pieces of information: where the car is now, and how it is moving. If the car is now passing Smith Road and heading north at 1 mile per minute, it will be 1 mile north of Smith Road in 1 minute.

Now, suppose you want to predict the weather. Again, you need two basic types of information: (1) the current weather and (2) how weather changes from one moment to the next.

You could attempt to predict the weather by creating a "model world." For example, you could overlay a globe of the Earth with graph paper and then specify the current temperature, pressure, cloud cover, and wind within each square. These are your starting points, or initial conditions. Next, you could input all the initial conditions into a computer, along with a set of equations (physical laws) that describe the processes that can change weather from one moment to the next.

Suppose the initial conditions represent the weather around the Earth at this very moment and you run your computer model to predict the weather for the next month in New York City. The model might tell you that tomorrow will be warm and sunny, with cooling during the next

week and a major storm passing through a month from now. Now suppose you run the model again but make one minor change in the initial conditions—say, a small change in the wind speed somewhere over Brazil. For tomorrow's weather, this slightly different initial condition will not change the weather prediction for New York City. For next week's weather, the new model may yield a slightly different prediction. But for next month's weather, the two predictions may not agree at all!

The disagreement between the two predictions arises because the laws governing weather can cause very tiny changes in initial conditions to be greatly magnified over time. This extreme sensitivity to initial conditions is sometimes called the *butterfly effect:* If initial conditions change by as much as the flap of a butterfly's wings, the resulting prediction may be very different.

The butterfly effect is a hallmark of *chaotic systems.* Simple systems are described by linear equations in which, for example, increasing a cause produces a proportional increase in an effect. In contrast, chaotic systems are described by nonlinear equations, which allow for subtler and more intricate interactions. For example, the economy is nonlinear because a rise in interest rates does not automatically produce a corresponding change in consumer spending. Weather is nonlinear because a change in the wind speed in one location does not automatically produce a corresponding change in another location. Many (but not all) nonlinear systems exhibit chaotic behavior.

Despite their name, chaotic systems are not completely random. In fact, many chaotic systems have a kind of underlying order that explains the general features of their behavior even while details at any particular moment remain unpredictable. In a sense, many chaotic systems are "predictably unpredictable." Our understanding of chaotic systems is increasing at a tremendous rate, but much remains to be learned about them.

---

twice as long as Earth seasons because a Martian year is almost twice as long as an Earth year.

A planet's changing distance from the Sun can affect the severity of seasons. Earth's nearly circular orbit makes this effect unimportant. But Mars has a more elliptical orbit that puts it significantly closer to the Sun during southern hemisphere summer, making it warmer than summer in the northern hemisphere, and farther from the Sun during southern hemisphere winter, making it colder than winter in the northern hemisphere (Figure 10.11). Mars therefore has more extreme seasons in its southern hemisphere than in its northern hemisphere.

### Global Wind Patterns

*Winds* are flows of air caused by pressure differences between different regions of a planet. On a local scale,

winds vary as much as the weather, blowing in different directions and with different strengths at different times. But certain wind patterns are fixed on a global scale, creating what we call **global wind patterns** (or *global circulation*).

The first major factor affecting global wind patterns is atmospheric heating. In general, the equatorial regions of a planet receive more heat from the Sun than do polar regions. The excess heat makes the atmosphere expand above the equator, and air spills northward and southward at high altitudes (Figure 10.12). By itself, this process creates two huge **circulation cells** resembling convection cells but much larger. (They are often called *Hadley cells* after the person who first suggested their existence in 1735.) The circulation cells serve to transport heat both from lower to higher altitudes and from the equator to the poles. If this circulation is very efficient and if the atmosphere is dense enough to carry a lot of thermal energy, the resulting winds can equalize planetary temperatures from equator to pole. That is the case on Venus, where temperatures near the poles are essentially the same as those at the equator.

**TIME OUT TO THINK** *Suppose a planet rotated synchronously with its orbit around the Sun, so that it kept the same face toward the Sun at all times. What kind of circulation pattern would you expect on this planet? Explain. (Hint: Which regions of the planet receive the most sunlight, and which regions receive the least sunlight?)*

The second major factor affecting global wind patterns is the planet's rotation. It's easiest to understand this effect by analogy. The movement of air over a planet is like the motion of a ball rolled on a merry-go-round (Figure 10.13). Imagine that you are sitting near the edge of a merry-go-round. Your speed around the axis will be higher than the speeds of the inner parts of the merry-go-round. If you roll a ball toward the center, the ball begins with your relatively high speed around the axis. As it rolls inward, this high speed around the axis makes it move ahead of the slower-moving inner regions. If your merry-go-round rotates counterclockwise, the ball therefore deviates to the right instead of heading straight inward. The deviation caused by the merry-go-round's rotation is called the **Coriolis effect**. It also works in reverse: If you roll the ball outward from the center, the ball lags behind the faster-moving outer regions, again deviating to the right. If your merry-go-round instead rotates clockwise, the deviations are to the left.

The Coriolis effect occurs on rotating planets because equatorial regions travel faster around the rotation axis than do polar regions (see Figure 1.10). On Earth, air moving away from the equator deviates ahead of the Earth's rotation to the east, and air moving toward the equator deviates behind the Earth's rotation to the west (Figure 10.14a). Note that, either way, the deviation is to the *right* in the Northern Hemisphere and to the *left* in the Southern Hemisphere. One result is that air flowing toward low-pressure zones ends up circulating around them counterclockwise in the Northern Hemisphere and clockwise in the Southern Hemisphere (Figure 10.14b). Low-pressure regions ("L" on weather maps) are often associated with storms, including hurricanes. Because the circulating winds prevent air from flowing in to equalize the pressure, low-

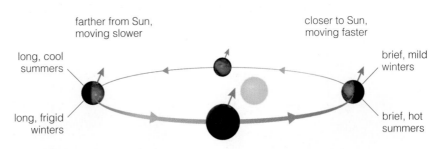

farther from Sun, moving slower

long, cool summers

long, frigid winters

closer to Sun, moving faster

brief, mild winters

brief, hot summers

**FIGURE 10.11** The ellipticity of Mars's orbit makes the severity of seasons different in the northern and southern hemispheres.

Cool air descends over poles.

Warm air rises over equator.

**FIGURE 10.12** Circulation cells. Heat rises above the equator, setting up a flow of warm air toward the poles at high altitudes and a flow of cool air toward the equator near the surface. The planet's rotation is neglected for the moment. (Figure 10.15 shows how rotation affects circulation cells on Earth.)

**FIGURE 10.13** The Coriolis effect on a merry-go-round rotating counterclockwise: A ball rolled inward starts with a speed around the center faster than that of regions nearer the center; this "extra" speed makes the ball deviate to the right. A ball rolled outward starts with a speed around the center slower than that of regions farther out; this "lag" also makes the ball deviate to the right. If the merry-go-round were rotating clockwise, both balls would veer to the left.

**a** The Coriolis effect causes air moving across the surface toward low-pressure regions to be diverted into a circular flow around the regions. The direction of rotation is opposite in the two hemispheres.

**b** You can see the direction of flow in a satellite photo of storms in the Pacific.

**FIGURE 10.14** The Coriolis effect drives wind patterns on rotating planets.

### Common Misconceptions: Do Toilets Flush Backward in the Southern Hemisphere?

A common myth holds that water circulates "backward" in the Southern Hemisphere; that is, toilets flush the opposite way, water spirals down sink drains the opposite way, and so on. If you visit an equatorial town, you may even find charlatans who, for a small fee, will demonstrate how to change the direction of water spiraling down a drain simply by stepping across the equator. This myth sounds similar to the Coriolis effect—which really does make hurricanes spiral in opposite directions in the two hemispheres—but it is completely untrue. The Coriolis effect is noticeable only when material moves significantly closer to or farther from the Earth's rotation axis—which means scales of hundreds of kilometers. Its effect is completely negligible on small scales, such as the scale of toilets or drains. Apart from the shape of the basin, the only thing that affects the direction in which the water in a toilet or sink swirls is the initial angular momentum, which you can affect by swirling the water in one direction or the other. Conservation of angular momentum [Section 5.1] then dictates that the water will swirl faster and faster as it gets closer to the drain. You can find water in toilets and sinks swirling in either direction, and even tornadoes twisting in either direction, in both hemispheres.

pressure regions tend to remain stable for many days, during which time prevailing winds can carry them thousands of kilometers across the planet. High-pressure regions ("H" on weather maps) can also last for days and travel great distances, but they are usually storm-free.

The Coriolis effect also diverts the global wind patterns. On Earth, this diversion causes each of the two huge circulation cells (shown in Figure 10.12) to split into three smaller cells (Figure 10.15a). Note that surface winds in the cells near the equator and near the poles flow toward the equator and hence are diverted westward by the Coriolis effect. In contrast, surface winds in the mid-latitude cells flow toward the poles and are diverted eastward by the Coriolis effect (Figure 10.15b). You've probably noticed that surface winds generally blow from west to east at mid-latitudes, which is why storms generally first hit the west coast of North America and then progress eastward.

**TIME OUT TO THINK** *Study Figure 10.15 a bit more. If you want to take maximum advantage of the prevailing winds, what course should you plot for a sailing trip from Europe to North America and back?*

The strength of the Coriolis effect depends on a planet's size and rotation rate: It is weakest on planets that are small and rotating slowly. Venus has a

**FIGURE 10.15** The Coriolis effect breaks up the circulation pattern shown in Figure 10.12.

**a** On a rapidly rotating planet like Earth, the Coriolis effect causes each of the two large circulation cells of a slowly rotating planet (see Figure 10.12) to split into three cells.

**b** The resulting surface wind patterns. Note that, at mid-latitudes such as over North America, the surface winds blow from the west. These motions combine with those of Figure 10.14a to give the overall wind patterns.

very weak Coriolis effect because of its slow rotation and hence has very slow surface winds; it lacks hurricane-like storms. The top wind speeds measured by the Soviet Union's Venera landers were no more than about 6 kilometers per hour. Apart from faster winds near the top of the atmosphere (of unknown cause), Venus is a rather dull place in terms of weather. Its temperature is nearly the same everywhere, and the surface winds are calm.

Mars has a rotation period very close to that of Earth, but its smaller size means a weaker Coriolis effect. Its circulation cells therefore do not split like those on Earth. Moreover, its thin atmosphere means that the circulation cells transport very little heat, so the poles remain much colder than the equator. Polar temperatures in the winter are so low (about 145 K, or −130°C) that carbon dioxide condenses into "dry ice" at the polar caps (Figure 10.16a). Because carbon dioxide is the major constituent of the Martian atmosphere, this condensation changes the atmospheric

pressure by as much as 20% from season to season. The condensation occurring at the winter pole draws $CO_2$ out of the atmosphere, which is replenished by winds blowing from the opposite polar cap, where the dry ice *sublimes* into $CO_2$ gas [Section 4.3]. The combination of these pole-to-pole winds, circulation cells, and the Coriolis effect gives Mars very dynamic weather.

The direction of the pole-to-pole winds on Mars changes with the alternating seasons. Sometimes these winds initiate huge dust storms (Figure 10.16b), particularly when the more extreme summer approaches in the southern hemisphere. At times, the surface is so shrouded by airborne dust that surface markings are hidden from view and large dunes form and shift with strong winds. As the dust settles out onto the surface, it can change the color or albedo over vast areas—thereby creating the seasonal changes in appearance that fooled some astronomers in the late 1800s and early 1900s into thinking they saw

**FIGURE 10.16** Polar ice caps and dust storms on Mars.

**b** Mars Global Surveyor photo of a dust storm (curving clouds) brewing over Mars's northern polar cap. (Image is 1000 kilometers across.)

**a** This photo, taken by the *Viking Orbiter,* shows the ice cap at a Martian pole during the Martian winter. (Image is 400 kilometers across.)

**c** Close-up of the edge of a polar cap, showing alternating layers of ice and dust. Each layer is a few dozen meters thick and may take thousands of years to form. (Image is about 40 kilometers across.)

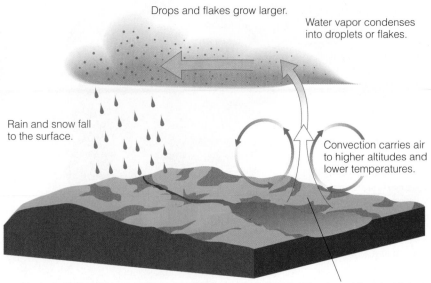

Drops and flakes grow larger.

Water vapor condenses into droplets or flakes.

Rain and snow fall to the surface.

Convection carries air to higher altitudes and lower temperatures.

Evaporation (or sublimation) injects water vapor into lower atmosphere.

**FIGURE 10.17** The cycle of water on Earth's surface and in the atmosphere. Other atmospheric ingredients on Earth and other planets have important cycles but may not be as apparent to the eye.

changes in vegetation [Section 9.5]. Dust also settles onto the polar caps, making alternating layers of darker dust and brighter frost (Figure 10.16c). The dust storms leave Mars with a perpetually dusty sky, giving it a pale pink color.

### Clouds and Precipitation

We may think of clouds as imperfections on a sunny day, but they have profound effects on a planet. Clouds fundamentally change the appearance of a planet, reflecting sunlight back to space and thus reducing the amount of sunlight that warms the surface. Clouds are also important to planetary geology because they are a prerequisite for rain, a major cause of erosion. Despite these significant effects, clouds on most planets form from very minor ingredients of the atmosphere (see Table 10.1).

Clouds form when one of the gases in the air condenses into liquid or solid form, a process usually resulting from convection (Figure 10.17). On Earth, evaporation of surface water (or sublimation of ice and snow) releases water vapor into the atmosphere. Convection carries the water vapor to high, cold regions of the troposphere, where it condenses into droplets or flakes of ice. Thus, clouds on Earth consist of countless tiny water droplets or ice flakes, a fact you can feel if you walk through a cloud on a mountaintop. The droplets or flakes grow within the clouds until they become so large that the upward convection currents can't hold them aloft. They then begin to fall toward the surface as rain, snow, or hail.

Strong convection means more clouds and precipitation. Thunderstorms often form on late summer afternoons when the sunlight-warmed surface

**FIGURE 10.18** Clouds on Venus are all that can be seen in this ultraviolet image taken by the *Pioneer Venus Orbiter*.

drives stronger convection. Earth's equatorial regions also experience more convection and rain than other regions. When you combine this fact with the global wind patterns (see Figure 10.15b), you can understand why jungles lie at the equator and deserts lie at latitudes 20°–30° north and south of the equator. The equatorial rain depletes the moisture in the air as the winds carry it north or south, leaving little moisture to rain on the deserts.

Venus is covered with clouds because its high surface temperature drives strong convection and circulation (Figure 10.18). In contrast to Earth's water clouds, the clouds of Venus are made of sulfuric acid ($H_2SO_4$) dissolved in water droplets. These droplets form high in Venus's troposphere, where temperatures are 400 K cooler than on the surface. The droplets grow in the clouds until they form a sulfuric acid rain that falls toward the surface. But the droplets evaporate completely long before they reach the ground. Thus, it never rains on the surface of Venus, and the lower 30 kilometers of the atmosphere is very clear. The sulfuric acid is formed by chemical reactions involving sulfur dioxide ($SO_2$) and water, both of which come from volcanic eruptions. Because Venus lacks an ultraviolet-absorbing stratosphere, water molecules in its atmosphere are broken apart by ultraviolet light from the Sun. The atmosphere also loses sulfur dioxide through chemical reactions with surface rocks. The presence of sulfuric acid clouds therefore suggests that volcanoes on Venus must still be active, erupting at least occasionally to replenish sulfur dioxide and water.

Clouds can also form when winds blowing over mountains carry air parcels to higher altitudes. Droplets form in an air parcel when it is pushed to high altitude over a mountain. These droplets then evaporate as the air parcel descends to the valley or plains below. The result is that droplets constantly form in the air over the mountain, creating a cloud that remains stationary even though strong winds are blowing. This process forms clouds over terrestrial mountain ranges like the Rockies, and also over tall Martian mountains like Olympus Mons (Figure 10.19). The clouds over the Martian mountains consist of water-ice crystals, and water-ice fog sometimes fills Martian canyons. But the total amount of water vapor in the Martian atmosphere is so small that it would make a frost layer less than 1/100 millimeter thick on the planet. Carbon dioxide clouds can also form on Mars at much higher altitudes, but they are very rare.

Interestingly, Mars possesses far more water than we ever see in its clouds. The polar caps contain large amounts of water ice in addition to frozen carbon dioxide. In fact, all the carbon dioxide at the northern polar cap sublimes during the northern summer, exposing a frozen-water polar cap. So much carbon dioxide is deposited on the southern polar cap during the long, deep winter that it does not all sublime during the relatively short summer. We therefore do not know how much water is hidden below. At high latitudes, water ice probably also permeates the Martian soil 1–2 meters below the surface, where not even the heat of a summer day can penetrate. This *ground ice* probably has had important geological effects. The Martian craters that look as if they were made in mud (see Figure 9.13b) probably formed when impacts melted the ground ice, and catastrophic flooding in the Martian past may have occurred when sudden volcanic heating melted the ground ice into liquid water.

**FIGURE 10.19** High-altitude clouds (the blue streaks in the upper right corner) over Olympus Mons, photographed by the *Mars Global Surveyor.*

### Long-Term Climate Change

We know that long-term climate change can occur. For example, the Earth has been in and out of ice ages throughout its history. What can change the climate of an entire planet?

At least four factors can cause climate change. First, the Sun slowly grows in brightness as it ages [Section 14.3]. The Sun was about 30% fainter when the solar system first formed than it is today. Planets therefore may have been cooler early in the history of the solar system, or perhaps greenhouse gases were more abundant.

Second, changes in the tilt of a planet's axis can cause climate change. The axis tilt may slowly change over thousands or millions of years because of small gravitational tugs from moons, other planets, or the Sun. Although *average* planetary temperature may not be affected by the axis tilt, temperatures in different regions may change a great deal. A smaller axis tilt means year-round reduced sunlight in polar regions. Temperatures therefore drop in the polar regions, and perhaps even in mid-latitudes, causing *ice ages*. Earth and Mars probably both experience ice ages for this reason, and several of the icy satellites of the outer solar system undergo analogous cycles.

A third influence on climate change is changes in a planet's albedo. If a planet reflects more sunlight, it absorbs less—which can lead to planet-wide cooling. Ice ages may lead to further planetary cooling because the extra ice covering can increase the planet's albedo. Microscopic dust particles, or *aerosols,* released by volcanic eruptions can have the same effect. If the dust particles are blasted all the way into the stratosphere, they will remain suspended there for years, reflecting sunlight back to space. Human activity may be changing Earth's albedo. Smog particles can act like volcanic dust, reflecting sunlight before it reaches the ground. Deforestation can also increase Earth's albedo by removing sunlight-absorbing plants. But some human activity decreases albedo, such as paving a road with blacktop. Clearly, the overall human effect on Earth's albedo is not easy to gauge.

The fourth major cause of climate change is varying atmospheric conditions, particularly the abundance of greenhouse gases. If the abundance of greenhouse gases increases, the planet generally will warm. If the planet warms enough, increased evaporation and sublimation may add substantial amounts of gases to the planet's atmosphere, leading to an increase in atmospheric pressure. Conversely, if the abundance of greenhouse gases decreases, the planet generally will cool, and atmospheric pressure may decrease as gases freeze. We'll apply all four of these concepts to the planets in the next section to understand their evolving climates.

## 10.5 Atmospheric Origins and Evolution

Today's headlines are full of stories about the human effect on Earth's atmosphere, such as ozone depletion, global warming, and air pollution. But the atmospheres of Earth and the other terrestrial planets have seen much larger changes in their billions of years of history. What causes such large changes? To answer this question, we must examine both how a planet gets its atmospheric gases and how it can lose them.

### How Atmospheres Are Created

The jovian planets obtained their atmospheres by capturing gas from the solar nebula, but the terrestrial worlds were too small to capture significant amounts of gas before the solar wind cleared away the nebula [Section 8.4]. Any gas that the terrestrial worlds did capture from the solar nebula consisted primarily of hydrogen and helium (just like the solar nebula as a whole). But these light gases escape easily from the terrestrial worlds and by now are long gone. The atmospheres of the terrestrial worlds therefore must have formed after the worlds themselves. Terrestrial atmospheres can get their gas from three different processes: *outgassing, evaporation/sublimation,* and *bombardment* (Figure 10.20).

The most important process is **outgassing**, the release of gases from the planetary interior by volcanic eruptions. Recall that interior gases were originally brought to the terrestrial planets by comets and volatile-rich asteroids during the early bombardment that ended about 4 billion years ago [Section 8.5]. The high pressures inside the planets trapped these gases in rocks in much the same way a pressurized bottle traps the bubbles of carbonated beverages. When the rocks melt and erupt onto the surface as lava, the release of pressure expels the gases. The gases may be released with the lava itself or from nearby vents (Figure 10.21). The most common gases expelled are water ($H_2O$), carbon dioxide ($CO_2$), nitrogen ($N_2$), and sulfur-bearing gases ($H_2S$ or $SO_2$). (Aside from water, none of the gases existed in the solar nebula. Instead, they were created by chemical reactions that occurred *inside* the planets.) Because outgassing depends on volcanism, it is most important on larger planets that retain their internal heat longer. Outgassing supplied most of the gas that became the atmospheres of Venus, Earth, and Mars.

**FIGURE 10.20** Three processes by which atmospheres gain gas.

outgassing

evaporation/sublimation

bombardment

Once outgassing creates an atmosphere, some of the gases may condense onto the surface. Earth's first volcanoes may have belched out water vapor over a dry, barren planet. As more and more water vapor filled the atmosphere, some of it began to condense and fall as rain—eventually filling our oceans. Similarly, Martian volcanoes outgassed large volumes of carbon dioxide, some of which is now frozen in the Martian polar caps. Surface liquids and ices continually exchange gas with the atmosphere. Sometimes the amount of gas released by *evaporation* (from liquids) or *sublimation* (from ices) exceeds the amount returning by condensation (from the atmosphere back into liquid or ice). Evaporation/sublimation is considered the second most important way in which gases are supplied to an atmosphere. Even though the gases first entered the atmosphere through outgassing, sublimation and evaporation can resupply gases that the atmosphere had lost.

Sublimation is most important on relatively cold bodies where ices form. It adds gas to the Martian atmosphere with the changing Martian seasons, as the warmer southern summer releases vast amounts of carbon dioxide from the south polar cap. It is even more important on some of the icy bodies of the outer solar system and for comets that happen to enter the inner solar system [Section 12.4].

Planets and satellites where outgassing and sublimation are negligible may still have thin atmospheres created by a third process: *bombardment* by micrometeorites, microscopic particles in the solar wind, or energetic solar photons. Bombardment can make only a thin atmosphere (a denser atmosphere would protect the surface from the bombarding particles), but it is the primary source of the atmospheres of the

**FIGURE 10.21** Volcanoes National Park, Hawaii. Volcanoes give off $H_2O$, $CO_2$, $N_2$, and sulfur-bearing gases. Some gas is given off from the lava itself, and some leaks out from nearby gas vents.

Moon and Mercury. The atmosphere may be composed both of vaporized surface materials and of any gas released by the material doing the bombardment.

### How Atmospheric Gases Are Lost

Just as several processes can add gas to a planetary atmosphere, an atmosphere can lose gas in several ways: *thermal escape, bombardment, atmospheric cratering, condensation,* and *chemical reactions* (Figure 10.22). The terrestrial planets lost any original

**FIGURE 10.22** The five major processes by which atmospheres lose gas.

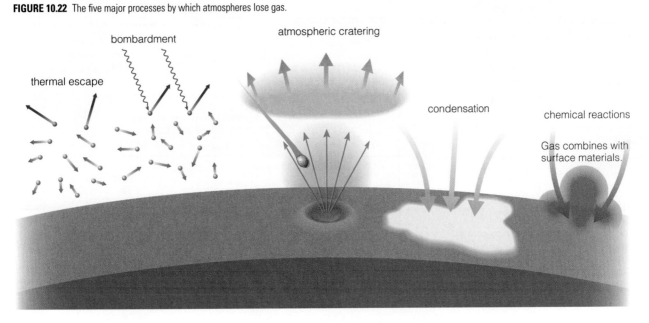

thermal escape | bombardment | atmospheric cratering | condensation | chemical reactions

Gas combines with surface materials.

hydrogen and helium they had captured from the solar nebula through the process of **thermal escape**, in which an atom or molecule in the exosphere moves fast enough to escape the pull of gravity. Three factors determine whether an atmospheric gas can be lost to space by thermal escape:

1.  The planet's *escape velocity,* or the speed at which a particle must travel to escape the pull of gravity—assuming it is traveling in the right direction and doesn't collide with anything else. The more massive the planet, the higher its escape velocity [Section 5.6].

2.  The temperature. Individual particles in a gas move with a wide range of random speeds [Section 4.2], but the higher the temperature, the faster their *average* speed.

3.  The mass of the gas particles. At a particular temperature, lighter particles (such as H or He) move around at faster average speeds than heavier ones (such as $O_2$ or $CO_2$) and therefore are more likely to achieve escape velocity.[5]

---

[5]At a particular temperature, all gas particles have the same *average kinetic energy.* Because the kinetic energy is described by the formula $\frac{1}{2}mv^2$, low-mass particles must have higher average speeds ($v$) than high-mass particles of the same kinetic energy.

Mercury cannot hold much of an atmosphere because its small size and high temperature mean that nearly all gas particles eventually achieve escape velocity. Gases escape about as easily from the Moon because it is smaller than Mercury, even though it is also somewhat cooler. Light gases such as hydrogen and helium escape any planet much more easily than heavier gases. That is why Venus, Earth, and Mars retained heavier gases but lost light gases—including any hydrogen released when molecules such as $H_2O$ were broken apart by solar ultraviolet radiation.

**TIME OUT TO THINK** *Suppose Mercury had formed at a much greater distance from the Sun, say, somewhere beyond the orbit of Mars. How would its lower surface temperature affect its ability to hold an atmosphere? Considering all you know about planetary formation and how atmospheric gases are created and lost, do you think Mercury would have a thicker atmosphere in this case? Explain.*

A second process that can cause atmospheric loss is *bombardment* by microscopic particles and photons—the same process that creates the atmospheres of the Moon and Mercury. Just as bombardment can eject atoms from a surface into a thin atmosphere, it can also eject atmospheric particles from a planet's exosphere altogether. Bombardment by solar wind

---

## Mathematical Insight 10.2    Thermal Escape from an Atmosphere

Whether an atmosphere loses gas by thermal escape depends on how many of the gas particles (atoms or molecules) are moving faster than the escape velocity. In general, particles of a particular type in a gas move at a wide range of speeds that depend on the temperature. For example, Figure 10.23 shows the range of speeds of sodium atoms at the temperature of the Moon's extremely thin atmosphere. The peak in the figure represents the most common speed of the sodium atoms. This speed, called the *peak thermal velocity* of the sodium atoms, is given by the following formula:

$$v_{thermal} = \sqrt{\frac{2kT}{m}}$$

where $m$ is the mass of a single atom, $T$ is the temperature in Kelvin, and $k = 1.38 \times 10^{-23}$ joule/Kelvin is *Boltzmann's constant.* This formula shows that higher temperatures mean higher thermal velocities for the atoms or molecules in a gas. It also shows that, for a given temperature, particles of lighter gases (smaller $m$) move at faster speeds than particles of heavier gases.

peak thermal velocity

$$v_{thermal} = \sqrt{\frac{2kT}{m}}$$

Most atoms are moving too slowly to escape.

This small fraction has escape velocity.

number of atoms at that speed

escape velocity

speed (km/s)

**FIGURE 10.23** In a gas at a given temperature, different atoms are always moving at different speeds. This plot shows the range of speeds of sodium atoms in the lunar atmosphere.

particles is particularly important because it can sweep ionized atoms from high in the atmosphere into space. Bombardment by energetic solar photons can also be important, because ultraviolet photons can break apart molecules and send fragments flying off at speeds faster than escape velocity. Note that bombardment can eject atoms that are too heavy for thermal escape. In general, planets with protective magnetic fields—such as Earth—are less susceptible to this type of atmospheric loss.

Larger impacts can also cause atmospheric escape. The same impacts that create craters on the surface may blast away a significant amount of the atmosphere as well, a process sometimes called *atmospheric cratering*. For the most part, atmospheric cratering happened only early in the solar system's history. We expect it to have been most important on smaller worlds, where gravity's hold on the atmosphere is weaker. Mars probably lost a significant amount of atmospheric gas through atmospheric cratering.

Thermal escape, bombardment, and atmospheric cratering all cause a planet to lose gas permanently into space. Two other processes allow atmospheric gas to be absorbed back into the solid planet. Gases may simply *condense* into liquid or solid form if a planet cools down, especially in the cold polar regions. On Mars, carbon dioxide condenses into the polar caps during winter. Condensation probably also

explains the presence of water ice in craters near the Moon's poles, discovered by the *Lunar Prospector* orbiter in 1998. The water probably came from comet impacts that each briefly created a thin lunar atmosphere. The water molecules from these impacts bounced around the surface at random until they condensed into ice in the polar craters. The bottoms of these craters lie in nearly perpetual shadow, keeping them so cold that the water remains perpetually frozen. Recent radar observations of Mercury suggest that it, too, may have water ice in its polar craters, probably for the same reason.

Finally, gases may become locked up in the surface through *chemical reactions* with rocks or liquids. On Earth, for example, carbon dioxide dissolves in the oceans, where it ultimately undergoes reactions that create *carbonate* rocks, such as limestone, on the ocean floor [Section 13.3]. Volcanoes have outgassed huge amounts of carbon dioxide into Earth's atmosphere over its history, but nearly all this gas has been converted into limestone by chemical reactions.

### Putting It All Together

We've seen that the processes by which atmospheric gases are created and lost are closely tied to planetary formation properties and other planetary processes. We now have the perspective to link what we have learned about planetary atmospheres with our

---

If the peak thermal velocity of a particular type of gas is higher than the escape velocity, then most of the gas particles will be traveling fast enough to escape the atmosphere, and the planet will lose this atmospheric gas to space fairly quickly. However, even if the peak thermal velocity is lower than the escape velocity, the wide range of particle speeds in a gas means that some small fraction of the gas particles may be traveling faster than the escape velocity. These fast-moving particles will escape, as long as they're moving upward and don't hit another particle on their way out. Collisions among the remaining gas particles will continually ensure that a few always attain escape velocity, and thus the atmosphere can slowly leak away into space. In general, most of the gas particles of a particular type will escape over the age of the solar system if the peak thermal velocity is 20% or more of the escape speed.

*Example:* The temperature on the dayside of the Moon is $T = 400$ K. Calculate the peak thermal velocities of both hydrogen atoms and sodium atoms. Then explain why the Moon (escape velocity $\approx 2.4$ km/s) cannot retain a hydrogen atmosphere for very long but retains a thin exosphere of sodium. The mass of a hydrogen atom is $1.67 \times 10^{-27}$ kg; the mass of a sodium atom is 23 times greater, or $3.84 \times 10^{-26}$ kg.

*Solution:* From the formula above, the peak thermal velocity of the hydrogen atoms on the dayside of the Moon is:

$$v_{thermal} = \sqrt{\frac{2 \times (1.38 \times 10^{-23} \frac{joule}{K}) \times (400 \text{ K})}{1.67 \times 10^{-27} \text{ kg}}}$$

$$\approx 2,600 \text{ m/s} = 2.6 \text{ km/s}$$

Similarly, the thermal velocity of the sodium atoms is:

$$v_{thermal} = \sqrt{\frac{2 \times (1.38 \times 10^{-23} \frac{joule}{K}) \times (400 \text{ K})}{3.84 \times 10^{-26} \text{ kg}}}$$

$$\approx 540 \text{ m/s} = 0.54 \text{ km/s}$$

Note that the peak thermal velocity of the hydrogen atoms is slightly greater than the Moon's escape velocity of about 2.4 km/s. Thus, the Moon cannot retain a hydrogen atmosphere. However, the peak thermal velocity of sodium is only about one-fifth, or about 20%, of the escape velocity. Thus, the Moon cannot hold a sodium atmosphere indefinitely, but it can hold some of the sodium atoms that are continually entering its atmosphere through bombardment.

**a** Mercury's atmosphere. Color-coded contours represent the gas density from lowest (black) to highest (red). Mercury's partially illuminated disk is indicated as the gibbous-shaped blue contour near the center (just within the yellow region); the Sun lies to the left along the direction of the dashed line.

**b** The Moon's atmosphere. This composite image represents the gas density from lowest (green) to highest (red). The Moon itself was blocked to make this image, resulting in the central black area of no data. The Moon's size is shown schematically by the white circle.

**FIGURE 10.24** The atmospheres of Mercury and the Moon—which are essentially exospheres only—viewed through instruments sensitive to emission lines from sodium atoms. Although these are extremely low density atmospheres, they extend quite high.

understanding of planetary geology from the previous chapter. In particular, we are in a better position to appreciate how planetary size affects the amount of outgassing and therefore the abundance of atmospheric gases. A closer look at atmospheric change will allow us to understand the different erosional histories of Earth, Mars, and Venus, which we left unresolved in the last chapter. Before you read further, you should refresh your memory of the "planetary flowcharts" in Chapter 9 and make your own analysis of atmospheric change on each of the terrestrial worlds.

## 10.6 History of the Terrestrial Atmospheres

We are now ready to return to the issue with which we began the chapter: how and why the terrestrial atmospheres came to differ so profoundly. Let's take a "historical tour" of the terrestrial atmospheres, in order of increasing planetary size.

### The Moon and Mercury

The extremely thin atmospheres of the Moon and Mercury are the easiest to explain (Figure 10.24). Volcanic outgassing ceased long ago on these small worlds, and any early atmosphere was lost. Both Mercury and the Moon may have some ice in craters

near their poles, but it remains perpetually frozen. Thus, the only source of atmospheric gas is bombardment. The relatively few particles blasted into the atmosphere by bombardment collide more often with the surface than with one another. They bounce around the surface like tiny rubber balls, arcing hundreds of kilometers into the sky before crashing back down. Sometimes these particles travel fast enough to escape the pull of gravity (thermal escape). Other times they are stripped away by bombardment by solar wind particles. Thus, gas does not accumulate in these atmospheres, but a small amount is always present because bombardment occurs continuously. Both atmospheres are relatively hot and extend high above the surface.

### Mars

Mars is only 40% larger in radius than Mercury, but its surface tells of a much more fascinating and complex atmospheric history. Pictures show clear evidence that water once flowed on the Martian surface. The abundant geological signs of water erosion on Mars present a major enigma to our understanding of the planet. The evidence includes not only obvious features such as dried-up streambeds (see Figure 9.27a), but also subtler features such as eroded crater rims and floors. Further evidence comes from the study of meteorites believed to have come to Earth from Mars [Section 12.3]. These *Martian meteorites* contain types of minerals (clays and carbonates) that can form only in the presence of liquid water. Some planetary geologists even believe they have found evidence in Mars images for ancient oceans and glaciers on Mars, although these conclusions are controversial (Figure 9.27).

The fact that liquid water once flowed on Mars means that its past must have been very different from its current "freeze-dried" state. The surface temperature must have been much warmer, and therefore Mars must have had a much stronger greenhouse effect and much higher atmospheric pressure. Computer simulations show that these requirements can be met by a carbon dioxide atmosphere about 400 times denser (i.e., having greater pressure) than the current Martian atmosphere—or about twice as thick as Earth's atmosphere.

The idea that Mars had a much denser atmosphere in the past is reasonable. Mars has plenty of ancient volcanoes, and calculations show that these volcanoes could have supplied all of the carbon dioxide needed to warm the planet. Even $CO_2$ ice clouds could have helped hold heat in the Martian troposphere. Moreover, if Martian volcanoes outgas carbon dioxide and water in the same proportions as do volcanoes on Earth, Mars would have had enough water to fill oceans tens or even hundreds of meters deep.

The bigger question is not whether Mars once had a denser atmosphere but where those atmospheric gases are today. Mars must somehow have lost most of its carbon dioxide gas. This loss reduced the strength of the greenhouse effect until the planet essentially froze over. The fate of the lost carbon dioxide is not completely clear. Some is locked up in the polar caps, and some in carbonate minerals like those identified in the Martian meteorites. Some of the gas in the early Martian atmosphere may have been blasted away by large impacts (atmospheric cratering). But, according to magnetic field measurements from the *Mars Global Surveyor* [Section 9.3], the final blow to Mars's atmosphere was probably bombardment by solar wind particles. Early in Mars's history, the warm convecting interior produced both volcanic outgassing and a magnetospheric bubble to protect the atmosphere. As the small planet cooled, the magnetic field weakened, and eventually bombardment by the solar wind stripped away the atmosphere. Had Mars kept its magnetic field, it might have retained much of its atmosphere and kept its moderate climate.

The vast amounts of water once present on Mars are also gone. Some is tied up in the polar caps and underground ice, but most was probably lost forever. Mars lacks an ultraviolet-absorbing stratosphere, and water molecules are easily broken apart by ultraviolet photons. Once water molecules were broken apart, the hydrogen atoms would have been rapidly lost to space through thermal escape. Some of the remaining oxygen was probably lost by solar wind bombardment, and the rest was probably drawn out of the atmosphere through chemical reactions with surface rock. This oxygen literally rusted the Martian rocks, giving the "red planet" its distinctive tint.

The history of the Martian atmosphere holds important lessons for us on Earth. Mars was apparently once a world with pleasant temperatures and streams, rain, glaciers, lakes, and possibly oceans. It had all the necessities for "life as we know it." But the once hospitable planet turned into a frozen and barren desert at least 3 billion years ago, and it is unlikely that Mars will ever be warm enough for its frozen water to flow again (without human intervention). If life once existed on Mars, it is either extinct or hidden away in a few choice locations, such as hot springs around not-quite-dormant volcanoes. As we think about the possibility of future climate change on Earth, Mars presents us with an ominous example of how much things can change.

### Venus

Venus presents a stark contrast to Mars. Its thick carbon dioxide atmosphere creates an extreme greenhouse effect that bakes the surface to unbearable temperatures. Venus's larger size allowed it to retain more interior heat than Mars, leading to greater volcanic activity [Section 9.5]. The associated outgassing produced the vast quantities of carbon dioxide in Venus's atmosphere, as well as the much smaller amounts of nitrogen and sulfur dioxide. But the outgassing presents a quandary when we consider water. We expect similar gases to come out of volcanoes on Earth and Venus, since both planets have similar overall compositions. Water vapor is the most common gas from volcanic outgassing on Earth, but Venus is incredibly dry, with only minuscule amounts of water vapor in its atmosphere and not a drop on the surface. Did Venus once have huge amounts of water? If so, what happened to it?

The leading theory suggests that Venus did indeed outgas plenty of water. But Venus's proximity to the Sun kept surface temperatures too high for oceans to form as they did on Earth. Outgassed water vapor accumulated in the atmosphere along with carbon dioxide and other gases. Because both water and carbon dioxide are strong greenhouse gases, Venus rapidly grew warmer still. Before the water disappeared, the surface temperature may have been double its current high value. Solar ultraviolet photons broke water molecules apart, and the high temperature allowed rapid escape of hydrogen (just as on Mars). The remaining oxygen was lost to a combination of chemical reactions with surface rocks and bombardment by the solar wind. Thus, the water that once was on Venus is gone forever. In fact, Venus may have lost so much water that its crust and mantle also dried out.

It's difficult to prove that Venus lost an ocean's worth of water billions of years ago, but some evidence comes from the gases that didn't escape. Recall that most hydrogen nuclei contain just a single proton. But a tiny fraction of all hydrogen atoms in the universe contain a neutron in addition to the proton. This isotope of hydrogen, called *deuterium,* can be present in water molecules in place of one of the hydrogen atoms (making molecules of "heavy water." The deuterium atom can be released into the atmosphere when an ultraviolet photon breaks apart such a water molecule. Both hydrogen and deuterium can escape from the atmosphere, but less deuterium escapes due to its higher mass. If Venus once had huge amounts of water molecules that broke apart, the more rapid escape of ordinary hydrogen should have left its atmosphere enriched in deuterium. And, indeed, measurements show that deuterium is at least a hundred times more abundant (relative to ordinary hydrogen) on Venus than anywhere else in the solar system.[6]

The next time you see Venus shining brightly as the morning or evening "star," consider the radically different path it has taken from that of Earth—and thank your lucky star. If Earth had formed a bit closer to the Sun or if the Sun had been a shade hotter, our planet might have suffered the same greenhouse-baked fate.

### Earth

In this chapter, we have used Earth as the "typical" planet for understanding the structure of a terrestrial world's atmosphere and weather. Astronomers began their studies of Mars and Venus expecting these planets to be variants of Earth. Instead we've discovered that they are fundamentally different from Earth, particularly in the areas of atmospheric composition and climate. Rather than being a "role model" for understanding other planets, Earth looks more like the odd one out. The lesson of planetary exploration is that understanding Earth requires understanding the solar system as a whole: its formation, geological processes, atmospheres, and even the jovian planets, asteroids, and comets. We are more than halfway through this list already, and after two more chapters we will come full circle, ready to explore and explain Earth's unique circumstances in Chapter 13.

---

[6]Some scientists remain skeptical that Venus lost huge amounts of water, instead suggesting that it was "born dry"—perhaps because it never received as much water as Earth or Mars. In that case, Venus's extraordinary abundance of deuterium relative to ordinary hydrogen requires an alternative explanation.

## THE BIG PICTURE

With what we have learned in this chapter and the previous chapter, we now have a complete "big picture" view of how the terrestrial planets started out so similar yet ended up so different. As you continue, keep the following important ideas in mind:

- Planetary atmospheres are collections of gas particles in search of balance. The vertical spread of an atmosphere is a balance between gravity and random thermal motions of molecules. Temperatures at different altitudes are in balance with the amount of light absorbed at each altitude.

- Weather and climate change are the planets' vain attempts to equalize temperatures and pressures over their surfaces. It's a losing battle, because solar heating can never be uniform. But it's the very nature of gases to move toward equilibrium, even if they never attain it.

- The many levels of balance rely on an active, not static, atmosphere. From the unseen vibrations and rotations of speeding molecules to planet-wide winds and weather, atmospheres are in motion.

- The long-term evolution of planetary atmospheres reflects an imbalance between atmospheric gains and losses, which vary over billions of years. Complete atmospheric transformation over the age of the solar system appears to be the rule for large terrestrial planets, not the exception.

### Review Questions

1. What is an atmosphere? List a few of the most common atmospheric gases. Where does an atmosphere end?

2. Explain the microscopic origin of *gas pressure.* What is 1 *bar* of pressure?

3. Briefly describe the three factors that would determine planetary temperatures in the absence of *greenhouse gases.* How do the "no greenhouse" temperatures of the terrestrial planets compare to their actual temperatures? Why?

4. What types of gases absorb infrared light? Ultraviolet light? X rays? Explain how these interactions between light and matter lead to the generic atmospheric structure profile shown in Figure 10.5.

5. Briefly explain why the sky is blue in the daytime and why sunrises and sunsets are red.

6. Give a few examples of greenhouse gases. Briefly describe how the *greenhouse effect* makes a planetary surface warmer than it would be otherwise.

7. What is convection? Briefly explain why it occurs in the *troposphere* but not in the *stratosphere*.

8. Briefly explain why a planet can have a stratosphere only if it has ultraviolet-absorbing molecules in its atmosphere. What molecule plays this role on Earth?

9. Explain how X-ray absorption in the *thermosphere* creates an *ionosphere* and how the ionosphere affects radio communications.

10. Briefly describe the actual atmospheric structure of each of the five terrestrial worlds; contrast these structures with the generic structure in Figure 10.5.

11. What is a *magnetosphere*? What are *charged particle belts*? Briefly describe how the solar wind affects magnetospheres and how auroras are produced.

12. Briefly distinguish between *weather* and *climate*.

13. Explain why Earth and Mars have seasons but Venus does not. How do seasons on Mars differ from seasons on Earth? Why does atmospheric pressure on Mars change during the seasons, while atmospheric pressure on Earth remains steady year-round?

14. What do we mean by *global wind patterns*? Briefly explain why terrestrial planets tend to have huge *circulation cells* carrying warm air toward the poles and cool air toward the equator.

15. What is the origin of the *Coriolis effect*? How does it affect global wind patterns?

16. Briefly describe how clouds form and how they affect planetary weather. What causes rain?

17. Briefly describe the four factors that can lead to long-term climate change and the effects of each factor.

18. Briefly describe the three processes that can add gas to a planetary atmosphere and the five processes by which a planetary atmosphere can lose gas.

19. Why do Mercury and the Moon have only thin exospheres? Why may there be ice in some polar craters on these worlds?

20. Briefly describe the atmospheric history of Mars.

21. Why should we expect Venus and Earth to have had very similar early atmospheres? How did the two planetary atmospheres become so different?

## Discussion Questions

1. *Charting Atmospheric Evolution.* How would you develop "planetary flowcharts" for the atmospheric source and loss processes analogous to those developed for geological processes in Chapter 9? Develop two charts, one for a source process and one for a loss process. Be sure your flowchart includes all the relevant connections described in this chapter.

2. *Mars: Past and Future.* Summarize the evolution of the Martian atmosphere since planetary formation, emphasizing the important source and loss processes. What is your prediction for the future of the Martian atmosphere?

## Problems

*Plausible Claims?* For **problems 1–7**, suppose you heard someone make the given claim. Decide whether the claim seems plausible. Explain.

1. If the Earth's atmosphere did not contain molecular nitrogen, X rays from the Sun would reach the surface.

2. When Mars had a thicker atmosphere in the past, it probably also had a stratosphere.

3. If the Earth rotated faster, storms would probably be more common and more severe.

4. Mars would not have seasons if it had a circular rather than an elliptical orbit around the Sun.

5. If the solar wind were much stronger, Mercury might develop a carbon dioxide atmosphere.

6. The Earth's oceans probably formed at a time when no greenhouse effect operated on Earth.

7. Mars once may have been warmer, but because it is farther from the Sun than is Earth, it's not possible that it could ever have been warmer than the Earth.

8. *Cool Venus.* Table 10.2 shows that Venus's temperature in the absence of the greenhouse effect is lower than Earth's, even though it is closer to the Sun.

   a. Explain this unexpected result in a sentence or two.

   b. Now suppose that Venus had neither clouds nor greenhouse gases. What do you think would happen to the temperature of Venus? Why?

   c. How are clouds and volcanoes linked on Venus? What change in volcanism might result in the disappearance of clouds? Explain.

9. *Atmospheric Structure.* Study Figure 10.5, which shows the atmospheric structure for a generic terrestrial planet. For each of the following cases, make a sketch similar to Figure 10.5 showing how the atmospheric structure would be different and explain the differences in words.

   a. Suppose the planet had no greenhouse gases.

   b. Suppose the Sun emitted no solar ultraviolet light.

   c. Suppose the Sun had a higher output of X rays.

10. *Inversions.* Consider a local inversion, in which the air is colder near the surface than higher up in the troposphere.

   a. Explain why convection is suppressed in an inversion.

   b. Cities that experience frequent inversions, such as Los Angeles and Denver, often have more serious problems with air pollution than other cities of similar size. Explain how an inversion can trap pollutants, keeping them close to the city in which they are generated.

11. *Coastal Winds.* During the daytime, heat from the Sun tends to make the air temperature warmer over land near the coast than over the water offshore. But at night, when land cools off faster than the sea, the temperatures tend to be cooler over land than over the sea. Use these facts to predict the directions in which winds generally blow during the day and at night in coastal regions; for example, do the winds blow out to sea or in toward the land? (*Hint:* How are these conditions similar to those that cause planetary circulation cells?) Explain your reasoning in a few sentences. Diagrams may help.

12. *A Swiftly Rotating Venus.* Suppose Venus had rotated as rapidly as Earth throughout its history. Briefly explain how and why you would expect it to be different in terms of each of the following: geological processes, atmospheric circulation, magnetic field, and atmospheric evolution. Write a few sentences about each.

13. *Sources and Losses.* Choose one atmospheric source process and one atmospheric loss process. Describe for each the ways in which the process is related to the four planetary formation properties discussed in Chapter 9. (For example, how is the creation of atmospheric gas by bombardment related to a planet's size, distance from the Sun, composition, and rotation rate?) (*Hint:* A process may not depend on all four formation properties.)

14. *Project: Atmospheric Science in the Kitchen.*
    a. Find an empty plastic bottle, such as a water bottle with a screwtop that makes a good seal. Warm the air inside by filling the bottle partway with hot water, and then shaking and emptying the bottle. Seal the bottle and place it in the refrigerator or freezer. What happens after 15 minutes or so? Explain why this happens, imagining that you could see the individual air molecules.
    b. You may have noticed that loose ice cubes in the freezer gradually shrink away to nothing or that frost sometimes builds up in old freezers. What are the technical terms used in this chapter for these phenomena? On what terrestrial planet do these same processes play a major role in controlling the atmosphere?

*15. *Habitable Planet Around 51 Peg?* A recently discovered planet orbits the star 51 Pegasi at a distance of only 0.051 AU. The star is approximately as bright as our Sun. The planet has a mass 0.6 times that of Jupiter, but no one knows if it is more similar to our jovian or to our terrestrial planets (if either).
    a. Suppose it is a terrestrial-type planet with an albedo of 0.15 (i.e., without clouds). Calculate its "no greenhouse" temperature, assuming it rotates fast enough to have the same tempera-

tures on its dayside and its nightside. How does this temperature compare to that of Earth?
    b. Repeat part (a), but this time assume that the planet is covered in very reflective clouds, giving it an albedo of 0.8.
    c. Based on your answers to parts (a) and (b), do you think it is likely that the conditions on this planet are conducive to life? Explain your answer in one or two paragraphs.

*16. *Escape from Venus.*
    a. Calculate the escape velocity from Venus's exosphere (about 200 km above Venus's surface). (*Hint:* See Mathematical Insight 5.3.)
    b. Calculate and compare the thermal speeds of hydrogen and deuterium atoms at the exospheric temperature of 350 K. The mass of a hydrogen atom is $1.67 \times 10^{-27}$ kg, and the mass of a deuterium atom is about twice the mass of a hydrogen atom.
    c. Comment in a few sentences on the relevance of the calculations in parts (a) and (b) to atmospheric evolution on Venus.

## Web Projects

Find useful links for Web projects on the text Web site.

1. *Spacecraft Study of Atmospheres.* Learn about a current or planned mission to study the atmosphere of one of the terrestrial worlds. Write a one- to two-page essay describing the mission and what it may teach us about terrestrial planet atmospheres.

2. *Martian Weather.* Find the latest weather report for Mars from spacecraft and other satellites. What season is it in the northern hemisphere? When was the most recent dust storm? What surface temperature was most recently reported from Mars's surface, and where was the lander located? Summarize your findings by writing a 1-minute script for a television news update on Martian weather.

3. *Terraforming Mars.* Some people have proposed that we might someday *terraform* Mars, making it more Earth-like so that we might live there more easily. Research some proposals for terraforming Mars. Do you think the proposals could work? Do you think it would be a good idea to terraform Mars? Write a one- to two-page essay summarizing your findings and defending your opinions.

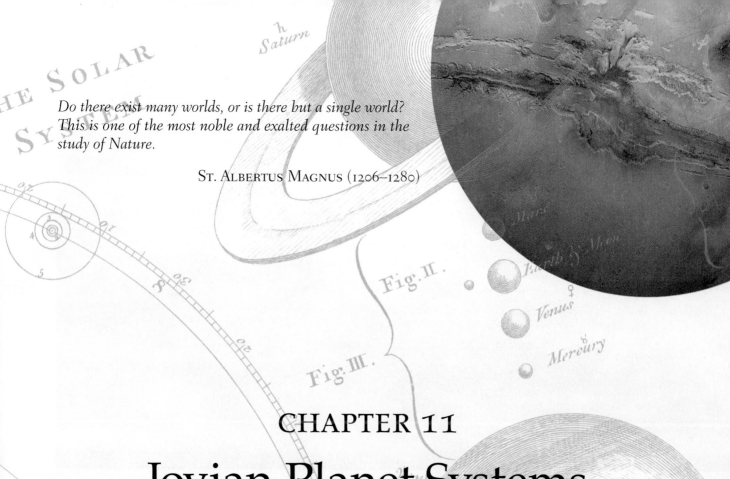

*Do there exist many worlds, or is there but a single world?
This is one of the most noble and exalted questions in the
study of Nature.*

ST. ALBERTUS MAGNUS (1206–1280)

# CHAPTER 11

# Jovian Planet Systems

In Roman mythology, the namesakes of the jovian planets are rulers among gods: Jupiter is the king of the gods, Saturn is Jupiter's father, Uranus is the lord of the sky, and Neptune rules the sea. But even the most imaginative of our ancestors did not foresee the true majesty of the jovian planets. The smallest, Neptune, is still large enough to contain the volume of more than 50 Earths. The largest, Jupiter, has a volume some 1,400 times that of Earth. These worlds are totally unlike the terrestrial planets. They are essentially giant balls of gas, with no solid surface on which to stand.

Why should we care about a set of worlds so different from our own? Apart from satisfying natural curiosity about the diversity of the solar system, the jovian planet systems serve as a testing ground for our general theories of comparative planetology. Are our theories good enough to predict the nature of these planets and their elaborate satellite systems, or are different processes at work? We'll find out in this chapter as we investigate the nature of the jovian planets, along with their intriguing moons and beautifully complex rings.

**FIGURE 11.1** Jupiter, Saturn, Uranus, and Neptune, shown to scale with Earth for comparison.

## 11.1 The Jovian Worlds: A Different Kind of Planet

The jovian planets have long held an important place in many human cultures. Jupiter is the third-brightest object that appears regularly in our night skies, after the Moon and Venus, and ancient astronomers carefully charted its 13-year trek through the constellations of the zodiac. Saturn is fainter and slower-moving, but people of many cultures also mapped its 27-year circuit of the sky. Ancient skywatchers did not know of the planets Uranus and Neptune, but astronomers charted their orbits soon after their discoveries in 1781 and 1846, respectively.

Scientific study of the jovian worlds dates back to Galileo in the early 1600s; however, scientists did not fully appreciate the differences between terrestrial and jovian planets until they established the absolute scale of the solar system (that is, in units such as kilometers instead of AU). Once distances were established, scientists could calculate the truly immense sizes of the jovian planets from their *angular* sizes (as measured through telescopes) [Section 7.1]. Knowing the distance scale also allowed calculating jovian planet masses by applying Newton's version of Kepler's third law [Section S.4] to observed orbital characteristics of jovian moons. Together, the measure-

ments of size and mass revealed the low densities of the jovian planets, proving that these worlds are very different from the Earth.[1]

The slow pace of discovery about the jovian planets gave way to revolutionary advances with the era of spacecraft exploration. The first spacecraft to the outer planets, *Pioneer 10* and *Pioneer 11*, flew past Jupiter and Saturn in the early 1970s. The Voyager missions followed less than a decade later [Section 7.6]. *Voyager 2* continued on a "grand tour" of the jovian planets, flying past Uranus in 1986 and Neptune in 1989. The results were spectacular. Figure 11.1 shows a montage of the jovian planets compiled by the Voyager spacecraft. Exploration of the jovian planet systems continued with the Galileo spacecraft, which went into orbit around Jupiter in 1995. Still ahead is the Cassini mission, scheduled for arrival at Saturn in 2004.

Jupiter, Saturn, Uranus, and Neptune are so different from the terrestrial planets that we must create an entirely new mental image of the term *planet*. Table 11.1 summarizes the bulk properties of these

---

[1] Isaac Newton proved that Jupiter was *relatively* less dense than the Earth before anyone could measure the *absolute* density of either.

**Table 11.1. Comparison of Bulk Properties of the Jovian Planets**

| Planet | Average Distance from Sun (AU) | Mass (Earth masses) | Radius (Earth radii) | Average Density (g/cm$^3$) | Bulk Composition |
|---|---|---|---|---|---|
| Jupiter | 5.20 | 317 | 11.2 | 1.33 | Mostly H, He |
| Saturn | 9.53 | 90 | 9.4 | 0.70 | Mostly H, He |
| Uranus | 19.2 | 14 | 4.11 | 1.32 | Hydrogen compounds and rocks, H and He |
| Neptune | 30.1 | 17 | 3.92 | 1.64 | Hydrogen compounds and rocks, H and He |

giant worlds. The most obvious difference between the jovian and terrestrial planets is size. Earth's mass in comparison to that of Jupiter is like the mass of a squirrel in comparison to that of a full-grown person. By volume, Earth in comparison to Jupiter is like a pea in a cup of soup. (Recall that volume is proportional to the cube of the radius. Thus, because Jupiter's radius is 11.2 times Earth's, its volume is $11.2^3 = 1{,}405$ times Earth's.)

The overall composition of the jovian planets—particularly Jupiter and Saturn—is more similar to that of the Sun than to any of the terrestrial worlds. Their primary chemical constituents are the light gases hydrogen and helium, although their atmospheres also contain many hydrogen compounds and their cores consist of a mixture of rocks, metals, and hydrogen compounds. Although these cores are small in proportion to the jovian planet volumes, each is still more massive than any terrestrial planet. Moreover, the pressures and temperatures near the cores are so extreme that the "surfaces" of the cores do not resemble terrestrial surfaces at all. In a sense, the general structures of the jovian planets are opposite those of the terrestrial planets: Whereas the terrestrial planets have thin atmospheres

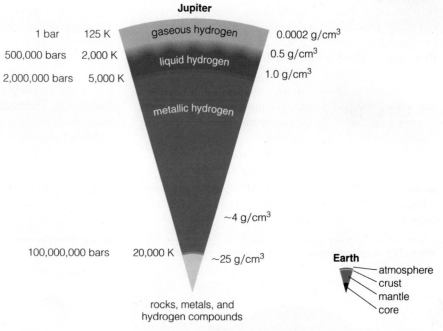

**FIGURE 11.2** Jupiter's interior structure, labeled with the pressure, temperature, and density at various depths. Earth's interior structure is shown to scale for comparison. Note that Jupiter's core is only slightly larger than Earth but is about 10 times more massive.

around rocky bodies, the jovian planets have proportionally small, rocky cores surrounded by massive layers of gas (Figure 11.2). A spacecraft descending into Jupiter, for example, would have to travel *tens of thousands* of kilometers before reaching the core.

The jovian planets may be Sun-like in composition, but their masses are far too low to provide the interior temperatures and densities needed for nuclear fusion. Calculations show that nuclear fusion is possible only with a mass at least 80 times that of Jupiter. (Some people have called Jupiter a "failed star" for this reason, but we prefer to think of it as a very successful planet.) The jovian planets have undoubtedly lost internal heat during the more than 4 billion years since their formation and thus must have been much warmer in the distant past. This heat may have "puffed up" their atmospheres, making them larger and brighter in the past. If so, Jupiter would have been even more prominent in Earth's sky billions of years ago than it is today.

The jovian planets rotate much more rapidly than any of the terrestrial worlds, but precisely defining their rotation rates can be difficult because they are not solid. We can measure a terrestrial rotation period simply by watching the apparent movement of a mountain or crater as a planet rotates, but on jovian planets we can observe only the movements of clouds. Cloud movements can be deceptive, because their apparent speeds may be affected by winds as well as by planetary rotation. Nevertheless, observations of clouds at different latitudes suggest that the jovian planets rotate faster near their equators than near their poles. (The Sun also exhibits this type of *differential rotation* [Section 14.5].) We can measure the rotation rates of the jovian interiors by tracking emissions from charged particles trapped in their *magnetospheres* [Section 10.3]. This technique allows us to observe the rotation period of a magnetosphere, which should be the same as the rotation period deep in the interior, where the magnetic fields are generated. These measurements show that the jovian

"days" range from only about 10 hours on Jupiter and Saturn to 16–17 hours on Uranus and Neptune.

**TIME OUT TO THINK** *How would you measure the rotation period of Earth if you made telescopic observations from Mars? How might Earth's clouds mislead you if you focused on them?*

Even the shapes of the jovian planets are somewhat different from the shapes of the terrestrial planets. Gravity makes the jovian planets approximately spherical, but their rapid rotation rates make them slightly squashed (Figure 11.3). Material near the equator, where speeds around the rotation axis are highest, is flung outward in the same way that you feel yourself flung outward when you ride a merry-go-round. The result is that jovian planets bulge noticeably around the equator. The size of the equatorial bulge depends on the balance between the strength of gravity pulling the material inward and the rate of rotation pushing the material outward. The balance tips most strongly toward flattening on Saturn, with its rapid 10-hour rotation period and its relatively weak surface gravity. Saturn is about 10% wider at its equator than at its poles. In addition to altering a planet's appearance, the equatorial bulge itself exerts an extra gravitational pull that helps keep satellites and rings aligned with the equator.

We can trace almost all the major characteristics of the jovian planets back to their formation [Section 8.4]. The jovian planets formed far from the Sun where icy grains condensed in the solar nebula, yielding far more solid matter to accrete into planetesimals. As the massive ice/rock cores of the future jovian planets accreted, their strong gravity captured hydrogen and helium gas from the surrounding neb-

**FIGURE 11.3** The jovian planets are not quite spherical.

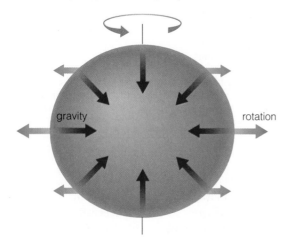

**a** Gravity alone makes a planet spherical, but rapid rotation flattens out the spherical shape by flinging material near the equator outward.

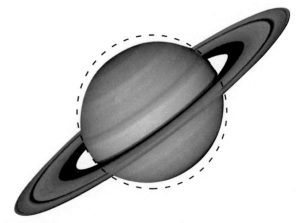

**b** Saturn is clearly not spherical. Compare its actual shape to the dashed circle.

ula. Some of this gas formed flattened "miniature solar nebulae" (or *jovian nebulae*) around the jovian planets. Just as solid grains condensed and combined into planets in the full solar nebula, solid grains in the nebulae surrounding the jovian planets condensed to form satellite systems. The deviations from the general patterns, such as the large 98° axis tilt of Uranus,[2] probably arose from giant impacts as the planets were forming. In the rest of this chapter, we will explore the features of the jovian planets and their satellites in greater depth, putting our theories of planetary development to the test.

## 11.2 Jovian Planet Interiors

As was the case with the terrestrial planets, developing a true understanding of the jovian planets requires looking deep inside them. Probing jovian planet interiors is even more difficult than probing terrestrial interiors, but several techniques allow us to learn what lies below the clouds. We've already discussed how Earth-based observations yielded the sizes and average densities of the jovian planets and how spacecraft measurements of magnetic and gravitational fields provide additional clues to their interior structure. Detailed observations of planetary shapes also provide information about interior structure; for example, computer models using shape data tell us that Saturn's core makes up a larger fraction of its mass than Jupiter's core.

Spectroscopy from Earth and from spacecraft reveals the chemical compositions of the jovian upper atmospheres. Their deeper atmospheres are generally more difficult to probe, but two recent events provided rare opportunities. In July 1994, fragments of comet Shoemaker–Levy 9 slammed into Jupiter, blasting material from deeper in the atmosphere out into the open, where astronomers could study it through telescopes [Section 12.6]. Then, in December 1995, NASA's Galileo spacecraft dropped a scientific probe into Jupiter's atmosphere. The Galileo probe survived to a depth of about 300 kilometers—a significant distance, but still much less than 1% of Jupiter's 70,000-kilometer radius—providing our first direct data from within a jovian world.

Beneath the depths at which we have compiled direct data, we learn about the jovian interiors by combining laboratory studies and theoretical models. These studies tell us how the ingredients of the jovian planets (especially hydrogen and helium) act

under the tremendous temperatures and pressures expected deep below the cloud tops. Nowadays, elaborate computer models successfully match the observed sizes, densities, atmospheric compositions, and even shapes of the jovian planets. We therefore believe that we have a fairly clear understanding of their interiors. We'll begin our discussion of the jovian interiors by using Jupiter as a prototype; then we'll apply the principles of comparative planetology to understand the other jovian planet interiors.

### Inside Jupiter

Imagine plunging head-on into Jupiter in a futuristic space suit that allows you to survive the incredible interior conditions. Near the cloud tops, you'll find the temperature to be a brisk 125 K (−148°C), the density to be a low 0.0002 $g/cm^3$, and the atmospheric pressure to be about 1 bar [Section 10.1]—the same as the pressure at sea level on Earth. The deeper you go, the higher the temperature, density, and pressure become (see Figure 11.2). By a depth of 7,000 km—about 10% of the planet's radius—you'll find that the temperature has increased to a scorching 2,000 K, the density has reached 0.5 $g/cm^3$ (half that of water), and the pressure is about 500,000 bars. Under these conditions, hydrogen acts more like a liquid than a gas.

At a depth of 14,000 km, you'll find a density about the same as that of water, a temperature near 5,000 K, and a pressure of 2 million bars. This extreme pressure forces hydrogen into an even more compact form: *metallic hydrogen,* in which all the atoms share electrons, just as happens in everyday metals.[3] The metallic and hence electrically conducting nature of this interior hydrogen is important in generating Jupiter's strong magnetic field.

Continuing your descent, you'll reach Jupiter's core at a depth of 60,000 km, about 10,000 km from the center. The core is a mix of hydrogen compounds, rocks, and metals, but these materials bear little resemblance to familiar solids or liquids because of the extreme 20,000-K temperature and 100-million-bar pressure. The core materials probably remain mixed together, with a density of about 25 $g/cm^3$, rather than separating into layers of different composition as in the terrestrial planets. The total mass of Jupiter's core is about 10 times that of Earth, so the core alone would make an impressive planet.

---

[2]The 98° tilt is measured by assuming that Uranus was "supposed to" rotate counterclockwise as seen from above Earth's North Pole—just like most other planets. We could equivalently say that Uranus has an 82° tilt (180° − 98° = 82°) but rotates backward.

[3]This phase change from nonmetal to metal does not occur in any everyday substance under normal conditions on Earth, and for a long time it was a theoretical prediction without experimental verification. Metallic hydrogen was finally produced under extreme pressure in laboratories in the early 1990s.

Our study of the terrestrial planets taught us that internal heat sources can have a strong effect on the behavior of planets, so it is natural to ask if Jupiter and the other jovian planets are also affected by internal heat sources. Jupiter has a tremendous amount of internal heat—so much that it emits almost twice as much energy as it receives from the Sun. (For comparison, Earth's internal heat adds only 0.005% as much energy to the surface as does sunlight.) This internal heating is much too large to be explained by radioactive decay alone, so we must search for other explanations. The most probable explanation is that Jupiter is still slowly contracting, as if it has not quite finished forming from a jovian nebula. This *gravitational contraction* [Section 14.1] is so gradual that we cannot measure it directly, but it converts gravitational potential energy to thermal energy, keeping Jupiter hot inside.

### Comparing Jovian Planet Interiors

Now that we've discussed the interior of Jupiter, what can we say about the other jovian planets? Look back at the bulk properties of the jovian planets in Table 11.1. Although there are no obvious correlations between size, density, and composition, we can explain the properties by examining the behavior of gaseous materials in more detail.

Building a planet of hydrogen and helium is a bit like making one out of very fluffy pillows (Figure 11.4a). Imagine assembling a planet pillow by

pillow. As each new pillow is added, those on the bottom are compressed more by those above. As the lower layers are forced closer together, their mutual gravitational attraction increases, compressing them even further. At first the stack grows substantially with each additional pillow, but eventually the growth slows until adding pillows hardly increases the height of the stack. This analogy explains why Jupiter is only slightly larger than Saturn in radius even though it is more than three times more massive. The extra mass of Jupiter compresses its interior to a much greater extent, making Jupiter's average density almost twice that of Saturn. In fact, Saturn's average density of 0.7 g/cm$^3$ is less than that of water. More precise calculations show that Jupiter's radius is almost the maximum possible for a jovian planet: If more gas were added to Jupiter, its weight would actually compress the interior enough to make the planet *smaller* instead of larger (Figure 11.4b). In fact, the smallest stars are significantly smaller in radius than Jupiter, even though they are 80 times more massive.

The pillow analogy suggests that a hydrogen/helium planet less massive than Saturn should have an even lower density. Because Uranus and Neptune have significantly higher densities than Saturn, we conclude that they cannot have the same hydrogen/helium composition. Instead, they must have a much larger fraction of higher-density material, such as hydrogen compounds and rocks, and a smaller fraction of "plain" hydrogen and helium.

---

**FIGURE 11.4** The growth of jovian planets.

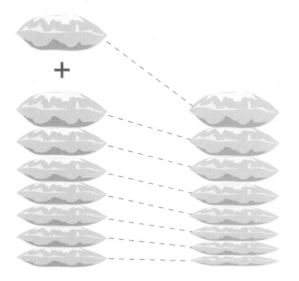

a Adding pillows to a stack may increase its height at first, but eventually it just compresses all the pillows in the stack. In a similar way, adding mass to a jovian planet would eventually just compress the planet to higher density without increasing the planet's radius.

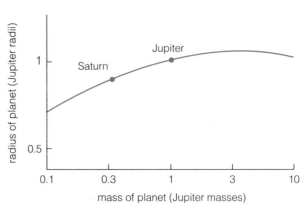

b This graph shows how the radius of a hydrogen/helium planet depends on the planet's mass. Jupiter's radius is only slightly larger than Saturn's, although it is three times more massive. For a planet much more massive than Jupiter, gravitational compression would actually make it smaller in size.

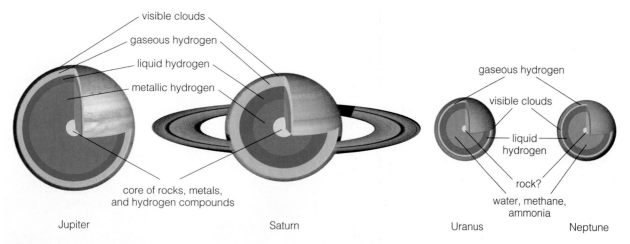

FIGURE 11.5 These diagrams compare the interior structures of the jovian planets (shown approximately to scale). All four planets have cores equal to about 10 Earth masses of rock, metal, and hydrogen compounds, and they differ primarily in the hydrogen/helium layers that surround the cores.

Computer models of the jovian interiors yield the somewhat surprising result that the cores of all four jovian planets are quite similar—about 10 Earth masses of rock, metal, and hydrogen compounds. This suggests that all four jovian planets began with about the same size "seed" from accretion and that their differences stem from their capturing different amounts of additional gas from the solar nebula. Jupiter captured more than 300 Earth masses of gas from the solar nebula, Saturn captured about one-fourth as much gas as Jupiter, and Uranus and Neptune captured only a few Earth masses of solar-nebula gas. This general pattern makes sense, because icy planetesimals took longer to accrete in the outer solar system, where planetesimals were more spread out. Thus, the more distant jovian planets didn't have as much time as Jupiter to capture solar-nebula gas before the nebula was cleared by the solar wind [Section 8.4].

The similar cores also mean that the interior structures of the jovian planets differ mainly in the hydrogen/helium layers that surround the cores (Figure 11.5). Saturn is large enough for interior densities, temperatures, and pressures to be high enough to force gaseous hydrogen into liquid and then metallic form, just as in Jupiter. But these conditions occur relatively deeper in Saturn than in Jupiter, because of its smaller size. Pressures within Uranus and Neptune are not high enough to form liquid or metallic hydrogen. However, their cores of rock, metal, and hydrogen compounds may be liquid, making for very odd "oceans" buried deep inside them.

Like Jupiter, Saturn emits nearly twice as much energy as it receives from the Sun. Saturn's mass is too small for it to be generating all its excess heat by contracting like Jupiter. Instead, its lower temperatures probably allow helium to condense and "rain down" from higher regions in the interior. The gradual rain of these relatively dense helium droplets

resembles the process of *differentiation* that once occurred in terrestrial planet interiors [Section 9.2]. Voyager observations confirmed that Saturn's atmosphere is somewhat depleted of helium (compared to Jupiter's atmosphere), just as we would expect if helium has been raining down into Saturn's interior for billions of years.

Neither Uranus nor Neptune has conditions that allow helium rain to form, and most of their original heat from accretion should have escaped long ago. This explains why Uranus emits virtually no excess internal energy. Neptune is much more mysterious: Like Jupiter and Saturn, it emits nearly twice as much energy as it receives from the Sun. The only reasonable explanation for Neptune's internal heat source is that the planet is somehow still contracting, rather like Jupiter, thereby converting gravitational potential energy into thermal energy. But no one knows why a planet of Neptune's size would still be contracting more than 4 billion years after its formation.

## 11.3 Jovian Planet Atmospheres

The jovian planets lack the geology of the terrestrial planets because they do not have solid surfaces. But whatever they lack in geology they more than make up for with their atmospheres. Fortunately, their atmospheric processes are quite similar to those we've already discussed for the terrestrial atmospheres, despite their much greater extent and very different compositions. Let's again begin with Jupiter.

### Jupiter's Atmosphere

Jupiter's atmosphere is almost entirely hydrogen and helium (about 75% hydrogen and 24% helium by mass), but it also contains trace amounts of many

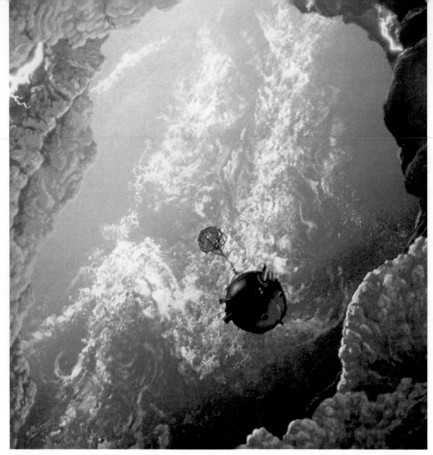

**a** Artist's conception of the Galileo probe entering Jupiter's atmosphere. This view, looking outward from beneath the clouds, shows the suitcase-size probe falling with its parachute extended above it.

**FIGURE 11.6** Jupiter's atmosphere.

other hydrogen compounds. Because oxygen, carbon, and nitrogen are the most common elements besides hydrogen and helium, the most common hydrogen compounds are methane ($CH_4$), ammonia ($NH_3$), and water ($H_2O$). Spectroscopy reveals the presence of more complex compounds, including acetylene ($C_2H_2$), ethane ($C_2H_6$), propane ($C_3H_8$), and larger molecules that can act like haze particles. Although hydrogen compounds make up only a minuscule fraction of Jupiter's atmosphere, they are responsible for virtually all aspects of its appearance. Some of these compounds condense to form the clouds so prominent in telescope and spacecraft images, and others are responsible for Jupiter's great variety of colors. Without these compounds, Jupiter would be a uniform, colorless ball of gas.

**TIME OUT TO THINK** *Jupiter possesses substantial amounts of gases like methane, propane, and acetylene, highly flammable fuels used here on Earth. There is plenty of lightning on Jupiter to provide sparks, so why aren't we concerned about Jupiter exploding? (Hint: What's missing from Jupiter's atmosphere that's necessary for ordinary fire?)*

Jupiter is the only jovian planet that we've directly sampled. On December 7, 1995, following a 6-year trip from Earth, the Galileo spacecraft released a scientific probe (the size of a large suitcase) into Jupiter's atmosphere (Figure 11.6a). The probe collected temperature, pressure, composition, and radiation measurements for about an hour as it descended, until it was destroyed by the ever-increasing pressures and temperatures. The probe sent its data via radio signals back to the Galileo spacecraft in orbit around Jupiter, which relayed the data back to Earth.

The Galileo probe helped confirm that the thermal structure of Jupiter's atmosphere is very similar to that of terrestrial atmospheres (Figure 11.6b). Let's follow its fiery descent. The probe plunged into Jupiter at a speed of over 200,000 km/hr, with a robust heat shield facing forward to protect the scientific instruments. Above the cloud tops, the probe

Graph labels:
- altitude above cloud tops (km): 250, 200, 150, 100, 50, 0, −50, −100, −150
- thermosphere
- stratosphere
- troposphere
- cold enough for ammonia to condense
- cold enough for ammonium hydrosulfide to condense
- cold enough for water to condense
- end of Galileo probe data
- pressure (bars): 0.01, 0.1, 1, 2, 10, 20
- temperature (K): 0, 100, 200, 300, 400, 500, 600, 700, 800, 900

**b** This graph shows the temperature structure of Jupiter's atmosphere (compare to Figure 10.5). Jupiter has at least three distinct cloud layers because different atmospheric gases condense at different temperatures and hence at different altitudes.

found very low density gas that is heated to perhaps 1,000 K by solar X rays and by energetic particles from Jupiter's magnetosphere. This thin, hot gas makes up Jupiter's *thermosphere*. Next, the probe encountered Jupiter's *stratosphere*, where solar ultraviolet photons are absorbed by a few minor ingredients in the atmosphere. This absorption gives the stratosphere a peak temperature of about 170 K. Chemical reactions driven by the solar ultraviolet photons also create a smoglike haze that masks the color and sharpness of the clouds below. Below the stratosphere lies Jupiter's *troposphere*, where the increased density greatly slowed the probe's descent; the probe then slowed further by jettisoning its heat shield and releasing a parachute. The temperature at the top of the troposphere is close to 125 K; it rises with depth because greenhouse gases trap both solar heat and Jupiter's own internal heat. The similarities between the atmospheric structures of Earth and Jupiter may seem surprising for two planets that are so different in other ways, but these similarities con-

firm that atmospheres are governed primarily by interactions between sunlight and gases.

The Galileo probe found tremendous winds and turbulence in the troposphere. As on the terrestrial planets, Jupiter's weather occurs mostly in its troposphere, where higher temperatures at lower altitudes drive vigorous convection. This convection is responsible for the thick clouds that enshroud Jupiter. As a parcel of gas rises upward through the troposphere, it encounters gradually lower temperatures. At relatively low altitudes, the surrounding temperature is low enough for water vapor to condense into liquid droplets or flakes of ice, forming water clouds similar to those on Earth. At higher altitudes, temperatures become low enough for another minor atmospheric ingredient, ammonium hydrosulfide ($NH_4SH$), to condense and form clouds. Still higher, the temperatures fall to the point at which ammonia ($NH_3$) condenses to form clouds of ammonia crystals—the prominent white clouds visible on Jupiter. Thus, Jupiter has several layers of clouds of different compositions (see Figure 11.6b). The relentless motion of Jupiter's atmosphere continuously regenerates the extensive clouds.

Jupiter also has planet-wide *circulation cells* similar to those on Earth, where solar heat causes equatorial air to expand and spill northward and southward toward the poles [Section 10.4]. However, whereas Earth's rotation splits its circulation cells into just three separate cells in each hemisphere, Jupiter's much more rapid rotation creates a strong Coriolis effect that causes its circulation cells to split into many huge bands encircling the entire planet at fixed latitudes (Figure 11.7a,b). The bands of rising air are called **zones**, and they appear white because of the ammonia clouds that form as the air rises to high, cool altitudes. Within the zones, ammonia "snowflakes" rain downward against the rising convective motions. The adjacent **belts** of falling air are depleted in the cloud-forming ingredients and do not contain any white ammonia clouds. They appear dark because we can see down to the red or tan ammonium-hydrosulfide clouds that form at lower altitudes. The distinction between Jupiter's belts and zones is analogous to the distinction on Earth between the cloudy, rainy equatorial zone (a region of generally rising air) and the clear desert skies found roughly 20°–30° north

**a** Belts and zones correspond to clouds of different composition at different altitudes. The Coriolis effect diverts motions in the circulation cells into strong easterly and westerly winds.

belt    zone    belt

The Coriolis effect diverts winds.

Rising air forms white ammonia cloud.

Snow depletes air of ammonia.

No cloud or snow in descending air; clouds below are visible.

ammonium hydrosulfide cloud

Belts are warm, red, low-altitude clouds.

Zones are cool, white, high-altitude clouds.

**b** The color difference between belts and zones is evident in this Hubble Space Telescope image.

**c** In this infrared image taken nearly simultaneously with (**b**), brightness indicates high temperatures.

**FIGURE 11.7** Jupiter's belts and zones.

and south of the equator (regions of descending air). Infrared images confirm the temperature differences between Jupiter's warm belts and cool zones (Figure 11.7b,c).

Jupiter's global wind patterns are shaped by these alternating bands of rising air in zones and falling air in belts. The rising air in the zones indicates higher pressures than in the adjacent belts, so winds must flow from the high-pressure zones toward the low-pressure belts. Figure 11.7a shows the northward winds flowing from a zone to a belt in the northern hemisphere. The northward winds are quickly diverted into fast eastward-flowing winds by the very strong Coriolis effect. Similarly, the southward-flowing winds from zones to belts in the northern hemisphere are diverted to the west. (Note that both these diversions of winds are to the right in the northern hemisphere; in the southern hemisphere, winds are diverted to the left [Section 10.4].) The winds are generally strongest

to Equator

N

H

high pressure

The Coriolis force diverts winds.

**FIGURE 11.8** This photograph shows Jupiter's Great Red Spot, a huge high-pressure storm that is large enough to swallow two or three Earths. The smaller photo (right) of the Great Red Spot is overlaid with a weather map of the region.

at the equator and at the boundaries between belts and zones. Peak wind speeds exceed 400 km/hr.

Jupiter's **Great Red Spot** is perhaps the most dramatic weather pattern in the solar system (Figure 11.8). We know that it has been prominent in Jupiter's southern hemisphere for at least three centuries, because it has been seen ever since telescopes became powerful enough to detect it. The Great Red Spot is huge—more than twice as wide as the Earth. Could it be a tremendous low-pressure storm like a hurricane on Earth? Not quite. Hurricane winds circulate around low-pressure regions and therefore circulate *clockwise* in the southern hemisphere [Section 10.4]. The winds in the Great Red Spot circulate counterclockwise, indicating that it is a *high*-pressure storm, possibly kept spinning by the influence of nearby belts and zones.

Other, smaller storms are always brewing in Jupiter's atmosphere—small only in comparison to the Great Red Spot. Brown ovals are low-pressure storms with their cloud tops deeper in Jupiter's atmosphere, and white ovals are high-pressure storms topped with ammonia clouds. No one knows what drives Jupiter's storms, why Jupiter has only one Great Red Spot, or why the Great Red Spot lasts so much longer than storms on Earth. Storms on Earth lose their strength when they pass over land, so perhaps Jupiter's biggest storms last for centuries because there is no solid surface below to sap their energy.

Jupiter's vibrant colors remain perplexing despite decades of intense study. Observations tell us that the high clouds of ammonia in the zones are usually white and that the lower clouds of ammonium hy-

drosulfide in the belts are brown or red. But pure ammonium-hydrosulfide crystals are as white as ammonia crystals, so the colors of the belt clouds must come from ingredients besides the ammonium-hydrosulfide crystals themselves. Sulfur compounds are a plausible suspect, because they form a variety of reds and tans (also seen on the surface of Jupiter's moon Io). Phosphorus compounds (including phosphine, $PH_3$) are another possibility. Whatever their origin, the red and tan compounds are found primarily at lower (and therefore warmer) altitudes. The chemical reactions that form them evidently require the extra energy of Jupiter's internal heat, or possibly lightning deep below the clouds. The bright red color of the very high altitude clouds in the Great Red Spot remains an even greater mystery. Perhaps chemical reactions caused by solar ultraviolet radiation produce the compounds responsible for these colors.

As far as we know, Jupiter's climate is steady and unchanging. Jupiter has no appreciable axis tilt and therefore has no seasons. In fact, Jupiter's polar temperatures are quite similar to its equatorial temperatures. Solar heating alone might leave the poles relatively cool, but Jupiter's internal heat source keeps the planet uniformly warm.

### Comparing Jovian Planet Atmospheres

The most striking difference among the jovian atmospheres is their colors. Starting with Jupiter's distinct red colors, the jovian planets turn to Saturn's more subdued yellows, to Uranus's faint blue-green tinge, and finally to Neptune's pronounced blue hue (see Figure 11.1). What's responsible for this regular progression of colors? The primary constituents in all the jovian atmospheres (hydrogen and helium) are colorless, so the planetary colors must come from trace gases or chemical reactions that create colored compounds. In fact, we can understand the color differences by comparing the atmospheric structures and compositions of the four planets. All four are quite similar, except for the effects of the lower temperatures and lower gravities on the more distant planets (Figure 11.9).

Saturn's reds and tans almost certainly come from the same compounds that produce these colors on Jupiter—whatever those compounds may be. As on Jupiter, these compounds are probably created by chemical reactions beneath the cloud layers and carried upward by convection. However, because of Saturn's lower temperatures, its cloud layers lie deeper in its atmosphere than Jupiter's. As a result, a thicker layer of tan "smog" overlies the clouds, washing out Saturn's colors. Saturn's lower gravity also means that its atmosphere is less compressed, so cloud layers are more spread out vertically. These thicker cloud layers prevent us from seeing down to the lower, more richly hued cloud levels that we see on Jupiter.

The blue colors of Uranus and Neptune have a completely different explanation: methane gas, which is at least 20 times more abundant (by percentage) on these planets than on Jupiter or Saturn. The highest-altitude clouds of Uranus and Neptune are made from flakes of methane ice; Jupiter and Saturn lack such clouds because their warmer temperatures prevent methane ice from condensing. Methane gas above these clouds absorbs red light but transmits blue light (Figure 11.10). The clouds then reflect (scatter) the blue light upward, where it is again transmitted through the gas above. Thus, we see this reflected blue light when we look at the atmospheres of Uranus and Neptune. Uranus and Neptune may also have red and tan cloud layers like those of Jupiter and Saturn, but if so they are hidden deep below the methane gas and clouds.

The fainter blue of Uranus compared to Neptune indicates that less sunlight penetrates the atmosphere to the level of the clouds. Instead, the light is probably scattered by abundant smoglike haze. The extra haze on Uranus may arise because its extreme axis tilt keeps one hemisphere in bright sunlight for decades at a time during its 84-year orbit, allowing more ultraviolet-driven chemical reactions. This continuous sunlight in one hemisphere may also explain why Uranus has a surprisingly hot thermosphere that extends thousands of kilometers above its cloud tops.

Voyager, Galileo, Cassini, and the Hubble Space Telescope cameras have monitored the meteorology of the four jovian planets with excellent resolution (Figure 11.11). Jupiter's weather phenomena (clouds, belts, zones, and other storms) are by far the strong-

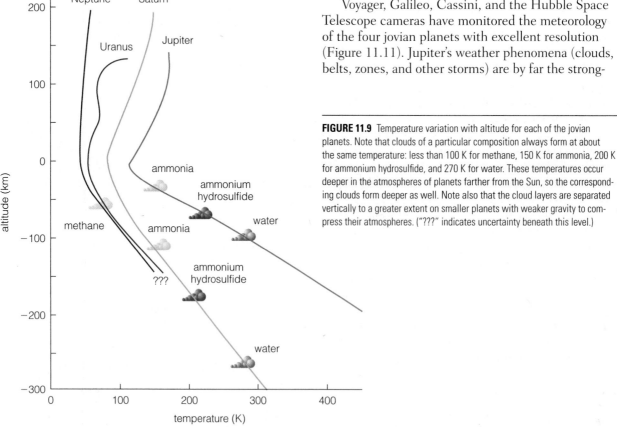

**FIGURE 11.9** Temperature variation with altitude for each of the jovian planets. Note that clouds of a particular composition always form at about the same temperature: less than 100 K for methane, 150 K for ammonia, 200 K for ammonium hydrosulfide, and 270 K for water. These temperatures occur deeper in the atmospheres of planets farther from the Sun, so the corresponding clouds form deeper as well. Note also that the cloud layers are separated vertically to a greater extent on smaller planets with weaker gravity to compress their atmospheres. ("???" indicates uncertainty beneath this level.)

est and most active. Saturn also possesses belts and zones (in more subdued colors), along with some small storms and an occasional large storm, but it lacks any weather feature as prominent as Jupiter's Great Red Spot. (For unknown reasons, Saturn's winds are even stronger than Jupiter's.) Neptune's atmosphere is also banded and has a high-pressure storm, called the Great Dark Spot, that acts much like Jupiter's Great Red Spot.

Seasonal changes play a relatively small role on most jovian planets. We might expect seasons on Saturn and Neptune because they have axis tilts similar to that of Earth, and some seasonal weather changes have been observed. But their internal heat sources maintain similar temperatures all over, just as Jupiter's internal heat keeps its polar and equatorial temperatures about the same. The greatest surprise in the weather patterns on the jovian planets is the weather on Uranus, the planet tipped on its side. When the Voyager spacecraft flew past in 1986, it was midsummer in Uranus's northern hemisphere, with the summer pole pointed almost directly at the Sun. Photographs revealed virtually no clouds, belts,

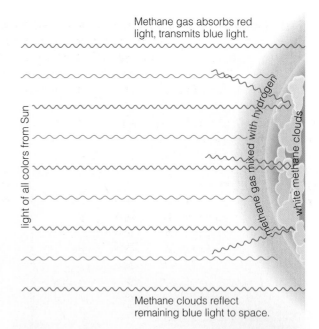

**FIGURE 11.10** Neptune and Uranus are blue because methane gas absorbs red light but transmits blue light. Clouds of methane-ice flakes reflect the transmitted blue light back to space.

**FIGURE 11.11** Close-ups of cloud patterns on the four jovian planets. Scientists combine series of images like these to make weather movies similar to those for Earth shown on the evening news. The reddish spots in the Uranus image are high clouds, and the Great Dark Spot is visible in the Neptune image to the left of center. Images for Jupiter, Saturn, and Neptune at visible wavelengths, Uranus at infrared wavelengths.

FIGURE 11.12 Auroras on Jupiter.

a Like Earth's magnetosphere (but much larger), Jupiter's magnetosphere has charged particle belts and auroras. In Jupiter's case, the charged particles come from the volcanically active moon Io.

or zones, which scientists attributed to the lack of a significant internal heat source on Uranus. But recently the Hubble Space Telescope has detected storms raging on the planet (bright spots in Figure 11.11). The seasons are changing, and the winter hemisphere is seeing sunlight for the first time in decades.

## 11.4 Jovian Planet Magnetospheres

Each jovian planet is surrounded by a bubblelike magnetosphere consisting of the planet's magnetic field and the particles trapped within it. The jovian planets themselves dwarf the terrestrial planets, and their magnetospheres are even more impressive. The Voyager spacecraft carried sophisticated instruments to measure magnetic fields and observe the charged particle belts encircling the planets. We learned not only about the magnetospheres themselves, but also about their interactions with the planets beneath them and the satellite systems within them.

### Jupiter's Magnetosphere

Jupiter's magnetic field is awesome—about 20,000 times stronger than Earth's. This strong magnetic field deflects the solar wind some 3 million km (about 40 Jupiter radii) before it even reaches Jupiter (Figure 11.12a). If our eyes could see this part of Jupiter's

b Images of Jupiter's aurora in the ultraviolet are overlaid on a visible-wavelength image of Jupiter for reference (Hubble Space Telescope photo).

magnetosphere, it would be larger than the full moon in our sky. The solar wind sweeps around Jupiter's magnetosphere, stretching it out on the far side of Jupiter all the way to Saturn's orbit. Just as on Earth, the magnetosphere traps charged particles and makes them spiral along the magnetic field lines. The more energetic particles cause *auroras* as they follow the magnetic field into Jupiter's upper atmosphere, colliding with atoms and molecules and causing them

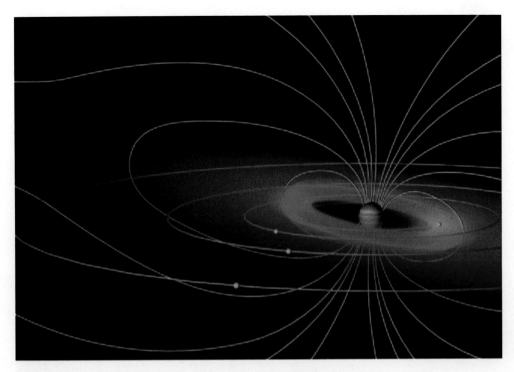

**FIGURE 11.13** Artist's conception of Jupiter's magnetosphere, with Io embedded deep within. An orange glow around Io represents its escaping atmosphere, and the red donut represents the Io torus—the charged particle belt formed by Io. The blue lines show Jupiter's strong magnetic field.

to radiate (Figure 11.12b). Jupiter's magnetosphere contains a great deal of plasma, some captured from the solar wind but most originating from Jupiter's volcanically active moon, Io.

Not only does Io help feed plasma into the magnetosphere, but the magnetosphere in turn has important effects on Io and other satellites of Jupiter. The charged particles bombard the surfaces of Jupiter's icy moons, with each particle blasting away a few atoms or molecules. This process alters the surface materials and can even generate thin bombardment atmospheres—just as bombardment creates the thin atmospheres of Mercury and the Moon [Section 10.5]. On Io, the bombardment leads to the continuous escape of the atmospheric gases released by volcanic outgassing. As a result, Io loses atmospheric gases faster than any other object in the solar system. The escaping gases (sulfur, oxygen, and a hint of sodium) are ionized and feed a donut-shaped charged particle belt, called the *Io torus*, that approximately traces Io's orbit (Figure 11.13).

### Comparing Jovian Planet Magnetospheres

The strength of each jovian planet's magnetic field depends primarily on the size of the electrically conducting layer buried in its interior. Jupiter, with its huge metallic-hydrogen layer, has by far the strongest magnetic field. Saturn has a thinner layer of metallic

hydrogen and hence a correspondingly weaker magnetic field. Uranus and Neptune have no metallic hydrogen at all. Their relatively weak magnetic fields must be generated in their core "oceans" of hydrogen compounds, rock, and metal. The actual size of a planet's magnetosphere depends on the pressure of the solar wind pushing on a planet's magnetic field, as well as on the magnetic-field strength itself. The pressure of the solar wind is weaker at greater distances from the Sun. Thus, the magnetospheric "bubbles" surrounding the outer planets, particularly Uranus and Neptune, are larger than they would be if these planets were closer to the Sun. This effect is not sufficient to offset the weak magnetic fields of Uranus and Neptune, however, so these planets have small magnetospheres (Figure 11.14).

While the trend of decreasing magnetic-field strengths makes sense, the magnetic fields still pose some unsolved problems. The magnetic fields of Jupiter and Saturn are fairly closely aligned with their rotation axes (10° tilt and 0° tilt, respectively), just as we might expect given that the magnetic fields are generated in their rotating interiors. But Voyager observations showed that the magnetic field of Uranus is tipped by a whopping 60° relative to its rotation axis (see Figure 11.14); its center is also significantly offset from the planet's center. Scientists briefly speculated that whatever giant impact caused the large

**FIGURE 11.14** Comparison of jovian planet magnetospheres. The size of Jupiter's magnetosphere is particularly impressive in light of the greater pressure from the solar wind nearer the Sun. (Planets enlarged for clarity.)

size of Sun
(to scale with
magnetospheres)

—— magnetic field lines

—— axis of rotation

—— orientation of magnetic field

—— solar wind

Jupiter

Saturn

Uranus

Neptune

tilt of Uranus's rotation axis also distorted the magnetic field. But this idea was discarded when Voyager discovered a similarly large magnetic field tilt (46°) for Neptune. Scientists still cannot explain the magnetic-field tilts of Uranus and Neptune.

No magnetosphere is as full of charged particles as Jupiter's, primarily because no other jovian planet has a satellite like Io. All magnetospheres trap particles from the solar wind, but Jupiter again captures the most. These trapped particles give Jupiter the brightest auroras; the more distant jovian planets have progressively weaker auroras.

## 11.5 A Wealth of Worlds: Satellites of Ice and Rock

Nearly 90 known moons (*satellites*) orbit the jovian planets. Figure 11.15 shows the larger ones, and Appendix C lists fundamental data for the known moons. It's worth taking a few minutes to study the

figure and the appendix, looking for patterns, before you read on.

Broadly speaking, the jovian moons can be divided into three groups: small moons less than about 300 km across, medium-size moons ranging from about 300 to 1,500 km in diameter, and large moons more than 1,500 km in diameter. Most of the known moons fall into the small category, and additional small moons may yet be discovered. The small moons generally look more like potatoes than like spheres (Figure 11.16), because their gravities are too weak to force their rigid material into spheres [Section 8.4]. Many of these moons (particularly those farther from their planets) also have unusual orbits, with significant eccentricities, large orbital tilts, or orbits that go backward relative to the planet's rotation. Such orbits are signs that the moons are captured asteroids rather than moons that formed from the "miniature solar nebulae" that surrounded each jovian planet. In a few cases, several small moons share similar orbits. For example, four moons orbit Jupiter backward at distances between 21 and 24 million kilometers and

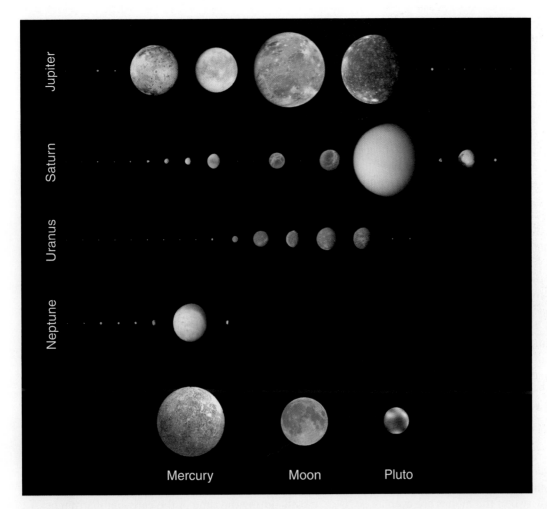

Jupiter

Saturn

Uranus

Neptune

Mercury      Moon      Pluto

**FIGURE 11.15** The larger moons of the jovian planets, with sizes (but not distances) shown to scale. Mercury, the Moon, and Pluto are included for comparison.

**FIGURE 11.16** A montage of the small moons of Saturn, shown to scale. The small moons of the other jovian planets also are probably not spherical. These photographs were taken by the Voyager spacecraft.

probably once were part of a larger captured asteroid that fragmented into several pieces.

Nearly all the medium-size and large moons follow the orbital patterns we expect from formation in "miniature solar nebulae": They have approximately circular orbits that lie close to the equatorial plane of their parent planet, and they orbit in the same direction in which their planet rotates. These moons are planetlike in almost all ways. They are approximately spherical, each has a solid surface with its own unique geology, and some possess atmospheres, hot interiors, and even magnetic fields. A few are planetlike in size as well. The two largest moons—Jupiter's moon Ganymede and Saturn's moon Titan—are larger than the planet Mercury. Four others are larger than Pluto: Jupiter's moons Io, Europa, and Callisto, and Neptune's moon Triton.

Nearly all jovian moons share an uncanny trait: They always keep the same face turned toward their planet, just as our Moon always shows the same face to Earth (see Figure 2.20). This *synchronous rotation* arose from the strong tidal forces [Section 5.5] exerted by the jovian planets, which caused each moon to end up with equal rotational and orbital periods regardless of how fast the moon rotated when it formed.

### Ice Geology

Prior to the Voyager missions, most scientists expected the jovian moons to be cold and geologically dead. After all, only two of the moons are even as large as Mercury, and Mercury has been geologically dead for a long time. Instead, Voyager provided many surprises, revealing worlds with spectacular past and present geological activity. We've since learned even more—about Jupiter's moons in particular—thanks primarily to data from the Galileo spacecraft.

How can moons have so much more geological activity than similar-size (or larger) planets? In a few cases, the answer involves unforeseen heat sources that we'll discuss shortly. But another important factor is the icy composition of most jovian moons. These moons accreted from solid particles that condensed in the "miniature solar nebulae" around the jovian planets. Because they were so far from the Sun, temperatures in these nebulae were quite cool and were rich with ice crystals of various hydrogen compounds (mostly water, but also small amounts of ammonia and methane). As a result, the jovian planet satellites contain much higher proportions of ice relative to rock than do the terrestrial planets. We even find distinctions among the jovian satellite systems: Jupiter's satellites have the highest proportion of rock, while the satellites of more distant planets contain higher proportions of the more volatile methane and ammonia ices.

We can understand why icy moons have more geological activity than similar-size rocky moons by investigating how ices compare to rocks in three geologically important properties: strength (or rigidity), radioactive content, and melting point. In terms of strength, the differences might be smaller than you would expect. Ice at a temperature of 100 K is almost as rigid as rock at a few hundred Kelvin. Nevertheless, the difference is great enough to cause ice mountains and ice cliffs on the jovian moons to sag and fade away more quickly than similar features made of rock on terrestrial planets. Most radioactive elements are found in rocks, not ices, so icy moons have relatively little internal heat generated by radioactive decay and hence lower internal temperatures. But ices also have much lower melting points than rocks, so the heat of accretion in many medium-size and large moons was enough to cause differentiation of their interiors. Thus, most of these moons have internal structures similar to those of the terrestrial planets but with an additional, icy layer on the outside. Despite the icy composition, no satellite surface is "clean as the driven snow"; the ices are "dirtied" by rocky and carbon-rich compounds. Each satellite has its own proportions of rock and ice. Some are cleaner, some are dirtier, and some are clean on one side and dirty on the other.

All in all, the *ice geology* of the jovian moons bears many similarities to the rock geology of the terrestrial planets [Section 9.4]. *Impact cratering,* occurring mostly during the time of the early bombardment more than 4 billion years ago, probably left all the satellites with battered surfaces. *Volcanism* is certainly present on some jovian moons, and *tectonics* seems likely as well. Both of these processes are driven by internal heat and hence take place more easily on icy moons than on rocky planets, because ice becomes deformable and melts at lower temperatures than rock. We know very little about *erosion* in the outer solar system, although we expect it to be relatively rare. Most satellites possess either no atmosphere or a very thin one, so in most cases wind or rain erosion is unlikely. Nevertheless, many of the jovian moons have interesting features that go beyond simple generalities. There are far too many moons to study all of them in depth here, but as we undertake our brief tour of the jovian moon systems, we will stop to investigate a few of the more intriguing moons in detail.

### The Galilean Satellites of Jupiter: Io, Europa, Ganymede, and Callisto

The first stops on our tour are the Galilean satellites of Jupiter—the four moons that Galileo saw through his telescope and that disproved the idea that all celestial bodies circle the Earth [Section 5.3]. These four moons are large enough that they would count as planets if they orbited the Sun. They bear the names of four mythological lovers of the Roman god Jupiter: Io, Europa, Ganymede, and Callisto. Their densities decrease with distance from Jupiter, just as the densities of the planets decrease with distance from the Sun, suggesting that similar condensation and accretion patterns occurred within the "miniature solar nebula" around Jupiter and in the solar nebula. Io, the innermost Galilean satellite, formed from rocky and metallic condensates with little or no icy condensates. Europa is mostly rocky, but it formed with enough ice to give it an icy outer shell. Ganymede and Callisto, the outermost Galilean moons, formed from a mix of icy and rocky condensates.

*Io* Just a few months before the Voyager spacecraft reached Jupiter, a group of scientists made the astonishing prediction that we would find active volcanism on Io. This prediction went against the common belief that only much larger bodies could have substantial geological activity. But the prediction proved correct.[4] Direct proof came from the discovery of towering volcanic plumes reaching hundreds of kilometers above the surface and spreading fallout over almost a million square kilometers of Io's surface (Figure 11.17a). The indirect proof was just as mind-boggling: the complete lack of impact craters on the surface—not a single one, to the resolution of Voyager's cameras. Io's eruptions have buried *all* its impact craters.

Despite Io's unusual colors and frost-covered surface, planetary scientists found volcanic eruptions remarkably similar to those of basalt volcanoes on Earth (Figure 11.17b). When the flowing lava comes in contact with frost, the resulting "steam" jets off at high speed to make the plume. The process is similar to lava flowing into the ocean on Earth, but Io's relative lack of atmosphere and low gravity let the plumes reach great altitude (Figure 11.17c). Not all of Io's volcanoes erupt so violently. Lava flows out of some vents, and sulfur gas expelled from the volcano coats the surface in red patches (Figure 11.17d). Some of the higher mountains were probably built by basaltic lava flows similar to those of terrestrial volcanoes (Figure 11.17e). Many of Io's volcanic vents glow red-hot (Figure 11.17f). Tectonic processes are probably also active on Io, but evidence for them

is covered by the frequent lava flows and plume deposits everywhere on Io's surface. Galileo and Voyager images showed that fallout from volcanic plumes can cover an area the size of Arizona in a matter of months (Figure 11.17g).

Io's volcanoes also produce a very thin sulfur-dioxide atmosphere about a billion times less dense than our own atmosphere. It is too thin to cause erosion, and Io's weak gravity allows a steady escape of the atmospheric gases. These volcanic gases supply the plasma in the Io torus (see Figure 11.13) and in Jupiter's magnetosphere.

Why is Io so geologically active? After all, it is about the size of our own geologically dead Moon, and it is not as icy in composition as most other jovian satellites. Io must have an additional internal heat source besides the usual combination of accretion, differentiation, and radioactivity that heats the interiors of the terrestrial worlds [Section 9.3]. This fourth internal heat source is **tidal heating**, and its theory was the basis for the pre-Voyager prediction of volcanic activity on Io.

How does tidal heating work? Tidal forces lock Io in synchronous rotation so that it keeps the same face toward Jupiter. But Io's orbit is slightly elliptical, so its orbital speed and distance from Jupiter vary. As a result, the strength and even the direction of the tidal force change very slightly over its orbit: Io is continuously flexed by Jupiter (Figure 11.18a). The flexing of Io's rocky crust and interior releases heat, just as flexing warms Silly Putty. In fact, Io's tidal heating releases more than 200 times more heat (per gram of mass) than the radioactive heat driving Earth's geology, which explains why Io is the most volcanically active body in the solar system.

But why is Io's orbit slightly elliptical, when almost all other large satellites' orbits are virtually circular? Io's neighbors are responsible: Gravitational nudges between Io, Europa, and Ganymede maintain **orbital resonances** between them (Figure 11.18b). During the time in which Ganymede completes one orbit of Jupiter, Europa completes exactly two orbits and Io completes exactly four orbits. The satellites therefore line up periodically, and the gravitational tugs these satellites exert on one another add up over time. The satellites are always tugged in exactly the same direction, and the satellite orbits become very slightly elliptical as a result. (If the satellites didn't line up periodically, the tugs would be exerted in random directions at random times—as ineffective as pushing a child on a swing at random times.) The resulting tidal forces are strongest on Io because it is closest to Jupiter, but they are also important on Europa and Ganymede.

---

[4]The heroes of this extraordinary discovery are theoreticians Pat Cassen, Stan Peale, and Ray Reynolds, and Linda Morabito, the Voyager navigation engineer who first spotted the plumes in calibration images.

**a** Most of the black, brown, and red spots are recently active volcanic features. The white and yellow areas are sulfur and sulfur-dioxide deposits from volcanic gases. Colors in this Galileo image are slightly enhanced.

**b** Galileo close-up of eruptions reveals intensely hot lava, probably similar in composition to basalt volcanoes on Earth.

**c** When basaltic lava flows over sulfur-dioxide ice, the explosive sublimation creates huge plumes. This plume rises 80 km high.

**FIGURE 11.17** Io is the most volcanically active body in the solar system.

*Europa* Europa's bizarre, fractured crust is proof enough that tidal heating has taken hold there (Figure 11.19a). The icy surface is nearly devoid of impact craters and may be only a few million years old. Jumbled icebergs (Figure 11.19b) suggest that an ocean of liquid water lies just a few kilometers below the surface, extending down to perhaps 100 km deep. The icy shell overlying the ocean is repeatedly flexed by tidal forces, resulting in a global network of cracks. Close-up images of the cracks taken by the Galileo orbiter show that most have a remarkable double-ridged pattern, perhaps the result of debris piling up around a crack that is repeatedly opened and closed by tidal flexing (Figure 11.19c,d). On Earth, changing winds form similar double ridges in

**d** The reddish color surrounding this volcano comes from sulfur gas expelled from the lava.

**e** This photo shows a shield volcano on Io that may be made of basaltic lava.

**g** This enhanced-color photo shows fallout (dark patch) from a volcanic plume on Io. The fallout region covers an area the size of Arizona. (The orange ring is the fallout from another volcano.)

sea ice in the Arctic Ocean, though on much smaller scales. (We do not expect winds on Europa, although it does have a very thin atmosphere created by magnetospheric bombardment.)

In some ways, Europa resembles a rocky terrestrial planet wrapped in an icy crust. (Some scientists suggest that the icy shell has not always rotated at exactly the same rate at the rocky center, leading to even greater cracking of the crust.) The rocky object that makes up most of Europa is undoubtedly geologically active below the layer of ocean and ice. Perhaps basaltic lavas erupt on Europa's seafloors, sometimes violently enough to jumble up the icy crust above (Figure 11.20). And, just possibly, tidal heating makes Europa's oceans as hospitable for life as our own oceans [Section 13.6].

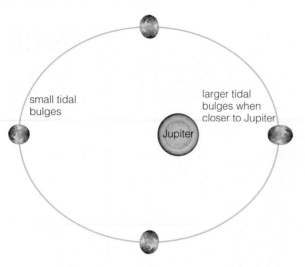

small tidal bulges

larger tidal bulges when closer to Jupiter

Jupiter

**a** Because Io's orbit is slightly elliptical, the strength and direction of Io's tidal bulges change. The bulges and orbital eccentricity are exaggerated.

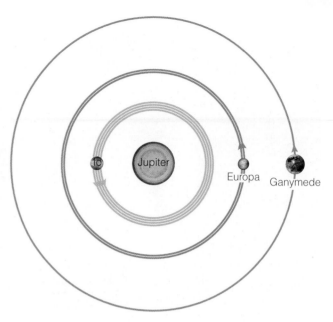

Io

Jupiter

Europa

Ganymede

**b** About every seven Earth days (one Ganymede orbit, two Europa orbits, and four Io orbits), the three moons line up as shown. The small gravitational tugs repeat and make all three orbits slightly elliptical.

**FIGURE 11.18** Orbital resonances cause tidal heating on Io, Europa, and Ganymede.

---

**a** Europa's icy crust is criss-crossed with cracks.

**b** Some regions show jumbled crust with icebergs, apparently frozen in slush.

Tidal flexing closes crack, grinds up ice.

Ridge builds up a little each time the crack opens and closes.

Tidal flexing opens crack. Debris in middle falls into crack.

**c** Close-up photos show that surface cracks have a double-ridged pattern.

**FIGURE 11.19** Europa is one of the most intriguing moons in the solar system.

**d** A possible mechanism for making the double-ridged surface cracks.

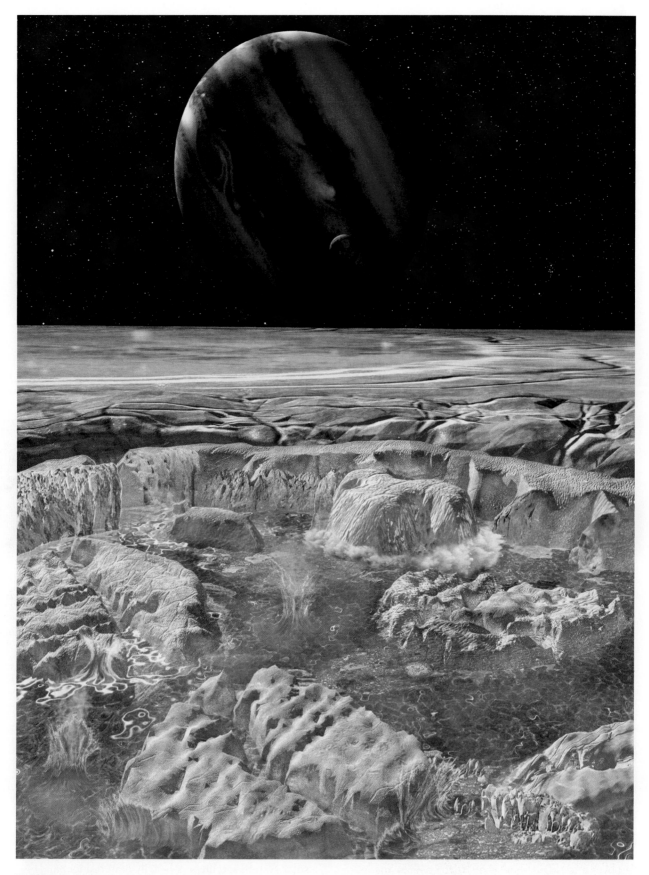

**FIGURE 11.20** Tidal heating may give Europa a subsurface ocean beneath its icy crust. This artist's conception imagines a region where the crust has been disrupted by an undersea volcano.

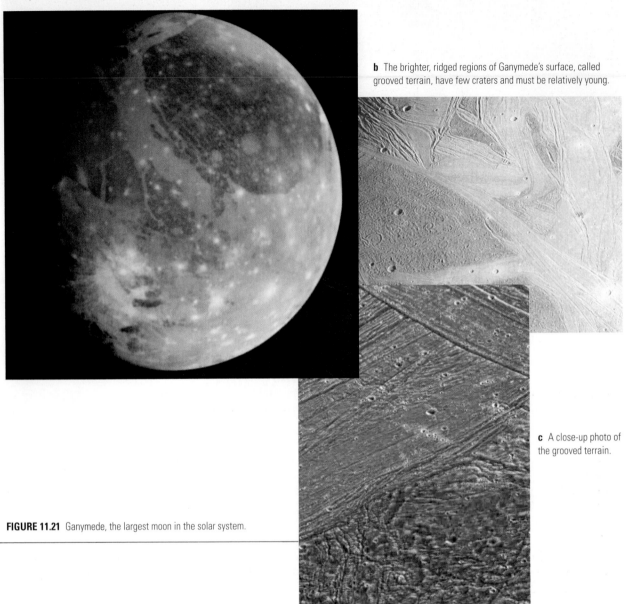

**a** Ganymede's numerous craters (bright spots) show that its surface is older than Europa's.

**b** The brighter, ridged regions of Ganymede's surface, called grooved terrain, have few craters and must be relatively young.

**c** A close-up photo of the grooved terrain.

**FIGURE 11.21** Ganymede, the largest moon in the solar system.

*Ganymede* Photographs of Ganymede tell the story of an interesting geological history. Parts of the surface have many impact craters, indicating that these regions are billions of years old (Figure 11.21a). But other areas show unusual "grooved terrain" unlike anything we've seen in terrestrial geology (Figure 11.21b,c). The grooves may form either from tectonic stresses or from water erupting along a crack in the surface; because ice expands when it solidifies (unlike rock), the grooves may form as the surface refreezes. A freezing surface patch on Ganymede therefore pushes outward, perhaps creating the grooves and ridges seen on its surface. Ganymede also shows some evidence of tectonics similar to plate tectonics on Earth: Some chunks of the surface appear to have shifted relative to one another. Ero-

sion is unimportant on Ganymede, because it has just a hint of an atmosphere generated by bombardment. The precise nature of Ganymede's internal heating remains mysterious, although it certainly is some combination of tidal heating and radioactive decay. Surprisingly, Ganymede has its own magnetic field—perhaps indicating a molten, convecting core. It may even harbor a liquid-water layer below the ice, but evidence for such an ocean is still quite tentative.

*Callisto* The outermost Galilean satellite, Callisto, looks most like what scientists first expected for outer solar system satellites: a heavily cratered iceball (Figure 11.22a). The bright patches on its surface are the result of cratering: Large impactors dug up cleaner ice from deep down and spread it over the surface. The odd rings in the upper left of Callisto's image

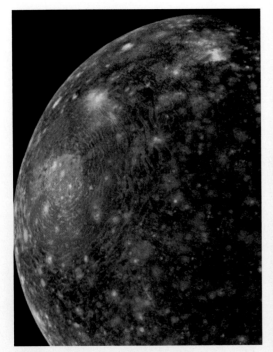

a Heavy cratering indicates an ancient surface.

b Close-up photos show a dark powder overlying the low areas of the surface.

**FIGURE 11.22** Callisto shows no evidence of volcanic or tectonic activity.

also came from impacts: The largest impactors shattered the icy sphere in a way that produced concentric rings around the impact site.

Despite its relatively large size (the third-largest moon in the solar system), Callisto lacks volcanic and tectonic features. Internal heat sources must be very small. In fact, gravity measurements by the Galileo spacecraft show that Callisto never underwent differentiation: Dense rock and lighter ice are still thoroughly mixed throughout. Callisto has no tidal heating because it shares no orbital resonances with other satellites. Nonetheless, Callisto appears to have a magnetic field, which could be generated in a salty ocean below the ice. The surface also holds some surprises. Close-up images show the surface to be covered by a dark, powdery substance concentrated in low-lying areas, leaving ridges and crests bright white (Figure 11.22b). No one knows the nature of this material or how it got there.

### Titan and the Medium-Size Moons of Saturn

Leaving Jupiter's moons behind, our satellite tour takes us next to Saturn. Here we find an amazing moon shrouded in a thick atmosphere: Titan. It is Saturn's only large moon and is the second-largest moon in the solar system after Ganymede.

Titan's hazy and cloudy atmosphere hides its surface (Figure 11.23a). The atmosphere is about 90% nitrogen, making it the only world besides Earth where nitrogen is the dominant atmospheric constituent. However, on Earth the rest of the atmosphere is mostly oxygen, while the rest of Titan's atmosphere consists of argon, methane, and other hydrogen compounds, including ethane ($C_2H_6$). Thus, we could not breathe the air on Titan and live. The methane and ethane actually give Titan an appreciable greenhouse effect, but the surface temperature is still a frigid 93 K ($-180°C$). The surface pressure on Titan is only somewhat higher than that on Earth—about 1.5 bars at the surface, which would be fairly comfortable if not for the lack of oxygen and the cold temperatures.

How did Titan end up with such an unusual atmosphere? Titan is composed mostly of ices, including methane and ammonia ice. Some of this ice sublimed long ago to form an atmosphere on Titan. Over billions of years, solar ultraviolet light broke apart the ammonia molecules ($NH_3$) into hydrogen and nitrogen. The light hydrogen escaped from the atmosphere (through thermal escape [Section 10.5]), but the heavier nitrogen molecules remained and accumulated.

We encounter a particularly intriguing idea when we examine what happened to the methane gas that sublimed into Titan's atmosphere long ago. Methane

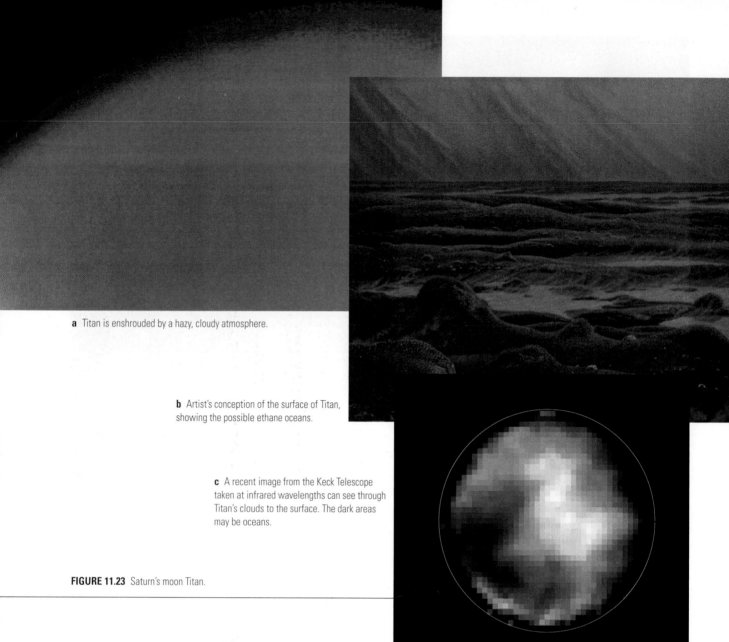

**a** Titan is enshrouded by a hazy, cloudy atmosphere.

**b** Artist's conception of the surface of Titan, showing the possible ethane oceans.

**c** A recent image from the Keck Telescope taken at infrared wavelengths can see through Titan's clouds to the surface. The dark areas may be oceans.

**FIGURE 11.23** Saturn's moon Titan.

is no longer present in large quantities, so some process must have removed it from the atmosphere. The most likely process is chemical reactions, triggered by solar ultraviolet light, that transform methane into ethane. If this idea is correct, atmospheric ethane may form clouds and rain on Titan, perhaps creating oceans of liquid ethane on the surface (Figure 11.23b). According to some calculations, Titan may have produced enough ethane over its history to create ethane oceans a kilometer deep. Recent infrared pictures (Figure 11.23c) have probed through the clouds to the surface, but we cannot yet determine whether such oceans really exist.

Because we cannot see its surface clearly, we do not know whether Titan is geologically active. However, given its relatively large size and icy composition, it seems likely that Titan has a rich geological history. Our understanding of Titan should improve dramatically when the Cassini spacecraft reaches Saturn in 2004 [Section 7.6]. In addition to cameras and spectrographs, Cassini carries a radar mapper similar to the Magellan radar that mapped the surface of Venus [Section 9.5]. Thus, we will see the surface of Titan at high resolution and at last will learn about its geology—and determine whether ethane oceans (or even lakes) exist. *Cassini* will also drop a probe (named *Huygens*, for a seventeenth-century pioneer in astronomy and optics) into Titan's atmosphere that will take pictures and measure atmospheric properties on the way down. Just in case, the probe is designed to float in liquid ethane.

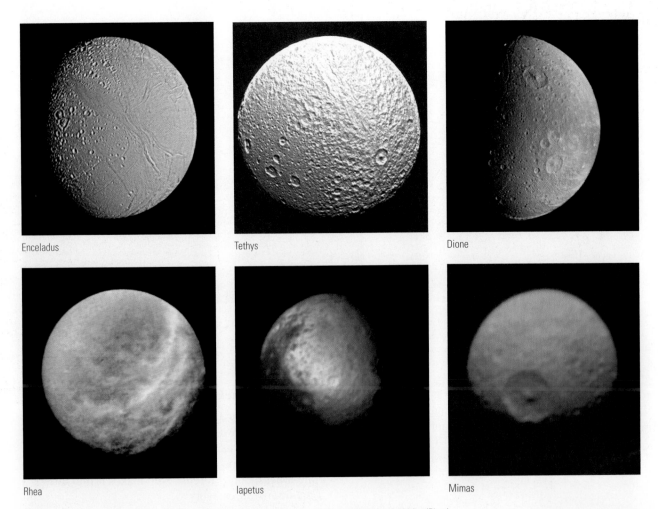

Enceladus

Tethys

Dione

Rhea

Iapetus

Mimas

**FIGURE 11.24** Saturn's six medium-size moons, which range in diameter from 390 km (Mimas) to 1,530 km (Rhea). All but Mimas show some evidence of volcanism and/or tectonics.

**TIME OUT TO THINK** *Based on your understanding of the four geological processes on icy satellites, what kind of surface features do you think might be present on Titan?*

Given that Titan and Ganymede are similar in both size and composition, it's natural to wonder why Titan has so much atmosphere and Ganymede has so little. One possibility is that cooler temperatures in the solar nebula at Saturn's greater distance from the Sun allowed more methane and ammonia ice to condense. These ices are more volatile than the water ice that makes up Jupiter's satellites and hence are more likely to sublime and form an atmosphere. Alternatively, atmospheric cratering [Section 10.5] may have stripped away Ganymede's atmosphere but not Titan's. Atmospheric cratering was probably more important on Ganymede than on Titan because Jupiter's stronger gravity accelerates impactors to higher speeds. No one yet knows which of these two processes—condensation in the solar nebula or atmospheric cratering—bears more responsibility for the differences between Ganymede and Titan.

Saturn's medium-size moons (Rhea, Iapetus, Dione, Tethys, Enceladus, and Mimas) show evidence of substantial geological activity (Figure 11.24). While all show some cratered surfaces, Enceladus has grooved terrain similar to Ganymede's, and the others show evidence of flows of "ice lava." But these satellites are considerably smaller than Ganymede: Enceladus is barely 500 kilometers across—small enough to fit inside the borders of Colorado. How can such small moons support so much geological activity? The answer probably lies with "ice geology," in which icy combinations of water, ammonia, and methane can melt, deform, and flow at remarkably low temperatures. Thus, even small objects with relatively little internal heat can sustain fascinating geological activity. Iapetus is particularly bizarre, with some regions distinctly bright and others distinctly dark. The dark regions appear to be covered by a thin veneer of dark material, but we still don't know what it is or how it got there.

Mimas (radius = 195 km), the smallest of the "medium-size" moons of Saturn, is essentially a heav-

**FIGURE 11.25** The surface of Miranda shows astonishing tectonic activity despite its small size. The cliff walls seen in the inset are higher than those of the Grand Canyon on Earth.

ily cratered iceball. One huge crater is sometimes called "Darth Crater" because of Mimas's resemblance to the Death Star in the *Star Wars* movies. (The official name of the crater is Herschel.) The impact that created this crater probably came close to breaking Mimas apart.

### The Medium-Size Moons of Uranus

Uranus is orbited by 5 medium-size moons (see Figure 11.15) and 10 smaller moons discovered by Voyager. Astronomers have recently discovered 6 more moons, including several that orbit the planet backward.

The medium-size moons pose several puzzles. For example, Ariel and Umbriel are virtual twins in size, yet Ariel shows evidence of volcanism and tectonics, while the heavily cratered surface of Umbriel suggests a lack of geological activity. Titania and Oberon also are twins in size, but Titania appears to have had much more geological activity than Oberon. No one knows why these two pairs of similar-size moons should vary so greatly in geological activity.

Miranda, the smallest of Uranus's medium-size moons (radius = 235 km), is the most surprising (Figure 11.25). Prior to the Voyager flyby, scientists expected Miranda to be a cratered iceball like Saturn's similar-size moon Mimas (see Figure 11.24). Instead, Voyager images of Miranda show tremendous tectonic features and relatively few craters. Why should Miranda be so much more geologically active than Mimas? Our best guess is an episode of tidal heating from a temporary orbital resonance with another satellite of Uranus billions of years ago. Evidently, Mimas never underwent a similar period of tidal heating.

### Triton, the Backward Moon of Neptune

Last stop on our satellite tour is Neptune, so distant that only two of its moons (Triton and Nereid) were known to exist before the Voyager visit. Triton is the only large moon in the Neptune system, and only one other moon (Proteus) even makes it into our "medium-size" category.

Triton may appear to be a typical satellite, but it is not. Its orbit is retrograde (it travels in a direction opposite to Neptune's rotation) and highly inclined to Neptune's equator. These are telltale signs of a captured satellite. But Triton is not small and potato-shaped like most captured asteroids. Instead it is large, spherical, and icy. In fact, it is larger than the planet Pluto. As such, Triton presents many challenges to our understanding of satellite capture. Nonetheless, it is almost certain that Triton once orbited the Sun instead of orbiting Neptune.

A quick study of the Triton photos in Figure 11.26 reveals a surface unlike any other in the solar system, and one that poses many unanswered questions. Are the flat surfaces like the lunar maria? Are the wrinkly ridges (nicknamed "cantaloupe terrain") tectonic in nature? Are the bright polar caps similar to those on Mars? Why is Triton's surface composition (a mixture of ices of nitrogen, methane, carbon dioxide, and carbon monoxide) unlike that of any other satellite? Clearly, Triton is more than a cratered iceball. The undisturbed craters suggest that major geological activity has subsided, but Triton appears to have undergone some sort of icy volcanism in the past. Such geological activity is astonishing in light of Triton's extremely low (40 K) surface temperature,

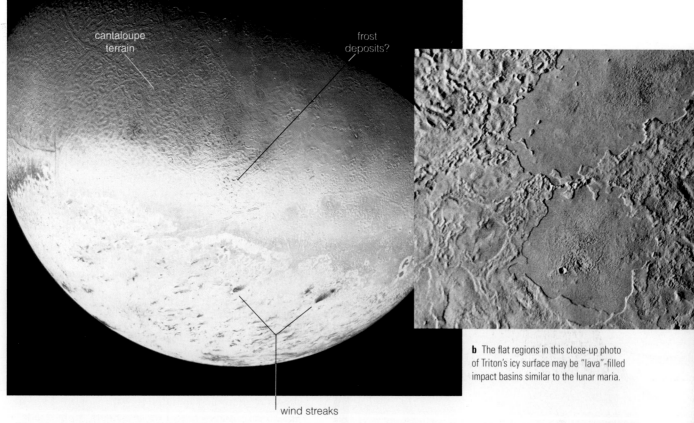

cantaloupe terrain

frost deposits?

wind streaks

**a** Triton's southern hemisphere as seen by *Voyager 2*.

**b** The flat regions in this close-up photo of Triton's icy surface may be "lava"-filled impact basins similar to the lunar maria.

**FIGURE 11.26** Neptune's moon Triton.

but it probably involved low-melting-point mixtures of water, methane, and ammonia ices. The internal heating source for Triton's geological activity is not known, but it may have involved tidal heating. Triton probably had a very elliptical orbit and a more rapid rotation when it was first captured by Neptune, but tidal forces would have circularized its orbit, slowed it to synchronous rotation, and possibly heated its interior enough to cause geological activity.

To cap off Triton's odd geology, the sublimation of surface ices creates a thin atmosphere. Thin as it is, the atmosphere creates wind streaks on the surface, and unknown processes pump unusual plumes of gas and particles into the atmosphere. The combination of Triton's large orbital inclination and the substantial tilt of Neptune's rotation axis leads to extreme seasonal swings, and polar caps probably grow, shrink, and migrate from pole to pole. All of this takes place on a satellite that, because of its high albedo, is even colder than Pluto. In fact, Triton is the coldest of all the planets and satellites in the solar system.

If Triton really is a captured satellite, where did it come from? Could other objects like it still be orbiting the Sun? Intriguingly, we know of at least one object that appears to be quite similar to Triton: the planet Pluto. But that's a story to be discussed in the next chapter.

### Satellite Summary: The Active Outer Solar System

Our brief tour has taken us to most of the medium-size and large moons in the solar system. The major lesson of the tour is that icy-satellite geology is harder to predict than terrestrial-planet geology. Size isn't everything when it comes to geological activity. Ices form lavas more easily than rocks, so icy worlds can have more geological activity than a rocky world of the same size. Satellites made of ices that include methane and ammonia may have even greater potential geological activity. In addition, we saw how tidal heating can supply added heat even when other internal heat sources are no longer important, as is the case on Io and Europa and as occurs to lesser extents on Ganymede, Triton, and possibly Miranda.

Satellite atmospheres also revealed surprises. We found examples of all three atmospheric sources (outgassing, sublimation, and bombardment [Section 10.5]). Io's atmosphere comes from volcanic outgassing, while Europa's and Ganymede's atmospheres are attributed to bombardment. Titan's thick atmosphere probably came from sublimation, followed by extensive chemistry aided by solar ultraviolet light. Sublimation is also responsible for Triton's thin atmosphere, even out at the frigid edges of our solar system. The jovian planet satellites are far more interesting and instructive than anyone could have imagined before the Voyager and Galileo expeditions.

## 11.6 Jovian Planet Rings

We have completed our comparative study of the jovian planets themselves and of their major moons, but we have one more topic left to cover: their amazing rings. Saturn's rings have dazzled and puzzled astronomers since Galileo first saw them through his small telescope and suggested that they resembled "ears" on Saturn. For a long time, Saturn's rings were thought to be unique in the solar system, but we now know that all four jovian planets have rings. As we did for the planets themselves, we'll look at one ring system in detail and then examine the others for important similarities and differences. Saturn's rings are the clear choice as the standard for comparison.

### Saturn's Rings

You can see Saturn's rings through a backyard telescope, but learning about their nature requires higher resolution. Even through large telescopes on Earth, the rings appear to be continuous, concentric sheets of material separated by gaps (Figure 11.27a). Spacecraft images reveal these "sheets" to be made of many more individual rings, each broken up into even smaller concentric *ringlets,* and different regions of a ring to range from transparent to opaque (Figure 11.27b). But even these appearances are somewhat deceiving. If we could wander into the rings, we'd see that they are made of countless individual particles orbiting Saturn together, each obeying Kepler's laws and occasionally colliding with nearby particles (Figure 11.27c). The particles range in size from large boulders to dust grains—far too small to be photographed, even when spacecraft like *Voyager* or *Cassini* pass nearby.

Spectroscopy reveals that Saturn's ring particles are made of relatively reflective (high-albedo) water ice. The rings look bright where there are enough particles to intercept most of the Sun's light and scatter it back toward us, and they appear more transparent where there are fewer particles. In regions where light cannot easily pass through, neither can another ring particle. In the densest parts of the rings, each particle collides with another every few hours.

**TIME OUT TO THINK** *Which ring particles travel faster, those at the inner edge of Saturn's rings or those at the outer edge? (Hint: Think about Kepler's third law.) Can you think of a way to confirm your answer with telescopic observations?*

Saturn's rings lie in a thin plane directly above the planet's bulging equator, so they share Saturn's 27° axis tilt. Over the course of Saturn's year, the rings present a changing appearance to the Earth and Sun, appearing wide open at Saturn's solstices and edge-on at its equinoxes. The rings are perhaps the thin-

a  Earth-based telescopic view of Saturn.

b  Voyager image of Saturn's rings against the disk.

c  Artist's conception of particles in a ring system. All the particles are moving slowly relative to one another and occasionally collide.

**FIGURE 11.27**  Looking closer at Saturn's rings.

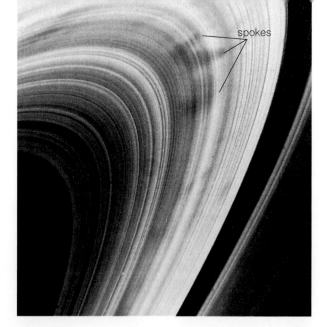

**FIGURE 11.28** The dark patches in Saturn's rings are called spokes.

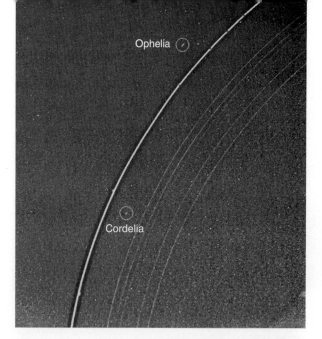

**FIGURE 11.29** Voyager's best photograph of shepherd moons came during the *Voyager 2* Uranus flyby. Two satellites shepherd one of Uranus's rings. The satellite images are smeared out by their motion during the exposure.

nest known astronomical structure: They are over 270,000 kilometers across but only a few tens of *meters* thick. Collisions help keep the rings thin. You can see why by imagining adding a new ring particle with an orbit tilted relative to the other particles. (The existence of many particles on tilted orbits would make the ring thicker.) The new particle would collide with other particles each time its orbit intersected the ring plane, and its orbital tilt would be reduced with every collision. It wouldn't be long before these collisions would force the particle to conform to the orbital pattern of the other particles. Similarly, a new ring particle with a highly elliptical orbit would soon end up with a circular orbit.

Where do the rings come from? An important clue is that the rings lie close to the planet in a region where tidal forces are very influential. Within two to three planetary radii (of any planet), the tidal forces tugging an object apart become comparable to the gravitational forces holding it together. This region is called the **Roche tidal zone**. Only relatively small objects held together by nongravitational forces (such as the electrostatic forces that hold solid rock—or spacecraft or human beings—together) can survive within the Roche tidal zone. Thus, there are two basic scenarios for the origin of the rings. One possibility is that a wandering moon strayed too close to Saturn and was torn apart. A more likely scenario is that tidal forces prevented the material in Saturn's rings from accreting into a single large moon, instead forming many smaller moons.

Among the many mysteries of Saturn's rings are unusual dusty patches, called *spokes,* that can appear and change dramatically in a matter of hours (Figure 11.28). They are probably particles of microscopic dust that have been levitated out of the ring plane by forces associated with Saturn's magnetic field.

### Rings and Gaps

By the time the Voyager spacecraft approached Saturn, astronomers knew of at least six distinct rings around Saturn. Voyager scientists had hoped to find reasons for the six rings, but instead they found that the total number of individual rings and gaps may be as high as 100,000. Theorists are still struggling to explain all the rings and gaps, but some general ideas are now clear.

Rings and gaps are caused by particles bunching up at some orbital distances and being forced out at others. This bunching happens when gravity nudges the orbits of ring particles in some particular way. One source of nudging is tiny moons—called *gap moons*—located within the rings themselves. The gravity of a gap moon tugs gently on nearby particles, effectively nudging them farther away to other orbits.[5] This clears a gap in the rings around the moon's orbit. Voyager spacecraft photographed a few gap moons, and there may be thousands more that are too small to see in the Voyager images. In some cases, Voyager images show two gap moons forcing particles trapped between them into line; the best such example comes from Uranus (Figure 11.29), but we find similar examples in Saturn's ring system. The gap moons are said to act as *shepherd moons* in such cases, because they shepherd the ring particles.

---

[5]It may seem counterintuitive that a gap moon's gravitational attraction should nudge a ring particle *farther away,* but theoretical models show that this happens as a result of the combined gravitational interactions between the gap moon, the ring particles, and the planet.

Cassini division

**a** The largest gap in Saturn's rings, called the Cassini division, is caused by an orbital resonance with the moon Mimas.

**b** Another Mimas resonance creates remarkable ripples in Saturn's rings. The dark spots in the image are calibration marks for the camera.

**FIGURE 11.30** Gaps in Saturn's rings.

In some cases, ring particles orbiting Saturn may also be nudged by the gravity from Saturn's larger and more distant moons. For example, a ring particle orbiting about 120,000 km from Saturn's center will circle the planet in exactly half the time it takes the moon Mimas to orbit. Every time Mimas returns to a certain location, the ring particle will also return to its original location and will experience the same gravitational nudge from Mimas. The nudges reinforce one another and eventually clear a gap in the rings (Figure 11.30a). This "Mimas 2:1 resonance" is essentially the same type of *orbital resonance* that affects the orbits of Io, Europa, and Ganymede. It is responsible for a large gap in Saturn's rings that is easily visible from Earth (called the *Cassini division*). Many similar resonances are responsible for other gaps, and resonances can even create beautiful ripples within the rings (Figure 11.30b).

Although we now know three causes of rings and gaps—gap moons, shepherd moons, and orbital resonances—we have not yet identified specific causes for the vast majority of the features within Saturn's rings. Perhaps the Cassini spacecraft will identify more gap moons and shepherd moons, or perhaps it will reveal even more puzzling structures.

### Comparing Planetary Rings

The ring systems of Jupiter, Uranus, and Neptune are so much fainter than Saturn's ring system that it took almost four centuries longer to discover them. Ring particles in these three systems are far less numerous, generally smaller, and much darker. Saturn's rings were the only ones known until 1977, when the rings of Uranus were discovered during observations of a *stellar occultation*—a star passing

behind Uranus as seen from the Earth. During the occultation, the star "blinked" on and off nine times before it disappeared behind Uranus, and nine more times as it emerged. Scientists concluded that these nine "blinks" were caused by nine thin rings encircling Uranus. Similar observations of stars passing behind Neptune gave more confounding results: Rings appeared to be present some of the time, but not at other times. Could Neptune's rings be incomplete or transient?

The Voyager spacecraft provided some answers. Voyager cameras first discovered thin rings around Jupiter in 1979. Then, after providing incredible images of Saturn's rings, *Voyager* 2 confirmed the existence of rings around Uranus as it flew past in 1986. In 1989, *Voyager* 2 passed by Neptune and found that it does, in fact, have partial rings—at least when seen from Earth. The space between the ring segments is filled with dust not detectable from Earth.

How do Voyager images distinguish between boulders and dust? The secret is to look at how the ring particles scatter light (Figure 11.31a). Tiny particles like dust are not much bigger than the wavelengths of visible light, so they scatter sunlight only by very small angles from its original direction. Thus, rings that scatter light mostly forward must be made of tiny dust-size particles. Dust on your windshield scatters light in the same way, which is why it's so hard to see the road when you're driving into the Sun. Larger particles—marble- or boulder-size— mostly reflect light back toward the Sun. Thus, the Voyager spacecraft saw mostly the larger particles on their way toward each planet and saw mostly dust-size particles when they looked back toward the Sun after passing each planet (Figure 11.31b). In fact,

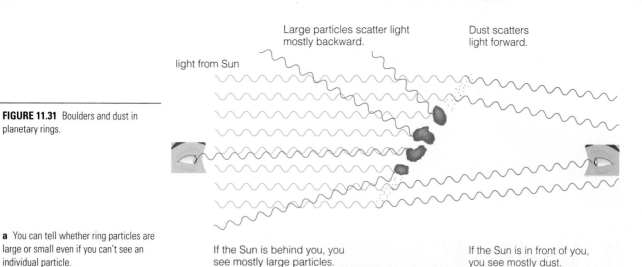

*Large particles scatter light mostly backward.*

*Dust scatters light forward.*

light from Sun

**FIGURE 11.31** Boulders and dust in planetary rings.

**a** You can tell whether ring particles are large or small even if you can't see an individual particle.

If the Sun is behind you, you see mostly large particles.

If the Sun is in front of you, you see mostly dust.

*Voyager 2* detected vast dust sheets between the widely separated rings of Uranus and Neptune.

**TIME OUT TO THINK** *Turn on a flashlight or projector in a dark room. Set it down and walk a few steps away from it. Explain why you see so much airborne dust when you look back toward the projector but not when you look forward in the direction of the beam. How is this phenomenon similar to the scattering of light by ring particles?* (Note: *You can see this effect particularly well if you look back toward the projector in a movie theater.*)

A family portrait of the jovian ring systems shows many similarities (Figure 11.32). All rings lie in their planet's equatorial plane within the Roche tidal zone. Particle orbits are fairly circular, with small orbital tilts relative to the equator. Gaps and ringlets are probably due to gap moons, shepherd moons, and orbital resonances. The differences also offer important insights: The larger size, higher reflectivity, and much greater number of particles in Saturn's rings compel us to wonder if different processes are at work there. The newly discovered rings brought challenges as well. The reasons for the slight tilt and eccentricity of Uranus's thin rings and the arcs within Neptune's rings are not yet understood.

### Origin of the Rings

Where do rings come from? How old are they? Did they form with their planet out of the nebula, or are they a more recent phenomenon? These questions long puzzled astronomers when they had only one case (Saturn) to study, but the discovery that all jovian planets have rings has made the answers clearer.

Part of the answer lies in determining how long rings will last. Unlike planets and large satellites, ring particles may not last very long. Ring particles orbiting Saturn bump into one another every few hours, and even with low-velocity collisions the particles are chipped away over time. Basketball-size ring particles

**b** The rings of Uranus seen before the spacecraft arrived (top; Sun behind the spacecraft) and after it passed by (bottom; looking back toward the Sun). Only the larger particles that scatter light back toward the Sun are visible in the top image. Abundant dust particles become visible looking back toward the Sun (bottom).

around Saturn are ground away to dust in a few million years. Other processes dismantle rings around the other jovian planets. The thermosphere of Uranus extends into its Roche tidal zone, so atmospheric drag slowly causes ring particles to spiral into the planet. Dust orbiting Jupiter is slightly slowed by the flood of solar photons passing by, and the particles we now see in Jupiter's ring will fall into the planet in only a few million years. In summary, particles in the four ring systems cannot last as long as the 4.6-billion-year age of our solar system.

If ring particles are rapidly disappearing, some source of new particles must keep the rings supplied. The most likely source is collisions. As ring particles are ground away by collisions, small moons (perhaps the gap moons) occasionally collide and create more ring particles. Meteorites may also strike these moons, with the impacts releasing even more ring particles. We now believe that the "miniature solar nebulae" that surrounded the jovian planets formed many

Jupiter

Saturn

Uranus

Neptune

**FIGURE 11.32** Four ring systems. The planets are not shown to scale. Uranus's rings were photographed by the Hubble Space Telescope, the others by Voyager. The Neptune frame is made of two images taken on either side of the bright planet.

small satellites and that the gradual dismantling of these satellites creates the dramatic ring systems we see today. The appearance of any particular ring system probably changes dramatically over millions and billions of years. The spectacle of Saturn's brilliant rings may be a special treat of our epoch, one that could not have been seen a billion years ago and that may not last long on the time scale of our solar system.

## THE BIG PICTURE

In this chapter, we saw that the jovian planets really are a "different kind of planet"—and, indeed, a different kind of planetary system. The jovian planets dwarf the terrestrial planets, and some of their moons are as large as terrestrial worlds. As you continue your study of the solar system, keep the following "big picture" ideas in mind:

- The jovian planets may lack solid surfaces on which geology can work, but they are interesting and dynamic worlds with rapid winds, huge storms, strong magnetic fields, and interiors in which common materials behave in unfamiliar ways.

- Despite their relatively small sizes and frigid temperatures, many jovian satellites are geologically active by virtue of their icy compositions. Ironically, it was cold temperatures in the solar nebula that led to icy compositions and hence geological activity.

- Ring systems owe their existence to small satellites formed from the "miniature solar nebulae" that produced the jovian planets billions of years ago. The rings we see today are composed of particles liberated from those satellites surprisingly recently.

- Understanding the jovian planets forced us to modify many of our earlier ideas about the solar system, in particular by adding the concepts of ice geology, tidal heating, and orbital resonances. Each new set of circumstances offers further opportunities to learn how the universe works.

## Review Questions

1. Briefly describe the past and present space exploration of the jovian worlds. Summarize what we've learned about the jovian planets in terms of composition, rotation rate, and shape.

2. Describe the interior structure of Jupiter. Contrast Jupiter's interior structure with the structures of the other jovian planets. Why is Jupiter denser than Saturn? Why is Neptune denser than Saturn?

3. How do we think Jupiter generates its internal heat? How do other jovian planets generate internal heat?

4. Describe the composition and temperature structure of Jupiter's atmosphere and contrast it with Earth's. Compare the temperature structures of the other jovian planets to that of Jupiter.

5. Why does Jupiter have several distinct layers of clouds?

6. How are the circulation cells on Jupiter similar to and different from those on Earth? What are *belts* and *zones*?

7. What is the *Great Red Spot*? Is it the same type of storm as a hurricane on Earth? Explain.

8. Describe the possible origins of Jupiter's vibrant colors. Contrast these with the origins of the colors of the other jovian planets.

9. Does Jupiter have seasons? Why or why not? Do other jovian planets have seasons? Explain.

10. Why does Jupiter have auroras? Contrast Jupiter's magnetosphere with those of the Earth and the other jovian planets.

11. What is the Io torus? Why doesn't Saturn, Uranus, or Neptune have a similar "torus"?

12. Briefly describe some of the general characteristics of the jovian moons.

13. How is the ice geology of the jovian moons similar to the rock geology of the terrestrial planets? How is it different?

14. Describe the volcanoes of Io and the mechanism of *tidal heating* that generates Io's internal heat.

15. What are *orbital resonances*? Explain how the resonance between Io, Europa, and Ganymede makes their orbits slightly elliptical.

16. Describe the evidence suggesting that Europa may have a subsurface ocean of liquid water.

17. Describe the general surface characteristics of Ganymede and Callisto. What do these characteristics tell us about internal heating on these worlds?

18. Describe the atmosphere of Titan. What evidence suggests that Titan may have oceans of liquid ethane?

19. Describe a few general features of Saturn's medium-size moons. Why is it surprising to find evidence of geological activity on some of these moons, and how do we explain it?

20. Describe a few general features of Uranus's medium-size moons. Why is the geological activity on Ariel and Titania puzzling? How do we explain the odd appearance of Miranda?

21. How do we know that Triton is not a typical large jovian satellite? Describe Triton's general characteristics and give possible ideas of where Triton came from.

22. Describe the appearance and structure of Saturn's rings. Why are the rings so thin? Where do the rings lie in relation to Saturn's *Roche tidal zone*?

23. Briefly describe how gap moons and orbital resonances can lead to gaps within ring systems.

24. Contrast the rings of the other jovian planets with Saturn's rings.

25. Describe two possible scenarios for the origin of planetary rings. What makes us think that ring systems must be continually replenished?

## Discussion Questions

1. *A Miniature Solar System?* In what ways is the Jupiter system similar to a miniature solar system? In what ways is it different?

2. *Jovian Mission.* We can study terrestrial planets up close by landing on them, but jovian planets have no surfaces to land on. Suppose you are in charge of planning a long-term mission to "float" in the atmosphere of a jovian planet. Describe the technology you will use and how you will ensure survival for any people assigned to this mission.

3. *Extrasolar Planets.* Many of the newly discovered planets orbiting other stars are more massive than Jupiter and much closer to their stars. Assuming that they are in fact jovian (as opposed to terrestrial or something else), how would you expect these new planets to differ from the jovian planets of our solar system? How would any magnetospheres, satellites, or rings be different? Explain.

## Problems

*Surprising Discoveries?* For **problems 1–8**, suppose someone claimed to make the discovery described. (These are *not* real discoveries.) Decide whether the discovery should be considered reasonable or surprising. More than one right answer may be possible, so explain your answer clearly.

1. Saturn's core is pockmarked with impact craters and dotted with volcanoes erupting basaltic lava.

2. Neptune's deep blue color is not due to methane, as previously thought, but instead is due to its surface being covered with an ocean of liquid water.

3. A jovian planet in another star system has a moon as big as Mars.

4. An extrasolar planet is discovered that is made primarily of hydrogen and helium; it has approximately the same mass as Jupiter but is 10 times larger than Jupiter in radius.

5. A new small moon is discovered to be orbiting Jupiter. It is smaller than any other of Jupiter's moons and orbits slightly farther from Jupiter than any of the other moons, but it has several large, active volcanoes.

6. A new moon is discovered to be orbiting Neptune. The moon orbits in Neptune's equatorial plane and in the same direction in which Neptune rotates, but it is made almost entirely of metals such as iron and nickel.

7. An icy, medium-size moon is discovered to be orbiting a jovian planet in a star system that is only a few hundred million years old. The moon shows evidence of active tectonics.

8. A jovian planet is discovered in a star system that is much older than our solar system. The planet has no moons at all, but it has a system of rings as spectacular as the rings of Saturn.

9. *The Importance of Rotation.* Suppose the material that formed Jupiter came together without any rotation, so that no "jovian nebula" formed and the planet today wasn't spinning. How else would the jovian system be different? Think of as many effects as you can, and explain each in a sentence.

10. *The Great Red Spot.* Based on the infrared and visible-wavelength images in Figure 11.7, is Jupiter's Great Red Spot warmer or cooler than nearby clouds? Does this mean it is higher or lower in altitude than the nearby clouds? (*Hint:* Use what you know about the belts and zones as you study these images.)

11. *Comparing Jovian Planets.* You can do comparative planetology armed only with telescopes and an understanding of gravity.

    a. The satellite Amalthea orbits Jupiter at just about the same distance in kilometers at which Mimas orbits Saturn. Yet Mimas takes almost twice as long to orbit. What can you deduce from this difference, qualitatively?

    b. Jupiter and Saturn are not very different in radius. When you combine this information with your answer to part (a), what can you conclude?

12. *Minor Ingredients Matter.* Suppose the jovian planet atmospheres were composed 100% of hydrogen and helium rather than 98% of hydrogen and helium. How would the atmospheres be different in terms of color and weather? Explain.

*13. *Disappearing Satellite.* Io loses about a ton (~1,000 kg) of sulfur dioxide per second to Jupiter's magnetosphere.

    a. At this rate, what fraction of its mass would Io lose in 5 billion years?

    b. Suppose sulfur dioxide currently makes up 1% of Io's mass. When will Io run out of this gas at the current loss rate?

*14. *Ring Particle Collisions.* Each ring particle in the densest part of Saturn's rings collides with another about every 5 hours. If a ring particle survived for the age of the solar system, how many collisions would it undergo? Do you consider it likely that the ring particles we see in Saturn's rings today have been there since the formation of the solar system? Explain the ramifications of your answer for understanding the origin of the jovian planet rings.

15. *Project: Jupiter's Moons.* Using binoculars or a small telescope, view the moons of Jupiter. Make a sketch of what you see, or take a photograph. Repeat your observations several times (nightly, if possible) over a period of a couple of weeks. Can you determine which moon is which? Can you measure their orbital periods? Can you determine their approximate distances from Jupiter? Explain.

16. *Project: Saturn and Its Rings.* Using binoculars or a small telescope, view the rings of Saturn. Make a sketch of what you see, or take a photograph. What season is it in Saturn's northern hemisphere? How far above Saturn's atmosphere do the rings extend? Can you identify any gaps in the rings? Describe any other features you notice.

## Web Projects

Find useful links for Web projects on the text Web site.

1. *Galileo and Cassini Missions.* Find the latest news on the Galileo and Cassini missions.

    a. Print out (or describe) an image from the Galileo mission of interest to you, and interpret it using the techniques developed in this chapter.

    b. In a few sentences, describe the main scientific goals of the Cassini mission. What is the current health of the spacecraft, and how is the mission progressing?

2. *Oceans of Europa.* The possibility of subsurface oceans on Europa holds great scientific interest and may even mean that life could exist on Europa. Find some of the latest research concerning Europa and learn about proposed missions to Europa. Write a one- to two-page summary of what you learn.

*As we look out into the Universe and identify the many accidents of physics and astronomy that have worked to our benefit, it almost seems as if the Universe must in some sense have known that we were coming.*

FREEMAN DYSON

# CHAPTER 12

# Remnants of Rock and Ice
## Asteroids, Comets, and Pluto

Asteroids and comets might seem insignificant in comparison to the planets and satellites we've been discussing. But there is strength in numbers, and the trillions of small bodies orbiting our Sun are far more important than their small size might suggest.

Few topics in astronomy have the potential to touch our lives more directly than asteroids and comets. The appearance of comets has more than once altered the course of human history, when our ancestors acted upon superstitions related to comet sightings. More profoundly, asteroids or comets falling to the Earth have scarred our planet with impact craters and altered the course of biological evolution.

Asteroids and comets are also important for a very different reason: They are remnants from the birth of our solar system and therefore provide an important testing ground for our theories of how our solar system came to be. In this chapter, we will explore asteroids, comets, and those bodies that fall to Earth as meteorites. We will also examine the smallest planet, Pluto, and see that, while it may be a misfit among planets, it may be right at home among the smaller objects of our solar system.

## 12.1 Remnants from Birth

The objects we've studied so far—terrestrial planets, jovian planets, and large moons—have changed dramatically since their formation. Most planets have been transformed in almost every way. Their interiors have differentiated, their surfaces have been reshaped by geological processes, and their atmospheres have changed as some gases escape while others are added. But many small bodies remain virtually unchanged since their formation some 4.5 billion years ago. Thus, comets, asteroids, and meteorites carry the history of our solar system encoded in their compositions, locations, and numbers.

Using these small bodies to understand planetary formation is a bit like picking through the trash in a carpenter's shop to see how furniture is made. By studying the scraps, sawdust, paint chips, and glue, we can develop a rudimentary understanding of how the carpenter builds furniture. Similarly, the "scraps" left over from the formation of our solar system allow us to understand how the planets and larger moons came to exist. Indeed, much of our modern theory of solar system formation was developed from studies of asteroids, comets, and meteorites.

As we discussed in Chapter 8, the leftovers from the process of accretion in the early solar system fall into three fairly distinct groups, distinguished by their physical and orbital properties: *asteroids, Kuiper belt comets,* and *Oort cloud comets.* Asteroids are rocky or metallic in composition, and most orbit the Sun between the orbits of Mars and Jupiter. In contrast, comets are mostly icy in composition and spend most of their time well outside the orbits of the planets. This compositional difference is directly related to where the objects formed: Asteroids formed inside the *frost line* of the solar nebula, and comets formed outside [Section 8.4]. Kuiper belt comets have orbits like those of the planets, lying close to the ecliptic plane and orbiting the Sun counterclockwise as viewed from above Earth's North Pole. Their distance from the Sun ranges between about 30 AU (about the distance of Neptune) and 100 AU (more than twice the average distance of Pluto). Oort cloud comets have orbits that are randomly inclined to the ecliptic plane, and they generally lie at much greater distances from the Sun than the Kuiper belt comets—in some cases, perhaps halfway to the nearest stars.

In this chapter, we will investigate what we have learned from these remnants from the birth of our solar system. We'll also discuss the cosmic collisions that sometimes occur between leftover planetesimals and the existing planets. Before we continue, however, it's worth noting that the terminology used to describe these objects has a long history that can sometimes be confusing. The word *comet* comes from the Greek word for "hair," and comets get their name from the long, hairlike tails they display on the rare occasions when they come close enough to the Sun to be visible in our sky. *Asteroid* means "starlike," but asteroids are starlike only in their appearance through a telescope, not in their fundamental properties. The term *meteor* refers to a bit of interplanetary dust burning up in our atmosphere; literally, it means "a thing in the air." Meteors are also sometimes called *shooting stars* or *falling stars* because some people once believed that they really were stars falling from the sky. Larger chunks of rock that survive the plunge through the atmosphere and hit the ground are called *fallen stars* or *meteorites,* which means "associated with meteors." To keep potential confusion to a minimum, we will use only the following terms and definitions in this book:

- *Asteroid:* a rocky leftover planetesimal orbiting the Sun.

- *Comet:* an icy leftover planetesimal orbiting the Sun—regardless of its size or whether or not it has a tail.

- *Meteor:* a flash of light in the sky caused by a particle entering the atmosphere, whether the particle comes from an asteroid or a comet.

- *Meteorite:* any piece of rock that fell to the ground from space, whether from an asteroid, a comet, or even another planet.

## 12.2 Asteroids

Asteroids are virtually undetectable to the naked eye and went unnoticed for almost two centuries after the invention of the telescope. The first asteroids were discovered about 200 years ago when astronomers were searching the "extra wide" gap between the orbits of Mars and Jupiter in hopes of discovering a previously unknown planet. It took 50 years to discover the first 10 asteroids (all large and bright); today, modern telescopes with advanced detectors discover that many on a typical night. Once an asteroid's orbit is calculated and verified, the asteroid is assigned a number (in order of verification), and the discoverer chooses a name (subject to the approval of the International Astronomical Union). The earliest discovered asteroids bear names of mythological figures; more recent discoveries carry names of scientists, cartoon heroes, pets, and rock stars.

The radius of the largest asteroid, Ceres, is about 500 kilometers—about half that of Pluto. About a dozen others are large enough that we would call them medium-size moons if they orbited a planet. Most asteroids are much smaller. There are probably more than 100,000 small asteroids with diameters of 1 kilometer or more. Despite their large numbers, asteroids don't add up to much: If they could all be put together, they'd make an object less than 1,000 kilometers in radius—far smaller than any terrestrial planet.

Painstaking observations have revealed the precise orbits of thousands of asteroids. The main **asteroid belt** lies between 2.2 and 3.3 AU from the Sun, though some interesting asteroids lie outside the belt (Figure 12.1). Asteroid orbits are distinctly elliptical and can be inclined relative to the ecliptic by as much as 20°–30°, but all orbit the Sun in the same direction as the planets. Science fiction movies often show the asteroid belt as a crowded and hazardous place, but the average distance between asteroids is millions of kilometers. Spacecraft must be carefully guided to fly close enough to study an asteroid, and accidental collisions with spacecraft are extremely unlikely.

### Origin and Evolution of the Asteroid Belt

Why are asteroids concentrated in the asteroid belt, and why didn't a full-fledged planet form in this region? The answers probably lie with *orbital resonances*. Recall that an orbital resonance occurs whenever one object's orbital period is a simple ratio of another object's period, such as $\frac{1}{2}$, $\frac{1}{4}$, or $\frac{5}{3}$. In such cases, the two objects periodically line up with each other, and the extra gravitational attractions at these times can affect the objects' orbits. Consider, for example, the orbital resonances between Saturn's moons and particles in its rings: The moons are much larger than the ring particles and therefore force the ring particles out of resonant orbits, clearing *gaps* in the rings [Section 11.6]. In the asteroid belt, similar orbital resonances occur between asteroids and Jupiter, the most massive planet by far. For example, any asteroid in an orbit that takes 6 years to circle the Sun—half of Jupiter's 12-year orbital period—would receive the same gravitational nudge from Jupiter every 12 years and thus would soon be pushed out of this orbit. The same is true for asteroids with orbital periods of 4 years ($\frac{1}{3}$ of Jupiter's period) and 3 years ($\frac{1}{4}$ of Jupiter's period). (Music offers an elegant analogy: When a vocalist sings into an open piano, the strings of notes "in resonance" with the voice are "nudged" and begin to vibrate—not just the note being sung, but also notes with a half or a quarter of the note's frequency.)

Today, we see the results of these orbital resonances when we graph the number of asteroids with various orbital periods. Just as we would expect, there are virtually no asteroids with periods exactly $\frac{1}{2}$, $\frac{1}{3}$, or $\frac{1}{4}$ of Jupiter's. Thus, there are no asteroids with average distances from the Sun (semimajor axes) that correspond to these orbital periods. Figure 12.2 shows

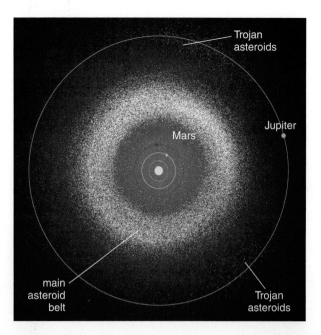

**FIGURE 12.1** Positions of 8,777 asteroids for midnight, 1 January 2002. The asteroids themselves are much smaller than the dots on this scale. The Trojan asteroids are found 60° ahead of and behind Jupiter in its orbit.

several other gaps in the asteroid belt (often called *Kirkwood gaps*, after their discoverer), corresponding to orbital resonances that make other simple ratios with Jupiter's orbital period. (By a *gap* in the asteroid belt we mean a gap in *average* distance; because asteroid orbits are elliptical, some asteroids pass through the gaps on parts of their orbits.)

The gravitational tugs from Jupiter that created the gaps in the asteroid belt probably also explain why no planet ever formed in this region. Early in the history of the solar nebula, the asteroid belt probably contained enough rocky planetesimals to form a planet as large as Earth or Mars. Just as in other parts of the solar nebula, collisions among these planetesimals frequently disrupted their orbits. However, the asteroid belt had an additional source of disruption: gravitational resonances with the forming planet Jupiter. The result was that planetesimals could not collect together to form a planet. Over the past 4.5 billion years, the ongoing orbital disruptions have gradually kicked pieces of this "unformed planet" out of the asteroid belt altogether. Once booted from the main asteroid belt, these objects eventually either crash into a larger object (Sun, planet, or moon) or are flung out of the solar system. (In extremely rare cases, they may become "captured" moons.) Thus, the asteroid belt slowly loses mass, explaining why the total mass of all its asteroids is now less than that of any terrestrial planet.

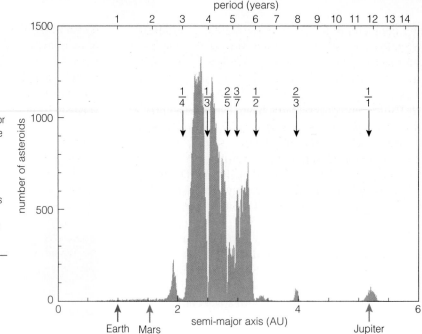

**FIGURE 12.2** This graph shows the numbers of asteroids with different average distances (semimajor axes) from the Sun. Note the gaps—distances where we see few if any asteroids. The ratio labeling each gap shows how the orbital period of objects at this distance compares to the 12-year orbital period of Jupiter. For example, the label $\frac{1}{3}$ means that the orbital period of objects with this average distance is $\frac{1}{3}$ of Jupiter's orbital period, or about 4 years. Most orbital resonances result in gaps, though some (such as $\frac{1}{1}$ and $\frac{2}{7}$) happen to gather up asteroids.

**TIME OUT TO THINK** *How is the process that prevented asteroids from accreting into a planet similar to that which prevented Saturn's ring particles from accreting into a single moon? How is it different?*

The overlapping elliptical orbits of the remaining asteroids still lead to a major collision somewhere in the asteroid belt every 100,000 years or so. (By comparison, collisions occur somewhere within Saturn's rings many times per second, which has circularized the orbits and flattened the rings.) Thus, larger asteroids continue to be broken into smaller ones, with each collision also creating numerous dust-size particles. The asteroid belt has been grinding itself down in this way for over 4 billion years and will continue to do so for as long as the solar system exists.

Most of the asteroids found outside the asteroid belt—including the *Earth-approaching asteroids* that pass near Earth's orbit—are probably "impacts waiting to happen." But asteroids can safely congregate in two stable zones outside the main belt. These zones are found along Jupiter's orbit 60° ahead of and behind Jupiter (see Figure 12.1). The asteroids found in these two zones are called the *Trojan asteroids,* and the largest are named for the mythological Greek heroes of the Trojan War. The Trojan asteroids are stable because of a different type of orbital resonance with Jupiter. In this case, any asteroid that wanders away from one of these zones is nudged back *into* the zone by Jupiter's gravity. The existence of such stable orbital resonances was first predicted by the French

mathematician Joseph Lagrange more than 200 years ago—135 years before the discovery of the first asteroid in such an orbit.[1] It is possible that the population of Trojan asteroids is as large as that of main-belt asteroids, but the greater distance to the Trojan asteroids makes them more difficult to study or even count from Earth.

### Learning About Asteroids

The general locations and orbits of asteroids tell us a lot about their origin, but we would like to know many other properties, such as masses, sizes, densities, shapes, and compositions. The first step in learning about an asteroid is determining its precise orbit. Asteroids are recognizable in telescopic images because they move noticeably relative to the stars in just a short time (Figure 12.3). Once we detect an asteroid, we can calculate its orbit by applying Kepler's laws [Section 5.3]—even if we've observed only a small part of one complete orbit.

Most asteroids appear as little more than points of light even to our largest Earth-based telescopes, so the best way to study an asteroid in depth is to send a spacecraft out to meet it. Spacecraft have visited

---

[1]The locations of these stable zones are called *Lagrange points.* Similar Lagrange points lie 60° ahead of and behind the Moon in its orbit around the Earth. These locations have been suggested for space colonies because of their stability. Three additional Lagrange points lie along the line connecting any two massive objects (such as the Earth and the Moon). They are not quite stable but also are good places to "park" spacecraft because staying in place doesn't take much fuel.

**FIGURE 12.3** Because asteroids orbit the Sun, they move relative to the stars just as planets do. In this photograph, stars show up as white dots, and the motion of an asteroid makes it show up as a short streak.

only a handful of asteroids close-up in their native environment of the asteroid belt and a few other presumed asteroids "in captivity" in orbit around other planets (e.g., Phobos and Deimos orbiting Mars, and the backward outer satellites of Jupiter). The Galileo spacecraft on its way to Jupiter photographed the asteroid Gaspra (Figure 12.4a) and an asteroid pair known as Ida and Dactyl (Figure 12.4b). The Near-Earth Asteroid Rendezvous mission (NEAR) photographed the asteroid Mathilde (Figure 12.4c) on its way to the asteroid Eros. NEAR orbited Eros (Figure 12.4d) for a full year, studying its entire surface at close range, before setting down on its surface. These spacecraft images reveal battered worlds that are probably fragments of larger asteroids shattered by collisions.

**a** Gaspra (16 km across). Photographed by the Galileo spacecraft on its way to Jupiter.

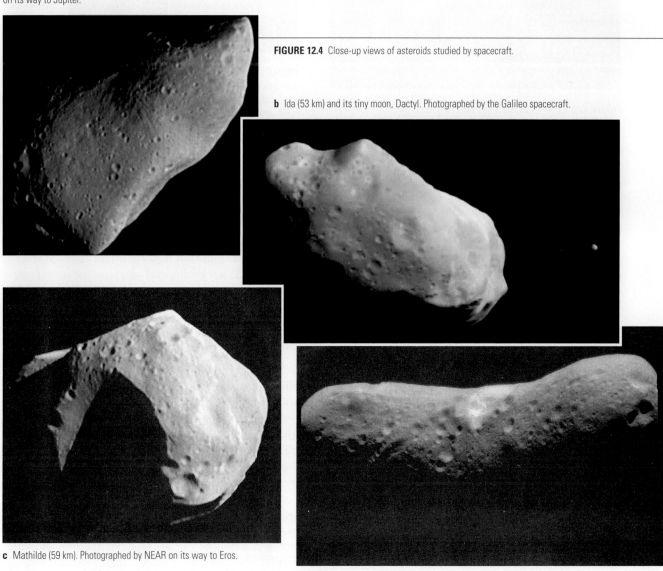

**FIGURE 12.4** Close-up views of asteroids studied by spacecraft.

**b** Ida (53 km) and its tiny moon, Dactyl. Photographed by the Galileo spacecraft.

**c** Mathilde (59 km). Photographed by NEAR on its way to Eros.

**d** Eros (40 km). The NEAR spacecraft orbited Eros for a year before landing on it.

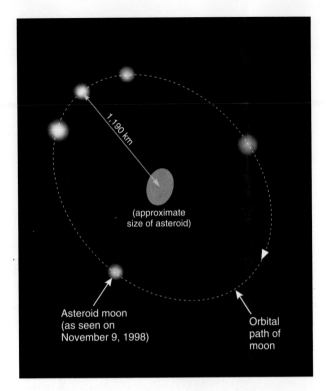

**FIGURE 12.5** By comparing measurements of reflected sunlight and thermal emission in the infrared, we can learn about asteroid albedos. Once we know an asteroid's albedo, we can determine its size.

**FIGURE 12.6** Asteroid masses can be measured only if we have observed the asteroid's gravitational effect on a passing spacecraft or, in very rare cases, if the asteroid has its own tiny moon. One case of an asteroid with a moon is Ida, with its moon Dactyl (see Figure 12.4b). Another is shown here, in an image made by a telescope using adaptive optics [Section 7.4]. The image shows a small moon observed in five positions in its orbit around asteroid Eugenia. The asteroid itself was blocked out during the observations and is shown as the white oval in the image.

We can directly measure the size of an asteroid only when we've seen it close up or in the rare cases when an asteroid is large enough to be resolved in a telescope. (We calculate physical size from the asteroid's angular size and distance [Section 7.1].) In many other cases, we can indirectly determine asteroid sizes by analyzing their light. The total amount of sunlight that an asteroid reflects depends on its size and albedo [Section 10.2]. For example, if two asteroids have the same albedo, the one that reflects more light must be larger. We can determine an asteroid's albedo by taking advantage of the fact that asteroids not only reflect visible light from the Sun, but also emit their own infrared thermal radiation. Because the temperature of an asteroid depends primarily on how much sunlight it absorbs, comparing its infrared thermal emission to its visible light reflection tells us its albedo. For example, an asteroid that is very reflective (high albedo) will not absorb much solar energy, so it will be cold and will give off very little infrared thermal emission (Figure 12.5). By using this technique, we have compiled good size estimates for more than a thousand asteroids.

**TIME OUT TO THINK** *Imagine that you discover an asteroid that is fairly bright through your telescope. What additional observations would you need to make to determine whether it is bright because it is very large, very close, or simply light-colored?*

Determining an asteroid's density can offer valuable insights into its origin and makeup but is possible only if we can measure the asteroid's mass as well as its size. Mass measurements have been made only in a few cases, because they require observing an asteroid's gravitational effect on another object, either a passing spacecraft or a tiny "moon" orbiting the asteroid (Figure 12.6). But these few cases have already revealed that different asteroids can have very different densities. For example, observations from the NEAR flyby of Mathilde yielded a density of 1.5 g/cm³, which is so low that the asteroid cannot be a solid rocky object. Indeed, the impact that formed the huge crater on Mathilde's surface (see Figure 12.4c) would have disintegrated a solid ob-

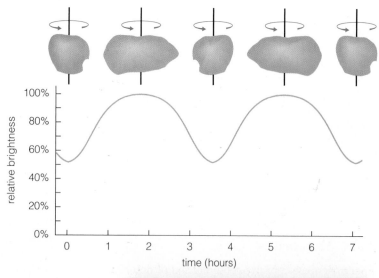

**a** Gaspra's irregular shape leads to large brightness variations as it rotates. The diagrams at the top show its appearance from Earth at different times during its rotation, and the graph shows the corresponding brightness at those times. Note that Gaspra appears brighter when we are looking at a larger face because it reflects more sunlight.

**FIGURE 12.7** In some cases, we can determine asteroid shapes from measurements made from Earth.

**b** The asteroid Kleopatra is shaped like a bone. The image shows the shape based on calculations from the results of radar observations.

ject. Mathilde must be a loosely bound "rubble pile" that could absorb the shock of impact without completely disintegrating. In contrast, NEAR found a relatively high density of 2.4 g/cm³ for Eros, which is close to the value expected for solid rock. Eros also has a subtle pattern of surface ridges and troughs (see Figure 12.4d), which hint at a set of parallel faults and fractures in its interior.

Determining asteroid shapes is even more challenging. One technique involves looking for brightness variations as an asteroid rotates. A uniform spherical asteroid will not change its brightness as it rotates, but a potato-shaped asteroid will reflect more light when it presents its larger side toward the Sun and our telescope (Figure 12.7a). Astronomers can also determine asteroid shapes by examining the shape of the shadows cast in starlight when an asteroid happens to pass right in front of a star. By combining the exact times of the star's disappearance and reappearance as clocked with telescopes in several different locations around the world, they can calculate the shape and size of the shadow and therefore the outline of the asteroid itself. Shape measurements show that only the largest asteroid (Ceres, 940-km diameter) is approximately spherical. The next two largest asteroids are somewhat oblong (Pallas, 540 km across, and Vesta, 510 km across). Smaller asteroids like Gaspra and Ida have still odder shapes. The strength of gravity on these smaller asteroids is evidently less than the strength of the rock.

In a few cases, astronomers have used radar to obtain more detailed shape information about aster-

oids that have passed close to the Earth. A radio dish sends out radio "pings" that bounce off the asteroid and reflect back to Earth.[2] By analyzing the reflected signals returned as the asteroid rotates, we can create a three-dimensional model of the asteroid. Such measurements revealed the odd shape of the asteroid Kleopatra (Figure 12.7b); in fact, the radar signals were reflected so strongly that scientists believe Kleopatra to be made almost entirely of metals. Radar images indicate that other asteroids are actually two objects held in contact with each other by a weak gravitational attraction. Apparently, this attraction is strong enough to hold the objects together, but not strong enough to force them to merge into a single body.

---

[2] The intense radar beacons beamed at these asteroids are probably the strongest human signals sent from Earth. Perhaps a distant alien civilization will someday pick up these signals and wonder what we were doing.

Finally, we can determine the compositions of asteroids through spectroscopy [Section 7.3]. Thousands of asteroids have been analyzed in this way, and they fall into three main categories: About 75% of asteroids are very dark and show absorption bands from carbon-rich materials. Another 15% are more reflective and show absorption bands characteristic of rocky materials. The remaining 10% include asteroids with spectral characteristics of metals such as iron. Overall, the wide range of asteroid properties reveals their varied histories and underscores planetary scientists' interest in visiting more asteroids.

## 12.3 Meteorites

Spectroscopy is a pretty good method of determining the composition of an asteroid, but wouldn't it be nice to study an asteroid sample in a laboratory? No spacecraft has yet returned an asteroid sample, but we have pieces of asteroids nonetheless—the rocks called *meteorites* that fall from the sky.

The reality of rocks falling from the sky wasn't always accepted. Stories of such events arose occasionally in human history, sometimes even influencing history. For example, the ancient Greek scientist Anaxagoras (500–428 B.C.) came up with his idea that planets and stars are flaming rocks in the heavens after hearing of "fallen stars." Later scientists were skeptical of such stories. Thomas Jefferson (who worked in science as well as politics), upon hearing of a meteorite fall in Connecticut, reportedly said, "It is easier to believe that Yankee professors would lie than that stones would fall from heaven."

Today we know that rocks really do sometimes fall from the heavens. Some are large enough to do significant damage, blasting huge craters upon impact. Despite the forces of erosion, more than 100 impact craters can still be seen on Earth (Figure 12.8).

The precise origin of meteorites was long a mystery, but today we know that most come from the asteroid belt. In recent decades, a few meteorite falls have been captured on film, allowing scientists to calculate the orbits that led them to crash to Earth.

**FIGURE 12.8** Large craters on Earth show that major impacts have played an important role in even relatively recent geological history.

**a** This map shows the locations of known impact craters.

Manicouagan Lakes crater

**b** The Manicouagan Lakes crater in Canada formed about 200 million years ago and has been heavily eroded by glaciers since then.

The results clearly show that the meteorites originated in the asteroid belt.

Rocks from space continue to rain down on Earth, and observers find a few meteorites every year by following the trajectories of very bright meteors called *fireballs*. Meteorites are often blasted apart in their fiery descent through our atmosphere, scattering fragments over an area several kilometers across. A direct hit on the head by a meteorite would be fatal, but there are no reliable accounts of human deaths from meteorites. However, meteorites have injured at least one human (by a ricochet, not a direct hit), damaged houses and cars, and killed animals (Figure 12.9). Most meteorites fall into the oceans, which cover three-quarters of Earth's surface area.

Many more meteorites—ones that fell to Earth at some time in the past—are found by accident or by organized meteorite searches. Antarctica offers the greatest treasure trove of meteorites, not because more fall there but because the icy surface makes meteorites easier to identify and the movement of glaciers carries rocky debris into a few small areas. The majority of meteorites in museums and laboratories come from Antarctica.

### Comparing Meteorites

Most meteorites are difficult to distinguish from terrestrial rocks without detailed scientific analysis, but a few clues can help. Meteorites are usually covered with a dark, pitted crust resulting from their fiery passage through the atmosphere. Some can be readily distinguished from terrestrial rocks by their high metal content. (Most types of meteorites contain enough metal to attract a magnet hanging on a string. If you suspect that you have found a meteorite, most science museums will analyze a small chip free of charge.) The ultimate judge of extraterrestrial origin is laboratory analysis of the rock's composition. Terrestrial rocks may differ from one another in composition, but all contain isotopes of particular elements in roughly the same ratios. Me-

teorites can be identified by their very different isotope ratios. The presence of certain rare elements, such as iridium, also indicates extraterrestrial origin; nearly all of Earth's iridium sank to the core long ago and hence is absent from surface rocks.

The tens of thousands of known meteorites fall into two basic categories. The vast majority of meteorites appear to be composed of a random mix of flakes from the solar nebula, and radioactive dating shows that they formed at the same time as the solar system itself—about 4.6 billion years ago [Section 8.6]. These **primitive meteorites** are our best source of information about conditions in the solar nebula

**FIGURE 12.9** Two perspectives on the risks of being hit by a meteorite.

**a** The impact crater in this Chevrolet was created by a 12-kg meteorite. Analysis of videotapes of the meteor's fiery passage over several East Coast states confirmed its origin in the asteroid belt.

**b** No humans have been killed by meteorite falls, but . . . .

AND IT SAYS HERE THAT NO ONE HAS BEEN KNOWN TO HAVE BEEN STRUCK BY A FALLING METEORITE..

ALTHOUGH A DOG WAS KILLED IN EGYPT BY A METEORITE YEARS AGO..

WHAT DO THEY MEAN, "ALTHOUGH" A DOG?

© 1994 United Feature Syndicate, Inc.

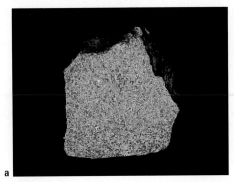

Stony primitive meteorite: metal flakes intermixed with rocky material.

Carbon-rich primitive meteorite: similar to meteorite at left, but with carbon compounds added in.

**b**

Differentiated iron meteorite: similar to planetary core.

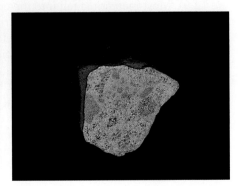

Differentiated stony meteorite: similar to volcanic rocks.

**FIGURE 12.10** (**a**) Two examples of primitive meteorites. (**b**) Two examples of processed meteorites.

(Figure 12.10a). Most primitive meteorites are composed of rocky minerals with an important difference from Earth rocks: A small but noticeable fraction of pure metallic flakes is mixed in. (Iron in Earth rocks is chemically bound in minerals.) Some primitive meteorites also contain substantial amounts of carbon compounds, and some even contain a small amount of water.

A much smaller group of meteorites appears to have undergone substantial change since the formation of the solar system, and radioactive dating shows some of these meteorites to be younger than the primitive meteorites. We call this group **processed meteorites**, because they apparently were once part of a larger object that "processed" the original material of the solar nebula into another form (Figure 12.10b).[3] Some processed meteorites resemble the Earth's core in composition: an iron/nickel mixture with trace amounts of other metals. These meteorites

have a relatively high density of about 7 g/cm³ and played an important role in human history: As the most accessible form of metallic iron available on the Earth's surface, they helped humans make the transition from the bronze age to the iron age. Other processed meteorites have much lower densities and are made of rocks more similar to the Earth's crust or mantle. A few even have a composition remarkably close to that of the basalts erupted from terrestrial volcanoes [Section 9.4].

### The Origin of Meteorites

We've seen that primitive meteorites may be either rocky or carbon-rich. Why are there two varieties? The answer lies in where they formed in the solar nebula. Carbon compounds condensed only at the relatively low temperatures that were found in the solar nebula beyond about 3 AU from the Sun. Thus, carbon-rich meteorites must come from the outer portion of the asteroid belt (beyond about 3 AU from the Sun). Laboratory spectra of these carbon-rich primitive meteorites confirm that they are a good match to the compositions of asteroids in the outer part of the asteroid belt. The remainder of the primi-

---

[3]The technical term for primitive meteorites is *chondrites*, because they contain seed-shaped "chondrules" that may be solidified droplets splashed out in the accretion process. Processed meteorites underwent major changes that destroyed the chondrules, so this category is called *achondrites*.

tive meteorites lack carbon compounds, so they presumably formed in the warmer, inner part of the asteroid belt. Curiously, most of the meteorites collected on Earth are of the rocky variety, even though most asteroids are of the carbon-rich variety. Evidently, orbital resonances are more effective at pitching asteroids our way from the inner part of the asteroid belt. All the primitive meteorites apparently survived untouched since the beginning of the solar system—at least until they came crashing down to Earth.

The processed meteorites tell a more complex story. Their compositions appear similar to the cores, mantles, or crusts of the terrestrial worlds. Thus, they must be fragments of worlds that underwent *differentiation* [Section 9.2]. That is, they are fragments of worlds that must have been heated to high enough temperatures to melt inside, allowing metals to sink to the center and rocks to rise to the surface. The processed meteorites with basaltic compositions must come from lava flows that occurred on some of the larger asteroids during a time when they had active volcanism. Perhaps as many as a dozen large asteroids were geologically active shortly after the formation of the solar system, but radioactive dating of processed meteorites suggests that these worlds soon became inactive.

Basaltic meteorites may simply have been chipped off the surface of a large asteroid by relatively small collisions. (By comparing meteorite and asteroid spectra, scientists have identified the asteroid Vesta as the likely source of some of these meteorites.) In contrast, the processed meteorites with corelike or mantlelike compositions must be fragments of worlds that completely shattered in collisions. These shattered worlds not only lost a chance to grow into planets, but they sent many fragments onto collision courses with other asteroids and other planets, including Earth. Thus, processed meteorites essentially offer us an opportunity to study a "dissected planet."

If fragments such as the basaltic meteorites can be chipped off the surface of an asteroid, is it possible that they might also be chipped off a larger object such as a moon or a planet? In fact, a few processed meteorites have been found that don't appear to match the compositions of asteroids but instead appear to match the composition either of the Moon or of Mars. We now believe that some of these meteorites in fact were chipped off the Moon in impacts and that others were chipped off Mars. The analysis of these *lunar meteorites* and *Martian meteorites* is providing new insights into the conditions on the Moon and Mars. In at least one case, a Martian meteorite may be offering us clues about whether life once existed on Mars [Section 13.6].

## 12.4 Comets

Humans have watched comets in awe for millennia. The occasional presence of a bright comet in the night sky was hard to miss before the advent of big cities, inexpensive illumination, and television. In some cultures, these rare intrusions into the unchanging heavens foretold bad or good luck, and in most cultures there was little attempt to interpret the event in astronomical terms. (Recall that comets were generally thought to be atmospheric phenomena until proved otherwise by Tycho Brahe [Section 5.3].) Nowadays, these leftover icy planetesimals can teach us about formation processes in the outer solar system, just as asteroids teach us about the inner solar system.

After Kepler developed his laws of planetary motion, other astronomers applied them to comets and found extremely eccentric orbits. Some comets visit the inner solar system only once before being ejected into interstellar space, others return on orbits spanning thousands of years, and a few come by more frequently. The most famous is Halley's comet, named for the English scientist Edmund Halley (1656–1742). Halley did not "discover" his comet but rather gained fame for recognizing that a comet seen in 1682 was the same one seen on a number of previous occasions. He used Newton's law of gravitation to calculate the comet's 76-year orbit and, in a book published in 1705, predicted that the comet would return in 1758. The comet was given his name when it reappeared as predicted, 16 years after his death. Halley's comet has returned on schedule ever since, including twice in the twentieth century—spectacularly in 1910 when it passed near the Earth, and unimpressively in 1986 when it passed by at a much greater distance. It will next visit in 2061.

Today, new comets carry a form of good luck. Thousands of amateur astronomers eagerly scan the skies with their telescopes and binoculars in hopes of discovering a new comet. The first discoverers (up to three) who report their findings to the International Astronomical Union have the comet named after them. Several comets are discovered every year, and most have never been seen before by human eyes. In 1996 and 1997, we were treated to back-to-back brilliant comets: comet Hyakutake and comet Hale–Bopp (Figure 12.11). The surprise champion of comet discovery is the SOHO spacecraft, an orbiting solar observatory. SOHO has detected more than 200 "Sun grazing" comets, most on their last pass by the Sun (Figure 12.12).

### The Flashy Lives of Comets

Comets are icy planetesimals from the outer solar system. Their composition has been described as "dirty snowballs": ices mixed with rocky dust. Comets

a

b

**FIGURE 12.11** Brilliant comets can appear at almost any time, as demonstrated by the back-to-back appearances of (**a**) comet Hyakutake in 1996 and (**b**) comet Hale–Bopp in 1997, photographed at Mono Lake in California.

**FIGURE 12.12** Comet SOHO-6's final blaze of glory. This "Sun grazing" comet was observed by the SOHO spacecraft a few hours before it passed just 50,000 km above the Sun's surface. The comet did not survive its passage, due to the intense solar heating and tidal forces. In this image, the Sun is blocked out behind the large, orange disk; the sun's size is indicated by the white circle.

**FIGURE 12.13** Anatomy of a comet. The inset photo is the nucleus of Halley's comet photographed by the Giotto spacecraft; the coma and tails shown are those of comet Hale–Bopp.

are completely frozen when they are far from the Sun, and most are just a few kilometers across. But a comet takes on an entirely different appearance when it comes closer to the Sun (Figure 12.13). The dirty snowball is the comet's **nucleus**. The sublimation of ices in the nucleus creates a rapidly escaping dusty atmosphere called the **coma**, along with a **tail** that points away from the Sun regardless of which way the comet is moving through its orbit. In most cases, we actually see two tails: a **plasma tail** made of ionized gas, and a **dust tail** made of small solid particles. Although much of comet science focuses on the dramatic tail and coma, we will begin our closer look at comets with the humbler nucleus.

Comet nuclei are rarely observable with telescopes, because they are quite small and are shrouded by the dusty coma. The European Space Agency's Giotto spacecraft provided our best view of a nucleus when it passed within 600 kilometers of comet Halley's nucleus in 1986. (The spacecraft was named for the Italian painter Giotto, who apparently was inspired by a passage of Halley's comet to include a comet in a 1304 religious painting.) The flyby revealed a dark, lumpy, potato-shaped nucleus about 16 kilometers long and 8 kilometers in width and depth. Despite its icy composition, comet Halley's nucleus is darker than charcoal, reflecting only 3% of the light that falls on it. (It doesn't take much rocky soil or carbon-rich material to darken a comet.) The ice is not packed very solidly; some estimates of the density of Halley's nucleus are considerably less than 1 g/cm$^3$—suggesting that the nucleus is part ice and part empty space.

How can such a small nucleus put on such a spectacular show? Comets spend most of their lives

in the frigid outer limits of our solar system. As a comet accelerates toward the Sun, its surface temperature increases and ices begin to sublime into gaseous form. By the time the comet comes within about 5 AU of the Sun, sublimation begins to form a noticeable atmosphere that easily escapes the comet's weak gravity. The escaping atmosphere drags away dust particles that were mixed with the ice and begins to create the dusty coma around the nucleus. Sublimation rates increase as the comet approaches the Sun, and gases jet away from patches on the nucleus at speeds of hundreds of meters per second (Figure 12.14). The jets can make faint pinwheel patterns within the coma, due to the slow rotation of comet nuclei. The rapid sublimation carries away so much dust that a spacecraft flyby is dangerous. The Giotto spacecraft, which approached Halley's nucleus at a relative speed of nearly 250,000 km/hr (70 km/sec), was sent reeling by dust impacts just minutes before closest approach, breaking radio contact with Earth.

As gas and dust move away from the comet, they are influenced by the Sun in different ways. The gases are ionized by ultraviolet photons from the Sun and then carried straight outward away from the Sun with the solar wind at speeds of hundreds of kilometers per second. These ionized gases form the *plasma tail*, which may extend hundreds of millions of kilometers away from the Sun. Dust-size particles experience a much weaker push caused by the pressure of sunlight itself (called *radiation pressure* [Section 16.4]), so the *dust tail* is swept away from the Sun in a slightly different direction (see Figure 12.13). The comet

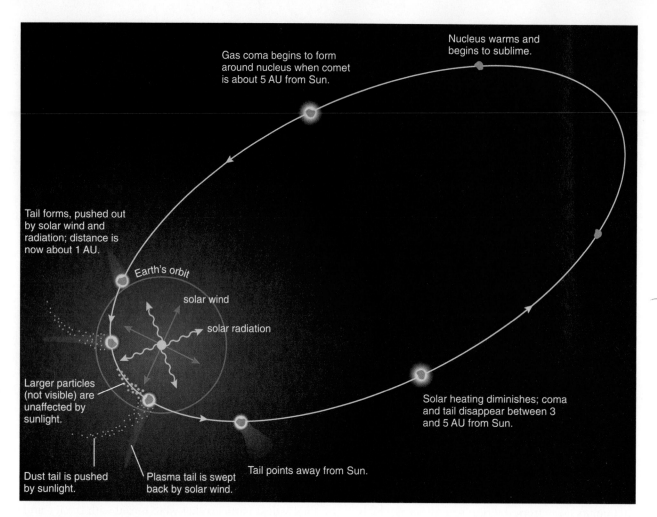

Gas coma begins to form
around nucleus when comet
is about 5 AU from Sun.

Nucleus warms and
begins to sublime.

Tail forms, pushed out
by solar wind and
radiation; distance is
now about 1 AU.

Earth's orbit

solar wind

solar radiation

Larger particles
(not visible) are
unaffected by
sunlight.

Solar heating diminishes; coma
and tail disappear between 3
and 5 AU from Sun.

Dust tail is pushed
by sunlight.

Plasma tail is swept
back by solar wind.

Tail points away from Sun.

**FIGURE 12.14** Comets exist as bare nuclei over most of their orbits and grow a coma and tails only when they approach the Sun. (Diagram not to scale.)

wheels around the Sun, always keeping its tails of dust and plasma pointed roughly away from the Sun. Comets also eject some larger, pebble-size particles that are not pushed away from the Sun. These form another, invisible "tail" extending along the comet's orbit; as we'll discuss in Section 12.6, these particles are responsible for meteor showers.

After the comet loops around the Sun and begins to head back outward, sublimation declines, the coma dissipates, and some of the dust settles back to the surface. Nothing happens until the comet again comes sunward—in a century, a millennium, a million years, or perhaps never.

Active comets cannot last forever. In a close pass by the Sun, a comet may shed a layer 1 meter thick. Dust that is too heavy to escape accumulates on the surface. This thick dusty deposit helps make comets dark and may eventually block the escape of interior gas that makes comets so phenomenal. A comet probably loses about 0.1% of its volatiles on every pass around the Sun. No one is certain what

happens after the volatiles stop escaping. Either the remaining dust disguises the dead comet as an asteroid, or it comes "unglued" without the binding effects of ices and simply disintegrates along its orbit.

Spectra of the coma and tail show emission lines and bands from water molecules and other hydrogen compounds that condensed in the outer regions of the solar nebula. They also show emission from carbon dioxide and carbon monoxide that condensed only in the coldest regions of the solar nebula, as well as a wide variety of more complex molecules. These emissions do not give a complete picture of a comet's ingredients, since sunlight and chemical reactions have altered the composition. Organic chemicals (containing carbon, hydrogen, oxygen, and nitrogen) may also be present, suggesting that comets carry the necessary building blocks for life. Comets may even contain some grains of interstellar dust that formed *before* our solar system. NASA's Stardust mission will gather some of these materials from comet Wild 2 and will return them to Earth in 2006. A complete understanding of the composition of comets still eludes us, but understanding comets' composition may have critical implications for understanding their formation in the outer solar nebula and their importance to the planets.

### The Origin of Comets

Comets are a rarity in the inner solar system, with only a handful coming within the orbit of Jupiter at any one time. However, because comets cannot survive very many passes by the Sun, comets must come from enormous reservoirs at much greater distances: the Kuiper belt and the Oort cloud (Figure 12.15). The existence of these reservoirs was first inferred by analysis of the orbits of comets that pass close to the Sun. Most comet orbits fit no pattern—they do not orbit the Sun in the same direction as the planets, and their elliptical orbits can be pointed in any direction. Comets Hyakutake and Hale–Bopp both fall into this class. It is believed that such comets are visitors from the Oort cloud. Other comets have a pattern to their orbits: They travel around the Sun in the same plane and direction as the planets, though on very elliptical orbits that take them beyond the orbit of Pluto. They also return much more frequently—typically every few decades or centuries—and are thought to be visitors from the Kuiper belt. Comets from either the Oort cloud or the Kuiper belt may occasionally pass near enough to a planet to have their orbits significantly altered, sometimes becoming trapped in the inner regions of the solar system. Halley's comet must have passed near a jovian planet in the distant past, causing it to end up on its current 76-year orbit of the Sun [Section 5.6]. Gravitational encounters with planets can also eject comets from the solar system altogether or send them crashing into the planets or the Sun.

Based on the number of comets that fall into the inner solar system, the Oort cloud must contain about a trillion ($10^{12}$) comets. However, Oort cloud comets normally orbit the Sun at such great distances—up to about 50,000 AU—that we have so far seen only the rare visitors to the inner solar system. The comets of the Oort cloud probably formed in the vicinity of the jovian planets and were flung into their large, random orbits by gravitational encounters with these planets. Oort cloud comets are so far from the Sun that the gravity of neighboring stars can alter their orbits, preventing some comets from ever returning

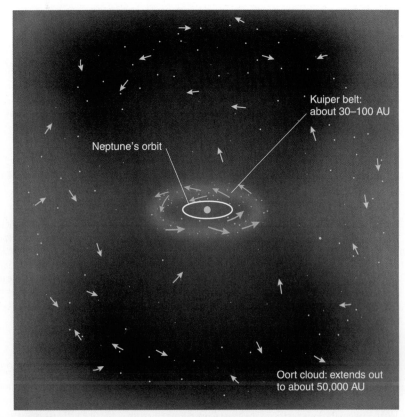

**FIGURE 12.15** The Kuiper belt and the Oort cloud. Arrows indicate representative orbital motions of objects in the two regions. (Figure not to scale.)

near the planets and sending others plummeting toward the Sun.

In contrast, the comets of the Kuiper belt probably still lie in the same general region in which they formed, which explains why their orbits match the pattern of the solar nebula as a whole. In the 1990s, astronomers began using the largest telescopes to search for Kuiper belt objects in their native environment rather than on their excursions into the inner solar system. The first discovery, given the name 1992QB1, orbits beyond Pluto with an orbital period of 296 years. It is a comet approximately 280 kilometers across. Subsequent searches have identified dozens of other objects that match the predicted orbital properties of Kuiper belt comets: fairly circular orbits in the same direction as the planets, with small orbital tilts. Nearly 400 Kuiper belt objects have been discovered so far, suggesting that at least 100,000 comets more than 100 km across must populate the Kuiper belt, along with a billion objects around 10 km across (the typical size of comets that enter the inner solar system). Thus, the total mass of the Kuiper belt is far greater than that of the asteroid belt. Spectroscopy has provided some preliminary information on the composition of Kuiper belt objects. Although they are undoubtedly rich in ices, the

Kuiper belt comets are covered with dark, carbon-rich compounds.

Planetary scientists would dearly love to compare samples of the ancient materials frozen inside the two types of comet. But comet samples falling to Earth burn up in the atmosphere and do not become meteorites, so we are limited to distant spectroscopic analysis of the gases sublimed off the nucleus. We cannot yet tell if Oort cloud comets show signs of having formed in closer, warmer, and denser regions of the solar nebula than their Kuiper belt counterparts. Spacecraft missions to these frigid regions of the solar system are prohibitive, so we must be content to wait for comets to come to us and watch as the Sun dissects them meter by meter.

How big can Kuiper belt objects be? The largest Kuiper belt comet discovered so far, designated 2000WR106, may be nearly 1,000 km across. If a comet can be 1,000 km across, could one be larger still? It's time to consider the odd planet Pluto.

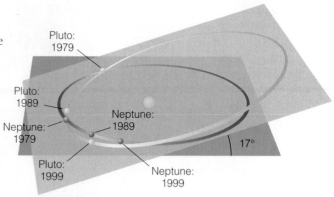

**FIGURE 12.16** Pluto's orbit is significantly more elliptical and more tilted relative to the ecliptic than that of any other planet. It comes closer to the Sun than Neptune for 20 years in each 248-year orbit, as was the case between 1979 and 1999. But there's no danger of a collision between Pluto and Neptune, because they share an orbital resonance in which Neptune completes three orbits for every two orbits by Pluto.

## 12.5 Pluto: Lone Dog or Part of a Pack?

Pluto was discovered in 1930 by American astronomer Clyde Tombaugh, culminating a search that began not long after the discovery of Neptune in 1846. Recall that Neptune's existence and location were predicted before its actual discovery by mathematical analysis of irregularities in the orbit of Uranus (see p. 20). Further analysis of Uranus's orbit suggested the existence of a "ninth planet," and Pluto was found only 6° from the predicted position of this planet. Initial estimates suggested that Pluto was much larger than Earth, but successively more accurate measurements derived ever-smaller sizes. We now know that Pluto has a radius of only 1,195 kilometers and a mass of just 0.0025 Earth mass—making it far too small to affect the orbit of Uranus. In fact, the discovery of Pluto near the predicted position of the "ninth planet" was coincidental; Uranus's supposed orbital irregularities were apparently just errors in measurement. Pluto might have escaped detection for decades without those errors.

Pluto has long seemed to be a misfit among the planets, fitting into neither the terrestrial nor the jovian category. Its 248-year orbit is unusually elliptical and significantly tilted relative to the ecliptic (Figure 12.16). Near perihelion, it actually comes closer to the Sun than Neptune—such was the case between 1979 and 1999. At aphelion, it is 50 AU from the Sun, putting it far beyond the realm of the jovian planets. Despite the fact that Pluto sometimes comes closer to the Sun than Neptune, there is no danger of the two planets colliding: For every two Pluto orbits, Neptune circles the Sun three times. Because of this stable *orbital resonance,* when Pluto is near Neptune's orbit, Neptune is always a safe distance away. The two will probably continue their dance of avoidance until the end of the solar system.

### Pluto and Its Moon

Pluto's great distance and small size make it difficult to study, but the task became much easier with the discovery of Pluto's moon Charon in 1978. The original discovery was made when astronomers noticed a "bump" on Pluto's blurry image that moved from side to side over a 6.4-day period (Figure 12.17a). Today we have much clearer pictures of Pluto and Charon from the Hubble Space Telescope (Figure 12.17b). The discovery of the moon enabled astronomers to accurately determine the mass of Pluto by applying Newton's version of Kepler's third law.[4] They also learned that Pluto's rotation axis is tipped 118° relative to its orbit, making it the third planet (in addition to Venus and Uranus) that rotates "backward."

---

[4]If you look in an astronomy text published before 1978, you'll often see Pluto's mass listed with some estimate followed by "?" because of the uncertainty. After the discovery of Charon in 1978, this uncertainty disappeared, providing a clear example of the power of Newton's version of Kepler's third law.

**a** The bump on the upper right of this fuzzy, black image of Pluto might not seem significant, but astronomers noticed that the bump moved from one side of Pluto to the other and back in six days.

**b** The bump (in **a**) is actually Pluto's moon Charon, clearly resolved in this Hubble Space Telescope image. The object on the left is Pluto, with Charon on the right.

**FIGURE 12.17** An improving view of Pluto and Charon.

Pluto's moon was discovered just in time, because astronomers soon learned that Charon's orbit was about to go edge-on as seen from the Earth, something that happens only every 124 years. From 1985 to 1990, astronomers monitored the combined brightness of Pluto and Charon as they alternately eclipsed each other every few days. Detailed analysis of brightness variations allowed calculation of accurate sizes, masses, and densities for both Pluto and Charon, as well as the compilation of rough maps of their surface markings. Charon's diameter is more than half Pluto's, and its mass is about one-eighth the mass of Pluto. Furthermore, Charon orbits only 20,000 kilometers from Pluto. (For comparison, our Moon has a mass 1/80th that of Earth and orbits 400,000 kilometers away.) Some astronomers argue that Pluto and Charon qualify as a "double planet," but others argue that neither is large enough to qualify as a planet at all.

Curiously, Pluto and Charon have slightly different densities and presumably slightly different compositions. Pluto's density of about 2 g/cm³ is a bit high for the expected ice/rock mix in the outer solar system, while Charon's density of 1.6 g/cm³ is a bit low. The leading explanation is that Charon was created by a giant impact similar to that thought to have formed our Moon. A large icy object impacting Pluto may have blasted away its low-density outer layers, which then formed a ring around Pluto and eventually reaccreted into the low-density moon Charon.

Pluto currently has a thin atmosphere of nitrogen and other gases formed by sublimation of surface ices. However, the atmosphere is steadily thinning because Pluto's elliptical orbit is now carrying it farther from the Sun. (Pluto will not reach aphelion until 2113.) As Pluto recedes, its atmospheric gases are refreezing onto its surface. Maps of surface markings generated from observation of eclipses and Hubble Space Telescope images show that the surface has bright and dark patches, but we don't yet have enough information to understand why (Figure 12.18).

Despite the cold, the view from Pluto would be stunning. Charon would dominate the sky, appearing almost 10 times larger in angular size than our Moon. Pluto and Charon's mutual tidal pulls long ago made them rotate synchronously with each other (see Figure 5.22). Thus, Charon is visible from only one side of Pluto and would hang motionless in the sky, always showing the same face. Moreover, the synchronous rotation means that Pluto's "day" is the same length as Charon's "month" (orbital period) of 6.4 Earth days. Charon would neither rise nor set in Pluto's skies but instead would cycle through its phases in place. The Sun would appear more than a thousand times fainter than it appears here on Earth, and it would be no larger in angular size than Jupiter is in our skies.

### Pluto: Planet or Kuiper Belt Object?

Pluto is an object in search of a category. It is a misfit among the planets, but it seems somewhat less out of place when considered in the context of the Kuiper belt. After all, it orbits in the same vicinity as Kuiper belt comets, it has a cometlike composition of icy and rocky materials, and it has a cometlike atmosphere that grows as it comes nearer the Sun in its orbit and fades as it recedes. Could Pluto be simply the largest known member of the Kuiper belt?

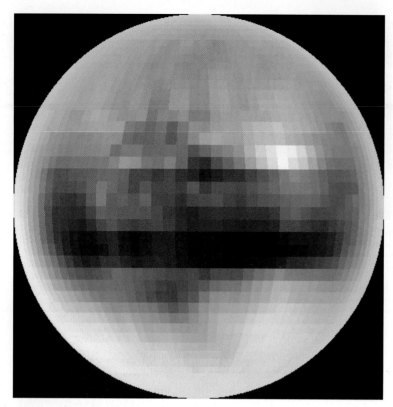

**FIGURE 12.18** The surface of Pluto in approximate true color, as derived from brightness measurements made during mutual eclipses between Pluto and Charon. The brown color probably comes from methane ice, but the origin of the dark equatorial band is unknown.

tune's moon Triton is quite similar to (and larger than) Pluto, and its orbit indicates that it must be a captured object. Thus, Triton was once a "planet" orbiting the Sun. Giant impacts of other large icy objects may have created Charon and might even have given Uranus its large tilt. Many Pluto-size objects probably roamed the Kuiper belt in its early days. Those that did not become trapped in stable resonances may have fallen inward to be accreted by the jovian planets or been thrown outward and ejected from the solar system. Pluto may be the largest surviving member of the Kuiper belt. However, it remains possible that we will someday discover other objects with sizes similar to that of Pluto, though probably farther away or considerably darker. As of 2001, only a small percentage of the sky had been thoroughly searched for large Kuiper belt objects.

**TIME OUT TO THINK** *What is your definition of a planet? Be as rigorous as possible. Exactly how many planets are there, according to your criteria? Does your list include Pluto, Charon, Ceres or other asteroids, or Triton (a captured cousin of Pluto)? How big would a new Kuiper belt object have to be to meet your definition? Try to convince a classmate of your definition. Is your definition useful?*

A closer look at the orbits of Kuiper belt objects uncovers an uncanny resemblance to the orbit of Pluto. Like Pluto, many Kuiper belt objects lie in stable orbital resonances with Neptune, and more than a dozen Kuiper belt objects have the same period and semimajor axis as Pluto itself (and are nicknamed "Plutinos"). Aside from Pluto's large size compared to the known comets, the most obvious difference between Pluto and Kuiper belt comets is their surface brightness. Comet nuclei generally have surfaces that are quite dark from carbon compounds, while Pluto's high reflectivity indicates an icy surface. However, this difference is easily explained. Whenever either Pluto or a smaller Kuiper belt comet approaches the Sun, the most volatile ices sublimate into an atmosphere. These atmospheric gases escape completely from the smaller Kuiper belt objects, but Pluto's gravity holds them until they refreeze onto the surface. Over time, the smaller Kuiper belt objects have become depleted in the most volatile ices, leaving behind the dark, carbon-rich compounds on their surfaces. Pluto has retained its volatile ices, giving it a bright, icy surface.

All in all, Pluto stands apart from Kuiper belt objects only in its size. But Pluto may not have been so unusual in the early solar system. Recall that Nep-

Planet or not, Pluto remains the largest known object in the solar system never visited by spacecraft. Close-up observations of its surface, atmosphere, and unusual moon are sure to teach us as much about icy bodies as past missions did about rocky bodies. NASA scientists and engineers are struggling with the difficult task of designing an affordable Pluto mission. Pluto presents real challenges: At typical spacecraft speeds it may take a decade to reach Pluto, but the faster a probe goes the less time it will have to study Pluto during its flyby. (A Pluto orbiter is simply too expensive.) Fortunately, recent advances in miniaturization are paying off. The current Pluto mission design fits on a coffee table but has instruments about as good as those on the Cassini spacecraft to Saturn, which is as large as a typical small classroom. (The Pluto probe design is also about 5–10 times cheaper than that of *Cassini*.) NASA's current goal is to send the mission to Pluto before its atmosphere completely refreezes onto the surface, but budget constraints may keep the mission from becoming a reality. (Check the text Web site for updates on the status of a Pluto mission.)

a This photo shows comet Shoemaker–Levy 9 after it was broken apart by tidal forces after passing close to Jupiter.

**FIGURE 12.19** Fragmented comets.

crater chain

b This chain of craters on Callisto probably formed long ago from impacts by fragments of a comet that, like comet Shoemaker–Levy 9, was broken apart by tidal forces while passing close to Jupiter. These impacts probably occurred just hours after the comet broke apart.

## 12.6 Cosmic Collisions: Small Bodies Versus the Planets

The hordes of small bodies orbiting the solar system are slowly shrinking in number through collisions with the planets and ejection from the solar system. Many more must have roamed the solar system in the days of the early bombardment, when most impact craters were formed [Section 8.5]. But there are still plenty left, and cosmic collisions still occur on occasion, with important ramifications for Earth as well as for other planets.

### Shoemaker–Levy 9 Impacts on Jupiter

We usually think about impacts in the context of solid bodies, because such impacts leave long-lasting scars in the form of impact craters. But impacts must be even more common on the jovian planets than on the terrestrial planets because of their larger size and stronger gravity, although no impact craters can form on gaseous worlds. It's estimated that a major impact occurs on Jupiter about once every 1,000 years. We were privileged to witness one in 1994.

The husband-and-wife team of Gene and Carolyn Shoemaker, along with their colleague David Levy, are among the premier "comet hunters" of modern times. During a routine search of the sky in March 1993, this team came across an unusual object that Carolyn Shoemaker described as a "squashed comet." The trio's ninth joint discovery, the comet was called *Shoemaker–Levy 9*, or *SL9* for short. On closer examination, the "squashed comet" turned out to be a string of comet nuclei all in a row (Figure 12.19a). The reason for SL9's odd appearance became clear

when astronomers calculated its orbit backward in time. The calculations showed that it had passed very close to Jupiter only a few months earlier (in July 1992). Because it had passed well within Jupiter's Roche tidal zone [Section 11.6], it apparently was ripped apart by tidal forces. Prior to that, SL9 was probably a single comet nucleus orbiting Jupiter, unnoticed by human observers. Similar breakups of comets near Jupiter have occurred before, as evidenced by a chain of craters on Callisto that must have formed when a string of comet nuclei crashed into its icy surface (Figure 12.19b).

The orbital calculations also showed that, thanks to gravitational nudges from the Sun, SL9 was on a collision course with Jupiter. Astronomers had more than a year to plan for observations of the impacts due in July 1994. The impacts of the 22 identified nuclei would take almost a week, and virtually every telescope on Earth and in space would be ready and watching. The only uncertainty was whether or not anything would happen. Even the best Hubble Space Telescope images were unable to determine whether the comet nuclei were massive kilometer-size chunks or merely insubstantial puffs of dust.

The answer came within minutes of the first impact: Infrared cameras recorded an intense fireball

**a** The Galileo spacecraft, on its way to Jupiter at the time, got a direct view of the impacts on Jupiter's night side.

**b** In under 20 minutes, the Hubble Space Telescope observed an impact plume rise thousands of kilometers above Jupiter's clouds and then collapse back down.

**c** This infrared photo shows the brilliant glow of a rising fireball from one of the impacts. Most of Jupiter appears dark because methane gas in its atmosphere absorbs infrared light.

**FIGURE 12.20** The SL9 impacts allowed astronomers their most direct view ever of cosmic collisions.

of hot gas rising thousands of kilometers above the impact site, which lay just barely on Jupiter's far side (Figure 12.20). As Jupiter's rapid rotation carried the scene into view, the collapsing plume smashed down on Jupiter's atmosphere, leading to another episode of heating and more infrared glow. The Hubble Space Telescope caught impact plumes in action as they rose into sunlight and collapsed back down, leaving dust clouds high in Jupiter's stratosphere. The impact scars lingered for months, but Jupiter has recovered—for now.

Material splashed out by the impacts provided us with a unique opportunity to study material from well beneath the layers of Jupiter that are ordinarily visible. More important, we learned much about the impact process itself. Many scientists correctly predicted the behavior of a rising plume of gas from an impact but did not consider the effects of the plume reimpacting on Jupiter. The reimpact of the plumes turned out to have even more significant global effects than the impact itself, heating an area 10,000 kilometers across and leaving dark, dusty clouds that eventually encircled the planet.

The SL9 impacts on Jupiter also provided two important sociological lessons. First, "Comet Crash Week" proved to be one of the best examples of international collaboration in history. With the aid of the Internet, scientists quickly and effectively shared data from observatories around the world. Second, extensive media coverage helped the event capture the public imagination, providing awareness that impacts are not relegated only to ancient geological history. Each individual fragment of SL9 crashing into Jupiter carried the equivalent force of a million hydrogen bombs. If such violent impacts can happen on other planets in our lifetime, could they also happen on Earth?

### Comet Tails and Meteor Showers

Far smaller impacts happen on Earth all the time, lighting up the sky as *meteors*. If you watch the sky on a clear night, you'll typically see a few meteors each hour. Most meteors are created by single pieces of comet dust, each no larger than a pea, that enter our atmosphere at speeds of up to 250,000 km/hr (70 km/s). (A small fraction of meteors may be dust from asteroids rather than comets, and the brightest meteors come from larger particles.) The particles and the surrounding atmosphere are heated so much that we see a brief but brilliant flash. Meteor particles are completely vaporized at altitudes of 50–100 kilometers, so we never get complete cometary

**d** This infrared photo shows high clouds created by several impacts. These clouds reflect infrared light from the Sun because they lie high above the methane gas that absorbs infrared light.

**e** In this visible-light photo from the Hubble Space Telescope, the high, dusty clouds left by the impacts appear as dark "scars" on Jupiter.

**f** This Hubble Space Telescope photo shows how the impact scars became smeared due to atmospheric winds. The scars disappeared completely within a few months.

**g** Artist's conception of the impacts viewed from the surface of Io.

"meteorites" to study. An estimated 25 million meteors occur worldwide every day, adding hundreds of tons of comet dust to the Earth daily.

Comet orbits tend to be filled with small particles ejected as the comets pass near the Sun. When Earth passes through a comet orbit, the particles striking our atmosphere produce a *meteor shower,* during which we may see dozens of meteors per hour. Earth's orbit intersects many comet orbits over the course of the year, and each produces a meteor shower (Table 12.1). The most famous meteor shower, the *Perseids,* occurs every August when the Earth passes through the orbit of comet Swift–Tuttle. Although meteors all strike the Earth on parallel tracks, meteor showers appear to radiate from a particular direction in the sky. You may have experienced a similar illusion while driving into a blizzard at night: The snowflakes seems to diverge from a single direction that depends on the combination of your speed and the wind speed (Figure 12.21a,b). (This illusion occurs even before the air flow around the car deflects the motion of the snowflakes.) The Perseids get their name because they appear to radiate from the constellation Perseus. (Figure 12.21c shows the Leonids from Leo.) The Earth runs into more meteors on the side facing in the direction of Earth's orbital motion (just as more snow hits the front windshield while the car is moving), so the predawn sky is the best place to watch for meteors.

**TIME OUT TO THINK** *The associated "comet" for the Geminid meteor shower is an object called Phaethon, which is classified as an asteroid because we've never seen a coma or tail associated with it. How is it possible that Phaethon looks like an asteroid today but once shed the particles that create the Geminid meteor shower?*

**Table 12.1  Major Annual Meteor Showers**

| Shower Name | Approximate Date |
|---|---|
| Quadrantids | January 3 |
| Lyrids | April 22 |
| Eta Aquarids | May 5 |
| Delta Aquarids | July 28 |
| Perseids | August 12 |
| Orionids | October 22 |
| Taurids | November 3 |
| Leonids | November 17 |
| Geminids | December 14 |
| Ursids | December 23 |

**FIGURE 12.21** Snowflakes and meteor showers.

**a** Driving into a blizzard.

**b** Geometry of a meteor shower: The Earth is moving through a swarm of comet debris.

**c** Meteors photographed during the intense Leonid meteor shower in 1966. Star images trailed across the photo from lower left to upper right during the time exposure. Meteors appear to streak away from the top center of the frame. Note one meteor at top center made a dot instead of a streak; it's headed straight for the camera.

**FIGURE 12.22** Meteor Crater in Arizona was created about 50,000 years ago by an asteroid impact. The crater is more than a kilometer across and almost 200 meters deep, but the asteroid that made it was only about 50 meters across.

## Impacts and Mass Extinctions

Meteorites and impact craters bear witness to the fact that much larger impacts occasionally occur on Earth. Meteor Crater in Arizona (Figure 12.22) formed about 50,000 years ago when a metallic impactor roughly 50 meters across crashed to Earth with the explosive power of a 20-megaton hydrogen bomb. Although the crater is only a bit more than 1 kilometer across, an area covering hundreds of square kilometers was probably battered by the blast and ejecta. Far bigger impacts have occurred, sometimes with catastrophic consequences for life on Earth.

Collecting geological samples in Italy in 1978, the father–son team of Luis and Walter Alvarez discovered a thin layer of dark sediments that had apparently been deposited 65 million years ago—about the same time that the dinosaurs and many other organisms suddenly became extinct. Subsequent studies found similar sediments deposited at the same time at many sites around the world (Figure 12.23). Careful analysis showed this worldwide sediment layer to be rich in the element iridium, which is rare on Earth's surface. But iridium is common in primitive meteorites, which led the Alvarezes to a stunning conclusion: The extinction of the dinosaurs was caused by the impact of an asteroid or comet. This conclusion was not immediately accepted and still generates some controversy, but it now seems clear that a major impact coincided with the death of the dinosaurs. Moreover, while the dinosaurs were the most famous victims of this **mass extinction**, it seems that up to 99% of all living things were killed and that 75% of all *species* living on Earth were wiped out at that time.

How could an impact lead to mass extinction? The amount of iridium deposited worldwide suggests that the impactor must have been about 10 kilometers across. After a decade-long search, scientists identified what appears to be the impact crater from the event. Located off the coast of Mexico's Yucatán peninsula (Figure 12.24), it is 200 kilometers across, which is close to what we expect for a 10-kilometer

**FIGURE 12.23** The arrow points to a layer of sediment laid down by the impact of 65 million years ago. At the time, the rock layers above the arrow did not exist. Dust from the impact and soot from global wildfires settled down through the atmosphere onto the seafloor that once occupied this location in Colorado.

impactor, and dates to 65 million years ago. Further evidence that the Yucatán crater is the right one comes from the distribution of small glassy spheres that formed when the molten impact ejecta solidified as it rained back to Earth. More of these glassy spheres are found in regions near the crater, and careful study of their distribution suggests that the impactor crashed to Earth at a slight angle. The impact almost immediately sent a shower of debris raining across much of North America and generated huge waves that may have sloshed more than 1,000 kilometers inland (Figure 12.25). Many North American species may have been wiped out shortly after impact. For the

**FIGURE 12.24** This false-color image, made with the aid of precise measurements of the strength of gravity, shows an impact crater with its center near the northwest coast of Yucatán. This crater, known as the Chicxulub crater, is thought to have been formed by the impact that killed the dinosaurs and most other species present 65 million years ago. The red box on the inset map shows the region covered by the image; the white lines on the image correspond to the coastlines and borders of Mexican states.

rest of the world, death may have come more slowly. Heat from the impact and returning ejecta probably ignited wildfires in forests around the world. Evidence of such wildfires is found in the large amount of soot that is also present in the iridium-rich sediments from 65 million years ago. The impact sent huge quantities of dust high into the stratosphere, where it remained for several years, blocking out sunlight, cooling the surface, and affecting atmospheric chemistry. Plants died for lack of sunlight, and effects propagated through the food chain.

Perhaps the most astonishing fact is not that 75% of all species died, but that 25% survived. Among the survivors were a few small, rodentlike mammals. These mammals may have survived because they lived in underground burrows and managed to store enough food to outlast the long spell of cold, dark days. Small mammals had first arisen at about the same time as the dinosaurs, more than 100 million years earlier. But the sudden disappearance of the dominant dinosaurs made these mammals dominant. With an evolutionary path swept wide open, they rapidly evolved into a large assortment of much larger mammals—including us.

The event 65 million years ago was but one of at least a dozen mass extinctions in Earth's distant past. An even larger extinction event 250 million years ago has also been linked to an impact and the ensuing catastrophic effects. Could a similar event occur in the future, wiping out all that we have accomplished?

### The Asteroid Threat:
### Real Danger or Media Hype?

The first step in analyzing the threat of future impacts is to examine the past evidence more thoroughly. Only one significant impact has clearly occurred in modern times. In 1908, an unusual explosion occurred in a sparsely inhabited region of Siberia. (The impact is known as the *Tunguska event.*) Entire forests were flattened and set on fire, and air blasts knocked over people, tents, and furniture up to 200 kilometers away (Figure 12.26). Seismic disturbances were recorded at distances of up to 1,000 kilometers, and atmospheric pressure fluctuations were detected almost 4,000 kilometers away. Scientific studies were

delayed for almost 20 years (due to the remoteness of the impact area and the politics of the time), but investigators eventually found meteoritic dust at the site—but no impact crater. These wide-reaching effects were apparently caused by a weak, stony meteorite only 30 meters across that exploded in the air, before reaching the surface. Objects of this size probably strike our planet every century or so, usually over the ocean. But the death toll could be quite high if such an object struck a densely populated area.

Another way to gauge the threat of impacts is to look at asteroids that might strike Earth. The largest-known *Earth-approaching asteroid*, Eros, is about 40 kilometers long (see Figure 12.4d). Hundreds of smaller Earth-approaching asteroids are known, down to sizes of tens of meters across. Orbital calculations show that none of these known objects will impact Earth in the foreseeable future. However, the vast majority of Earth-approaching asteroids probably have not yet been detected. Astronomers estimate that some 1,000 undiscovered members of this class may be larger than 1 kilometer across, and another 100,000 may be larger than 100 meters across. Many search programs are under way, detecting hundreds of objects every year. NASA has set a goal of detecting 90% of all large Earth-approaching asteroids by 2010. Comets also pose a threat, particularly because their rapid plunge from the outer solar system gives little warning.

By combining observations of asteroids with information from past impact craters, we can estimate the frequency of impacts of various sizes (Figure 12.27). Larger impacts are obviously more devastating but thankfully are rare. Impactors a few meters across probably break up high in the Earth's atmosphere

**FIGURE 12.25** Instant geology—and biology: Artist's conception (clockwise from upper left) of the impact that led to a mass extinction 65 million years ago.

every few days, with each liberating the energy of an atomic bomb. However, the effects are dissipated before they reach the surface, so we do not notice them. (Military technology designed to detect nuclear bomb tests has recorded many such events.) Hundred-meter impactors that forge craters similar to Meteor Crater probably strike only about every 10,000 years or so. Impacts large enough to cause mass extinctions occur tens of millions of years apart.

Thus, while it seems a virtual certainty that the Earth will be battered by many more large impacts, the chance of a major impact happening in our life-time is quite small. Nevertheless, the chance is not zero, and until we know the orbits of *all* large Earth-approaching asteroids we cannot predict when the next impact might occur. Some people advocate a thorough search to find all potentially dangerous as-

**FIGURE 12.26** Damage from the 1908 impact over Tunguska, Siberia.

In this chapter, we focused on the solar system's smallest objects and found that they can have big consequences. Asteroids, comets, and meteorites teach us much about the evolution of the solar system. And, in the case of the impact 65 million years ago, one such object may have made our existence possible. Keep in mind the following "big picture" ideas as you continue your studies:

- The smallest bodies in the solar system—asteroids and comets—are our best evidence of how the solar system formed.

- The small bodies are subjected to the gravitational whims of the planets, particularly the jovian planets. The subtleties of resonances play a major role in sculpting the outer solar system.

- The interplay of large and small bodies brings us meteorites to teach us our origins, comets and meteor showers to light up the sky, and impacts that can alter or obliterate life as we know it.

- Pluto is called the ninth planet, but it bears much more similarity to the thousands of Kuiper belt comets than to the other eight planets.

teroids, a relatively cheap proposition. But others wonder whether the information would be useful: If you knew an asteroid would hit next year, could you do anything about it? Schemes to save Earth by using nuclear weapons to demolish or divert an asteroid abound, but no one knows whether current technology is up to the task. For the time being, we can only hope that our number does not come up soon.

While some people see danger in Earth-approaching asteroids, others see opportunity, because Earth-approaching asteroids bring valuable resources tantalizingly close to Earth. Iron-rich asteroids are particularly enticing, since they probably contain many precious metals that mostly sank to the core on Earth. In the not-too-distant future, it may prove technically feasible and financially profitable to mine metals from asteroids and bring these resources to Earth. It may also be possible to gather fuel and water from asteroids for use in missions to the outer solar system.

**FIGURE 12.27** This graph shows how the frequency of impacts—as well as the magnitude of their effects—depends on the size of the impactor; note that smaller impacts are much more frequent than larger ones.

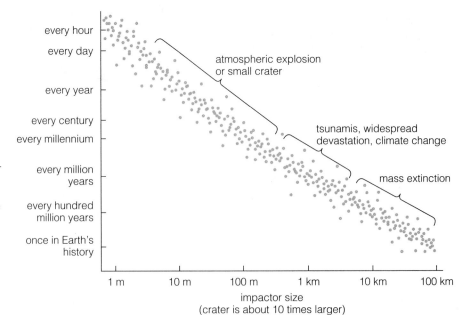

atmospheric explosion or small crater

tsunamis, widespread devastation, climate change

mass extinction

every hour
every day
every year
every century
every millennium
every million years
every hundred million years
once in Earth's history

1 m    10 m    100 m    1 km    10 km    100 km

impactor size
(crater is about 10 times larger)

## Review Questions

1. Briefly explain why comets, asteroids, and meteorites are so useful in terms of helping us understand the formation and development of our solar system.

2. What is the *asteroid belt,* and where is it located? How does the total mass of all the asteroids compare to the mass of a terrestrial world?

3. Briefly describe how orbital resonances with Jupiter have affected the asteroid belt.

4. How do we detect asteroids with telescopic images? How do we determine the orbit of an asteroid?

5. Briefly describe how we can estimate an asteroid's size, mass, density, and shape.

6. Describe the compositions of the three main groups of asteroids, as distinguished by spectroscopy.

7. How can we distinguish a meteorite from a terrestrial rock? Why do we find so many meteorites in Antarctica?

8. Distinguish between *primitive meteorites* and *processed meteorites* in terms of composition. How do the origins of these two groups of meteorites differ?

9. Why do primitive meteorites come in carbon-rich and rocky varieties?

10. How is the study of a processed meteorite an opportunity to look at a piece of a "dissected planet"?

11. How did Halley's comet get its name? How are comets named today?

12. Describe the anatomy of a comet. How does gas escape from the interior of the *nucleus* into space? Why do the *tails* point away from the Sun?

13. Why can't an active comet last forever? What happens to comets after many passes near the Sun?

14. Describe the Kuiper belt and the Oort cloud in terms of location and comet orbits. Explain how we infer the existence of these two comet reservoirs. How do we think comets came to exist in these two distinct reservoirs?

15. Describe Pluto and Charon. How were they discovered? Why won't Pluto collide with Neptune even though their orbits cross? How did Charon probably form?

16. Briefly summarize the evidence suggesting that Pluto is a Kuiper belt comet.

17. Describe the impact of comet Shoemaker–Levy 9 on Jupiter. How was the impact studied? What did we learn from this impact?

18. Explain how meteor showers are linked to comets. Why do meteor showers seem to originate from a particular location in the sky?

19. Describe the evidence suggesting that the *mass extinction* that killed off the dinosaurs was caused by the impact of an asteroid or comet. How did the impact lead to the mass extinction?

20. How often should we expect impacts of various sizes on Earth? How could we alleviate the risk of major impacts?

## Discussion Questions

1. *Impact Risk.* How can we compare the risk of death from an impact to the risk of death from other hazards? One proposed way to evaluate the risk is to multiply the probability of an impact by the number of people it would kill. For example, the probability of a major impact that could kill half the world's population, or some 3 billion people, is estimated to be about 0.0000001 ($10^{-7}$) in any given year. If we multiply this low probability by the 3 billion people that would be killed, we find the "average" risk from such an impact to be $10^{-7} \times (3 \times 10^9) = 300$ people killed per year—about the same as the average number of people killed in airplane crashes. Do you think it is valid to say that the risk of being killed by a major impact is about the same as the risk of being killed in an airplane crash? Should we pay to limit this risk, as we pay to limit airline crashes? Defend your opinions.

2. *Observational Bias.* Meteorites and long-tailed comets represent "free samples" of more distant objects.

   a. Carbon-rich asteroids make up about 5% of meteorite falls on the Earth. How does this compare with the observed fraction of carbon-rich asteroids in the asteroid belt? The odds of a particular comet we observe originating from the Oort cloud versus the Kuiper belt are about 50–50. How does this compare with the relative number of objects in these two regions?

   b. Your answers to part (a) should show that meteorite samples and comet observations suffer from *bias*—that is, what we learn from their study may not accurately reflect the complete populations of the objects they represent. How might a similar bias play a role in more down-to-earth situations? For example, do you and your classmates form a representative sample of your city, nation, or planet? How might this affect the accuracy of a report on world events you might write together or the fairness of a decision you might vote on? In what ways can the effects of bias be removed?

3. *Rise of the Mammals.* Suppose the impact 65 million years ago had not occurred. How do you think our planet would be different? For example, do you think that mammals would still have eventually come to dominate the Earth? Would we be here? Defend your opinions.

## Problems

*Surprising Discoveries?* For **problems 1–8**, suppose we made the discoveries described. (These are *not* real discoveries.) Decide whether the discovery should be considered reasonable or surprising. Explain.

1. A small asteroid that orbits within the asteroid belt has an active volcano.

2. Scientists discover a meteorite that, based on radioactive dating, is 7.9 billion years old.

3. An object that resembles a comet in size and composition is discovered to be orbiting in the inner solar system.

4. Studies of a large object in the Kuiper belt reveal that it is made almost entirely of rocky (as opposed to icy) material.

5. Astronomers discover a previously unknown comet that will produce a spectacular display in Earth's skies about 2 years from now.

6. A mission to Pluto finds that it has lakes of liquid water on its surface.

7. Geologists discover a crater from a 5-km object that impacted the Earth more than 100 million years ago.

8. Archaeologists learn that the fall of ancient Rome was caused in large part by an asteroid impact in southern Africa.

9. *Orbital Resonances.* How would our solar system be different if orbital resonances had never been important (for example, if Jupiter and asteroids continued to orbit the Sun but did not affect each other through resonances)? Describe at least five ways in which our solar system would be different. Which differences do you consider superficial, and which differences more profound? Consider the effects of orbital resonances discussed both in this chapter and in Chapter 11.

10. *Life Story of an Iron Atom.* Imagine that you are an iron atom in an iron meteorite recently fallen to Earth. Tell the story of how you got here, beginning from the time when you were in a gaseous state in the solar nebula 4.6 billion years ago. Include as much detail as possible. Your story should be scientifically accurate but also creative and interesting.

11. *Asteroid Discovery.* You have discovered two new asteroids and have named them Barkley and Jordan. Both lie at the same distance from the Earth and have the same brightness when you look at them through your telescope. But Barkley is twice as bright as Jordan at infrared wavelengths. What can you deduce about the two asteroids' relative reflectivities and sizes? Which would make a better target for a mission to mine metal? Which would make a better target for a mission to obtain a sample of a carbon-rich planetesimal? Explain your answers.

*12. *The "Near Miss" of Toutatis.* The 5-km asteroid Toutatis passed a mere 3 million km from the Earth in 1992.

   a. In one or two paragraphs, describe what would have happened to the Earth if Toutatis had hit it.

   b. Suppose Toutatis was destined to pass *somewhere* within 3 million km of Earth. Calculate the probability that this "somewhere" would have meant that it slammed into Earth. Based on your result, do you think it is fair to say that the 1992 passage was a "near miss"? Explain. (*Hint:* You can calculate the probability by considering an imaginary dartboard of radius 3 million km on which the bull's-eye has the Earth's radius of 6,378 km.)

*13. *Comet Temperatures.* Compare the strength of sunlight at 50,000 AU in the Oort cloud with its strength at 3 AU and 1 AU. Compare the "no greenhouse" temperatures for comets (see Mathematical Insight 10.1) at the three positions. At which location will the temperature be high enough for water ice to sublime (about 150 K)? Assume that the comets rotate rapidly and have an albedo of 3%.

14. *Project: Tracking a Meteor Shower.* Armed with an expendable star chart and a flashlight covered in red plastic, set yourself up comfortably to watch a meteor shower listed in Table 12.1. Each time you see a meteor, record its path on your star chart. Record at least a dozen, and try to determine the *radiant* of the shower—the point in the sky from which the meteors appear to radiate. Also record the direction of the Earth's motion, which you can find by determining which sign of the zodiac rises at midnight.

15. *Project: Dirty Snowballs.* If there is snow where you live or study, make a filthy snowball. (The ice chunks that form behind tires work well.) How much dirt does it take to darken snow? Find out by allowing your dirty snowball to melt and measuring the approximate proportions of water and dirt afterward.

## Web Projects

Find useful links for Web projects on the text Web site.

1. *The NEAR Mission.* Learn about the NEAR mission to the asteroid Eros. How did the mission reach Eros? How did it end? What did it accomplish? Write a one- to two-page summary of your findings.

2. *Stardust.* Learn about NASA's Stardust mission (launched in 1999) to bring back cometary material to Earth. What is the current status of the spacecraft? What do we hope to learn after it returns? Write a report about the mission status and its science.

3. *Asteroid and Comet Missions.* Learn about another proposed space mission to study asteroids or comets. Write a short report about the mission plans, goals, and prospects for success.

4. *Pluto Express.* NASA has gone back and forth for years about a mission to Pluto, the only planet not yet visited by spacecraft. Find the latest on plans for a mission to Pluto. Does the mission seem likely to take place anytime soon? Write a short report about the current status of a Pluto mission. Discuss the scientific goals of such a mission and the political realities that may dictate whether it occurs.

*Looking outward to the blackness of space, sprinkled with the glory of a universe of lights, I saw majesty—but no welcome. Below was a welcoming planet. There, contained in the thin, moving, incredibly fragile shell of the biosphere is everything that is dear to you, all the human drama and comedy. That's where life is; that's where all the good stuff is.*

LOREN ACTON, U.S. ASTRONAUT

# CHAPTER 13

# Planet Earth
## And Its Lessons on Life in the Universe

Perhaps you've heard the Earth described as the "third rock from the Sun." At first glance, the perspective of comparative planetology may seem to support this dispassionate view of the Earth. However, a deeper comparison between Earth and its neighbors reveals a far more remarkable planet.

Earth is unique in the solar system in many ways. It is the only planet with surface oceans of liquid water and substantial amounts of oxygen in its atmosphere, and its geological activity is more diverse than that of any other terrestrial world. Most important, Earth is the only world known to harbor life, which has played a considerable role in shaping the Earth's surface and atmosphere.

So far, we have found that our theories of solar system formation and planetary evolution explain most of the general features of our solar system. In this chapter, we will apply and extend what we've learned in order to form a coherent picture of the combined geological, atmospheric, and biological evolution of our planet. We'll also discuss a few important lessons that the solar system teaches us about our future on Earth and that the Earth teaches us about the possibility of life elsewhere in the universe.

## 13.1 How Is Earth Different?

Take a look at Figure 13.1. The abundant white clouds overlying the expanse of oceans show a planet unlike any other in our solar system. It is, of course, our own planet Earth.

In Chapters 9 and 10, we discussed many features of the Earth's geology and atmosphere. We found many similarities between the Earth and other terrestrial worlds, and also some important differences. For example, the Earth's surface is shaped by the same four geological processes (impact cratering, volcanism, tectonics, and erosion) that shape other worlds, but Earth is the only planet on which the lithosphere is clearly broken into plates that move around in what we call plate tectonics. The Earth's atmosphere shows even more substantial differences

from the atmospheres of its neighbors: It is the only planet with significant atmospheric oxygen and the only terrestrial world with an ultraviolet-absorbing stratosphere.

But the greatest differences between Earth and other worlds lie in two features totally unique to Earth. First, the surface of the Earth is covered by huge amounts of water. Oceans cover nearly three-fourths of the Earth's surface, with an average depth of about 3 kilometers (1.8 miles). Water is also significant on land, where it flows through streams and rivers, fills lakes and underground water tables, and sometimes lies frozen in glaciers. Frozen water covers nearly the entire continent of Antarctica in the form of the southern ice cap. The northern ice cap sits atop the Arctic Ocean and covers the large island of Greenland. Water plays such an important role on Earth that some scientists treat it as a distinct planetary layer, called the **hydrosphere**, between the lithosphere and the atmosphere.

The second totally unique feature of Earth is its diversity of life. We find life nearly everywhere on Earth's surface, throughout the oceans, and even underground. The layer of life on Earth is sometimes called the **biosphere**. As we will see shortly, the biosphere helps shape many of the Earth's physical characteristics. For example, the biosphere explains the presence of oxygen in Earth's atmosphere. Without life, Earth's atmosphere would be very different.

Comparative planetology compels us to explore these unique properties of Earth closely. If we find that the formation and evolution of our Earth violated the rules we've derived for other planets—if Earth is "irregular"—life might be unique to Earth. If Earth does follow the rules—if Earth is "regular" or even "standard"—then life may be common in the universe.

## 13.2 Our Unique Geology

It's not surprising that Earth shows much more geological activity than Mercury or the Moon, since those small worlds have cooled since their formation and are now geologically "dead." But why have Earth and Venus ended up so different, despite very similar sizes? And, although Earth is significantly larger than Mars, both planets probably once had similar surface conditions that allowed liquid water to flow. Why did Earth remain hospitable, while Mars is now dry and barren? These mysteries warrant a closer look.

Figure 13.2 shows shaded relief maps comparing the surfaces of Earth, Venus, and Mars. While the three planets have many superficial similarities, they also have important differences. We find fewer impact craters on Venus than on Mars, and fewer still on Earth. Most of Earth's volcanic mountains are

Venus

Earth

Mars

**FIGURE 13.2** These shaded relief maps compare the surfaces of Venus, Earth, and Mars; the map for Earth shows the seafloor as it would appear if there were no oceans. Despite superficial similarities, there are important differences. For example, Mars has the most craters, and Earth has the fewest. Also note the unique distinction between the two kinds of surface (seafloor and continent) on Earth.

seafloor crust (5–10 km thick, dense, young)

upper mantle

continental crust (20–70 km thick, lower-density, old)

**FIGURE 13.3** Earth has two distinct kinds of crust.

comes in two very different varieties: a relatively thick, low-density crust underlying the *continents*, and a thinner, denser crust underlying the *seafloors* (Figure 13.3). Seafloor crust is made of basalt and is typically only 5–10 km thick, whereas continental crust is made of lower-density rock (such as granite) and is 20–70 km thick. To understand these and other unique features of Earth's geology, we must look in more detail at how the four geological processes affect our planet.

Before we discuss the geological processes themselves, remember that they depend in many ways on a planet's interior structure. We know much more about Earth's interior structure than we do about that of any other planet, because geologists have created a three-dimensional "picture" of the interior by analyzing the propagation of seismic waves from earthquakes (Figure 13.4). The Earth's thin crust and the uppermost portion of the mantle make up a relatively cool and rigid *lithosphere* about 100 km thick [Section 9.2]. Below the lithosphere, the mantle is warm and partially molten in places; it supplies the magma for volcanic eruptions. Deeper in the mantle, higher pressures force the rock into the solid phase despite even higher temperatures. But even in solid form the mantle slowly flows, and convection continually carries heat up from below. The Earth's metallic core underlies the lower mantle. The outer region of the core is molten, but high pressures in the inner core force the metal into solid form. Thus, the Earth has all the

steep-sided and therefore must have been made from a much more viscous lava than that found on the other planets. And Earth shows far more evidence of tectonic activity—surface reshaping driven by internal stresses. To our current knowledge, Earth is the only terrestrial planet on which the lithosphere is split into distinct *plates*. Earth also has a crust that

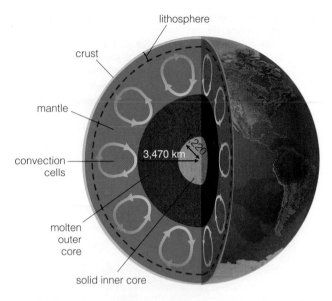

**FIGURE 13.4** Internal structure of the Earth, based on the study of seismic waves (Figure 9.6).

ingredients needed for exciting geology: a hot interior to supply energy for volcanism, convection to help generate tectonic stresses, and a relatively thin lithosphere that does not inhibit geological activity.

### The Four Geological Processes on Earth

The first of the four geological processes, *impact cratering,* should have occurred at roughly similar rates on all the terrestrial worlds. All were subject to the intense early bombardment during the solar system's first few hundred million years. Four billion years ago, the Earth's surface may have been as saturated with craters as the densely cratered lunar highlands are today [Section 9.5]. We find no 4-billion-year-old craters on Earth now, so these ancient impacts must have been erased by other geological processes. The impact rate fell substantially after the early bombardment, but occasional impacts still occur—sometimes with devastating consequences [Section 12.6]. The effects of erosion make impact craters surprisingly difficult to identify on Earth. Nevertheless, remnants of more than 100 impact craters have been found (see Figure 12.8). Large impacts should have occurred more or less uniformly over the Earth's surface, including both continents and seafloors, because large impactors are not stopped by the oceans. The relative absence of craters on the seafloor suggests that seafloor crust is much younger than is continental crust; it must have formed later than most of the impacts.

The rampant *erosion* on Earth arises primarily from processes involving water, but atmospheric winds also contribute. Wind tears away at geological fea-

tures created by other processes, blows dust and sand across the globe, and builds features such as sand dunes. Note that wind erosion is more effective on Earth than on either Venus or Mars: Venus has very little surface wind because of its slow rotation, and wind on Mars does little damage because of the low atmospheric pressure. On Earth, water contributes to erosion through a remarkable variety of processes (Figure 13.5). Perhaps the most obvious are rain and rivers breaking down mountains, carving canyons, and transporting sand and silt across continents to deposit them in the sea. But water erosion occurs on microscopic levels too: Water seeps into cracks and crevices in rocks and breaks them down from the inside, especially when this water freezes and expands. Further examples of water-erosion processes include the slow movement of glaciers, the flow of underground rivers, and the pounding of the ocean surf.

*Volcanism* and *tectonics* are also very important processes on Earth. The many active volcanoes prove that volcanism still reshapes the surface, and many small-scale cliffs and valleys offer evidence of tectonics similar to that found on other terrestrial worlds. But plate tectonics may be unique to Earth. To gain a deeper understanding of our planet's closely linked volcanism and tectonics, we must study plate tectonics in more detail.

### Plate Tectonics

If you cut up a map and rearrange the continents, you'll find that they fit together in surprising ways. For example, the east coast of South America fits quite nicely into the west coast of Africa (Figure 13.6). You might chalk this up to coincidence, but we also find similar types of distinct rocks and rare fossils in eastern South America and western Africa—suggesting that these two regions were once near each other. Based on such evidence, in 1912 German meteorologist and geologist Alfred Wegener proposed the idea of *continental drift:* that the continents gradually drift across the surface of the Earth, over time scales of tens of millions of years.

For decades after Wegener made his proposal, most geologists rejected the idea that continents could move, and many ridiculed the idea openly. However, the idea of continental drift gained favor in the 1950s as supporting evidence began to accumulate. Mapping of the seafloors revealed surprising structures (Figure 13.7): high *mid-ocean ridges* extending a total length of about 60,000 km along the ocean floors, and *trenches* in which the ocean depth can reach more than 8 kilometers. Geologists soon recognized that these features represented boundaries between **plates**—pieces of the lithosphere that apparently float upon the denser mantle below. Convection cells in the upper mantle move the plates around the surface, forcing them together, apart, or sideways at

**a** The Colorado River continues to carve the Grand Canyon after millions of years.

**b** Glaciers created Yosemite Valley during the ice ages.

**d** Erosional debris also creates geological features, as seen in this river delta.

**c** Surf pounds away at the California coastline.

**FIGURE 13.5** A few examples of water erosion.

Africa

South America

**FIGURE 13.6** The "fit" of South America into Africa.

**FIGURE 13.7** The discovery of mid-ocean ridges and deep trenches provided important evidence for continental drift. The relief map uses color to show elevation, progressing from blue (lowest) to red (highest). Solid lines show plate boundaries, and arrows represent directions in which the plates are moving. Important geological features discussed later in the text are identified.

their boundaries—with profound geological consequences. This discovery offered a model to explain how continents could drift about, and Wegener's idea finally gained acceptance under the new name **plate tectonics**. (Recall that tectonics is geological activity driven by internal stresses, so *plate tectonics* refers to the motion of plates driven by internal stresses.) Today we know that the Earth's lithosphere is broken into more than a dozen plates (Figure 13.7). Most major earthquakes and volcanic eruptions occur along plate boundaries.

**TIME OUT TO THINK** *Study the plate boundaries in Figure 13.7. Based on this diagram, explain why the West Coast states of California, Oregon, and Washington are more prone to earthquakes and volcanoes than other parts of the United States.*

Over millions of years, plate tectonics acts like a giant conveyor belt for the Earth's crust, carrying rock up from the mantle, transporting it across the seafloor, and then returning it down into the mantle (Figure 13.8). The mid-ocean ridges mark **spreading centers** between plates—places where hot mantle material rises upward and then spreads sideways, pushing the plates apart. New seafloor crust forms as the partially molten mantle material emerges through

a long string of underwater volcanoes, forming crust made of basalt [Section 9.4]. The newly formed basaltic crust cools and contracts as it spreads sideways from the central ridge, giving mid-ocean ridges their characteristic shape (see Figure 13.7). The new crust spreads throughout the area that opens as plates separate, forming only a relatively thin layer of crust over the mantle (see Figure 13.3). Worldwide along the mid-ocean ridges, new crust covers an area of about 2 square kilometers every year—enough to replace the entire seafloor within a geologically short time of about 200 million years. Meanwhile, as new crust spreads over the surface, older crust must be returned to the mantle. This return occurs at the locations of the deep ocean trenches, which mark places where one plate slides under another in a process called **subduction**. As we would expect from this model of seafloor crust formation, samples of seafloor crust are composed of basaltic material, and radioactive dating [Section 8.6] shows their age to be generally less than 200 million years.

The conveyor-like process of plate tectonics is undoubtedly driven by convection, although the precise nature of the convection remains uncertain. The crust may be simply dragged along by convection in the upper mantle. Alternatively, the tops of the convection cells may actually be the crust itself, with warm rock rising up under the ocean ridges and cooler,

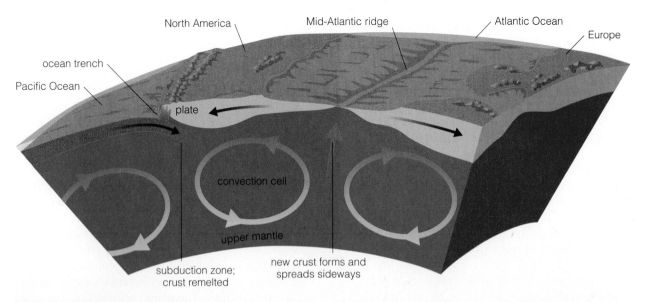

North America    Mid-Atlantic ridge    Atlantic Ocean    Europe

ocean trench

Pacific Ocean

plate

convection cell

upper mantle

subduction zone;
crust remelted

new crust forms and
spreads sideways

**FIGURE 13.8** Plate tectonics acts like a giant conveyor belt, driven by mantle convection, that carries rock up from the mantle at mid-ocean ridges, transports it across the seafloor, and returns it down into the mantle at ocean trenches.

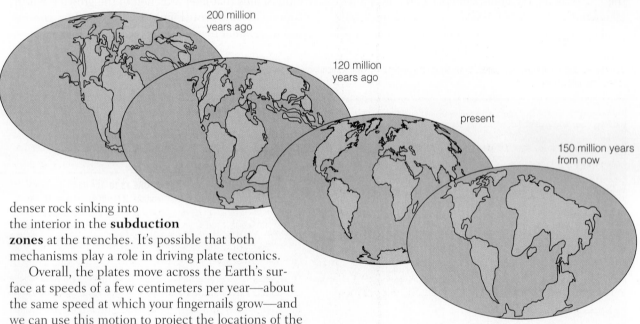

200 million
years ago

120 million
years ago

present

150 million years
from now

denser rock sinking into the interior in the **subduction zones** at the trenches. It's possible that both mechanisms play a role in driving plate tectonics.

Overall, the plates move across the Earth's surface at speeds of a few centimeters per year—about the same speed at which your fingernails grow—and we can use this motion to project the locations of the continents millions of years into the past or future. For example, at a speed of 2 centimeters per year, a plate will travel 2,000 kilometers in 100 million years. Over longer time scales, the plates may have altered their speeds and directions, but we can still project past locations of continents through careful comparisons of rock and fossil samples found in different places. For example, if 500-million-year-old rocks and fossils are very similar in two places, the two places were probably close together at that time, even if they are far apart now. Figure 13.9 shows several past arrangements of the continents, along with one future arrangement. Over the past billion years, the continents have slammed together, pulled apart, spun around, and changed places on the globe. Central

The Mediterranean Sea will become mountains, Australia will merge with Antarctica, and California will slide northward to Alaska.

**FIGURE 13.9** Past, present, and predicted future arrangements of the Earth's continents.

Africa once lay at Earth's South Pole, and Antarctica was once nearer the equator. At various times, such as was the case about 200 million years ago, the continents were all merged into a single giant continent, often called *Pangaea* (which means "all lands"). The current arrangement of the continents is no more permanent than any other.

*Subduction and the Origin of Continents* Where plates collide, subduction of seafloor crust creates continental crust. The seafloor crust remelts as subduction carries it back into the mantle, and the resulting magma separates by density. The lowest-density magma—which consists of rocks such as rhyolite, andesite, and granite—pushes upward to form continental crust. Thus, continental crust is made of lower-density material than seafloor crust. Plate tectonics has gradually built up thick continental crust over about 45% of the Earth's surface, and the fraction is still increasing. (Some of this continental crust is underwater—continental shelves—so land areas represent *less* than 45% of the Earth's surface.) Billions of years ago, Earth was even more of an ocean planet than it is today.

Despite being tens of kilometers thicker than seafloor crust, on average the continental crust rises only a few kilometers higher in altitude. The sheer weight of the continents presses down on the mantle, so most of their extra thickness goes deeper into the Earth. Thus, the continents poke up only a few kilometers higher than the seafloors (see Figure 13.3).

The present-day continents have been built up over billions of years; radioactive dating shows some rocks in continental crust to be as much as 4 billion years old.

The rising magma along plate boundaries creates tremendous volcanic activity. Where one seafloor plate subducts under another, the resulting eruptions form a long string of volcanic islands. Alaska's Aleutian Islands exemplify this process at an early stage. As the process continues, islands can grow and merge; this occurred with both Japan and the Philippines, each of which once contained many small islands that merged into the fewer islands we see today. As these islands continue to grow and merge, they may eventually create a new continent. In other cases, a plate carrying islands may run up against an existing continental plate. The dense seafloor crust surrounding the islands subducts below the continents, but the islands resist subduction because they are made of low-density rock. The islands are essentially scraped off the seafloor and stuck onto the continent. Alaska, British Columbia, Washington, Oregon, and most of California began their existence as numerous Pacific islands that later attached to the growing North American continent (Figure 13.10). Seafloor continues to subduct below these states and provinces.

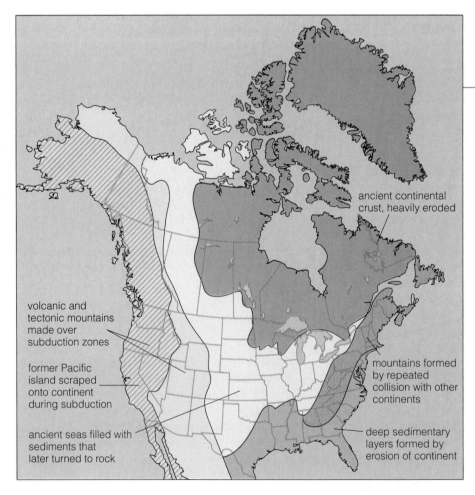

ancient continental crust, heavily eroded

volcanic and tectonic mountains made over subduction zones

former Pacific island scraped onto continent during subduction

ancient seas filled with sediments that later turned to rock

mountains formed by repeated collision with other continents

deep sedimentary layers formed by erosion of continent

**FIGURE 13.10** The major geological features of North America record the complex history of plate tectonics. Only the basic processes behind the largest features are shown here.

**b** The Himalayas are still slowly growing as the Indian plate (carrying India) pushes into the Eurasian plate (carrying most of the rest of Asia). (Satellite photo.)

**a** Tectonic forces have torn the Arabian peninsula from Africa. (Photo from Space Shuttle.)

**FIGURE 13.11** Tectonic forces on continent.

The low-density magmas generated by subduction have relatively high viscosity, which affects the kind of volcanoes they construct. The rhyolite and andesite lavas that emerge from volcanoes along plate boundaries create steep-sided *stratovolcanoes* [Section 9.4] like Mount St. Helens in Washington and the mountains of the Andes range in South America. Granite magma usually does not erupt onto the surface but instead builds mountains through vast underground intrusions that make the rock layers above them bulge up. The upper rock layers may gradually erode away, leaving granite mountain ranges such as the Sierra Nevada in California.

*Tectonic Stresses on Continents* Continental crust is relatively thick, strong, and low-density, so it resists both spreading and subduction. Instead of simply separating like seafloor crust on either side of a mid-ocean ridge, continental crust thins and creates a *rift valley* when mantle convection tugs it apart. One such rift valley runs through Africa; it will eventually tear the continent apart and create a seafloor spreading center. A similar process tore the Arabian peninsula from Africa in the past, creating the Red Sea (Figure 13.11a).

When two continent-bearing plates collide, neither plate can subduct (because of the low density of the crust), and the resulting pressure creates tremendous mountain ranges. The Indian Plate is currently ramming into the Eurasian Plate, forming the Himalayas (Figure 13.11b). These mountains, already the tallest on Earth, are still growing. The Appalachian range in the eastern United States formed by the same process as North America collided twice with South America and then with western Africa over a period of hundreds of millions of years. The Appala-

chians were probably once as tall as the Himalayas are now, but erosion has gradually transformed them into the fairly modest mountain range we see today. Similar processes contributed to forming the Rocky Mountains in the United States and Canada.

At other places on Earth, plates slip sideways relative to each other along a **fault**, or a fracture in a  Along California's San Andreas fault (and many other places in the world), plates are sliding sideways past each other. Asterisks indicate recent earthquakes.

b  The photo shows a place where a road is no longer straight because of this movement.

c  Earthquakes occur when plates slip violently along a fault. This photo shows damage from the 1995 earthquake in Kobe, Japan.

**FIGURE 13.12**  Plate tectonics on a human level.

the lithosphere. This is the case with the *San Andreas fault* in California, where plate motions are carrying Los Angeles on a 20-million-year trip to San Francisco (Figure 13.12a). Plates do not slip smoothly against each other. Instead, their rough surfaces resist slippage until the tension grows too high; then everything slips along the fault in the violent motion that we call an *earthquake* (Figure 13.12b,c). The motions associated with earthquakes can raise mountains, level cities, and set the whole planet vibrating with seismic waves. In contrast to the usual motion of plates at the rate of a few centimeters per year,

an earthquake can move plates by several *meters* in a few seconds. Although most earthquake faults lie along plate boundaries, a few more ancient faults are found elsewhere. As a result, devastating earthquakes occasionally occur in regions that we tend to think of as at low risk from seismic events. In fact, one of the largest earthquakes in U.S. history occurred in Missouri in 1811.

*Hot Spots and Mantle Plumes*  Not all volcanoes occur near plate boundaries. Sometimes, a plume of hot mantle material may rise in what we call a **hot spot** within a plate. The Hawaiian Islands are the

Aleutian
Trench

Kauai: heavily eroded valleys

Hawaii: recent lava flows

Midway: island eroded down to sea level

relative motion of
mantle plume

Hawaiian Islands

Loihi: future Hawaiian island
(in about a million years)

**FIGURE 13.13** The Hawaiian Islands are just the most recent of a very long string of volcanic islands made by a mantle hot spot. The black-and-white image of Loihi (lower right) was obtained by sonar, as it is still entirely under water.

result of a hot spot that has been erupting basaltic lava for tens of millions of years (Figure 13.13). The low viscosity of this lava produces broad *shield volcanoes* [Section 9.4]. Today, most of the lava erupts on the "Big Island" of Hawaii, giving much of this island a young, rocky surface. But about a million years ago, the mantle plume lay farther to the northwest—or, equivalently, the entire plate lay farther to the southeast. Back then, the eruptions built the island of Maui, parts of which are now heavily eroded and covered in lush vegetation. Before that, the mantle hot spot built the other islands of Hawaii, including

Oahu (3 million years ago) and Kauai (5 million years ago); it also created Midway Island (27 million years ago), which has now almost completely eroded back to sea level. Thus, this single hot spot created a vast string of islands (and smaller underwater mountains) as the plate gradually moved over it. The process continues today: A new island named Loihi is currently forming beneath the ocean surface and will rise above sea level southeast of Hawaii in a million years or so. Hot spots can also appear beneath continental crust. The geysers and hot springs of Yellowstone National Park result from the heating of a mantle plume. This hot spot is currently migrating to the northeast (relative to the continental crust) because of the southwestern motion of the plate.

### Summary of Earth's Geology

Two fundamental differences between the geology of Earth and that of other terrestrial worlds stand out:

1. Rampant erosion driven by the action of plentiful water—a direct result of Earth's atmospheric evolution, as we will see.

2. A different style of tectonics—plate tectonics—that recycles crust, drives high-viscosity volcanism to create continental crust, and causes frequent earthquakes.

Together, these two processes have reshaped the Earth's surface beyond recognition from its original state billions of years ago. They make the Earth's surface very young, perhaps the youngest in the solar system besides that of Io [Section 11.5].

But why does Earth's geology differ from that of our neighbors in these two ways? In the next section, we'll see how our unique atmosphere leads to the strong erosion on Earth. We'll also find that the interactions between our atmosphere and geology might help explain why Earth has plate tectonics while similar-size Venus does not.

## 13.3 Our Unique Atmosphere

In Chapter 10, we learned that the superficial differences in the atmospheres of the terrestrial planets are fairly easy to understand. For example, the Moon and Mercury lack substantial atmospheres because of their small sizes, and a very strong greenhouse effect causes the high surface temperature on Venus. We also learned how solar heating, seasonal changes, and the Coriolis effect that comes from rotation lead to differing global circulation patterns on different worlds. But explaining how the compositions of the atmospheres came to be so different is more challenging, especially when we consider the cases of Venus, Earth, and Mars. Outgassing produced all three of these atmospheres, and the same volatiles—primarily water and carbon dioxide—were outgassed in all three cases. How, then, did Earth's atmosphere end up so different? In particular, any study of Earth's atmosphere must address four major questions:

1. Why did Earth retain most of its water—in the form of the oceans and other components of the hydrosphere—while Venus and Mars lost theirs?

2. Why does Earth have so little carbon dioxide ($CO_2$) in its atmosphere, when Earth should have outgassed about as much of it as Venus?

3. Why does Earth have so much more oxygen ($O_2$) than Venus or Mars? Where did it come from, and how does this highly reactive gas remain present in the atmosphere?

4. Why does Earth have an ultraviolet-absorbing stratosphere, while Venus and Mars do not?

To answer these questions, we must look into the history of Earth's atmosphere. The answers to all four questions turn out to be closely connected.

**TIME OUT TO THINK** *Recall that water ice could not condense in the region of the solar nebula where the terrestrial planets formed. How, then, did the water outgassed from volcanoes get here in the first place? (Hint: See Section 8.5.)*

### Water and the Origin of the Hydrosphere

On a basic level, it's fairly easy to explain why the Earth retains so much water while Venus and Mars do not. As we learned in Chapter 10, Venus probably lost an "ocean-full" of water as solar ultraviolet photons split apart water molecules and the hydrogen atoms subsequently escaped to space. Mars probably lost some of its water in a similar way, and the rest is frozen at the polar caps and under the surface.

Let's look a little more closely at the sequence of events that led to these different histories. Picture a generic terrestrial planet, billions of years ago, with erupting volcanoes outgassing carbon dioxide, water vapor, and small amounts of nitrogen. As the outgassing continued, the water vapor might have either condensed into oceans, frozen out as snow, or remained gaseous in the atmosphere. In the case of Venus, proximity to the Sun made the planet warm enough to keep all its water gaseous in the atmosphere, even before it had a strong greenhouse effect. Because water vapor itself is a greenhouse gas, this caused significant greenhouse warming and ensured that additional water vapor would also remain gaseous and warm the planet further. This tendency of the greenhouse effect to reinforce itself is called the **runaway greenhouse effect**. At the other extreme, Mars's temperature was eventually low enough for the water vapor to freeze out of the atmosphere, resulting in thick polar caps.

On Earth, moderate temperatures allowed most of the water vapor to condense as rain, leading to the accumulation of liquid water in the oceans. A small amount of water vapor remained in the atmosphere and caused greenhouse warming, but not enough to create a runaway greenhouse effect. Additional water vapor released from volcanoes therefore also condensed, gradually forming the oceans and the other components of the hydrosphere. Thus, Venus lost its oceans because it was too hot, Mars lost its oceans because it was too cold, and Earth retained its oceans because conditions were "just right."

## Where Is All the CO$_2$?

Measurements of outgassing by active volcanoes and estimates of past volcanic activity suggest that Earth must have outgassed nearly as much carbon dioxide throughout its history as Venus. But Venus today has an atmosphere with a CO$_2$ concentration of 96%, a surface pressure 90 times greater than that on Earth, and about 500°C of greenhouse warming. In contrast, the proportion of carbon dioxide in Earth's atmosphere is much less than 1%; in fact, we usually measure CO$_2$ concentration on Earth in units of *parts per million*. (For example, 300 parts per million means $300 \div 1,000,000 = 0.0003 = 0.03\%$.) Clearly, some atmospheric loss process must have removed nearly all of the outgassed CO$_2$ on Earth.

The secret of Earth's CO$_2$ is wrapped up in the history of our oceans. The primary process that removes atmospheric CO$_2$ on Earth involves liquid water. Carbon dioxide can dissolve in water, and the oceans actually contain about 60 times more carbon dioxide than the atmosphere—but this is still a very small amount compared to the total amount that must have been outgassed. Most of the carbon dioxide is locked up in rocks on the seafloor through chemical reactions. Rainfall erodes silicate rocks on the Earth's surface and carries the eroded minerals to the oceans. There the minerals react with dissolved carbon dioxide to form *carbonate* minerals [Section 10.5], which fall to the ocean floor, building up thick layers of carbonate rock such as *limestone*. This is part of the **carbonate–silicate cycle** (Figure 13.14). Because the process requires liquid water, it operates only on Earth, where it has removed about as much CO$_2$ from Earth's atmosphere as now remains in Venus's atmosphere. (If Venus's CO$_2$ could somehow be removed, the remaining atmosphere would have about as much nitrogen as Earth's.) Had Earth been slightly closer to the Sun, its warmer temperature might have evaporated the oceans, leaving the CO$_2$ in the atmosphere and causing a runaway greenhouse effect as on Venus. Conditions might not have been so conducive to "life as we know it."

The interplay of atmosphere and geology may also explain why Earth has plate tectonics while Venus does not. The apparent lack of plate tectonics on Venus suggests that its lithosphere is stronger and thicker than Earth's. How can this be, given that

**FIGURE 13.14** Recycling of CO$_2$ and the carbonate–silicate cycle.

both planets probably have similar internal temperatures? The answer may lie in the history of Venus's atmosphere. As Venus lost its oceans, even the small amounts of water dissolved in the crust and mantle were baked out, removing the lubricating and softening effects of volatiles trapped in rocks. So Venus's atmospheric evolution may have thickened the lithosphere to the point where Earth-like plate tectonics cannot occur. This theory is still controversial (some planetary geologists think that Venus's lithosphere is actually thinner than Earth's), but it underscores the surprising possibility that a planet's atmosphere can affect its interior, not just the other way around.

## The Origin of Oxygen, Ozone, and the Stratosphere

While both water and carbon dioxide are products of outgassing, molecular oxygen (O$_2$) is not. In fact, no geological process can explain the great abundance of oxygen (about 20%) in Earth's atmosphere. Moreover, oxygen is a highly reactive chemical that would rapidly disappear from the atmosphere if it were not continuously resupplied. Fire, rust, and the discoloration of freshly cut fruits and vegetables are everyday examples of **oxidation**—chemical reactions that remove oxygen from the atmosphere. Similar reactions between oxygen and surface materials (especially iron-bearing minerals) give rise to the reddish appearance of many of Earth's rock layers, such as those in Arizona's Grand Canyon. Thus, we must explain not only how oxygen got into the Earth's atmosphere in the first place, but also how the amount of oxygen remains relatively steady even while oxidation reactions tend to bind oxygen into rocks at a rapid rate.

The answer to the oxygen mystery is *life*. The process that supplies oxygen to the atmosphere is *photosynthesis*, which converts $CO_2$ to $O_2$. The carbon becomes incorporated into amino acids, proteins, and other components of living organisms. Today, plants and single-celled photosynthetic organisms return oxygen to the atmosphere in approximate balance with the rate at which animals and oxidation reactions consume oxygen, so the oxygen content of the atmosphere stays relatively steady. Earth originally developed its oxygen atmosphere when photosynthesis added oxygen at a rate greater than these processes could remove it from the atmosphere.

**TIME OUT TO THINK** *Suppose that, somehow, photosynthetic life (e.g., plants) all died out. What would happen to oxygen in our atmosphere? Could animals (such as humans) survive?*

Life and oxygen also explain the presence of Earth's ultraviolet-absorbing stratosphere. In the upper atmosphere, chemical reactions involving solar ultraviolet light transform some of the $O_2$ into molecules of $O_3$, or *ozone*. The $O_3$ molecule is more weakly bound than $O_2$, which allows it to absorb solar ultraviolet energy even better, giving rise to the warm stratosphere and preventing harmful ultraviolet radiation from reaching the surface. Mars and Venus lack photosynthetic life and therefore have too little $O_2$ and too little ozone to form a stratosphere.

### Feedback Processes and Carbon Dioxide Balance

The Earth today is just warm enough for liquid water and "life as we know it" thanks to a moderate greenhouse effect caused by the presence of water vapor and carbon dioxide in our atmosphere. Our good fortune might seem to be based on atmospheric properties alone, but in fact our luck lies deeper—with Earth's geological processes. Much of the $CO_2$ is injected into the atmosphere by volcanoes near subduction zones: Carbonate rocks carried beneath the seafloor by subduction melt and release their $CO_2$ (see Figure 13.14). The balance between the rate at which carbonate rocks form in the oceans and the rate at which carbonate rocks melt in subduction zones largely determines the amount of $CO_2$ in Earth's atmosphere. If plate tectonics—especially subduction—stopped on Earth, or if it occurred at a substantially different rate, the amount of atmospheric

---

**Common Misconceptions: Ozone—Good or Bad?**

Ozone often generates confusion, because in human terms it is sometimes good and sometimes bad. In the stratosphere, ozone acts as a protective shield from the Sun's ultraviolet radiation. However, ozone is poisonous to most living creatures and therefore is a bad thing when it is found near the Earth's surface. In fact, ozone is one of the main ingredients in urban air pollution, produced as a by-product of automobiles and industry. Some people wonder whether we might be able to transport this ozone to the stratosphere and thereby alleviate the effects of ozone depletion. Unfortunately, this plan won't work. Even if we could find a way to transport this ozone, all the ozone ever produced in urban pollution would barely make a dent in the amount lost from the stratosphere.

---

$CO_2$ would undoubtedly be different. The eventual effect on Earth's temperature might prove fatal to us.

Life also plays a role in the $CO_2$ balance, because the photosynthetic cycle consumes carbon dioxide as it produces oxygen. (Life in the oceans plays an additional role: One mechanism by which carbonate rocks form in the ocean involves seashells that sink to the ocean floor.) Moreover, just as the carbon dioxide locked up in carbonate rocks can later be released, so can the carbon dioxide consumed by living organisms. When organic materials burn, their carbon reacts with atmospheric oxygen to produce carbon dioxide. Fossil fuels—oil, coal, and natural gas—are the remains of living organisms that died long ago. When we burn these fuels, we add carbon dioxide to the atmosphere, changing the $CO_2$ balance.

The full story of the Earth's carbon dioxide balance is even more complex because of **feedback relationships**—relationships in which a change in one property amplifies (*positive feedback*) or counteracts (*negative feedback*) the behavior of the rest of the system. You are probably familiar with audio feedback: If you bring a microphone too close to a loudspeaker, it picks up and amplifies small sounds from the speaker, and these amplified sounds are again picked up by the microphone and further amplified, causing a loud screech. This is an example of positive feedback. The screech usually leads to a form of negative feedback: The embarrassed person holding the microphone moves away from the loudspeaker, thereby stopping the positive audio feedback.

A planet's carbon dioxide balance, and hence its greenhouse-induced temperature, is also subject to both positive and negative feedback. The hotter a planet's surface, the more of its greenhouse gases will be in the atmosphere instead of in the oceans and crust. But this increase in greenhouse gases further increases the temperature—an example of positive feedback (which ultimately led to the runaway greenhouse effect on Venus). However, in some cases, warming temperatures can also lead to negative feedback, at least on planets with liquid water. The warmer temperature leads to more evaporation and cloud formation, and the higher albedo of clouds causes cooling as more sunlight is reflected back to space. Furthermore, higher temperatures increase the rate of carbonate rock formation, pulling more $CO_2$ from the atmosphere and cooling the planet. The complexity of these relationships makes predicting planetary climates difficult.

Geological evidence is mounting for an unusual stage in Earth's history that highlights the importance of feedback processes. The evidence suggests that some 600–700 million years ago glaciers resided in regions known to lie near the equator at that time. If this really occurred, the global temperature must have dipped enough for the oceans to start to freeze. Because ice has a much higher albedo than water (ice reflects about 90% of incoming sunlight, as opposed to just 5% for water), the small amount of freezing would have further cooled the planet, leading to more widespread ocean freezing. This positive feedback would have led quickly to what some geologists call "snowball Earth." How did the Earth recover from this "snowball" phase? After all, once covered with high-albedo ice, the planet must have become very cold. The answer lies in the carbonate–silicate cycle (Figure 13.14). If the oceans froze and snow fell instead of rain, the cycle was broken: $CO_2$ was no longer pulled from the atmosphere. It therefore built up in the atmosphere, warming the planet until the oceans melted and the carbonate–silicate cycle was restored.

**TIME OUT TO THINK** *How would the carbonate–silicate cycle be affected if plate tectonics did not occur? Without plate tectonics, could Earth recover from a "snowball" phase?*

Feedback processes probably also explain how the Earth has kept a fairly steady temperature despite a changing Sun: Stars like the Sun increase in brightness as they age, and billions of years ago our Sun was probably about 30% fainter than it is today [Section 14.3]. With Earth's current abundance of greenhouse gases, our planet would have been frozen over. Thus, greenhouse gases must have been more abundant early in Earth's history. Venus, on the other hand, might have ex-

perienced hospitable conditions if it possessed "only" its current inventory of greenhouse gases—but it probably also had more greenhouse gases in its early history, leading to its runaway greenhouse effect. On Mars, extra greenhouse gases once provided the warm temperatures needed for liquid water to flow, but Mars lost so much of this gas that it became colder even as the Sun grew brighter.

### Summary of Earth's Atmosphere

Venus, Earth, and Mars all began on similar paths, releasing similar gases into their atmospheres by outgassing. But only Earth had conditions "just right" to maintain liquid oceans. The oceans helped remove carbon dioxide from the atmosphere, ensuring that the greenhouse effect on Earth remained just strong enough to keep conditions hospitable for life, but not so strong as to create a runaway greenhouse effect like that on Venus.

The physical connections between the Earth's geology and its atmosphere cannot fully explain the conditions on Earth today. In particular, the presence of oxygen and ozone can be explained only as products of life. Thus, to complete our understanding of the unique place of Earth in the solar system, we must turn our attention to the role of life on Earth.

## 13.4 Life

Fossils, the petrified remains of living organisms, tell the story of life on Earth (Figure 13.15). Most fossils formed when dead organisms fell to the bottom of a body of water, where they were gradually buried by layers of sediment and eventually compressed into

**FIGURE 13.15** Dinosaur fossils.

**FIGURE 13.16** The rock layers of the Grand Canyon record 2 billion years of Earth history.

rocks. In some areas, such as in the Grand Canyon, layers of sediments have been deposited one on top of the other for millions or even billions of years, burying a detailed record of life in the process (Figure 13.16). Erosion or tectonic activity later exposes the fossils. Some fossils are remarkably well preserved, and we find fossils of large animals, plants, and even microscopic, single-celled organisms.

The key to reconstructing the history of life is to determine the dates at which fossil organisms lived. The *relative* ages of fossils found in different layers can be determined easily: Deeper layers formed earlier and contain more ancient fossils. Radioactive dating confirms these relative ages and gives us fairly accurate absolute ages for fossils [Section 8.6].

For relatively recent geological history, such as the age of the dinosaurs that began about 250 million years ago and ended abruptly 65 million years ago, the numerous fossil skeletons of extinct animals prove that life on Earth has undergone dramatic changes. Life in earlier epochs is more difficult to characterize. Primitive life-forms without skeletons leave fewer fossils, erosion erases much old fossil evidence, and subduction destroys other fossil evidence deep beneath the Earth's surface. Nevertheless, geologists and biologists have developed a fairly clear picture of the history of life on Earth, at least in broad outline. As we trace this history through time, you should ask yourself three key questions:

1. How did Earth's physical conditions affect the development of life?

2. How has life influenced the physical characteristics of Earth?

3. What can we learn about the prospects for finding life elsewhere in the solar system or universe?

### The Origin of Life (4.4–3.5 billion years ago)

Life arose on Earth at least 3.5 billion years ago, and possibly much earlier than that. We've found recognizable fossils in rocks as old as 3.5 billion years— microscopic fossils of single-celled bacteria and larger fossils of bacterial "colonies" called *stromatolites* (Figure 13.17). But indirect evidence suggests that life originated at least 350 million years earlier (3.85 billion years ago), even though such ancient rock samples are too contorted for fossils to remain recognizable. This evidence comes from analysis of different isotopes of carbon [Section 4.3]. Most carbon atoms are atoms of carbon-12 (6 protons and 6 neutrons), but a small proportion of carbon atoms are instead carbon-13 (6 protons and 7 neutrons). Living organisms incorporate carbon-12 slightly more easily than carbon-13, and as a result the fraction of carbon-13 is always a bit lower in fossils than in rock samples that lack fossils. In fact, all life and all fossils tested to date show the same characteristic ratio of the two carbon isotopes. Rocks as old as 3.85 billion years also show the same ratio, strongly suggesting that these rocks contain remnants of life. Beyond 3.85 billion years, we cannot yet determine whether life existed, because rocks more ancient than this no longer exist on Earth's surface. It is conceivable that life arose as early as 4.4 billion years ago.

**TIME OUT TO THINK** *You may have noticed that, while we've been talking about life, we haven't actually defined the term. In fact, it's surprisingly difficult to draw a clear boundary between life and nonlife. How would you define life? Explain your reasoning.*

If life did arise much before 3.85 billion years ago, it may have been in for a rough time. The transition from intolerable conditions during planetary

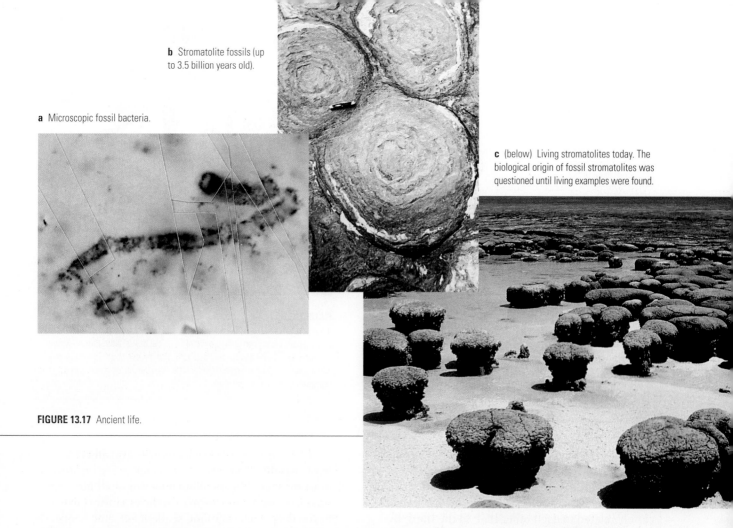

**b** Stromatolite fossils (up to 3.5 billion years old).

**a** Microscopic fossil bacteria.

**c** (below) Living stromatolites today. The biological origin of fossil stromatolites was questioned until living examples were found.

**FIGURE 13.17** Ancient life.

formation to more hospitable conditions was a gradual one. The early bombardment that continued after the end of accretion gradually died away over a period of a few hundred million years. But large impacts capable of sterilizing the planet by temporarily boiling all the oceans may have occurred as late as 4.0–3.8 billion years ago. Earthquakes and volcanic eruptions were probably more frequent and more violent as well, due to greater radioactive heating in Earth's interior. Plate tectonics may not yet have begun, and oceans may have covered the entire surface. Indeed, some biologists speculate that life may have arisen several times in the Earth's early history, only to be extinguished by the hostile conditions. If so, life might have turned out very different if one less—or one more—sterilizing impact had occurred.

An even deeper question concerns not just *when* life arose, but *how*. No one knows the precise answer to this question, but we are confident of one thing: Whether life arose once or multiple times, one particular type of organism came to dominate the entire Earth. That is, every organism living today apparently developed from a single ancestor.

The idea of a common ancestor comes from several lines of evidence based on the fact that all known life-forms share uncanny chemical resemblances to one another—similarities that are not expected on simple chemical grounds and that are far too improbable and numerous to be considered coincidences. First, all known organisms use virtually the same limited set of chemical building blocks. For example, proteins are made from building blocks called **amino acids**, and all living organisms use the same set of 20 different amino acids—even though more than 70 amino acids exist. Similarly, all living organisms use the same basic molecule (called ATP) to store energy within cells, and all use molecules of DNA to transmit their genes from one generation to the next. (Some viruses use RNA, rather than DNA, as their genetic material.)

A second line of evidence for a common ancestor comes from the fact that all living organisms share nearly the same **genetic code**—the "language" that living cells use to read the instructions chemically encoded in DNA. You are probably familiar with the structure of DNA, which consists of two long strands that look somewhat like train tracks, wound together in the shape of a double helix (Figure 13.18). Each letter shown along the DNA strands represents one of four *chemical bases*, denoted by A, G, T, and C (for the first letters of their chemical names). The instructions for assembling the cell are written in the precise arrangement of these four chemical bases: Genetic "words" composed of three consecutive bases represent particular amino acids. (For example, the "word" CAG represents one amino acid, and TCA represents a completely different amino acid. Chemical reactions between the DNA and its surroundings in effect read the codes.) There is no known reason why living organisms should follow a particular genetic code, and biochemists believe that DNA could use different sequences of these bases—or possibly even different bases altogether—to encode the same genetic information. Thus, the fact that all living organisms share a common genetic code implies a common ancestry.

A third line of evidence for a common ancestor comes from detailed analysis of the sequence of chemical bases in the DNA of different organisms. In particular, biologists have mapped out the sequence in many different organisms that holds the instructions for making a molecule called rRNA (ribosomal RNA). They've discovered that this sequence includes "unused" segments that apparently do not affect the structure or function of rRNA. Biologists can trace the process of evolution by comparing these unused segments. For example, suppose the unused segments look the same in two organisms but a little bit different in a third organism. Then we can conclude that the first two organisms are more closely related to each other than to the third. By making many such comparisons, biologists have developed an evolutionary "tree of life" (Figure 13.19). Although many details in the structure of this tree remain uncertain, it clearly shows that living organisms share a common ancestry.

**FIGURE 13.18** Left: A model of a small piece of a DNA molecule. Right: This diagram shows that a DNA molecule is made from two intertwined strands, with "ladder steps" connecting pairs of chemical bases. Note that A always connects to T, and G always connects to C. The genetic code is a language in which triplets (along a single strand) of the chemical bases make "words" that represent particular amino acids.

Comparison of DNA sequences also allows at least reasonable guesses as to which living organisms most resemble the common ancestor of all life. Surprisingly, the answer appears to be organisms living in the deep oceans around seafloor volcanic vents called *black smokers* (after the dark, mineral-rich water that flows out of them) and in hot springs in places like Yellowstone (Figure 13.20). These organisms thrive in temperatures as high as 125°C. (The high pressures at the seafloor prevent the water from

**FIGURE 13.19** The tree of life, showing evolutionary relationships according to modern biology as of early 2001. Note that just two small branches represent *all* plant and animal species.

a  Life around a black smoker deep beneath the ocean surface.

b  This aerial photo shows a hot spring in Yellowstone National Park that is filled with colorful bacterial life. The path in the lower left gives an indication of scale.

**FIGURE 13.20**  Life in hot water.

boiling until it reaches 450°C.) Unlike most life at the Earth's surface, which depends on sunlight, the ultimate energy source for these organisms is chemical reactions in water volcanically heated by the internal heat of the Earth itself.

Of course, knowing that all life shares a common ancestor still does not tell us how that ancestor first arose. The step from simple chemical building blocks to our common DNA-bearing ancestor (from non-life to life) is huge, to say the least. No fossils record the transition, nor has it ever been duplicated in the laboratory.

The bare necessities for "life as we know it"—chemicals, energy, and water—were undoubtedly available on the early Earth. The building blocks of life, including amino acids and nucleic acids, are composed primarily of carbon, oxygen, nitrogen, and hydrogen, chemicals that were readily available. Energy to fuel chemical reactions was present on the surface in the form of lightning and ultraviolet light from the Sun and was also present in the oceans in the heated water near undersea volcanoes. We know that oceans were present, because we find ancient carbonate rocks that must have formed in water.

Laboratory experiments demonstrate that the chemical building blocks of life could have formed spontaneously and rapidly in the conditions that prevailed early in Earth's history. In these experiments, researchers replicate the chemical conditions of the early Earth by, for example, including the types of ingredients outgassed by volcanoes and "sparking" the mixture with electricity to simulate lightning or other energy sources. Within just a few days, the mixture spontaneously becomes rich in amino acids and nucleic acids. Such chemical reactions were undoubtedly an important source of organic molecules on Earth, but they may not have been the only source—some meteorites contain complex organic molecules.

With the building blocks for life plentiful, it may only have been a matter of time before chemical reactions created a molecule that could make a copy of itself. Such a *self-replicating molecule* might have spread quickly through regions with hospitable conditions. If life really began in this way, then some ancient self-replicating molecule was the ancestor of modern DNA—and of all life on Earth.

### Early Evolution in the Oceans (3.5–2.0 billion years ago)

Regardless of its origin, life soon thrived in the oceans in the form of single-celled organisms, tapping a variety of energy sources including sunlight (i.e., through photosynthesis). Individual organisms that survived and reproduced passed on copies of their DNA to the next generation. However, the transmission of DNA from one generation to the next is not always perfect. **Mutations**—errors in the copying process—can change the arrangement of chemical bases in a strand of DNA, making the genetic information in a new cell slightly different from that of its parent. Mutations can be caused by many factors, including high-energy *cosmic rays* from space [Section 18.2], ultraviolet light from the Sun, particles emitted by the decay of radioactive elements in the Earth, and various toxic chemicals. Most mutations are lethal, killing the cell in which the mutation occurs. However, some mutations may make a cell better able to survive in its surroundings, and the cell then passes on this improvement to its offspring.

The process by which mutations that make an organism better able to survive get passed on to future generations is called **natural selection**. The idea of natural selection was proposed by Charles Darwin (1809–1882) as a way of explaining evolution (which simply means "change with time") in animal species. Today, we believe that natural selection is the primary mechanism by which evolution proceeds: Over time, natural selection may help individuals of a species become better able to compete for scarce resources and may also lead to the development of entirely new species from old ones. The fossil record provides strong evidence that evolution *has* occurred, while natural selection explains *how* it occurs.

Fossils show that evolution progressed remarkably slowly for most of Earth's history. For at least a billion years after life first arose, the most complex life-forms were still single-celled. Some 2 billion years ago, the land was still inhospitable because of the lack of a protective ozone layer. Continents much like those today were surrounded by oceans teeming with life, but the land itself was probably as barren as Mars is today, despite pleasant temperatures and plentiful rainfall.

**FIGURE 13.21** Thanks to the buildup of oxygen in the atmosphere (and small amounts dissolved in the oceans), animals like these trilobites became possible. Trilobites were among the most complex animals alive a few hundred million years ago. The largest specimens reached 75 cm (30 in.) in length.

### Altering the Atmosphere
### (beginning about 2 billion years ago)

The process of photosynthesis appears to have developed quite early in the history of life. Over billions of years, the abundant single-celled organisms in the ocean pulled carbon dioxide from the atmosphere and put back oxygen. Oxygen is a highly reactive gas, and for a long time it was pulled back out of the atmosphere by reactions with surface rocks. However, by about 2 billion years ago, the oxidation of surface rocks was fairly complete, and oxygen began to accumulate in the atmosphere. Today it constitutes about 20% of the atmosphere, but this fraction may vary over periods of millions of years.

The buildup of oxygen had two far-reaching effects for life on Earth. First, it made possible the development of oxygen-breathing *animals* (Figure 13.21). No one knows precisely how or when the first oxygen-breathing organism appeared, but for that animal the world was filled with food. You can imagine how quickly these creatures must have spread around the world, and the fact that other organisms could now be eaten changed the "rules of the game" for evolution.

The second major effect of the oxygen buildup was the formation of the ozone layer, which made it safe for life to move onto the land. Although it took

more than a billion years, natural selection eventually led to plants that could survive and thrive on land, and animals followed soon after, taking advantage of this new food source.

This epoch highlights the ability of life to fundamentally alter a planet. Not only did life change the Earth's atmosphere, but in doing so it made two other kinds of life possible: oxygen-breathing animals and land organisms.

### An Explosion of Diversity
### (beginning about 0.54 billion years ago)

As recently as 540 million years ago, most life-forms were still single-celled and tiny. Note that life had already been present on Earth for at least 3 billion years by that time, demonstrating the remarkable slowness with which evolution progressed for most of Earth's history. But the fossil record reveals a dramatic diversification of life beginning about 540 million years ago. Although this change occurred over a period of about 40 million years, it was so dramatic in comparison to the events of the previous 3 billion years that it is often called the *Cambrian explosion*. (Cambrian is the name geologists give the period from about 540 million to 500 million years ago.) We can trace the origin of most of today's plant and animal species—from insects to trees to vertebrates—back to this period. Apparently, once life began to diversify, the increased competition among the many more complex species accelerated the process of natural selection and the evolution of new species.

Some species have been more successful and more adaptable than others. Dinosaurs dominated the landscape of the Earth for more than 100 million years. But their sudden demise 65 million years ago paved the way for the evolution of large mammals—including us. The earliest humans appeared on the scene only a few million years ago (after 99.9% of

Earth's history), and our few centuries of industry and technology have come after 99.99999% of Earth's history. Despite our recent arrival (in geological terms), modern humans are by some measures the most successful species ever to inhabit the Earth. Humans survive and prosper in virtually every type of land environment. With proper equipment, we can survive underwater, and a few people have lived under the sea for extended periods of time in experimental habitats. We are even developing the technology to survive away from our planet, in the inhospitable environment of space. And our population has been growing exponentially for the past few centuries, roughly doubling in just the past 40 years (Figure 13.22).

The tremendous growth of the human population suggests a chilling analogy: Exponential growth is also the mark of a cancerous tumor—which may seem very successful at surviving while it is growing but ultimately dies when it kills its host. Is it possible that our tremendous success is killing our host, the Earth? We can gain some perspective on this question by looking at a few lessons that the solar system teaches us about our relationship with the Earth.

**TIME OUT TO THINK** *The pace of change in human existence has accelerated since the advent of modern humans a few million years ago: Civilization arose about 10 thousand years ago, the industrial revolution began just a couple of centuries ago, and the computer era started just a few decades ago. Do you think the pace of change can continue to accelerate? What do you think the next stage will be?*

## 13.5 Lessons from the Solar System

The United States and other nations have carried out the exploration of the solar system for many reasons, including scientific curiosity, national pride, and technological advancement. Perhaps the most important return on this investment was one not expected: an improved understanding of our own planet and an enhanced ability to understand some very important global issues. In this section, we explore three particularly important issues about which comparative planetology offers important insights: global warming, ozone depletion, and mass extinctions.

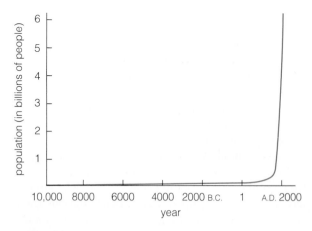

**FIGURE 13.22** This graph shows human population over the past 12,000 years. Note the tremendous population growth that has occurred in just the past few centuries.

### Global Warming

Venus stands as a searing example of the effects of large amounts of atmospheric carbon dioxide. Earth remains habitable only because natural processes have locked up most of its carbon dioxide on the seafloor. However, humans are now tinkering with this difference between the two planets by adding carbon dioxide and other greenhouse gases to the Earth's atmosphere. The primary way we release carbon dioxide is through the burning of fossil fuels (coal, natural gas, and oil)—the carbon-rich remains of plants buried millions of years ago. But other human actions, such as deforestation and the subsequent burning of trees, also affect the carbon dioxide balance of our atmosphere. The inescapable result is that the amount of atmospheric carbon dioxide has risen steadily since the dawn of the industrial age—and continues to rise (Figure 13.23)—nearly 20% in the past 50 years alone.

**FIGURE 13.23** These data, collected for many years on Mauna Loa (Hawaii), show the increase in atmospheric carbon dioxide concentration. Yearly wiggles represent seasonal variations in the concentration, but the long-term trend is clearly upward. The concentration is measured in parts per million (ppm).

Although it may seem logical to conclude that an increase in the concentration of greenhouse gases should warm the Earth, the Earth is a very complex system. As a result, the debate over whether human activity is changing the Earth's climate is fierce. Measuring even something as seemingly simple as the average temperature of the entire planet can be surprisingly difficult. Until the advent of satellite temperature measurements, temperature data came only from ground-based weather stations and were subject to bias. For example, most weather stations are restricted to land and are located near cities (which tend to be warmer than surrounding areas). Despite measurement difficulties, however, there is general scientific consensus that the average temperature of the Earth has warmed slightly (about 0.5°C) over the past 50 years—although there is much less agreement about why. Furthermore, glaciers, ice sheets, and even the snows of Mount Kilimanjaro are in retreat, while ocean levels are slowly rising. It's likely that the cause is the human addition of greenhouse gases to the atmosphere, but it's also possible that the change is natural and would have occurred even without human activity. Some scientists even suggest that the Sun itself may be warming and thus contributing to the global temperature rise.

The question of whether human activity is inducing global warming is not merely academic: The consequences of a significant continued warming could be widespread and disastrous. The primary way scientists try to predict the effects of global warming is by making sophisticated computer models of the climate. Different models give different results, but some predict a warming of more than 5°C during the next hundred years. Past ice ages occurred when the average temperature dropped by about 5°C; a similar increase could melt polar ice and flood the Earth's densely populated coastal regions. Such warming would also increase evaporation from the oceans, tending to make storms of all types both more frequent and more destructive: Coastal regions would be hit by more hurricanes, intense thunderstorms and associated tornadoes would strike more frequently, and even winter blizzards would be more severe and more damaging. Computer models also show that global warming would not affect all regions in the same way. Some regions would warm much more than the average, while others might even cool. Rainfall patterns would also shift, and much of the world's current cropland might become unusable. The most ominous possibility is the collapse of entire ecosystems. If a regional climate changes more rapidly than local species can adapt or migrate, these species might become extinct. Given the complex interactions of the Earth's biosphere, hydrosphere, and atmosphere, the consequences of such ecosystem changes are impossible to foresee.

The uncertainty in our understanding of global warming is underscored by the fact that most current computer models predict that the Earth should already have warmed to a greater degree than we've observed. This suggests that some process may be counteracting the effects of the added greenhouse gases. One hypothesis is that increased evaporation from the oceans might lead to more clouds that prevent sunlight from reaching the surface. Another is that recent volcanic eruptions, such as the 1991 eruption of Mount Pinatubo in the Philippines, have injected particles into the stratosphere that reflect sunlight, effectively increasing the Earth's albedo. The most frightening possibility is that reflective particles are indeed being injected into the atmosphere, but their source is sulfate particles from coal-burning industries. At first, this idea might seem to suggest that the pollutants from coal burning counter the effects of the added carbon dioxide, but in reality this can only postpone and worsen the problem: Sulfate particles fall out of the atmosphere in a matter of years, while carbon dioxide may remain for half a million years.

Given the current uncertainties, it is impossible for anyone to know for sure whether global warming will even be a serious problem in the coming century, let alone to make specific predictions of its severity. Our studies of the planets show that surface temperatures depend on many factors and that positive and negative feedback processes can alter climates in surprising ways. Nevertheless, the fact that we cannot explain the current climate conditions on Earth suggests that we should be very careful about tampering with them.

**TIME OUT TO THINK** *The most obvious way to prevent global warming is to stop burning the fossil fuels that add greenhouse gases to the atmosphere. But much of the world economy depends on energy produced from fossil fuels. Given the uncertainties about the effects of global warming in the next hundred years, what, if any, changes do you think are justified at present? What specific proposals would you make if you were a world leader?*

### Ozone Depletion

For 2 billion years, the Earth's ozone layer has shielded the surface from hazardous ultraviolet radiation, but in the past two decades humans have begun to destroy the shield. The idea that human activity might damage the ozone was first suggested in the early 1970s, but the magnitude of the problem was not recognized until the discovery of an **ozone hole** over Antarctica in the mid-1980s (Figure 13.24). The "hole" is a place where the concentration of ozone in

**FIGURE 13.24** The extent of the ozone hole over Antarctica in 1979 (left) and 1998 (right). The ozone hole grew substantially between 1979 and 1998. Red indicates normal ozone concentration, and blue indicates severe depletion.

the stratosphere is dramatically lower than it would naturally be. The ozone hole appears for a few months during each Antarctic spring and has gradually worsened over the years. Since its discovery, satellite measurements have suggested that **ozone depletion** has caused ozone levels to fall by as much as a few percent worldwide. If ozone levels continue to decline, more solar ultraviolet radiation will reach the surface. Humans will face substantially greater risk from skin cancer, and plants and animals will suffer more genetic damage from mutations induced by ultraviolet radiation—with unknown consequences for the biosphere as a whole.

The apparent cause of the ozone depletion is human-made chemicals known as CFCs (chlorofluorocarbons). CFCs were invented in the 1930s and have been widely used in air conditioners and refrigerators, in the manufacture of packaging foam, as propellants in spray cans, in industrial solvents used in the computer industry, and for many other purposes. Indeed, CFCs once seemed like an almost ideal chemical: They are useful in many industries, cheap and easy to produce, and chemically inert (i.e., they do not burn, break down, or react with anything on the Earth's surface). Ironically, their inertness is also their downfall; because CFCs are gases and are not destroyed by chemical reactions in the lower atmosphere, they eventually rise intact into the stratosphere. There they are broken down by the Sun's ultraviolet light, and one of the by-products is chlorine—a very

reactive gas that catalytically destroys ozone without being consumed in the process. On average, a single chlorine atom in the stratosphere can destroy 100,000 ozone molecules before it is consumed itself in some other chemical reaction. Chlorine's ability to attack ozone is enhanced at low temperatures, which explains why ozone depletion was first observed in the polar regions.

Mars and Venus each played an important role in our understanding of ozone and chlorine. Mars lacks an ozone layer, so ultraviolet radiation reaches the surface. As a result, the surface is sterile: Terrestrial life could not survive on the surface, and the building blocks of life would be torn apart when exposed to the Sun. But it was the study of Venus that first alerted scientists to the dangers on Earth. Chlorine is a minor but important ingredient of Venus's atmosphere, and models of its chemical cycles showed that chlorine could rapidly destroy weak molecules such as ozone. When the models were altered to apply to Earth's atmosphere, CFCs and ozone depletion were connected.

This tale of three planets may have a happy ending, thanks to the awareness it brought of the dangers posed by ozone destruction. Today, international treaties ban the production of CFCs, although previously existing CFCs may still be used and recycled. If these treaties are obeyed, continued ozone destruction probably will not be a serious problem in the future, but the ozone hole will probably take 50 years to recover. Most of the CFCs ever produced are still in intact air conditioners, refrigerators, or other products, and most of these CFCs will eventually escape into the atmosphere. Moreover, because the stratosphere lacks the weather of the troposphere [Section 10.2], CFCs (and their breakdown products) remain in the stratosphere for decades once they arrive. But the greater danger lies in the possibility of treaty failures. Some of the replacements for CFCs may be only marginally less damaging than the CFCs themselves. In addition, the replacements are generally much more expensive to produce than CFCs, and a large global black market now exists for CFCs produced in violation of the treaties. Like most global issues, the final outcome of the ozone problem remains in doubt.

**TIME OUT TO THINK** *You've just learned that your car air conditioner is broken and will cost $200 to fix. Then you hear about a shop that can fix it for only $100—undoubtedly by violating the laws concerning CFCs. Is the small benefit to our ozone layer worth the extra $100?*

### Mass Extinctions

When geology was a young science, its practitioners thought that entire mountain ranges and huge valleys were formed suddenly by cataclysmic events. Later geologists denounced this *catastrophism* and replaced it with *uniformitarianism,* which holds that geological change occurs gradually by processes acting over very long periods. Uniformitarianism certainly holds for three of our four geological processes, but impact cratering represents the "instant geology" of catastrophism. Many geologists initially rejected the importance of impact cratering as a geological process, but they were eventually convinced by the unambiguous evidence of impacts on the Moon, by astronomical studies of comets and asteroids, and by careful analysis of the few impact craters still present on Earth. Geology today is a combination of uniformitarianism and catastrophism.

Scientific ideas about evolution are undergoing a similar transformation. Biologists once assumed that evolution always proceeded gradually, with new species arising slowly and others occasionally becoming extinct. It now appears that the vast majority of all species in Earth's history died out in sudden *mass extinctions*—for which impacts are the prime suspect. The mass extinction that killed off the dinosaurs is only the most famous of these events [Section 12.6]; the fossil record shows evidence of at least a dozen other mass extinctions, some with even greater species loss than in the dinosaur event. While some species died out from direct effects of the impact,

most probably died due to the disappearance from their ecosystem of species on which they depended. Furthermore, the survival or extinction of species appears to be random during mass extinctions: Surviving species show no discernible advantage over those that perish. In a sense, mass extinctions clear the blackboard, allowing evolution to get a fresh start with a new set of species. If we re-formed the Earth from scratch, life (and even intelligent life) might well arise again, but there is no scientific basis for thinking that evolution would follow the same course.

The story of mass extinctions teaches us about the danger of large impacts, but it also teaches a potentially more important lesson: Even without an impact, the Earth may be undergoing a mass extinction right now. In the normal course of evolution, the rate of species extinction is fairly low—perhaps one species lost per century. According to some estimates, human activity is now driving species to extinction so rapidly that half of today's species may be lost by the end of the twenty-first century. It is not just that humans are hunting and fishing many species to extinction. Far more are lost due to habitat destruction and pollution. And when a few species are lost by direct human influence, entire ecosystems that depend on those species may collapse. If global warming alters the climate significantly or if ozone depletion leads to more genetic damage in plants and animals, the rate of species extinction might increase even more. In any case, the "event" of losing half the world's species in just a few hundred years certainly qualifies as a mass extinction on a geological time scale, and the biological effects could be as dramatic as those of any impact. Are we unwittingly clearing the way for a new set of dominant species?

## 13.6 Lessons from Earth: Life in the Solar System and Beyond

Just as comparative planetology teaches us much about the Earth, the study of the Earth can teach us much about other worlds. In particular, it teaches us about the conditions for life and may help us answer what is surely one of the deepest philosophical questions of all time: Are we alone in the universe? It is fitting to close our study of the Earth by extending our understanding of biology to the planets and beyond. The study of the possibility of life elsewhere in the universe, called *astrobiology* (or *exobiology*), is a logical extension of comparative planetology.

In the time between the Copernican revolution [Section 5.3] and the space age, many people expected the other planets in our solar system to be Earth-like and to harbor intelligent life. In fact, a reward was supposedly once offered for the first evidence of intelligent life on another planet *other than Mars.* Venus, a bit closer to the Sun than Earth, was often pictured as a tropical paradise. Such expectations were dashed by the bleak images of Mars returned by spacecraft and the discovery of the runaway greenhouse effect on Venus. Many scientists began to believe that only Earth has the right conditions for life, intelligent or otherwise. Recently, the pendulum has begun to swing the other way, spurred primarily by two developments. First, biologists are learning that life thrives under a much wider range of conditions than once imagined. Second, planetary scientists are developing a much better understanding of conditions on other worlds. It now seems quite likely that conditions in at least some places on other worlds might be conducive to life.

### The Hardiness, Diversity, and Probability of Life

Even on Earth, biologists long assumed that many environments were uninhabitable. But recent discoveries have found life surviving in a remarkable range of conditions. The teeming life surviving at temperatures as high as 125°C near underwater volcanic vents and in hot springs is only one of many surprises. Biologists have found microorganisms living deep inside rocks in the frozen deserts of Antarctica and inside basaltic rocks buried more than a kilometer underground. Some bacteria can even survive radiation levels once thought lethal—apparently, they have evolved cellular machinery that repairs mutations as fast as they occur. The newly discovered diversity of microscopic life has forced scientists to redraw the "tree of life" (see Figure 13.19), crowding familiar plants and animals into one corner. The majority of these microorganisms need neither sunlight, oxygen, nor "food" in the form of other organisms. Instead, they tap a variety of chemical reactions for their survival.

The new view of terrestrial biology forces us to rethink the possibility of life elsewhere. First, life on Earth thrives at extremes of temperature, pressure, and atmospheric conditions that overlap conditions found on other worlds. The Antarctic valleys, for example, are as dry and cold as certain parts of Mars, and the conditions found in terrestrial hot springs may have been duplicated on a number of planets and moons at certain times in the past. Second, life harnesses energy sources readily available on other planets. The basalt-dwelling bacteria, for example, would probably survive if they were transplanted to Mars. Third, life on Earth has evolved from a common ancestor into every imaginable ecological niche (and some unimaginable ones as well). The diversification of life on Earth has basically tested the limits of our planet, and there is no reason to doubt that

it would do so on other planets. Thus, if life ever had a foothold on any other planet in the past, some organisms might still survive in surprising ecological niches today even if the planet has undergone substantial changes. The only real question is whether life ever got started elsewhere in the first place.

What is the probability of life arising from nonliving ingredients? This is probably the greatest unknown in astrobiology. The fact that we exist and are asking the question does not tell us the probability; it merely tells us that it happened once. But the rapidity with which life arose on Earth may provide a clue. As we've discussed, we find fossil evidence for life dating almost all the way back to the end of the period of early bombardment in the solar system, suggesting that life arises easily and perhaps inevitably under the right conditions. In that case, we must search the solar system for those conditions, past or present.

**TIME OUT TO THINK** *The preceding discussion implies that the rapid appearance of life on Earth means that life is highly probable. Do you agree with this logic? What alternative conclusions could you reach?*

### Life in Our Solar System

Speculation about life in the solar system usually begins with Mars, for good reason. Before it dried out billions of years ago, its early atmosphere gave the surface hospitable conditions that rivaled those on Earth, with ample running water, the necessary raw chemical ingredients for life, and a variety of familiar energy sources. Many of Earth's organisms would have thrived under early Martian conditions, and some could even survive in places in today's Martian environment. Our first attempt to search for life on Mars came with the Viking missions to Mars in the 1970s, which included two landers equipped to search for the chemical signs of life [Section 9.5]. No life was found. But the landers sampled only two locations on the planet and tested soils only very near the surface. If life once existed on Mars, it either has become extinct or is hiding in other locations.

Today, a renewed debate about Martian life is under way, thanks in part to the study of a Martian meteorite found in Antarctica in 1984. The meteorite apparently landed in Antarctica 13,000 years ago, following a 16-million-year journey through space after being blasted from Mars by an impact. The rock itself dates to 4.5 billion years ago, indicating that it solidified shortly after Mars formed and therefore was present during the time when Mars was warmer and wetter. Painstaking analysis of the meteorite

**a** Microscopic view of seemingly lifelike structures in a Martian meteorite.

**b** A comparison of microscopic chains of magnetic crystals from Earth (top) and Mars (bottom).

**FIGURE 13.25** Evidence for life on Mars?

reveals indirect evidence of past life on Mars, including layered carbonate minerals and complex molecules (called polycyclic aromatic hydrocarbons), both of which are associated with life when they are found in Earth rocks. Even more intriguing, highly magnified images of the meteorite reveal eerily lifelike forms (Figure 13.25a). These forms bear a superficial resemblance to terrestrial bacteria, although they are about a hundred times smaller—about the same size as recently discovered terrestrial "nanobacteria" and viruses. Magnetic crystals have also been found within the rock—crystals that on Earth are only made by bacteria (Figure 13.25b). Nevertheless, many scientists dispute the conclusion that these features suggest the past existence of life on Mars, claiming that nonbiological causes can also explain the meteorite's unusual features.

Future missions to Mars will search for life using more sophisticated techniques than those used by the Viking missions. The best place to look for fossil remains of extinct life is probably in ancient valley bottoms or the sedimentary rocks of dried-up lake beds (Figure 9.27d). If any hot springs surround Mars's not-quite-dormant volcanoes, they may be a good place to look for surviving life. A thorough search for Martian life will probably require the return of rock samples to Earth or human exploration of the planet.

Martian meteorites also remind us that the planets may occasionally exchange rocks dislodged by major impacts. The harsh conditions under which some life on Earth exists suggest that living organisms might survive such impacts and even survive the journey from one planet to another. Earth's basalt-dwelling bacteria, for example, could probably survive an impact-cratering event, the ensuing millions of years in space, and a violent impact on Mars. If a meteorite from Earth once landed in hospitable conditions on Mars, it might have introduced life to Mars or wiped out life already present. In a sense, Earth, Venus, and Mars have been "sneezing" on one another for billions of years. Life could conceivably have originated on any of these three planets and been transported to the others. Some scientists even suggest that the life on Earth may have originated beyond our own solar system and been brought here by interstellar dust or meteorites.

**TIME OUT TO THINK** *Suppose we someday discover living organisms on Mars. How will we be able to tell whether these organisms share a common ancestor with living organisms on Earth?*

Besides Mars, the best places to search for life probably are the satellites of the jovian planets. Several of them may meet the requirements of having liquid water, appropriate chemicals, and energy sources for life. In particular, Europa may have a planet-wide ocean beneath its icy crust [Section 11.5]. The ice and rock from which Europa formed undoubtedly included the necessary chemicals, and its internal heating might lead to undersea volcanic vents. Thus, the real question about Europa may be whether it is possible that its ocean has existed for billions of years *without* developing life. NASA is considering missions to search for signs of life on Europa. The most ambitious involves landing a robotic spacecraft on the surface that will melt its way through the icy crust to reach the ocean below.

Another enticing place to look for life past or present is Saturn's moon Titan. We've already found evidence of complex chemical reactions on Titan, many involving the same elements used by life on Earth. Liquid water and energy are in shorter supply, but both might have been supplied by impacts that heated and melted the icy surface early in Titan's history. Life might have arisen in a slushy pond during the brief period that it remained liquid and might have survived after the pond froze. Unlike the case on Earth, where early impacts probably sterilized the planet, impacts on Titan may have made life possible.

Despite our new awareness of the diversity of life on Earth, we may still be underestimating the range of conditions in which life can exist. Could life arise in liquids other than water, or possibly in an atmosphere? Some people have speculated that life could develop in the clouds of Jupiter or other jovian planets. Might life be based on different elements than those used on Earth? Are there other energy sources that we have not considered? Is our definition of life too narrow? Clearly, it will be a long time before we know all the places where life might exist even within our solar system.

### Life Around Other Stars

Only a few places in our solar system seem hospitable to life, but many more hospitable worlds may be orbiting some of the hundred billion other stars in the Milky Way Galaxy or stars in some of the billions of other galaxies in the universe. Might some of the stars be orbited by planets that are as hospitable as our own Earth?

Interstellar clouds throughout the galaxy contain the basic chemical ingredients of life—carbon, oxygen, nitrogen, and hydrogen, as well as other elements. All stars are born from such interstellar clouds, so it seems likely that other solar nebulae should have given rise to planetary systems similar to our own [Section 8.7]. Terrestrial planets anywhere will receive light from their parent star, and if they are large enough, like Venus or Earth, they will have plenty of internal heat. Thus, the chemicals and energy sources for life should be present on many planets throughout the universe.

Planets with liquid water on their surfaces may be somewhat rarer, particularly if we consider only planets where oceans can endure for billions of years. Even if a planet is large enough to outgas substantial quantities of water and retain its atmosphere, the stories of Venus and Mars tell us that oceans are not guaranteed. To keep oceans for billions of years, the planet must lie within a range of distances from its star, sometimes called the **habitable zone**, that has temperatures just right for liquid water. How big is the habitable zone in our own solar system? We know that Venus is too close to the Sun, so this zone must begin outside the orbit of Venus. Mars is a borderline case: If it had been large enough to retain its atmosphere and sustain a stronger greenhouse effect, Mars might still be habitable today. Overall, the habitable zone around our star probably ranges from 0.8 to 1.5 AU. This zone may be broader around brighter stars and narrower around fainter stars. Computer models of solar system formation suggest that one or more terrestrial planets will usually form within a star's habitable zone, as long as the star is not part of a binary star system. Many of the extrasolar planets discovered recently lie within their star's habitable zone. Although the planets themselves are thought to be jovian—and therefore not habitable—moons orbiting the planets could be habitable. Even moons outside the habitable zone could harbor life if other energy sources (such as tidal heating) are available.

The bottom line is that, according to our theories of solar system formation, planets with all the necessities for life should be quite common in the universe. The only major question is whether these ingredients combine to form life. The fact that life arose very early in Earth's history suggests that it may be very easy to produce life under Earth-like conditions, but we will not know for sure unless and until we find other life-bearing planets. NASA is currently developing plans for orbiting telescopes that may be able to detect ozone in the spectra of planets around other stars—and, at least in our solar system, substantial ozone implies life. In addition, radio astronomers are searching the skies in hopes of receiving a signal from some extraterrestrial civilization [Section S5.3]. Perhaps, in a decade or two, we will discover unmistakable evidence of life. On that day, if it comes, we will know that we are not alone.

**TIME OUT TO THINK** *Consider the following statements: (1) We are the only intelligent life in the entire universe. (2) Earth is one of many planets inhabited by intelligent life. Which do you think is true? Do you find either philosophically troubling?*

## THE BIG PICTURE

Humans have observed the Sun, the Moon, and the planets for thousands of years, but only recently did we learn that these other worlds have much to teach us about our own Earth. Through our study of solar system formation and comparative planetology, we have learned to look at Earth from a very new perspective. Keep in mind the following "big picture" ideas:

- Earth has been shaped by the same geological and atmospheric processes that shaped the other terrestrial worlds. Earth is not a special case from a planetary point of view but rather a place where natural processes led to conditions conducive to life.

- Most of Earth's unique features can be traced to the fact that abundant water has remained liquid throughout our planet's history—thanks to our distance from the Sun and the size of our planet.

- Life arose early on Earth and played a crucial role in shaping our planet's history. The abundant oxygen in our atmosphere is just one of many phenomena that demonstrate how life can transform a planet.

- Humans are ideally adapted to the Earth today, but there is no guarantee that the Earth will remain as hospitable in the future. The study of our solar system teaches us how planets can change.

- The conditions necessary for "life as we know it" are probably common in the universe and may even be found in our own solar system. But so far we have no proof that life exists elsewhere.

### Review Questions

1. Briefly summarize how Earth is different from the other terrestrial planets. In particular, define *hydrosphere* and *biosphere*.

2. Briefly describe the interior structure of the Earth, including its molten outer core and its lithosphere.

3. How does seafloor crust differ from continental crust? Why do we find fewer craters on the seafloor than on the continents?

4. Why is erosion more important on Earth than on Venus or Mars? Describe how erosion affects the Earth's geology.

5. Briefly describe the conveyor-like process of *plate tectonics*. What are *spreading centers* and *subduction zones*?

6. Describe how *subduction* has created the continents over billions of years. Give examples of how this process has affected Japan, the Philippines, and the western United States.

7. Briefly describe how tectonic stresses can create rift valleys, tall mountain ranges, and *faults*. Give examples of places that have been affected in each of these ways.

8. What is a *hot spot*? Describe how hot spots affect Hawaii and Yellowstone.

9. What is a *runaway greenhouse effect*? Why did it occur on Venus but not on Earth?

10. Describe how the *carbonate–silicate cycle* helps maintain the relatively small $CO_2$ content of our atmosphere.

11. What are *oxidation* reactions? If there were no life on Earth, would Earth's atmosphere still contain significant amounts of oxygen or ozone?

12. Give examples of positive and negative *feedback relationships*. How does feedback affect the $CO_2$ balance in our atmosphere? What is "snowball Earth"?

13. Approximately when did life arise on Earth? How do we know?

14. What evidence tells us that all life today shares a common ancestor? How do biologists compare DNA sequences to establish the "tree of life"? Where do plants and animals fall on this diagram?

15. What are *mutations?* How do mutations drive the process of *natural selection?*

16. Briefly describe how life gradually altered the Earth's atmosphere until it reached its current state.

17. Summarize the slow evolution of life on the early Earth. What was the Cambrian explosion?

18. What is global warming? Briefly describe some of the potential dangers of global warming and why so many uncertainties are involved in knowing whether global warming represents a real threat.

19. Briefly describe the phenomena and causes of the Antarctic *ozone hole* and worldwide *ozone depletion.*

20. Is the Earth currently undergoing a mass extinction? Explain.

21. Summarize why we now think that life can survive in a much broader range of conditions than we did just a few decades ago. Why is this important to the prospect of finding life elsewhere?

22. Describe the evidence from Martian meteorites suggesting that life may once have existed on Mars. Explain how life might have originated on one terrestrial planet and been transferred to others.

23. Why are Europa and Titan considered prospects for harboring life?

24. What is a *habitable zone?* Using this idea, briefly describe the prospect of finding life on planets around other stars.

## Discussion Questions

1. *Evidence of Our Civilization.* Imagine a future archaeologist, say 10,000 years from now, trying to piece together a picture of human civilization at our time (i.e., around the year 2000). What types of evidence of our civilization are most likely to survive for 10,000 years? (Will our buildings survive? Our infrastructure, such as highways and water pipes? Information in the form of books or computer data?) What geological processes are likely to destroy evidence over the next 10,000 years? Next, discuss the evidence that will remain—and why—for an archaeologist living 100 million years from now. Be sure to consider the effects of all four geological processes, as well as continental drift.

2. *Cancer of the Earth?* In the text, we discussed how the spread of humans over the Earth resembles, at least in some ways, the spread of cancer in a human body. Cancers end up killing themselves because of the damage they do to their hosts. Do you think we are in danger of killing ourselves through our actions on the Earth? If so, what should we do to alleviate this danger? Overall, do you think the cancer analogy is valid or invalid? Defend your opinions.

3. *Contact.* Suppose we discover definitive evidence for microbial life on Mars or Europa. Would this discovery alter your view of our place in the universe? If so, how? What if we made contact with an intelligent species from another world? Do you think it is likely that either kind of life exists elsewhere in the universe? Do you think either kind will be discovered in your lifetime? Explain.

## Problems

*Surprising Discoveries?* For **problems 1–8**, suppose we made the discoveries described. (These are *not* real discoveries.) Decide whether the discovery should be considered reasonable or surprising. Explain. (In some cases, either view can be defended.)

1. A fossil of an organism that died more than 300 million years ago, found in the crust near a mid-ocean ridge.

2. Evidence that fish once swam in a region that is now high on a mountaintop.

3. A "lost continent" on which humans had a great city just a few thousand years ago but that now resides deep underground near a subduction zone.

4. A planet in another solar system that has an Earth-like atmosphere but no life.

5. A planet in another solar system that has an ozone layer but no ordinary oxygen ($O_2$) in its atmosphere.

6. Evidence that the early Earth had more carbon dioxide in its atmosphere than the Earth does today.

7. Discovery of life on Mars that also uses DNA as its generic molecule and that uses a genetic code very similar to that used by life on Earth.

8. Evidence of photosynthesis occurring on a planet in another solar system that lies outside that solar system's habitable zone.

9. *Change in Formation Properties.* Consider Earth's four formation properties of size, distance, composition, and rotation rate. Choose one property, and suppose it had been different (e.g., smaller size, greater distance). Describe how this change might have affected Earth's subsequent history and the possibility of life on Earth.

10. *Growing Population.* Since about 1950, human population has grown with a doubling time of about 40 years; that is, the population doubles every 40 years. The current population is about 6 billion. If population continues to grow with a doubling time of 40 years, what will it be in 40 years? In 80 years? Do you think this will actually happen? Why or why not?

11. *Feedback Processes in the Atmosphere.*

    a. Give an everyday example (not used in this book) of a positive or negative feedback process. Explain how the process works.

    b. As the Sun gradually brightens, how can the carbonate–silicate cycle respond to reduce the warming effect? Which parts of the cycle will be affected? Is this an example of positive or negative feedback?

12. *Defining Life.* Write a definition of life and explain the basis of your definition in a few sentences. Then evaluate whether each of the following three cases meets your definition. Explain why or why not in a paragraph for each case. (i) The first self-replicating molecule on Earth lies near the boundary of life and nonlife. Does it meet your definition of life? (ii) Modern-day viruses are essentially packets of DNA encased in a microscopic shell of protein. Viruses cannot replicate themselves; instead, they reproduce by infecting living cells and "hijacking" the cell's reproduction machinery to make copies of the viral DNA and proteins. Are viruses alive? (iii) Imagine that humans someday travel to other stars and discover a planet populated by what appear to be robots programmed to mine metal, refine it, and assemble copies of themselves. Examination of fossil "robots" shows that they have improved, perhaps because cosmic rays have caused errors in their programs. Is this race of robots alive? Would your answer depend on whether another race had built the first robots?

13. *Ozone Signature.* Suppose a powerful future telescope is able to take a spectrum of a terrestrial planet around another star. The spectrum reveals the presence of significant amounts of ozone. Why would this discovery strongly suggest the presence of life on this planet? Would it tell us whether the life is microscopic or more advanced? Summarize your answers in one or two paragraphs.

14. *Explaining Ourselves to the Aliens.* Imagine that someday we make contact with intelligent aliens and even learn to communicate. Even so, many facets of life we take for granted may be utterly incomprehensible to them: music (perhaps they have no sense of hearing), money (perhaps there has never been a need), love (perhaps they don't feel this emotion), meals (perhaps they photosynthesize). Write a page attempting to explain one of these concepts, or another of your choosing. Remember that even the words in your explanation require definition; start at the lowest possible level.

## Web Projects

Find useful links for Web projects on the text Web site.

1. *Life on Mars.* Find the latest information regarding the controversy over evidence for life in Martian meteorites. Write a one- to two-page report summarizing the current state of the controversy and your own opinion as to whether life once existed on Mars.

2. *Search for Life.* Learn about a proposed mission to search for life on Mars, Europa, or elsewhere in our solar system or beyond. Write a one- to two-page summary of the mission and its prospects for success.

3. *Human Threats to the Earth.* Write an in-depth research report, three to five pages in length, about current understanding and controversy regarding one of the following issues: global warming, ozone depletion, or the loss of species on Earth due to human activity. Be sure to address both the latest knowledge about the issue and proposals for alleviating any dangers associated with it. End your report by making your own recommendations about what, if anything, needs to be done to prevent damage to the Earth.

4. *Local Geology.* Write a one- to two-page report about the geology of an area you know well—perhaps the location of your campus or your hometown. Which of the four geological processes has played the most important role, in your opinion? Has plate tectonics played a direct role in shaping the area?

# A Deeper Look at Nature

*Henceforth space by itself, and time by itself, are doomed to fade away into mere shadows, and only a kind of union of the two will preserve an independent reality.*

HERMANN MINKOWSKI, 1908

# CHAPTER S2

# Space and Time

The universe consists of matter and energy moving through *space* with the passage of *time*. Up to this point in the book, we have discussed the concepts of space and time as though they are absolute and distinct—just as they appear in everyday life. But what if this appearance is deceiving?

About a century ago, Albert Einstein discovered that space and time are not what they appear to be. Instead, space and time are intertwined in a remarkable manner described by Einstein's *theory of relativity*. Because space and time are such fundamental concepts, understanding relativity is important to understanding the universe.

The theory of relativity is *not* difficult to understand, despite popular myths to the contrary. It does, however, require us to think in new ways. That is our task in this chapter and the next. By the time we are finished, you will see that Einstein brought about a revolution in human thinking with many important ramifications for understanding our place in the universe.

## S2.1 Einstein's Revolution

Imagine that, with the aid of a long tape measure, you carefully measure the distance you walk from home to work to be 5.0 kilometers. You wouldn't expect any argument about this distance. For example, if a friend drives her car along the same route and measures the distance with her car's odometer, she ought to get the same measurement of 5.0 kilometers—as long as her odometer is working properly.

Likewise, you would expect agreement about the time it takes you to walk from home to work. Suppose your friend continues driving and you call her on a cellular phone just as you leave your house at 8:00 A.M. and again just as you arrive at work at 8:45 A.M. You'd certainly be surprised if she argued that your walk took an amount of time other than 45 minutes.

Distances and times appear absolute and distinct in our daily lives. We expect everyone to agree on the distance between two points, such as the locations of home and work. We also expect agreement about the time between two events, such as leaving home and arriving at work. Thus, it came as a huge surprise to everyone when in 1905 Albert Einstein showed that these expectations are not strictly correct.

With extremely precise measurements, the distance you measure between home and work will be *different* from the distance measured by a friend in a car, and you and your friend will also disagree about the time it takes you to walk to work. At ordinary speeds, the differences will be so small as to be unnoticeable. But if your friend could drive at a speed close to the speed of light, the differences would be substantial.

Disagreements about distances and times are only the beginning of the astonishing ideas contained in Einstein's **theory of relativity**. Einstein developed this theory in two parts. His **special theory of relativity**, published in 1905, showed how space and time are intertwined but did not deal with the effects of gravity. His **general theory of relativity**, published in 1915, offered a surprising new view of gravity—a view that we will use to help us understand topics such as the expansion and fate of the universe and the strange objects known as *black holes*.

In this chapter, we will focus on the new view of space and time in Einstein's special theory of relativity. In particular, we will see how this theory supports each of the following ideas:

- Nothing can travel faster than the speed of light (in a vacuum), and no material object can even reach the speed of light.

- If you carefully observe anyone or anything moving by you at a speed close to the speed of light, time will run more slowly for the moving object.

That is, a person moving by you ages more slowly than you, a clock moving by you ticks more slowly than your clock, a computer moving by you runs more slowly than your similar computer, and so on.

- If you observe two events to occur simultaneously, such as flashes of light in two different places at the same time, a person moving by you at a speed close to the speed of light will not agree that the two events were simultaneous.

- If you carefully measure the size of something moving by you at a speed close to the speed of light, you will find that its length (in the direction of its motion) is shorter than it would be if the object were not moving.

- If you could measure the mass of something moving by you at a speed close to the speed of light, you would find its mass to be greater than the mass it would have if it were stationary. From this fact you can conclude, as did Einstein, that $E = mc^2$.

Although the consequences of special relativity may sound like science fiction or fantasy, their reality is supported by a vast body of observational and experimental evidence. They also follow logically from a few simple ideas. If you keep an open mind and think deeply as you read, you'll soon be confident and conversant in the ideas of relativity.

### What Is Relativity?

Suppose a supersonic airplane is flying at a speed of 1,650 km/hr from Nairobi, Kenya, to Quito, Ecuador. How fast is the plane going? At first, this question sounds trivial—we have just said that the plane is going 1,650 km/hr.

But wait. . . . Nairobi and Quito are both nearly on the Earth's equator, and the equatorial speed of the Earth's rotation is the same 1,650 km/hr that the plane is flying [Section 1.3]. Moreover, the east-to-west flight from Nairobi to Quito is opposite the direction of the Earth's rotation (Figure S2.1). Thus, if you could observe the plane from far off in space, it would appear to stay put *while the Earth rotated beneath it*. When the flight began, you would see the plane lift straight off the ground in Nairobi. The plane would then remain stationary while the Earth's rotation carried Nairobi away from it and Quito toward it. When Quito finally reached the plane's position, the plane would drop straight down to the ground.

We have two alternative viewpoints about the plane's flight. People on Earth say that the plane is traveling westward across the surface of the Earth. Observers in space say that the plane is stationary while the Earth rotates eastward beneath it. Both viewpoints are equally valid. In fact, there are many other equally valid viewpoints about the plane's flight. Observers looking at the solar system as a whole would see the plane moving at a speed of more than 100,000 km/hr—the Earth's speed in its orbit around the Sun. Observers living in a distant galaxy would see the plane moving away from them at a very high speed, carried along with the Earth and the Milky Way by the expansion of the universe. The only thing all these observers would agree on is that the plane is traveling at 1,650 km/hr *relative to* the surface of the Earth.

This example shows that questions like "Who is really moving?" and "How fast are you going?" have no absolute answers. Einstein's *theory of relativity* gets its name from the fact that it tells us that measurements of motion, as well as measurements of time and space, make sense only when we describe whom or what they are being measured relative to.

**TIME OUT TO THINK** *Suppose you are running on a treadmill and the readout says you are going 8 miles per hour. What is the 8 miles per hour measured relative to? How fast are you going relative to the ground? How fast would an observer on the Moon see you going? Describe a few other possible viewpoints on your speed.*

Note that the theory of relativity does *not* say that *everything* is relative. In particular, the theory claims that two things in the universe are absolute:

1. The laws of nature are the same for everyone.

2. The speed of light is the same for everyone.

As we'll see shortly, all the astounding consequences of relativity follow directly from these two seemingly innocuous statements.

### Making Sense of Relativity

One reason why relativity has a reputation for being difficult to grasp, despite its underlying simplicity, is that most of its ideas and consequences are not obvious in everyday life. They become obvious only when we deal with speeds close to the speed of light or with gravitational fields far stronger than that of the Earth. Because we don't commonly experience such extreme conditions, we have no *common* sense about them. Thus, to say that relativity violates common sense is not really accurate. The theory of relativity is perfectly consistent with everything we have come to expect in daily life.

Making sense of relativity really requires only that you learn to view your everyday experiences from a new, broader perspective. Fortunately, you have learned to

**FIGURE S2.1** A plane flying at 1,650 km/hr from Nairobi to Quito (westward) travels precisely opposite the Earth's eastward rotation. Thus, viewed from afar, the plane remains stationary while the Earth rotates underneath it.

broaden your perspective in a similar way before. At a very young age, you learned "common sense" meanings for *up* and *down: Up* is above your head, *down* is toward your feet, and things tend to fall down. One day, however, you learned that the Earth is round. When you looked at a globe with the Northern Hemisphere on the top, you were immediately confronted with a **paradox**—a situation that *seems* to violate common sense or to contradict itself. Your common sense told you that Australians should fall off the Earth (Figure S2.2a), but they don't. To resolve this paradox, you were forced to accept that your "common sense" about *up* and *down* was incorrect. You therefore revised your common sense to accept that *up* and *down* are determined relative to the center of the Earth (Figure S2.2b).

**TIME OUT TO THINK** *Why do you suppose most maps and globes show the Northern Hemisphere on the top and the Southern Hemisphere on the bottom? If you hung your map upside down and rewrote the words so they read right-side up, would the map be equally valid?*

**FIGURE S2.2** Learning that the Earth is round helps children revise their "common sense" understanding of *up* and *down.*

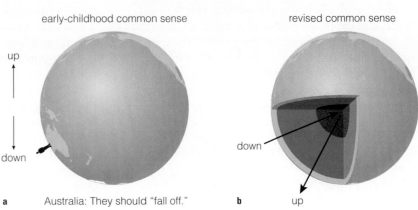

early-childhood common sense

up

down

**a** Australia: They should "fall off."

revised common sense

down

**b** up

**a** Observers in different reference frames measure different speeds for material objects.

**b** Everyone measures the same speed of light.

**FIGURE S2.3** Unlike the case with material objects, the speed of light is not additive.

As a teenager, Einstein wondered what the world would look like if he could travel at or beyond the speed of light. But he inevitably encountered paradoxes when he thought about this question. Ultimately, he resolved the paradoxes only when he recognized that our commonsense ideas about space and time must change if we are to extend them to the realm of very high speeds or very strong gravitational fields. Just as we all once learned a new common sense about up and down, we now must learn a new common sense about space and time.

## S2.2  Relative Motion

We will study relativity with the aid of *thought experiments* in which we create imaginary situations and logically follow them through to their conclusions. A starting point for our thought experiments will be the assumption that the two absolutes of relativity are true.

The first of the two absolutes, that the laws of nature are the same for everyone, is probably not surprising. If you're on an airplane with the shades drawn during a very smooth flight, you won't feel any sensation of motion. Thus, you should expect to get the same results from any experiments you perform on the airplane that someone else would get performing the same experiments on the ground. These equivalent results prove that the laws of nature are the same in the airplane and on the ground. In the language of relativity, the ground and the airplane represent different **frames of reference** (or *reference frames*) because they are moving relative to each other. The idea that the laws of nature are the same for everyone means that they do not depend on your frame of reference.

The second absolute of relativity, that the speed of light is the same for everyone, is far more surprising. In general, we expect people in different reference frames to give different answers for the speed of the same moving object. For example, suppose you roll a ball down the aisle of an airplane. The ball rolls slowly in your airplane reference frame, but moves fast—because it also has the airplane's speed—in the reference frame of a person on the ground (Figure S2.3a). However, if you turn on a flashlight and measure the speed of the emitted light, a person on the ground will find exactly the same speed for the light beam (Figure S2.3b). That is, people in different reference frames can disagree about the speeds of material objects, but everyone always agrees on the speed of light—regardless of where the light comes from.

How can we know that everyone always measures the same speed of light? Einstein reached this conclusion because it was the only way he could resolve the paradoxes he encountered when he thought about traveling at the speed of light. But observations and experiments are the ultimate judge of any scientific theory. Many observations and experiments, some of which we'll study later in the chapter, have verified that the speed of light really is an absolute in nature. *The absoluteness of the speed of light is an experimentally verified fact.*

This statement may not seem important, but it will force you to let go of many of your intuitive beliefs about how the universe works. We will investigate why this statement forces such a change by constructing a series of thought experiments about relative motion viewed from different reference frames. If you follow the logic of the thought experiments carefully, you will come to understand the strange predictions of relativity. Later, we will investigate the experimental evidence that shows these predictions to be accurate. Because special relativity does not deal with the effects of gravity, the thought experiments are easiest to visualize by imagining that they take place in deep space, far from any gravitational fields. We will use spaceships floating freely without engine power. Because everything in and around these spaceships is weightless and floats freely, we call the reference frames of these spaceships **free-float frames** (more traditionally called *inertial reference frames*).

### Thought Experiments at Ordinary Speeds

First, to make sure you're comfortable with ideas of relative motion in everyday life, let's analyze a few thought experiments involving ordinary speeds.

**Thought Experiment 1** (Figure S2.4) Imagine that you are floating freely in a spaceship. Because you feel no sensation of motion, you perceive yourself to be at rest, or traveling at zero speed. As you look out your window, you see your friend Jackie in her own spaceship, moving away at a constant speed of 90 km/hr. How does the situation appear to Jackie?

**FIGURE S2.4** Thought Experiment 1.

your point of view

Jackie's point of view

We can answer the question by logically analyzing the experimental situation. Because Jackie is moving at *constant velocity* relative to you, she must also be in a free-float frame. She therefore perceives *herself* to be at rest, and she would say that *you* are moving away from her at 90 km/hr.

Note that both points of view—yours and Jackie's—are equally valid. You both would find the same results for any experiments performed in your own spaceship, and your research would lead you to exactly the same laws of nature. You could argue endlessly about who is really moving, but your argument would be pointless because all motion is relative.

**Thought Experiment 2** (Figure S2.5) We begin with the same situation as in Thought Experiment 1, but this time you put on your spacesuit and strap yourself to the outside of your spaceship. You happen to have a baseball, which you throw in Jackie's direction at a speed of 100 km/hr. How is the ball moving relative to Jackie?

**FIGURE S2.5** Thought Experiment 2.

your point of view

Jackie's point of view

From your point of view, Jackie and the ball are both going in the same direction. Jackie is going 90 km/hr and the ball is going 100 km/hr, so the ball is going 10 km/hr faster than Jackie. The ball will therefore overtake and pass her.

From Jackie's point of view, *she* is stationary and *you* are moving away from her at 90 km/hr. Thus, she sees the ball moving toward her at 10 km/hr—the ball's speed of 100 km/hr relative to you *minus* the 90 km/hr at which you are moving relative to her. Note that both you and Jackie agree that the ball will pass her at a *relative* speed of 10 km/hr.

**Thought Experiment 3** (Figure S2.6) This time you throw a baseball in Jackie's direction at 90 km/hr. From your point of view, the ball is traveling at exactly the same speed as Jackie. Therefore, you'll see the ball forever chasing her through space, neither catching up nor falling behind.

**FIGURE S2.6** Thought Experiment 3.

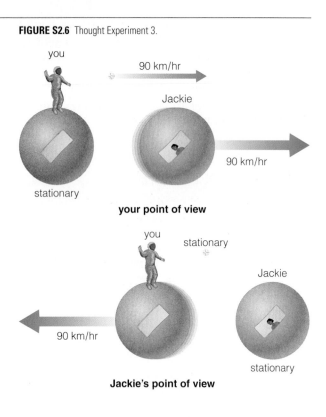

From Jackie's point of view, the 90 km/hr at which you threw the ball exactly matches your 90 km/hr speed away from her. Therefore, the ball is *stationary* in her reference frame. Think about this for a moment: Before you throw the baseball, Jackie sees it moving away from her at 90 km/hr because it is in your hand. At the moment you release the baseball, it suddenly becomes stationary in Jackie's reference frame, floating in space at a fixed distance from her spaceship. Many hours later, after you have traveled far away, Jackie will still see the ball floating in the same place. If she wishes, she can put on her spacesuit and go out to retrieve it. Or she can just leave it there—from her point of view, it's not going anywhere, and neither is she.

**TIME OUT TO THINK** *In Thought Experiment 3, suppose instead that you throw the ball in Jackie's direction at 80 km/hr. In that case, what will Jackie see the ball doing? Next, suppose that Jackie is moving* toward *you rather than* away *from you. What would she see the ball doing in that case?*

*Thought Experiments at High Speeds*

The absoluteness of the speed of light did not come into play in our first three thought experiments because the speeds were so small compared to the speed of light. For example, 100 km/hr is less than *1 ten-millionth* of the speed of light. Now let's raise the speeds way up and explore the strange consequences of the absoluteness of the speed of light.

**Thought Experiment 4** (Figure S2.7) Imagine that Jackie is moving away from you at 90% of the speed of light, or $0.9c$. (Recall that $c$ is the symbol for the speed of light, which is about 300,000 km/s.) How does the situation appear to Jackie?

**FIGURE S2.7** Thought Experiment 4.

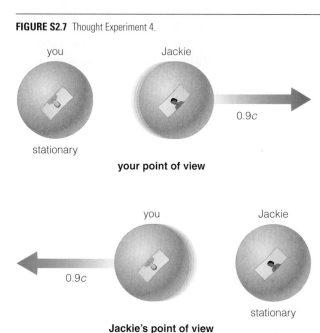

Other than the much higher speed, this situation is just like that in Thought Experiment 1. Jackie perceives *herself* to be at rest and sees *you* moving away from her at $0.9c$.

**Thought Experiment 5** (Figure S2.8) Now, instead of throwing a baseball, you climb out of your spaceship and point a flashlight in Jackie's direction. How is the beam of light moving relative to Jackie?

From your point of view, Jackie and the flashlight beam are both going in the same direction. Jackie is going at 90% of the speed of light, or $0.9c$, and the light beam is going at the full speed of light, or $c$. Thus, you see the light beam going $0.1c$ faster than Jackie.[1] Nothing should be surprising so far.

---

[1]You can't actually *see* a light beam moving forward. When we say that you see the beam moving at the speed of light, we really mean that you would find it to be moving at this speed if you made a careful measurement with instruments at rest in your reference frame.

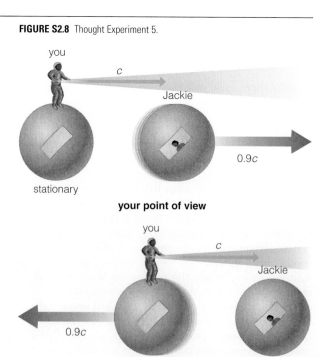

**your point of view**

**Jackie's point of view**

From Jackie's point of view, *she* is stationary and *you* are moving away from her at 0.9*c*. Following the "old common sense" used in our earlier thought experiments, we would expect Jackie to see the light moving toward her at 0.1*c*—the light's speed of *c* minus your speed of 0.9*c*. *But this answer is wrong!* Relativity tells us that the speed of light is always the same for everyone. Therefore, Jackie must see the beam of light coming toward her at *c*, *not* at 0.1*c*.

Note that you and Jackie no longer agree about her speed *relative* to the speed of the light beam: She'll see the light beam pass by her at the speed of light, *c*, but you'll see it going only 0.1*c* faster than she is going. By our old common sense, this result sounds preposterous. But we found it by using simple logic, starting with the assumption that the speed of light is the same for everyone. As long as this assumption is true—and, remember, the absoluteness of the speed of light is an experimentally verified fact—our conclusions follow logically.

**TIME OUT TO THINK** *Suppose Jackie is moving away from you at a speed of 0.99999c, which is short of the speed of light by only 0.00001c, or 3 km/s. How much faster than Jackie will you see the light going? How fast will Jackie see the light going as it passes her?*

### You Can't Reach the Speed of Light

You might be wondering what Jackie would see if she were moving away from you at the speed of light or faster—which is essentially the same question Einstein asked when he wondered how the world would look if he could travel at or beyond the speed of light. However, once we accept the absoluteness of the speed of light, it's easy to prove that neither she nor you nor any other material object can ever reach the speed of light, let alone exceed it.

**Thought Experiment 6** You have just built the most incredible rocket imaginable, and you are taking it on a test ride. Soon you are going faster than anyone had ever imagined possible—and then you put the rocket into second gear! You keep going faster and faster and faster. Here is the key question: Are you ever traveling faster than the speed of light?

Before we answer this question, the fact that all motion is relative forces us to answer another question: In what reference frame is your speed being measured? Let's begin with *your* reference frame. Imagine that you turn on your rocket's headlights. Because the speed of light is absolute, you must see the headlight beams travel away from you at *c* = 300,000 km/s. Note that this is true no matter how long you have been firing your rocket engines; in your own reference frame, you cannot possibly outrace your own headlight beams.

Could someone in a different reference frame say that you are traveling faster than the speed of light? Observers in different reference frames will measure your speed differently, but *all* observers will agree on two key points: (1) Your headlight beams are moving out ahead of you, and (2) these light beams are traveling at *c* = 300,000 km/s. Clearly, if you are being outraced by your headlights and if the headlights are traveling at the speed of light, you must be traveling *slower* than the speed of light. It does not matter who is measuring your speed; it can be you, someone on Earth, or anyone else in any other reference frame. No one can ever observe you to be traveling as fast as a light beam.

In case you are still not convinced, let's turn the situation around. Imagine that, as you race by some planet, a person on the planet turns on a light beam. Because the speed of light is absolute, you will see the light beam race past you at *c* = 300,000 km/s. The person on the planet will also see the light traveling at *c* = 300,000 km/s and will see the light outrace you. Thus, again, everyone will agree that you are traveling slower than the speed of light.

The same argument applies to any moving object. As long as the speed of light is absolute, no material object can reach or exceed it. Building a spaceship to travel at the speed of light is not a mere technological challenge—it simply cannot be done.

### What If Light Can't Catch You?

If you're like most students learning about relativity for the first time, you're probably already looking for loopholes in the logic of our thought experiments. For example, confronted with Thought Experiment 6, you might be tempted to ask, "What happens if you're traveling away from some planet faster than light, so the light from the planet can't catch you?" While it's surely true that light couldn't catch you if you were going faster than the speed of light, it also makes the question somewhat moot: If you can't see light from the planet, there is no way for you to know that the planet even exists.

In fact, what relativity really tells us about the speed of light is that it is a limit on the speed at which *information* can be transmitted. There are numerous circumstances in the universe in which, on philosophical grounds, an object may *seem* to be exceeding the speed of light. However, these circumstances do not provide any means of sending information or objects at speeds faster than the speed of light.

As an example, consider the implications of the fact that the universe is expanding [Section 1.3]. Recall that the more distant a galaxy, the faster the expansion of the universe is carrying it away from us. In principle, somewhere far away, there could be a point beyond which the expansion is carrying galaxies away from us faster than the speed of light. However, we cannot observe such galaxies because their light cannot reach us. Scientifically, we say that such galaxies are beyond the bounds of our observable universe, and the observable universe is the only "universe" that we can study.

Other examples of things that *seem* to move faster than the speed of light arise frequently in the strange world of quantum mechanics (see Chapter S4). According to quantum principles, measuring a particle in one place can (in certain specific circumstances) affect a particle in another place *instantaneously*—even if the particle is many light-years away. In fact, this process has been observed in laboratories over short distances. This instantaneous effect of one particle on another may at first seem to violate relativity, but it does not. The built-in randomness of quantum mechanics prevents this technique from being used to transmit useful information to a distant point. Moreover, if we wish to confirm that the second particle really was affected, we will have to receive a signal carrying information about the particle—and that signal can travel no faster than the speed of light.

## S2.3 The Reality of Space and Time

In the beginning of this chapter, we listed five key predictions of the theory of relativity. So far, we have shown only how the first one—that no material object can reach or exceed the speed of light—follows from the two absolutes of relativity. Let's continue on and see why our old conceptions of time and space must be revised.

### Time Differs in Different Reference Frames

In preparation for our next thought experiment, imagine that you are on a moving train tossing a ball straight up so that it bounces straight back down from the ceiling. How do the path and speed of the ball appear to an observer along the tracks outside the train? As shown in Figure S2.9, the outside observer sees the ball going forward with the train at the same time that it is going up and down, so the ball's path always slants forward. Because the outside observer sees the ball moving with this forward speed *in addition to* its up-and-down speed while you see the ball going only up and down, he would measure a *faster* overall speed for the ball than you would. If the

Inside the train, the ball goes up and down.

Outside the train, the ball appears to be going faster: It has the same up-and-down speed, plus the forward speed of the train.

The faster the train is moving, the faster the ball appears to be going to the outside observer.

**FIGURE S2.9** A ball tossed straight up and down on a moving train follows a slanted path according to an outside observer.

train is moving slowly, the outside observer sees the ball's path slant forward only slightly and would say that the ball's overall speed is only slightly faster than you would report. If the train is moving rapidly, the ball's path leans much farther forward, and the ball appears to be going considerably faster to the outside observer than to you.

**Thought Experiment 7** (Figure S2.10) Inside her spaceship, Jackie has a laser on her floor that is pointed up to a mirror on her ceiling. She momentarily flashes the laser light and uses a very accurate clock to time how long it takes the light to travel from the floor to the ceiling and back. As Jackie zips by you at a speed close to the speed of light, you observe her experiment through a window in her spaceship. Using your own very accurate clock, you also time the laser light's trip from Jackie's floor to her ceiling and back.

**FIGURE S2.10** Thought Experiment 7.

Jackie

**Jackie's point of view**

Jackie

**your point of view**

Because Jackie, the laser, and the mirror are all moving from your point of view, the light's path looks slanted as it goes from floor to ceiling and back. Thus, from your point of view, the light travels a *longer* path in going from the floor to the ceiling than it does from Jackie's point of view, just as the ball tossed in a train took a longer path from the outside observer's point of view.

By our old common sense, this would be no big deal. You and Jackie would agree on how long it takes the light to go from the floor to the ceiling and back, just as you and an outside observer would agree on how long it takes you to toss a ball up and down on a train. You would explain the light's longer path by

saying that the light is moving faster relative to you than it is relative to Jackie, just as the outside observer sees the tossed ball moving faster because of the forward motion of the train. But, because we are dealing with *light*, you and Jackie must both see its speed to be the *same*—300,000 km/s—even though you see its path slanted forward with the movement of the spaceship.

So what? Both you and Jackie see the light traveling at the same speed, but *you* see it traveling a longer distance—and, at a given speed, it takes more time to travel a longer distance. Thus, *your clock will record more time* than Jackie's as the light travels from floor to ceiling and back. That is, if you watch Jackie's clock, you will see it running slower than your own. It doesn't matter what you and Jackie use to measure the time for the light trip. *Anything* that can measure time will be going slower in Jackie's reference frame than in yours, including mechanical clocks, electrical clocks, heartbeats, and biochemical reactions. Our astonishing conclusion: From your point of view, *time itself* is running slower for Jackie.

How much slower is time running for Jackie? It depends on her speed relative to you. If she is moving slowly compared to the speed of light, you will scarcely be able to detect the slant, and your clock and Jackie's clock will tick at nearly the same rate. The faster she is moving, the more slanted the light path you see and the greater the difference between the rate of her clock and that of yours. Generalizing, we reach the following conclusion:

*From your point of view, time runs slower in the reference frame of anyone moving relative to you. The faster the other reference frame is moving, the slower time passes within it.*

This effect is called **time dilation** because it tells us that time is *dilated*, or expanded, in a moving reference frame.

### The Relativity of Simultaneity

Our old common sense tells us that everyone must agree when two events happen at the same time or when one event happens before another. If you see two apples—one red and one green—fall from two different trees and hit the ground at the same time, you expect everyone else to agree that they landed at the same time (assuming you've accounted for any difference in the light travel times from the two trees). If you see the green apple land before the red apple, you are very surprised if someone else says that the red apple hit the ground first. Prepare yourself to be surprised, because our next thought experiment will show that observers in different reference frames will not necessarily agree about the order or simultaneity of events that occur in different places.

Before we go on, note that observers in different reference frames *must* agree about the order of events that occur in the *same* place. For example, suppose you grab a cookie and eat it. In your reference frame, both events (picking up the cookie and eating it) occur in the same place. Thus, it could not possibly be the case that someone else would see you eat the cookie before you pick it up.

**Thought Experiment 8** Jackie is coming toward you in a brand new, extra-long spaceship. She is in the center of her spaceship, which is totally dark. At the instant that Jackie happens to pass you, two lights flash at either end of her spaceship. After a brief moment, the two flashes reach you at *exactly the same time*: a flash of green light from the front of her spaceship, and a flash of red light from the rear of her

## Mathematical Insight S2.1    The Time Dilation Formula

Look at the different paths that you and Jackie see the light take from the floor to the ceiling in Figure S2.10. We can form a right triangle from these paths, which we can use to find an exact formula for time dilation. Recall that *distance = speed × time*, and note how the sides are constructed in Figure S2.11a:

- *You* see the light take a slanted path from Jackie's floor to ceiling because of her motion relative to you. Let's use $t$ to represent the time that *you* measure as the light travels this path. Because the light travels at the speed of light, $c$, the length of this path is $c \times t$.

- The distance that *you* see Jackie travel while the light goes from her floor to her ceiling is $v \times t$, where $v$ is her speed relative to you.

- We know that Jackie measures time differently than you, so we'll use $t'$ (read "t-prime") to represent the time *she* measures as the light travels from her floor to her ceiling. The distance she sees the light travel therefore is $c \times t'$.

Because we have a right triangle, we can solve for the time on Jackie's clock ($t'$) in terms of the time on your clock ($t$) by using the Pythagorean theorem and a bit of algebra. (Recall that the Pythagorean theorem states that $a^2 + b^2 = c^2$ for a right triangle with side lengths $a$, $b$, and $c$, where $c$ is the hypotenuse.)

Start with the Pythagorean theorem:
$$(ct')^2 + (vt)^2 = (ct)^2$$

Expand the squares:
$$c^2 t'^2 + v^2 t^2 = c^2 t^2$$

Subtract $v^2 t^2$ from both sides:
$$c^2 t'^2 = c^2 t^2 - v^2 t^2$$

Divide both sides by $c^2 t^2$:
$$\frac{t'^2}{t^2} = \frac{c^2 - v^2}{c^2}$$

Simplify:
$$\frac{t'^2}{t^2} = \frac{c^2}{c^2} - \frac{v^2}{c^2} = 1 - \left(\frac{v}{c}\right)^2$$

Take the square root of both sides:
$$\frac{t'}{t} = \sqrt{1 - \left(\frac{v}{c}\right)^2} \quad \text{or} \quad t' = t\sqrt{1 - \left(\frac{v}{c}\right)^2}$$

The final result, called the *time dilation formula*, tells us the *ratio* of time in a moving reference frame to time in a reference frame at rest. This ratio is graphed against speed in Figure S2.11b. Note that $t'/t \approx 1$ at speeds that are small compared to the speed of light, meaning that clocks in both reference frames tick at about the same rate. But as $v$ approaches $c$, the amount of time passing in the moving reference frame gets smaller and smaller compared to the time passing in the reference frame at rest.

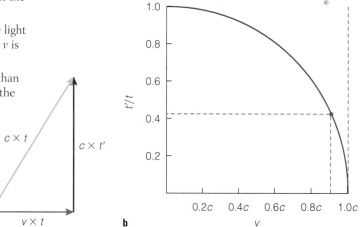

**FIGURE S2.11** (a) The setup for finding the time dilation formula. (b) The time dilation factor graphed against speed.

*Example:* Suppose Jackie is moving past you at a speed of $0.9c$. While 1 hour passes for you, how much time passes for Jackie?

*Solution:* Jackie's speed of $v = 0.9c$ means $v/c = 0.9$. The variable $t$ represents *your* time, so $t = 1$ hour. Substituting into the time dilation formula yields:

$$t' = t\sqrt{1 - \left(\frac{v}{c}\right)^2}$$
$$= (1 \text{ hr}) \sqrt{1 - (0.9)^2}$$
$$= (1 \text{ hr}) \sqrt{1 - 0.81}$$
$$= (1 \text{ hr}) \sqrt{0.19} \approx 0.44 \text{ hr}$$

which is about 26 minutes. Thus, while 1 hour passes for you, only 26 minutes passes for Jackie. Note that you can also find this answer from the graph in Figure S2.11b: At a speed of $v = 0.9c$, the graph shows that the ratio of Jackie's time to your time is 0.44.

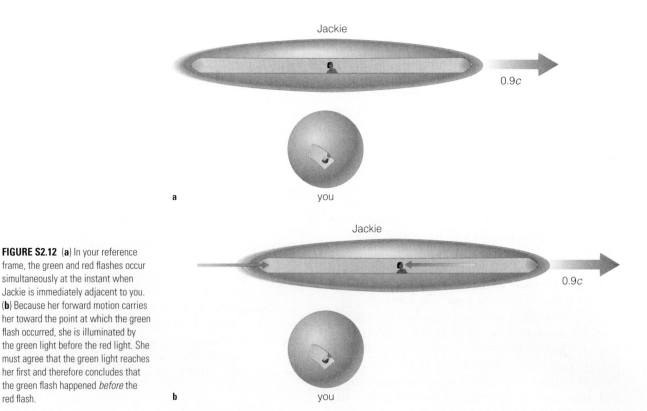

Jackie

0.9*c*

**a**

you

Jackie

0.9*c*

**FIGURE S2.12** (**a**) In your reference frame, the green and red flashes occur simultaneously at the instant when Jackie is immediately adjacent to you. (**b**) Because her forward motion carries her toward the point at which the green flash occurred, she is illuminated by the green light before the red light. She must agree that the green light reaches her first and therefore concludes that the green flash happened *before* the red flash.

**b**

you

spaceship (Figure S2.12a). However, during the very short time that the light flashes are traveling toward Jackie, her speed carries her toward the point where you saw the green flash occur and away from the point where you saw the red flash occur (Figure S2.12b). Therefore, the green flash will reach her before the red flash: You'll see her illuminated first by green light and then by red light. Jackie must also see herself first turn green and then turn red, agreeing with you that the green light reached her before the red light.

So far, nothing is surprising. But remember that Jackie considers herself to be in the center of a *stationary* spaceship. From her point of view, the flashes from the front and the rear both travel toward her at the *same speed* (the speed of light), and both have the same distance to travel. Therefore, because the green flash from the front of the spaceship reaches her *before* the red flash from the rear, she must conclude that the green flash happened first and the red flash happened some time later. Thus, while you say that the two flashes were simultaneous, Jackie disagrees: She says that the green flash occurred before the red flash.

### Effects on Length and Mass

The fact that time is different in different reference frames means that lengths (or distances) and masses must also be affected, although the explanations are a bit subtler. The following two thought experiments use the idea of time dilation to help us understand the effects on length and mass.

**Thought Experiment 9** Jackie is back in her original spaceship, coming toward you at high speed. As usual, both you and she agree on your *relative* speed; you disagree only about who is stationary and who is moving. Now imagine that Jackie tries to measure the length of your spaceship as she passes by you. In your reference frame, you'll see Jackie's time running slower. Because her clocks record less time than yours as she passes from one end of your spaceship to the other, she must measure the length of your spaceship to be shorter than you measure it to be. (Recall that distance is speed × time.) Similarly, you will measure Jackie's spaceship as having a shorter length than it would have if it were at rest in your reference frame, an effect called **length contraction** (Figure S2.13). Note that lengths are affected only in the direction of motion; her spaceship is shorter from your point of view, but its height and depth

**FIGURE S2.13** People and objects moving relative to you are contracted in their direction of motion.

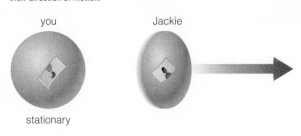

you

Jackie

stationary

are unaffected. Generalizing, we reach the following conclusion:

*From your point of view, lengths of objects moving by you (or distances between objects moving by you) are shorter in their direction of motion than they would be if the objects were at rest. The faster the objects are moving, the shorter the lengths.*

**Thought Experiment 10** Imagine that Jackie has an identical twin sister with an identical spaceship, and suppose that her sister is at rest in your reference frame while Jackie is moving by you at high speed. At the instant Jackie passes by, you give both Jackie and her sister identical pushes (Figure S2.14). If Jackie and her sister are truly identical, the force of your push should have the same effect on each of them; for example, it might cause each of them to gain 1 km/s of speed relative to you. However, because you'll see Jackie's time running slower than yours and her sister's, you will conclude that Jackie feels the force of your push for a *shorter* time than her sister feels your push. (For example, if you and Jackie's sister measure the duration of the push to be 1 microsecond, Jackie's clock will show the duration to be less than 1 microsecond.) Because Jackie feels the force of your push for a shorter time than her sister, the push must have a *smaller* effect on Jackie's veloc-ity. In other words, you'll find that your push has less effect on Jackie than on her sister, despite the fact that you gave them identical pushes. According to Newton's laws of motion [Section 5.2], the only way the same push can have a smaller effect on Jackie's velocity is if her mass is *greater* than her sister's mass. This effect is sometimes called **mass increase**:

*From your point of view, objects moving by you have greater mass than they have at rest. The faster an object is moving, the greater the increase in its mass.*

Mass increase provides another way of under-standing why no material object can reach the speed of light. The faster an object is moving relative to you, the greater mass you'll find it to have. Thus, at higher speeds, the same force will have less effect on an object's velocity. In fact, as an object approaches the speed of light, you will find its mass to be head-ing toward infinity. No force can accelerate an infi-nite mass, so the object can never gain that last little bit of speed needed to push it to the speed of light.

### Velocity Addition

We have just one more important effect to discuss: As the next thought experiment shows, you and Jackie will disagree about the speed of a material object

---

**FIGURE S2.14** Thought Experiment 10.

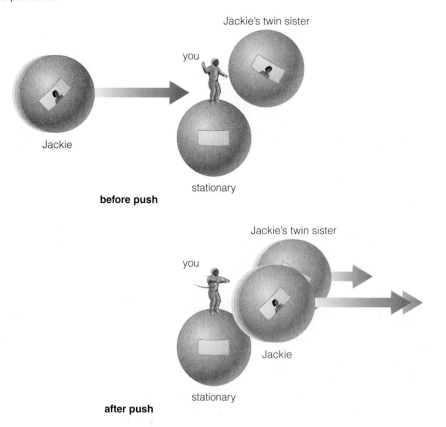

moving relative to both of you. The only speed you will agree on is the speed of light.

**Thought Experiment 11** (Figure S2.15) Jackie is moving toward you at 0.9*c*. Your friend Bob jumps into his spaceship and starts heading in Jackie's direction at 0.8*c* (from your point of view). How fast will Jackie see him approaching her?

By our old common sense, Jackie should see Bob coming toward her at $0.9c + 0.8c = 1.7c$. But we know this answer is wrong, because 1.7*c* is faster than the speed of light. Jackie must see Bob coming toward her at a speed less than *c*, but he will be coming faster than the speed of 0.9*c* at which she sees you coming. Thus, she'll conclude that Bob's speed is somewhere between 0.9*c* and *c*. (In this case, it turns out that she'll see him coming at 0.988*c*; see Mathematical Insight S2.2.)

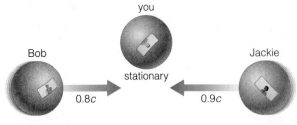

you

Bob      stationary      Jackie

0.8*c*      0.9*c*

**your point of view**

you

Bob      0.9*c*      Jackie

0.988*c*

**Jackie's point of view**

stationary

---

## Mathematical Insight S2.2    Formulas of Special Relativity

We found a formula for time dilation in Mathematical Insight S2.1. Although we will not go through the derivations, it is possible to find similar formulas for length contraction and mass increase. In summary, the three formulas are:

$$\underset{\text{(moving frame)}}{\text{time}} = \underset{\text{(rest frame)}}{\text{time}} \times \sqrt{1 - \left(\frac{v}{c}\right)^2}$$

$$\underset{\text{(moving frame)}}{\text{length}} = (\text{rest length}) \times \sqrt{1 - \left(\frac{v}{c}\right)^2}$$

$$\text{moving mass} = \frac{(\text{rest mass})}{\sqrt{1 - \left(\frac{v}{c}\right)^2}}$$

There's also a simple formula for velocity addition. Suppose you see Jackie moving at speed $v_1$ and Jackie sees a second object moving relative to her at speed $v_2$. By our old common sense, you would see the second object moving at speed $v_1 + v_2$. But the speed that you actually see is:

$$\text{speed of second object} = \frac{v_1 + v_2}{1 + \left(\frac{v_1}{c} \times \frac{v_2}{c}\right)}$$

*Example 1: Length Contraction.* Suppose Jackie is moving by you at 0.99*c*. Because her spaceship is the same model as yours, you know that it is 100 meters long when it is at rest. How long is her spaceship as it moves by you?

*Solution:* We use the length contraction formula to calculate the length of the moving spaceship:

$$\underset{\text{(moving frame)}}{\text{length}} = (\text{rest length}) \times \sqrt{1 - \left(\frac{v}{c}\right)^2}$$

$$= (100 \text{ m}) \times \sqrt{1 - (0.99)^2} = 14 \text{ m}$$

You would measure her spaceship as only 14 meters long, instead of its rest length of 100 meters.

*Example 2: Mass Increase.* A fly has a mass of 1 gram at rest. It is an unusual fly, however, in that it can travel at 0.9999*c*. What is the mass of the fly at that speed?

*Solution:* We use the mass increase formula to calculate the mass of the moving fly:

$$\text{moving mass} = \frac{(\text{rest mass})}{\sqrt{1 - \left(\frac{v}{c}\right)^2}}$$

$$= \frac{1 \text{ g}}{\sqrt{1 - (0.9999)^2}} = 70.7 \text{ g}$$

At 0.9999*c*, the mass of the fly is almost 71 grams, or more than 70 times its rest mass.

*Example 3: Velocity Addition.* Jackie is moving toward you at 0.9*c*. Your friend Bob jumps into his spaceship and starts heading in Jackie's direction at 0.8*c* (from your point of view). How fast will Jackie see him approaching her? (See Figure S2.15.)

*Solution:* According to Jackie, your speed is $v_1 = 0.9c$. Bob's speed *relative to you* is $v_2 = 0.8c$ in the same direction. Thus, she sees him coming at:

$$\underset{\text{(relative to Jackie)}}{\text{Bob's speed}} = \frac{v_1 + v_2}{1 + \left(\frac{v_1}{c} \times \frac{v_2}{c}\right)}$$

$$= \frac{0.9c + 0.8c}{1 + (0.9 \times 0.8)}$$

$$= \frac{1.7c}{1.72} = 0.988c$$

She sees him moving at almost 99% of the speed of light.

## Measuring the Speed of Light

The only reason it is difficult to measure the speed of light is that light travels so fast. If you stand a short distance from a mirror and turn on a light, the reflection seems to appear instantaneously. Such observations led Aristotle (384–322 B.C.) to conclude that light travels at infinite speed, a view that was still held by many scientists as recently as the late 1600s.

One way to make the measurement easier is to place a mirror at increasingly great distances. If the speed of light truly were infinite, the reflection would always appear instantaneously. However, if it takes time for the light to travel to and from the mirror, you should eventually find a delay between the time you turn on the light and the time you see the reflection. Galileo tried a version of this experiment using the distance between two tall hills, but he was unable to detect any delay (instead of using a mirror, he stationed an assistant on the distant hill to signal back when he saw the light). He concluded that the speed of light, if not infinite, was too fast to be measured between hills on Earth with the technology of his day.

A delay in seeing reflected light was first detected in 1675 by the Danish astronomer Olaus Roemer, who used the four largest moons of Jupiter as his "mirrors." By that time, the orbital periods of the moons were well known, so it was possible to predict the precise moments at which each moon would be eclipsed by Jupiter. To his surprise, Roemer found that the eclipses occurred progressively earlier than expected during those times of year when Earth was moving toward Jupiter in its orbit and progressively later when Earth was moving away from Jupiter. He realized that the eclipses actually were occurring at the predicted times, but the light was taking longer to reach us when we were farther from Jupiter. Roemer's observations proved that the speed of light is finite and led to the correct value of 300,000 km/s for its speed. (The measurement depends on knowing the Sun–Earth and Sun–Jupiter distances, which were not well known in 1675. As a result, Roemer calculated the speed of light to be 227,000 km/s. Redoing his calculations using the modern values of these distances yields 300,000 km/s.)

As technology advanced, it became possible to measure light travel time between mirrors at much closer distances. In 1849 and 1850, the French physicists Fizeau and Foucault (also famous for the Foucault pendulum) performed a series of experiments using rotating mirrors to measure the speed of light much more precisely. Modern devices for measuring the speed of light take advantage of the wave properties of light, particularly the fact that light waves can interfere with one another. Such devices, called *interferometers,* were refined by A. A. Michelson in the early 1880s and used in the Michelson–Morley experiment. Details of how these experiments work can be found in many physics texts.

## S2.4 Is It True?

We've shown how all the major predictions of special relativity follow directly from the absoluteness of the speed of light and from the fact that the laws of nature are the same for everyone. But despite the clear logic of our thought experiments, our conclusions remain tentative until they pass observational or experimental tests. Are the bizarre predictions of relativity true?

### The Absoluteness of the Speed of Light

The first thing we might wish to test is the surprising premise of relativity: the absoluteness of the speed of light. In principle, we can test this premise by measuring the speed of light coming from many different objects and going in many different directions, and verifying that the speed is always the same.

The speed of light was first measured in the late 1600s, but experimental evidence for the *absoluteness* of the speed of light did not come until 1887, when A. A. Michelson and E. W. Morley performed their now-famous *Michelson–Morley experiment*. This experiment showed that the speed of light is not affected by the motion of the Earth around the Sun. Countless subsequent experiments verified and extended the results of the Michelson–Morley experiment: The speed of light is always the same.

### Experimental Tests of Special Relativity

Although *we* cannot yet travel at speeds at which the effects of relativity should be obvious, tiny subatomic particles can reach such speeds. In machines called *particle accelerators*, physicists accelerate subatomic particles to speeds near the speed of light and study what happens when the particles collide. The collisions involve large amounts of kinetic energy, some of which is converted into mass-energy that emerges as a shower of newly produced particles [Section 4.2]. Many of these particles have very short lifetimes, at the end of which they decay (change) into other particles. For example, a particle called the $\pi^+$ ("pi plus") meson has a lifetime of about 18 nanoseconds (billionths of a second) when produced at rest. But $\pi^+$ mesons produced at speeds close to the speed of light in particle accelerators last much longer than 18 nanoseconds—just as predicted by the time dilation formula.

Particle accelerators also offer experimental evidence that nothing can reach the speed of light. It is relatively easy to get particles traveling at 99% of the speed of light in particle accelerators. But no matter how much more energy is put into the accelerators, the particle speeds get only fractionally closer to the speed of light. Some particles have been accelerated to speeds within 0.00001% of the speed of light, but none have ever reached the speed of light.

Although the effects of relativity are obvious only at very high speeds, modern techniques of measuring time are so precise that effects can be measured even at ordinary speeds. For example, a 1975 experiment compared the amount of time that passed on an airplane flying in circles to the time that passed on the ground. Over 15 hours, the airborne clocks lost a bit under 6 nanoseconds to the ground clocks, matching the result expected from relativity.

## A Great Conspiracy?

Perhaps you're thinking "I still don't believe it." After all, how can you know that the scientists who report the experimental evidence are telling the truth? Perhaps physicists are making up the whole thing as part of a great conspiracy designed to confuse everyone else so they can take over the world!

What you need is evidence that you can see for yourself. What about nuclear energy? Einstein's famous formula $E = mc^2$, which explains the energy release in nuclear reactions, is a direct consequence of the special theory of relativity—and one that you can derive for yourself with a bit of algebra (see Mathematical Insight S2.3). Every time you see film of an atomic bomb, use electrical power from a nuclear power plant, or feel the energy of sunlight that was generated in the Sun by nuclear fusion, you are gaining experimental evidence of relativity.

Another test you can do yourself is to look through a telescope at a binary star system. If the speed of

---

## Mathematical Insight S2.3  Deriving $E = mc^2$

We can derive $E = mc^2$ from the mass increase formula, calling the moving mass $m$ and the rest mass $m_0$:

$$\text{moving mass} = \frac{(\text{rest mass})}{\sqrt{1 - \left(\frac{v}{c}\right)^2}}$$

or

$$m = m_0 \left(1 - \frac{v^2}{c^2}\right)^{-\frac{1}{2}}$$

We also need a special mathematical approximation: If $x$ is small compared to 1, then:

$$(1 + x)^{-\frac{1}{2}} \approx 1 - \frac{1}{2}x \quad (\text{for } x \text{ small compared to 1})$$

You can verify this approximation by using your calculator to check that it holds for a few small values of $x$, such as $x = 0.05$ or $x = 0.001$.

Note what happens if we substitute $x = -v^2/c^2$ in this approximation:

Start with the approximation:

$$(1 + x)^{-\frac{1}{2}} \approx 1 - \frac{1}{2}x$$

Substitute $x = -v^2/c^2$:

$$\left(1 + -\frac{v^2}{c^2}\right)^{-\frac{1}{2}} \approx 1 - \frac{1}{2}\left(-\frac{v^2}{c^2}\right)$$

Simplify:

$$\left(1 - \frac{v^2}{c^2}\right)^{-\frac{1}{2}} \approx 1 + \frac{1}{2}\frac{v^2}{c^2}$$

We can use this new form of the approximation to rewrite the mass increase formula. The condition that $x$

must be small compared to 1 now means that $-v^2/c^2$ must be small; that is, the speed $v$ must be small compared to the speed of light, $c$.

Start with the mass increase formula:

$$m = m_0 \left(1 - \frac{v^2}{c^2}\right)^{-\frac{1}{2}}$$

Substitute $\left(1 - \frac{v^2}{c^2}\right)^{-\frac{1}{2}} \approx 1 + \frac{1}{2}\frac{v^2}{c^2}$:

$$m \approx m_0 \left(1 + \frac{1}{2}\frac{v^2}{c^2}\right)$$

Expand the right side:

$$m \approx m_0 + \frac{1}{2}\frac{m_0 v^2}{c^2}$$

Multiply both sides by $c^2$:

$$mc^2 \approx m_0 c^2 + \frac{1}{2}m_0 v^2$$

You may recognize the last term on the right as the *kinetic energy* [Section 4.2] of an object with mass $m_0$. Because the other two terms also have units of mass multiplied by speed squared, they also must represent some kind of energy. Einstein recognized that the term on the left represents the *total* energy of a moving object. He then noticed that, even if the speed is *zero* ($v = 0$) so that there is *no* kinetic energy, the equation states that the total energy is *not* zero; instead, it is $m_0 c^2$. In other words, when an object is not moving at all, it still contains energy by virtue of its mass. Thus, $E = mc^2$ is a direct consequence of Einstein's theory of relativity.

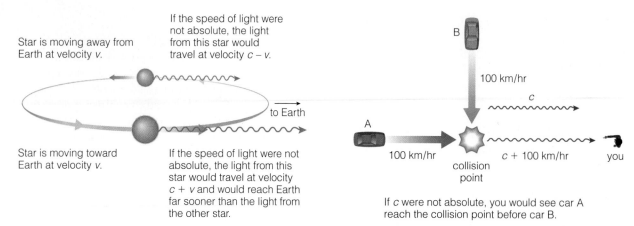

If the speed of light were not absolute, the light from this star would travel at velocity c – v.

Star is moving away from Earth at velocity v.

to Earth

Star is moving toward Earth at velocity v.

If the speed of light were not absolute, the light from this star would travel at velocity c + v and would reach Earth far sooner than the light from the other star.

**FIGURE S2.16** If the speed of light were *not* absolute, the speed at which light from each star in a binary system comes toward Earth would depend on its velocity toward us in the binary orbit.

B

100 km/hr

c

A

100 km/hr          c + 100 km/hr          you

collision point

If c were not absolute, you would see car A reach the collision point before car B.

**FIGURE S2.17** If the speed of light were *not* absolute, the light from a car coming toward you would approach you faster than the light from a car going across your line of sight.

light were *not* absolute, the speed at which light from each star comes toward Earth would depend on its velocity toward us in the binary orbit (Figure S2.16). Imagine, for example, that one star is currently moving directly away from us in its orbit. Light from the star at this point would approach us at speed c − v. Some time later, when the same star is moving toward us in its orbit, its light would approach us at speed c + v. This light would therefore tend to catch up with the light that the star emitted from the other side of its orbit. If the orbital speed and distance were just right, we might see the same star on both sides of the orbit at once! More generally, because the light from each star would come toward us at a different speed from each point in its orbit, we would see each star in multiple positions in its orbit simultaneously. Thus, each star would appear as a short line of light rather than as a point—if the speed of light were not absolute. The fact that we always see distinct stars in binary systems therefore demonstrates that the speed of light *is* absolute.[2]

Finally, you can explore the paradoxes that would occur if the speed of light were not absolute. For example, imagine that two cars, both going about 100 km/hr, collide at an intersection (Figure S2.17). You witness the collision from far down one street. If the speed of light were *not* absolute, the light from the car that was coming toward you would have a

speed of c + 100 km/hr, while the light from the other car would approach you only at c. You therefore would see the car coming toward you reach the intersection slightly *before* the other car and thus would see events unfold differently than the passengers in the car or eyewitnesses in other locations. This difference would be scarcely noticeable, because 100 km/hr is only about *one-millionth* the speed of light, but the difference would increase if you could watch from *very* far away. For example, if you had a super telescope and watched such a collision on a planet in a galaxy 1 million light-years from Earth, you'd see the first car reach the intersection a *year* before the second car. This is a serious paradox: From the viewpoint of the passengers in the cars, they have collided, yet you saw one car reach the collision point long before the other car had even started its journey!

**TIME OUT TO THINK** *The preceding paradox presents us with a choice. If the speed of light is not absolute, different people can witness the same events in very different ways. If the speed of light is absolute, measurements of time and space are relative. Einstein preferred the latter choice. Do you? Explain.*

Of course, like any scientific theory, the theory of relativity can never be *proved* beyond all doubt. But it is supported by a tremendous body of evidence, some of which you can see for yourself. This evidence is real and cannot be made to disappear. If anyone ever comes up with an alternative theory, the new theory will still have to explain the many experimental results that seem to support relativity so well.

---

[2]This conclusion would not follow if light waves were carried by a medium in the same way that sound waves are carried by air. Scientists in the 1800s believed that such a medium, which they called the *ether*, permeated all of space. The Michelson–Morley experiment ruled out the existence of such a medium, so we are left with the conclusion that c is absolute.

## S2.5 Toward a New Common Sense

We've used thought experiments to show that our old common sense doesn't work, and we've discussed how actual experiments verify the ideas of our thought experiments. But we haven't yet figured out what new common sense should replace the old. Surprisingly, another thought experiment that may at first make everything seem even more bizarre will help us understand what is really going on.

**Thought Experiment 12** Suppose Jackie is moving by you at a speed close to the speed of light. From our earlier thought experiments, we know that you'll measure her time as running slow, her length as having contracted, and her mass as having increased. But what would *she* say?

From Jackie's point of view, she's not going anywhere—you are moving by *her* at high speed. Because the laws of nature are the same for everyone, she must reach exactly the same conclusions from her point of view that you reach from your point of view. That is, she'll say that *your* time is running slow, *your* length is contracted, and *your* mass is increased!

Now we have a severe argument on our hands. Imagine that you are looking into Jackie's spaceship with a super telescope. You can clearly see that her time is running slow because everything she does is in slow motion. You send her a radio message saying "Hi Jackie! Why are you doing everything in slow motion?" Because the radio message travels at the absolute speed of light, Jackie has no trouble receiving your message, and she responds with her own radio message back to you.

As you listen to her response, you'll hear it in slow motion—"Hheeeellllloooo tthhheeerrreee"— thus verifying that her time is running slow. But once you record the entire message and use your computer to speed up her voice so that it sounds normal, you'll hear Jackie say, "I'm not moving in slow motion, *you are!*"

You can argue back and forth all you want, but it will get neither of you anywhere. Then you come up with a brilliant idea. You hook up a video camera to your telescope and record a film showing that Jackie's clock is moving slower than yours. You put your videotape in a very fast rocket and shoot it off toward her. When the video arrives and she watches it, she'll see that you are right and that *she* is in slow motion.

Before you declare victory in the argument, one slight problem remains. Jackie had the same brilliant idea, and a rocket from Jackie arrives with a videotape that she made. You put it into the videotape player and watch what appears to be clear proof that Jackie is right—her tape shows that *you* are in slow motion!

How can it be that you see Jackie's time running slow while she sees your time running slow? Think

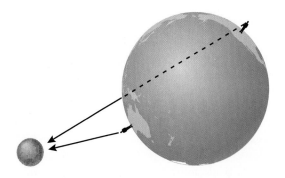

**FIGURE S2.18** The Moon is up for the Australian observer but down for the American observer. (Not to scale.)

back to our earlier discussion of up and down, and imagine that an American child and an Australian child are talking on the telephone. The Australian says, "Isn't the Moon beautiful up in the sky right now?" The American replies, "What are you talking about? The Moon isn't up right now!" According to childhood common sense about up and down, the two children appear to be contradicting each other and could argue endlessly. However, once they realize that up and down are measured *relative* to the center of the Earth, they realize that the argument stems only from incorrect definitions of *up* and *down* (Figure S2.18).

In a similar way, the argument between you and Jackie arises because you are using the old common sense in which we think of space and time as absolutes and expect the speed of light to be relative. The theory of relativity tells us that we have it backward. The speed of light is the absolute, and time and space are relative. By the new common sense, the fact that you and Jackie disagree about whose time is running slow is no more surprising than the fact that the two children disagree about whether the Moon is up or down. The disagreement is meaningless because it involves inadequate definitions of time and space. What counts are *results,* and every experiment that you perform will agree with every experiment that Jackie performs. You are both experiencing the same laws of nature, albeit in ways different from those our old common sense would have suggested.

## S2.6 Ticket to the Stars

The fact that we cannot exceed the speed of light might at first make distant stars seem forever out of reach. But time dilation and length contraction actually offer a ticket to the stars, if we can ever build spaceships capable of traveling at speeds close to the speed of light.

Suppose you want to take a trip to the star Vega, about 25 light-years away. Further, suppose you have a ship that can travel at very close to the speed of light—say, at 0.999c. The trip will take you about 25 years from our point of view on Earth (since you are going at nearly the speed of light over a distance of 25 light-years), and the return trip will take another 25 years. If you leave in the year 2025, you will arrive at Vega in the year 2050 and return to Earth in 2075.

However, from your point of view, you remain stationary while Earth rushes away from you and Vega rushes toward you at 0.999c. You'll therefore find the length from Earth to Vega contracted from its rest length of 25 light-years; with the length contraction formula, the contracted distance turns out to be just over 1 light-year. Because Vega is coming toward you at 0.999c and has only 1 light-year to travel from your point of view, you'll be at Vega in only about 1 year. Your return trip to Earth will also take about 1 year, so the round-trip time is only about 2 years from your point of view (Figure S2.19). If you leave at age 40, you'll return as a 42-year-old.

Although it sounds contradictory by our old common sense, both points of view are correct.[3] If you

leave in 2025 at age 40, you'll return to Earth at age 42—but in the year 2075. That is, while you will have aged only 2 years, all your surviving friends and family will be 50 years older than when you left.

You could make even longer trips within your lifetime with a sufficiently fast spaceship. For example, the Andromeda Galaxy is about 2.5 million light-years away, so the round-trip to any star in the Andromeda Galaxy would take at least 5 million years from the point of view of observers on Earth. However, if you could travel at a speed within 50 parts in a trillion of the speed of light (i.e., $c - 5 \times 10^{-11}c$), the trip would take only about 50 years from your point of view. You could leave Earth at age 30 and return at age 80—but you would return to an Earth on which your friends, your family, and everything you knew had been gone for 5 million years.

In terms of time, relativity offers only a one-way ticket to the stars. You can go a long distance and return to the *place* that you left, but you cannot return to the epoch from which you left.

---

[3]Given that you see the Earth–Vega distance contracted, shouldn't you also claim that it is *Earth's* time running slow, rather than yours? This question underlies the so-called *twin paradox,* in which you make the trip while your twin sister stays home on Earth (see Chapter S3). The resolution comes from the fact that, because you must turn around at Vega, you effectively change reference frames relative to Earth at least once during your trip. A careful analysis of the changing reference frames is beyond the scope of this book, but it turns out that you do indeed measure less total time than your stay-at-home twin.

---

**FIGURE S2.19** At high speed, a traveler to a distant star will age less than people back home on Earth.

round-trip time ≈ 50 years

**reference frame of Earth**

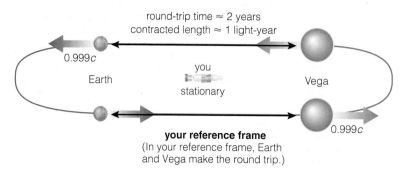

**your reference frame**
(In your reference frame, Earth and Vega make the round trip.)

## THE BIG PICTURE

In this chapter, we have studied Einstein's special theory of relativity, learning that space and time are intertwined in remarkable ways that are quite different from what we might have expected from everyday experience. As you look back on our new viewpoint about space and time, keep in mind the following "big picture" ideas.

- The ideas of relativity all derive from two simple facts: The laws of nature are the same for everyone, and the speed of light is absolute. The thought experiments in this chapter simply derived the consequences of these facts.

- Thought experiments are useful, but the ultimate judge of any theory is observation or experiment. The theory of relativity has been extensively tested and verified.

- Although the ideas of relativity may sound strange at first, you can understand them simply and logically if you allow yourself to develop a "new common sense" that incorporates them.

- Space and time are properties of the universe itself, and the new understanding of them gained through the theory of relativity will enable you to better appreciate how the universe works.

### Review Questions

1. What is the *theory of relativity?* How does *special relativity* differ from *general relativity?*

2. List five major predictions of the special theory of relativity.

3. Suppose you are riding on a stationary bike and the speedometer says you are going 30 km/hr. What does this number mean? What does it tell you about the idea of relative motion?

4. According to the theory of relativity, what are the two absolutes in the universe? Which one is more surprising, and why?

5. What is a *paradox?* How can a paradox lead us to a deeper understanding of an issue?

6. What do we mean by a *frame of reference?* What is a *free-float frame?*

7. Suppose you see a friend moving by you at some constant speed. Explain why your friend can equally well say that he is stationary and you are moving by him.

8. In your own words, restate Thought Experiment 6 to prove that no material object can be observed to travel at or above the speed of light.

9. What is *time dilation?* Explain how and why your measurements of time will differ from those of someone moving by you.

10. Explain why observers in different reference frames will not necessarily agree about the order of two events that occur in different places.

11. What is *length contraction?* How will your measurements of the size of a spaceship differ for a spaceship moving by you and the same spaceship at rest in your reference frame?

12. What is *mass increase?* How does the mass of an object moving by you compare to its rest mass?

13. Construct your own variation on Thought Experiment 11 to show why velocities must add up differently than we would expect according to our "old common sense."

14. Briefly describe several experimental tests that support special relativity.

15. Why do tests of $E = mc^2$ also test special relativity? Describe several tests of $E = mc^2$ that you can see for yourself.

16. If you watch a friend moving by you, you'll say that her time is running slow, her length is contracted, and her mass is greater than her rest mass. How will she perceive her own time, length, and mass? Why? How will she perceive *your* time, length, and mass?

17. Suppose you could take a trip to a distant star at a speed very close to the speed of light. Explain how relativity makes it possible for you to make this trip in a reasonably short amount of time. What will you find when you return home to Earth?

### Discussion Questions

1. *Common Sense.* Discuss the meaning of the term *common sense.* How do we develop common sense? Can you think of other examples, besides the example of the meaning of *up* and *down,* in which you've had to change your common sense? Do you think that the theory of relativity contradicts common sense? Why or why not?

2. *Photon Philosophy.* Extend the ideas of time dilation and length contraction to think about how the universe would look if you were a photon traveling at the speed of light. Do you think there's any point to thinking about how a photon "perceives" the universe? If so, discuss any resulting philosophical implications. If not, explain why not.

3. *Ticket to the Stars.* Suppose that we someday acquire the technology to travel among the stars at speeds near the speed of light. Imagine that many people make journeys to many places. Discuss some of the complications that would arise from people aging at different rates depending on their travels.

## Problems

1. *Relative Motion Practice.* In all of the following, assume that you and your friends are in free-float reference frames.

   a. Bob is coming toward you at a speed of 75 km/hr. You throw a baseball in his direction at 75 km/hr. What does he see the ball doing?

   b. Shawn is traveling away from you at a speed of 120 km/hr. He throws a baseball that, according to him, is going 100 km/hr in your direction. What do you see the ball doing?

   c. Carol is going away from you at 75 km/hr, and Sam is going away from you in the opposite direction at 90 km/hr. According to Carol, how fast is Sam going?

   d. Consider again the situation in part (c). Suppose you throw a baseball in Sam's direction at a speed of 120 km/hr. What does Sam see the ball doing? What does Carol see the ball doing?

2. *Moving Spaceship.* Suppose you are watching a spaceship go past at a speed close to the speed of light.

   a. How do clocks on the spaceship run, compared to your own clocks?

   b. If you could measure the length, width, and height of the spaceship as it passed by, how would these measurements compare to the spaceship's size if it were stationary?

   c. If you could measure the mass of the spaceship, how would it compare to its rest mass?

   d. How would a passenger on the spaceship view your time, size, and mass?

3. *Relativity of Simultaneity.* Consider the situation in Thought Experiment 8, about the green and red flashes of light at opposite ends of Jackie's spaceship. Suppose your friend Bob is traveling in a spaceship in the opposite direction from Jackie. Further imagine that he is also precisely aligned with you and Jackie at the instant the two flashes of light occur (in your reference frame).

   a. According to Bob, is Jackie illuminated first by the green flash or the red flash? Explain.

   b. According to you, which flash illuminates Bob first? Why?

   c. According to Bob, which flash occurred first? Explain. How does Bob's view of the order of the flashes compare to your view and to Jackie's view?

*4. *Time Dilation 1.* A clever student, after learning about the theory of relativity, decides to apply his knowledge in order to prolong his life. He decides to spend the rest of his life in a car, traveling around the freeways at 55 miles per hour (89 km/hr). Suppose he drives for a period of time during which 70 years pass on Earth; how much time will pass in the car? (*Hint:* If you are unable to find a difference, be sure to explain why.)

*5. *Time Dilation 2.* An even more clever student, upon realizing the folly of the student in the previous problem, decides on a better approach for prolonging her life. She decides to spend time cruising around the local solar neighborhood at a speed of 0.95c (95% of the speed of light). How much time will pass on her spacecraft during a period in which 70 years pass on Earth?

*6. *Time Dilation with Subatomic Particles.* Recall that a $\pi^+$ meson produced at rest has a lifetime of 18 nanoseconds ($1.8 \times 10^{-8}$ s). Thus, in its own reference frame, a $\pi^+$ meson will always "think" it is at rest and therefore will decay after 18 nanoseconds. Suppose a $\pi^+$ meson is produced in a particle accelerator at a speed of 0.998c.

   a. Use the time dilation formula to calculate how long scientists will see the particle last before it decays.

   b. Briefly explain how an experiment like this helps verify the special theory of relativity.

*7. *Ticket to the Stars.* Suppose you stay home on Earth while your twin sister takes a trip to a distant star and back in a spaceship that travels at 99% of the speed of light. If both of you are 25 years old when she leaves and you are 45 years old when she returns, how old is your sister when she gets back?

*8. *The Betelgeuse Red Stars.* Like the fans in Boston, the fans of interstellar baseball at Betelgeuse (in the constellation Orion) have been deprived of a championship team for a long time. In fact, the Betelgeuse Red Stars have not won the Universe Series for nearly 200,000 years. (They did, however, come very close to winning 75,000 years ago; their defeat was sealed only when a routine ground ball went through the legs of the infamous Zargon Buckner.) Realizing that time may be running out for their team—Betelgeuse is expected to explode as a supernova within the next 100,000 years—the Red Stars management has decided to break some league rules (hopefully without getting caught) in hopes of winning the series. It has therefore extended a lucrative offer to Hideo Nomo, of planet Earth, if he will leave his home and join the Betelgeuse Red Stars as their new pitcher. Although he was reluctant to leave friends and family behind, Nomo finally was swayed to join the Red Stars. Interestingly, in an interview with the *Intergalactic Press*, Nomo said it was the travel opportunity, rather than the money, that lured him to Betelgeuse. Nomo was given a ticket to travel to Betelgeuse on an express spaceship at 95% of the speed of light. During the trip, he decided to try some pitching in the ship's on-board stadium. He found that, with the replacement body parts provided by the Red Stars management, his fastball was considerably improved: He was now able to throw a pitch at 80% of the speed of light. Assuming that he throws a pitch in the same direction the spacecraft is traveling, use the formula for velocity addition to calculate how fast we would see the ball moving from Earth.

*9. *Racing a Light Beam, Part 1.* A long time ago, in a galaxy far away, there was a civilization that hosted an Olympic competition every 4 of their years. One year, during an Olympiad held in the city of Sole in the nation of Kira, a sprinter by the name of Jo shattered their world record for the 100-meter dash. Alas, Jo was disqualified for having ingested illegal substances, and his record was eliminated from the books. Rather than sulk, however, Jo decided that human competition was too easy anyway. He announced that he would instead race a beam of light. Sponsors lined up, crowds gathered, and the event was sold to a pay-per-view audience. Everything was set. The starting gun went off. Jo raced out of the starting blocks and shattered the old world record, running the 100 meters in 8.7 seconds. The light beam, represented by a flashlight turned on at precisely the right moment, of course emerged from its "blocks" at the speed of light. How long did it take the light beam to cover the 100-meter distance? What can you say about the outcome of this race?

*10. *Racing a Light Beam, Part 2.* Following his humiliation in the race against the light beam, Jo went into hiding for the next 2 years. By that time, most people had forgotten about both him and the money they had wasted on the pay-per-view event. However, Jo was secretly in training during his hiding. He worked out hard and tested new performance-enhancing substances. One day, he emerged from hiding and called a press conference. "I'm ready for a rematch," he announced. Sponsors were few this time and spectators scarce in the huge Olympic stadium where Jo and the flashlight lined up at the starting line. But those who were there will never forget what they saw, although it all happened very quickly! Jo blasted out of the starting blocks at 99.9% of the speed of light. The light beam, emitted from the flashlight, took off at the speed of light. The light beam won again—but barely! After the race, TV commentators searched for Jo, but he seemed to be hiding again. Finally, they found him in a corner of the locker room, sulking under a towel. "What's wrong? You did great!" said the commentators. Jo looked back sadly, saying, "Two years of training and experiments, for nothing!" Let's investigate what happened.

a. As seen by spectators in the grandstand, how much faster than Jo is the light beam?

b. As seen by Jo, how much faster is the light beam than he is? Explain your answer clearly.

c. Using your results from parts (a) and (b), explain why Jo can say that he was beaten just as badly as before, while the spectators can think he gave the light beam a good race.

d. Although Jo was disappointed by his performance against the light beam, he did find one pleasant surprise: The 100-meter course seemed short to him. In Jo's reference frame during the race, how long was the 100-meter course?

## Web Projects

Find useful links for Web projects on the text Web site.

1. *Relativity Simulations.* Explore some of the simulations of the effects of special relativity available on the Web. Write a short report on what you learn.

2. *Einstein's Life.* Learn more about Einstein's life and work and how he has influenced the modern world. Write a short essay describing some aspect of his life or work.

3. *The Michelson–Morley Experiment.* Find details about the famous Michelson–Morley experiment. Write a one-page description of the experiment and its results, including a diagram of the experimental setup.

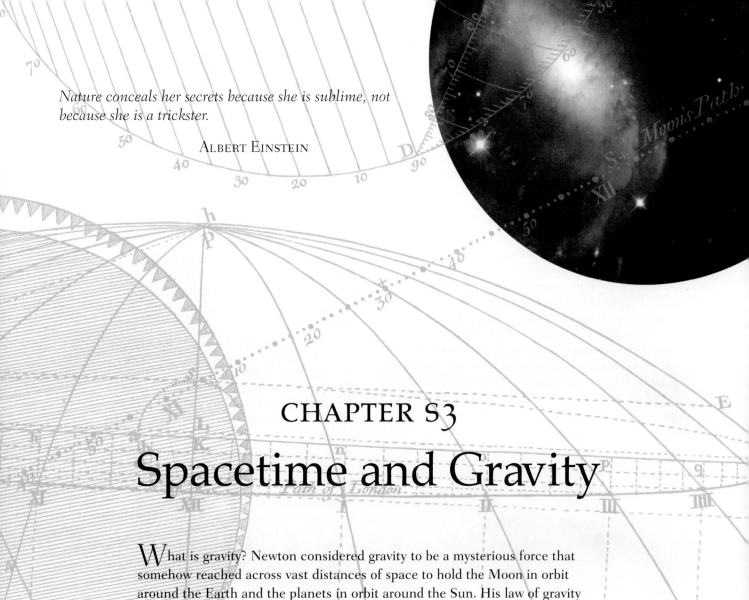

*Nature conceals her secrets because she is sublime, not because she is a trickster.*

ALBERT EINSTEIN

# CHAPTER S3

# Spacetime and Gravity

What is gravity? Newton considered gravity to be a mysterious force that somehow reached across vast distances of space to hold the Moon in orbit around the Earth and the planets in orbit around the Sun. His law of gravity explained the actions and consequences of this mysterious force but said nothing about how the force was transmitted through space.

Einstein removed the mystery of how gravity acts at a distance. As he extended his theory of relativity, Einstein found that he could explain gravity in terms of the structure of space and time. In Einstein's view, the orbits of the Moon and the planets are as natural as motion in a straight line.

As we investigate Einstein's revolutionary view of gravity, we will see that the consequences of his discoveries abound in astronomy and explain phenomena ranging from the peculiar orbit of Mercury to the expansion of the universe. We will also see how space and time merge into a four-dimensional *spacetime* and that our universe is a strange world of curved space and altered time containing *black holes* through which material can leave the universe, never to return.

## S3.1 Einstein's Second Revolution

Imagine that you and everyone around you believe the Earth to be flat. As a wealthy patron of the sciences, you decide to sponsor an expedition to the far reaches of the world. You select two fearless explorers and give them careful instructions. Each is to journey along a perfectly straight path, but they are to travel in opposite directions. You provide each with a caravan for land-based travel and boats for water crossings, and you tell each to turn back only after discovering "something extraordinary."

Some time later, the two explorers return. You ask, "Did you discover something extraordinary?" To your surprise, they answer in unison, "Yes, but we both discovered the same thing: We ran into each other, despite having traveled in opposite directions along perfectly straight paths."

Although this outcome would be extraordinarily surprising if you truly believed the Earth to be flat, we are not surprised because we know that the Earth is round (Figure S3.1). In a sense, the explorers followed the *straightest possible paths*, but these "straight" lines follow the curved surface of the Earth.

**FIGURE S3.1** Travelers going in opposite directions along paths that are as straight as possible will meet as they go around the Earth.

Now let's consider a somewhat more modern scenario. You are floating freely in a spaceship somewhere out in space. Hoping to learn more about space in your vicinity, you launch two small probes along straight paths in opposite directions. Each probe is equipped with a camera that transmits pictures back to your spaceship. Imagine that, to your astonishment, the probes one day transmit pictures of each other! That is, although you launched them in opposite directions and neither has ever fired its engines, the probes have somehow met. In fact, this situation arises quite naturally with any orbiting objects in space. If you launch two probes in opposite directions from a space station, they will meet as they orbit the Earth.

Since the time of Newton, we've generally explained the curved paths of the two probes as an effect caused by the force of gravity. However, by analogy with the explorers journeying in opposite directions on the Earth, might we instead conclude that the probes meet because *space* is somehow curved? The idea that space could be curved certainly sounds strange at first. While it's easy to visualize a surface curving *through* space, our mind cannot visualize three-dimensional space as being curved. The idea that space can be curved lies at the heart of Einstein's second revolution—a revolutionary view of gravity contained in his *general theory of relativity,* published in 1915.

From the special theory of relativity, we already know that space and time are inextricably linked. In fact, the three dimensions of space and the one dimension of time together form an inseparable, *four-*dimensional combination called **spacetime**. General relativity tells us that matter shapes the "fabric" of spacetime in a manner analogous to the way heavy weights distort a taut rubber sheet or trampoline (Figure S3.2). Of course, we cannot place weights "upon" spacetime because all matter exists *within* spacetime, and we cannot visualize distortions of spacetime. But, using a rubber sheet as an analogy, we can begin to appreciate the principles of general relativity that govern the structure of space and time.

It is difficult to overstate the significance of general relativity to our understanding of the universe. For example, all the following ideas come directly from Einstein's general theory of relativity:

- Gravity arises from distortions of spacetime. It is *not* a mysterious force that acts at a distance. The presence of mass causes the distortions, and the resulting distortions determine how other objects move through spacetime.

- Time runs slow in gravitational fields. The stronger the gravity, the slower time runs.

- *Black holes* can exist in spacetime, and falling into a black hole means leaving the observable universe.

- The universe has no boundaries and no center, yet it might still have a finite volume.

- Large masses that undergo rapid changes in motion or structure emit *gravitational waves* that travel at the speed of light.

**FIGURE S3.2** A rubber-sheet analogy to spacetime: Matter distorts the "fabric" of four-dimensional spacetime in a manner analogous to the way heavy weights distort a taut, two-dimensional rubber sheet. The greater the mass, the greater the distortion of spacetime.

## S3.2 The Equivalence Principle

Special relativity shows that there is no single, absolute answer to the question "Who is moving?" when two people pass each other at a constant velocity. Each individual can claim to be at rest, and each claim is equally valid. However, the situation seems quite different when accelerations are involved.

Imagine that you and your friend Jackie from Chapter S2 are both floating freely in space when your rocket engine fires (Figure S3.3). Jackie sees you accelerating away, with your speed growing ever faster, so she sends you a radio message saying "Good-bye, have a nice trip!"

**TIME OUT TO THINK** *Suppose you start from rest in Jackie's reference frame and she sees you accelerate at 1g ($\approx$ 10 m/s²). Approximately how fast will Jackie see you going after 1 second? After 10 seconds? After a minute? (Hint: See Section 5.1.)*

From your perspective, it is Jackie who is receding into the distance at ever-faster speeds, so you reply: "Thanks, but I'm not going anywhere. You're the one accelerating into the distance." On closer examination, however, your reply seems to have a flaw. If you had been moving at constant velocity relative to Jackie, you both would have been floating freely, making it impossible to determine who was "really" moving. However, your acceleration makes you feel a force. Instead of floating weightlessly like Jackie, you are held to the floor of your spaceship. If you happen to be accelerating at 1g, or 9.8 m/s², you'll feel just as you feel when you are stationary on Earth, with your normal Earth weight. Thus, Jackie can re-

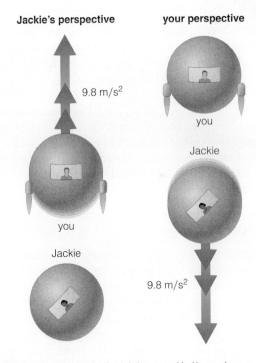

**FIGURE S3.3** Jackie is floating freely in her spaceship. Your engines are firing, and you feel a force allowing you to stand on the floor of your spaceship.

spond: "Oh yeah? If you're not going anywhere, why are you stuck to the floor of your spaceship, and why do you have your engines turned on? Furthermore, if I'm accelerating, why don't I feel any forces?"

You must admit that Jackie is asking very good questions. It certainly *looks* as if you really are the

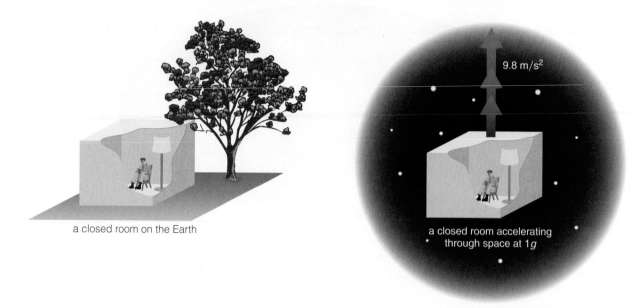

9.8 m/s²

a closed room accelerating
through space at 1*g*

**FIGURE S3.4** The equivalence principle states that the effects of gravity are exactly equivalent to the effects of acceleration. Thus, according to the equivalence principle, you cannot tell the difference between being in a closed room on Earth and being in a closed room accelerating through space at 1*g*.

one who is moving and that you *cannot* legitimately claim to be stationary. Einstein didn't like the appearance of situations like this one, because he believed that *all* motion should be relative.

In 1907, Einstein hit upon what he later called "the happiest thought of my life." His revelation consisted of the idea that, whenever you feel weight (as opposed to weightlessness), you can equally well attribute it to effects of either acceleration or gravity. This idea is called the **equivalence principle**. Stated more precisely, it says:

*The effects of gravity are exactly equivalent to the effects of acceleration.*

To clarify the meaning of the equivalence principle,[1] imagine that you are sitting inside with doors closed and window shades pulled down when your room is magically removed from the Earth and sent hurtling through space with an acceleration of 1*g* (Figure S3.4). According to the equivalence principle, you have no way of knowing that you've left the Earth. Any experiment you performed, such as dropping balls of different weights, would yield the same results you'd get on the Earth.

Now back to Jackie's questions. She claims that *you* must be accelerating because you feel weight as you stand in your spaceship. The equivalence prin-

ciple tells us that, with equal validity, you can claim to feel weight because of gravity. From this perspective, space is filled with a gravitational field pointing "downward" toward the back of your spaceship. You are stationary only because your rocket engine prevents you from falling, and you feel weight just as a person hovering in a helicopter over the Earth does. Jackie, because she is not using her engines, is falling through the gravitational field. As you may recall, anyone in *free-fall* feels weightless [Section 5.1]. In summary, you can claim that the situation is much as it would be if you were hovering over a cliff while Jackie had fallen over the edge (Figure S3.5). Thus, you can respond: "Sorry, Jackie, but I still say that you have it backward. I'm using my engines to prevent my spaceship from falling, and I feel weight because of *gravity*. You're weightless because you're in free-fall. I hope you won't be hurt by hitting whatever lies at the bottom of this gravitational field!"

The equivalence principle allows us to claim that *all* motion is relative; it is the starting point for general relativity. Just as we derived the strange consequences of special relativity from the idea that the speed of light is absolute, the astounding predictions of general relativity follow from the equivalence principle. And, just as special relativity led us to recognize some underlying truths about nature, such as that space and time are different for observers in different reference frames, general relativity also leads us to a new and deeper understanding of the universe.

---

[1]Technically, this equivalence holds only within small regions of space. Over larger regions, we can detect *tidal forces* that can arise from gravity but not from acceleration.

### Einstein's Leap

Given that the similarities in the effects of gravity and acceleration were well known to scientists as far back in time as Newton, you may be wondering why the equivalence principle is so surprising. The answer is that the similarities were generally attributed to coincidence—although a very puzzling coincidence. It is as if other scientists imagined that nature was showing them two boxes, one labeled "effects of gravity" and the other labeled "effects of acceleration." They shook, weighed, and kicked the boxes but could never find any obvious differences between them. They concluded: "What a strange coincidence! The boxes seem the same from the outside even though they contain different things." Einstein's revelation was, in essence, to look at the boxes and say that it is not a coincidence at all. The boxes appear the same from the outside because they contain the same thing.

In many ways, Einstein's assertion of the equivalence principle represented a leap of faith—although it was a faith he would willingly test through scientific experiment. He made the assertion because he thought the universe would make more sense if it were true, not because of any compelling observational or experimental evidence for it at the time. This leap of faith sent him on a path far ahead of his scientific colleagues.

From a historical viewpoint, special relativity was a "theory waiting to happen" because it was needed to explain two significant problems left over from the nineteenth century: the perplexing constancy of the speed of light, demonstrated in the Michelson–Morley experiment [Section S2.4], and some seeming peculiarities of the laws of electromagnetism. Indeed, several other scientists were very close to discovering the ideas of special relativity when it was published by Einstein in 1905, and *someone* was bound to come up with special relativity around that time. In contrast, general relativity was a tour de force by Einstein. He recognized that unsolved problems remained after completing the theory of special relativity, and he alone took the leap of faith required to accept the equivalence principle. Without Einstein, general relativity probably would have remained undiscovered for several decades beyond 1915, the year he completed and published the theory.

**FIGURE S3.5** If you hover over a cliff while Jackie falls, you feel weight, you need your engines to keep you from falling, and Jackie is weightless because she is in free-fall.

## S3.3 Understanding Spacetime

It's easy to say that you can equally well attribute your weight to effects of gravity or acceleration, but the two effects tend to *look* very different. A person standing on the surface of the Earth appears to be motionless, while an astronaut accelerating through space continually gains speed. How can gravity and acceleration produce such similar effects when they look so different? The theory of general relativity answers that we're not seeing the whole picture: Instead of looking just at the three dimensions of space, we must learn to "look" at the *four* dimensions of spacetime.

### Four Dimensions

The concept of **dimension** describes the number of independent directions in which movement is possible. A **point** has zero dimensions. If you were a geometric prisoner confined to a point, you'd have no place to go. Sweeping a point back and forth along one direction generates a **line** (Figure S3.6). The line is one-dimensional because only one direction of motion is possible (going backward is considered the same as going forward by a negative distance). Sweeping a line back and forth generates a two-dimensional **plane**. The two directions of possible motion are horizontal and vertical; any other direction is just a combination of these two. If we sweep a plane back and

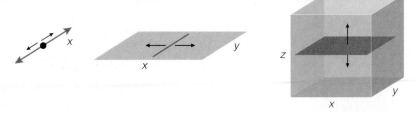

**FIGURE S3.6** We can generate one-, two-, and three-dimensional spaces by sweeping back and forth a point, a line, and a plane, respectively.

forth, it fills three-dimensional **space**, with the three independent directions of length, width, and depth.

We live in three-dimensional space, so we cannot visualize any direction that is distinct from length, width, and depth (and combinations thereof). However, just because we cannot see "other" directions doesn't mean they don't exist. Thus, we can imagine sweeping space back and forth in some "other" direction to generate a **four-dimensional space**. Although we have no hope of visualizing a four-dimensional space, we can easily describe it mathematically. In algebra, we do one-dimensional problems with the single variable $x$, two-dimensional problems with the variables $x$ and $y$, and three-dimensional problems with the variables $x$, $y$, and $z$. A four-dimensional problem simply requires adding a fourth variable, as in $x$, $y$, $z$, and $w$. We could continue to five dimensions, six dimensions, and many more. Any space with more than three dimensions is called a **hyperspace**, which means "beyond space."

### Spacetime

Spacetime is a four-dimensional space in which the four directions of possible motion are length, width, depth, and *time*. Note that time is not "the" fourth dimension; it is simply one of the four. (However, time differs in an important way from the other three dimensions; see Mathematical Insight S3.1.) We cannot picture all four dimensions of spacetime at once, but we can imagine what things would look like if we could. In addition to the three spatial dimensions of spacetime that we ordinarily see, every object would be stretched out through time. Objects that we see as three-dimensional in our ordinary lives would appear as "solid" four-dimensional objects in spacetime. If we could see in four dimensions, we could look through time just as easily as we look to our left or right. If we looked at a person, we could see every event in the person's life. If we wondered what really happened during some historical event, we'd simply look to find the answer.

**TIME OUT TO THINK** *Try to imagine how you would look in four dimensions. How would your body, stretched through time, appear? Imagine that you bumped into someone on the bus yesterday. What would this event look like in spacetime?*

This spacetime view of objects provides a new way of understanding why different observers can disagree about measurements of time and distance. Because we can't visualize four dimensions, let's use a three-dimensional analogy. Suppose you give the same book to many different people and ask each person to measure the book's dimensions. Everyone will get the same results, agreeing on the three-dimensional structure of the book (Figure S3.7a). Now suppose instead that you show each person only a two-dimensional picture of the book rather than the book itself. The pictures can look very different, even though they show the same book in all cases (Figure S3.7b). If the people believed that the two-dimensional pictures reflected reality, they might argue endlessly about what the pictured object really looks like.

In our ordinary lives, we perceive only three dimensions, and we assume that this perception reflects reality. But spacetime is actually four-dimensional. Just as different people can see different two-dimensional pictures of the same three-dimensional book, different observers can see different three-dimensional "pictures" of the same spacetime reality. These different "pictures" are the differing perceptions of time and space of observers in different reference frames. Thus, different observers will get different results when they measure time, length, or mass, even though all are actually looking at the same spacetime reality. In the words of a famous textbook on relativity:

> *Space is different for different observers.*
> *Time is different for different observers.*
> *Spacetime is the same for everyone.*[2]

---

[2]From E. F. Taylor and J. A. Wheeler, *Spacetime Physics*, 2d ed., Freeman, 1992.

10 in.

2 in.

8 in.

**a** A book has an unambiguous three-dimensional shape.

**b** Two-dimensional pictures of the book can look very different.

**FIGURE S3.7** Two-dimensional views of a three-dimensional object (like a book) can appear different, even though the object has only a single real shape. In a similar way, observers in different reference frames may measure space and time differently (because they perceive only three dimensions at once) and even though they are all observing the same four-dimensional spacetime reality.

## Mathematical Insight S3.1    Spacetime Geometry

As you read this chapter, you hopefully will not find the basic ideas of four-dimensional geometry and spacetime difficult to grasp. However, working with spacetime geometry is mathematically complex because the four dimensions are not all equivalent. In particular, time enters the equations of spacetime geometry in a different way than do the three dimensions of space.

To gain insight into the nature of spacetime geometry, consider two points in a plane separated by amounts $x = 3$ along the horizontal axis and $y = 4$ along the vertical axis (Figure S3.8a). You may recall from geometry that the *distance* between the two points is $\sqrt{x^2 + y^2}$. Now consider the same two points viewed from a coordinate system that happens to be rotated so that both points lie along the $x$-axis (Figure S3.8b). In this coordinate system, the horizontal separation is $x = 5$ and the vertical separation is $y = 0$. However, the distance $\sqrt{x^2 + y^2}$ between the points is still the same. This fact should not be surprising: *Distance* is a real, physical quantity, while the $x$ and $y$ separations are artifacts of a chosen coordinate system. The same idea holds if we add a $z$-axis, perpendicular to both $x$ and $y$ (you can represent the $z$-axis with a pencil that sticks straight up out of the page), to make a three-dimensional coordinate system: Different stationary observers using different coordinate systems can disagree about the $x$, $y$, and $z$ separations, but they will always agree on the distance $\sqrt{x^2 + y^2 + z^2}$.

We can think of spacetime as having a fourth axis, which we will call the $t$-axis, for time. We might expect that, just as different observers always agree on the three-dimensional distance between two points, they will also agree on some kind of four-dimensional "distance" that has the formula $\sqrt{x^2 + y^2 + z^2 + t^2}$. However, it turns out that different observers will instead agree on the value of the quantity $\sqrt{x^2 + y^2 + z^2 - t^2}$, which is called the *interval*.

(Technically, the interval formula should use $ct$ rather than $t$ so that all the terms have units of length.) That is, different observers can disagree about the values of $x$, $y$, $z$, and $t$ separating two events, but all will agree on the interval between the two events.

**FIGURE S3.8** The distance between two points in a plane is the same regardless of how we set up a coordinate system.

It is the *minus sign* that goes with the time dimension in the interval formula that makes the geometry of spacetime surprisingly complex. For example, the three-dimensional distance between two points can be zero only if the two points are in the same place. But the interval between two events can be zero even if they are in different places in spacetime, as long as $x^2 + y^2 + z^2 = t^2$. (For example, the interval is zero between any two events connected by a light path on a spacetime diagram.) If you study general relativity further, you will see many more examples of how this strange geometry comes into play.

Car comes to a
stop at work.

Car slows for arrival at work.

Car reaches
60 km/hr.

Car accelerates
from rest.

Car is at rest.

Car decelerates for a red light.

Car reaches
60 km/hr.

Car accelerates
from rest.

**a** A trip from home to work on a straight road.

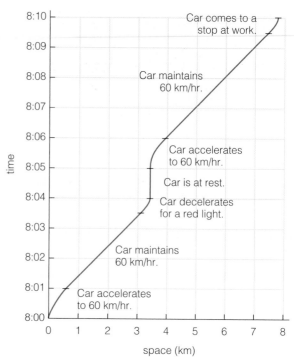

**b** Spacetime diagram for the trip.

**FIGURE S3.9** The process of creating a spacetime diagram for a simple car trip.

### Spacetime Diagrams

Suppose you drive your car along a straight road from home to work as shown in Figure S3.9a. At 8:00 A.M., you leave your house and accelerate to 60 km/hr. You maintain this speed until you come to a red light, where you decelerate to a stop. After the light turns green, you accelerate again to 60 km/hr, which you maintain until you slow to a stop when you reach work at 8:10. What does your trip look like in spacetime?

If we could see all four dimensions of spacetime, we'd see all three dimensions of your car and your trip stretched out through the 10 minutes of time taken for your trip. We can't visualize all four dimensions at once, but in this case we have a special situation: Your trip progressed along only one dimension of space because you took a straight road. Therefore, we can represent your trip in spacetime by drawing a graph showing your path through one dimension of space on the horizontal axis and your path through time on the vertical axis (Figure S3.9b). This type of graph is called a **spacetime diagram**.

The car's path through four-dimensional spacetime is called its **worldline**. Any particular point along a worldline represents a particular **event**. That

is, an event is a specific place and time. For example, the lowest point on the worldline in Figure S3.9b represents the event of your leaving your house: The place is 0 km from home, and the time is 8:00 A.M. You can see three very important properties of any worldline in Figure S3.9b:

1. The worldline of an object at rest is vertical (i.e., parallel to the *time* axis). The object is going nowhere in space, but it still moves through time.

2. The worldline of an object moving at constant velocity is straight but slanted. The more slanted the worldline, the faster the object is moving.

3. The worldline of an accelerating object is curved. If the object's speed is increasing, its worldline curves toward the horizontal. If its speed is decreasing, its worldline gradually becomes more vertical.

In Figure S3.9b, we used units of minutes for time and kilometers for distance. In relativity it is easiest to work with spacetime diagrams in which we use units related to the speed of light, such as *seconds* for time and *light-seconds* for distance. In this case, light follows 45° lines on the spacetime diagram be-

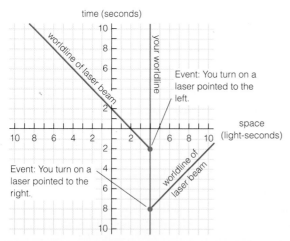

**a** Light follows 45° lines on a spacetime diagram that uses units of seconds for time and light-seconds for space.

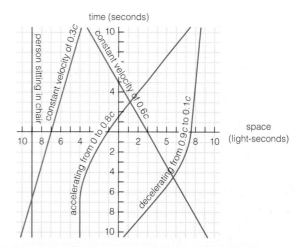

**b** This spacetime diagram shows several sample worldlines. Note that objects at rest have vertical worldlines, objects moving at constant velocity have straight but slanted worldlines, and accelerating objects have curved worldlines.

**FIGURE S3.10** Spacetime diagrams marked with units of seconds for time and light-seconds for space.

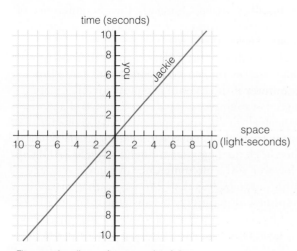

**a** The spacetime diagram from your point of view.

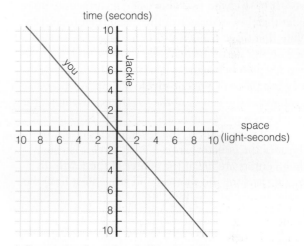

**b** The spacetime diagram from Jackie's point of view.

**FIGURE S3.11** Spacetime diagrams for the situation in which Jackie is moving by you at 0.9c.

cause it travels 1 light-second of distance with each second of time. For example, suppose you are sitting still in your chair, so that your worldline is vertical (Figure S3.10a). If at some particular time you flash a laser beam pointed to your right, the worldline of the light goes diagonally to the right. If you flash the laser to the left a few seconds later, its worldline goes diagonally to the left. Worldlines for several other objects are shown in Figure S3.10b.

**TIME OUT TO THINK** *Explain why, in Figure S3.10, the worldlines of objects we see in our everyday life would be nearly vertical.*

We can use spacetime diagrams to clarify the relativity of time and space. Suppose you see Jackie moving past you in a spaceship at 0.9c. Figure S3.11a shows the spacetime diagram from your point of view: You are at rest and therefore have a vertical world-line; Jackie is moving and has a slanted worldline. Of course, Jackie claims that *you* are moving by her and therefore would draw the spacetime diagram shown in Figure S3.11b, in which her worldline is vertical and yours is slanted. Special relativity tells us that you would see Jackie's time running slow, while she sees *your* time running slow (along with effects on length and mass). We know there is no contradiction here, just a problem with our old common sense about space and time. From a four-dimensional perspective, the problem is that the large angle between your worldline and Jackie's means that neither of you is looking at the other "straight-on" in spacetime. Thus, you and Jackie are both looking at the same four-dimensional reality but from different three-dimensional perspectives. Like two people looking at each other cross-eyed, it's not surprising that if you see Jackie's time running slow she sees the same thing when she looks at you.

### *Spacetime Curvature*

So far, we've been viewing spacetime diagrams drawn on the flat pages of this book. But, as we discussed in the beginning of this chapter, spacetime can be curved. Unfortunately, while it's easy to visualize the curvature of a two-dimensional surface, we have no hope of visualizing the curvature of space or spacetime. What, then, do we mean when we talk about space or spacetime being curved?

The answer lies in the rules of geometry, which are easiest to study on two-dimensional surfaces. Consider the curved surface of the Earth (Figure S3.12a). Note that there really is no such thing as a "straight" line on the Earth. Instead, the shortest and *straightest possible* path between two points on the Earth's surface is a piece of a **great circle**—a circle whose center is at the center of the Earth. For example, the equator is a great circle, and any "line" of longitude is part of a great circle. However, circles of latitude (besides the equator) are *not* great circles because their centers are *not* at the center of the Earth. If you are seeking the shortest and straightest route between two cities, you must follow a *great-circle route*. For example, Philadelphia and Beijing are both at about 40°N latitude, but the shortest route between

them does *not* follow the circle of 40°N latitude; instead, it follows a great-circle route that extends far to the north (Figure S3.12b).

**TIME OUT TO THINK** *Find a globe and locate New Orleans and Katmandu (Nepal). Explain why the shortest route between these two cities goes almost directly over the North Pole. Why do you think airplanes generally follow great-circle routes?*

Now let's contrast the rules of geometry on the surface of the Earth or any other sphere with the rules of geometry in a flat plane. You are probably familiar with the rules of geometry illustrated in Figure S3.13a, such as that two parallel lines never meet and that the circumference of a circle is $2\pi r$. However, as shown in Figure S3.13b, these rules do *not* hold if we draw lines and shapes on the surface of a sphere. For example, if we draw two great circles that look parallel in one place, they do *not* obey the "flat plane" rule that parallel lines never meet; instead, they eventually converge. Similarly, the circumference of a circle on the surface of the sphere is *not* $2\pi r$. Instead, it is *less than* $2\pi r$.

Generalizing these ideas to more than two dimensions, we say that space, or spacetime, has a **flat geometry** if the rules of geometry for a flat plane hold. For example, if the circumference of a circle in space really is $2\pi r$, then space has a flat geometry. (Flat geometry is also known as *Euclidean geometry,* after the Greek mathematician Euclid [c. 325–270 B.C.].) However, if the circumference of a circle in space turns out to be less than $2\pi r$, we say that space has a **spherical geometry** because the rules are those that hold on the surface of a sphere. Flat and spherical geometries are two of three general types of ge-

---

**FIGURE S3.12** The straightest possible path between any two points on a sphere must be a segment of a great circle.

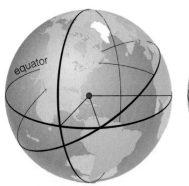

The three circles shown are great circles because their centers are at the center of the Earth.

Except for the equator, lines of latitude are not great circles.

**a** A great circle is any circle on the surface of the Earth that has its center at the center of the Earth.

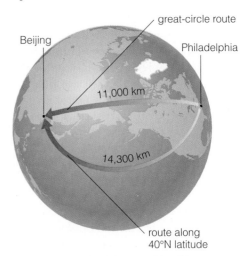

**b** The shortest and straightest possible path between two points on Earth is always a piece of a great circle.

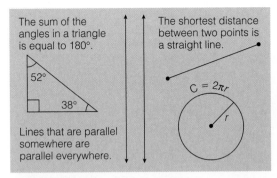

The sum of the angles in a triangle is equal to 180°.

52°
38°

Lines that are parallel somewhere are parallel everywhere.

The shortest distance between two points is a straight line.

$C = 2\pi r$

r

**a** Rules of flat geometry.

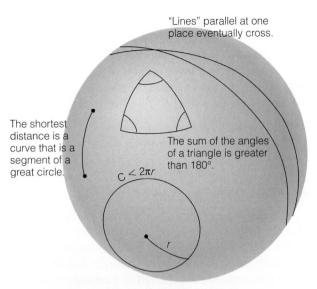

"Lines" parallel at one place eventually cross.

The shortest distance is a curve that is a segment of a great circle.

The sum of the angles of a triangle is greater than 180°.

$C < 2\pi r$

r

**b** Rules of spherical geometry.

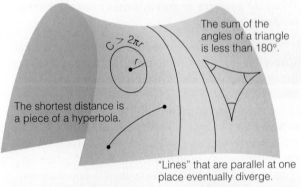

$C > 2\pi r$

r

The sum of the angles of a triangle is less than 180°.

The shortest distance is a piece of a hyperbola.

"Lines" that are parallel at one place eventually diverge.

**c** Rules of saddle-shaped geometry.

**FIGURE S3.13** These diagrams contrast three basic types of geometry.

ometry. The third general type of geometry is called **saddle-shaped geometry** (also called *hyperbolic geometry*) because its rules are most easily visualized on a two-dimensional surface shaped like a saddle (Figure S3.13c). In this case, the circumference of a circle is *greater* than $2\pi r$.

The actual geometry of spacetime turns out to be a mixture of all three general types. That is, just as a two-dimensional surface can look flat in some places, like a piece of a sphere in others, and like a piece of a saddle in still others, different regions of spacetime obey different sets of geometrical rules.

### "Straight" Lines in Curved Spacetime

One of the keys to understanding spacetime is being able to tell whether an object is following the *straightest possible path* between two points in spacetime. However, given that we can visualize neither the time part of spacetime nor the curvature of spacetime, how do we know whether an object is traveling on the straightest possible path through spacetime?

Einstein used the equivalence principle to provide the answer. According to the equivalence principle, we can attribute a feeling of weight either to experiencing a force generated by acceleration or to being in a gravitational field. Similarly, any time we feel weightless, we may attribute it either to being in free-fall or to traveling at constant velocity far from any gravitational fields. Because traveling at constant velocity means traveling in a straight line, Einstein reasoned that objects experiencing weightlessness for *any* reason must be traveling in a "straight" line—that is, along a line that is the straightest possible path between two points in spacetime.

*If you are floating freely, then your worldline is following the straightest possible path through spacetime. If you feel weight, then you are not on the straightest possible path.*

This conclusion provides us with a remarkable way to examine the geometry of spacetime. Recall that any orbit is a free-fall trajectory. The Space Station is always free-falling toward the Earth, but its forward velocity always moves it ahead just enough to "miss" hitting the ground. The Earth is constantly free-falling toward the Sun, but its orbital speed keeps us going around and around instead of ever hitting the Sun. According to the equivalence principle, all orbits represent paths of objects that are following the straightest possible path through spacetime. Thus, the shapes and speeds of orbits reveal the geometry of spacetime, which leads us to an entirely new view of gravity.

**TIME OUT TO THINK** *Suppose you are standing on a scale in your bathroom. Is your worldline following the straightest possible path through spacetime? Explain.*

### S3.4 A New View of Gravity

Newton's law of gravity claims that every mass exerts a gravitational attraction on every other mass, no matter how far away it is. However, on close examination, this idea of "action at a distance" is rather mysterious. For example, how does the Earth feel the Sun's attraction and know to orbit it? Newton himself was troubled by this idea. A few years after publishing his law of gravity in 1687, Newton wrote:

> *That one body may act upon another at a distance through a vacuum, . . . and force may be conveyed from one to another, is to me so great an absurdity, that I believe no man, who has . . . a competent faculty in thinking, can ever fall into it.*[3]

Einstein's general theory of relativity removes the idea of "action at a distance" by stating that the Earth feels *no* forces—it simply follows the straightest possible path through spacetime. Thus, the fact that the Earth goes around the Sun tells us that spacetime itself is curved. In other words,

***What we perceive as gravity arises from the curvature of spacetime.***

We cannot picture curvature of four-dimensional spacetime, but a two-dimensional analogy illustrates many of the basic ideas. We use a stretched rubber sheet to represent spacetime and assume also that there is no friction on the rubber sheet just as there is no friction in space. We represent the Sun by placing a heavy mass on the rubber sheet, which causes the sheet to curve and form a bowl-like depression (Figure S3.14). Freely moving objects follow paths that are as straight as possible given the curvature of the rubber sheet; the central mass is not grabbing them, communicating with them, or doing anything else to influence their motion. The path of an object coming from far away bends as it passes by the central mass—this path is the type we called an *unbound orbit* in Chapter 5. Other objects are "trapped" in the bowl and therefore follow circular or elliptical orbits around the central mass. By analogy, Einstein tells us that planets orbit the Sun because the Sun's mass curves spacetime in such a way that no other motion could be more natural. In summary:

***Mass causes spacetime to curve, and the curvature of spacetime determines the paths of freely moving masses.***

The rubber-sheet analogy to spacetime is useful, but we should keep three very important subtleties in mind:

- The rubber sheet is supposed to represent the universe, and it makes no sense to think of placing a mass "upon" the universe; instead, we should

[3]Letter from Newton, 1692–1693, as quoted in J. A. Wheeler, *A Journey into Gravity and Spacetime*, Scientific American Library, 1990, p. 2.

c  circular orbit
e  elliptical orbit
u  unbound orbit

**FIGURE S3.14** On a rubber sheet, marbles "orbit" a central mass by following the straightest paths that are possible.

think of the masses as being *within* the rubber sheet.

- The rubber sheet allows us to picture orbits in only two dimensions. For example, it allows us to show that different planets orbit at different distances from the Sun and that some have more highly elliptical orbits than others, but it does not allow us to represent the fact that not all planets orbit the Sun in the same plane.

- The rubber-sheet analogy does not show the *time* part of spacetime at all. Bound orbits on the sheet or in space appear to return to the same point with each circuit of the Sun. However, objects cannot return to the same point in spacetime because they always move forward through time. For example, with each orbit of the Sun, the Earth returns to the same place in space (relative to the Sun) but to a time that is a year later (Figure S3.15).

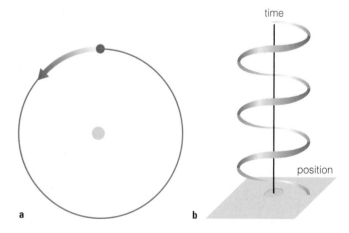

**FIGURE S3.15** (**a**) If we ignore time, the Earth appears to return to the same point with each orbit of the Sun. (**b**) If we include a time axis, we see that the Earth never returns to the same point in spacetime because it always moves forward in time.

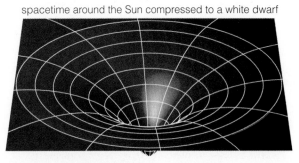

spacetime around the Sun today

spacetime around the Sun compressed to a white dwarf

**a** The left diagram represents the curvature of space around the Sun today; the yellow circle in the center represents the Sun itself. The right diagram represents the curvature that would result if the Sun were compressed to the size of a white dwarf (about the size of the Earth). There is no change beyond the old boundaries of the Sun, but the curvature becomes much greater within the region formerly occupied by the Sun.

spacetime around the Sun compressed to a black hole

**b** If we kept compressing the Sun, the curvature within the region where the Sun used to be would be greater and greater, eventually creating a *black hole* in the universe.

**FIGURE S3.16** These rubber-sheet diagrams represent the curvature of space around an object with the mass of our Sun. Remember that these diagrams have limitations, as described in the three bullets on page 416.

### The Strength of Gravity

The more spacetime curves, the stronger gravity becomes. The rubber-sheet analogy shows that there are two basic ways to increase the curvature of spacetime. First, a larger mass results in greater curvature at particular distances away from it. For example, the Sun curves spacetime more than any planet, and the Earth curves spacetime more than the Moon. Second, for an object of a given mass, spacetime curvature is greater near the object's surface if the object is denser (and hence smaller in size). For example, suppose we could compress the Sun into a type of "dead" star called a *white dwarf* [Section 17.2]. Because its total mass is still the same, there is no effect on the curvature of spacetime far from the Sun, but spacetime is much more curved near the compressed Sun's surface (Figure S3.16a). Thus, gravity feels much stronger on a white dwarf star than on the Sun.

If we continued to compress the Sun to smaller and smaller size, spacetime would curve more and more at the Sun's surface. Eventually, we could create a bottomless pit in spacetime, which is what we call a **black hole** (Figure S3.16b). Nothing can escape from within a black hole, and we can never again detect or observe an object that falls into a black hole. The boundary that marks the "point of no return" is called the **event horizon**, because events that occur within this boundary can have no influence on our observable universe. Thus, a black hole is truly a hole in the observable universe. (We'll discuss black holes further in Chapter 17.)

### Gravitational Time Dilation

Given that gravity arises from curvature of spacetime, you should not be surprised to learn that gravity affects time as well as space. We can learn about the effects of gravity on time by considering the effects of accelerated motion and then invoking the equivalence principle.

Imagine that you and Jackie are floating weightlessly at opposite ends of a spaceship. You both have watches that flash brightly each second and that you have synchronized beforehand. Because you are both floating freely with no relative motion between you, you are both in the same reference frame. Therefore, you will see each other's watches flashing at the same rate.

Now suppose you fire the spaceship engines so that the spaceship begins to accelerate, with you at the front and Jackie at the back. When the ship be-

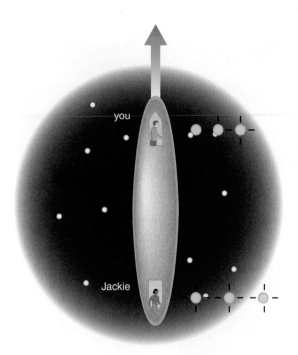

**a** A thought experiment with flashing watches shows that time runs slower at the back of an accelerating spaceship. The yellow dots represent the flashes from the watches, and the spacing between the dots represents the time between the flashes.

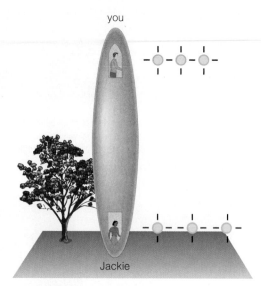

**b** By the equivalence principle, time must also run slower at lower altitudes in a gravitational field.

**FIGURE S3.17** A thought experiment demonstrating why time must run slower when gravity is stronger.

gins accelerating, you and Jackie will no longer be weightless. But the acceleration introduces an even more important change into the situation, which we can understand by imagining the view of someone floating weightlessly outside the spaceship. Remember that observers moving at different relative speeds are in different reference frames. When the spaceship is accelerating, its speed is constantly increasing relative to the outside observer, which means that both you and Jackie are constantly changing reference frames. Moreover, the flashes from your watches take a bit of time to travel the length of the spaceship. Thus, by the time a particular flash from Jackie's watch reaches you (or a flash from your watch reaches Jackie), both of your reference frames are different from what they were at the time the flash was emitted.

Because you are in the *front* of the accelerating spaceship, your changing reference frames are always carrying you *away* from the point at which each of Jackie's flashes is emitted. Thus, the light from each of her flashes will take a little *longer* to reach you than it would have if the ship were not accelerating. As a result, instead of seeing Jackie's flashes 1 second apart, you'll see them coming a little *more* than 1 second apart. That is, you'll see Jackie's watch flashing slower than yours (Figure S3.17a). You will therefore conclude that time is running slow at the back end of the spaceship.

From Jackie's point of view at the *back* of the accelerating spaceship, her changing reference frames are always carrying her *toward* the point at which each of your flashes is emitted. Thus, the light from each of your flashes will take a little *less* time to reach her than it would have if the ship were not accelerating, so she'll see them coming a little *less* than 1 second apart. She will see your watch flashing *faster* than hers and conclude that time is running *fast* at the front end of the spaceship. Note that you and Jackie agree: Time is running slower at the back end of the spaceship and faster at the front end. The greater the acceleration of the spaceship, the greater the difference in the rate at which time passes at the two ends of the spaceship.

Now we apply the equivalence principle, which tells us that we should get the same results for a spaceship at rest in a gravitational field as we do for a spaceship accelerating through space. Thus, if the spaceship were at rest on a planet, time would also have to be running slower at the bottom of the spaceship than at the top (Figure S3.17b). That is, time must run slower at lower altitudes than at higher altitudes in a gravitational field. This effect is known as **gravitational time dilation**.

The stronger the gravity—and hence the greater the curvature of spacetime—the larger the factor by which time runs slow. Time runs slower on the surface of the Sun than on the Earth, and slower on the surface of a white dwarf star than on the Sun. Perhaps you've already guessed that the extreme case is a black hole: As seen by anyone watching from a distance, time comes to a stop at the event horizon. If you could observe clocks placed at varying distances from the black hole, you'd see that clocks nearer the event horizon run slower and clocks *at* the event horizon show time to be frozen.

**TIME OUT TO THINK** *Where would you age more slowly, on the Earth or on the Moon? Explain.*

### The Geometry of the Universe

On a small scale, the surface of the Earth appears flat in some places and curved by hills and valleys in others. However, when we expand our view to the entire Earth, it's clear that the overall geometry of the Earth's surface is like the surface of a sphere. In a similar way, but in two more dimensions, the four-dimensional spacetime of our universe presumably has some overall geometry determined by the masses within it. This overall geometry must be one of the three general types of geometry discussed earlier: flat, spherical, or saddle-shaped (see Figure S3.13).

In geometry, a plane is infinite in extent. An idealized, saddle-shaped (hyperbolic) surface is also infinite in extent. In the same way, spacetime would be infinite in extent if the universe were flat or saddle-shaped overall, and therefore the universe would have no center and no edges. If the overall geometry of the universe were spherical, spacetime would be finite like the surface of the Earth, but it would still have no center and no edges. Just as you can sail or fly around the Earth's surface endlessly, you could fly through the universe forever and never encounter an edge. And just as the *surface* of the Earth has no center—New York is no more "central" than Beijing or any other place on the Earth's surface—there is no center to the universe. (The three-dimensional Earth *does* have a center, but this center is not part of the two-dimensional surface of the Earth. Similarly, if four-dimensional spacetime is spherical, any "center" will be visible only by looking in at least five dimensions. Such a center has no meaning, because it is not part of the four spacetime dimensions of our universe.)

## S3.5  Is It True?

Starting from the principle of equivalence, we've used logic and analogies to develop the ideas of general relativity. However, as always, we should not accept these theoretical conclusions unless they withstand observational and experimental tests. Like the pre-

dictions of special relativity, those of general relativity have faced many tests and have passed with flying colors.

### Mercury's Peculiar Orbit

The first observational test passed by the theory of general relativity involved observations of the orbit of Mercury. Newton's law of gravity predicts that Mercury's orbit should precess slowly around the Sun because of the gravitational influences of other planets (Figure S3.18). Careful observations of Mercury's orbit during the 1800s showed that it does indeed precess, with each precession cycle taking more than 20,000 years. However, careful calculations made with Newton's law of gravity could not completely account for the observed precession. Although the discrepancy was small, further observations verified that it was real.

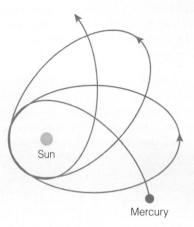

Note: The amount of precession with each orbit is highly exaggerated in this picture.

**FIGURE S3.18** Mercury's orbit slowly precesses around the Sun. Note: The amount of precession with each orbit is highly exaggerated in this picture.

Einstein was aware of this discrepancy and had hoped that he would be able to explain it from the time he first thought of the equivalence principle in 1907. When he finally succeeded in November 1915, he was so excited that he was unable to work for the next 3 days. He later called the moment of this success the high point of his scientific life.

In essence, Einstein showed that the discrepancy arose because Newton's law of gravity assumes that time is absolute and space is flat. In reality, time runs slower and space is more curved on the part of Mercury's orbit that is nearer the Sun. The equations of general relativity take this distortion of spacetime into account, providing a predicted orbit for Mercury that precisely matches its observed orbit.

## The Twin Paradox

Imagine two twins, one of whom stays on Earth while the other takes a high-speed trip to a distant star and back. In Chapter S2, we said that the twin who takes the trip will age less than the twin who stays home on Earth. But shouldn't the traveling twin be allowed to claim that she stayed stationary while Earth made a trip away from her and back? And in that case, shouldn't the twin on Earth be the one who ages less? This question underlies the so-called *twin paradox*. It can be analyzed in several different ways, but we will take an approach that offers some insights into the nature of spacetime.

Suppose you and Jackie are floating weightlessly next to each other with synchronized watches. While you remain weightless, Jackie uses her engines to accelerate a short distance away from you, decelerate to a stop a bit farther away, and then turn around and return. From your point of view, Jackie's motion means that you'll see her watch ticking slower than yours. Thus, upon her return, you expect to find that less time has passed for her than for you. But how does Jackie view the situation?

The two of you can argue endlessly about who is really moving, but one fact is obvious to both of you: During the trip, you remained weightless while Jackie felt *weight* holding her to the floor of her spaceship. Jackie can account for her weight in either of two ways. First, she can agree with you that she was the one who accelerated. But, because we know that time runs slow in an accelerating spaceship, she'll therefore agree that her watch ran slower than yours. Alternatively, she can claim that she felt weight because her engines counteracted a gravitational field in which she was stationary while you fell freely. But we also know that time runs slow in gravitational fields, and therefore she'll still agree that her watch ran slower than yours. Thus, no matter how you or Jackie looks at it, the result is the same: Less time passes for Jackie.

Figure S3.18a shows a spacetime diagram for this experiment. You and Jackie both moved between the same two events in spacetime: the start and end points of Jackie's trip. However, note that your path between the two events is shorter than Jackie's. Because we have already concluded that less time passes for Jackie, we are led to a remarkable insight about the passage of time:

*Between any two events in spacetime, more time passes on the shorter (and hence straighter) path.*

The maximum amount of time you can record between two events in spacetime occurs if you follow the straightest possible path—that is, the path on which you are weightless.

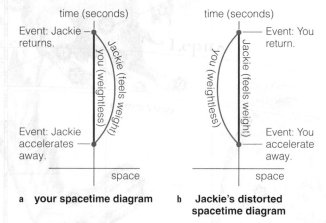

**FIGURE S3.19** (**a**) A person floating weightlessly must be following the straightest possible path through spacetime. Because this is not the case in Jackie's diagram (**b**), her diagram must be distorted.

a   **your spacetime diagram**

b   **Jackie's distorted spacetime diagram**

**TIME OUT TO THINK** *Suppose the perihelion of Mercury's orbit were even closer to the Sun than it actually is. Would you expect the discrepancy between the actual orbit and the orbit predicted by Newton's laws to be greater than or less than it actually is? Explain.*

### Gravitational Lensing

We can also test Einstein's claim that space is curved by observing the trajectories of light rays moving through the universe. Because light always travels at the same speed, never accelerating or decelerating, light must always follow the straightest possible path. If space itself is curved, then light paths will appear curved as well.

Suppose we could carefully measure the angular separation between two stars during the daytime, just when the light from one of the stars passes near the Sun. The curvature of space near the Sun forces the light beam passing closer to the Sun to curve more than the light beam from the other star (Figure S3.21). Therefore, the angular separation of the two stars will appear smaller than their true angular separation (which we would know from nighttime measurements). This effect was first observed during a total eclipse in 1919. This second spectacular success of general relativity brought Einstein worldwide fame.

Even more dramatic effects occur when a distant star or galaxy, as seen from Earth, lies directly behind another object with a strong gravitational field (Figure S3.22). The mass of the intervening object curves spacetime in its vicinity, altering the trajectories of

The subtlety arises if Jackie chooses to claim that she is at rest and attributes her weight to gravity. In that case, she might be tempted to draw the spacetime diagram in Figure S3.19b, on which you appear to have the longer path through spacetime. The rule that time runs slower on longer paths would then seem to imply that *your* watch should have recorded less time, contradicting our earlier claims. But the contradiction is an illusion. If Jackie wishes to assert that she felt gravity, she must also claim that the gravity she felt implies that spacetime is curved in her vicinity, and therefore she should *not* have drawn a spacetime diagram on a flat piece of paper.

Jackie's problem is analogous to that of a pilot who plans a trip from Philadelphia to Beijing on a flat map of the Earth (Figure S3.20). On the flat map, it appears that the pilot has plotted the straightest possible path. However, this appearance is an illusion: The shortest and straightest path really is the great-circle route that appears curved on the flat map of the Earth. A flat map of the Earth distorts reality because the actual geometry of the Earth's surface is spherical. Just as the distortions in a map of the world do not change the actual distances between cities, the way we choose to draw a spacetime diagram does not alter the reality of spacetime. The solution to the twin paradox is that the two twins do not share identical situations: The twin who turns around at the distant star must have a more strongly curved worldline than the stay-at-home twin. Thus, more time must pass for the stay-at-home twin, and the traveler does indeed age less during the journey.

**FIGURE S3.20** On a flat map of the Earth, what looks like a straight line is not really as straight as possible.

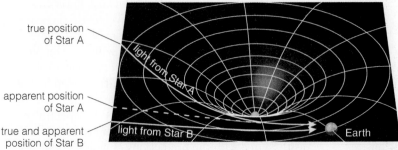

**FIGURE S3.21** Light from Star A passes through a more highly curved region of spacetime than light from Star B, making the angular separation of the two stars appear smaller than their true angular separation.

**FIGURE S3.22** Gravitational lensing can create distorted or multiple images of a distant object whose light passes by a massive object on its way to Earth.

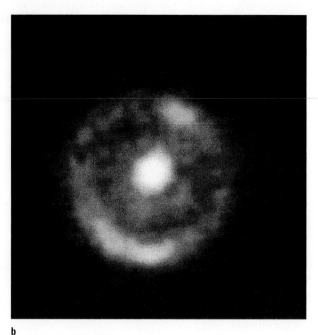

a                                          b

**FIGURE S3.23** (**a**) In this case of gravitational lensing, called Einstein's Cross, the gravity of a foreground galaxy (center) bends light from a single bright background object so that it reaches us along four different paths—creating four distinct images of a single object. (**b**) When one galaxy lies directly behind another, the foreground galaxy can bend light on all sides so that the light converges on the Earth, forming an Einstein Ring like that pictured here.

light beams passing nearby. Different light paths can curve so much that they end up converging at Earth, grossly distorting the appearance of the star or galaxy. Depending on the precise four-dimensional geometry of spacetime between us and the observed star or galaxy, the image we see may be magnified or distorted into arcs, rings, or multiple images of the same object (Figure S3.23). This type of distortion is called **gravitational lensing**, analogous to the bending of light by a glass lens. (The cover of this book shows another example of gravitational lensing.)

### Effects on Time

The prediction of gravitational time dilation can be tested by comparing clocks located in places with different gravitational field strengths. Even in the Earth's weak gravity, experiments have demonstrated that clocks at low altitude tick more slowly than identical clocks at higher altitude. The effect is extremely small—it would add up to only a few billionths of a second over a human lifetime—but the differences agree precisely with the predictions of general relativity.

Surprisingly, it's even easier to compare the passage of time on Earth with the passage of time on the surface of the Sun and other stars. Because stellar gases emit and absorb *spectral lines* with particular frequencies [Section 6.4], they serve as natural atomic

clocks. Suppose that, in a laboratory on Earth, we find that a particular type of gas emits a spectral line with a frequency of 500 trillion cycles per second. If this same gas is present on the Sun, it will also emit a spectral line with a frequency of 500 trillion cycles per second. General relativity claims that time should be running very slightly slower on the Sun than on Earth; that is, 1 second on the Sun lasts *longer* than 1 second on Earth, or, equivalently, a second on Earth is shorter than a second on the Sun. Thus, during 1 second on Earth, we will see *fewer* than 500 trillion cycles from the gas on the Sun. Because lower frequency means longer or redder wavelength, the spectral lines from the Sun ought to be *redshifted*. Note that this redshift has nothing to do with the Doppler shifts that we see from moving objects [Section 6.5]. Instead, it is a **gravitational redshift**, caused by the fact that time runs slow in gravitational fields. Gravitational redshifts have been measured for spectral lines from the Sun and from many other stars. The results agree with the predictions of general relativity.

### The Search for Gravitational Waves

If the curvature of space suddenly changes somewhere, it can have effects on distant parts of the universe. For example, the effect of a star suddenly imploding or exploding is rather like the effect of dropping a rock into a pond, generating ripples of curvature that propagate outward through space. Similarly, two massive stars orbiting each other closely and rapidly generate ripples of curvature in space rather like those of a blade turning in water. Einstein called these ripples **gravitational waves**. Similar in character to light waves but far weaker, gravitational waves have no mass and travel at the speed of light.

The distortions of space carried by gravitational waves should compress and expand objects they pass by. In principle, we could detect gravitational waves by looking for such waves of compression and expansion, but these effects are expected to be extremely weak. No one has yet succeeded in detecting gravitational waves. However, a new observatory dedicated to the search for gravitational waves should be fully operational by 2003. Called the Laser Interferometer Gravitational Wave Observatory, or LIGO, it consists of two large detectors—one in Louisiana and one in Washington State—that will search in tandem for telltale signs of gravitational waves.

Despite the lack of direct detection, we are quite certain that gravitational waves exist because of a special set of observations carried out over the past quarter-century. In 1974, astronomers Russell Hulse and Joseph Taylor discovered an unusual binary star system in which both stars are highly compressed (they are neutron stars [Section 17.3]), allowing them to orbit each other extremely closely and rapidly. General relativity predicts that this system should be emitting a substantial amount of energy in gravitational waves. If the system is losing energy to these waves, the orbits of the two stars should be steadily decaying. Observations show that the rate at which the orbital period is decreasing matches the prediction of general relativity, a strong suggestion that the system really is losing energy by emitting gravitational waves (Figure S3.24).

## S3.6 Hyperspace, Wormholes, and Warp Drive

If you're a fan of *Star Trek, Star Wars,* or other science fiction, you've seen spaceships bounding about the galaxy with seemingly little regard for Einstein's prohibition on traveling faster than the speed of light. In fact, these stories do not necessarily have to violate the precepts of relativity as long as they exploit potential "loopholes" in the known laws of nature.

Let's begin with an analogy. Suppose you want to take a trip between Hawaii and South Africa, which happen to lie diametrically opposite on the Earth (Figure S3.25). Ordinarily, we are restricted to traveling along the Earth's surface by car, boat, or plane, and the most direct trip covers about 20,000 kilometers. But suppose you could somehow drill a hole

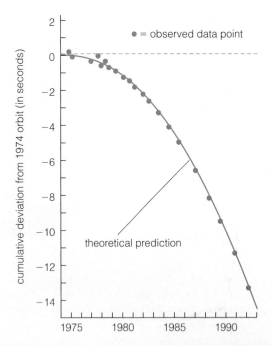

**FIGURE S3.24** The decrease in the orbital period of the Hulse–Taylor binary star system matches what we expect if the system is emitting gravitational waves.

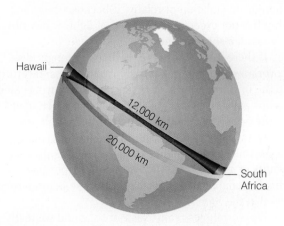

**FIGURE S3.25** If you could take a shortcut *through* the Earth, the trip from Hawaii to South Africa would be shorter than is possible on the *surface* of the Earth.

through the center of the Earth and fly through the hole from Hawaii to South Africa. In that case, the trip would be only about 12,000 kilometers.

Now consider a trip from Earth to the star Vega, about 25 light-years away. From the point of view of someone who stays home on Earth, this trip must take at least 25 years in each direction. But suppose space happens to be curved in such a way that Earth and Vega are much closer together as viewed from a multidimensional *hyperspace,* just as Hawaii and

**FIGURE S3.26** The curved sheet represents our universe, in which a trip from Earth to Vega covers a distance of 25 light-years. This trip could be much shorter if there were a wormhole that created a shortcut through hyperspace.

South Africa are closer together if we can go through the Earth than if we must stay on its surface. Further, suppose there is a tunnel through hyperspace, often called a **wormhole**, through which we can travel (Figure S3.26). If the tunnel is short—perhaps only a few kilometers in length—then a spaceship needs to travel only a few kilometers through the wormhole to go from Earth to Vega. The trip might take only a few minutes in each direction! Note that there is no violation of relativity, because the spaceship has not exceeded the speed of light. It has simply taken a shortcut through hyperspace.

If there is no wormhole, perhaps we might discover a way to "jump" through hyperspace and return to the universe anywhere we please. Such hyperspace jumps are the fictional devices used for space travel in the *Star Wars* movies. Or perhaps we might discover a way to warp spacetime to our own specifications, thereby allowing us to make widely separated points in space momentarily touch in hyperspace—this fictional device is the basic premise behind *warp drive* in the *Star Trek* series.

Do wormholes really exist? If so, could we really travel through them? Is it possible that we might someday discover a way to jump into hyperspace or create a warp drive? Our current understanding of physics is insufficient to answer these questions definitively. For the time being, the known laws of physics do not prohibit any of these exotic forms of travel. These loopholes are therefore ideal for science fiction writers, because they might allow rapid travel among distant parts of the universe without violating the established laws of relativity.

However, many scientists believe we will eventually find that these exotic forms of travel are *not* possible. Their primary objection is that wormholes seem to make time travel possible. If you could jump through hyperspace to another place in our universe, couldn't you also jump back to another *time*? If you

used a trip through hyperspace to travel into the past, could you prevent your parents from ever meeting?

The paradoxes we encounter when we think about time travel are severe and seem to have no resolution. Most scientists therefore believe that time travel will prove to be impossible, even though we don't yet know any laws of physics that prohibit it. In the words of physicist Stephen Hawking, time travel should be prohibited "to keep the world safe for historians."

If time travel is not possible, it is much more difficult to see how shortcuts through hyperspace could be allowed. Nevertheless, neither time travel nor travel through hyperspace can yet be categorically ruled out in the same way that we can rule out the possibility of exceeding the speed of light. Until we learn otherwise, the world remains safe for science fiction writers who choose their fictional space travel techniques with care, avoiding any conflicts with relativity and other known laws of nature.

## S3.7 The Last Word

We now know that space and time are intertwined in ways that would have been difficult to imagine before Einstein's work. So, for the last word in our study of relativity, let's turn to Einstein himself. Here is what he said about a month before his death on April 18, 1955:

> *"Death signifies nothing. . . . the distinction between past, present, and future is only a stubbornly persistent illusion."*[4]

---

[4]This quotation was found with the aid of Alice Calaprice, author of *The Quotable Einstein,* Princeton University Press, 1996.

## THE BIG PICTURE

Just as the Copernican revolution overthrew the ancient belief in an Earth-centered universe, Einstein's revolution overthrew the ancient belief that space and time are distinct and absolute. Now that we have explored Einstein's revolution in some detail in the past two chapters, keep in mind the following "big picture" ideas:

- We live in four-dimensional spacetime. Disagreements among different observers about measurements of time and space occur because the different observers are looking at this four-dimensional reality from different three-dimensional perspectives.

- Gravity arises from curvature of spacetime. Once we recognize this fact, the orbits of planets, moons, and all other objects are perfectly natural consequences of the curvature, rather than results of a mysterious "force" acting over great distances.

- Although the predictions of relativity may seem quite bizarre, they have been verified many times by observations and experiments.

- Some questions remain well beyond our current understanding. In particular, we do not yet know whether travel through hyperspace might be possible, thereby allowing some of the imaginative ideas of science fiction to become reality.

### Review Questions

1. Explain what we mean by the straightest possible path on the Earth's surface.

2. What do we mean by *spacetime?*

3. List five major ideas that come directly from the general theory of relativity.

4. What is the *equivalence principle?* Give an example that clarifies its meaning.

5. What do we mean by *dimension?* Describe a *point,* a *line,* a *plane,* a *three-dimensional space,* and a *four-dimensional space.* What does *hyperspace* mean?

6. Explain the meaning of the following statement: "Space is different for different observers. Time is different for different observers. Spacetime is the same for everyone."

7. What is a *spacetime diagram?* What is an *event?* What is a *worldline?*

8. Consider a spacetime diagram that shows worldlines for three objects: One worldline is vertical, one is straight but slanted, and one is curved. In the reference frame of the person who drew the diagram, how is each object moving?

9. Briefly describe how the rules of geometry are different depending on whether the geometry is *flat, spherical,* or *saddle-shaped.*

10. How can you tell whether you are following the straightest possible path through spacetime?

11. According to general relativity, what is gravity? In this view, why does the Earth orbit the Sun?

12. Briefly describe the idea behind the rubber-sheet analogy to spacetime. List three ways in which this analogy is limited.

13. Explain why the curvature of spacetime near a star depends on both the star's mass and its size.

14. What is a *black hole?* What do we mean by the *event horizon* of a black hole?

15. What is *gravitational time dilation?* What determines how much time is slowed in a gravitational field?

16. Explain how the universe can be finite yet have no center and no edges.

17. Briefly describe several observational tests that support general relativity.

18. What is *gravitational lensing?* According to general relativity, why does it occur?

19. Why do we see a *gravitational redshift* when we look at spectral lines from the Sun?

20. What are *gravitational waves?* What evidence supports their existence?

21. What is the current evidence regarding the possibility of travel through hyperspace, wormholes, or warp drive? Explain how a *wormhole* might allow us to travel between two places that are 10 light-years apart in less than 10 years.

### Discussion Questions

1. *Relativity and Fate.* In principle, if we could see all four dimensions of spacetime, we could see future events as well as past events. In his novel *Slaughterhouse Five,* writer Kurt Vonnegut used this idea to argue that our futures are predetermined and that there is no such thing as free will. Do you agree with this argument? Why or why not?

2. *Philosophical Implications of Relativity.* According to our description of spacetime, you exist in spacetime as a "solid" object stretching through time. In that sense, you cannot erase anything you've ever said or done from spacetime; if we could see in four dimensions, we would be able to see everything you've ever said or done. Do you think these ideas have any important philosophical implications? Discuss.

3. *Wormholes and Causality.* Suppose it turns out that travel through wormholes *is* possible and that it is possible to travel into the past. Discuss some of the paradoxes that would occur. In light of these paradoxes, do you believe that travel through wormholes will turn out to be prohibited? Why or why not?

## Problems

1. *Worldlines at Low Speed.* Make a spacetime diagram and draw worldlines for each of the following situations. Explain your drawings.

   a. A person sitting still in a chair.

   b. A person driving by at a constant velocity of 50 km/hr.

   c. A person driving by at a constant velocity of 100 km/hr.

   d. A person accelerating from a stop sign to a speed of 50 km/hr.

   e. A person decelerating from 50 km/hr to a stop.

2. *Worldlines at High Speed.* Make a spacetime diagram on which the time axis is marked in seconds and the space axis is marked in light-seconds. Assume you are floating weightlessly and therefore consider yourself at rest. You see Sebastian moving to your right at $0.5c$ and Michaela moving to your left at $0.7c$. Sebastian passed your location 2 seconds ago, and Michaela passed your location 4 seconds ago. Draw worldlines for Sebastian, Michaela, and yourself. Explain your diagrams.

3. *Galileo and the Equivalence Principle.* Galileo demonstrated that all objects near the Earth's surface should fall with the same acceleration, regardless of their mass. According to general relativity, why shouldn't the mass of a falling object affect its rate of fall? Explain in one or two paragraphs.

4. *Long Trips at Constant Acceleration.* On a realistic trip to the stars, we could not suddenly jump to a speed near the speed of light without being killed by the forces associated with the sudden acceleration. Thus, a more realistic trip would have us accelerate at a comfortable rate, such as $1g$, until we are halfway to our destination and then decelerate at the same rate until we reach our destination. Explain why we would be comfortable with this acceleration. By our own reckoning, would we notice anything unusual about lengths, masses, or the passage of time on our spaceship? Why or why not?

5. *Long Trips at Constant Acceleration: Earth Time.* Suppose you stay on Earth and watch a spaceship leave on a long trip at a constant acceleration of $1g$.

   a. At an acceleration of $1g$, approximately how long will it take before you see the spaceship traveling away from Earth at *half* the speed of light? Explain. (Use $g = 9.8$ m/s$^2$.)

   b. Describe how you will see its speed change as it continues to accelerate. Will it keep gaining speed at a rate of 9.8 m/s each second? Why or why not?

   c. Suppose the ship travels to a star that is 500 light-years away. According to you back on Earth, *approximately* how long will this trip take? Explain.

6. *Movie Science Fiction.* Choose a popular science fiction movie that involves interstellar travel and study it closely as you watch it. What aspects of the movie are consistent with relativity and other laws of physics? What aspects of the movie violate the laws of relativity or other laws of physics? Write a two- to three-page summary of your findings.

7. *Research: The Eötvös Experiment.* Galileo's result that all objects fall to the Earth with the same acceleration (neglecting air resistance) is very important to general relativity—if it were not true, general relativity would be in serious trouble. Describe the experiments of Baron Roland von Eötvös, who tested Galileo's conclusions in the late 1800s. How did the results of these experiments influence Einstein as he worked on general relativity? Write a one- to two-page summary of your findings.

8. *Research: Wormholes.* Some scientists have thought seriously about wormholes and their consequences. Find and read a popular article or book about wormholes. Write a short summary of the article, and discuss your opinion of the implications of wormholes according to the article.

*9. *Long Trips at Constant Acceleration: Spaceship Time.* Consider again the spaceship on a long trip with a constant acceleration of $1g$. Although the derivation is beyond the scope of this book, it is possible to show that, as long as the ship is gone from Earth for many years, the amount of time that passes on the spaceship during the trip is approximately:

$$T_{ship} = \frac{2c}{g} \ln\left(\frac{g \times D}{c^2}\right)$$

In this formula, $D$ is the distance to the destination and ln stands for the natural logarithm. (Your calculator probably has a key for taking natural logarithms [usually labeled "ln"], so you can use this formula even if you are not familiar with them.) If $D$ is in meters, $g = 9.8$ m/s$^2$, and $c = 3 \times 10^8$ m/s, the answer will be in units of *seconds*.

   a. Suppose the ship travels to a star that is 500 light-years away. How much time will pass on the ship? Compare this to the amount of time that passes on Earth (see problem 5c). (*Hint:* Be sure you convert the distance from light-years to meters and convert your answer from seconds to years.)

   b. Suppose the ship travels to the center of the Milky Way Galaxy, about 28,000 light-years away. How much time will pass on the ship? Compare this to the amount of time that passes on Earth.

c. The Andromeda Galaxy is about 2.5 million light-years away. Suppose you had a spaceship that could constantly accelerate at 1g. Could you go to the Andromeda Galaxy and back within your lifetime? Explain. What would you find when you returned to Earth?

## Web Projects

Find useful links for Web projects on the text Web site.

1. *Person of the Century.* Read the article "A Brief History of Relativity" by Stephen Hawking (on the *Time* magazine Web site) to learn why *Time* chose Einstein as their "Person of the Century." Write a short essay explaining the reasons and whether you agree with the choice. Defend your opinion.

2. *Gravity Probe-B.* A NASA satellite called *Gravity Probe-B,* scheduled for launch in 2002 or 2003, will test some of the predictions of general relativity with great precision. Learn more about this satellite and its mission, and write a short report about your findings.

3. *LIGO.* Learn more about the Laser Interferometer Gravitational Wave Observatory (LIGO) and how it will attempt to detect gravitational waves. Write a short report on your findings.

*There is a theory which states that if ever anyone discovers exactly what the Universe is for and why it is here, it will instantly disappear and be replaced by something even more bizarre and inexplicable.*
*There is another which states that this has already happened.*

DOUGLAS ADAMS,
FROM *THE RESTAURANT AT THE END OF THE UNIVERSE*

# CHAPTER S4
# Building Blocks of the Universe

The microscopic realm of atoms and nuclei seems far removed from the vast realm of planets, stars, and galaxies. Nevertheless, much of what we know about the cosmos today would have remained mysterious without a thorough understanding of these tiny particles. They are the building blocks from which all else is made, and the behavior of very large objects frequently depends on the laws that govern their tiniest pieces.

We've already seen that matter and energy behave in some strange ways when we break them down into small units. For example, we know that electrons in atoms can have only specific energies and that photons act sometimes like particles and sometimes like waves. These are only a few of the strange realities in the realm of the very small, where the laws of nature can seem utterly bizarre to even the most practiced scientists.

In this chapter, we will examine the laws of nature that underlie the structure of matter. We will look more deeply into the building blocks of nature, investigating current knowledge of the fundamental particles and forces that make up the universe. We will see that the strange laws of the microscopic world play a fundamental role in diverse processes such as nuclear fusion in the Sun and the collapse of a star into a black hole.

## S4.1 The Quantum Revolution

Around the same time that Einstein was discovering the principles of relativity, he and others were also investigating the behavior of matter and energy. Their discoveries in this area were no less astonishing. In 1905, the same year he published the special theory of relativity, Einstein showed that light behaves like particles (photons) in addition to behaving like waves [Section 6.2]. In 1911, British physicist Ernest Rutherford (1871–1937) discovered that atoms consist mostly of empty space, begging the question of how matter can ever feel solid. In 1913, Danish physicist Niels Bohr (1885–1962) discovered that electrons in atoms can have only particular energies; that is, electron energies are *quantized* [Section 4.4]. Thus, the realm of the very small is often called the *quantum realm,* and the science of the quantum realm is called **quantum mechanics**.

Other scientists soon built upon the work of Einstein, Rutherford, and Bohr. By the mid-1920s, our ideas about the structure and nature of atoms and subatomic particles were undergoing a total revolution. The repercussions of this *quantum revolution* continue to reverberate today. They have forced us to reexamine our "common sense" about the fundamental nature of matter and energy. They have also driven a technological revolution, because the laws of quantum mechanics make modern electronics possible. Most important, at least from an astronomical point of view, the combination of new ideas and new technology is enabling us to look ever deeper into the heart of matter and energy—the ultimate building blocks of the universe.

This chapter discusses key ideas of the quantum revolution that are important to the study of astronomy. The following are among these surprising new ideas:

- The protons, neutrons, and electrons that we usually consider the building blocks of atoms are not truly fundamental. Instead, the building blocks of ordinary matter are *quarks* and *leptons*. Quarks and leptons, in turn, belong to a category called *fermions*, while photons belong to an entirely distinct category of particles called *bosons*.

- *Antimatter* is real and is readily produced in the laboratory. When a particle and its antiparticle meet, the result is mutual annihilation and release of energy.

- Just four forces govern all interactions between particles: gravity, electromagnetism, and the strong and weak nuclear forces. In fact, these four forces are themselves manifestations of a smaller number of truly fundamental forces. Perhaps a single unified force rules all of nature.

- Our everyday common sense tells us that particles and waves are different, but the quantum laws show that *all* tiny particles exhibit the same *wave–particle duality* that Einstein demonstrated for photons.

- The quantum laws have important astronomical consequences. For example, a strange quantum effect called *degeneracy pressure* can prevent the core of a dying star from collapsing. *Quantum tunneling* helps make nuclear fusion possible in the Sun. And phantomlike *virtual particles* may be important to the ultimate fate of black holes and the universe itself.

No matter how bizarre the quantum laws may seem, they lead to concrete predictions that can be tested experimentally and observationally. Some of these tests require sophisticated technological equipment found only in advanced physics laboratories. Others require billion-dollar particle accelerators. But some are performed every day, right before your eyes. Every time you see a ray of sunlight, you are seeing the product of nuclear reactions that are made possible by the quantum laws. And every time you turn on a computer, a calculator, a television, or any other "high-tech" electronic device, the strange laws of quantum mechanics are being put to work for your benefit.

## S4.2 Fundamental Particles and Forces

More than 2,400 years ago, Democritus proposed that matter is made from building blocks that he called *atoms* [Section 4.3]. He believed that atoms were **fundamental particles**, the most basic units of matter, impossible to divide any further. By this definition, the particles we now call atoms are not truly fundamental. By the 1930s, we had learned that atoms themselves are made of protons, neutrons, and electrons. Following this realization, scientists briefly hoped that these three particles were the true fundamental building blocks of the universe. However, under more extreme conditions, matter starts to display greater variety, and strange new particles begin to appear.

We can generate many unusual particles with the aid of **particle accelerators** (sometimes called *atom smashers*), such as Fermilab near Chicago and CERN on the border between Switzerland and France (Figure S4.1). The large magnets inside particle accelerators accelerate familiar particles such as electrons or protons to very high speeds—often extremely close to the speed of light. When these particles collide with one another or with a stationary target, they

**FIGURE S4.1** Aerial photograph of the Fermilab particle accelerator in Illinois.

release a substantial amount of energy within a very small space. Some of this energy spontaneously turns into mass, producing a shower of particles. (Recall that $E = mc^2$ tells us not only that mass can turn into energy, but also that energy can turn into mass.) Scientists recognize particles of different types by their differing behavior. Whenever scientists observe a particle that behaves in previously unseen ways, it is cataloged as a new type of particle and given a name.

Hundreds of different particles had been discovered by the early 1960s, and scientists began to wonder whether any of them were truly fundamental. At about that time, physicist Murray Gell-Mann proposed a scheme in which all these particles could be built from just a few fundamental components. Gell-Mann's scheme has since blossomed into what physicists call the *standard model* for the structure of matter. The standard model has proved very successful and has even predicted the existence of new particles later discovered in particle accelerators. In this section, we briefly describe the fundamental particles according to the standard model, along with their special relationships with the forces of nature.

### Properties of Particles

Each particular type of subatomic particle, such as an electron, proton, or neutron, has its own peculiar behavior that is determined by just a few basic prop-

erties. The most important of these basic properties are *mass, charge,* and *spin.* Mass is already very familiar to you, and the effects of charge, such as static electricity or lightning, are also part of your everyday experience. Spin, on the other hand, is a property evident only in the quantum realm of the very small.

The word *spin* indicates that this property is related to angular momentum. Recall that a spinning ice skater or a spinning baseball has rotational angular momentum [Section 5.2]. By analogy, we say that a subatomic particle, such as an electron, has **spin angular momentum**—or **spin**, for short—as it "spins" on its axis. However, because an electron is not a particle in the same sense as a baseball, it does not actually spin in the same sense as a baseball. *Spin* is simply a term used to describe the angular momentum that belongs to the electron. Just as all electrons have exactly the same mass and electric charge, all electrons have exactly the same amount of spin. Similar considerations hold for all other types of subatomic particle: Every particle of a particular type has a particular amount of mass, charge, and spin.

In fact, spin is a very important property for subatomic particles, since all particles turn out to fall into one of two broad classes based on their spin: the **fermions**, named for Enrico Fermi (1901–1954), and the **bosons**, named for Satyendra Bose (1894–

1974).[1] The most familiar fermions are electrons, neutrons, and protons. The most familiar bosons are photons. In this book, we will not deal with the distinction between fermions and bosons except as a matter of classification. However, one more important aspect of spin applies to fermions such as electrons, protons, and neutrons: The spin can be oriented in two ways, usually called *spin up* and *spin down*. These two orientations, which correspond to the two opposite senses of rotation, clockwise and counterclockwise, are often represented by arrows (Figure S4.2). Be sure to remember that denoting a particle's spin by a small dot with an arrow is a representation of convenience; subatomic particles are *not* tiny spinning balls.

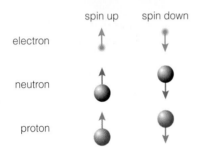

**FIGURE S4.2** The two possible states of an electron's, neutron's, or proton's spin are spin up and spin down, represented by arrows.

## Quarks and Leptons: The Building Blocks of Matter

While electrons appear to be truly fundamental, protons and neutrons are made from even smaller particles, called **quarks**. Protons and neutrons each contain two different types of quarks: the **up quark**, which has an electric charge of $+\frac{2}{3}$, and the **down quark**, which has an electric charge of $-\frac{1}{3}$. (Charge values are given relative to the $-1$ charge of electrons.) Two up quarks and one down quark form a proton, giving it an overall charge of $+\frac{2}{3} + \frac{2}{3} - \frac{1}{3} = +1$. One up quark and two down quarks form a neutron, making it neutral: $+\frac{2}{3} - \frac{1}{3} - \frac{1}{3} = 0$ (Figure S4.3).

To sum up so far, the fundamental building blocks of atoms are the up quark, the down quark, and the electron. But what about the hundreds of other particles discovered by scientists? The standard model organizes all these particles into a relatively simple hierarchy. First, as we discussed earlier, particles are classified as either fermions or bosons, depending on

**FIGURE S4.3** The quark composition of protons and neutrons.

their *spin*. Quarks, electrons, protons, and neutrons are all fermions. Next, the fermions fall into two groups: those made from quarks and those not made from quarks. Fermions not made from quarks, such as electrons, are called **leptons**.[2]

**TIME OUT TO THINK** *In most high school science classes, students are told that the fundamental building blocks of atoms are protons, neutrons, and electrons. However, based on the preceding discussion, explain why our current understanding really holds that the fundamental building blocks of atoms are* quarks *and* leptons.

Particles made from quarks can consist of either two or three quarks. Interestingly, experiments in particle accelerators indicate that a single quark cannot exist in isolation; it must always live either in a pair or in a threesome with other quarks.

We can determine what types of quarks a particle is made of by analyzing the particle's behavior. In the standard model, a total of six different types (or "flavors") of quarks are needed to explain the characteristics of all particles observed to date. We have already met the up and down quarks that make up protons and neutrons; the other four quarks have the rather exotic names *strange, charmed, top,* and *bottom.* Six different types of leptons go with the six types of quarks: the electron and the *electron neutrino,* the *muon* and the *mu neutrino,* and the *tauon* and the *tau neutrino.* All the quarks and leptons are listed in Table S4.1. All six quarks and all six leptons have been detected in experiments. The detection of the top quark was a particularly impressive success of the standard model: It was first predicted to exist in the 1970s and was verified experimentally in 1995.

At this point, you may be wondering what all these bizarrely named particles have to do with astronomy. In part, the answer is simply that these particles are the fundamental building blocks of everything, from atoms to people, planets, stars, and galaxies. In

---

[1]Physicists measure the angular momentum of subatomic particles in units of Planck's constant divided by $2\pi$. In these special units, *fermions* have half-integer spins (e.g., $\frac{1}{2}, \frac{3}{2}, \frac{5}{2}$), and *bosons* have integer spins (e.g., 0, 1, 2).

[2]There is also a name for the particles made from quarks: They are called *hadrons.* However, in this book we simply refer to them as "particles made from quarks."

## Table S4.1 Fundamental Fermions

| The Quarks | The Leptons |
|---|---|
| Up | Electron |
| Down | Electron neutrino |
| Strange | Muon |
| Charmed | Mu neutrino |
| Top | Tauon |
| Bottom | Tau neutrino |

addition, in Chapter 22, we'll see that the events that unfolded during the first fraction of a second after the Big Bang depended critically on the various types of fundamental particles. We'll also see that *neutrinos,* in particular, are important in several astronomical processes, including nuclear fusion, the explosion of stars, and the fate of the universe.

Incidentally, neutrinos get their name, which means "little neutral ones," from the fact that they are electrically neutral and extremely lightweight—far less massive than even electrons. No one has yet succeeded in measuring the precise masses of neutrinos. But neutrinos turn out to be extremely common—they outnumber protons, neutrons, and electrons combined by a factor of roughly a billion. As a result, their total mass could be a significant part of the total mass of the universe.

### Antimatter

Anyone who has watched *Star Trek* has heard of **antimatter**. Although *Star Trek* is science fiction, antimatter is not. It really exists. In fact, every quark and every lepton has a corresponding *antiquark* and *antilepton.* The antiparticle is like an exact opposite of its corresponding ordinary particle. For example, an *antielectron* (also called a *positron*) is identical to an ordinary electron except that it has a positive charge instead of a negative charge.

When a particle and its corresponding antiparticle meet, the result is mutual **annihilation** (Figure S4.4a). The combined mass of the particle and antiparticle turns completely into energy in accord with $E = mc^2$. Because our universe is made predominantly of ordinary matter, antimatter generally does not last very long. Whenever an antiparticle is produced, it quickly meets an ordinary particle, and the two annihilate each other to make energy.

This process also works in reverse. When conditions are right, pure energy can turn into a particle–antiparticle pair. For example, whenever an electron "pops" into existence, an antielectron also pops into existence with it (Figure S4.4b). This process of **pair production** happens routinely in particle accelera-

tors here on Earth and on a much grander scale in outer space. In fact, during the first few moments after the Big Bang, the universe's energy fields were so intense that particle–antiparticle pairs popped rapidly in and out of existence at virtually every point in space.

When we include antiparticles, the total number of quarks and leptons really is twice as high as shown in Table S4.1. That is, there are really 12 quarks: the six quarks listed and their six corresponding antiquarks (e.g., up quark and anti–up quark). Similarly, there are 12 leptons: the six listed and their six corresponding antileptons. The net total of 24 different fundamental particles is quite complex.[3] As we'll see shortly, this complexity leads many scientists to believe that additional simplifying principles of particle physics still await discovery.

### Forces

Without forces, the universe would be infinitely boring, a uniform sea of fundamental particles drifting aimlessly about. Forces supply the means through which particles communicate and exchange momentum, attracting or repelling one another depending on their properties. For example, particles with mass interact with other massive particles via the force of *gravity,* and particles with charge interact with other charged particles via the force of *electromagnetism.* Electromagnetism rules the processes of chemistry and biology, grouping electrons and protons into

---

[3]Moreover, each of the six quarks and six antiquarks is believed to come in three distinct varieties, called *colors.* (The term *color* is not meant to be literal; rather, it describes a property of quarks that we cannot visualize.) For example, the up quark comes in three colors, often called red, green, and blue.

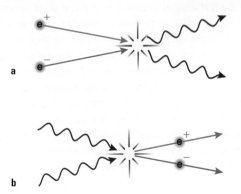

**FIGURE S4.4** (**a**) In this representation, an electron and a positron (antielectron) annihilate each other to make energy in the form of a pair of photons. (**b**) Here, a concentration of energy leads to pair production of an electron and a positron.

## Table S4.2 The Four Forces

| Force | Relative Strength Within Nucleus* | Relative Strength Beyond Nucleus | Exchange Particles | Major Role |
|---|---|---|---|---|
| Strong | 100 | 0 | Gluons | Holding nuclei together |
| Electromagnetic | 1 | 1 | Photons | Chemistry and biology |
| Weak | $10^{-5}$ | 0 | Weak bosons | Nuclear reactions |
| Gravity | $10^{-43}$ | $10^{-43}$ | Gravitons | Large-scale structure |

*The force laws for the strong and weak forces are more complex than the inverse square laws for the electromagnetic force and gravity; hence, the numbers given for the strong and weak forces are very rough.

atoms, atoms into molecules, and molecules into living cells. Gravity drives the action on larger scales, holding people on planets, planets in solar systems, and stars in galaxies.

Besides gravity and electromagnetism, we know of two other fundamental forces in the universe, called the **strong force** and the **weak force**. Both act only on extremely short-distance scales—so short that these forces can be felt only *within* atomic nuclei. You can see why the strong force must exist by remembering that the nuclei of all elements except hydrogen (which has just a single proton) contain more than one proton. Protons are positively charged, so the electromagnetic force pushes them apart. If the electromagnetic force were unopposed, atomic nuclei would always fly apart. The strong force, so named because it is strong enough to overcome electromagnetic repulsion, is what holds nuclei together. The weak force, also very important in nuclear reactions, is a bit more subtle. All particles made from quarks respond to the strong force, but neutrinos, for example, feel only the weak force.

According to the standard model, each force is transmitted by an **exchange particle** that transfers momentum between two interacting particles. Photons are the exchange particle for the electromagnetic force. That is, photons carry electromagnetic force through the universe. Motions of electrons in a star create photons. The photons then cross light-years of space to our eyes, where they generate an electromagnetic disturbance that we see as starlight. Similarly, *gravitons* carry the gravitational force through the universe.[4] *Gluons,* which get their name because they act like glue to bind nuclei together, carry the strong force. The weak force is carried by particles sometimes called *weak bosons.* (All of the

exchange particles are bosons.) The four forces and their exchange particles are listed in Table S4.2.

Table S4.2 also has columns describing the relative strengths of the four forces. For example, note that within an atomic nucleus the strong force is about 100 times stronger than the electromagnetic force, enabling the strong force to hold nuclei together. Outside atomic nuclei, the strong and weak forces vanish, leaving only gravity and electromagnetism to be felt in our daily lives.

Given the weakness of gravity in comparison to the other forces, you might wonder why it is important at all. The answer is that the other forces are out of the picture when we deal with large masses. The strong and weak forces vanish beyond atomic nuclei. The electromagnetic force cancels itself out in large objects, because such objects contain virtually equal numbers of protons and electrons, making them electrically neutral and unresponsive to the electromagnetic force. In contrast, all the matter we know about has positive mass, so gravity never cancels itself out. Thus, gravity is the only force left to act between massive enough objects. That is why gravity dominates the universe on large scales.

### The Quest for Simplicity

The standard model involves four forces that mediate interactions between particles built from six types of quarks and six types of leptons, plus their corresponding antiparticles. It explains many experimental and observational results quite successfully; however, some scientists think that this model is still too complicated. They seek an even more basic theory of matter that reduces the number of forces and fundamental particles.

Theoretical work in the 1970s, verified experimentally in the 1980s, showed that the electromagnetic and weak forces are really just two different aspects of a single force, called the *electroweak force.* Many scientists hope that future discoveries will show three or even all four forces to be simply different aspects of a single, unified force governing *all*

---

[4]*Gravitons* is the name for the particles that correspond to gravitational waves in general relativity, analogous to the correspondence between photons and electromagnetic waves. Gravitons have not yet been detected.

interactions in nature. As we will see in Chapter 22, these *unified theories* might be necessary to understanding the goings-on during the first fraction of a second after the Big Bang.

## S4.3 The Uncertainty Principle

So far, we've used the word *particle* as if we were talking about tiny balls of matter. However, subatomic particles frequently act like waves, too. Unfortunately, our intuition is not accustomed to this dual wave–particle nature of subatomic particles. Nevertheless, we managed to invent the science of quantum mechanics, which enables us to determine with great accuracy the properties of matter.

Two fundamental laws that lie at the heart of quantum mechanics lead to most of its bizarre predictions. The first of these two laws is the **uncertainty principle**, discovered by Werner Heisenberg (1901–1976) in 1927. Here is one way of stating it:

*The more we know about where a particle is located, the less we can know about its momentum, and the more we know about its momentum, the less we can know about its position.*

We can illuminate the meaning of the uncertainty principle by considering how we might measure the trajectories of a baseball and an electron. In the case of a baseball, we could photograph it with a blinking strobe light. The resulting photograph shows us both where the ball was and where it was going at each moment in time (Figure S4.5). In scientific terms, knowing the path of the baseball means that we are measuring both its *location* and its *velocity* at each instant or, equivalently, its location and its *momentum*. (Recall that momentum is mass times velocity.)

Now imagine trying to observe an electron in the same way. We will detect the electron only if it manages to scatter some of the photons streaming by it. But whereas the photons are tiny particles of light compared to a baseball, they are quite large compared to the minuscule electron. The precision with which we can pinpoint the electron's location depends on the wavelengths of the photons. If we use visible light with a wavelength of 500 nanometers, we can measure the electron's location only to within 500 nanometers—which is about 5,000 *times* the size of a typical atom. That is, if we see a flash from a row of 5,000 atoms, we do not even know which atom contains the electron that caused the flash! To locate the electron more precisely, we must use

**FIGURE S4.5** A photograph of a ball taken with a blinking strobe light allows us to determine both where the ball was and where it was going at each moment in time.

shorter-wavelength light, such as ultraviolet or X rays. But now we encounter our next problem: To determine the electron's path, we must observe the flashes from its interactions with one photon after another. Yet each photon's energy delivers a "kick" that disturbs the electron, thereby changing the momentum that we are trying to measure. The higher the energy of the photon—which means the shorter its wavelength—the more it alters the electron's momentum.

It is almost as if nature is playing a perverse trick on us. Locating the electron precisely requires hitting it with a short-wavelength photon, but the high energy of this photon prevents us from determining the electron's momentum. Conversely, measuring the electron's momentum requires hitting it with a low-energy photon that will not disturb it much. Because low-energy light has long wavelengths, we'll no longer have a very good idea of where the electron is located.

**TIME OUT TO THINK** *Colloquially, we often express the uncertainty principle by saying that we can't know both where a particle is and where it is going. How does this statement relate to the more precise statement that we can't know both the particle's location and its momentum? In what ways is the colloquial statement accurate, and in what ways is it an oversimplification?*

The uncertainty principle applies to *all* particles, not just to electrons. In fact, it applies even to large

## Does God Play Dice?

Suppose we knew all the laws of nature and, at some particular moment in time, what every single particle in the universe was doing. Could we then predict the future of the universe for all time?

Until the twentieth century, nearly every philosopher would have answered yes. The idea was so pervasive that many philosophers concluded that God was like a watchmaker: God simply started up the universe, and the future was forever after determined. This idea that everything in the universe is predictable from its initial state is called *determinism*; a universe that runs predictably, like a watch, is called a *deterministic universe.*

The discovery of the uncertainty principle shattered the idea of a deterministic universe by telling us that, at best, we can only make statements about the *probability* of the precise future location of a subatomic particle. Because everything is made of subatomic particles, the uncertainty principle implies a degree of built-in randomness to the universe.

The idea that nature is governed by probability rather than certainty unsettled many people, including Einstein. Although he was well aware that the theories of quantum physics had survived many experimental tests, Einstein maintained a belief that the theories were incomplete. He believed that scientists would one day discover a deeper

level of nature at which uncertainty would be removed. To summarize his philosophical objections to uncertainty, Einstein said, "God does not play dice."

Einstein did more than simply object on philosophical grounds. He also proposed a number of thought experiments in which he showed that the uncertainty principle implied paradoxical results. Claiming that such paradoxes made no sense, he argued that the uncertainty principle must not be correct. In the years since Einstein's death in 1955, advances in technology have made performing some of Einstein's thought experiments possible. The results have proved to be just as paradoxical as Einstein claimed they would be. That is, the experiments have confirmed the uncertainty principle at the same time that they have posed apparent logical paradoxes.

What can we make of an idea, such as the uncertainty principle, that seems to violate common sense at the same time that it survives every experimental test? Under the tenets of science, experiment is the ultimate judge of theory, and we must accept the results despite philosophical objections. In a sense, Einstein's objection that "God does not play dice" reflected his beliefs about how the universe *should* behave. Niels Bohr argued instead that nature need not fit our preconceptions with his famous reply to Einstein: "Stop telling God what to do."

"particles" such as baseballs, but it is unnoticeable at this level. Consider what happens when we look at a baseball with visible light of 500-nanometer wavelength. Just as with the electron, we can locate any part of the baseball only to within 500 nanometers, but an uncertainty of 500 nanometers (about 0.00002 inch) is negligible in comparison to the size of the baseball. Moreover, the energy of visible light is so small compared to the energy of the baseball (including its mass-energy) that it has no noticeable effect on the baseball's momentum. That is why Newton's laws work perfectly well when we deal with the motion of baseballs, cars, planets, or other objects in the macroscopic world. (The prefix *macro* comes from the Greek word for "large," and the term *macroscopic* is used to contrast the large world of objects visible to the naked eye with the microscopic world visible only through microscopes.) But Newton's laws fail us in the microscopic quantum realm, where we must deal with the implications of the uncertainty principle.

### Wave–Particle Duality

Our thought experiment suggested that a particle such as an electron somehow "hides" its precise path from us. However, the uncertainty principle runs

deeper than this—it implies that the electron *does not even have* a precise path. From this point of view, the concepts of location and momentum do not exist independently for electrons in the way that they appear to exist for objects in everyday life. Instead of imagining the electron as following some complex but hidden path, we need to think of the electron as being "smeared out" over some volume of space [Section 4.3]. This "smearing out" of electrons and other particles holds the essence of the idea of wave–particle duality.

If we choose to regard the electron as a particle, we are imagining that we can locate it precisely by hitting it with a short-wavelength photon. In that case, we know the precise location of the electron at each instant but can never predict where it will be at the next instant. We see the electron in one place at one moment and in another place at another moment, but we have no idea how it passed through the regions in between. A mathematical description of quantum mechanics allows us to calculate the *probability* that we'll find the electron in any particular place at any particular time. For example, Figure S4.6 shows the probability patterns for the electron in several energy levels of hydrogen; the brighter the region on the diagram, the higher the probability of finding the electron at any particular instant. From the point of view of the electron as a particle, the "smeared out"

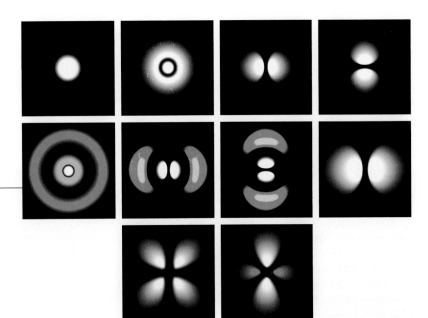

**FIGURE S4.6** Probability patterns for the electron in several energy levels of hydrogen.

## Mathematical Insight S4.1   Electron Waves in Atoms

In the text, we've said that an electron in an atom is "smeared out" over some volume of space. In fact, the physics is much more precise than this vague statement implies. If we choose to view the electron as a wave, an electron in an atom can be regarded as a *standing wave*. You are probably familiar with standing waves on a string that is anchored in place at its two ends, such as a violin string (Figure S4.7a). Such waves are called standing waves because each point on the string vibrates up and down, but the wave does not appear to move along the length of the string. Moreover, because the string is anchored at both ends, only wave patterns with a half-integer (e.g., 0, $\frac{1}{2}$, 1, $\frac{3}{2}$, 2) number of wavelengths along the string are possible. Other patterns, such as having three-fourths of a wavelength along the string (Figure S4.7b), are not possible without breaking one end of the string away from its anchor point.

An electron viewed as a standing wave is anchored by the electromagnetic force holding it in the atom. Like the waves on a string, only particular wave patterns are possible. However, these patterns are more complex than waves on a string because they are three-dimensional wave patterns. The allowed wave patterns for an electron in an atom can be calculated with the famous *Schrödinger equation*, developed by Erwin Schrödinger in 1926. These allowed wave patterns correspond directly to the allowed energies of the electron in the atom, and thus the Schrödinger equation enables scientists to predict what energies should be allowed in different atoms. The fact that the Schrödinger equation successfully predicts the energy levels that are measured in the laboratory (by analysis of spectral lines) is one of the great triumphs of quantum mechanics.

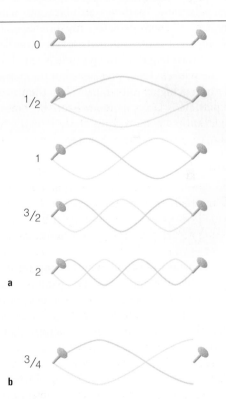

**FIGURE S4.7** (**a**) Standing waves on a string must have a half-integer number of wavelengths. (**b**) Any other number of wavelengths is not possible without breaking the string away from one of its anchors.

**FIGURE S4.8** A wave has a well-defined momentum (represented by the arrows) but not a single, precise location.

electron cloud around the hydrogen nucleus represents those places where we are most likely to find the electron at any instant.

Alternatively, we can choose to regard the electron as a wave. We can measure the momentum of a wave, such as that of a ripple moving across a pond, but we cannot say that a wave has a single, precise location (Figure S4.8). Instead, the wave is spread out over some region of the water in the same way that an electron is "smeared out" over some volume of space.

The fact that electrons exhibit both particle and wave properties demonstrates that our common sense from the macroscopic world does not translate well to the quantum world. We say that electrons, like photons of light, exhibit wave–particle duality. In fact, all subatomic "particles" exhibit wave–particle duality; we call them *particles* only for convenience. Like a photon of light, each particle has a wavelength.[5] When the wavelength of the particle is small, we can locate the particle fairly precisely, but the particle's momentum is highly uncertain. When the wavelength of the particle is large, its momentum becomes well defined, but its location grows fuzzy.

### Quantifying the Uncertainty Principle

We can quantify the uncertainty principle with a simple mathematical statement:

$$\frac{\text{uncertainty}}{\text{in location}} \times \frac{\text{uncertainty}}{\text{in momentum}} \approx \text{Planck's constant}$$

Planck's constant is a fundamental constant in nature rather like the gravitational constant ($G$) in Newton's law of gravity and the speed of light; its numerical value is $6.626 \times 10^{-34}$ joule $\times$ s. (Recall that Planck's constant appears in the formula for the energy of a photon [Section 6.2].)

---

[5]Electrons usually have very small wavelengths and therefore can be used to locate other particles with high precision. This is the principle behind *electron microscopes,* in which short-wavelength electrons are used to study microscopic objects. Whereas the resolution of visible-light microscopes is limited to the roughly 500-nanometer wavelength of visible light, electron microscopes can achieve resolutions of less than 0.1 nanometer.

This formula quantifies what we have already learned: Because the product of the uncertainties is roughly constant, when one uncertainty (either location or momentum) goes down, the other must go up. For example, if we determine the location of an electron with a particular amount of uncertainty, such as to within 500 nanometers, we can use the formula to calculate the amount of uncertainty in the electron's momentum. Note that the numerical value of Planck's constant is quite small, which explains why uncertainties are scarcely noticeable for macroscopic objects.

A second way of writing the uncertainty principle is mathematically equivalent but leads to additional insights. Instead of expressing the uncertainty principle in terms of location and momentum, this alternative version expresses it in terms of the amount of *energy* that a particle has and *when* it has this energy. This version reads:

$$\frac{\text{uncertainty}}{\text{in energy}} \times \frac{\text{uncertainty}}{\text{in time}} \approx \text{Planck's constant}$$

An amusing way to gain further appreciation for the uncertainty principle in both its forms is to imagine a game of "quantum baseball." Suppose a quantum pitcher is pitching an electron that you try to hit with your quantum bat. You'll find it extremely difficult! With the first version of the uncertainty principle, the problem is that you'll never know both where the electron is and where it is headed next. You might see it right in front of you, but because you don't know which direction it's going, you can't know whether to swing straight, up, down, or sideways. With the second version of the uncertainty principle, your problem is that you might know the electron's energy, which tells you how hard you need to swing, but you'll never know *when* to swing. Either way, your chances of hitting the electron are completely random, governed by probabilities that can be calculated with quantum mechanics.

**TIME OUT TO THINK** *Explain why real baseball players don't have the same problems that would arise with quantum baseball. (Hint: How do the quantum uncertainties compare to the size of a real baseball and a real bat?)*

## S4.4 The Exclusion Principle

The uncertainty principle is the first of the two fundamental laws that lie at the heart of quantum mechanics. The second fundamental law, called the **exclusion principle**, was discovered by Wolfgang Pauli (1900–1958) in 1925. In its simplest sense, the exclusion principle says that two particles cannot be in the same place at the same time. (It applies only to fermions, not to bosons.) A more complete understanding of the exclusion principle requires investigating the properties of particles a little more deeply.

### The Quantum State of a Particle

Scientists use the term *state* to describe the current conditions of an object. For example, if you are relaxing in a chair, a scientist might say that you are in a "state of rest." A more precise description of your state in the chair might be something like "Your current state is a velocity of zero (at rest), a heart rate of 65 beats per minute, a breathing rate of 12 breaths per minute, a body temperature of 37°C, a metabolic rate of 200 Calories per hour," and so on.

**TIME OUT TO THINK** *Suppose you have the following information about the current state of a friend: velocity of 5 km/hr, heart rate of 160 beats per minute, metabolic rate of 1,200 Calories per hour. Which of the following is your friend most likely doing: walking slowly as she reads a book, driving in her car, riding a bicycle down a hill, or swimming at a hard pace? How do you know?*

Completely describing a person's state is quite complicated. Fortunately, describing the state of a subatomic particle such as an electron, proton, or neutron is much easier. In general, a complete description of the state of a subatomic particle—called its **quantum state**—specifies only its location, momentum, orbital angular momentum, and spin to the extent allowed by the uncertainty principle. Like the energy of an electron in an atom, each property that describes a particle's quantum state is *quantized*, meaning that it can take on only particular values and not other values in between.

### Statement and Meaning of the Exclusion Principle

Above we described the exclusion principle in simple terms by saying that two particles cannot be in the same place at the same time. Now let us state the exclusion principle more precisely:

*Two fermions of the same type cannot occupy the same quantum state at the same time.*

This principle has many important implications. One of the most important is in chemistry, where it dictates how electrons occupy their various states in atoms. For example, an electron occupying the lowest energy level in an atom necessarily has a particular amount of orbital angular momentum and a restricted range of locations. The electron's energy level fully determines its quantum state, except for its spin. Because electrons have only two possible spin states, up or down, only two electrons can occupy the lowest energy level (Figure S4.9). If you tried to put a third electron into the lowest energy level, it would have the same spin—and hence the same quantum state—as one of the two electrons already there. The exclusion principle won't allow that, so the third electron must go into a higher energy level. If you take a course in chemistry, you'll learn how a similar analysis of higher energy levels explains the chemical properties of all the elements, including their arrangement in the periodic table of the elements (see Appendix B).

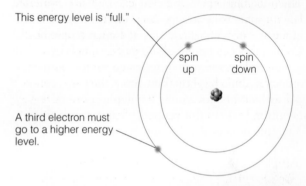

**FIGURE S4.9** Only two electrons, one with spin up and the other with spin down, can share a single energy level in an atom.

This energy level is "full."

spin up    spin down

A third electron must go to a higher energy level.

The uncertainty principle and the exclusion principle together determine the sizes of atoms and of everything made of atoms, including your own body. The uncertainty principle ensures that electrons cannot be packed into infinitesimally tiny spaces. If you tried to confine an electron in too small a space in an atom, its momentum would become so large that the electromagnetic attraction of the nucleus could no longer retain it. The exclusion principle ensures that each electron has to have its own space. Thus, despite the fact that atoms are almost entirely empty, the two fundamental laws of quantum mechanics explain the solidity of matter. In the words of physicist Richard Feynman (1918–1988), "It is the fact that electrons cannot all get on top of each other that makes tables and everything else solid."

The exclusion and uncertainty principles also govern the behavior of tightly grouped protons, neutrons, and all other kinds of fermions. Just as these principles give atoms their size, they also determine the size of nuclei, because they limit how closely protons and neutrons can pack together. As we will see shortly, these quantum effects can even influence the lives of stars.

Before we go on to discuss some astronomical implications of the quantum laws, it's worth noting that photons and other bosons do *not* obey the exclusion principle. For example, laser beams are so intense because many photons *can* be in the same state at the same time. In addition, it is possible under special conditions for two or more fermions to act together like a single boson. Such conditions lead to some amazing behavior, including *superconductivity*, in which electricity flows without any resistance, and *superfluidity*, in which extremely cold liquids can "creep" up the walls of a container. Many popular books on quantum laws explain these phenomena in more detail.

## S4.5 Key Quantum Effects in Astronomy

The uncertainty principle and the exclusion principle lead to some truly strange consequences in the sub-atomic realm. Amazingly, this odd microscopic behavior produces important effects on much larger scales. In fact, we cannot fully understand how stars are born, shine brightly throughout their lives, and die without understanding the implications of the quantum laws. In this section, we investigate three quantum effects of great importance in astronomy: degeneracy pressure, quantum tunneling, and virtual particles.

### Degeneracy Pressure

Under ordinary conditions in gases, pressure and temperature are closely related. For example, suppose we inflate a balloon, filling it with air molecules. The individual molecules zip around inside the balloon, continually bouncing off its walls (Figure S4.10).

The force of these molecules striking the walls of the balloon creates **thermal pressure**, which keeps the balloon inflated. If we cool the balloon by, say, putting it in a freezer, the molecules slow down. Slowing the molecules reduces the force with which they strike the walls, reducing the thermal pressure and shrinking the balloon. Heating the balloon speeds up the molecules, raising the thermal pressure and causing the balloon to expand. (Thus, thermal pressure gets its name because it depends on temperature.)

Thermal pressure is the dominant type of pressure at low to moderate densities. However, quantum effects produce an entirely different type of pressure under conditions of extremely high density, one that does not depend on temperature at all. Consider what happens when we compress a *plasma*, a mixture of positively charged ions and free electrons [Section 4.3]. At first, the energy we expend in crushing the plasma makes the electrons and protons move faster and faster, increasing the pressure and the temperature. Now suppose we let the plasma cool off for a while. As the plasma cools, its pressure drops, enabling us to compress it further. Continuing this process of cooling and compression, we can squeeze the plasma down to a very dense state. However, we cannot continue this process indefinitely. According to the exclusion principle, no two electrons can have exactly the same position, momentum, and spin. Just as in an atom, all the electrons can't get on top of one another at once. The compression must stop at some point, no matter how cold the plasma. This resistance to compression, stemming from the exclusion principle, is what we call **degeneracy pressure**.

The following analogy might help you visualize how degeneracy pressure works. Imagine a small number of people in an auditorium filled with folding chairs. Each person can move freely about and sit in any empty chair. The chairs represent available quan-

**FIGURE S4.10** Higher temperature means higher thermal pressure, so a balloon expands. Lower temperature means lower thermal pressure, so the balloon contracts. The dots represent molecules in the balloon, and the lengths of the arrows represent the speeds of the molecules.

**a** When there are many more available quantum states (chairs) than electrons (people), an electron is unlikely to try to enter the same state as another electron. The only pressure comes from the temperature-related motion of the electrons, which is the thermal pressure.

**b** When the number of electrons (people) approaches the number of available quantum states (chairs), finding an available state requires that the electrons move faster than they would otherwise. This extra motion creates degeneracy pressure.

**FIGURE S4.11** The auditorium analogy to degeneracy pressure. Chairs represent available quantum states, and people moving from chair to chair represent electrons.

---

tum states, the people represent electrons darting from place to place, and their motions represent thermal pressure as the electrons move from one quantum state to the next. The exclusion principle corresponds to the rule that two people cannot sit in the same chair at the same time. As long as the chairs greatly outnumber the people, two people will rarely fight over the same chair (Figure S4.11a).

Suppose that ushers begin removing chairs from the front of the auditorium (compression), gradually forcing people to move to the back. Soon everyone has to crowd toward the back of the auditorium, where the number of remaining chairs is just slightly larger than the number of people. Now when a person moves to a particular chair, there's a good chance that it's already occupied. Ultimately, when the number of people equals the number of chairs, people can still move from place to place, but only if they swap seats with somebody else (Figure S4.11b). The ushers can't take away any more chairs, and the compression must stop. In other words, all the available states are filled.

The uncertainty principle also influences degeneracy pressure, though in a way that does not perfectly fit this analogy. In a highly compressed plasma, the available space for each electron is very small, so the electrons' positions must be precisely defined. According to the uncertainty principle, their momentum must then be extremely uncertain, which means that the electrons must be moving very fast on average. This requirement that highly compressed electrons have to move quickly holds *even if the object is cold.*[6] This quantum-mechanical trade-off between position and momentum is at the root of degeneracy pressure. If you want to compress lots of electrons into a tiny space, you need to exert an enormous force to rein in their momentum.

---

[6]In this sense, an object is *cold* if there's no way to get heat from it. Consider a plasma in which all the available momentum states are filled up to a certain level. To extract heat from the plasma, you'd have to slow down some of its particles. But that means moving them to lower-momentum states, which are already taken. The exclusion principle thus prevents any energy from escaping, so the plasma is cold even though the electrons may be moving at high speeds.

Degeneracy pressure caused by the crowding of electrons, or **electron degeneracy pressure**, affects the lives of stars in several different ways. In some cases, it can prevent a collapsing cloud of gas from becoming a star in the first place, creating what is called a *brown dwarf* [Section 16.2]. In stars like the Sun, it determines how they begin burning helium near the end of their lives [Section 16.3]. When stars die, most leave behind an extremely dense stellar corpse called a *white dwarf,* which is also supported by electron degeneracy pressure [Section 17.2].

Not all stars meet this fate, because electron degeneracy pressure cannot grow infinitely strong. Under extreme compression, the average speed of the electrons begins to approach the speed of light. Nothing can go faster than the speed of light, so we eventually reach a limit to how much degeneracy pressure the electrons can exert. Once a dying star reaches that limit, electron degeneracy pressure cannot prevent it from shrinking further. The star then collapses until it becomes a ball of neutrons, called a *neutron star* [Section 17.3]. Neutron stars support themselves through **neutron degeneracy pressure**, which is just like electron degeneracy pressure except that it is caused by neutrons and occurs at much higher densities. (Neutron degeneracy pressure comes into play only at much higher densities, because neutrons have much greater mass than electrons. A neutron near the speed of light possesses over 1,800 times more momentum than an electron at the same speed. Thus, the positions of neutrons can be over 1,800 times more precise, enabling them to occupy a much smaller volume of space.)

Neutron degeneracy pressure cannot grow infinitely strong either. It begins to fail when the speed of the neutrons approaches the speed of light. According to our present understanding, nothing can stop the collapse of an object once its gravity overcomes neutron degeneracy pressure. Such an object collapses indefinitely, becoming the mysterious type of structure in spacetime that we call a *black hole.*

### Quantum Tunneling

The next quantum effect we'll investigate arises from the uncertainty principle and has important implications not only in astronomy, but also in modern technology. Imagine that, as an unfortunate result of a case of mistaken identity, you're sitting on a bench in a locked jail cell (Figure S4.12a). Another bench is on the other side of the cell wall. If you could magically transport yourself from the bench on the inside to the bench on the outside, you'd be free. Alas, no such magic ever occurs for humans.

But what if you were an electron? In that case, the uncertainty principle would prevent us from pre-

**FIGURE S4.12** (**a**) A person is confined to the bench inside the jail cell, even though it would take no more energy to sit on the outside bench. (**b**) If you were an electron, you could "magically" become free through the process of quantum tunneling.

dicting your precise location. At best, we could state only the probability of your being in various locations. While the probability that you remain in your cell might be greatest, there is always some small probability that you will be found outside your cell. With a bit of luck, you might suddenly find yourself free, thanks to the uncertainty principle (Figure S4.12b). This process, in which an electron or any other subatomic particle "magically" goes through a wall-like barrier, is called **quantum tunneling**.

We can gain a deeper understanding of quantum tunneling by thinking in terms of the *energy* needed to cross a barrier. If you are sitting in a jail cell, the barrier is the wall of the cell. The reason you cannot escape the cell is that you don't have enough energy to crash through the wall. Just as the cell wall keeps you imprisoned, a barrier of electromagnetic repulsion can imprison an electron that does not have enough energy to crash through it. However, recall that we can write the uncertainty principle in the following form:

$$\frac{\text{uncertainty}}{\text{in energy}} \times \frac{\text{uncertainty}}{\text{in time}} \approx \text{Planck's constant}$$

Because of the uncertainty inherent in energy, there is always *some* chance that the electron will have more energy than we think at a particular moment, allowing it to cross the barrier anyway. From this point of view, quantum tunneling comes about because of uncertainty in energy rather than uncertainty in location.

Both points of view on quantum tunneling are equivalent, but the latter viewpoint illustrates a rather remarkable "loophole" in the law of conservation of energy. To cross the barrier, the particle must briefly gain some excess energy. Thanks to the uncertainty principle, this "stolen" energy need not come from anywhere as long as the particle returns it within a time period *shorter* than the uncertainty in time. In that case, we cannot be certain that any energy was ever missing! It's like stealing a dollar and putting it right back before anyone notices, so that no harm is done—except that the particle uses the stolen energy to cross the barrier before returning it.

This tale of phantom quantum energy thefts may sound utterly ridiculous at first, but the process of quantum tunneling is readily observed, and it is extremely important. In fact, the "microchips" used in all modern computers and many other modern electronic devices work because of quantum tunneling by electrons. We can control the rate of quantum tunneling, and hence the electric current, by adjusting the "height" of the energy barrier. The higher the energy barrier, the less likely it is that particles will tunnel through it.

Even more amazingly, our universe would look much different were it not for quantum tunneling. The nuclear fusion reactions that power stars occur when atomic nuclei smash together so hard that they stick. However, nuclei tend to repel each other, because they are positively charged (they contain only positive protons and neutral neutrons) and like charges repel. This repulsion creates an electromagnetic barrier that prevents nuclear fusion under most conditions. Inside the electromagnetic barrier, the attraction of the strong force takes over. But, even at the high temperatures inside stars, atomic nuclei don't have enough energy to crash through the electromagnetic barrier. Instead, they rely on quantum tunneling to sneak through to the region where the strong force dominates. In other words, quantum tunneling is what makes nuclear fusion possible in stars like our Sun. (Quantum tunneling is not as crucial to fusion in stars with core temperatures much higher than the Sun's.)

### Virtual Particles

Now we investigate the third quantum effect of importance to astronomy. The same "loophole" in the law of conservation of energy that allows particles to tunnel through otherwise impenetrable barriers permits even bigger crimes. Entire particles can "pop" into existence from nowhere—their mass made from stolen energy—as long as they "pop" back out of existence before anyone can verify that they ever existed. A somewhat fanciful analogy will help us understand this bizarre concept.

Imagine that the law of conservation of energy is enforced by a "great cosmic accountant." (In reality, of course, the law is enforced naturally.) Further, imagine that the cosmic accountant keeps a storehouse of energy in a large bank vault and ensures that anytime something borrows some energy it returns the energy in a precisely equal amount. A particle that pops into existence is like a bank robber who steals some energy from the vault. If the particle is caught by the cosmic accountant, someone will have to pay for the stolen energy. However, the particle won't be caught as long as it pops back out of existence quickly enough, returning the stolen energy. The length of time the particle is allowed to exist is so short that the uncertainty principle prevents anyone from knowing that energy is missing.

Particles that pop in and out of existence before anyone can possibly detect them are called **virtual particles**. Although these particles are undetectable themselves, quantum theories predict that virtual particles should exert real, measurable effects on those particles we can detect. Remarkably, many of these predictions have been verified experimentally. In fact, modern theories of the universe propose that empty space—what we call a *vacuum*—actually "bubbles" with virtual particles that pop rapidly in and out of existence.

**TIME OUT TO THINK** *Imagine that you write a check for $100, but you have no money in your checking account. Your check is not necessarily doomed to bounce—as long as you deposit the needed $100 before the check clears. Explain how this $100 of "virtual money" is similar in concept to virtual particles.*

Astronomically speaking, the most important process involving virtual particles concerns black holes. We can understand the process by extending our analogy to the case of a virtual electron popping into existence near a black hole. The virtual electron cannot pop into existence alone; it must be accompanied by a virtual positron (an antielectron) so that electric charge is conserved. The virtual electron–positron pair must return the stolen energy before being caught by our imaginary "great cosmic accountant," and they do so by annihilating each other (Figure S4.13a). But suppose a virtual electron–positron pair appears very close to, but outside of, the event horizon of a black hole. The electron and positron are supposed to annihilate each other quickly, but a terrible problem comes up: One of the particles crosses the event horizon during its brief, virtual existence (Figure S4.13b). From the perspective of

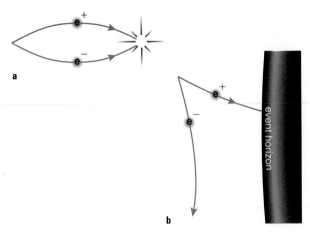

**a**

**b**

event horizon

**FIGURE S4.13** (**a**) Pairs of virtual electrons and positrons can pop into existence, as long as they annihilate each other before they can be detected. (**b**) Near the event horizon of a black hole, one member of a virtual pair may cross the event horizon; the other particle is then left with no partner and cannot annihilate itself.

our cosmic accountant, this virtual particle was never accounted for in the first place, so there's no problem with the fact that it will never be seen again. But the other particle is suddenly caught like a deer in the headlights. Without its virtual mate, it has no way to annihilate itself, and it is caught red-handed by the great cosmic accountant.

If we strip away the fanciful imagery of a cosmic accountant, the end result is the creation of *real* particles, not virtual ones, just outside the event horizon of a black hole. Note that nothing escapes from in-

side the black hole. Rather, these real particles are created from the gravitational potential energy of the black hole. Around the black hole, these real electrons and positrons annihilate each other, producing real photons that are radiated into space. To an outside observer, the black hole would appear to be radiating, even though nothing ever escapes from inside it. This effect was first predicted by Stephen Hawking in the 1970s and is therefore called **Hawking radiation**. As we've just seen, the ultimate source of Hawking radiation is the gravitational potential energy of the black hole. The continual emission of Hawking radiation causes the black hole to shrink slowly in mass, or *evaporate,* over very long periods of time.

The idea that black holes can evaporate remains untested, but if it is true it may have profound implications for both the origin and the fate of the universe. Some scientists speculate that black holes of all sizes might have been created during the Big Bang. If so, some of the smaller ones should be evaporating today. The fact that we have not yet detected any such evaporation sets limits on the number of small black holes that might have formed in the Big Bang. At the other end of time, if the universe continues to expand forever, black holes may be the last large masses left after all the stars have died. In that case, the slow evaporation caused by Hawking radiation will mean that even black holes cannot last forever, and the universe eventually will contain nothing but a fog of photons and subatomic particles, separated from one another by incredible distances as the universe continues to grow in size.

## THE BIG PICTURE

In this chapter, we have studied the quantum revolution and its astronomical consequences. As you look back, keep in mind the following "big picture" ideas:

- The quantum revolution is arguably the third great revolution in our understanding of the universe. The first was the Copernican revolution, which demolished the ancient belief in an Earth-centered universe. The second was relativity, which radically revised our ideas about space, time, and gravity. The quantum revolution has changed our ideas about the fundamental nature of matter and energy.

- Strange as the laws of quantum mechanics may seem, they can be readily tested and confirmed through observation and experiment. The quantum laws, like relativity, now stand on very solid ground. So far, they have passed every experimental test devised for them.

- The tiny quantum realm may seem remote from the large scales we are accustomed to in astronomy, but it is exceedingly important. The laws of quantum mechanics are necessary for understanding many astronomical processes, including nuclear fusion in the Sun, the degeneracy pressure that supports stellar corpses, and the possible evaporation of black holes.

### Review Questions

1. What do we mean by the quantum realm? What is *quantum mechanics*?

2. List five major ideas that come directly from the laws of quantum mechanics.

3. What do we mean by *fundamental particles*? How do we investigate fundamental particles in *particle accelerators*?

4. What is *spin*? What are the two basic categories of particles based on spin?

5. What are *quarks* and *leptons*? Explain why we say that quarks and leptons are subsets of the *fermions*.

6. List the six quarks and six leptons in the standard model. Describe the quark composition of a proton and of a neutron.

7. What are neutrinos? Why might they turn out to be important to the fate of the universe?

8. What is *antimatter*? How does a positron differ from an electron? What happens when a particle and its antiparticle meet?

9. How is antimatter produced, and why is it always produced along with matter in *pair production*?

10. List the four basic forces in nature and the *exchange particles* for each.

11. The *strong force* and the *weak force* are sometimes called nuclear forces. Why?

12. Why do many scientists believe that the standard model will eventually be replaced by a simpler model of nature?

13. What is the *uncertainty principle*? How is it related to the idea of wave–particle duality?

14. Describe two ways of quantifying the uncertainty principle, and give an example showing the meaning of each.

15. What do we mean by the *quantum state* of a particle?

16. What is the *exclusion principle*? What types of particles obey it? Briefly explain how the exclusion principle determines how electrons fill energy levels in atoms.

17. What is *degeneracy pressure*? How does it differ from *thermal pressure*? Describe the auditorium analogy for degeneracy pressure.

18. Explain why the uncertainty principle implies that the particles in a highly compressed plasma must move at very high speeds. How does this fact explain why there is a limit to the strength of degeneracy pressure? Why is this limit higher for *neutron degeneracy pressure* than for *electron degeneracy pressure*?

19. What is *quantum tunneling*? How is it important to modern electronics? How is it important to nuclear fusion in the Sun?

20. What do we mean by *virtual particles*? Briefly explain how the concept of virtual particles suggests that black holes may be able to evaporate through *Hawking radiation*.

### Discussion Questions

1. *Common Sense Versus Experiment.* Even the most highly trained physicists find the results of quantum mechanics to be strange and counter to our everyday common sense. Yet the predictions of quantum mechanics have passed every experimental test yet posed for them. Discuss whether it is important to reconcile our common sense with experimental results and, if so, how we can do it.

2. *The Meaning of the Uncertainty Principle.* When first hearing about it, many people assume that the uncertainty principle means that we cannot *measure* the position and momentum of a particle precisely. But, according to current understanding, it really tells us that the particle *does not have* a precise position and momentum in the sense that we would expect from everyday life. How do these two viewpoints differ? Discuss the different philosophical consequences of these two viewpoints.

3. *Antimatter Engines.* In the *Star Trek* series, starships are powered by matter–antimatter annihilation. Explain why matter–antimatter annihilation is the most efficient possible source of power. What practical problems would we face in developing matter–antimatter engines?

## Problems

1. *The Strong Force.* The strong nuclear force is the force that holds the protons and neutrons in the nucleus together. Based on the fact that atomic nuclei can be stable, briefly explain how you can conclude that the strong force must be even stronger than the electromagnetic force, at least over very short distances.

2. *Chemistry and Biology Are Electromagnetic.* All chemical and biological reactions involve the creation and breaking of chemical bonds, which are bonds between the electrons of one atom and the electrons of others. Given this fact, explain why the electromagnetic force governs all chemical and biological reactions. Also explain why the strong force, the weak force, and gravity play no role in these reactions.

3. *Why Does Gravity Dominate on Large Scales?* As shown in Table S4.2, the electromagnetic force between two charged particles is much greater than the strength of gravity between them, no matter how far apart they are. Nevertheless, it is *gravity*, rather than the electromagnetic force, that dominates the universe on large scales. Briefly explain why.

4. *Quantum Tunneling and Life.* In one or two paragraphs, explain the role of quantum tunneling in creating the elements from which we are made. (*Hint:* Recall that we are *star stuff* in the sense that the elements of our bodies were produced by nuclear fusion inside stars.)

*5. *Comparing Gravity and the EM Force.* In this problem, we compare the strength of gravity to the strength of the electromagnetic (EM) force for two interacting electrons. Because both electrons are negatively charged, they will want to *repel* each other according to the EM force; because electrons have

mass, they will want to *attract* each other according to gravity. Let's see which effect will dominate. You will need the following information for this problem:

- The force law for gravitation is:

$$F_g = G\frac{M_1 M_2}{d^2} \quad \left(G = 6.67 \times 10^{-11}\ \frac{\text{N} \times \text{m}^2}{\text{kg}^2}\right)$$

  where $M_1$ and $M_2$ are the masses of the two objects, $d$ is the distance between them, and $G$ is the gravitational constant. ("N" is the abbreviation for *newton*, the metric unit of force.)

- The force law for electromagnetism is:

$$F_{EM} = k\frac{q_1 q_2}{d^2} \quad \left(k = 9.0 \times 10^9\ \frac{\text{N} \times \text{m}^2}{\text{Coul}^2}\right)$$

  where $q_1$ and $q_2$ are the *charges* of the two objects (in *Coulombs*, the standard unit of charge), $d$ is the distance between them, and $k$ is a constant. ("Coul" is an abbreviation for *Coulomb*.)

- The *mass* of an electron is $9.10 \times 10^{-31}$ kg.

- The *charge* of an electron is $-1.6 \times 10^{-19}$ Coul.

  a. Calculate the gravitational force, in *newtons*, that attracts the two electrons if they are separated by a distance of $10^{-10}$ meter (about the size of an atom).

  b. Calculate the electromagnetic force, in *newtons*, that repels the two electrons.

  c. How many times stronger is the electromagnetic repulsion than the gravitational attraction for the two electrons?

*6. *Evaporation of Black Holes.* The time it takes for a black hole to evaporate through the process of Hawking radiation can be calculated using the following formula, in which $M$ is the mass of the black hole in kilograms and $t$ is the lifetime of the black hole in seconds:

$$t = 10{,}240\,\pi^2\,\frac{G^2 M^2}{hc^4} \quad \left(h = 6.63 \times 10^{-34}\ \frac{\text{kg} \times \text{m}^2}{\text{s}};\right.$$
$$\left.G = 6.67 \times 10^{-11}\ \frac{\text{m}^3}{\text{kg} \times \text{s}^2}\right)$$

  a. Without doing any calculations, explain how this formula implies that lower-mass black holes have much shorter lifetimes than more massive ones and that the evaporation process accelerates as a black hole loses mass.

  b. What is the lifetime of a black hole with the mass of the Sun ($M_{Sun} = 2.0 \times 10^{30}$ kg)? How does this compare to the current age of the universe?

  c. In Chapter 22, we will see that some scientists speculate that the universe will eventually consist only of gigantic black holes and scattered subatomic particles. The largest black holes that conceivably might form would have a mass of about a trillion ($10^{12}$) Suns. Calculate the lifetime of such a giant black hole. (*Hint:* Your calculator probably will be unable to handle the large numbers involved in this problem; you will need to rearrange the numbers so that you can calculate the powers of 10 without your calculator.)

*7. *Mini–Black Holes.* Some scientists speculate that black holes of many different masses might have been formed during the early moments of the Big Bang. Some of these black holes might be mini–black holes, much smaller in mass than those that can be formed by the crush of gravity in today's universe.

   a. Calculate the lifetime of a mini–black hole with the mass of the Earth (about $6 \times 10^{24}$ kg). Compare this to the current age of the universe.

   b. Calculate the mass of a black hole that might have formed in the Big Bang and be completing the evaporation today. Compare this to the mass of the Earth. For this calculation, assume that the universe is 12 billion years old.

## Web Projects

Find useful links for Web projects on the text Web site.

1. *Fermilab and CERN.* Visit the Web site for either the Fermilab or CERN particle accelerator. Take a virtual tour, and learn about the work at the laboratory. Write a short report about what you learn.

2. *The Higgs Particle.* Learn about how the so-called Higgs particle fits into the standard model and how physicists are searching for it. Write a short summary of your findings, including your opinion as to when we are likely to acquire evidence in support of (or against) the existence of the Higgs particle.

3. *Quantum Computing.* Learn how computer scientists hope to harness quantum effects to build computers much more powerful than any existing today. Briefly summarize the ideas, and write an essay stating your opinion concerning the benefits and drawbacks of developing this technology.

# PART V
# Stellar Alchemy

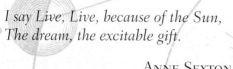

*I say Live, Live, because of the Sun,*
*The dream, the excitable gift.*

ANNE SEXTON (1928–1974)

# CHAPTER 14

# Our Star

Today, astronomy involves the study of the entire universe, but the root of the word *astronomy* originally came from the Greek word for "star." Although we have learned a lot about the universe up to this point in the book, only now do we turn our attention to the study of the stars, the namesakes of our subject.

When we think of stars, we usually think of the beautiful points of light visible on a clear night. But the nearest and most easily studied star is visible only in the daytime—our Sun. Of course, the Sun is important to us in many more ways than as an object for astronomical study. The Sun is the source of virtually all light, heat, and energy reaching the Earth, and life on Earth's surface could not survive without it.

In this chapter, we will study the Sun in some depth. We will learn how the Sun makes life possible on Earth. Equally important, we will study our Sun as a star, so that in subsequent chapters we can more easily understand stars throughout the universe.

## 14.1 Why Does the Sun Shine?

Ancient peoples recognized the vital role of the Sun in their lives. Some worshiped the Sun as a god, and others created elaborate mythologies to explain its daily rise and set. Only recently, however, have we learned how the Sun provides us with light and heat.

Most ancient thinkers viewed the Sun as some type of fire, perhaps a lump of burning coal or wood. The Greek philosopher Anaxagoras (c. 500–428 B.C.) imagined the Sun to be a very hot, glowing rock about the size of the Greek peninsula of Peloponnesus (comparable in size to Massachusetts), making him one of the first people in history to believe that the heavens and the Earth are made from the same types of materials.

By the mid-1800s, the size and distance of the Sun were reasonably well known, and scientists seriously began to address the question of how the Sun shines. Two early ideas held either that the Sun was a cooling ember that had once been much hotter or that the Sun generated energy from some type of chemical burning similar to the burning of coal or wood. Although simple calculations showed that a cooling or chemically burning Sun could shine for a few thousand years—an age that squared well with biblically based estimates of the age of the Earth that were popular at the time—these ideas suffered from fatal flaws. If the Sun were a cooling ember, it would have been much hotter just a few hundred years earlier, making it too hot for civilization to have existed. Chemical burning was ruled out because it cannot generate enough energy to account for the rate of radiation observed from the Sun's surface.

A more plausible hypothesis of the late 1800s suggested that the Sun generates energy by contracting in size, a process called **gravitational contraction**. If the Sun were shrinking, it would constantly be converting gravitational potential energy into thermal energy, thereby keeping the Sun hot. Because of its large mass, the Sun would need to contract only very slightly each year to maintain its temperature—so slightly that it would be unnoticeable. Calculations showed that the Sun could shine for up to about 25 million years generating energy by gravitational contraction. However, geologists of the late 1800s had already established the age of the Earth to be far older than 25 million years, leaving astronomers in an embarrassing position.

Only after Einstein published his special theory of relativity, which included his discovery of $E = mc^2$, did the true energy-generation mechanism of the Sun become clear. We now know that the Sun generates energy by *nuclear fusion*, a source so efficient that the Sun can shine for about 10 billion years. Because the Sun is only 4.6 billion years old today [Section 8.6], we expect it to keep shining for some 5 billion years to come.

**FIGURE 14.1** An acrobat stack is in gravitational equilibrium: The lowest person supports the most weight and feels the greatest pressure, and the overlying weight and underlying pressure decrease for those higher up.

Our current model of solar-energy generation by nuclear fusion means that the Sun's size is generally stable, maintained by a balance between the competing forces of gravity pulling inward and pressure pushing outward. This balance is called **gravitational equilibrium** (also referred to as *hydrostatic equilibrium*). It means that, at any point within the Sun, the weight of overlying material is supported by the underlying pressure. A stack of acrobats provides a simple example of this balance (Figure 14.1). The bottom person supports the weight of everybody above him, so the pressure on his body is very great. At each higher level, the overlying weight is less, so the pressure decreases. Gravitational equilibrium in the Sun means that the pressure increases with depth, making the Sun extremely hot and dense in its central core (Figure 14.2).

**TIME OUT TO THINK** *The Earth's atmosphere is also in gravitational equilibrium, with the weight of upper layers supported by the pressure in lower layers. Use this idea to explain why the air gets thinner at higher altitudes.*

Interestingly, while gravitational contraction is not an important energy-generation mechanism in the

**FIGURE 14.2** Gravitational equilibrium in the Sun: At each point inside, the pressure pushing outward balances the weight of the overlying layers.

Sun today, it was important in the distant past and will be important again in the distant future. Our Sun was born from a collapsing cloud of interstellar gas. The contraction of the cloud released gravitational potential energy, raising the interior temperature higher and higher. When the central temperature and density reached the values necessary to sustain nuclear fusion, the newly released energy provided enough pressure to halt the collapse. That is, the onset of fusion brought the Sun into gravitational equilibrium. About 5 billion years from now, when the Sun finally exhausts its nuclear fuel, the internal pressure will drop, and gravitational contraction will begin once again. As we will see later, some of the most important and spectacular processes in astronomy hinge on this ongoing "battle" between the crush of gravity and a star's internal sources of pressure.

Thus, the answer to the question "Why does the Sun shine?" is that about 4.6 billion years ago *gravitational contraction* made the Sun hot enough to sustain nuclear fusion in its core. Ever since, energy liberated by fusion has maintained the Sun's *gravitational equilibrium* and kept the Sun shining steadily, supplying the light and heat that sustain life on Earth.

## 14.2 Plunging to the Center of the Sun: An Imaginary Journey

In the rest of this chapter, we will discuss in detail how the Sun produces energy and how that energy travels to Earth. But first, to get a "big picture" view of the Sun, let's imagine you have a spaceship that can somehow withstand the immense heat and pres-

sure of the solar interior and take an imaginary journey from Earth to the center of the Sun.

As you begin your voyage from Earth, the Sun appears as a whitish ball of glowing gas. With spectroscopy [Section 7.3], you verify that the Sun's mass is 70% hydrogen and 28% helium. Heavier elements make up the remaining 2%. The total power output of the Sun, called its **luminosity**, is an incredible $3.8 \times 10^{26}$ watts. That is, every second, the Sun radiates a total of $3.8 \times 10^{26}$ joules of energy into space (recall that 1 watt = 1 joule/s). If we could somehow capture and store just 1 second's worth of the Sun's luminosity, it would be enough to meet current human energy demands for roughly the next 500,000 years! Of course, only a tiny fraction of the Sun's total energy output reaches Earth, with the rest dispersing in all directions into space. Most of this energy is radiated in the form of visible light, but once you leave the protective blanket of the Earth's atmosphere you'll encounter significant amounts of other types of solar radiation, including dangerous ultraviolet and X rays. You'll need substantial shielding on your spaceship to prevent serious radiation burns from these high-energy forms of light.

Through a telescope, you can see that the Sun seethes with churning gases, and at most times you'll see at least a few **sunspots** blotching its surface (Figure 14.3). If you focus your telescope solely on a sunspot, you'll find that it is blindingly bright; sunspots appear dark only in contrast to the even brighter solar surface that surrounds them. A typical sunspot is large enough to swallow the entire Earth, dramatically illustrating that the Sun is immense by any earthly standard: The Sun's radius is nearly 700,000 kilometers, and its mass is $2 \times 10^{30}$ kilograms—about 300,000 times more massive than the Earth.

**FIGURE 14.3** This photo of the visible surface of the Sun shows several dark sunspots.

**Table 14.1  Basic Properties of the Sun**

| | |
|---|---|
| Radius ($R_{Sun}$) | 696,000 km (about 109 times the radius of the Earth) |
| Mass ($M_{Sun}$) | $2 \times 10^{30}$ kg (about 300,000 times the mass of the Earth) |
| Luminosity ($L_{Sun}$) | $3.8 \times 10^{26}$ watts |
| Composition (by percentage of mass) | 70% hydrogen, 28% helium, 2% heavier elements |
| Rotation rate | 27 days (equator) to 31 days (poles) |
| Surface temperature | 5,800 K (average); 4,000 K (sunspots) |
| Core temperature | 15 million K |

You can determine that the Sun is rotating by watching the sunspots day after day. If you watch very carefully, you may notice that sunspots near the solar equator circle the Sun faster than those at higher solar latitudes. This observation reveals that, unlike a spinning ball, the entire Sun does *not* rotate at the same rate. Instead, the solar equator completes one rotation in about 27 days, and the rotation period increases with latitude to about 31 days near the solar poles. Table 14.1 summarizes some of the basic properties of the Sun.

**TIME OUT TO THINK** *As a brief review, describe how we measure the mass of the Sun using Newton's version of Kepler's third law.* (Hint: *Look back at Chapter 5.*)

As you and your spaceship continue to fall toward the Sun, you notice an increasingly powerful headwind exerting a bit of drag on your descent. This headwind, called the **solar wind**, is created by the energy of photons, ions, and subatomic particles flowing outward from the solar surface. The solar wind helps shape the magnetospheres of planets and blows off the material that forms the tails of comets [Section 12.4].

A few million kilometers above the solar surface, you enter the solar **corona**, the tenuous uppermost layer of the Sun's atmosphere (Figure 14.4). Here you find the temperature to be astonishingly high—about 1 million Kelvin. This region emits most of the Sun's X rays. However, the density here is so low that your spaceship feels relatively little heat despite the million-degree temperature [Section 4.2]. Nearer the surface, the temperature suddenly drops to about 10,000 K in the **chromosphere**, the primary source of the Sun's ultraviolet radiation. At last, you plunge through the visible surface of the Sun, called the **photosphere**, where the temperature averages just under 6,000 K. Although the photosphere looks like a well-defined surface from Earth, it consists of gas far less dense than the Earth's atmosphere.

Throughout the solar atmosphere, you notice that the Sun has its own version of weather, in which conditions at a particular altitude differ from one region to another. Some regions of the chromosphere and corona are particularly hot and bright, while other regions are cooler and less dense. In the photosphere, sunspots are cooler than the surrounding surface, though they are still quite hot and bright by earthly standards. In addition, your compass goes crazy as you descend through the solar atmosphere, indicating that solar weather is shaped by intense magnetic fields. Occasionally, huge magnetic storms occur, shooting hot gases far into space.

Up to this point in your journey, you have seen the Earth and the stars behind you, but as you slip beneath the photosphere, blazing light engulfs you. You are inside the Sun, and your spacecraft is tossed about by incredible turbulence. If you can hold steady long enough to see what is going on around you, you'll

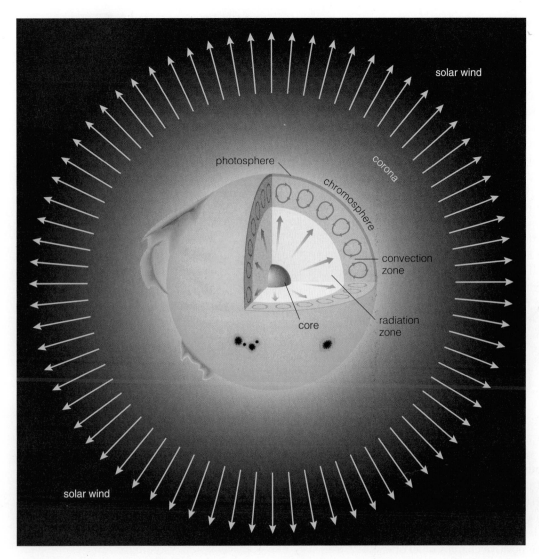

**FIGURE 14.4** The basic structure of the Sun.

notice spouts of hot gas rising upward, surrounded by cooler gas cascading down from above. You are in the **convection zone**, where energy generated in the solar core travels upward, transported by the rising of hot gas and falling of cool gas called *convection* [Section 9.3]. With some quick thinking, you may realize that the photosphere above you is the top of the convection zone and that convection is the cause of the Sun's seething, churning appearance.

As you descend through the convection zone, the surrounding density and pressure increase substantially, along with the temperature. Soon you reach depths at which the Sun is far denser than water; nevertheless, it is still a *gas*—more specifically, a *plasma* of positively charged ions and free electrons—because each particle moves independently of its neighbors [Section 4.3].

About a third of the way down to the center, the turbulence of the convection zone gives way to the stabler plasma of the **radiation zone**, where energy is carried outward primarily by photons of light. The temperature is now almost 10 million K, and your spacecraft is bathed in X rays trillions of times more intense than the visible light at the solar surface. No real spacecraft could survive, but your imaginary one keeps plunging straight down to the solar **core**. There you finally find the source of the Sun's energy: nuclear fusion transforming hydrogen into helium. At the Sun's center, the temperature is about 15 million K, the density is more than 100 times that of water, and the pressure is 200 billion times that on the surface of the Earth.

With your journey complete, it's time to turn around and head back home. We'll continue this chapter by studying fusion in the solar core and then tracing the flow of the energy generated by fusion as it moves outward through the Sun.

## 14.3 The Cosmic Crucible

The prospect of turning common metals like lead into gold enthralled medieval alchemists. Sometimes they tried primitive scientific approaches, such as melting various ores together in a vessel called a crucible. Other times they tried magic. But their get-rich-quick schemes never managed to work. Today we know that there is no easy way to turn other elements into gold, but it *is* possible to transmute one element or isotope into another. If a nucleus gains or loses protons, its atomic number changes and it becomes a different element. If it gains or loses neutrons, its atomic mass changes and it becomes a different isotope [Section 4.3]. The process of splitting a nucleus so that it loses protons or neutrons is called **nuclear fission**. The process of combining nuclei to make a nucleus with a greater number of protons or neutrons is called **nuclear fusion** (Figure 14.5). Human-built nuclear power plants rely on nuclear fission of uranium or plutonium. The nuclear power plant at the center of the Sun relies on nuclear fusion, turning hydrogen into helium.

**FIGURE 14.5** Nuclear fission splits a nucleus into smaller pieces, while nuclear fusion combines smaller nuclei into a larger nucleus.

At low speeds, electromagnetic repulsion prevents the collision of nuclei.

At high speeds, nuclei come close enough for the strong nuclear force to bind them together.

**FIGURE 14.6** Positively charged nuclei can fuse only if a high-speed collision brings them close enough for the strong nuclear force to come into play.

### Nuclear Fusion

The 15-million-K plasma in the solar core is like a "soup" of hot gas, with bare, positively charged atomic nuclei (and individual negatively charged electrons) whizzing about at extremely high speeds. At any one time, some of these nuclei are on high-speed collision courses with each other. In most cases, electromagnetic forces deflect the nuclei, preventing actual collisions, because positive charges repel one another. However, if nuclei collide with sufficient energy, they can stick together to form a heavier nucleus (Figure 14.6).

Sticking positively charged nuclei together is not easy. The **strong force**, which binds protons and neutrons together in atomic nuclei, is the only force in nature that can overcome the electromagnetic repulsion between two positively charged nuclei [Section S4.2]. In contrast to gravitational and electromagnetic forces, which drop off gradually as the distances between particles increase (by an inverse square law), the strong force is more like glue or Velcro: It overpowers the electromagnetic force over very small distances but is insignificant when the distances between particles exceed the typical sizes of atomic nuclei. The trick to nuclear fusion therefore is to push the positively charged nuclei close enough together for the strong force to outmuscle electromagnetic repulsion.

The high pressures and temperatures in the solar core are just right for fusion of hydrogen nuclei into helium nuclei. The high temperature is important

because the nuclei must collide at very high speeds if they are to come close enough together to fuse. (Quantum tunneling is also important to this process [Section S4.5].) The higher the temperature, the harder the collisions, making fusion reactions more likely at higher temperatures. The high pressure of the overlying layers is necessary because without it the hot plasma of the solar core would simply explode into space, shutting off the nuclear reactions. In the Sun, the pressure is high and steady, allowing some 600 million tons of hydrogen to fuse into helium every second.

### Hydrogen Fusion in the Sun:
### The Proton–Proton Chain

Recall that hydrogen nuclei are nothing more than individual protons, while the most common form of helium consists of two protons and two neutrons.

Thus, the overall hydrogen fusion reaction in the Sun is:

4 ¹H → 1 ⁴He + — energy —

However, collisions between two nuclei are far more common than three- or four-way collisions, so this overall reaction proceeds through steps that involve just two nuclei at a time. The sequence of steps that occurs in the Sun is called the **proton–proton chain** because it begins with collisions between individual protons (hydrogen nuclei); it is illustrated in Figure 14.7.

*Step 1.* Two protons fuse to form a nucleus consisting of one proton and one neutron, which is the isotope of hydrogen known as *deuterium*. Note that this step converts a proton into a neutron, reducing the total nuclear charge from +2 for the two fusing protons to +1 for the resulting deuterium nucleus. The lost positive charge is carried off by a *positron*, the antimatter version of an electron with a positive rather than negative charge [Section S4.2]. A *neutrino*—a subatomic particle with a very tiny mass—is also produced in this

step.[1] The positron won't last long; it soon meets up with an ordinary electron, resulting in the creation of two gamma-ray photons through matter–antimatter annihilation.

*Step 2.* A fair number of deuterium nuclei are always present along with the protons and other nuclei in the solar core, since step 1 occurs so frequently in the Sun (about $10^{38}$ times per second). Step 2 occurs when one of these deuterium nuclei collides and fuses with a proton. The result is a nucleus of helium-3, a rare form of helium with two protons and one neutron. This reaction also produces a gamma-ray photon.

*Step 3.* The third and final step of the proton–proton chain requires the addition of another neutron to the helium-3, thereby making normal helium-4. This final step can proceed in several different ways, but the most common route involves a collision of two helium-3 nuclei. Each of these helium-3 nuclei resulted from a prior, separate occurrence of step 2 somewhere in the solar core.

---

[1]Producing a neutrino is necessary because of a law called *conservation of lepton number*: The number of leptons (e.g., electrons or neutrinos [see Chapter S4]) must be the same before and after the reaction. The lepton number is zero before the reaction because there are no leptons. Among the reaction products, the positron (antielectron) has lepton number −1 because it is antimatter, and the neutrino has lepton number +1. Thus, the total lepton number remains zero.

---

**FIGURE 14.7** Hydrogen fuses into helium in the Sun by way of the proton–proton chain. In step 1, two protons fuse to create a deuterium nucleus consisting of a proton and a neutron. In step 2, the deuterium nucleus and a protons fuse to form helium-3, a rare form of helium. In step 3, two helium-3 nuclei fuse to form helium-4, the common form of helium.

**Key:**

| | | | |
|---|---|---|---|
| e⁻ electron | | ⟿ gamma ray | |
| neutrino | | n neutron | |
| e⁺ positron | | p proton | |

**Total reaction**

The final result is a normal helium-4 nucleus and two protons.

*Total reaction.* Note that, somewhere in the solar core, steps 1 and 2 must each occur twice to make step 3 possible. Six protons go into each complete cycle of the proton–proton chain, but two come back out. Thus, the overall proton–proton chain converts four protons (hydrogen nuclei) into a helium-4 nucleus, two positrons, two neutrinos, and two gamma rays.

Each resulting helium-4 nucleus has a mass that is slightly less (by about 0.7%) than the combined mass of the four protons that created it. Overall, fusion in the Sun converts about 600 million tons of hydrogen into 596 million tons of helium every second; the "missing" 4 million tons of matter becomes energy in accord with Einstein's formula $E = mc^2$. About 2% of this energy is carried off by the neutrinos. Neutrinos rarely interact with matter (because they respond only to the weak force [Section S4.2]), so most of the neutrinos created by the proton–proton chain pass unscathed from the solar core, through the solar surface, and out into space. The rest of the energy emerges as kinetic energy of the nuclei and radiative energy of the gamma rays. As we will see, this energy slowly percolates to the solar surface, eventually emerging as the sunlight that bathes the Earth.

### The Solar Thermostat

The rate of nuclear fusion in the solar core, which determines the energy output of the Sun, is very sensitive to temperature. A slight increase in temperature would mean a much higher fusion rate, and a slight decrease in temperature would mean a much lower fusion rate. If the Sun's rate of fusion varied erratically, the effects on the Earth might be devastating. Fortunately, the Sun's central temperature is steady thanks to gravitational equilibrium—the balance between the pull of gravity and the push of internal pressure.

Suppose the core temperature rose very slightly. The rate of nuclear fusion would soar, generating excess energy that would increase the pressure. The push of this pressure would temporarily exceed the pull of gravity, causing the core to expand and cool. With this cooling, the fusion rate would drop back down. The expansion and cooling would continue until gravitational equilibrium was restored, at which point the fusion rate would be back at its original value. An opposite process restores the normal fusion rate if the core temperature drops. A decrease in core temperature would lead to decreased nuclear burning, a drop in the central pressure, and contraction of the core. As the core shrank, its temperature would rise until the burning rate returned to normal.

The response of the core pressure to changes in the nuclear fusion rate is essentially a *thermostat* that keeps the Sun's central temperature steady. Any change in the core temperature is automatically corrected by the change in the fusion rate and the accompanying change in pressure.

While the processes involved in gravitational equilibrium prevent erratic changes in the fusion rate, they also ensure that the fusion rate gradually rises over billions of years. Because each fusion reaction converts *four* hydrogen nuclei into *one* helium nucleus, the total number of *independent particles* in the solar core is gradually falling. This gradual reduction in the number of particles causes the solar core to shrink. The slow shrinking of the solar core means that it must generate energy more rapidly in order to counteract the stronger compression of gravity, so the solar core gradually gets hotter as it shrinks. Theoretical models indicate that the Sun's core temperature should have increased enough to raise its fusion rate and the solar luminosity by about 30% since the Sun was born 4.6 billion years ago.

The gradual increase in the solar luminosity poses a bit of a puzzle, because geological evidence shows that the Earth's temperature has remained fairly steady since the Earth finished forming over 4 billion years ago. How has the Earth maintained its temperature while the Sun's energy output has increased by some 30%? Apparently, the Earth has its own thermostat that keeps the surface temperature steady even as the Sun increases in brightness. This "Earth thermostat" is probably related to the greenhouse effect [Section 13.3], which may have been much stronger in the distant past than it is today. Studying how the Sun changes with time and how the Earth responds to these changes may teach us much about how the Earth's physical and biological systems regulate the greenhouse effect.

### "Observing" the Solar Interior

We cannot see inside the Sun, so you may be wondering how we can know so much about what goes on underneath its surface. The primary way we learn about the interior of the Sun and other stars is by creating *mathematical models* that use the laws of physics to predict the internal conditions. A basic model uses the Sun's observed composition and mass as inputs to equations that describe gravitational equilibrium and the solar thermostat. With the aid of a computer, we can use the model to calculate the Sun's temperature, pressure, and density at any depth. We can then predict the rate of nuclear fusion in the solar core by combining these calculations with knowledge about nuclear fusion gathered in laboratories here on Earth. Remarkably, such models correctly "predict" the radius, surface temperature, luminosity, age, and many other properties of the Sun. However, current models do not predict *everything* about the Sun correctly, so scientists are constantly working to discover what is missing from them. The fact that the models successfully predict so many observed characteristics of the Sun gives us confidence that they are on the right track and that we really do understand what is going on inside the Sun.

A second way to learn about the inside of the Sun is to observe "sun quakes"—vibrations of the Sun that are similar to the vibrations of the Earth caused by earthquakes, although they are generated very differently. Earthquakes occur when the Earth's crust suddenly shifts, generating *seismic waves* that propagate through the Earth's interior [Section 13.2]. We can learn about the Earth's interior by recording seismic waves on the Earth's surface with seismographs. Sun quakes result from waves of pressure (sound waves) that propagate deep within the Sun at all times. These waves cause the solar surface to vibrate when they reach it. Although we cannot set up seismographs on the Sun, we can detect the vibrations of the surface by measuring Doppler shifts [Section 6.5]: Light from portions of the surface that are rising toward us is slightly blueshifted, while light from portions that are falling away from us is slightly red-shifted. The vibrations are relatively small but measurable (Figure 14.8). In principle, we can deduce a great deal about the solar interior by carefully analyzing these

**FIGURE 14.8** Vibrations on the surface of the Sun can be detected by Doppler shifts. In this schematic representation, red indicates falling gas, and blue indicates rising gas.

## Mathematical Insight 14.1    Mass–Energy Conversion in the Sun

We can calculate how much mass the Sun loses through nuclear fusion by comparing the input and output masses of the proton–proton chain. A single proton has a mass of $1.6726 \times 10^{-27}$ kg, so four protons have a mass of $6.690 \times 10^{-27}$ kg.

A helium-4 nucleus has a mass of only $6.643 \times 10^{-27}$ kg, slightly less than the mass of the four protons. The difference is:

$6.690 \times 10^{-27}$ kg $- 6.643 \times 10^{-27}$ kg $= 4.7 \times 10^{-29}$ kg

which is 0.7%, or 0.007, of the original mass. Thus, for example, when 1 kilogram of hydrogen fuses, the resulting helium weighs only 993 grams, while 7 grams of mass turn into energy.

To calculate the *total* amount of mass converted to energy in the Sun each second, we use Einstein's equation $E = mc^2$. The total energy produced by the Sun each second is $3.8 \times 10^{26}$ joules, so we can solve for the total mass converted to energy each second:

$$E = mc^2 \quad \Rightarrow \quad m = \frac{E}{c^2}$$

$$= \frac{3.8 \times 10^{26} \text{ joules}}{\left(3.0 \times 10^8 \frac{m}{s}\right)^2} = 4.2 \times 10^9 \text{ kg}$$

The Sun loses about 4 billion kilograms of mass every second, which is roughly equivalent to the combined mass of nearly 100 million people.

*Example:* How much hydrogen is converted to helium each second in the Sun?

*Solution:* We have already calculated that the Sun loses $4.2 \times 10^9$ kg of mass each second and that this is only 0.7% of the mass of hydrogen that is fused:

$4.2 \times 10^9$ kg $= 0.007 \times$ (mass of hydrogen fused)

We now solve for the mass of hydrogen fused:

$$\text{mass of hydrogen fused} = \frac{4.2 \times 10^9 \text{ kg}}{0.007}$$

$$= 6.0 \times 10^{11} \text{ kg} \times \frac{1 \text{ metric ton}}{10^3 \text{ kg}}$$

$$= 6.0 \times 10^8 \text{ metric tons}$$

The Sun fuses 600 million metric tons of hydrogen each second, of which about 4 million tons becomes energy, and the remaining 596 million tons becomes helium.

vibrations. (By analogy to seismology on Earth, this type of study of the Sun is called *helioseismology* [recall that *helios* means "sun"].) Results to date confirm that mathematical models of the solar interior are on the right track and at the same time provide data that can be used to improve the models further.

### The Solar Neutrino Problem

Another way to study the solar interior is to observe the neutrinos coming from fusion reactions in the core. Don't panic, but as you read this sentence about a thousand trillion solar neutrinos will zip through your body. Fortunately, they won't do any damage, because neutrinos rarely interact with anything. Neutrinos created by fusion in the solar core fly quickly through the Sun as if passing through empty space. In fact, while an inch of lead will stop an X ray, stopping an average neutrino would require a slab of lead more than a light-year thick! Clearly, counting neutrinos is dauntingly difficult, because virtually all of them stream right through any detector built to capture them.

**TIME OUT TO THINK** *Is the number of solar neutrinos zipping through our bodies significantly lower at night? (Hint: How does the thickness of the Earth compare with the thickness of a slab of lead needed to stop an average neutrino?)*

Nevertheless, neutrinos *do* occasionally interact with matter, and it is possible to capture a few solar neutrinos with a large enough detector. Neutrino detectors are usually placed deep inside mines so that the overlying layers of rock block all other kinds of particles coming from outer space except neutrinos, which pass through rock easily. The first major solar neutrino detector, built in the 1960s, was located 1,500 meters underground in the Homestake gold mine in South Dakota (Figure 14.9). The detector for this "Homestake experiment" consisted of a 400,000-liter vat of chlorine-containing dry-cleaning fluid. It turns out that, on very rare occasions, a chlorine nucleus can capture a neutrino and change into a nucleus of radioactive argon. By looking for radioactive argon in

the tank of cleaning fluid, experimenters could count the number of neutrinos captured in the detector.

Remarkably, from the many trillions of solar neutrinos that passed through the tank of cleaning fluid each second, experimenters expected to capture an average of just one neutrino per day. This predicted capture rate was based on measured properties of chlorine nuclei and models of nuclear fusion in the Sun. However, over a period of more than two decades, neutrinos were captured only about once every 3 days on average. That is, the Homestake experiment detected only about one-third of the predicted number of neutrinos. This disagreement between model predictions and actual observations is called the **solar neutrino problem**.

**TIME OUT TO THINK** *Although the observed number of neutrinos falls short of theoretical predictions, experiments like Homestake have shown that at least some neutrinos are coming from the Sun. Explain why this provides direct evidence that nuclear fusion really is taking place in the Sun right now. (Hint: See Figure 14.7.)*

The shortfall of neutrinos found with the Homestake experiment has led to many more recent attempts to detect solar neutrinos using more sophisticated detectors (Figure 14.10). The chlorine nuclei in the Homestake experiment could capture only high-energy neutrinos that are produced by one of

**FIGURE 14.9** This tank of dry-cleaning fluid (visible underneath the catwalk), located deep within South Dakota's Homestake mine, was a solar neutrino detector. The chlorine nuclei in the cleaning fluid turned into argon nuclei when they captured neutrinos from the Sun.

the rare pathways of step 3 in the proton–proton chain. More recent experiments can detect lower-energy neutrinos, including those produced by step 1 of the proton–proton chain, and therefore offer a better probe of fusion in the Sun. To date, all these experiments have found fewer neutrinos than current models of the Sun predict. This discrepancy between model and experiment probably means one of two things: Either something is wrong with our models of the Sun, or something is missing in our understanding of how neutrinos behave.

For the moment, many physicists and astronomers are betting that we understand the Sun just fine and that the discrepancy has to do with the neutrinos themselves. One intriguing idea arises from the fact that neutrinos come in three types: electron neutrinos, muon neutrinos, and tau neutrinos [Section S4.2]. Fusion reactions in the Sun produce only electron neutrinos, and most solar neutrino detectors can detect only electron neutrinos. However, recent experiments have shown that some of the electron neutrinos might change into muon and tau neutrinos as they fly out through the solar plasma. In that case, our detectors would count fewer than the expected number of electron neutrinos. Early results from the Sudbury Neutrino Observatory in Canada, a new detector designed to search for all types of neutrinos, suggests that neutrinos changing type is indeed the solution to the solar neutrino problem. However, the observations are ongoing, and it will probably be several more years before this solution can be definitively confirmed.

## 14.4 From Core to Corona

Energy liberated by nuclear fusion in the Sun's core must eventually reach the solar surface, where it can be radiated into space. The path that the energy takes to the surface is long and complex. In this section, we follow the long path that energy travels after its production in the core.

### The Path Through the Solar Interior

In Chapter 6, we discussed how atoms can absorb or emit photons. In fact, photons can also interact with any charged particle, and a photon that "collides" with an electron can be deflected into a completely new direction. Deep in the solar interior, the plasma is so dense that the gamma-ray photons resulting from fusion travel only a fraction of a millimeter

**a** Scientists inspecting individual detectors within Super-Kamiokande.

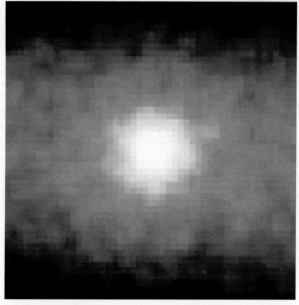

**b** An image of the Sun based on neutrinos detected by Super-Kamiokande.

**FIGURE 14.11** A photon in the solar interior bounces randomly among electrons, slowly working its way outward in a process called radiative diffusion.

before colliding with an electron. Because each collision sends the photon in a random new direction, the photon bounces around the core in a haphazard way, sometimes called a *random walk* (Figure 14.11). With each random bounce, the photon drifts farther and farther, on average, from its point of origin. As a result, photons from the solar core gradually work their way outward. The technical term for this slow, outward migration of photons is **radiative diffusion** (to *diffuse* means to "spread out"; *radiative* refers to the photons of light or radiation). Along the way, the photons exchange energy with their surroundings; because the surrounding temperature declines as the photons move outward through the Sun, they are gradually transformed from gamma rays to photons of lower energy. (Because energy must be conserved, each gamma-ray photon becomes many lower-energy photons.) By the time the energy of fusion reaches the surface, the photons are primarily visible light. On average, the energy released in a fusion reaction takes about a million years to reach the solar surface.

**TIME OUT TO THINK** *Radiative diffusion is just one type of diffusion. Another is the diffusion of dye through a glass of water. If you place a concentrated spot of dye at one point in the water, each individual dye molecule begins a random walk as it bounces among the water molecules. The result is that the dye gradually spreads through the entire glass. Can you think of any other examples of diffusion in the world around you?*

Radiative diffusion is the primary way by which energy moves outward through the *radiation zone,* which stretches from the core to about 70% of the Sun's radius (see Figure 14.4). Above this point, where the temperature has dropped to about 2 million K, the solar plasma absorbs photons more readily (rather than just bouncing them around). This is the beginning of the solar *convection zone,* where the build-

up of heat resulting from photon absorption causes bubbles of hot plasma to rise upward in the process known as **convection** [Section 9.3]. Convection occurs because hot gas is less dense than cool gas. Like a hot-air balloon, a hot bubble of solar plasma rises upward through the cooler plasma above it. Meanwhile, cooler plasma from above slides around the rising bubble and sinks to lower layers, where it is heated. The rising of hot plasma and sinking of cool plasma form a cycle that transports energy outward from the top of the radiation zone to the solar surface (Figure 14.12a).

### The Solar Surface

The Earth has a solid crust, so its surface is well defined. In contrast, the Sun is made entirely of gaseous plasma. Defining where the surface of the Sun begins is therefore something like defining the surface of a cloud: From a distance it looks quite distinct, but up close the surface is fuzzy, not sharp. We generally define the solar surface as the layer that appears distinct from a distance. This is the layer we identified as the *photosphere* when we took our imaginary journey into the Sun. More technically, the photosphere is the layer of the Sun from which photons finally escape into space after the million-year journey of solar energy outward from the core.

Most of the energy produced by fusion in the solar core ultimately leaves the photosphere as thermal radiation [Section 6.4]. The average temperature of the photosphere is about 5,800 K, corresponding to a thermal radiation spectrum that peaks in the green portion of the visible spectrum, with substantial energy coming out in all colors of visible light. The Sun appears whitish when seen from space, but in our sky the Sun appears somewhat more yellow—and even red at sunset—because the Earth's atmosphere scatters blue light. It is this scattered light from the Sun that makes our skies blue [Section 10.2].

Although the average temperature of the photosphere is 5,800 K, actual temperatures vary significantly from place to place. The photosphere is marked throughout by the bubbling pattern of **granulation** produced by the underlying convection (Figure 14.12b). Each *granule* appears bright in the center, where hot gas bubbles upward, and dark around the edges, where cool gas descends. If we made a movie of the granulation, we'd see it bubbling rather like a pot of boiling water. Just as bubbles in a pot of boiling water burst on the surface and are replaced by new bubbles, each granule lasts only a few minutes before being replaced by other granules bubbling upward.

**a** This schematic diagram shows how hot gas (white arrows) rises while cooler gas (orange arrows) descends around it. Bright spots appear on the solar surface in places where hot gas is rising from below, creating the granulated appearance of the solar photosphere.

**b** Granulation is evident in this photo of the Sun's surface. Each bright granule is the top of a rising column of gas. At the darker lines between the granules, cooler gas is descending below the photosphere.

**FIGURE 14.12** Convection transports energy outward in the Sun's convection zone.

### Sunspots and Magnetic Fields

Sunspots are the most striking features on the solar surface. The temperature of the plasma in sunspots is about 4,000 K, significantly cooler than the 5,800-K plasma of the surrounding photosphere. If you think about this for a moment, you may wonder how sunspots can be so much cooler than their surroundings. What keeps the surrounding hot plasma from heating the sunspots? Something must be preventing hot plasma from entering the sunspots, and that "something" turns out to be magnetic fields.

Detailed observations of the Sun's spectral hues reveal sunspots to be regions of intense magnetic activity. Strong magnetic fields can alter the energy levels in atoms and ions and therefore can alter the spectral lines they produce. More specifically, magnetic fields cause some spectral lines to split into two or more closely spaced lines (Figure 14.13). This effect, called the *Zeeman effect*, enables scientists to map magnetic fields on the Sun by studying the spectral lines in light from different parts of the solar surface.

Magnetic fields are invisible, but in principle we could visualize a magnetic field by laying out many compasses; each compass needle would point to local magnetic north. We can represent the magnetic field by drawing a series of lines, called **magnetic field lines**, connecting the needles of these imaginary compasses (Figure 14.14a). The strength of the magnetic field is indicated by the spacing of the lines: Closer lines mean a stronger field (Figure 14.14b). Because these imaginary field lines are so much easier to visualize than the magnetic field itself, we

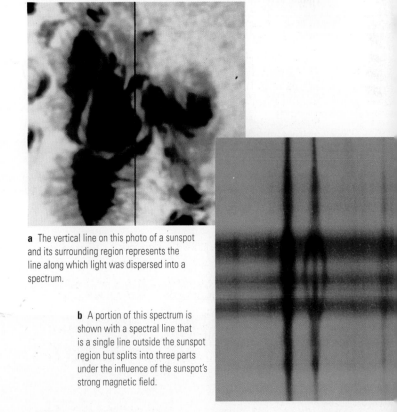

**a** The vertical line on this photo of a sunspot and its surrounding region represents the line along which light was dispersed into a spectrum.

**b** A portion of this spectrum is shown with a spectral line that is a single line outside the sunspot region but splits into three parts under the influence of the sunspot's strong magnetic field.

**FIGURE 14.13** Sunspots are regions of intense magnetic activity.

**a** Magnetic field lines follow the directions that compass needles would point.

weaker magnetic field

stronger magnetic field

weaker magnetic field

**b** Lines closer together indicate a stronger field.

**c** Charged particles follow paths that spiral along magnetic field lines.

**FIGURE 14.14** We draw magnetic field lines to represent invisible magnetic fields.

**FIGURE 14.15** Loops of magnetic field lines can arch high above the solar surface.

Magnetic fields trap gas.

sunspots
T ≈ 4,500 K

T ≈ 5,800 K

T ≈ 5,800 K

convection cells

Magnetic fields of sunspots suppress convection and prevent surrounding plasma from sliding sideways into sunspot.

**b** Pairs of sunspots are connected by tightly wound magnetic field lines.

**a** This X-ray photo (from NASA's TRACE mission) shows hot gas trapped within looped magnetic field lines.

usually discuss magnetic fields by talking about how the field lines would appear. Charged particles, such as the ions and electrons in the solar plasma, follow paths that spiral along the magnetic field lines (Figure 14.14c). Thus, the solar plasma can move freely *along* magnetic field lines but cannot easily move perpendicular to them.

The magnetic field lines act somewhat like elastic bands, twisted into contortions and knots by turbulent motions in the solar atmosphere. Sunspots occur where the most taut and tightly wound magnetic fields poke nearly straight out from the solar interior. Note that sunspots tend to occur in pairs connected by a loop of magnetic field lines. These tight magnetic field lines suppress convection within each sunspot and prevent surrounding plasma from sliding sideways into the sunspot. With hot plasma unable to enter the region, the sunspot plasma becomes cooler than that of the rest of the photosphere.

The magnetic field lines connecting two sunspots often soar high above the photosphere, through the chromosphere, and into the corona (Figure 14.15). These vaulted loops of magnetic field sometimes appear as **solar prominences**, in which the field traps gas that may glow for days or even weeks. Some prominences rise to heights of more than 100,000 kilometers above the Sun's surface (Figure 14.16).

The most dramatic events on the solar surface are **solar flares**, which emit bursts of X rays and fast-moving charged particles into space (Figure 14.17). Flares generally occur in the vicinity of sunspots, leading us to suspect that they occur when the magnetic field lines become so twisted and knotted that they can bear the tension no longer. The magnetic field lines suddenly snap like tangled elastic bands twisted beyond their limits, releasing a huge amount of energy. This energy heats the nearby plasma to 100 million K over the next few minutes to few hours, generating X rays and accelerating some of the charged particles to nearly the speed of light.

**FIGURE 14.16** A gigantic solar prominence erupts from the solar surface at the upper right of this ultraviolet-light photo (from the SOHO mission). The gas within this prominence, which is over 20 times the size of Earth, is quite hot but still cooler than the million-degree gas of the surrounding corona.

**FIGURE 14.17** This photo (from TRACE) of ultraviolet light emitted by hydrogen atoms shows a solar flare erupting from the Sun's surface.

**FIGURE 14.18** An X-ray image of the Sun reveals the corona: Brighter regions of this image correspond to regions of stronger X-ray emission. (From the Yohkoh space observatory.)

### *The Chromosphere and Corona*

The high temperatures of the chromosphere and corona perplexed scientists for decades. After all, temperatures gradually decline as we move outward from the core to the top of the photosphere. Why should this decline suddenly reverse? Some aspects of this atmospheric heating remain a mystery today, but we have at least a general explanation: The Sun's strong magnetic fields carry energy upward from the churning solar surface to the chromosphere and corona. More specifically, the rising and falling of gas in the convection zone probably shakes magnetic field lines beneath the solar surface. This shaking generates waves along the magnetic field lines that carry energy upward to the solar atmosphere. Precisely how the waves deposit their energy in the chromosphere and corona is not known, but the waves agitate the low-density plasma of these layers, somehow heating them to high temperatures. Much of this heating appears to happen near where the magnetic field lines emerge from the Sun's surface.

Note that, according to this model of solar heating, the same magnetic fields that keep sunspots cool make the overlying plasma of the chromosphere and corona hot. We can test this idea observationally. The gas of the chromosphere and corona is so tenuous that we cannot see it with our eyes except during a total eclipse, when we can see the faint visible light scattered by electrons in the corona [Section 2.3]. However, the roughly 10,000-K plasma of the chromosphere emits strongly in the ultraviolet, and the million-K plasma of the corona is the source of virtually all X rays coming from the Sun. Figure 14.18 shows an X-ray image of the Sun: As the solar heating model predicts, the brightest regions of the corona tend to be directly above sunspot groups.

Some regions of the corona, called **coronal holes**, barely show up in X-ray images. More detailed analyses show that the magnetic field lines in coronal holes project out into space like broken rubber bands, allowing particles spiraling along them to escape the Sun altogether. These particles streaming outward from the corona constitute the *solar wind,* which blows through the solar system at an average speed of about 500 kilometers per second and has important effects on planetary surfaces, atmospheres, and magnetospheres [Section 10.3]. Somewhere beyond the orbit of Neptune, the pressure of interstellar gas must eventually halt the solar wind. The Pioneer and Voyager spacecraft that visited the outer planets in the 1970s and 1980s are still traveling outward from our solar system and may soon encounter this "boundary" (called the *heliopause*) of the realm of the Sun. It's also worth noting that, in the same way that meteorites provide us with samples of asteroids we've never visited, solar wind particles captured by satellites provide us with a sample of material from the Sun. Analysis of these solar particles has reassuringly verified that the Sun is made mostly of hydrogen, just as we conclude from studying the Sun's spectrum.

## 14.5 Solar Weather and Climate

Individual sunspots, prominences, and flares are short-lived phenomena, somewhat like storms on the Earth, and constitute what we call *solar weather* or **solar activity**. You know from personal experience that the Earth's weather is notoriously unpredictable,

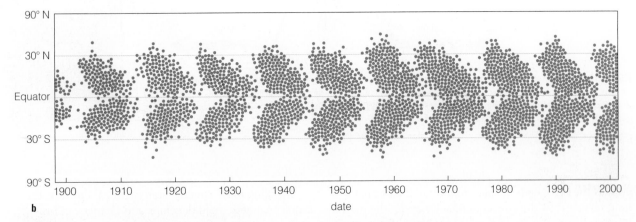

**FIGURE 14.19** Sunspot cycle during the last century. (**a**) This graph shows how the number of sunspots on the Sun changes with time. Note the approximately 11-year cycle. (**b**) This graph shows how the latitudes at which sunspot groups appear tend to shift during a single sunspot cycle. Each dot represents a group of sunspots and indicates the year (horizontal axis) and latitude (vertical axis) at which the group appeared.

and the same is true for the Sun: We cannot predict precisely when or where a particular sunspot or flare will appear. The Earth's *climate,* on the other hand, is quite regular from season to season. So it is with the Sun, where despite day-to-day variations the general nature and intensity of solar activity follow a predictable cycle.

### The Sunspot Cycle

Long before we realized that sunspots were magnetic disturbances, astronomers had recognized patterns in sunspot activity. The most notable pattern is the number of sunspots visible on the Sun at any particular time. Thanks to telescopic observations of the Sun recorded by astronomers since the 1600s, we know that the number of sunspots gradually rises and falls in a **sunspot cycle** with a period of about 11 years (Figure 14.19a). At the time of **solar maximum**, when sunspots are most numerous, we may see dozens of sunspots on the Sun at one time. In contrast, we see few if any sunspots at the time of **solar minimum**. Note that the sunspot cycle is not perfectly predictable: The interval between solar maxima is sometimes as long as 15 years or as short as

7 years. More dramatically, sunspot activity virtually ceased between the years 1645 and 1715, a period sometimes called the *Maunder minimum* (after E. W. Maunder, who identified it in historical sunspot records). The frequency of prominences and flares also follows the sunspot cycle, with these events being most common at solar maximum and least common at solar minimum.

Another feature of the sunspot cycle is a gradual change in the solar latitudes at which individual sunspots form and dissolve (Figure 14.19b). As a cycle begins at solar minimum, sunspots form primarily at mid-latitudes (30° to 40°) on the Sun. The sunspots tend to form at lower latitudes as the cycle progresses, appearing very close to the solar equator as the next solar minimum approaches.

A less obvious feature of the sunspot cycle is that at each solar minimum something peculiar happens to the Sun's magnetic field. The field lines connecting all pairs of sunspots (see Figure 14.15) tend to point in the same direction throughout an 11-year solar cycle (within each hemisphere); for example, all compass needles might point from the easternmost sunspot to the westernmost sunspot in a pair. How-

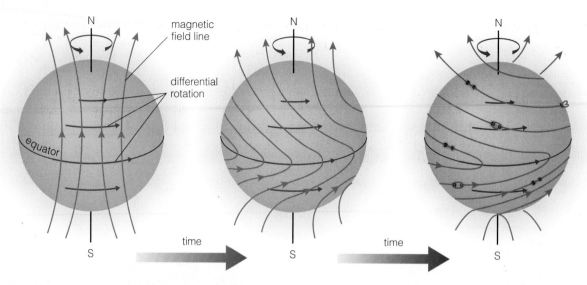

**FIGURE 14.20** The Sun rotates more quickly at its equator than it does near its poles, a behavior known as differential rotation. Because gas circles the Sun faster at the equator, it drags the Sun's north-south magnetic field lines into a more twisted configuration. The magnetic field lines linking pairs of sunspots, depicted here as green and black blobs, trace out the directions of these stretched and distorted field lines.

ever, as the cycle ends at solar minimum, the magnetic field reverses: In the subsequent solar cycle, the field lines connecting pairs of sunspots point in the opposite direction. Apparently, the entire magnetic field of the Sun flip-flops every 11 years. These magnetic reversals hint that the sunspot cycle is related to the generation of magnetic fields on the Sun. They also tell us that the *complete* magnetic cycle of the Sun, called the *solar cycle,* really averages 22 years, since it takes two 11-year cycles before the magnetic field is back the way it started.

### What Causes the Sunspot Cycle?

The causes of the Sun's magnetic fields and the sunspot cycle are not well understood, but we believe we know the general nature of the processes involved. Convection is thought to dredge up weak magnetic fields generated in the solar interior, amplifying them as they rise. The Sun's **differential rotation**—faster at its equator than near its poles—then stretches and shapes these fields.

Imagine what happens to a magnetic field line that originally runs along the Sun's surface directly from the north pole to the south pole. At the equator, the field line circles the Sun in 27 days, but at higher latitudes the field line lags behind. Gradually, differential rotation winds the field line more and more tightly around the Sun (Figure 14.20). This process, operating at all times over the entire Sun, produces the contorted field lines that generate sunspots and other solar activity.

Making more specific statements about how the Sun's magnetic field develops and changes in time requires the aid of sophisticated computer models. Scientists are working hard on such models, but the behavior of these fields is so complex that approximations are necessary even with the best supercomputers. Using these computer models, scientists have successfully replicated some features of the sunspot cycle, such as changes in the number and latitude of sunspots and the magnetic field reversals that occur about every 11 years. However, much still remains mysterious, including why the period of the sunspot cycle varies and why solar activity is different from one cycle to the next.

### Solar Activity and the Earth

During solar maximum, solar flares and other forms of solar activity feed large numbers of highly energetic charged particles (protons and electrons) into the solar wind. Do these forms of solar weather affect the Earth? In at least some ways, the answer is a definitive yes.

The solar wind continually carries charged particles from the solar corona to the Earth. These particles then stream along the Earth's magnetic field lines, piling up near the poles (Figure 14.21a). Most of these charged particles collide with atoms in the Earth's upper atmosphere, causing electrons in the atoms to jump to higher energy levels [Section 4.4]. These excited atoms subsequently emit visible-light photons as they drop to lower energy levels, creating the shimmering light of the *aurora* (Figure 14.21b).

## Long-Term Change in Solar Activity

Figure 14.19 shows that the sunspot cycle varies in length and intensity, and it sometimes seems to disappear altogether. With these facts as background, many scientists are searching for longer-term patterns in solar activity. Unfortunately, the search for longer-term variations is difficult because telescopic observations of sunspots cover a period of only about 400 years. Some naked-eye observations of sunspots recorded by Chinese astronomers go back almost 2,000 years, but these records are sparse, and naked-eye observations may not be very reliable. We can also guess at past solar activity from descriptions of solar eclipses recorded around the world: When the Sun is more active, the corona tends to have longer and brighter "streamers" visible to the naked eye.

Another way to gauge past solar activity is to study the amount of carbon-14 in tree rings. High-energy *cosmic rays* [Section 18.2] coming from beyond our own solar system produce radioactive carbon-14 in the Earth's atmosphere. During periods of high solar activity, the solar wind tends to grow stronger, shielding the Earth from some of these cosmic rays. Thus, production of carbon-14 drops when the Sun is more active. All the while, trees steadily breathe in atmospheric carbon, in the form of carbon dioxide, and incorporate it year by year into each ring. We can therefore estimate the level of solar activity in any given year by measuring the level of carbon-14 in the corresponding ring. No clear evidence has yet been found of longer-term cycles of solar activity, but the search goes on.

Theoretical models predict a very long term trend. The Sun must have rotated much faster when it was young [Section 8.4]. Because a combination of convection and differential rotation generates solar activity, a faster rotation rate should have meant much more activity. Observations of other stars that are similar to the Sun but rotate faster confirm that these stars are much more active. We find evidence for many more "starspots" on these stars than on the Sun, and their relatively bright ultraviolet and X-ray emissions suggest that they have brighter chromospheres and coronas—just as we would expect if they are more active than the Sun.

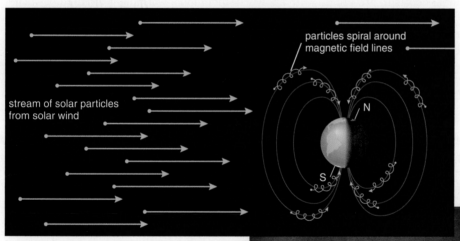

**a** The Earth's magnetic field captures charged particles from the solar wind and directs them toward the poles.

**b** Because energetic charged particles impact the atmosphere near the poles, the aurora is most commonly seen at high latitudes. However, solar storms can bring the aurora closer to mid-latitudes. This photograph shows the aurora borealis, or "northern lights," in August 2000 seen from Sunrise Point in Mount Rainier National Park, Washington. (In the Southern Hemisphere, the aurora is called the aurora australis.)

**FIGURE 14.21** Particles from the Sun cause auroras on Earth.

Particles streaming from the Sun after the occurrence of solar flares or other major solar storms can also have practical impacts on society. For example, these particles can hamper radio communications, disrupt electrical power delivery, and damage the electronic components in orbiting satellites. During a particularly powerful magnetic storm on the Sun in March 1989, the U.S. Air Force temporarily lost track of over 2,000 satellites, and powerful currents induced in the ground circuits of the Quebec hydroelectric system caused it to collapse for more than 8 hours. The combined cost of the loss of power in the United States and Canada exceeded $100 million. In January 1997, AT&T lost contact with a $200-million communications satellite, probably because of damage caused by particles coming from another powerful solar storm.

Satellites in low-Earth orbit are particularly vulnerable during solar maximum, because the increase in solar X rays and energetic particles heats the Earth's upper atmosphere, causing it to expand. The density of the gas surrounding low-flying satellites therefore rises, exerting drag that saps their energy and angular momentum. If this drag proceeds unchecked, the satellites ultimately plummet back to Earth. Satellites in low orbits, including the Hubble Space Telescope, therefore require occasional boosts to prevent them from falling out of the sky.

Connections between solar activity and the Earth's climate are much less clear. The period from 1645 to 1715, when solar activity seems to have virtually ceased, was a time of exceptionally low temperatures in Europe and North America known as the *Little Ice Age*. Did the low solar activity cause these low temperatures, or was their occurrence a coincidence? No one knows for sure. Some researchers have claimed that certain weather phenomena, such as drought cycles or frequencies of storms, are correlated with the 11- or 22-year cycles of solar activity. However, the data supporting these correlations are weak in many cases, and even real correlations may be coincidental.

Part of the difficulty in linking solar activity with climate is that no one understands how the linkage might work. Although emissions of ultraviolet light, X rays, and high-energy particles increase substantially from solar minimum to solar maximum, the total luminosity of the Sun barely changes at all. (The Sun becomes slightly brighter during solar maximum, but only by about 0.1%.) Thus, if solar activity really is affecting Earth's climate, it must be through some very subtle mechanism. For example, perhaps the expansion of the Earth's upper atmosphere that occurs with solar maximum somehow causes changes in weather.

The question of how solar activity is linked to the Earth's climate is very important, because we need to know whether global warming is affected by solar activity in addition to human activity. Unfortunately, for the time being at least, we can say little about this question.

## THE BIG PICTURE

In this chapter, we have examined our Sun, the nearest star. When you look back at this chapter, make sure you understand these "big picture" ideas:

■ The ancient riddle of why the Sun shines is now solved. The Sun shines with energy generated by fusion of hydrogen into helium in the Sun's core. After a million-year journey through the solar interior and an 8-minute journey through space, a small fraction of this energy reaches the Earth and supplies sunlight and heat.

■ Gravitational equilibrium, the balance between pressure and gravity, determines the Sun's interior structure and maintains its steady nuclear burning rate. If the Sun were not so steady, life on Earth might not have been possible.

■ The Sun's atmosphere displays its own version of weather and climate, governed by solar magnetic fields. Solar weather has important influences on the Earth.

■ The Sun is important not only as our source of light and heat, but also because it is the only star near enough for us to study in great detail. In the coming chapters, we will use what we've learned about the Sun to help us understand other stars.

1. Briefly describe how *gravitational contraction* generates energy and when it was important in the Sun's history.

2. What two forces are balanced in *gravitational equilibrium*? How does gravitational equilibrium determine the pressure at any depth within a planet or star?

3. What is the Sun made of? How do we know?

4. Briefly describe the Sun's luminosity, mass, radius, and average surface temperature.

5. Briefly describe the distinguishing features of each of the Sun's major layers shown in Figure 14.4.

6. What are *sunspots*? Why do they appear dark in pictures of the Sun?

7. Distinguish between *nuclear fission* and *nuclear fusion*. Which one is used in nuclear power plants? Which one is used by the Sun?

8. Why does fusion require high temperatures and pressures? What role does the *strong force* play?

9. What is the overall nuclear fusion reaction in the Sun? Briefly describe the *proton–proton chain*.

10. How does the idea of gravitational equilibrium explain why the Sun's core temperature and fusion rate are self-regulating, like a thermostat?

11. Explain how mathematical models allow us to predict conditions inside the Sun. How can we be confident that the models are on the right track?

12. How are "sun quakes" similar to earthquakes? How are they different? Describe how we can observe them and how they help us learn about the solar interior.

13. What is the *solar neutrino problem*? Describe a possible solution to this problem.

14. Why does the energy produced by fusion in the solar core take so long to reach the solar surface? Describe the process of *radiative diffusion*.

15. What is *convection*? Describe how convection transports energy through the Sun's convection zone.

16. Describe the appearance and temperature of the Sun's *photosphere*. What is *granulation*? How would granulation appear in a movie?

17. Briefly describe how *magnetic field lines* are related to what we would see if we placed compasses in a magnetic field.

18. How are magnetic fields related to sunspots? Describe how magnetic fields explain each of the following: the fact that sunspot plasma is cool, the existence and appearance of *prominences*, and the dramatic explosions of *solar flares*.

19. Why is the *chromosphere* best viewed with ultraviolet telescopes? Why is the *corona* best viewed with X-ray telescopes?

20. Describe the current theory of how the chromosphere and corona are heated. What evidence supports it?

21. What are *coronal holes*? How are they related to the solar wind?

22. What do we mean by *solar activity*? Explain how it is similar to weather on short time scales and to climate on longer time scales.

23. Describe the *sunspot cycle*. What do we mean by *solar maximum* and *solar minimum*? Explain why the complete cycle is really 22 years rather than 11 years.

24. Describe a few known ways solar activity affects the Earth. Why is it so difficult to establish links between solar activity and the Earth's climate?

## *Discussion Questions*

1. *The Solar Neutrino Problem.* Discuss the solar neutrino problem and its potential solutions. How serious do you consider this problem? Do you think current theoretical models of the Sun could be wrong in any fundamental way? Why or why not?

2. *The Sun and Global Warming.* One of the most pressing environmental issues on Earth concerns the extent to which human emissions of greenhouse gases are warming our planet. Some people claim that part or all of the observed warming over the past century may be due to changes on the Sun, rather than to anything humans have done. Discuss how a better understanding of the Sun might help us understand the threat posed by greenhouse gas emissions. Why is it so difficult to develop a clear understanding of how the Sun affects the Earth's climate?

## *Problems*

*Sensible Statements?* For **problems 1–7**, decide whether the statement is sensible and explain why it is or is not.

1. Before Einstein, gravitational contraction appeared to be a perfectly plausible mechanism for solar energy generation.

2. A sudden temperature rise in the Sun's core is nothing to worry about, because conditions in the core will soon return to normal.

3. If fusion in the solar core ceased today, worldwide panic would break out tomorrow as the Sun began to grow dimmer.

4. Astronomers have recently photographed magnetic fields churning deep beneath the solar photosphere.

5. Neutrinos probably can't harm me, but just to be safe I think I'll wear a lead vest.

6. If you want to see lots of sunspots, just wait for solar maximum!

7. News of a major solar flare today caused concern among professionals in the fields of communications and electrical power generation.

8. *Differential Rotation.* The Sun and Jupiter exhibit differential rotation, but Earth does not.

   a. Explain clearly what we mean by *differential rotation.*

   b. Briefly explain why it is possible for jovian planets to rotate differentially, but it is not possible for terrestrial planets to do so.

   c. Would you expect differential rotation to be common among other stars? Why or why not?

*9. *Number of Fusion Reactions in the Sun.* Use the fact that each cycle of the proton–proton chain converts $4.7 \times 10^{-29}$ kg of mass into energy (see Mathematical Insight 14.1), along with the fact that the Sun loses a total of about $4.2 \times 10^9$ kg of mass each second, to calculate the total number of times the proton–proton chain occurs each second in the Sun.

*10. *The Lifetime of the Sun.* The total mass of the Sun is about $2 \times 10^{30}$ kg, of which about 75% was hydrogen when the Sun formed. However, only about 13% of this hydrogen ever becomes available for fusion in the core; the rest remains in layers of the Sun where the temperature is too low for fusion.

   a. Based on the given information, calculate the total mass of hydrogen available for fusion over the lifetime of the Sun.

   b. Combine your results from part (a) and the fact that the Sun fuses about 600 billion kg of hydrogen each second to calculate how long the Sun's initial supply of hydrogen can last. Give your answer in both seconds and years.

   c. Given that our solar system is now about 4.6 billion years old, when will we need to worry about the Sun running out of hydrogen for fusion?

*11. *Solar Power Collectors.* This problem leads you through the calculation and discussion of how much solar power can be collected by solar cells on Earth.

   a. Imagine a giant sphere surrounding the Sun with a radius of 1 AU. What is the surface area of this sphere, in square meters? (*Hint:* The formula for the surface area of a sphere is $4\pi r^2$.)

   b. Because this imaginary giant sphere surrounds the Sun, the Sun's entire luminosity of $3.8 \times 10^{26}$ watts must pass through it. Calculate the power passing through each square meter of this imaginary sphere in *watts per square meter*. Explain why this number represents the maximum power per square meter that can be collected by a solar collector in Earth orbit.

   c. List several reasons why the average power per square meter collected by a solar collector on the ground will always be less than what you found in part (b).

   d. Suppose you want to put a solar collector on your roof. If you want to optimize the amount of power you can collect, how should you orient the collector? (*Hint:* The optimum orientation depends on both your latitude and the time of year and day.)

*12. *Solar Power for the United States.* The total annual U.S. energy consumption is about $2 \times 10^{20}$ joules.

   a. What is the average *power* requirement for the United States, in watts? (*Hint:* 1 watt = 1 joule/s.)

   b. With current technologies and solar collectors on the ground, the best we can hope is that solar cells will generate an average (day and night) power of about 200 watts/$m^2$. (You might compare this to the maximum power per square meter you found in problem 11b.) What total area would we need to cover with solar cells to supply all the power needed for the United States? Give your answer in both square meters and square kilometers.

   c. The total surface area of the United States is about $2 \times 10^7$ km$^2$. What fraction of the U.S. area would have to be covered by solar collectors to generate all of the U.S. power needs? In one page or less, describe potential environmental impacts of covering so much area with solar collectors. Also discuss whether you think these environmental impacts would be greater or lesser than the impacts of using current energy sources such as coal, oil, nuclear power, and hydroelectric power.

*13. *The Color of the Sun.* The Sun's average surface temperature is about 5,800 K. Use Wien's law (see Mathematical Insight 6.2) to calculate the wavelength of peak thermal emission from the Sun. What color does this wavelength correspond to in the visible-light spectrum? In light of your answer, why do you think the Sun appears white or yellow to our eyes?

## Web Projects

Find useful links for Web projects on the text Web site.

1. *Current Solar Activity.* Daily information about solar activity is available at NASA's Web site sunspotcycle.com. Where are we in the sunspot cycle right now? When is the next solar maximum or minimum expected? Have there been any major solar storms in the past few months? If so, did they have any significant effects on Earth? Summarize your findings in a one- to two-page report.

2. *Solar Observatories in Space.* Visit NASA's Web site for the Sun–Earth connection and explore some of the current and planned space missions designed to observe the Sun. Choose one mission to study in greater depth, and write a one- to two-page report on the mission status and goals and what it has taught or will teach us about the Sun.

3. *Sudbury Neutrino Observatory.* Visit the Web site for the Sudbury Neutrino Observatory (SNO) and learn how it may help solve the solar neutrino problem. Write a one- to two-page report describing the observatory, any recent results, and what we can expect from it in the future.

*"All men have the stars," he answered, "but they are not the same things for different people. For some, who are travelers, the stars are guides. For others they are no more than little lights in the sky. For others, who are scholars, they are problems. For my businessman they were wealth. But all these stars are silent. You—you alone—will have the stars as no one else has them."*

ANTOINE DE SAINT-EXUPERY,
FROM *THE LITTLE PRINCE*

# CHAPTER 15

# Stars

On a clear, dark night, a few thousand stars are visible to the naked eye. Many more become visible through binoculars, and with a powerful telescope we can see so many stars that we could never hope to count them. Like individual people, each individual star is unique. Like the human family, all stars share much in common.

Today, we know that stars are born from clouds of interstellar gas, shine brilliantly by nuclear fusion for millions or billions of years, and then die, sometimes in dramatic ways. This chapter outlines how we study and categorize stars and how we have come to realize that stars, like people, change over their lifetime.

## 15.1 Snapshot of the Heavens

Imagine that an alien spaceship flies by Earth on a simple but short mission: The visitors have just 1 minute to learn everything they can about the human race. In 60 seconds, they will see next to nothing of each individual person's life. Instead, they will obtain a collective "snapshot" of humanity that shows people from all stages of life engaged in their daily activities. From this snapshot alone, they must piece together their entire understanding of human beings and their lives, from birth to death.

We face a similar problem when we look at the stars. Compared with stellar lifetimes of millions or billions of years, the few hundred years humans have spent studying stars with telescopes is rather like the aliens' 1-minute glimpse of humanity. We see only a brief moment in any star's life, and our collective snapshot of the heavens consists of such frozen moments for billions of stars. From this snapshot, we try to reconstruct the life cycles of stars while also analyzing what makes one star different from another.

Thanks to the efforts of hundreds of astronomers studying this snapshot of the heavens, stars are no longer mysterious points of light in the sky. We now know that all stars form in great clouds of gas and dust. All stars begin their life with roughly the same chemical composition: About three-quarters of the star's mass at birth is hydrogen, and about one-quarter is helium, with no more than about 2% consisting of elements heavier than helium. During most of any star's life, the rate at which it generates energy depends on the same type of balance between the inward pull of gravity and the outward push of internal pressure that governs the rate of fusion in our Sun. Despite these similarities, stars appear different from one another for two primary reasons: They differ in mass, and we see different stars at different stages of their lives.

The key that finally unlocked these secrets of stars was an appropriate classification system. Before the twentieth century, humans classified stars primarily by their brightness and location in our sky. The brightest stars within each constellation still bear Greek letters designating their order of brightness. For example, the brightest star in the constellation Centaurus is Alpha Centauri, the second brightest is Beta Centauri, the third brightest is Gamma Centauri, and so on. However, a star's brightness and membership in a constellation tell us little about its true nature. A star that appears bright could be either extremely powerful or unusually close, and two stars that appear right next to each other in our sky might not be true neighbors if they lie at significantly different distances from Earth.

Today, astronomers classify a star primarily according to its *luminosity* and *surface temperature*. Our

task in this chapter is to learn how this extraordinarily effective classification system reveals the true natures of stars and their life cycles. We begin by investigating how to determine a star's luminosity, surface temperature, and mass.

## 15.2 Stellar Luminosity

A star's **luminosity** is the total amount of power it radiates into space, which can be stated in *watts* [Section 14.2]. For example, the Sun's luminosity is $3.8 \times 10^{26}$ watts. We cannot measure a star's luminosity directly, because its brightness in our sky depends on its distance as well as its true luminosity. For example, our Sun and Alpha Centauri A (the brightest of the three stars in the Alpha Centauri system [Section 1.2]) are similar in luminosity. But Alpha Centauri A is a feeble point of light in the night sky, while our Sun provides enough light and heat to sustain life on Earth. The difference in brightness arises because Alpha Centauri A is about 270,000 times farther from Earth than is the Sun.

More precisely, we define the **apparent brightness** of any star in our sky as the amount of light reaching us *per unit area*. (A more technical term for apparent brightness is *flux*.) The apparent brightness of any light source obeys an *inverse square law* with distance, similar to the inverse square law that describes the force of gravity [Section 5.4]. If we viewed the Sun from twice the Earth's distance, it would appear dimmer by a factor of $2^2 = 4$. If we viewed it from 10 times the Earth's distance, it would appear $10^2 = 100$ times dimmer. From 270,000 times the Earth's distance, it would look like Alpha Centauri A—dimmer by a factor of $270,000^2$, or about 70 billion.

Figure 15.1 shows why apparent brightness follows an inverse square law. The same total amount of light must pass through each imaginary sphere surrounding the star. If we focus our attention on the light passing through a small square on the sphere located at 1 AU, we see that the same amount of light must pass through *four* squares of the same size on the sphere located at 2 AU. Thus, each square on the sphere at 2 AU receives only $\frac{1}{2^2} = \frac{1}{4}$ as much light as the square on the sphere at 1 AU. Similarly, the same amount of light passes through *nine* squares of the same size on the sphere located at 3 AU. Thus, each of these squares receives only $\frac{1}{3^2} = \frac{1}{9}$ as much light as the square on the sphere at 1 AU. Generalizing, we see that the amount of light received per unit area decreases with increasing distance by the square of the distance—an inverse square law.

This inverse square law leads to a very simple and important formula relating the apparent brightness, luminosity, and distance of any light source. We will call it the **luminosity–distance formula**:

$$\text{apparent brightness} = \frac{\text{luminosity}}{4\pi \times (\text{distance})^2}$$

Note that, because the standard units of luminosity are watts, the units of apparent brightness are *watts per square meter*. Because we can always measure the apparent brightness of a star, this formula provides a way to calculate a star's luminosity if we can first measure its distance or to calculate a star's distance if we somehow know its luminosity. (The luminosity–distance formula is strictly correct only if interstellar dust does not absorb or scatter the starlight along its path to Earth.)

## Mathematical Insight 15.1
## The Luminosity–Distance Formula

We can derive the luminosity–distance formula by extending the idea illustrated in Figure 15.1. Suppose we are located a distance $d$ from a star with luminosity $L$. The apparent brightness of the star is the power per unit area that we receive at our distance $d$. We can find this apparent brightness by imagining that we are part of a giant sphere with radius $d$, similar to any one of the three spheres in Figure 15.1. The surface area of this giant sphere is $4\pi \times d^2$, and the star's entire luminosity $L$ must pass through this surface area. (Recall that the surface area of any sphere is $4\pi \times \text{radius}^2$.) Thus, the apparent brightness at distance $d$ is the power per unit area passing through the sphere:

$$\text{apparent brightness} = \frac{\text{star's luminosity}}{\text{surface area of imaginary sphere}}$$

$$= \frac{L}{4\pi \times d^2}$$

This is our luminosity–distance formula.

*Example:* What is the apparent brightness of sunlight as seen from the Earth?

*Solution:* The Sun's luminosity is $L_{\text{Sun}} = 3.8 \times 10^{26}$ watts, and the Earth's distance from the Sun is $d = 1.5 \times 10^{11}$ meters. Thus, the apparent brightness of sunlight at the Earth's surface is:

$$\frac{L}{4\pi \times d^2} = \frac{3.8 \times 10^{26} \text{ watts}}{4\pi \times (1.5 \times 10^{11} \text{ m})^2}$$

$$= 1.3 \times 10^3 \text{ watts/m}^2$$

This apparent brightness of about 1,300 watts per square meter represents the maximum power that could be collected by a detector on Earth that directly faces the Sun, such as a solar power (or *photovoltaic*) cell. In reality, the apparent brightness is usually lower because the Earth's atmosphere absorbs some sunlight, particularly when it is cloudy.

Although watts are the standard units for luminosity, it's often more meaningful to describe stellar luminosities in comparison to the Sun by using units of **solar luminosity**: $L_{Sun} = 3.8 \times 10^{26}$ watts. For example, Proxima Centauri, the nearest of the three stars in the Alpha Centauri system and hence the nearest star besides our Sun, is only about 0.0006 times as luminous as the Sun, or $0.0006 L_{Sun}$. Betelgeuse, the bright left-shoulder star of Orion, has a luminosity of $38,000 L_{Sun}$, meaning that it is 38,000 times more luminous than the Sun.

### Measuring the Apparent Brightness

We can measure a star's apparent brightness by using a detector, such as a CCD, that records how much energy strikes its light-sensitive surface each second. For example, such a detector would record an apparent brightness of $2.7 \times 10^{-8}$ watt per square meter from Alpha Centauri A. The only difficulties involved in measuring apparent brightness are making sure the detector is properly calibrated and, for ground-based telescopes, taking into account the absorption of light by the Earth's atmosphere.

No detector can record light of all wavelengths, so we necessarily measure apparent brightness in only some small range of the complete spectrum. For example, the human eye is sensitive to visible light but does not respond to ultraviolet or infrared photons. Thus, when we perceive a star's brightness, our eyes are measuring the apparent brightness only in the visible region of the spectrum. Clearly, when we measure the apparent brightness in visible light, we can calculate only the star's *visible-light luminosity*. Similarly, when we observe a star with a spaceborne X-ray telescope, we measure only the apparent brightness in X rays and can calculate only the star's *X-ray luminosity*. We will use the terms **total luminosity** and **total apparent brightness** to describe the luminosity and apparent brightness we would measure *if* we could detect photons across the entire electromagnetic spectrum. (Astronomers refer to the total luminosity as the *bolometric* luminosity.)

### Measuring Distance Through Stellar Parallax

Once we have measured a star's apparent brightness, the next step in determining its luminosity is to measure its distance. The most direct way to measure the distances to stars is with *stellar parallax,* the small annual shifts in a star's apparent position caused by the Earth's motion around the Sun [Section 2.4]. Recall that you can observe parallax of your finger by holding it at arm's length and looking at it alternately with first one eye closed and then the other. Astronomers measure stellar parallax by comparing observations of a nearby star made 6 months apart (Figure 15.2).

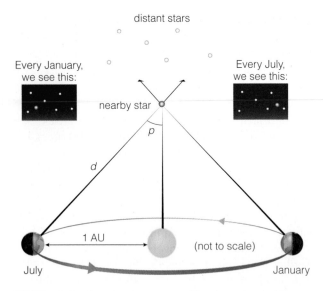

**FIGURE 15.2** Parallax makes the apparent position of a nearby star shift back and forth with respect to distant stars over the course of each year. If we measure the parallax angle $p$ in arcseconds, the distance $d$ to the star in parsecs is $\frac{1}{p}$. The angle in this figure is greatly exaggerated: All stars have parallax angles of less than 1 arcsecond.

The nearby star appears to shift against the background of more distant stars because we are observing it from two opposite points of the Earth's orbit. The star's **parallax angle** is defined as *half* the star's annual back-and-forth shift.

Measuring stellar parallax is difficult because stars are so far away, making their parallax angles very small. Even the nearest star, Proxima Centauri, has a parallax angle of only 0.77 arcsecond. For increasingly distant stars, the parallax angles quickly become too small to measure even with our highest-resolution telescopes. Current technology allows us to measure parallax only for stars within a few hundred light-years—not much farther than what we call our *local solar neighborhood* in the vast, 100,000-light-year-diameter Milky Way Galaxy.

By definition, the distance to an object with a parallax angle of 1 arcsecond is one **parsec**, abbreviated **pc**. (The word *parsec* comes from the words *parallax* and *arcsecond*.) With a little geometry and Figure 15.2, it is possible to show that:

$$1 \text{ pc} = 3.26 \text{ light-years} = 3.09 \times 10^{13} \text{ km}$$

If we use units of arcseconds for the parallax angle, a simple formula allows us to calculate distances in parsecs:

$$d \text{ (in parsecs)} = \frac{1}{p \text{ (in arcseconds)}}$$

For example, the distance to a star with a parallax angle of 1/2 arcsecond is 2 parsecs, the distance to a star with a parallax angle of 1/10 arcsecond is 10 parsecs, and the distance to a star with a parallax angle of 1/100 arcsecond is 100 parsecs. Astronomers often express distances in parsecs or light-years interchangeably, so you should learn to convert quickly between them by remembering that 1 pc = 3.26 light-years. Thus, 10 parsecs is about 32.6 light-years; 1,000 parsecs, or 1 kiloparsec (1 kpc), is about 3,260 light-years; and 1 million parsecs, or 1 megaparsec (1 Mpc), is about 3.26 million light-years.

Enough stars have measurable parallax to give us a fairly good sample of the many different types of stars. For example, we know of over 300 stars within about 33 light-years (10 parsecs) of the Sun. About half are binary star systems consisting of two orbiting stars or multiple star systems containing three or more stars. Most are tiny, dim red stars such as Proxima Centauri—so dim that we cannot see them with the naked eye, despite the fact that they are relatively close. A few nearby stars, such as Sirius (2.6 parsecs), Vega (8 parsecs), Altair (5 parsecs), and Fomalhaut (7 parsecs), are white in color and bright in our sky, but many more of the brightest stars in the sky lie farther away. The intrinsic luminosities of stars must therefore span a wide range, since so many nearby stars appear dim while many more distant stars appear bright.

### The Magnitude System

Many amateur and professional astronomers describe stellar brightness using the ancient **magnitude system** devised by the Greek astronomer Hipparchus (c. 190–120 B.C.). The magnitude system originally classified stars according to how bright they look to

Hipparchus

---

## Mathematical Insight 15.2    The Parallax Formula

Here is one of several ways to derive the formula relating a star's distance and parallax angle. Figure 15.2 shows that the parallax angle $p$ is part of a right triangle, the side opposite $p$ is the Earth–Sun distance of 1 AU, and the hypotenuse is the distance $d$ to the object. You may recall that the *sine* of an angle in a right triangle is the length of its opposite side divided by the length of the hypotenuse. In this case, we find:

$$\sin p = \frac{\text{length of opposite side}}{\text{length of hypotenuse}} = \frac{1\ \text{AU}}{d}$$

If we solve for $d$, the formula becomes:

$$d = \frac{1\ \text{AU}}{\sin p}$$

By definition, 1 parsec is the distance to an object with a parallax angle of 1 arcsecond (1″), or 1/3,600 degree. (Recall that 1° = 60′ and 1′ = 60″.) Substituting these numbers into the parallax formula and using a calculator to find that $\sin 1'' = 4.84814 \times 10^{-6}$, we get:

$$1\ \text{pc} = \frac{1\ \text{AU}}{\sin 1''} = \frac{1\ \text{AU}}{4.84814 \times 10^{-6}} = 206{,}265\ \text{AU}$$

That is, 1 parsec = 206,265 AU, which is equivalent to $3.09 \times 10^{13}$ km or 3.26 light-years. (Recall that 1 AU = 149.6 million km.)

We need one more fact from geometry to derive the parallax formula given in the text. As long as the parallax angle, $p$, is small, $\sin p$ is proportional to $p$. For example, $\sin 2''$ is twice as large as $\sin 1''$, and $\sin \frac{1}{2}''$ is half as large as $\sin 1''$. (You can verify these examples with your calculator.) Thus, if we use $\frac{1}{2}''$ instead of 1″ for the parallax angle in the formula above, we get a distance of 2 pc instead of 1 pc. Similarly, if we use a parallax angle of $\frac{1}{10}''$, we get a distance of 10 pc. Generalizing, we get the simple parallax formula given in the text:

$$d\ (\text{in parsecs}) = \frac{1}{p\ (\text{in arcseconds})}$$

*Example:* Sirius, the brightest star in our night sky, has a measured parallax angle of 0.379″. How far away is it in parsecs? In light-years?

*Solution:* From the formula, the distance to Sirius in parsecs is

$$d\ (\text{in pc}) = \frac{1}{0.379} = 2.64\ \text{pc}$$

Because 1 pc = 3.26 light-years, this distance is equivalent to:

$$2.64\ \text{pc} \times 3.26\ \frac{\text{light-years}}{\text{pc}} = 8.60\ \text{light-years}$$

our eyes—the only instruments available in ancient times. The brightest stars received the designation "first magnitude," the next brightest "second magnitude," and so on. The faintest visible stars were magnitude 6. We call these descriptions **apparent magnitudes** because they compare how bright different stars *appear* in the sky. Star charts often use dots of different sizes to represent the apparent magnitudes of stars.

In modern times, the magnitude system has been extended and more precisely defined (see Mathematical Insight 15.3). As a result, stars can have fractional apparent magnitudes, and a few bright stars have apparent magnitudes *less than* 1—which means *brighter* than magnitude 1. For example, the brightest star in the night sky, Sirius, has an apparent magnitude of −1.46.

The modern magnitude system also defines **absolute magnitudes** as a way of describing stellar luminosities. A star's absolute magnitude is the apparent magnitude it would have *if* it were at a distance of 10 parsecs from Earth. For example, the Sun's absolute magnitude is about 4.8, meaning that the Sun would have an apparent magnitude of 4.8 *if* it were 10 parsecs away from us—bright enough to be visible, but not conspicuous, on a dark night.

It's worth acquainting yourself with the magnitude system, because it is still commonly used. However, for the calculations in this book, it's much easier to work with the luminosity–distance formula, so we will avoid using magnitude formulas in this book.

## 15.3 Stellar Surface Temperature

The second basic property of stars (besides luminosity) needed for modern stellar classification is surface temperature. Measuring a star's surface temperature is somewhat easier than measuring its luminosity because the measurement is not affected by the star's distance. Instead, we determine surface temperature directly from the star's color or spectrum. One note of caution: We can measure only a star's *surface temperature,* not its interior temperature. (Interior temperatures are calculated with theoretical models [Section 14.3].) When astronomers speak of the "temperature" of a star, they usually mean the surface temperature unless they say otherwise.

A star's surface temperature determines the color of light it emits. A red star is cooler than a yellow star, which in turn is cooler than a blue star. The naked eye can distinguish colors only for the brightest stars, but colors become more evident when we view stars through binoculars or a telescope (Figure 15.3). Astronomers can determine the "color" of a star more precisely by comparing its apparent brightness as viewed through two different filters [Section 7.3]. For example, a cool star such as Betelgeuse, with a surface temperature of about 3,400 K, emits more red light than blue light and therefore looks much brighter when viewed through a red filter than when viewed through a blue filter. In contrast, a hotter star such as Sirius, with a surface temperature of about 9,400 K, emits more blue light than

---

## Mathematical Insight 15.3    The Modern Magnitude Scale

The modern magnitude system is defined so that each difference of 5 magnitudes corresponds to a factor of exactly 100 in brightness. For example, a magnitude 1 star is 100 times brighter than a magnitude 6 star, and a magnitude 3 star is 100 times brighter than a magnitude 8 star. Because 5 magnitudes corresponds to a factor of 100 in brightness, a single magnitude corresponds to a factor of $(100)^{1/5} \approx$ 2.512. The following formula summarizes the relationship between stars of different magnitudes:

$$\frac{\text{apparent brightness of Star 1}}{\text{apparent brightness of Star 2}} = (100^{1/5})^{m_2 - m_1}$$

where $m_1$ and $m_2$ are the apparent magnitudes of Stars 1 and 2, respectively. If we replace the apparent magnitudes with absolute magnitudes (designated $M$ instead of $m$), the same formula applies to stellar luminosities:

$$\frac{\text{luminosity of Star 1}}{\text{luminosity of Star 2}} = (100^{1/5})^{M_2 - M_1}$$

*Example 1:* On a clear night, stars dimmer than magnitude 5 are quite difficult to see. Today, sensitive instruments on large telescopes can detect objects as faint as magni-

tude 30. How much more sensitive are such telescopes than the human eye?

*Solution:* We imagine that our eye sees "Star 1" with magnitude 5 and the telescope detects "Star 2" with magnitude 30; then we compare:

$$\frac{\text{apparent brightness of Star 1}}{\text{apparent brightness of Star 2}} = (100^{1/5})^{30-5} = (100^{1/5})^{25}$$

$$= 100^5 = 10^{10}$$

The magnitude 5 star is $10^{10}$, or 10 billion, times brighter than the magnitude 30 star, so the telescope is 10 billion times more sensitive than the human eye.

*Example 2:* The Sun has an absolute magnitude of about 4.8. Polaris, the North Star, has an absolute magnitude of −3.6. How much more luminous is Polaris than the Sun?

*Solution:* We use Polaris as Star 1 and the Sun as Star 2:

$$\frac{\text{luminosity of Polaris}}{\text{luminosity of Sun}} = (100^{1/5})^{4.8-(-3.6)} = (100^{1/5})^{8.4}$$

$$= 100^{1.7} \approx 2,500$$

Polaris is about 2,500 times more luminous than the Sun.

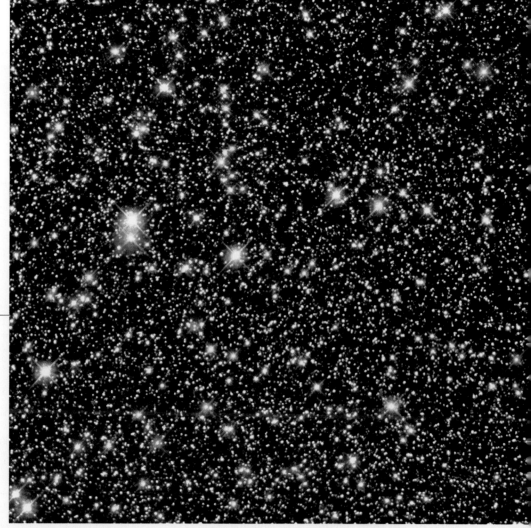

**FIGURE 15.3** This Hubble Space Telescope view through the heart of our Milky Way Galaxy reveals that stars come in many different colors.

red light and looks much brighter through a blue filter than through a red filter.

### Spectral Type

The emission and absorption lines in a star's spectrum provide an independent and more accurate way to measure its surface temperature. Stars displaying spectral lines of highly ionized elements must be fairly hot, while stars displaying spectral lines of molecules must be relatively cool [Section 6.4]. Astronomers classify stars according to surface temperature by assigning a **spectral type** determined from the spectral lines present in a star's spectrum. The hottest stars, with the bluest colors, are called spectral type O, followed in order of declining surface temperature by spectral types B, A, F, G, K, and M. The time-honored mnemonic for remembering this sequence, OBAFGKM, is "Oh Be A Fine Girl/Guy, Kiss Me!" Table 15.1 summarizes the characteristics of each spectral type.

Each spectral type is subdivided into numbered subcategories (e.g., B0, B1, . . . , B9). The larger the number, the cooler the star. For example, the Sun is designated spectral type G2, which means it is slightly hotter than a G3 star but cooler than a G1 star.

**TIME OUT TO THINK** *Invent your own mnemonic for the OBAFGKM sequence. To help get you thinking, here are two examples: (1) Only Bungling Astronomers Forget Generally Known Mnemonics; and (2) Only Business Acts For Good, Karl Marx.*

### History of the Spectral Sequence

You may wonder why the spectral types follow the peculiar order of OBAFGKM. The answer lies in the history of stellar spectroscopy. Astronomical research never paid well, and many astronomers of the 1800s were able to do research only because of family wealth. One such astronomer was Henry Draper (1837–1882), an early pioneer of stellar spectroscopy. After Draper died in 1882, his widow made a series of large donations to Harvard College Observatory for the purpose of building upon his work. The observatory director, Edward Pickering (1846–1919), used the gifts to improve the facilities and to hire numerous assistants, whom he called "computers"; Pickering added money of his own, as did other wealthy donors.

Most of Pickering's hired computers were women who had studied physics or astronomy at women's colleges such as Wellesley and Radcliffe. Women had few opportunities to advance in science at the time; Harvard, for example, did not allow women as either students or faculty. But Pickering's project of studying and classifying stellar spectra provided plenty of work and opportunity for his computers, and many of the Harvard Observatory women ended up among the most prominent astronomers of the late 1800s and early 1900s. One of the first computers was Williamina Fleming (1857–1911). Following Pickering's suggestion, Fleming classified stellar spectra according to the strength of their hydrogen lines: Type A for the strongest hydrogen lines, type B for slightly weaker hydrogen lines, and so on to type O, for stars with the weakest hydrogen lines. Pickering published Fleming's classifications of more than 10,000 stars in 1890.

As more stellar spectra were obtained and spectra were studied in greater detail, it became clear that the classification scheme based solely on hydrogen lines was inadequate. Ultimately, the task of finding a better classification scheme fell to Annie Jump Cannon (1863–1941), who joined Pickering's team in 1896 (Figure 15.4). Building on the work of Fleming and another of Pickering's computers, Antonia Maury (1866–1952), Cannon soon realized that the spectral classes fell into a natural order—but it was not the alphabetical order determined by hydrogen lines alone. Moreover, she

**Table 15.1  The Spectral Sequence**

| Spectral Type | Example(s) | Temperature Range | Key Absorption Line Features |
|---|---|---|---|
| O | Stars of Orion's Belt | >30,000 K | Lines of ionized helium, weak hydrogen lines |
| B | Rigel | 30,000 K–10,000 K | Lines of neutral helium, moderate hydrogen lines |
| A | Sirius | 10,000 K–7,500 K | Very strong hydrogen lines |
| F | Polaris | 7,500 K–6,000 K | Moderate hydrogen lines, moderate lines of ionized calcium |
| G | Sun, Alpha Centauri A | 6,000 K–5,000 K | Weak hydrogen lines, strong lines of ionized calcium |
| K | Arcturus | 5,000 K–3,500 K | Lines of neutral and singly ionized metals, some molecules |
| M | Betelgeuse, Proxima Centauri | <3,500 K | Molecular lines strong |

found that some of the original classes overlapped others and could be eliminated. Cannon discovered that the natural sequence consisted of just a few of Pickering's original classes in the order OBAFGKM; she also added the subdivisions by number. Cannon became so adept that she could properly classify a stellar spectrum with little more than a momentary glance. During her lifetime, she personally classified over 400,000 stars. She became the first woman ever awarded an honorary degree by Oxford University, and in 1929 the League of Women Voters named her one of the 12 greatest living American women.

The astronomical community adopted Cannon's system of stellar classification in 1910. However, no one at that time knew *why* spectra followed the OBAFGKM sequence. Many astronomers guessed, incorrectly, that the different sets of spectral lines reflected different compositions for the stars. The correct answer—that all stars are made primarily of hydrogen and helium and that a star's surface temperature determines the strength of its spectral lines—was discovered by Cecilia Payne-Gaposchkin (1900–1979), another woman working at Harvard Observatory. Relying on insights from what was then the newly developing science of quantum mechanics, Payne-Gaposchkin showed that the differences in spectral lines from star to star merely reflected changes

**FIGURE 15.4** Women astronomers pose with Edward Pickering at Harvard College Observatory in 1913. Annie Jump Cannon is fifth from the left in the back row.

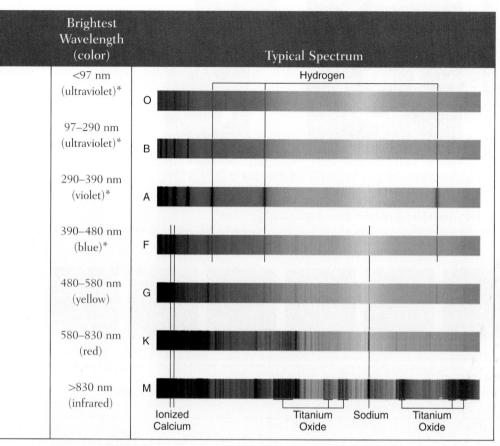

| Brightest Wavelength (color) | Typical Spectrum |
|---|---|
| <97 nm (ultraviolet)* | O |
| 97–290 nm (ultraviolet)* | B |
| 290–390 nm (violet)* | A |
| 390–480 nm (blue)* | F |
| 480–580 nm (yellow) | G |
| 580–830 nm (red) | K |
| >830 nm (infrared) | M |

Hydrogen

Ionized Calcium · Titanium Oxide · Sodium · Titanium Oxide

*All stars above 6,000 K look more or less white to the human eye because they emit plenty of radiation at all visible wavelengths.

in the ionization level of the emitting atoms. For example, O stars have weak hydrogen lines because, at their high surface temperatures, nearly all their hydrogen is ionized. Without an electron to "jump" between energy levels, ionized hydrogen can neither emit nor absorb its usual specific wavelengths of light. At the other end of the spectral sequence, M stars are cool enough for some particularly stable molecules to form, thus explaining their strong molecular absorption lines. Payne-Gaposchkin described her work and her conclusions in a dissertation published in 1925. A later review of twentieth-century astronomy called her work "undoubtedly the most brilliant Ph.D. thesis ever written in astronomy."

Cecilia Payne-Gaposchkin

## 15.4 Stellar Masses

The most important property of a star is its mass, but stellar masses are harder to measure than luminosi-

ties or surface temperatures. The most dependable method for "weighing" a star relies on Newton's version of Kepler's third law [Section 5.4]:

$$p^2 = \frac{4\pi^2}{G(M_1 + M_2)}a^3$$

where $G$ is the gravitational constant, $M_1$ and $M_2$ are the masses of two orbiting objects, and $p$ and $a$ are the orbital period and average radius (semimajor axis) of the orbiting star system. This law can be applied only when we can measure both $p$ and $a$. Thus, in most cases we can measure stellar masses only in binary star systems in which we have determined the orbital properties of the two stars.

### Types of Binary Star Systems

About half of all stars orbit a companion star of some kind, and these star systems fall into three classes:

■ A **visual binary** is a pair of stars that we can see distinctly (with a telescope) as the stars orbit each other. Mizar, the second star in the handle of the Big Dipper, is one example of a visual binary

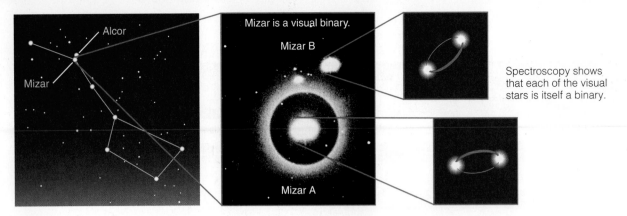

FIGURE 15.5 Mizar looks like one star to the naked eye but is actually a system of four stars. Through a telescope Mizar appears to be a visual binary made up of two stars, Mizar A and Mizar B, that gradually change positions, indicating that they orbit every few thousand years. However, each of these two stars is actually a spectroscopic binary, making a total of four stars. (The star Alcor appears very close to Mizar to the naked eye but does *not* orbit it.)

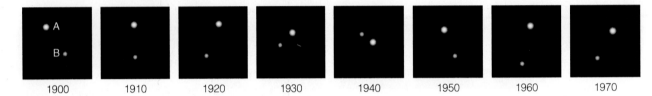

FIGURE 15.6 Each frame represents the relative positions of Sirius A and Sirius B at 10-year intervals from 1900 to 1970. The back-and-forth "wobble" of Sirius A allowed astronomers to infer the existence of Sirius B even before the two stars could be resolved in telescopic photos.

(Figure 15.5). Sometimes we observe a star slowly shifting position in the sky as if it were a member of a visual binary, but its companion is too dim to be seen. For example, slow shifts in the position of Sirius, the brightest star in the sky, revealed it to be a binary star long before its companion was discovered (Figure 15.6).

- An **eclipsing binary** is a pair of stars that orbit in the plane of our line of sight (Figure 15.7). When neither star is eclipsed, we see the combined light of both stars. But when one star eclipses the other, the apparent brightness of the system drops because some of the light is blocked from view. A *light curve*, or graph of apparent brightness against time, reveals the pattern of the eclipses. The most famous example of an eclipsing binary is Algol, the "demon star" in the constellation Perseus (*algol* is Arabic for "the ghoul"). Algol becomes three times dimmer for a few hours about every 3 days as the brighter of its two stars is eclipsed by its dimmer companion.

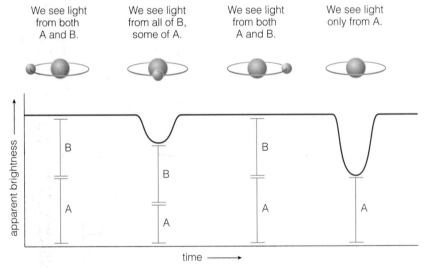

FIGURE 15.7 The apparent brightness of an eclipsing binary system drops when either star eclipses the other.

- If a binary system is neither visual nor eclipsing, we may be able to detect its binary nature by observing Doppler shifts in its spectral lines [Section 6.5]. If one star is orbiting another, it periodically moves toward us and away from us in its orbit, and its spectral lines show blueshifts and redshifts as a result of this motion (Figure 15.8). Because we detect the binary nature of such star systems by studying their spectra, they are called

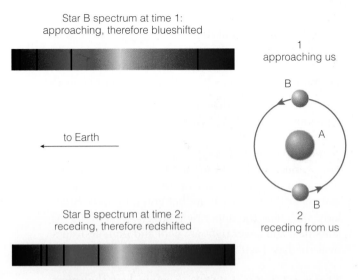

Star B spectrum at time 1:
approaching, therefore blueshifted

to Earth

Star B spectrum at time 2:
receding, therefore redshifted

1
approaching us

A

B

2
receding from us

**FIGURE 15.8** The spectral lines of a star in a binary system are alternately blueshifted as it comes toward us in its orbit and redshifted as it moves away from us.

spectroscopic binary systems. Sometimes we see two sets of lines shifting back and forth—one set from each of the two stars in the system (a *double-lined* spectroscopic binary). Other times we see a set of shifting lines from only one star because its companion is too dim to be detected (a *single-lined* spectroscopic binary). Interestingly, each of the two stars in the visual binary Mizar is itself a spectroscopic binary.

### Measuring Masses in Binary Systems

Even for a binary system, we can apply Newton's version of Kepler's third law only if we can measure both the orbital period and separation of the two stars. Measuring orbital period is fairly easy: In a visual binary, we simply observe how long each orbit takes (or extrapolate from part of an orbit); in an eclipsing binary, we measure the time between eclipses; and in a spectroscopic binary, we measure the time it takes the spectral lines to shift back and forth.

Determining the average separation of the stars in a binary system is usually much more difficult. Except in rare cases in which we can measure the separation directly, we can calculate the separation only if

---

## Mathematical Insight 15.4  Orbital Separation and Newton's Version of Kepler's Third Law

Measurements of stellar masses rely on Newton's version of Kepler's third law [Section 5.4], for which we need to know the orbital period $p$ and semimajor axis $a$. As described in the text, it's generally easy to measure $p$ for binary star systems. We can rarely measure $a$ directly, but we can calculate it in cases in which we can measure the orbital velocity of one star relative to the other. If we assume that the first star traces a circle of radius $a$ around its companion, the circumference of its orbit is $2\pi a$. Because the star makes one circuit of this circumference in one orbital period $p$, its velocity relative to its companion is:

$$v = \frac{\text{distance traveled in one orbit}}{\text{period of one orbit}} = \frac{2\pi a}{p}$$

Solving for $a$, we find:

$$a = \frac{pv}{2\pi}$$

Once we know both $p$ and $a$, we can use Newton's version of Kepler's third law to calculate the *sum* of the masses of the two stars $(M_1 + M_2)$. We can then calculate the individual masses of the two stars by taking advantage of the fact that the relative velocities of the two stars around their common center of mass are inversely proportional to their relative masses.

*Example:* The spectral lines of two stars in a particular eclipsing binary system shift back and forth with a period of 2 years ($p = 6.2 \times 10^7$ seconds). The lines of one star (Star 1) shift twice as far as the lines of the other (Star 2); the amount of the Doppler shift indicates an orbital speed of $v = 100{,}000$ m/s for Star 1 relative to Star 2. What are

the masses of the two stars? Assume that each of the two stars traces a circular orbit around their center of mass.

*Solution:* We will find the masses by using Newton's version of Kepler's third law, solved for the masses:

$$p^2 = \frac{4\pi^2}{G(M_1 + M_2)}a^3 \Rightarrow (M_1 + M_2) = \frac{4\pi^2}{G} \cdot \frac{a^3}{p^2}$$

We are given the orbital period $p = 6.2 \times 10^7$ s, and we find the semimajor axis $a$ of the system from the given orbital velocity $v$:

$$a = \frac{pv}{2\pi} = \frac{(6.2 \times 10^7 \text{ s}) \times (100{,}000 \text{ m/s})}{2\pi}$$
$$= 9.9 \times 10^{11} \text{ m}$$

Now we calculate the sum of the stellar masses by substituting the values of $p$, $a$, and the gravitational constant $G$ [Section 5.4] into the mass equation above:

$$(M_1 + M_2) = \frac{4\pi^2}{\left(6.67 \times 10^{-11} \dfrac{\text{m}^3}{\text{kg} \times \text{s}^2}\right)} \times \frac{(9.9 \times 10^{11} \text{ m})^3}{(6.2 \times 10^7 \text{ s})^2}$$
$$= 1.5 \times 10^{32} \text{ kg}$$

The fact that the lines of Star 1 shift twice as far as those of Star 2 tells us that Star 1 moves twice as fast as Star 2, and hence that Star 1 is half as massive as Star 2. In other words, Star 2 is twice as massive as Star 1. Using this fact and their combined mass of $1.5 \times 10^{32}$ kg, we conclude that the mass of Star 2 is $1.0 \times 10^{32}$ kg and the mass of Star 1 is $0.5 \times 10^{32}$ kg.

we know the actual orbital speeds of the stars from their Doppler shifts. Unfortunately, a Doppler shift tells us only the portion of a star's velocity that is directly toward us or away from us. Because orbiting stars generally do not move directly along our line of sight, their actual velocities can be significantly greater than those we measure through the Doppler effect.

The exceptions are eclipsing binary stars; because they orbit in the plane of our line of sight, their Doppler shifts can tell us their true orbital velocities.[1] Eclipsing binaries are therefore particularly important to the study of stellar masses. As an added bonus, eclipsing binaries allow us to measure stellar radii directly: Because we know how fast the stars are moving across our line of sight as one eclipses the other, we can determine their radii by timing how long each eclipse lasts.

**TIME OUT TO THINK** *Suppose two orbiting stars are moving in a plane perpendicular to our line of sight. Would the spectral features of these stars appear shifted in any way? Explain.*

## 15.5 The Hertzsprung–Russell Diagram

During the first decade of the twentieth century, a similar thought occurred independently to astronomers Ejnar Hertzsprung, working in Denmark, and Henry Norris Russell, working in the United States at Princeton University: Each decided to make a graph plotting stellar luminosities on one axis and spectral types on the other. Such graphs are now called **Hertzsprung–Russell (H–R) diagrams**. Soon after they began making their graphs, Hertzsprung and Russell uncovered some previously unsuspected patterns in the properties of stars. As we will see shortly, understanding these patterns and the H–R diagram is central to the study of stars.

### A Basic H–R Diagram

Figure 15.9 displays an example of an H–R diagram. Note that:

- The horizontal axis represents stellar surface temperature, which, as we've discussed, corresponds to spectral type. Temperature increases *from right to left* because Hertzsprung and Russell based their diagrams on the spectral sequence OBAFGKM.

- The vertical axis represents stellar luminosity, in units of the Sun's luminosity ($L_{Sun}$). Stellar luminosities span a wide range, so we keep the graph compact by making each tick mark represent a luminosity 10 times larger than the prior tick mark.

Each dot on the diagram represents the spectral type and luminosity of a single star. For example, the dot representing the Sun in Figure 15.9 corresponds to the Sun's spectral type, G2, and its luminosity, $1 L_{Sun}$. Because luminosity increases upward on the diagram and surface temperature increases leftward, stars near the upper left are hot and luminous. Similarly, stars near the upper right are cool and luminous, stars near the lower right are cool and dim, and stars near the lower left are hot and dim.

**TIME OUT TO THINK** *Explain how the colors of the stars in Figure 15.9 help indicate stellar surface temperature. Do these colors tell us anything about interior temperatures? Why or why not?*

The H–R diagram also provides direct information about stellar radii, because a star's luminosity depends on both its surface temperature and its surface area or radius. Recall that surface temperature determines the amount of power emitted by the star *per unit area*: Higher temperature means greater power output per unit area [Section 6.4]. Thus, if two stars have the same surface temperature, one can be more luminous than the other only if it is larger in size. Stellar radii therefore must increase as we go from the high-temperature, low-luminosity corner on the lower left of the H–R diagram to the low-temperature, high-luminosity corner on the upper right.

### Patterns in the H–R Diagram

Figure 15.9 also shows that stars do not fall randomly throughout the H–R diagram. Instead, they fall into several distinct groups:

- Most stars fall somewhere along the **main sequence**, the prominent streak running from the upper left to the lower right on the H–R diagram. Note that our Sun is a main-sequence star.

- The stars along the top are called **supergiants** because they are very large in addition to being very bright.

- Just below the supergiants are the **giants**, which are somewhat smaller in radius and lower in luminosity (but still much larger and brighter than main-sequence stars of the same spectral type).

- The stars near the lower left are small in radius and appear white in color because of their high temperature; we call these stars the **white dwarfs**.

---

[1]In other binaries, we can calculate an actual orbital velocity from the velocity obtained by the Doppler effect if we also know the system's orbital inclination. Astronomers have developed techniques for determining orbital inclination in a relatively small number of cases.

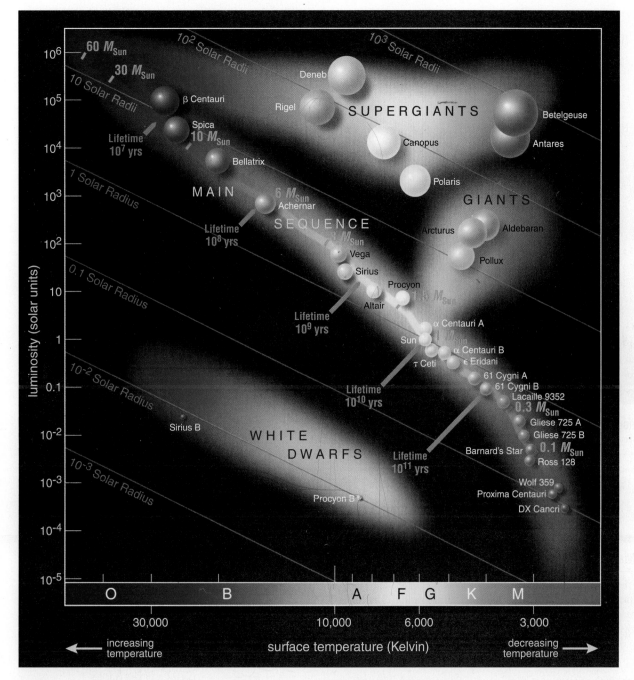

**FIGURE 15.9** An H–R diagram, one of astronomy's most important tools, shows how the surface temperatures of stars (plotted along the horizontal axis) relate to their luminosities (plotted along the vertical axis). Several of the brightest stars in the sky are plotted here, along with a few of the closest to Earth. They are not drawn to scale—the diagonal lines, labeled in solar radii, indicate how large they are compared to the Sun. The lifetime and mass labels apply only to main-sequence stars (see Figure 15.10). (Star positions on this diagram are based on data from the Hipparcos satellite.)

When classifying a star, astronomers generally report both the star's spectral type and a **luminosity class** that describes the region of the H–R diagram in which the star falls. Table 15.2 summarizes the luminosity classes. Note that luminosity class I represents supergiants, luminosity class III represents giants, luminosity class V represents main-sequence

stars, and luminosity classes II and IV are intermediate to the others. For example, the complete spectral classification of our Sun is G2 V: The G2 spectral type means it is yellow in color, and the luminosity class V means it is a main-sequence star. Betelgeuse is M2 I, making it a *red supergiant*. Proxima Centauri

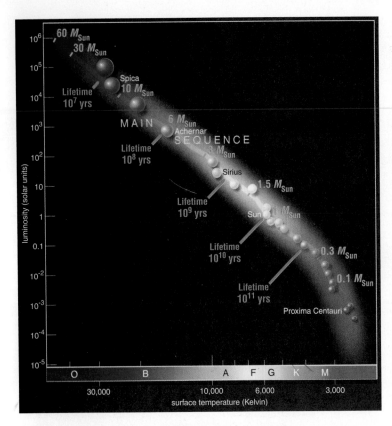

**FIGURE 15.10** Along the main sequence, more massive stars are brighter and hotter but have shorter lifetimes. (Stellar masses are given in units of solar masses: $1\,M_{Sun} = 2 \times 10^{30}$ kg.)

is M5 V—similar in color and surface temperature to Betelgeuse, but far dimmer because of its much smaller size. White dwarfs are usually designated with the letters *wd* rather than with a Roman numeral.

### The Main Sequence

The common trait of main-sequence stars is that, like our Sun, they are fusing hydrogen into helium in their cores. Because stars spend the majority of their lives fusing hydrogen, most stars fall somewhere along the main sequence of the H–R diagram.

But why do main-sequence stars span such a wide range of luminosities and surface temperatures? By measuring the masses of stars in binary systems, astronomers have discovered that stellar masses increase upward along the main sequence (Figure 15.10). At the upper end of the main sequence, the hot, luminous O stars can have masses as high as 100 times that of the Sun ($100M_{Sun}$). On the lower end, cool, dim M stars may have as little as 0.08 times the mass of the Sun ($0.08M_{Sun}$). Many more stars fall on the lower end of the main sequence than on the upper end, which tells us that low-mass stars are much more common than high-mass stars.

## Mathematical Insight 15.5 Calculating Stellar Radii

Almost all stars are too distant for us to measure their radii directly. However, we can calculate a star's radius from its luminosity with the aid of the thermal radiation laws. As given in Mathematical Insight 6.2, the amount of thermal radiation emitted by a star of surface temperature $T$ is:

$$\text{emitted power per unit area} = \sigma T^4$$

where the constant $\sigma = 5.7 \times 10^{-8}$ watt/(m$^2 \times$ Kelvin$^4$). The luminosity $L$ of a star is its power per unit area multiplied by its total surface area. If the star has radius $r$, its surface area is given by the formula $4\pi r^2$. Thus:

$$L = 4\pi r^2 \times \sigma T^4$$

With a bit of algebra, we can solve this formula for the star's radius $r$:

$$r = \sqrt{\frac{L}{4\pi\sigma T^4}}$$

*Example:* Betelgeuse has a luminosity of $38,000 L_{Sun}$ and a surface temperature of about 3,400 K. What is its radius?

*Solution:* First, we must make our units consistent by converting the luminosity of Betelgeuse into watts. Remembering that $L_{Sun} = 3.8 \times 10^{26}$ watts, we find:

$$L_{Bet} = 38,000 \times L_{Sun} = 38,000 \times 3.8 \times 10^{26} \text{ watts}$$
$$= 1.4 \times 10^{31} \text{ watts}$$

Now we can use the formula derived above to calculate the radius of Betelgeuse:

$$r = \sqrt{\frac{L}{4\pi\sigma T^4}}$$

$$= \sqrt{\frac{1.4 \times 10^{31} \text{ watts}}{4\pi \times (5.7 \times 10^{-8} \frac{\text{watt}}{\text{m}^2 \times \text{K}^4}) \times (3,400 \text{ K})^4}}$$

$$= \sqrt{\frac{1.4 \times 10^{31} \text{ watts}}{9.6 \times 10^7 \frac{\text{watts}}{\text{m}^2}}} = 3.8 \times 10^{11} \text{ m}$$

The radius of Betelgeuse is about 380 billion meters or, equivalently, 380 million kilometers. Note that this is more than twice the Earth–Sun distance of 150 million kilometers.

**Table 15.2 Stellar Luminosity Classes**

| Class | Description |
|-------|-------------|
| I | Supergiants |
| II | Bright giants |
| III | Giants |
| IV | Subgiants |
| V | Main sequence |

The orderly arrangement of stellar masses along the main sequence tells us that *mass* is the most important attribute of a hydrogen-burning star. Luminosity depends directly on mass because the weight of a star's outer layers determines the nuclear burning rate in its core; more weight means the star must sustain a higher nuclear burning rate in order to maintain gravitational equilibrium [Section 14.3]. The nuclear burning rate, and hence the luminosity, is very sensitive to mass. For example, a $10M_{Sun}$ star on the main sequence is about 10,000 times more luminous than the Sun.

The relationship between mass and surface temperature is a little subtler. In general, a very luminous star must either be very large or have a very high surface temperature, or some combination of both. Stars on the upper end of the main sequence are thousands of times more luminous than the Sun but only about 10 times larger than the Sun in radius. Thus, their surfaces must be significantly hotter than the Sun's surface to account for their high luminosities. Main-sequence stars more massive than the Sun therefore have higher surface temperatures than the Sun, and those less massive than the Sun have lower surface temperatures. That is why the main sequence slices diagonally from the upper left to the lower right on the H–R diagram.

### Main-Sequence Lifetimes

A star has a limited supply of core hydrogen and therefore can remain as a hydrogen-fusing main-sequence star for only a limited time—the star's **main-sequence lifetime** (or *hydrogen-burning lifetime*). Because stars spend the vast majority of their lives fusing hydrogen into helium, we sometimes refer to the main-sequence lifetime as simply the "lifetime." Like masses, stellar lifetimes vary in an orderly way as we move up the main sequence: Massive stars near the upper end of the main sequence have *shorter* lives than less massive stars near the lower end (see Figure 15.10).

Why do more massive stars live shorter lives? A star's lifetime depends on both its mass and its luminosity. Its mass determines how much hydrogen fuel the star initially contains in its core. Its luminosity determines how rapidly the star uses up its fuel. Massive stars live shorter lives because, even though they start their lives with a larger supply of hydrogen, they consume their hydrogen at a prodigious rate.

The main-sequence lifetime of our Sun is about 10 billion years [Section 14.1]. A 30-solar-mass star has roughly 30 times more hydrogen than the Sun but burns it with a luminosity some 300,000 times greater. Consequently, its lifetime is roughly 30/300,000 = 1/10,000 as long as the Sun's—corresponding to a lifetime of only a few million years. Cosmically speaking, a few million years is a remarkably short time, which is one reason why massive stars are so rare: Most of the massive stars that have ever been born are long since dead. (A second reason is that lower-mass stars form in larger numbers than higher-mass stars [Section 16.2].) The fact that any massive stars exist tells us that stars form continuously in our galaxy. The massive, bright O stars in our galaxy today formed only recently and will die long before they have a chance to complete even one orbit around the center of the galaxy.

**TIME OUT TO THINK** *Would you expect to find life on planets orbiting massive O stars? Why or why not? (Hint: Compare the lifetime of an O star to the amount of time that passed from the formation of our solar system to the origin of life on Earth.)*

On the other end of the scale, a 0.3-solar-mass star emits a luminosity just 0.01 times that of the Sun and consequently lives roughly 0.3/0.01 = 30 times longer than the Sun. In a universe that is now between 12 and 16 billion years old, even the most ancient of these small, dim M stars still survive and will continue to shine faintly for hundreds of billions of years to come.

### Giants, Supergiants, and White Dwarfs

Giants and supergiants are stars nearing the ends of their lives because they have already exhausted their core hydrogen. Surprisingly, stars grow more luminous when they begin to run out of fuel. As we will discuss in the next chapter, a star generates energy furiously during the last stages of its life as it tries to stave off the inevitable crushing force of gravity. As ever-greater amounts of power well up from the core, the outer layers of the star expand, making it into a giant or supergiant. The largest of these celestial behemoths have radii more than 1,000 times that of the Sun. If our Sun were this big, it would engulf the planets, out to Jupiter.

Because they are so bright, giants and supergiants can be seen even when they are not especially close to us. Many of the brightest stars visible to the naked eye are giants or supergiants; they are often identifiable by their reddish color. Nevertheless, giants and supergiants are rarer than main-sequence stars because, in our snapshot of the heavens, we catch most stars in the act of hydrogen burning and relatively few in a later stage of life.

Giants and supergiants eventually run out of fuel entirely. A giant with a mass similar to that of our Sun ultimately ejects its outer layers, leaving behind a "dead" core in which all nuclear fusion has ceased. White dwarfs are these remaining embers of former giants. They are hot because they are essentially exposed stellar cores, but they are dim because they lack an energy source and radiate only their leftover heat into space. A typical white dwarf is no larger in size than the Earth, although it may have a mass as great as that of our Sun. (Giants and supergiants with masses much larger than that of the Sun ultimately explode, leaving behind neutron stars or black holes as corpses [Section 16.4].)

### Pulsating Variable Stars

Not all stars shine steadily like our Sun. Any star that significantly varies in brightness with time is called a *variable star*. A particularly important type of variable star has a peculiar problem with achieving the proper balance between the power welling up from its core and the power being radiated from its surface. Sometimes the upper layers of such a star are too opaque; energy and pressure build up beneath the photosphere, and the star expands in size. However, this expansion puffs the upper layers outward, making them too transparent. So much energy then escapes that the underlying pressure drops, and the star contracts again. In a futile quest for a steady equilib-

rium, the atmosphere of such a **pulsating variable star** alternately expands and contracts, causing the star to rise and fall in luminosity. Figure 15.11 shows a typical light curve for a pulsating variable star, with the star's brightness graphed against time. Any pulsating variable star has its own particular period between peaks in luminosity, which we can discover easily from its light curve. These periods can range from as short as several hours to as long as several years.

Most pulsating variable stars inhabit a strip (called the *instability strip*) on the H–R diagram that lies between the main sequence and the red giants (Figure 15.12). A special category of very luminous pulsating variables lies at the top of this strip: the **Cepheid variables**, or **Cepheids** (so named because the first identified star of this type was the star Delta Cephei).

Cepheids fluctuate in luminosity with periods of a few days to a few months. In 1912, another woman astronomer at Harvard, Henrietta Leavitt, discovered that the periods of these stars are very closely related to their luminosities: The longer the period, the more luminous the star. This **period–luminosity relation** holds because larger (and hence more luminous) Cepheids take longer to pulsate in and out in size.

Once we measure the period of a Cepheid variable, we can use the period–luminosity relation to determine its luminosity. We can then calculate its distance with the luminosity–distance formula. In fact, as we'll discuss in Chapter 19, Cepheids provide our primary means of measuring distances to other galaxies and thus teach us the true scale of the cosmos. The next time you look at the North Star, Polaris, gaze upon it with renewed appreciation. Not only has it guided generations of navigators in the Northern Hemisphere, but it is also one of these special Cepheid variable stars.

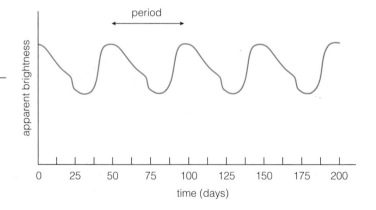

**FIGURE 15.11** A typical light curve for a Cepheid variable star. Cepheids are giant, whitish stars whose luminosities regularly pulsate over periods of a few days to about a hundred days. The pulsation period of this Cepheid is about fifty days.

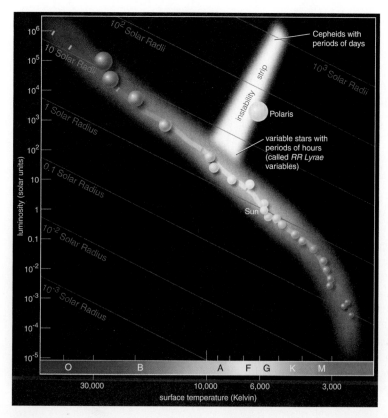

**FIGURE 15.12** An H–R diagram with the instability strip highlighted.

Labels within figure:
- $10^2$ Solar Radii
- 10 Solar Radii
- 1 Solar Radius
- 0.1 Solar Radius
- $10^{-2}$ Solar Radius
- $10^{-3}$ Solar Radius
- $10^3$ Solar Radii
- instability strip
- Cepheids with periods of days
- Polaris
- variable stars with periods of hours (called *RR Lyrae* variables)
- Sun
- luminosity (solar units)
- surface temperature (Kelvin)
- O  B  A  F  G  K  M
- 30,000  10,000  6,000  3,000

## 15.6 Star Clusters

All stars are born from giant clouds of gas. Because a single interstellar cloud can contain enough material to form many stars, stars almost inevitably form in groups. In our snapshot of the heavens, many stars still congregate in the groups in which they formed. These groups are of two basic types: modest-size **open clusters** and densely packed **globular clusters**.

Open clusters of stars are always found in the disk of the galaxy. They can contain up to several thousand stars and typically span about 30 light-years (10 parsecs). The most famous open cluster is the *Pleiades,* a prominent clump of stars in the constellation Taurus (Figure 15.13). The Pleiades are often called the *Seven Sisters,* although only six of the cluster's several thousand stars are easily visible to the naked eye. Other cultures have other names for this beautiful group of stars; in Japanese it is *Subaru,* which is why the logo for Subaru automobiles is a diagram of the Pleiades.

Globular clusters are found in both the halo and the disk of our galaxy. A globular cluster can contain more than a million stars concentrated in a ball typically 60 to

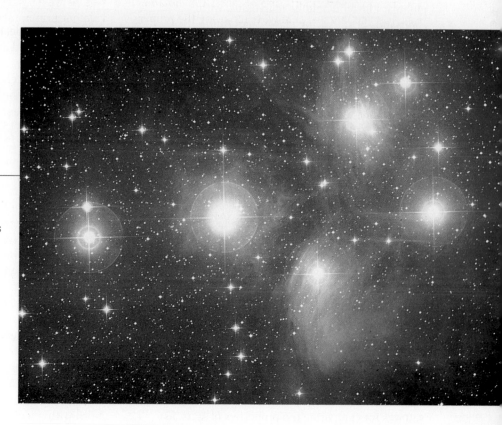

**FIGURE 15.13** A photo of the Pleiades, a nearby open cluster of stars. The most prominent stars in this open cluster are of spectral type B, indicating that the Pleiades are no more than 100 million years old, relatively young for a star cluster.

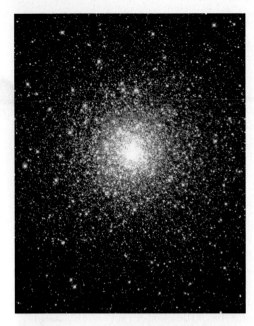

FIGURE 15.14 This globular cluster, known as M80, is over 12 billion years old. The prominent reddish stars in this Hubble Space Telescope photo are red giant stars nearing the ends of their lives.

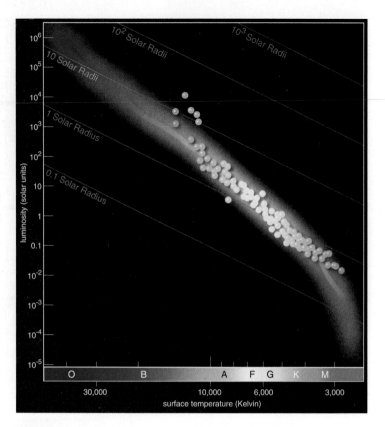

FIGURE 15.15 An H–R diagram for the stars of the Pleiades. Note that the Pleiades cluster is missing its upper main-sequence stars, indicating that these stars have already ended their hydrogen-burning lives. The main-sequence turnoff point at about spectral type B6 tells us that the Pleiades are about 100 million years old.

150 light-years across (20 to 50 parsecs). Its innermost region can have 10,000 stars packed within just a few light-years (Figure 15.14). The view from a planet in a globular cluster would be marvelous, with thousands of stars lying closer than Alpha Centauri is to the Sun. Because a globular cluster's stars nestle so closely, they engage in an intricate and complex dance choreographed by gravity. Some stars zoom from the cluster's core to its outskirts and back again at speeds approaching the escape velocity from the cluster, while others orbit the dense core more closely. When two stars pass especially close to each other, the gravitational pull between them deflects their trajectories, altering their speeds and sending them careening off in new directions. Occasionally, a close encounter boosts one star's velocity enough to eject it from the cluster. Through such ejections, globular clusters gradually lose stars and grow more compact.

Star clusters are extremely useful to astronomers for two key reasons:

1. All the stars in a cluster lie at about the same distance from Earth.

2. Cosmically speaking, all the stars in a cluster formed at about the same time (i.e., within a few million years of one another).

Astronomers can therefore use star clusters as laboratories for comparing the properties of stars, as yardsticks for measuring distances in the universe [Section 19.3], and as timepieces for measuring the age of our galaxy.

We can use clusters as timepieces because we can determine their ages from H–R diagrams of cluster stars. To understand how the process works, consider Figure 15.15, which shows an H–R diagram for the Pleiades. Note that most of the stars in the Pleiades fall along the standard main sequence, with one important exception: The Pleiades' stars trail away to the right of the main sequence at the upper end. That is, the Pleiades are missing the hot, short-lived O main-sequence stars. Apparently, the Pleiades are old enough for its O stars to have already ended their hydrogen-burning lives. At the same time, they are young enough for some of its B stars to still survive on the main sequence.

The precise point on the H–R diagram at which the Pleiades' main sequence diverges from the standard main sequence is called the **main-sequence turnoff** point. In this cluster, it occurs around spectral type B6. The main-sequence lifetime of a B6 star is roughly 100 million years, so this must be the age of the Pleiades. Any star in the Pleiades that was born with a main-sequence spectral type hotter than B6 had a lifetime shorter than 100 million years

**FIGURE 15.16** This H–R diagram shows stars from four clusters with very different ages. Each star cluster has a different main-sequence turnoff point. The youngest cluster, h+χ Persei, still contains main-sequence O and B stars, indicating that it is only about 14 million years old. Stars at the main-sequence turnoff point for the oldest cluster, NGC 188, are only slightly more luminous and massive than the Sun, indicating an age of 7 billion years.

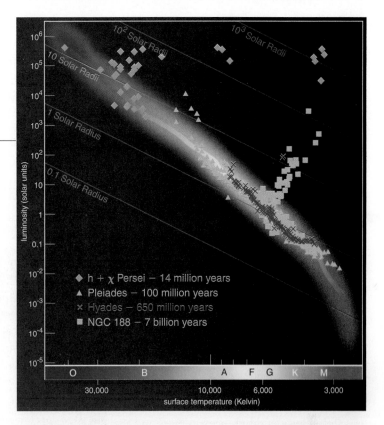

and hence is no longer found on the main sequence. Stars with lifetimes longer than 100 million years are still fusing hydrogen and hence remain as main-sequence stars.

Over the next few billion years, the B stars in the Pleiades will die out, followed by the A stars and the F stars. Thus, if we could make H–R diagrams for the Pleiades every few million years, we would find that the main sequence gradually grows shorter. Comparing the H–R diagrams of other open clusters makes this effect more apparent (Figure 15.16). In each case, we determine the cluster's age from the lifetimes of the stars at its main-sequence turn-off point:

age of the cluster = lifetime of stars
at main-sequence
turnoff point

Thus, stars in a particular cluster that once resided above the turnoff point on the main sequence have already exhausted their core supply of hydrogen, while stars below the turnoff point remain on the main sequence.

**TIME OUT TO THINK** *Suppose a star cluster is precisely 10 billion years old. On an H–R diagram, where would you expect to find its main-sequence turnoff point? Would you expect this cluster to have any main-sequence stars of spectral type A? Would you expect it to have main-sequence stars of spectral type K? Explain. (Hint: What is the lifetime of our Sun?)*

The technique of identifying main-sequence turnoff points is our most powerful tool for evaluating the ages of star clusters. We've learned, for example, that most open clusters are relatively young and that very few are older than about 5 billion years. In contrast, the stars at the main-sequence turnoff points in globular clusters are usually less massive than our Sun (Figure 15.17). Because stars like our Sun have a lifetime of about 10 billion years and these stars have already died in globular clusters, we conclude that globular-cluster stars are older than 10 billion years. More precise studies

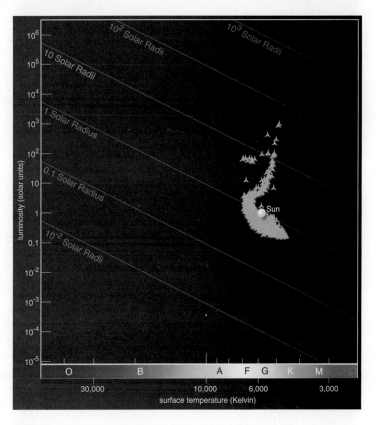

**FIGURE 15.17** This H–R diagram shows stars from the globular cluster Palomar 3. The main-sequence turnoff point is in the vicinity of stars like our Sun, indicating an age for this cluster of around 10 billion years. A more technical analysis of this cluster places its age at around 12 to 14 billion years. (Stars in globular clusters tend to contain virtually no elements other than hydrogen and helium. Because of their different composition, these stars are somewhat bluer and more luminous than stars of the same mass and composition as that of our Sun.)

of the turnoff points in globular clusters, coupled with theoretical calculations of stellar lifetimes, place the ages of these clusters at between 12 and 16 billion years, making them the oldest known objects in the galaxy. In fact, globular clusters place a constraint on the possible age of the universe: If stars in globular clusters are 12 billion years old, then the universe must be at least this old.

## THE BIG PICTURE

We have classified the diverse families of stars visible in the night sky. Much of what we know about stars, galaxies, and the universe itself is based on the fundamental properties of stars introduced in this chapter, so make sure you understand the following "big picture" ideas:

■ All stars are made primarily of hydrogen and helium, at least at the time they form. The differences between stars come about primarily because of differences in mass and age.

■ Much of what we know about stars comes from studying the patterns that appear when we plot stellar surface temperatures and luminosities in an H–R diagram. Thus, the H–R diagram is one of the most important tools of astronomers.

■ Stars spend most of their lives as main-sequence stars, fusing hydrogen into helium in their cores. The most massive stars live only a few million years, while the least massive stars will survive until the universe is many times its present age.

■ Much of what we know about the universe comes from studies of star clusters. Here again, H–R diagrams play a vital role. For example, H–R diagrams of star clusters allow us to determine their ages.

### Review Questions

1. Briefly explain how we can learn about the lives of stars, despite the fact that stellar lives are far longer than human lives.

2. What basic composition are all stars born with? Given that all stars begin their lives with this same basic composition, why do stars differ from one another?

3. What do we mean by a star's *luminosity?* What are the standard units for luminosity? Explain what we mean when we measure luminosity in units of $L_{Sun}$.

4. What do we mean by a star's *apparent brightness?* What are the standard units for apparent brightness? Explain how a star's apparent brightness depends on its distance from us.

5. State the *luminosity–distance formula,* and explain why it is so important.

6. What do we mean by a star's visible-light luminosity or visible-light apparent brightness? By its X-ray luminosity or X-ray apparent brightness? Explain why we sometimes talk about such wavelength-specific measures, rather than *total luminosity* and *total apparent brightness.*

7. Briefly explain how we calculate a star's distance in parsecs by measuring its *parallax angle* in arcseconds.

8. What is the *magnitude system?* What are its origins? Briefly explain what we mean by the *apparent magnitude* and *absolute magnitude* of a star.

9. Briefly describe how a star's *spectral type* is related to its surface temperature. List the seven basic spectral types in order of decreasing temperature. How are the spectral types subdivided by number (e.g., A3, G5)?

10. Briefly summarize the roles of Annie Jump Cannon and Cecilia Payne-Gaposchkin in discovering the spectral sequence and its meaning.

11. Describe and distinguish between *visual binary* systems, *eclipsing binary* systems, and *spectroscopic binary* systems.

12. Describe how we measure stellar masses and why eclipsing binaries are so important to such measurements.

13. Draw a sketch of a basic *Hertzsprung–Russell diagram (H–R diagram).* Label the *main sequence, giants, supergiants,* and *white dwarfs.* Where on this diagram do we find stars that are cool and dim? Cool and luminous? Hot and dim? Hot and bright?

14. What do we mean by a star's *luminosity class?* On your sketch of the H–R diagram, identify the regions for luminosity classes I, III, and V.

15. Explain how mass determines the luminosity and surface temperature of a main-sequence star. How do masses differ as we look along the main sequence on an H–R diagram?

16. What do we mean by a star's *main-sequence lifetime?* Explain why more massive stars live shorter lives.

17. What are *pulsating variable stars?* Why do they vary periodically in brightness?

18. What are *Cepheid variables?* What is the *period–luminosity relation* for Cepheids, and why is it useful for distance measurements?

19. Describe in general terms how *open clusters* and *globular clusters* differ in their numbers of stars, ages, and locations in the galaxy. Why are star clusters so important to astronomers?

20. Explain why H–R diagrams look different for star clusters of different ages. How does the location of the *main-sequence turnoff point* tell us the age of the star cluster?

## Discussion Question

1. *Classification.* Edward Pickering's team of female "computers" at Harvard University made many important contributions to astronomy, particularly in the area of systematic stellar classification. Why do you think rapid advances in our understanding of stars followed so quickly on the heels of their efforts? Can you think of other areas in science where huge advances in understanding followed directly from improved systems of classification?

## Problems

*True Statements?* For **problems 1–10**, decide whether the statements are true or false and clearly explain how you know.

1. Two stars that look very different must be made out of different kinds of elements.

2. Sirius is the brightest star in the night sky, but if we moved it 10 times farther away it would look only one-tenth as bright.

3. Sirius looks brighter than Alpha Centauri, but we know that Alpha Centauri is closer because its apparent position in the sky shifts by a larger amount as the Earth orbits the Sun.

4. Stars that look red-hot have hotter surfaces than stars that look blue.

5. Some of the stars on the main sequence of the H–R diagram are not converting hydrogen into helium.

6. The smallest, hottest stars are plotted in the lower left-hand portion of the H–R diagram.

7. Stars that begin their lives with the most mass live longer than less massive stars because it takes them a lot longer to use up their hydrogen fuel.

8. Star clusters with lots of bright, blue stars are generally younger than clusters that don't have any such stars.

9. All giants, supergiants, and white dwarfs were once main-sequence stars.

10. Most of the stars in the sky are more massive than the Sun.

11. *Stellar Data.* Consider the following data table for several bright stars. Note that $M_v$ is absolute magnitude and $m_v$ is apparent magnitude.

| Star | $M_v$ | $m_v$ | Spectral Type | Luminosity Class |
|---|---|---|---|---|
| Aldebaran | −0.2 | +0.9 | K5 | III |
| Alpha Centauri A | +4.4 | 0.0 | G2 | V |
| Antares | −4.5 | +0.9 | M1 | I |
| Canopus | −3.1 | −0.7 | F0 | II |
| Fomalhaut | +2.0 | +1.2 | A3 | V |
| Regulus | −0.6 | +1.4 | B7 | V |
| Sirius | +1.4 | −1.4 | A1 | V |
| Spica | −3.6 | +0.9 | B1 | V |

Answer each of the following questions, including a brief explanation with each answer.

a. Which star appears brightest in our sky?

b. Which star appears faintest in our sky?

c. Which star has the greatest luminosity?

d. Which star has the smallest luminosity?

e. Which star has the highest surface temperature?

f. Which star has the lowest surface temperature?

g. Which star is most similar to the Sun?

h. Which star is a red supergiant?

i. Which star has the largest radius?

j. Which stars have finished burning hydrogen in their cores?

k. Among the main-sequence stars listed, which one is the most massive?

l. Among the main-sequence stars listed, which one has the longest lifetime?

12. *Data Tables.* Study the spectral types listed in Appendix F for the 20 brightest stars and for the stars within 12 light-years. Why do you think the two lists are so different? Explain.

*13. *The Inverse Square Law for Light.* The Earth is about 150 million km from the Sun, and the apparent brightness of the Sun in our sky is about 1,300 watts/m². Using these two facts and the inverse square law for light, determine the apparent brightness we would measure for the Sun *if* we were located at the following positions.

a. Half the Earth's distance from the Sun.

b. Twice the Earth's distance from the Sun.

c. Five times the Earth's distance from the Sun.

*14. *The Luminosity of Alpha Centauri A.* Alpha Centauri A lies at a distance of 4.4 light-years and has an apparent brightness in our night sky of $2.7 \times 10^{-8}$ watt/m². Recall that 1 light-year = $9.5 \times 10^{12}$ km = $9.5 \times 10^{15}$ m.

a. Use the luminosity–distance formula to calculate the luminosity of Alpha Centauri A.

b. Suppose you have a light bulb that emits 100 watts of visible light. (*Note:* This is *not* the case for a standard 100-watt light bulb, in which most of its 100 watts goes to heat and only about 10–15 watts is emitted as visible light.) How far away would you have to put the light bulb for it to have the same apparent brightness as Alpha Centauri A in our sky? (*Hint:* Use the 100 watts as $L$ in the luminosity–distance formula, and use the apparent brightness given above for Alpha Centauri A. Then solve for the distance.)

*15. *More Practice with the Luminosity–Distance Formula.* Use the luminosity–distance formula to answer each of the following questions.

    a. Suppose a star has the same luminosity as our Sun ($3.8 \times 10^{26}$ watts) but is located at a distance of 10 light-years. What is its apparent brightness?

    b. Suppose a star has the same apparent brightness as Alpha Centauri A ($2.7 \times 10^{-8}$ watt/m$^2$) but is located at a distance of 200 light-years. What is its luminosity?

    c. Suppose a star has a luminosity of $8 \times 10^{26}$ watts and an apparent brightness of $3.5 \times 10^{-12}$ watt/m$^2$. How far away is it? Give your answer in both kilometers and light-years.

    d. Suppose a star has a luminosity of $5 \times 10^{29}$ watts and an apparent brightness of $9 \times 10^{-15}$ watt/m$^2$. How far away is it? Give your answer in both kilometers and light-years.

*16. *Parallax and Distance.* Use the parallax formula to calculate the distance to each of the following stars. Give your answers in both parsecs and light-years.

    a. Alpha Centauri: parallax angle of 0.742″.

    b. Procyon: parallax angle of 0.286″.

*17. *The Magnitude System.* Use the definitions of the magnitude system to answer each of the following questions.

    a. Which is brighter in our sky, a star with apparent magnitude 2 or a star with apparent magnitude 7? By how much?

    b. Which has a greater luminosity, a star with absolute magnitude +4 or a star with absolute magnitude −6? By how much?

*18. *Measuring Stellar Mass.* The spectral lines of two stars in a particular eclipsing binary system shift back and forth with a period of 6 months. The lines of both stars shift by equal amounts, and the amount of the Doppler shift indicates that each star has an orbital speed of 80,000 m/s. What are the masses of the two stars? Assume that each of the two stars traces a circular orbit around their center of mass. (*Hint:* See Mathematical Insight 15.4.)

*19. *Calculating Stellar Radii.* Sirius A has a luminosity of $26L_{Sun}$ and a surface temperature of about 9,400 K. What is its radius? (*Hint:* See Mathematical Insight 15.5.)

## Web Projects

Find useful links for Web projects on the text Web site.

1. *Women in Astronomy.* Until fairly recently, men greatly outnumbered women in professional astronomy. Nevertheless, many women made crucial discoveries in astronomy throughout history. Do some research about the life and discoveries of a woman astronomer from any time period, and write a two- to three-page scientific biography.

2. *The Hipparcos Mission.* The European Space Agency's Hipparcos mission, which operated from 1989–1993, made precise parallax measurements for more than 40,000 stars. Learn about how Hipparcos allowed astronomers to measure smaller parallax angles than they could from the ground and how Hipparcos discoveries have affected our knowledge of the universe. Write a one- to two-page report on your findings.

3. *Future Parallax Missions.* Astronomers have plans for missions that will further extend our ability to measure distances through parallax. Write a one- to two-page report on one such mission, such as NASA's Space Interferometry Mission (SIM; launch planned for 2009) or the European Space Agency's GAIA mission (launch scheduled for 2012).

# CHAPTER 16

# Star Stuff

We inhale oxygen with every breath. Iron-bearing hemoglobin carries this oxygen through the bloodstream. Chains of carbon and nitrogen form the backbone of the proteins, fats, and carbohydrates in our cells. Calcium strengthens our bones, while sodium and potassium ions moderate communications of the nervous system. What does all this have to do with astronomy? The profound answer, recognized only in the latter half of the twentieth century, is that these elements were created by stars.

We've already discussed in general terms how the elements in our bodies came to exist: Hydrogen and helium were produced in the Big Bang, and heavier elements were created later by stars and scattered into space by stellar explosions. There, in the spaces between the stars, these elements mixed with interstellar gas and became incorporated into subsequent generations of stars.

In this chapter, we will discuss the origins of the elements in greater detail by delving into the lives of stars. As you read, keep in mind that no matter how far the stars may seem to be removed from our everyday lives, they actually are connected to us in the most intimate way possible: Without the births, lives, and deaths of stars, none of us would be here.

## 16.1 Lives in the Balance

The story of a star's life is in many ways the story of an extended battle between two opposing forces: gravity and pressure. The most common type of pressure in stars is **thermal pressure**—the familiar type of pressure that keeps a balloon inflated and that increases when the temperature or thermal energy increases.

A star can maintain its internal thermal pressure only if it continually generates new thermal energy to replace the energy it radiates into space. This energy can come from two sources: *nuclear fusion* of light elements into heavier ones and the process of *gravitational contraction*, which converts gravitational potential energy into thermal energy [Section 14.1]. These energy-production processes operate only temporarily, although in this case "temporarily" means millions or billions of years. In contrast, gravity acts eternally, and any time gravity succeeds in shrinking a star's core the strength of gravity grows. (Recall that the force of gravity inside an object grows stronger if it either gains mass or shrinks in radius [Section 5.4].) Because a star cannot rely on thermal energy to resist gravity forever, its ultimate fate depends on whether something other than thermal pressure manages to halt the unceasing crush of gravity.

The outcome of a star's struggle between gravity and pressure depends almost entirely on its birth mass. All stars are born from spinning clumps of gas, but newborn stars can have masses ranging from less than 10% of the mass of our Sun to about 100 times that of our Sun. The most massive stars live fast and die young, proceeding from birth to explosive death in just a few million years. The lowest-mass stars consume hydrogen so slowly that they will continue to shine until the universe is many times older than it is today.

Because stars come in such a great variety of masses, we can simplify our discussion of stellar lives by dividing stars into three basic groups: **low-mass stars** are born with less than about two times the mass of our Sun, or less than 2 *solar masses* ($2M_{Sun}$) of material; **intermediate-mass stars** have birth weights between about 2 and 8 solar masses; and **high-mass stars** include all stars born with masses greater than about 8 solar masses. Both low-mass and intermediate-mass stars swell into red giants near the ends of their lives and ultimately become white dwarfs. High-mass stars also become red and large in their latter days, but their lives end much more violently. We will focus most of our discussion in this chapter on the dramatic differences between the lives of low- and high-mass stars. Because the life stages of intermediate-mass stars are quite similar to the corresponding stages of high-mass stars until the very ends of their lives, we include them in our discussion of high-mass stars.

Given the brevity of human history compared to the life of any star, you might wonder how we can know so much about stellar life cycles. As with any scientific inquiry, we study stellar lives by comparing theory and observation. On the theoretical side, we use mathematical models based on the known laws of physics to predict the life cycles of stars. On the observational side, we study stars of different mass but the same age by looking in star clusters whose ages we have determined by main-sequence turnoff [Section 15.6]. Occasionally, we even catch a star in its death throes. Theoretical predictions of the life cycles of stars now agree quite well with these observations. In the remainder of this chapter, we will examine in detail our modern understanding of the life stories of stars and how they manufacture the variety of elements—the *star stuff*—that make our lives possible.

## 16.2 Star Birth

A star's life begins in an interstellar cloud (Figure 16.1). Star-forming clouds tend to be quite cold—typically only 10–30 K. (Recall that 0 K is absolute zero, and temperatures on Earth are around 300 K.) They also tend to be quite dense compared to the rest of the gas between the stars, although they would qualify as a superb vacuum by earthly standards. Like the galaxy as a whole, star-forming clouds are made almost entirely of hydrogen and helium.

The clouds that form stars are sometimes called **molecular clouds**, because their low temperatures allow hydrogen atoms to pair up to form hydrogen molecules ($H_2$). The relatively rare atoms of elements heavier than helium can also form molecules, such as carbon monoxide or water, or tiny, solid grains of dust. More important, the cold temperatures and relatively high densities allow gravity to overcome thermal pressure more readily in molecular clouds than elsewhere in interstellar space, initiating the gravitational collapse that gives birth to new stars.

### From Cloud to Protostar

As a piece of a molecular cloud starts to collapse, gravitational contraction increases the cloud's thermal energy. However, the cloud quickly radiates this thermal energy away, preventing the pressure from building enough to resist gravity. During this early phase of collapse, the temperature remains below 100 K, and the cloud glows in long-wavelength infrared light (Figure 16.2).

The ongoing collapse increases the cloud's density, making it increasingly difficult for radiation to

**FIGURE 16.1** A star-forming cloud of molecular hydrogen gas in the constellation Scorpius extends from the upper-right corner of this photo through the center. The cloud appears dark because dust particles within it obscure the light from more distant stars lying behind it. Blue-white blotches near the edges of the dark cloud are newly formed stars. They appear fuzzy because some of their light is reflecting off patchy gas in their vicinity.

**FIGURE 16.2** This false-color picture shows infrared radiation from star-forming regions in the constellation Orion. The colors correspond to the temperature of the emitting gas: Red is cooler, and white is hotter. Star formation is most intense in the yellow-white regions, which have been heated to 60–100 K (but note that this is still quite cold). The Orion Nebula, home to many protostars, is the prominent yellow-white area near the bottom. Betelgeuse, a red supergiant, appears as a blue-white dot near the center.

escape. Eventually, its central regions grow completely opaque, trapping much of the thermal energy produced by gravitational contraction. Because thermal energy can no longer escape easily, the cloud's internal temperature and pressure rise dramatically. This rising pressure begins to fight back against the crush of gravity, and the dense cloud fragment becomes a **protostar**—the seed from which a star will grow. A protostar looks starlike, but its core is not yet hot enough for fusion.

The law of conservation of angular momentum [Section 5.2] implies that a **protostellar disk** should encircle a forming protostar, similar to the *proto-planetary disk* from which the planets of our solar system formed [Section 8.3]. A collapsing cloud fragment necessarily starts with some overall angular

**FIGURE 16.3** Artist's conception of star birth. A cloud fragment (top left) necessarily has some angular momentum, which causes it to spin faster and flatten into a protostellar disk as it collapses (center). In the late stages of collapse (bottom right), the central protostar has a strong protostellar wind and may fire jets of high-speed gas outward along its rotation axis.

momentum (the sum total of the angular momenta of every constituent gas particle), although it might be unmeasurable when the fragment is large. But conservation of angular momentum ensures that the fragment spins faster and faster as it collapses (Figure 16.3). The rotating cloud flattens to form the protostellar disk as it shrinks. Protostellar disks sometimes coalesce into true planetary systems, but we do not yet know how commonly this occurs.

**TIME OUT TO THINK** *The term* protostellar disk *refers to any disk of material surrounding a protostar. The term* protoplanetary disk *refers to a disk of material that later produces full-fledged planets. Do you think that all protostellar disks are also protoplanetary disks? If so, why? If not, what do you think might prevent planets from forming in some protostellar disks?*

The protostellar disk probably plays a large role in eventually slowing the rotation of the protostar. The protostar's rapid rotation generates a strong magnetic field. As the magnetic field lines sweep through the protostellar disk, they transfer some of the protostar's angular momentum outward, slowing its rotation [Section 8.4]. The strong magnetic field also helps gen-

erate a strong **protostellar wind**—an outward flow of particles similar to the *solar wind* [Section 14.2]—that may carry additional angular momentum from the protostar to interstellar space.

Rotation is likely to be responsible for the formation of some binary star systems. Protostars that are unable to rid themselves of enough angular momentum spin too fast to become a stable single star and tend to split in two. Each of these two fragments can go on to form a separate star. If the stars are particularly close together, the resulting pair is called a **close binary** system, in which two stars coexist in close proximity, rapidly orbiting each other.

Observations show that the latter stages of a star's formation can be surprisingly violent. Besides the strong wind, many young stars also fire high-speed streams, or **jets**, of gas into interstellar space (Figure 16.4). No one knows exactly how protostars generate these jets, but two high-speed streams generally flow out along the rotation axis of the protostar, shooting in opposite directions. We also sometimes see blobs of material along the jets (called *Herbig–Haro objects* after their discoverers). These blobs appear to be collections of gas swept up as the jet plows into the surrounding interstellar material. Together, winds

protostellar
disk

proto-star

jet

**a** Schematic illustration of protostellar disk–jet structure.

**b** Photograph of a protostellar disk and jet. We are seeing the disk edge-on, as in (**a**). The disk's top and bottom surfaces, illuminated by the protostar, are shown in green, and the jets emerging along the disk's axis are shown in red. The dark central layers of the disk block our view of the protostar itself.

**c** A wider-angle photograph of a jet emanating from a protostar (left) and ramming into surrounding interstellar gas (right).

**FIGURE 16.4** Some protostars can be seen shooting jets of matter into interstellar space.

and jets play an important role in clearing away the cocoon of gas that surrounds a forming star, eventually allowing the star to emerge into view.

### A Star Is Born

A full-fledged star is born when the core temperature of the protostar exceeds 10 million K—hot enough for hydrogen fusion to operate efficiently by the *proton–proton chain* [Section 14.3]. The ignition of fusion halts the protostar's gravitational contraction. The new star's interior structure stabilizes, with the thermal energy generated by fusion maintaining the balance between gravity and pressure that we call *gravitational equilibrium* [Section 14.1]. The star is now a hydrogen-burning, *main-sequence* star [Section 15.5].

The length of time from the formation of a protostar to the birth of a main-sequence star depends on the star's mass. Remember that massive stars do everything faster. The collapse of a high-mass protostar may take only a million years or less. Collapse into a star like our Sun takes about 50 million years, and collapse into a small star of spectral type M may take more than a hundred million years. Thus, the most massive stars in a young star cluster may live

and die before the smallest stars finish their prenatal period.

We can summarize the transitions that occur during star birth with a special type of H–R diagram. Recall that a standard H–R diagram shows luminosities and surface temperatures for many different stars [Section 15.5]. In contrast, this special H–R diagram shows part of a **life track** (also called an *evolutionary track*) for a single star; for reference, the diagram also shows the standard main sequence. Each point along a star's life track represents its surface temperature and luminosity at some moment during its life. Figure 16.5 shows a life track for the prenatal period in the life of a $1M_{Sun}$ star like our Sun. Note that this period includes four distinct stages:

*Stage 1.* When the protostar first assembles from a cloud of gas, its surface temperature is quite low, putting it far to the right on the H–R diagram. However, its surface area is quite large at this time, so its luminosity is also quite large—perhaps 100 times the luminosity it will have when it becomes a Sun-like main-sequence star.

*Stage 2.* Because of its large luminosity, the young protostar rapidly loses the energy it generates through gravitational contraction, and its collapse

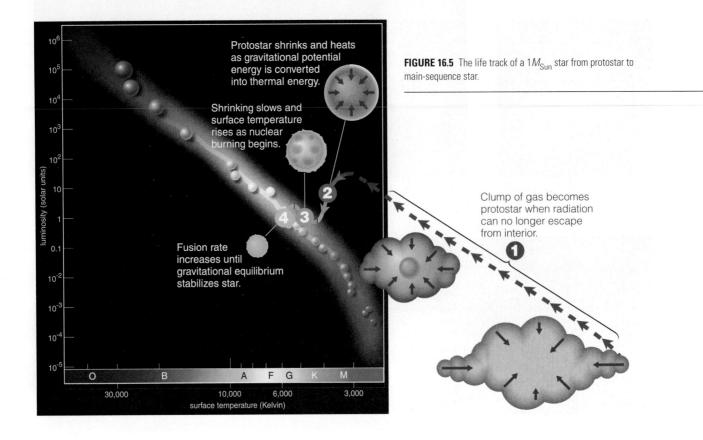

Protostar shrinks and heats as gravitational potential energy is converted into thermal energy.

Shrinking slows and surface temperature rises as nuclear burning begins.

Fusion rate increases until gravitational equilibrium stabilizes star.

Clump of gas becomes protostar when radiation can no longer escape from interior.

continues at a relatively rapid rate. Its surface temperature warms only slightly during the next few million years, but its shrinking size reduces its luminosity dramatically. The life track therefore progresses almost straight downward on the H–R diagram.

**Stage 3.** When the core temperature reaches a few million K, hydrogen nuclei begin to fuse into helium. However, the rate of fusion is still not high enough to halt the collapse of the star, although the rate of shrinkage slows considerably. As the star shrinks, its surface temperature rises. The net result of this shrinkage and heating is a slight increase in luminosity over the next 10 million years. The life track therefore progresses leftward and slightly upward on the H–R diagram.

**Stage 4.** The core temperature and rate of fusion continue to increase gradually for the next few tens of millions of years. Finally, the rate of fusion becomes high enough to establish gravitational equilibrium. At this point, fusion becomes self-sustaining and the star settles into its hydrogen-burning, main-sequence life.

Stars of different masses follow a similar set of stages during their prenatal periods. Figure 16.6 illustrates life tracks on an H–R diagram for the prenatal stages of several stars of different masses.

**TIME OUT TO THINK** *Explain in your own words what we mean by a life track for a star. Why do we say that Figures 16.5 and 16.6 show only pre-main-sequence life tracks? In general terms, predict the appearance on Figure 16.6 of pre-main-sequence life tracks for a $25 M_{Sun}$ star and for a $0.1 M_{Sun}$ star.*

### Stellar Birth Weights

A single group of molecular clouds can contain thousands of solar masses of gas, which is why stars generally are born in clusters. We do not yet fully understand the processes that govern the clumping and fragmentation of these clouds into protostars with a wide array of masses. However, we can observe the results. In a newly formed star cluster, stars with low masses greatly outnumber stars with high masses. For every star with a mass between 10 and 100 solar masses, there are typically 10 stars with masses between 2 and 10 solar masses, 50 stars with masses between 0.5 and 2 solar masses, and a few hundred stars with masses below $0.5 M_{Sun}$. Thus, although the Sun lies toward the middle of the overall range of stellar masses, most stars in a new star cluster are less massive than the Sun. With the passing of time, the balance tilts even more in favor of the low-mass stars as the high-mass stars die away.

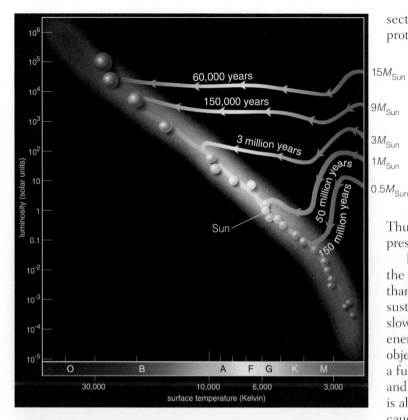

**FIGURE 16.6** Life tracks from protostar to the main sequence for stars of different masses. A high-mass protostar becomes a main-sequence star much more quickly than a lower-mass star, and its luminosity does not decline as much as it collapses.

The masses of stars have limits. Theoretical models indicate that stars above about $100M_{Sun}$ generate power so furiously that gravity cannot contain their internal pressure. Such stars effectively blow themselves apart and drive their outer layers into space. Observations confirm the absence of stars much larger than $100M_{Sun}$; if any stars this massive existed nearby, they would be so luminous that we would easily detect them.

On the other end of the scale, calculations show that the central temperature of a protostar with less than $0.08M_{Sun}$ never climbs above the 10-million-K threshold needed for efficient hydrogen fusion. Instead, a strange effect called **degeneracy pressure** halts the gravitational contraction of the core before hydrogen burning can begin. The quantum mechanical origins of degeneracy pressure are discussed in Chapter S4; you can visualize the origin of degeneracy pressure with an analogy to an auditorium in which the chairs represent all possible places that subatomic particles (electrons, in this case) can be located and people represent the particles. Protostars with masses above $0.08M_{Sun}$ are like auditoriums with many more available chairs than people, so the people (particles) can easily squeeze into a smaller

section of the auditorium. But the cores of protostars with masses below $0.08M_{Sun}$ are like auditoriums with so few chairs that the people (particles) fill nearly all of them. Because there are no extra chairs available, the people (particles) cannot squeeze into a smaller section of the auditorium. This resistance to squeezing is why degeneracy pressure halts gravitational contraction. Note that the degeneracy pressure arises *only* because particles have no place else to go. Thus, unlike thermal pressure, degeneracy pressure has nothing to do with temperature.

Because degeneracy pressure halts the collapse of a protostellar core with less than $0.08M_{Sun}$ before fusion becomes self-sustaining, the result is a "failed star" that slowly radiates away its internal thermal energy, gradually cooling with time. Such objects, called **brown dwarfs**, occupy a fuzzy gap between what we call a planet and what we call a star. (Note that $0.08M_{Sun}$ is about 80 times the mass of Jupiter.) Because degeneracy pressure does *not* rise and fall with temperature, the gradual cooling of a brown dwarf's interior does not weaken its degeneracy pressure. In the constant battle of any "star" to resist the crush of gravity, brown dwarfs are winners, albeit dim ones: Their degeneracy pressure will not diminish with time, so gravity will never gain the upper hand.

Brown dwarfs radiate primarily in the infrared and actually look deep red in color rather than brown. But they are far dimmer than normal stars and therefore are extremely difficult to detect, even if they are quite nearby. The first bona fide brown dwarf was discovered in 1995—a $0.05M_{Sun}$ object (called Gliese 229B) in orbit around a much brighter star (Gliese 229A). Many more brown dwarfs are now known. If the trend that makes small stars far more common than massive stars continues to masses below $0.08M_{Sun}$, brown dwarfs might outnumber ordinary stars by a huge margin.

## 16.3 Life as a Low-Mass Star

In the grand hierarchy of stars, our Sun ranks as rather mediocre. We should be thankful for this mediocrity. If the Sun had been a high-mass star, it would have lasted only a few million years, dying before life could have arisen on Earth. Instead, the Sun has shone steadily for nearly 5 billion years and will continue to do so for about 5 billion more. In this section, we investigate the lives of low-mass stars like our Sun.

### Slow and Steady

Low-mass stars spend their main-sequence lives fusing hydrogen into helium in their cores slowly and steadily via the *proton–proton chain* [Section 14.3]. As in the Sun, the energy released by nuclear fusion in the core may take a million years to reach the surface, where it finally escapes into space as the star's luminosity. The energy moves outward from the core through a combination of *radiative diffusion* and *convection* [Section 14.4]. Recall that radiative diffusion transports energy through the random bounces of photons from one electron to another and that convection transports energy by the rising of hot plasma and the sinking of cool plasma.

Radiative diffusion is more effective at transporting energy outward in the deeper, hotter plasma near a star's core. In higher layers, where the temperature is cooler, some of the ions in the plasma retain electrons. These ions can absorb photons and thereby tend to prevent photons from continuing outward by radiative diffusion. When the energy welling up from fusion in the core reaches the point at which radiative diffusion is inhibited, convection must take over as the means of transporting energy outward. This point represents the beginning of a star's *convection zone* (Figure 16.7). In the Sun, the temperature is cool enough to allow convection in the outer one-third of its interior. More massive stars have hotter interiors and hence shallower convection zones.

Lower-mass stars have cooler interiors and deeper convection zones. In very low mass stars, the convection zone extends all the way down to the core. The highest-mass stars have no convection zone at all near their surface, but they have a convective core because they produce energy so furiously.

The depth of the convection zone plays a major role in determining whether a star has activity similar to that of the sunspot cycle on our Sun [Section 14.5]. Recall that the Sun's activity arises from the twisting and stretching of its magnetic fields by convection and rotation. The most dramatically active stars are low-mass M stars that happen to have fast rotation rates in addition to their deep convection zones. The churning interiors of these stars are in a constant state of turmoil, twisting and knotting their magnetic field lines. When these field lines suddenly snap, the result can be a spectacular flare. For a few minutes or hours, the flare can produce more radiation in X rays than the total amount of light coming from the star in infrared and visible light. Life on a planet near one of these **flare stars** might be quite difficult. Proxima Centauri, the nearest star to the Sun, is a flare star.

A low-mass star gradually consumes its core hydrogen, converting it into helium over a period of billions of years. In the process, the declining number of independent particles in the core (four independent protons fuse into just one independent helium nucleus) causes the core to shrink and heat very gradually, pushing the luminosity of the main-sequence star slowly upward as it ages [Section 14.3]. But the most dramatic changes occur when nuclear fusion exhausts the hydrogen in the star's core.

high-mass star

$1 M_{Sun}$ star

very low mass star

**FIGURE 16.7** Among main-sequence stars, convection zones extend deeper in lower-mass stars. High-mass stars have convective cores but have no convection zones near their surfaces.

## Red Giant Stage

The energy released by hydrogen fusion during a star's main-sequence life maintains the thermal pressure that holds gravity at bay. But when the core hydrogen is finally depleted, nuclear fusion ceases in the star's core. With no fusion to supply thermal energy, the core pressure can no longer resist the crush of gravity, and the core begins to shrink more rapidly.

Surprisingly, the star's outer layers expand outward while the core is shrinking. On an H–R diagram, the star's life track moves almost horizontally to the right as the star grows in size to become a **subgiant** (Figure 16.8). Then, as the expansion of the outer layers continues, the star's luminosity begins to increase substantially, and the star slowly becomes a **red giant**. For a $1M_{Sun}$ star, this process takes about a billion years, during which the star's radius increases about 100-fold and its luminosity grows by an even greater factor. (Like all phases of stellar lives, the process occurs faster for more massive stars and slower for less massive stars.) This process may at first seem paradoxical: Why does the star grow bigger and more luminous at the same time that its core is shrinking?

We can find the answer by considering the interior structure of the star. The core is now made of helium—the "ash" left behind by hydrogen fusion—but the surrounding layers still contain plenty of fresh hydrogen. Gravity shrinks both the *inert* (nonburning) helium core and the surrounding *shell* of hydrogen, and the shell soon becomes hot enough to sustain hydrogen fusion (Figure 16.9). In fact, the shell becomes so hot that this **hydrogen shell burning** proceeds at a higher rate than core hydrogen fusion did during the star's main-sequence life. The result is that the star becomes more luminous than ever before. The thermal pressure generated by the hydrogen shell burning overcomes gravity in the star's upper layers, pushing them to expand outward. What was once a fairly dim main-sequence star balloons into a luminous red giant. Note that the red giant is large on the outside but most of its mass is buried deep in a shrunken stellar core.

The situation grows more extreme as long as the helium core remains inert. Recall that, in a main-sequence star like the Sun, a rise in the fusion rate causes the core to inflate and cool until the fusion rate drops back down; in Chapter 14, we referred to this self-correcting process as the solar *thermostat*

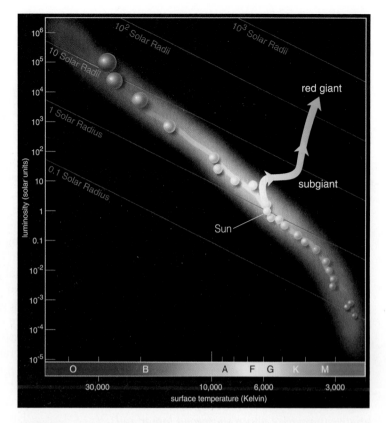

**FIGURE 16.8** The life track of a $1M_{Sun}$ star on an H–R diagram from the end of its main-sequence life until it becomes a red giant.

**FIGURE 16.9** After a star ends its main-sequence life, its inert helium core contracts while hydrogen shell burning begins. The high rate of fusion in the hydrogen shell forces the star's upper layers to expand outward.

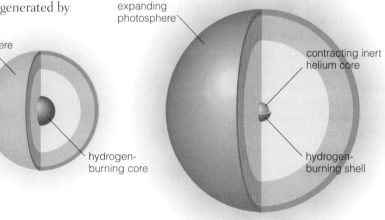

main-sequence star                    expanding subgiant

[Section 14.3]. But thermal energy generated in the hydrogen-burning shell of a red giant cannot do anything to inflate the inert core that lies underneath. Instead, newly produced helium keeps adding to the mass of the helium core, amplifying its gravitational pull and shrinking it further. The hydrogen-burning shell shrinks along with the core, growing hotter and denser. The fusion rate in the shell consequently rises, feeding even more helium ash to the core. The star is caught in a vicious circle. The core and shell continue to shrink in size and grow in luminosity, while thermal pressure continues to push the star's upper layers outward. This cycle breaks down only when the inert helium core reaches a temperature of about 100 million K, at which point helium nuclei can fuse together. (In a very low mass star, the inert helium core may never become hot enough to fuse helium. The core collapse will instead be halted by degeneracy pressure, ultimately leaving the star a *helium white dwarf.*) Throughout the expansion phase, **red-giant winds** carry away much more matter than the solar wind does for our Sun, but at much slower speeds.

**TIME OUT TO THINK** *Before you read on, briefly summarize why a star grows larger and brighter after it exhausts its core hydrogen. When does the growth of a red giant finally halt, and why? Would a star's red giant stage be different if the temperature required for helium fusion were around 200 million K, rather than 100 million K? Why?*

### Helium Burning

Recall that fusion occurs only when two nuclei come close enough together for the attractive *strong force* to overcome electromagnetic repulsion [Section 14.3]. Helium nuclei have two protons (and two neutrons) and hence a greater positive charge than the single proton of a hydrogen nucleus. The greater charge means that helium nuclei repel one another more strongly than hydrogen nuclei. **Helium fusion** therefore occurs only when nuclei slam into one another at much higher speeds than those needed for hydrogen fusion. Therefore, helium fusion requires much higher temperatures. The helium fusion process (often called the "triple-alpha" reaction because helium nuclei are sometimes called "alpha par-

ticles") converts three helium nuclei into one carbon nucleus:

Energy is released because the carbon-12 nucleus has a slightly lower mass than the three helium-4 nuclei, and the lost mass becomes energy in accord with $E = mc^2$.

There's one subtlety in the ignition of helium burning in low-mass stars. Theoretical models show that, in the inert helium core of a low-mass star, the thermal pressure is too low to counteract gravity. Instead, the models show that the pressure fighting against gravity is *degeneracy pressure*—the same strange type of pressure that supports brown dwarfs. Because degeneracy pressure does *not* increase with temperature, the onset of helium fusion heats the core rapidly *without* causing it to inflate. The rising temperature causes the helium fusion rate to rocket upward in what is called a **helium flash**.

The helium flash dumps enormous amounts of new thermal energy into the core. In a matter of seconds, the rapidly rising thermal pressure becomes the dominant pressure pushing back against gravity; the core is no longer degenerate and begins to expand. This core expansion pushes the hydrogen-burning shell outward, lowering its temperature and its burning rate. The result is that, even though the star now has core helium fusion *and* hydrogen shell burning taking place simultaneously (Figure 16.10),

---

**FIGURE 16.10** Core structure of a helium-burning star. Helium fusion causes the core and hydrogen-burning shell to expand and slightly cool, thereby reducing the overall energy generation rate in comparison to the rate during the red giant stage. The outer layers shrink back, so a helium-burning star is smaller than a red giant of the same mass.

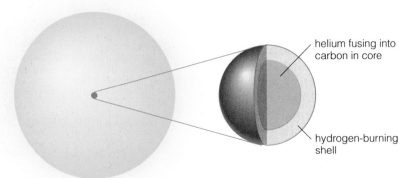

**FIGURE 16.11** The onset of helium fusion.

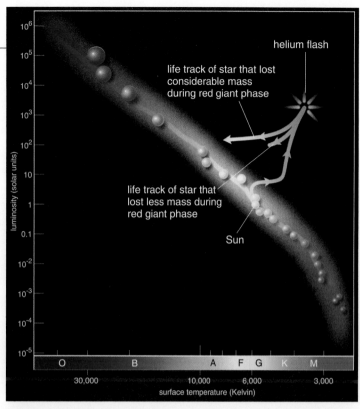

**a** After the helium flash, a star's surface shrinks and heats, so the star's life track moves downward and to the left on the H–R diagram.

the total energy production falls from its peak during the red giant phase. The reduced total energy output of the star reduces its luminosity, thereby allowing its outer layers to contract from their peak size during the red giant phase. As the outer layers contract, the star's surface temperature also increases somewhat.

Because the helium-burning star is now smaller and hotter than it was as a red giant, its life track on the H–R diagram drops downward and to the left (Figure 16.11a). The helium cores of all low-mass stars fuse helium into carbon at about the same rate, so these stars all have about the same luminosity. However, the outer layers of these stars can have different masses, depending on how much mass they lost through their red-giant winds. Stars that lost more mass end up with smaller radii and higher surface temperatures and hence are farther to the left on the H–R diagram. In a cluster of stars, those stars that are currently in their helium-burning phase therefore all have about the same luminosity but differ in surface temperature. Thus, on an H–R diagram for a cluster of stars, the helium-burning stars are arranged along a **horizontal branch** (Figure 16.11b). Note that the cluster H–R diagram clearly shows the main-sequence turnoff point. Stars that have recently left the main sequence are subgiants on their way to becoming red giants. In the upper-right corner of the red giant region are stars that are almost ready for the helium flash. The stars that have already become helium-burning, horizontal-branch stars are slightly dimmer and hotter.

### Last Gasps

It is only a matter of time until a horizontal-branch star fuses all its core helium into carbon. The core helium in a low-mass star will run out in about a hundred million years. When the core helium is exhausted, fusion turns off, and the core begins to shrink once again under the crush of gravity.

The basic processes that changed the star from a main-sequence star into a red giant now resume, but this time it is helium fusion

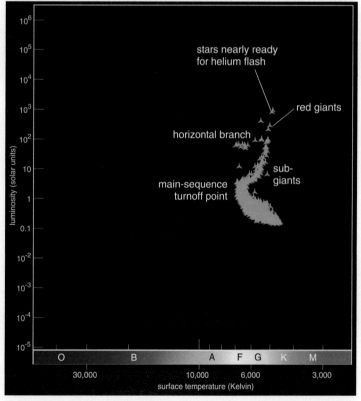

**b** This H–R diagram plots the luminosity and surface temperature of individual stars in a cluster (i.e., it does *not* show life tracks). Helium core–burning stars occupy the horizontal branch of the diagram. A star's position along the horizontal branch depends on how much mass it lost during the red giant phase.

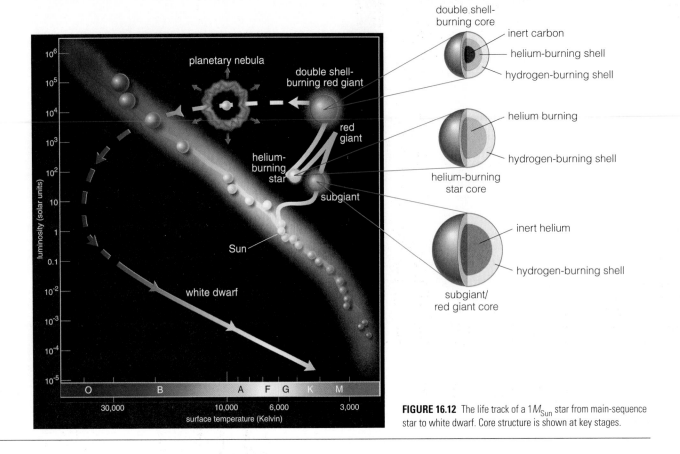

**FIGURE 16.12** The life track of a $1M_{Sun}$ star from main-sequence star to white dwarf. Core structure is shown at key stages.

that ignites in a shell around an inert carbon core. Meanwhile, the hydrogen shell still burns atop the helium layer. Both shells contract along with the inert core, driving their temperatures and fusion rates much higher. The luminosity of this double-shelled star grows greater than ever, and its outer layers swell to an even huger size. On the H–R diagram, the star's life track once again turns upward (Figure 16.12). Theoretical models show that helium burning inside such a star never finds a happy equilibrium but instead proceeds in a series of **thermal pulses** during which the fusion rate spikes upward every few thousand years.

The furious burning in the helium and hydrogen shells cannot last long—maybe a few million years or less for a $1M_{Sun}$ star. The star's only hope of extending its life lies with the carbon core, but this is a false hope in the case of low-mass stars. Carbon fusion is possible only at temperatures above about 600 million K. Before the core of a low-mass star ever reaches such a lofty temperature, degeneracy pressure halts its gravitational collapse.

For a low-mass star with a carbon core, the end is near. The huge size of the dying star means that it has a very weak grip on its outer layers. As the star's luminosity and radius keep rising, matter flows from its surface at increasingly high rates. Meanwhile, during each thermal pulse, strong convection dredges up carbon from the core, enriching the surface of the

star with carbon. Red giants whose atmospheres become especially carbon-rich in this way are called **carbon stars**. Carbon stars have cool, low-speed stellar winds, and the temperature of the gas in these winds drops with distance from the stellar surface. At the point at which the temperature has dropped to 1,000–2,000 K, some of the gas atoms in these slow-moving winds begin to stick together in microscopic clusters, forming small, solid particles of dust. These dust particles continue their slow drift with the stellar wind into interstellar space, where they become **interstellar dust grains**. The process of particulate formation is very similar to the formation of smoke particles in a fire. Thus, in a sense, carbon stars are the most voluminous polluters in the universe. However, this "carbon smog" is essential to life: Most of the carbon in your body (and in all life on Earth) was manufactured in carbon stars and blown into space by their stellar winds.

**TIME OUT TO THINK** *Suppose the universe contained only low-mass stars. Would elements heavier than carbon exist? Why or why not?*

Before a low-mass star dies, it treats us to one last spectacle. Through winds and other processes, the star ejects its outer layers into space. The result is a huge shell of gas expanding away from the inert, degenerate carbon core. The exposed core is still very hot and therefore emits intense ultraviolet radia-

**a** The Ring Nebula

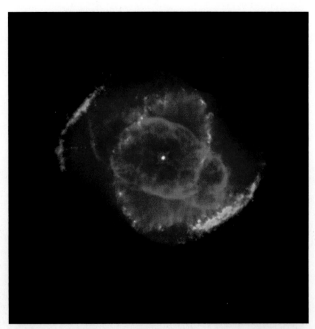

**b** The Cat's Eye Nebula

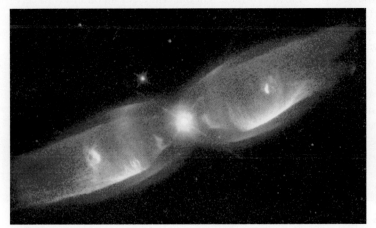

**c** The Twin Jet Nebula

**FIGURE 16.13** Planetary nebulae occur when low-mass stars in their final death throes cast off their outer layers of gas, as seen in these photos from the Hubble Space Telescope. The hot core that remains ionizes and energizes the richly complex envelope of gas surrounding it.

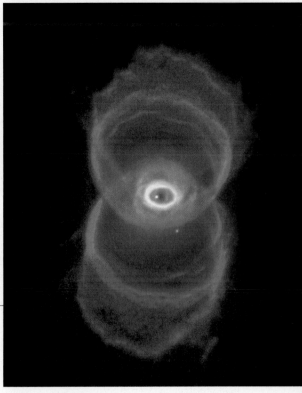

**d** The Hourglass Nebula

tion that ionizes the gas in the expanding shell, causing it to glow brightly as what we call a **planetary nebula**. Despite their name, planetary nebulae have nothing to do with planets. The name comes from the fact that nearby nebulae look disk-shaped (like planets) through a small telescope. Through a larger telescope, more detail is visible. The famous Ring Nebula in the constellation Lyra is a planetary nebula; many others are also quite beautiful (Figure 16.13).

The glow of the planetary nebula fades as the exposed core cools and the ejected gas disperses into space. The nebula will disappear within a million years, leaving behind the cooling carbon core. On the H–R diagram, the life track now represents this "dead" core (see Figure 16.12). At first the life track heads to the left, because the core is initially quite hot and luminous. But the life track soon veers downward and to the right as the remaining ember cools and fades. You already know these naked, inert cores by another name: *white dwarfs* [Section 15.5].

In the ongoing battle between gravity and a star's internal pressure, white dwarfs are a sort of stalemate. As long as no mass is added to the white dwarf from some other source (such as a companion star in a binary system), neither the strength of gravity nor the strength of the degeneracy pressure that holds gravity at bay will ever change. Thus, a white dwarf is little more than a decaying corpse that will cool for the indefinite future, eventually disappearing from view as a *black dwarf*.

### The Fate of Life on Earth

The evolutionary stages of low-mass stars are immensely important to the Earth, because we orbit a low-mass star—the Sun. The Sun will gradually brighten during its remaining time as a main-sequence star; it has already been doing so for the past 4 billion years, perhaps with no serious consequences for life on Earth. (Apparently, Earth's climate self-adjusts to maintain stable temperatures as the Sun heats over long time scales.) However, somewhere around the year A.D. 5,000,000,000, the hydrogen in the solar core will run out. The Sun will then expand to a subgiant about three times as large and twice as bright as it is today. This increased luminosity will evaporate the oceans, perhaps leading to a runaway greenhouse effect that could raise Earth's average temperature to something similar to that of Venus and probably hotter [Section 13.3]. If any life survives, it will have to be very tolerant of heat.

Things will only get worse as the Sun grows into a red giant over the next several hundred million years. Just before helium flash, the Sun will be about 100 times larger in radius and over 1,000 times more luminous than it is today. Earth's surface temperature will exceed 1,000 K, and the oceans will long since have boiled away. By this time, any surviving humans will need to have found a new home. Saturn's moon Titan [Section 11.5] might not be a bad choice: Its surface temperature will have risen from well below freezing today to about the present temperature of Earth. The Sun will shrink somewhat after helium burning begins, providing a temporary lull in incineration while the Sun spends 100 million years as a helium-burning star.

Anyone who survives the Sun's helium-burning phase will need to prepare for one final disaster. After exhausting its core helium, the Sun will expand again during its last million years. Its luminosity will soar to thousands of times what it is today, and it will grow so large that solar prominences might lap at the Earth's surface. Then it will eject its outer layers as a planetary nebula that will engulf Jupiter and Saturn and drift on past Pluto into interstellar space. If the Earth is not destroyed, its charred surface will be cold and dark in the faint, fading light of the white dwarf that the Sun has become. From then on, the Earth will be little more than a chunk of rock circling the corpse of our once-brilliant star.

---

THINKING ABOUT . . .

### Five Billion Years

The Sun's demise in about 5 billion years might at first seem worrisome, but 5 billion years is a very long time. It is longer than Earth has yet existed, and human time scales pale by comparison. A single human lifetime, if we take it to be about 100 years, is only $2 \times 10^{-8}$, or two hundred-millionths, of 5 billion years. Because $2 \times 10^{-8}$ of a human lifetime is about 1 minute, we can say that a human lifetime compared to the life expectancy of the Sun is roughly the same as 60 heart beats in comparison to a human lifetime.

What about human creations? The Egyptian pyramids have often been described as "eternal." But they are slowly eroding due to wind, rain, air pollution, and the impact of tourists, and all traces of them will have vanished within a few hundred thousand years. While a few hundred thousand years may seem like a long time, the Sun's remaining lifetime is more than 1,000 times longer.

On a more somber note, we can gain perspective on 5 billion years by considering evolutionary time scales. During the past century, our species has acquired suffi-cient technology and power to destroy human life totally, if we so choose. However, even if we make that unfortunate choice, some species (including many insects) are likely to survive. Would another intelligent species ever emerge on Earth? There is no way to know, but we can look to the past for guidance. Many species of dinosaurs were biologically quite advanced, if not truly intelligent, when they were suddenly wiped out about 65 million years ago. Some small rodentlike mammals survived, and here we are 65 million years later. We therefore might guess that another intelligent species could evolve some 65 million years after a human extinction. If these beings also destroyed themselves, another species could evolve 65 million years after that, and so on. But even at 65 million years per shot, the Earth would have *nearly* 80 more chances for an intelligent species to evolve in 5 billion years (5 billion ÷ 65 million ≈ 77). Perhaps one of those species will not destroy itself, and future generations might move on to other star systems by the time the Sun finally dies. Perhaps this species will be our own.

## 16.4 Life as a High-Mass Star

Human life would be impossible without both low-mass stars and high-mass stars. The long lives of low-mass stars allow evolution to proceed for billions of years, but only high-mass stars produce the full array of elements on which life depends. Fusion of elements heavier than helium to produce elements heavier than carbon requires extremely high temperatures in order to overcome the larger electromagnetic repulsion of more highly charged nuclei. Reaching such temperatures requires an extremely strong crush of gravity on a star's core—a crush that occurs only under the immense weight of the overlying gas in high-mass stars.

In the final stages of their lives, the highest-mass stars proceed to fuse increasingly heavy elements until they have exhausted all possible fusion sources. When fusion ceases, gravity drives the core to implode suddenly, which, as we will soon see, causes the star to self-destruct in the titanic explosion we call a *supernova*. The fast-paced life and cataclysmic death of a high-mass star—surely one of the great dramas of the universe—are the topics of this section.

### Brief but Brilliant

During its main-sequence life, the strong gravity of a high-mass star compresses its hydrogen core to higher temperatures than we find in lower-mass stars. You already know that the rate of fusion via the proton–proton chain increases substantially at higher tem-peratures, but the even hotter core temperatures of high-mass stars enable protons to slam into carbon, oxygen, or nitrogen nuclei as well as into other protons. Although carbon, nitrogen, and oxygen make up less than 2% of the material from which stars form in interstellar space, this 2% is more than enough to be useful in a stellar core. The carbon, nitrogen, and oxygen act as catalysts for hydrogen fusion, making it proceed at a far higher rate than would be possible by the proton–proton chain alone. (A *catalyst* is something that aids the progress of a reaction without being consumed in the reaction.) The lives of high-mass stars are truly brief but brilliant.

The chain of reactions that leads to hydrogen fusion in high-mass stars is called the **CNO cycle**; the letters *CNO* stand for carbon, nitrogen, and oxygen, respectively. The six steps of the CNO cycle are shown in Figure 16.14. Note that, just as in the proton–proton chain [Section 14.3], four hydrogen nuclei go in while one helium-4 nucleus comes out. The amount of energy generated in each reaction cycle therefore is the same as in the proton–proton chain: It is equal to the difference in mass between the four hydrogen nuclei and the one helium nucleus multiplied by $c^2$. The CNO cycle is simply another, faster way to accomplish hydrogen fusion.

The escalated fusion rates in high-mass stars generate remarkable amounts of power. Many more photons stream from the photospheres of high-mass stars than from the Sun, and many more photons are

**FIGURE 16.14** This diagram illustrates the six steps of the CNO cycle by which massive stars fuse hydrogen into helium. Note that the overall result is the same as that of the proton–proton chain: Four hydrogen nuclei fuse to make one helium nucleus. The carbon, nitrogen, and oxygen nuclei help the cycle proceed, but overall these nuclei are neither consumed nor created in the cycle.

bouncing around inside. Although photons have no mass, they act like particles and carry *momentum* [Section 5.1], which they can transfer to anything they hit, imparting a very slight jolt. The combined jolts from the huge number of photons streaming outward through a high-mass star apply a type of pressure called **radiation pressure**.

**TIME OUT TO THINK** *We have now discussed three types of pressure: thermal pressure, degeneracy pressure, and radiation pressure. Before continuing, briefly review each type of pressure and describe the conditions under which each is important.*

Radiation pressure can have dramatic effects on high-mass stars. In the most massive stars, radiation pressure is even more important than thermal pressure in keeping gravity at bay. Near the photosphere, the radiation pressure can drive strong, fast-moving stellar winds. The wind from a very massive star can expel as much as $10^{-5}$ solar mass of gas per year at speeds greater than 1,000 km/s. This wind would cross the United States in about 5 seconds and would send a mass equivalent to that of our Sun hurtling into space in only 100,000 years. Such a wind cannot last long because it would blow away all the mass of even a very massive star in just a few million years.

### Advanced Nuclear Burning

The exhaustion of core hydrogen in a high-mass star sets in motion the same processes that turn a low-mass star into a red giant, but the transformation proceeds much more quickly. The star develops a hydrogen-burning shell, and its outer layers begin to expand outward. At the same time, the core contracts, and this gravitational contraction releases energy that raises the core temperature until it becomes hot enough to fuse helium into carbon. However, there is no helium flash in stars of more than 2 solar masses. The high core temperatures induced by core contraction keep the thermal pressure high, preventing degeneracy pressure from being a factor. Helium burn-

ing therefore ignites gradually, just as hydrogen burning did at the beginning of the star's main-sequence life.

A high-mass star fuses helium into carbon so rapidly that it is left with an inert carbon core after just a few hundred thousand years or less. Once again, the absence of fusion leaves the core without a thermal energy source to fight off the crush of gravity. The inert carbon core shrinks, the crush of gravity intensifies, and the core pressure, temperature, and density all rise. Meanwhile, a helium-burning shell forms between the inert core and the hydrogen-burning shell. The star's outer layers swell again.

Up to this point, the life stories of intermediate-mass stars ($2$–$8M_{Sun}$) and high-mass stars ($>8M_{Sun}$) are very similar, except that all stages proceed more rapidly in higher-mass stars. However, degeneracy pressure prevents the cores of intermediate-mass stars from reaching the temperatures required to burn carbon or oxygen into anything much heavier. These stars eventually blow away their upper layers and finish their lives as white dwarfs. The rest of a high-mass star's life, on the other hand, is unlike anything that a low- or intermediate-mass star ever experiences.

The crush of gravity in a high-mass star is so overwhelming that degeneracy pressure never comes into

**FIGURE 16.15** A few of the many nuclear reactions that occur in the final stages of a high-mass star's life. Fusion of two silicon nuclei and some other processes that lead to iron actually first produce nickel-56 (28 protons and 28 neutrons), but this decays rapidly to cobalt-56 (27 protons and 29 neutrons) and then to iron-56 (26 protons and 30 neutrons).

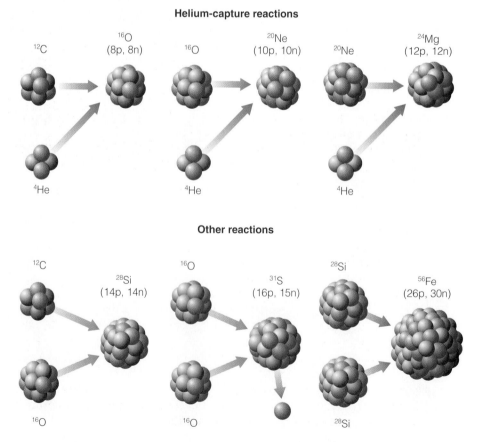

**Helium-capture reactions**

$^{12}$C    $^{16}$O (8p, 8n)    $^{16}$O    $^{20}$Ne (10p, 10n)    $^{20}$Ne    $^{24}$Mg (12p, 12n)

$^4$He    $^4$He    $^4$He

**Other reactions**

$^{12}$C    $^{28}$Si (14p, 14n)    $^{16}$O    $^{31}$S (16p, 15n)    $^{28}$Si    $^{56}$Fe (26p, 30n)

$^{16}$O    $^{16}$O    $^{28}$Si

play in the collapsing carbon core. The gravitational contraction of the core continues, and the core temperature soon reaches the 600 million K required to fuse carbon into heavier elements. Carbon fusion provides the core with a new source of energy that restores the balance versus gravity, but only temporarily. In the highest-mass stars, carbon burning may last only a few hundred years. When the core carbon is depleted, the core again begins to collapse, shrinking and heating until it can fuse a still-heavier element. The star is engaged in the final phases of a desperate battle against the ever-strengthening crush of gravity. Each successive stage of core nuclear burning proceeds more rapidly than prior stages. In a field in which we usually think in terms of millions or billions of years, we are suddenly dealing with time scales that are short even for humans.

The nuclear reactions in the star's final stages of life become quite complex, and many different reactions may take place simultaneously (Figure 16.15). The simplest sequence of fusion stages involves **helium capture**—the fusing of helium nuclei into progressively heavier elements. (Some helium nuclei still remain in the core, but not enough to continue helium fusion efficiently.) Helium capture can fuse carbon into oxygen, oxygen into neon, neon into magnesium, and so on. At high enough temperatures, a star's core plasma can fuse heavy nuclei to one another. For example, fusing carbon to oxygen creates silicon, fusing two oxygen nuclei creates sulfur, and fusing two silicon nuclei generates iron. Some of these heavy-element reactions release free neutrons, which may fuse with heavy nuclei to make still rarer elements. The star is forging the variety of elements that, in our solar system at least, became the stuff of life.

Each time the core depletes the elements it is fusing, it shrinks and heats until it becomes hot enough for other fusion reactions. Meanwhile, a new type of shell burning ignites between the core and the overlying shells of fusion. Near the end, the star's central region resembles the inside of an onion, with layer upon layer of shells burning different elements (Figure 16.16). During the star's final few days, iron begins to pile up in the silicon-burning core.

Despite the dramatic events taking place in its interior, the high-mass star's outer appearance changes only slowly. As each stage of core fusion ceases, the

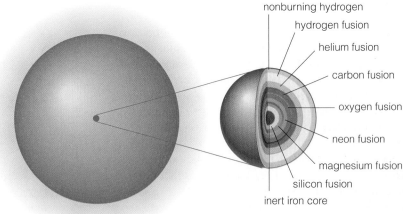

**FIGURE 16.16** The multiple layers of nuclear burning in the core of a high-mass star during the final days of its life.

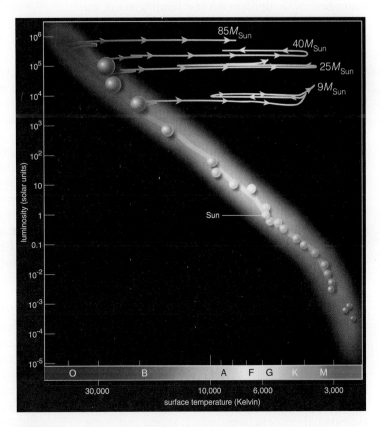

**FIGURE 16.17** Life tracks on the H–R diagram from main-sequence star to red supergiant for selected high-mass stars. Labels on the tracks give the star's mass at the beginning of its main-sequence life. Because of the strong wind from such a star, its mass can be considerably smaller when it leaves the main sequence. (Based on models from A. Maeder and G. Meynet.)

surrounding shell burning intensifies and further inflates the star's outer layers. Each time the core flares up again, the outer layers may contract a bit. The result is that the star's life track zigzags across the top of the H–R diagram (Figure 16.17). In very massive stars, the core changes happen so quickly that the outer layers don't have time to respond, and the star progresses steadily toward becoming a red supergiant.

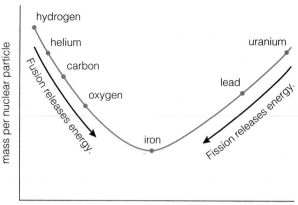

Betelgeuse, the upper-left shoulder star of Orion, is the best-known red supergiant star. Its radius is over 500 solar radii, or more than twice the distance from the Sun to Earth. We have no way of knowing what stage of nuclear burning is now taking place in Betelgeuse's core. Betelgeuse may have a few thousand years of nuclear burning still ahead, or we may be seeing it as iron piles up in its core. If the latter is the case, then sometime in the next few days we will witness one of the most dramatic events that ever occurs in the universe.

### Iron: Bad News for the Stellar Core

As a high-mass star develops an inert core of iron, the core continues shrinking and heating while iron continues to pile up from nuclear burning in the surrounding shells. If iron were like the other elements in prior stages of nuclear burning, this core contraction would stop when iron fusion ignited. However, iron is unique among the elements in a very important way: It is the one element from which it is *not* possible to generate any kind of nuclear energy.

To understand why iron is unique, remember that only two basic processes can release nuclear energy: *fusion* of light elements into heavier ones, and *fission* of very heavy elements into not-so-heavy ones. Recall that hydrogen fusion converts four protons (hydrogen nuclei) into a helium nucleus that consists of two protons and two neutrons. Thus, the total number of *nuclear particles* (protons and neutrons combined) does not change. However, this fusion reaction generates energy (in accord with $E = mc^2$) because the *mass* of the helium nucleus is less than the combined mass of the four hydrogen nuclei that fused to create it—despite the fact that the *number* of nuclear particles is unchanged.

In other words, fusing hydrogen into helium generates energy because helium has a lower *mass per nuclear particle* than hydrogen. Similarly, fusing three helium-4 nuclei into one carbon-12 nucleus generates energy because carbon has a lower mass per nuclear particle than helium—which means that some mass disappears and becomes energy in this fusion reaction. In fact, the decrease in mass per nuclear particle from hydrogen to helium to carbon is part of a general trend shown in Figure 16.18: The mass per nuclear particle tends to decrease as we go from light elements to iron, which means that fusion of light nuclei into heavier nuclei generates energy. This trend reverses beyond iron: The mass per nuclear particle tends to *increase* as we look to still heavier elements. As a result, elements heavier than iron can generate nuclear energy only through fission into lighter elements. For example, uranium has a greater mass per nuclear particle than lead, so uranium fission (which ultimately leaves lead as a by-product) must convert some mass into energy.

**FIGURE 16.18** Overall, the average mass per nuclear particle declines from hydrogen to iron and then increases. Selected nuclei are labeled to provide reference points. (This graph shows the most general trends only; a more detailed graph would show numerous up-and-down bumps superimposed on the general trend.)

Iron has the lowest mass per nuclear particle of all nuclei and therefore cannot release energy by either fusion or fission. Thus, once the matter in a stellar core turns to iron, it can generate no further thermal energy or pressure. The iron core's only hope of resisting the crush of gravity lies with degeneracy pressure. But iron keeps piling up in the core until degeneracy pressure can no longer support it either. What ensues is the ultimate nuclear-waste catastrophe.

**TIME OUT TO THINK** *How would the universe be different if hydrogen, rather than iron, had the lowest mass per nuclear particle? Why?*

### Supernova

The degeneracy pressure that briefly supports the inert iron core arises because the laws of quantum mechanics prohibit electrons from getting too close together [Section S4.5]. But once gravity pushes the electrons past the quantum mechanical limit, they can no longer exist freely. The electrons disappear by combining with protons to form neutrons, releasing neutrinos in the process (Figure 16.19). The electron degeneracy pressure suddenly vanishes, and gravity has free rein.

In a fraction of a second, an iron core with a mass comparable to that of our Sun and a size larger than that of Earth collapses into a ball of neutrons just a few kilometers across. The collapse halts only because the neutrons have a degeneracy pressure of their own. The entire core then resembles a giant atomic nucleus. If you recall that ordinary atoms are made almost entirely of empty space [Section 4.3] and that almost all their mass is in their nuclei, you'll realize that a giant atomic nucleus must have an astoundingly high density.

**FIGURE 16.19** During the final, catastrophic collapse of a high-mass stellar core, electrons and protons combine to form neutrons, accompanied by the release of neutrinos.

e⁻

n

p

neutrino

The gravitational collapse of the core releases an enormous amount of energy—more than a hundred times what the Sun will radiate over its entire 10-billion-year lifetime! Where does this energy go? It drives the outer layers off into space in a titanic explosion—a **supernova**. The ball of neutrons left behind is called a **neutron star**. In some cases, the remaining mass may be so large that gravity also overcomes neutron degeneracy pressure, and the core continues to collapse until it becomes a *black hole*.

Theoretical models of supernovae successfully reproduce the observed energy outputs of real supernovae, but the precise mechanism of the explosion is not yet clear. Two general processes could contribute to the explosion. In the first process, neutron degeneracy pressure halts the gravitational collapse, causing the core to rebound slightly and ram into overlying material that is still falling inward. Until recently, most astronomers thought that this *core-bounce* process ejected the star's outer layers. But current models of supernovae suggest that the more important process involves the neutrinos formed when electrons and protons combine to make neutrons. Although these ghostly particles rarely interact with anything [Section 14.3], so many are produced when the core implodes that they drive a shock wave that propels the star's upper layers into space.

The shock wave sends the star's former surface zooming outward at a speed of 10,000 km/s, heating it so that it shines with dazzling brilliance. For about a week, a supernova blazes as powerfully as 10 billion Suns, rivaling the luminosity of a moderate-size galaxy. The ejected gases slowly cool and fade in brightness over the next several months, but they continue to expand outward until they eventually mix with other gas in interstellar space. The scattered debris from the supernova carries with it the variety of elements produced in the star's nuclear furnace, as well as additional elements created when some of the neutrons produced during the core collapse slam into other nuclei. Millions or billions of years later, this debris may be incorporated into a new generation of stars.

### The Origin of Elements

Before we leave the subject of massive-star life cycles, it's useful to consider the evidence that indicates we actually understand the origin of the elements. We cannot see inside stars, so we cannot directly observe elements being created in the ways we've discussed. However, the signature of nuclear reactions in massive stars is written in the patterns of elemental abundances across the universe.

For example, if massive stars really produce heavy elements (that is, elements heavier than hydrogen and helium) and scatter these elements into space when they die, the total amount of these heavy elements in interstellar gas should gradually increase with time (because additional massive stars have died). Thus, we should expect stars born recently to contain a greater proportion of heavy elements than stars born in the distant past because they formed from interstellar gas that contained more heavy elements. Stellar spectra confirm this prediction: Older stars do indeed contain smaller amounts of heavy elements than younger stars. For very old stars in globular clusters, elements besides hydrogen and helium typically make up as little as 0.1% of the total mass. In contrast, about 2–3% of the mass of young stars that formed in the recent past is in the form of heavy elements.

We gain even more confidence in our model of elemental creation when we compare the abundances of different elements. For example, because helium-capture reactions add two protons (and two neutrons) at a time, we expect nuclei with even numbers of protons to outnumber those with odd numbers of protons that fall between them. Sure enough, even-numbered nuclei such as carbon, oxygen, and neon are relatively abundant (Figure 16.20). Similarly, because elements heavier than iron are made only

**FIGURE 16.20** This graph shows the observed relative abundances of elements in the galaxy in comparison to the abundance of hydrogen. For example, the abundance of nitrogen is about $10^{-4}$, which means that there are about $10^{-4} = 0.0001$ times as many nitrogen atoms in the galaxy as hydrogen atoms.

**FIGURE 16.21** The Crab Nebula is the remnant of the supernova observed in A.D. 1054. This photograph was taken with the new Very Large Telescope at the European Southern Observatory in Chile.

by rare fusion reactions shortly before and during a supernova, we expect these elements to be extremely rare. Again, this prediction made by our model of nuclear creation is verified by observations.

### Supernova Observations

The study of supernovae owes a great debt to astronomers of many different epochs and cultures. Careful scrutiny of the night skies allowed the ancients to identify several supernovae whose remains still adorn the heavens. The most famous example concerns the Crab Nebula in the constellation Taurus. The Crab Nebula is a **supernova remnant**—an expanding cloud of debris from a supernova explosion (Figure 16.21). A spinning neutron star lies at the center of the Crab Nebula, providing evidence that supernovae really do create neutron stars. Photographs taken years apart show that the nebula is growing larger at a rate of several thousand kilometers per second. Calculating backward from its present size, we can trace the nebula's birth to somewhere near A.D. 1100. Thanks to observations made by ancient astronomers, we can be even more precise.

The official history of the Sung Dynasty in China contains a record of a remarkable celestial event:

> *In the first year of the period Chih-ho, the fifth moon, the day chi-ch'ou, a guest star appeared approximately several [degrees] southeast of Thien-kuan. After more than a year it gradually became invisible.*

This description of the sudden appearance and gradual dimming of a "guest star" matches what we expect for a supernova, and the location "southeast of Thien-kuan" corresponds to the Crab Nebula's location in Taurus. Moreover, the Chinese date described in the excerpt corresponds to July 4, 1054, telling us precisely when the Crab supernova became visible on Earth. Descriptions of this particular supernova also appear in Japanese astronomical writings, in an Arabic medical textbook, and possibly in Native American paintings in the southwestern United States. Curiously, European records do not mention this supernova, even though it would have been clearly visible.

Historical records of supernovae allow us to age-date the remnants we see today to determine the kinds of supernovae that produced them and to assess how frequently stars explode in our region of the Milky Way Galaxy. At least four supernovae have been observed during the last thousand years, appearing as brilliant new stars for a few months in the years 1006, 1054, 1572, and 1604. The supernova of 1006, the brightest of these four, could be seen during the daytime and cast shadows at night. Supernovae may even have influenced human history. The Chinese were meticulous in recording their observations because they believed that celestial events foretold the future, and they may have acted in accord with such fortune-telling. The 1572 supernova was witnessed by Tycho Brahe, and it helped convince him and others that the heavens were not as perfect and unchanging as Aristotle had imagined [Section 5.3]. Kepler saw the 1604 supernova at a time when he was struggling to make planetary orbits fit perfect circles; perhaps this "imperfection" of the heavens helped push him to test elliptical orbits instead.

No supernova has been seen in our own galaxy since 1604, but today astronomers routinely discover supernovae in other galaxies. The nearest of these

**FIGURE 16.22** Before-and-after photos of the location of Supernova 1987A. In the before picture, the arrow indicates the star that exploded. The supernova actually appeared as a bright *point* of light; it appears larger than a point in the after photograph only because of overexposure.

before

after

extragalactic supernovae, and the only one near enough to be visible to the naked eye, burst into view in 1987. Because it was the first supernova detected that year, it was given the name **Supernova 1987A**. Supernova 1987A was the explosion of a star in the *Large Magellanic Cloud,* a small galaxy that orbits the Milky Way and is visible only from southern latitudes. The Large Magellanic Cloud is about 150,000 light-years away, so the star really exploded some 150,000 years ago.

As the nearest supernova witnessed in four centuries, Supernova 1987A provided a unique opportunity to study a supernova and its debris in detail. Astronomers from all over the planet traveled to the Southern Hemisphere to observe it, and several orbiting spacecraft added observations in many different wavelengths of light. Older photographs of the Large Magellanic Cloud allowed astronomers to determine precisely which star had exploded (Figure 16.22). It turned out to be a blue star, not the red supergiant expected when core fusion has ceased. The most likely explanation is that the star's outer layers were unusually thin and warm near the end of its life, changing its appearance from that of a red supergiant to a blue one. The surprising color of the preexplosion star demonstrates that we still have much to learn about supernovae. Reassuringly, most other theoretical predictions of stellar life cycles were well matched by observations of Supernova 1987A.

One of the most remarkable findings from Supernova 1987A was a burst of neutrinos, recorded by neutrino detectors in Japan and Ohio. The neutrino data confirmed that the explosion released most of its energy in the form of neutrinos, suggesting that we are correct in believing that the stellar core undergoes sudden collapse to a ball of neutrons. The capture of neutrinos from Supernova 1987A has spurred scientific interest in building more purposeful "neutrino telescopes." Perhaps these neutrino telescopes will open new fields of astronomical research in the coming decades.

**TIME OUT TO THINK** *When Betelgeuse explodes as a supernova, it will be more than 10 times brighter than the full moon in our sky. If Betelgeuse had exploded a few hundred or a few thousand years ago, do you think it could have had any effect on human history? How do you think our modern society would react if we saw Betelgeuse explode tomorrow?*

### Summary of Stellar Lives

We have seen that the primary factor determining how a star lives its life is its mass. Low-mass stars live long lives and die in planetary nebulae, leaving behind white dwarfs. High-mass stars live short lives and die in supernovae, leaving behind neutron stars and black holes. Both types of stars are crucial to life. Near the ends of their lives, low-mass stars can become carbon stars, which are the source of most of the carbon in our bodies. High-mass stars produce the vast array of other chemical elements on which life depends. Figure 16.23 summarizes the life cycles of stars of different masses.

**Protostars**: A star system forms when a cloud of interstellar gas collapses under gravity. The central protostar is surrounded by a protostellar disk in which planets may eventually form.

**Blue main-sequence star**: Star is fueled by hydrogen fusion in its core. In high-mass stars, hydrogen fusion proceeds by the series of reactions known as the CNO cycle.

**Red supergiant**: After core hydrogen is exhausted, the core shrinks and heats. Hydrogen shell burning begins around the inert helium core, causing the star to expand into a red supergiant.

**Helium core-burning supergiant**: Helium fusion begins when enough helium has collected in the core. The core then expands, slowing the fusion rate and allowing the star's outer layers to shrink somewhat. Hydrogen shell burning continues at a reduced rate.

**Life of a 20M$_{Sun}$ Star.**
Main-sequence lifetime: 8 million years
Duration of later stages: 1 million years

**Multiple shell-burning supergiant**: After core helium is exhausted, the core shrinks until carbon fusion begins, while helium and hydrogen continue to burn in shells surrounding the core. Late in its life, the star fuses heavier elements like carbon and oxygen in shells while iron collects in the inert core.

**Supernova**: Iron cannot provide fusion energy, so it accumulates in the core until the mass of the iron core approaches the 1.4$M_{Sun}$ limit. Then it can no longer support its own weight and collapses, leading to the catastrophic explosion of the star.

**Neutron star**: During the core collapse of the supernova, electrons combine with protons to make neutrons. The leftover core is therefore made almost entirely of neutrons.

**Yellow main-sequence star**: Star is fueled by hydrogen fusion in its core, which converts four hydrogen nuclei into one helium nucleus. In low-mass stars, hydrogen fusion proceeds by the series of reactions known as the proton-proton chain.

**FIGURE 16.23** Summary of stellar lives. The life stages of a high-mass star (on the left) and a low-mass star (on the right) are depicted in clockwise sequences beginning with the protostellar stage in the upper-left corner. (Stars not drawn to scale.)

**Helium core-burning star**: Helium fusion, in which three helium nuclei fuse to form a single carbon nucleus, begins when enough helium has collected in the core. The core then expands, slowing the fusion rate and allowing the star's outer layers to shrink somewhat. Hydrogen shell burning continues at a reduced rate.

**Red giant star**: After core hydrogen is exhausted, the core shrinks and heats. Hydrogen shell burning begins around the inert helium core, causing the star to expand into a red giant.

**Double shell-burning red giant**: After core helium is exhausted, the core again shrinks and heats. Helium shell burning begins around the inert carbon core and the star enters its second red giant phase. Hydrogen shell burning continues.

**Life of a 1M$_{Sun}$ Star.**
Main-sequence lifetime: 10 billion years
Duration of later stages: 1 billion years

**Planetary nebula**: The dying star expels its outer layers in a planetary nebula, leaving behind the exposed inert core.

**White dwarf**: The remaining white dwarf is made primarily of carbon and oxygen because the core never grew hot enough to fuse these elements into anything heavier.

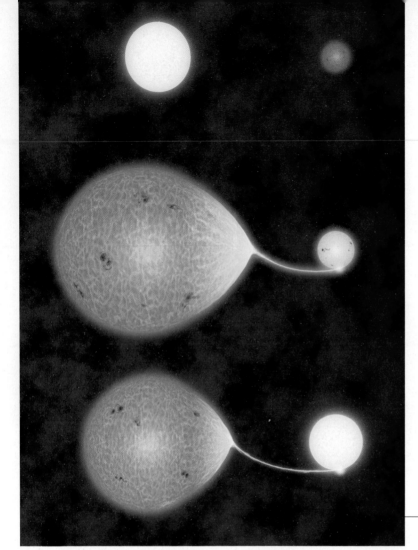

Algol shortly after its birth. The higher-mass main-sequence star (left) evolved more quickly than its lower-mass companion (right).

Algol at onset of mass transfer. When the more massive star expanded into a red giant, it began losing some of its mass to its main-sequence companion.

Algol today. As a result of the mass transfer, the red giant has shrunk to a subgiant, and the main-sequence star on the right is now the more massive of the two stars.

**FIGURE 16.24** Artist's conception of the development of the Algol close binary system.

## 16.5 The Lives of Close Binary Stars

For the most part, stars in binary systems proceed from birth to death as if they were isolated and alone. The exceptions are close binary stars. Algol, the "demon star" in the constellation Perseus, consists of two stars that orbit each other closely: a $3.7M_{Sun}$ main-sequence star and a $0.8M_{Sun}$ subgiant. A moment's thought reveals that something quite strange is going on. The stars of a binary system are born at the same time and therefore must both be the same age. We know that more massive stars live shorter lives, and therefore the more massive star must exhaust its core hydrogen and become a subgiant before the less massive star does. How, then, can Algol's less massive star be a subgiant while the more massive star is still burning hydrogen as a main-sequence star?

This so-called *Algol paradox* reveals some of the complications in ordinary stellar life cycles that can arise in close binary systems. The two stars in close binaries are near enough to exert significant tidal forces on each other [Section 5.5]. The gravity of each star attracts the near side of the other star more strongly than it attracts the far side. The stars therefore stretch into football-like shapes rather than remaining spherical. In addition, the stars become *tidally locked* so that they always show the same face to each other, much as the Moon always shows the same face to Earth.

During the time that both stars are main-sequence stars, the tidal forces have little effect on their lives. But when the more massive star (which exhausts its core hydrogen sooner) begins to expand into a red giant, gas from its outer layers can spill over onto its companion. This **mass exchange** occurs when the giant grows so large that its tidally distorted outer layers succumb to the gravitational attraction of the smaller companion star. The companion then begins to gain mass at the expense of the giant.

The solution to the Algol paradox should now be clear (Figure 16.24). The $0.8M_{Sun}$ subgiant *used to be* much more massive. As the more massive star, it was the first to begin expanding into a red giant.

But as it expanded, so much of its matter spilled over onto its companion that it is now the less massive star.

The future may hold even more interesting events for Algol. The $3.7 M_{Sun}$ star is still gaining mass from its subgiant companion. Thus, its life cycle is actually accelerating as its increasing gravity raises its core hydrogen fusion rate. Millions of years from now, it will exhaust its hydrogen and begin to expand into a red giant itself. At that point, it can begin to transfer mass *back* to its companion. Even stranger things can happen in other mass-exchange systems, particularly when one of the stars is a white dwarf or a neutron star. But that is a topic for the next chapter.

## THE BIG PICTURE

In this chapter, we answered the question of the origin of elements that we first discussed in Chapter 1. As you look back over this chapter, remember these "big picture" ideas:

- Virtually all elements besides hydrogen and helium were forged in the nuclear furnaces of stars. Carbon can be released from low-mass stars near the ends of their lives (carbon stars), and many other elements are released into space by massive stars in supernova explosions.

- The tug-of-war between gravity and pressure determines how stars behave from the time of their birth in a cloud of molecular gas to their sometimes violent death.

- Low-mass stars like our Sun live long lives and die with the ejection of a planetary nebula, leaving behind a white dwarf.

- High-mass stars live fast and die young, exploding dramatically as supernovae.

- Close binary stars can exchange mass, altering the usual course of stellar evolution.

## Review Questions

1. What is *thermal pressure?* What are the two energy sources that can help a star maintain its internal thermal pressure?

2. What is a *molecular cloud?* Briefly describe the process by which a *protostar* and *protostellar disk* form from gas in a molecular cloud.

3. Under what conditions does a *close binary* form?

4. Describe some of the activity seen in protostars, such as strong *protostellar winds* and *jets.*

5. What do we mean by a star's *life track* on an H–R diagram? How does an H–R diagram that shows life tracks differ from a standard H–R diagram?

6. Describe the observed trends in the number of stars that are born with different masses. What types of stars are most common? What types are least common?

7. What is *degeneracy pressure?* How does it differ from thermal pressure? Explain why degeneracy pressure can support a stellar core against gravity even when the core becomes very cold.

8. What is a *brown dwarf?* Explain why brown dwarfs may be common, even though they are difficult to detect.

9. What happens to the core of a star when it exhausts its hydrogen supply? Why does *hydrogen shell burning* begin around the inert core?

10. Why does *helium fusion* require much higher temperatures than hydrogen fusion? Briefly describe the overall reaction by which helium fuses into carbon.

11. Why does helium burning begin with a *helium flash* in low-mass stars? How do the core structure and rate of fusion change after the helium flash?

12. Explain why a star's overall radius shrinks from its peak size as a red giant after helium fusion begins. Why do helium-burning stars in a star cluster all fall on a *horizontal branch* on an H–R diagram?

13. What is a *planetary nebula?* What happens to the core of a star after a planetary nebula occurs?

14. Briefly describe how the Sun will change, and how Earth will be affected by these changes, over the next several billion years.

15. What is *radiation pressure?* Why is it more important in high-mass stars than in low-mass stars? What effects does radiation pressure have on the structure of a high-mass star?

16. Describe some of the nuclear reactions that can occur in high-mass stars after they exhaust their core helium. Why does this continued nuclear burning occur in high-mass stars but not in low-mass stars?

17. What special feature of iron nuclei determines how massive stars end their lives? What happens during a *supernova?*

18. Summarize some of the observational evidence supporting our ideas about how the elements formed and showing that supernovae really occur.

19. What is the Algol paradox? What is its resolution? Use your answer to summarize how the lives of stars in close binaries can differ from the lives of single stars.

### Discussion Questions

1. *Connections to the Stars.* In ancient times, many people believed that our lives were somehow influenced by the patterns of the stars in the sky, a belief that survives to this day in astrology. Modern science has not found any evidence to support this belief but instead has found that we have a connection to the stars on a much deeper level: In the words of Carl Sagan, we are "star stuff." Discuss in some detail our real connections to the stars as established by modern astronomy. Do you think these connections have any philosophical implications in terms of how we view our lives and our civilization? Explain.

2. *Humanity in A.D. 5,000,000,000.* Do you think it is likely that humanity will survive until the Sun begins to expand into a red giant 5 billion years from now? Why or why not? If the human race does survive, how do you think people in A.D. 5,000,000,000 will differ from people today? What do you think they will do when faced with the impending death of the Sun? Debate these questions, and see if you and your friends can come to any agreement on possible answers.

### Problems

*Sensible Statements?* For **problems 1–6**, decide whether the statement is sensible and explain why it is or is not.

1. The iron in my blood came from a star that blew up over 4 billion years ago.

2. A protostellar cloud spins faster as it contracts because it is gaining angular momentum.

3. When helium fusion begins in the core of a low-mass star, the extra energy generated causes the star's luminosity to rise.

4. Humanity will eventually have to find another planet to live on, because one day the Sun will blow up as a supernova.

5. I sure am glad hydrogen has a higher mass per nuclear particle than many other elements. If it had the lowest mass per nuclear particle, none of us would be here.

6. I just discovered a $3.5M_{Sun}$ main-sequence star orbiting a $2.5M_{Sun}$ red giant. I'll bet that red giant was more massive than $3M_{Sun}$ when it was a main-sequence star.

*Homes to Civilizations.* We do not yet know how many stars have Earth-like planets, nor do we know the likelihood that such planets might harbor advanced civilizations like our own. However, some stars can probably be ruled out as candidates for advanced civilizations. For example, given that it took a few billion years for humans to evolve on Earth, it seems unlikely that advanced life would have had time to evolve around a star that is only a few million years old. For each of the stars in **problems 7–12**, decide whether you think it is possible that it could harbor an advanced civilization, and explain your reasoning in one or two paragraphs.

7. A $10M_{Sun}$ main-sequence star.

8. A flare star.

9. A carbon star.

10. A $1.5M_{Sun}$ red giant.

11. A $1M_{Sun}$ horizontal branch star.

12. A red supergiant.

13. *Rare Elements.* Lithium, beryllium, and boron are elements with atomic numbers 3, 4, and 5, respectively. But despite their being three of the five simplest elements, Figure 16.20 shows that they are rare compared to many heavier elements. Suggest a reason for their rarity. (*Hint:* Consider the process by which helium fuses into carbon.)

14. *Future Skies.* As a red giant, the Sun's angular size in the Earth's sky will be about 30°. What will sunset and sunrise be like? About how long will they take? Do you think the color of the sky will be different from what it is today? Explain.

15. *Research: Historical Supernovae.* As discussed in the text, historical accounts exist for supernovae in the years 1006, 1054, 1572, and 1604. Choose one of these supernovae and learn more about historical records of the event. Did the supernova influence human history in any way? Write a two- to three-page summary of your research findings.

### Web Projects

Find useful links for Web projects on the text Web site.

1. *Coming Fireworks in Supernova 1987A.* Astronomers believe that the show from Supernova 1987A is not yet over. In particular, sometime between now and about 2010, the expanding cloud of gas from the supernova is expected to ram into surrounding material, and the heat generated by the impact is expected to create a new light show. Learn more about how Supernova 1987A is changing and what we might expect to see from it in the future. Summarize your findings in a one- to two-page report.

2. *Picturing Star Birth and Death.* Photographs of stellar birthplaces (i.e., molecular clouds) and death places (e.g., planetary nebulae and supernova remnants) can be strikingly beautiful, but only a few such photographs are included in this chapter. Search the Web for additional photographs of these types; look not only for photos taken in visible light, but also for false-color photographs made from observations in other wavelengths of light. Put each photograph you find into a personal on-line journal, along with a one-paragraph description of what the photograph shows. Try to compile a journal of at least 20 such photographs.

# CHAPTER 17

# The Bizarre Stellar Graveyard

Welcome to the afterworld of stars, the fascinating domain of white dwarfs, neutron stars, and black holes. To scientists, these dead stars are ideal laboratories for testing the most extreme predictions of general relativity and quantum theory. To most other people, the eccentric behavior of stellar corpses demonstrates that the universe is stranger than they had ever imagined.

Dead stars behave in unusual and unexpected ways that challenge our minds and stretch the boundaries of what we believe is possible. Stars that have finished nuclear burning have only one hope of staving off the crushing power of gravity: the strange quantum mechanical effect of degeneracy pressure. But even this strange pressure cannot save the most massive stellar cores, which collapse into oblivion as black holes. Prepare to be amazed by the eerie inhabitants of the stellar graveyard!

## 17.1 A Star's Final Battle

In the previous chapter, we saw that an ongoing "battle" between the inward crush of gravity and the outward push of pressure governs a star's life from the time when it first begins to form in an interstellar cloud to the time when it finally exhausts its nuclear fuel. Throughout most of this time, the pressure that holds gravity at bay is *thermal pressure,* which results from the heat produced as the star fuses light elements into heavier ones in its core. But the nuclear fuel eventually runs out. In the end, after the star dies in a planetary nebula or supernova, the fate of the stellar corpse lies in the outcome of a final battle between gravity and pressure—but this time the source of the pressure is the quantum mechanical effect called *degeneracy pressure.*

We have already discussed how degeneracy pressure successfully resists the crush of gravity in the stellar corpses known as white dwarfs and neutron stars, as well as in several other cases (e.g., brown dwarfs and inert stellar cores). Because these objects are supported by degeneracy pressure, they are known collectively as *degenerate objects,* and the matter within them is called *degenerate matter.* Recall that degeneracy pressure arises when subatomic particles are packed as closely as the laws of quantum mechanics allow [Section S4.5]. More specifically, white dwarfs are supported against the crush of gravity by **electron degeneracy pressure**, in which the pressure arises from densely packed electrons. In neutron stars, it is *neutrons* that are packed tightly together, thereby generating **neutron degeneracy pressure**.

White dwarfs and neutron stars would be strange enough if the story ended here, but it does not. Sometimes, gravity wins the battle with degeneracy pressure, and the stellar corpse collapses without end, crushing itself out of existence and forming a *black hole*. A black hole is truly a hole in the universe. If you enter a black hole, you leave our observable universe and can never return. In this chapter, we will study the bizarre properties and occasional catastrophes of the stellar corpses known as white dwarfs, neutron stars, and black holes.

## 17.2 White Dwarfs

A **white dwarf** is the inert core left over after a star has ceased nuclear burning, so its composition reflects the products of the star's final nuclear-burning stage. The white dwarf left behind by a $1M_{Sun}$ star like our Sun will be made mostly of carbon, the product of the star's final helium-burning stage (Figure 17.1). The cores of very low mass stars never become hot enough to fuse helium and thus end up as helium white dwarfs. Some intermediate-mass stars progress to carbon burning but do not create any iron (and hence do not explode as supernovae). These stars leave behind white dwarfs containing large amounts of oxygen or even heavier elements.

Despite the ordinary-sounding compositions of white dwarfs, their degenerate matter is unlike anything ever seen on Earth. Gravity and electron degeneracy pressure have battled to a draw in white dwarfs. Electron degeneracy pressure finally halts the collapse of a $1M_{Sun}$ stellar corpse when it shrinks to about the size of the Earth. If you recall that our Earth is smaller than a typical sunspot, it should be clear that it's no small feat to pack the entire mass of the Sun into the volume of the Earth. The density of such a white dwarf is so high that a pair of standard dice made from its material would weigh about 5 tons.

Surprisingly, more massive white dwarfs are smaller in size than less massive ones. For example, a $1.3M_{Sun}$ white dwarf is half the diameter of a $1.0M_{Sun}$ white dwarf (Figure 17.2). The more massive white dwarf is smaller—even though it contains more matter—because its greater gravity can compress this matter to a much greater density. As a white dwarf becomes denser, its electrons must move faster, and degeneracy pressure becomes stronger [Section S4.5]. The most massive white dwarfs are therefore the smallest, because they must be extremely dense for degeneracy pressure to balance their greater gravity.

The fact that adding mass to a white dwarf makes it shrink also explains why red giants become more luminous as they age [Section 16.3]. Recall that degeneracy pressure supports the inert helium core of a low-mass red giant, so this core is essentially a white dwarf buried inside a star. As the hydrogen-burning shell deposits more helium ash onto the degenerate core, the mass of the core continually increases. Therefore the core continually contracts, and the surrounding shell of hydrogen shrinks along with it. Because the shell gets hotter as it shrinks, its hydrogen fusion rate increases, steadily raising the luminosity of the red giant.

### The White Dwarf Limit

Theoretical calculations show that the mass of a white dwarf cannot exceed a **white dwarf limit** of about $1.4M_{Sun}$, commonly called the *Chandrasekhar limit* after its discoverer. The limit comes about because the electron speeds are higher in more massive white dwarfs, and these speeds approach the speed of light in white dwarfs with masses approaching $1.4M_{Sun}$. Neither electrons nor anything else can travel faster than the speed of light, so electrons can do nothing to halt the crush of gravity in a stellar

**FIGURE 17.1** The binary star system Sirius as seen in X-ray light by the Chandra Telescope. Sirius A, the brightest star in the night sky to human eyes, is actually the dimmer of the two stars in this picture. Sirius B, its white dwarf companion, is much hotter and therefore much brighter in X-ray light. (The spikes emanting from Sirius B are not real; they are artifacts created by the telescope's optics.)

corpse with a mass above the white dwarf limit. Such an object must inevitably collapse into a compact ball of neutrons, at which point *neutron* degeneracy pressure can stop the crush of gravity.

Strong observational evidence supports this theoretical limit on the mass of a white dwarf. Many known white dwarfs are members of binary systems, and hence their masses can be measured [Section 15.4]. In every observed case, the white dwarfs have masses below $1.4M_{Sun}$, just as we would expect from theory.

### White Dwarfs in Close Binary Systems

Left to itself, a white dwarf will never succumb to the crush of gravity because its electron degeneracy pressure does not lessen even as the white dwarf cools into a cold black dwarf. However, white dwarfs in close binary systems do not necessarily rest in peace.

A white dwarf in a close binary system can gain substantial quantities of mass if its companion is a main-sequence or giant star. When a clump of mass first spills over from the companion to the white dwarf, it has some small orbital velocity. The law of conservation of angular momentum dictates that the clump must orbit faster and faster as it falls toward the white dwarf's surface. The infalling matter therefore forms a whirlpool-like disk around the white dwarf

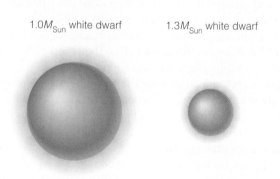

$1.0M_{Sun}$ white dwarf      $1.3M_{Sun}$ white dwarf

**FIGURE 17.2** Contrary to what you might expect, more massive white dwarfs are actually *smaller* (and thus denser) than less massive white dwarfs.

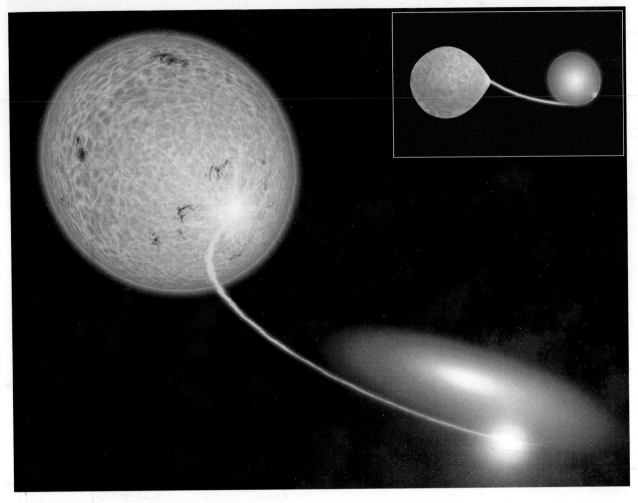

**FIGURE 17.3** This artist's conception shows how mass spilling from a companion star (left) toward a white dwarf (right) forms an accretion disk around the white dwarf. The white dwarf itself is in the center of the accretion disk—too small to see on this scale. Matter streaming onto the disk creates a hot spot at the point of impact. The inset shows how the system looks from above the pole, which you can relate to the perspective shown in the painting.

(Figure 17.3). The process in which material falls onto another body is called *accretion* [Section 8.4], so this rapidly rotating disk is called an **accretion disk**.

**TIME OUT TO THINK** *Explain why the infalling matter forms a disk around the white dwarf (as opposed to making, say, a spherical distribution of matter). (Hint: See Sections 8.3 and 16.2.) How is an accretion disk similar to a protoplanetary disk? How is it different?*

Accreting gas gradually spirals inward through the accretion disk and eventually falls onto the surface of the white dwarf. This happens because the individual gas particles in the accretion disk, like anything else that orbits a massive body, obey Kepler's laws [Section 5.3]. Gas in the inner parts of the accretion disk moves faster than gas in the outer parts; because of these differences in orbital speed, gas in any par-

ticular part of the accretion disk "rubs" against slower-moving gas just outside of it. This "rubbing" generates friction and heat in the same way that rubbing your palms together makes them warm. The friction slowly causes the orbits of individual gas particles to decay, making the orbits smaller and smaller until they fall onto the white dwarf surface. Meanwhile, additional gas spilling over from the companion constantly replenishes the accretion disk.

Accretion can provide the "dead" white dwarf with a new energy source. Theory predicts that the heat generated by friction should make the accretion disk hot enough to radiate optical and ultraviolet light, and sometimes even X rays. Thus, although accretion disks are far too small to be seen directly, we should be able to detect their intense ultraviolet or X-ray radiation. Searches for this radiation have turned up strong evidence for accretion disks around many white

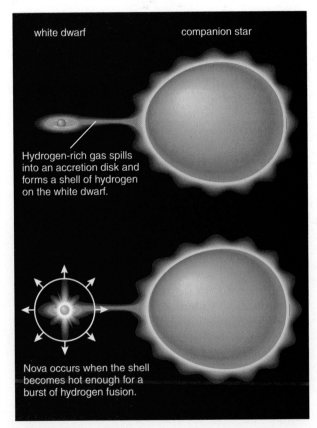

white dwarf                    companion star

Hydrogen-rich gas spills into an accretion disk and forms a shell of hydrogen on the white dwarf.

Nova occurs when the shell becomes hot enough for a burst of hydrogen fusion.

**a** Diagram of the nova process.

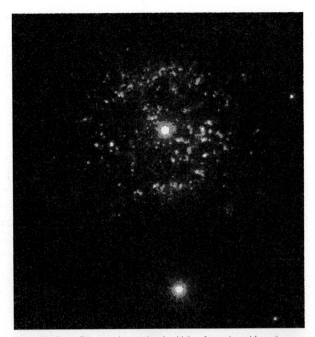

**b** Hubble Space Telescope image showing blobs of gas ejected from the nova T Pyxidis. The bright spot at the center of the blobs is the binary star system that generated the nova.

**FIGURE 17.4** A nova occurs when hydrogen fusion ignites on the surface of a white dwarf in a binary star system.

dwarfs. In some cases, the brightness of these systems is highly variable—sudden increases in brightness by a factor of 10 or more may persist for a few days and then fade away, only to repeat a few weeks or months later. Such brightening probably arises when instabilities in the accretion disk cause some of the matter to fall suddenly onto the white dwarf surface, with an accompanying release of gravitational potential energy. (This type of brightening is sometimes called a *dwarf nova*.)

Accreting white dwarfs occasionally flare up even more dramatically. Remember that a white dwarf is "dead" because it has no hydrogen left to fuse. This situation changes in an accreting white dwarf. The gas spilling onto an accreting white dwarf comes from the upper layers of its companion star and thus is composed mostly of hydrogen. A thin shell of fresh hydrogen builds up on the surface of the white dwarf as more and more material rains down from the accretion disk. The pressure and temperature at the bottom of this shell increase as the shell grows, and hydrogen fusion ignites when the temperature exceeds 10 million K. The white dwarf suddenly blazes back to life as its hydrogen shell burns. This thermonuclear flash causes the binary system to shine for a few glorious weeks as a **nova**, which can radiate as brightly as 100,000 Suns (Figure 17.4a). The nova

generates heat and pressure, ejecting most of the material that has accreted onto the white dwarf. This material expands outward, creating a *nova remnant* that sometimes remains visible years after the nova explosion (Figure 17.4b).

Accretion resumes after a nova explosion subsides, so the entire process can repeat itself. The time between successive novae in a particular system depends on the rate at which hydrogen accretes on the white dwarf surface and on how highly compressed this hydrogen becomes. The compression of hydrogen is greatest for the most massive white dwarfs, which have the strongest surface gravities. In some cases, novae have been observed to repeat after just a few decades. More commonly, accreting white dwarfs may have 10,000 years between nova outbursts.

Note that, according to our modern definitions, a nova and a supernova are quite different events: A nova is a relatively minor detonation of hydrogen fusion on the surface of a white dwarf in a close binary, while a supernova is the total explosion of a star. However, the word *nova* simply means "new," and historically a nova referred to any star that appeared to the naked eye where none was visible before. Because supernovae generate far more power than novae— the light of 10 billion Suns in a supernova versus

100,000 Suns in a nova—a very distant supernova can appear as bright in our sky as a nova that is relatively close. Thus, people could not distinguish between novae and supernovae prior to modern times.

### White Dwarf Supernovae

Each time a nova occurs, the white dwarf ejects some of its mass. Each time a nova subsides, the white dwarf begins to accrete matter again. Theoretical models cannot yet tell us whether the net result is a gradual increase or decrease in the white dwarf's mass. Nevertheless, in at least some cases, accreting white dwarfs in binary systems continue to gain mass as time passes. If such a white dwarf gains enough mass, it can one day reach the $1.4M_{Sun}$ white dwarf limit. This day is the white dwarf's last.

The electron degeneracy pressure that has been supporting the white dwarf gives out as soon as it reaches the $1.4M_{Sun}$ limit. Gravity is suddenly unopposed, and the white dwarf begins to collapse. The gravitational potential energy released in the collapse quickly heats the white dwarf, which soon reaches the temperature needed for carbon fusion. Because the white dwarf material is degenerate, carbon fusion ignites almost instantly throughout the star. This "carbon bomb" detonation is similar to the helium flash that occurs in low-mass red giants, but it releases far more energy [Section 16.3]. The white dwarf explodes completely in what we will call a **white dwarf supernova**.

**TIME OUT TO THINK** *Why do we expect that most collapsing white dwarfs undergo carbon fusion, as opposed to fusion of hydrogen, helium, or some other element?*

A white dwarf supernova shines as brilliantly as a supernova that occurs at the end of a high-mass

star's life [Section 16.4]. To distinguish the two types, we'll refer to the latter as a **massive star supernova**. Both white dwarf supernovae and massive star supernovae result in the destruction of a star. A massive star supernova is thought inevitably to leave behind either a neutron star or a black hole, but nothing remains after the "carbon bomb" detonation of a white dwarf supernova.

Astronomers can distinguish between white dwarf and massive star supernovae by studying their light.[1] Because white dwarfs contain almost no hydrogen, the spectra of white dwarf supernovae show no spectral lines of hydrogen. In contrast, massive stars usually have plenty of hydrogen in their outer layers at the time they explode, so hydrogen lines are prominent in the spectra of most massive star supernovae. A second way to distinguish the two types of supernovae is to plot *light curves* that show how their luminosity fades with time. Figure 17.5 contrasts typical light curves for white dwarf and massive star supernovae. Note that both types of supernovae reach a peak luminosity of about 10 billion Suns ($10^{10}L_{Sun}$), but white dwarf supernovae fade steadily while massive star supernovae fade in two distinct stages. Not only are white dwarf supernovae dramatic, but they also provide one of the primary means by which we measure large distances in the universe. Massive star supernovae differ in intrinsic brightness, but white dwarf supernovae always occur in white dwarfs

---

[1]Observationally, astronomers classify supernovae as *Type II* if their spectra show hydrogen lines, and *Type I* otherwise. All Type II supernovae are assumed to be massive star supernovae. However, a Type I supernova can be either a white dwarf supernova or a massive star supernova in which the star blew away all its hydrogen before exploding. Type I supernovae appear in three classes whose light curves differ, called *Type Ia, Type Ib,* and *Type Ic.* Only Type Ia supernovae are thought to be white dwarf supernovae.

**FIGURE 17.5** Typical light curves for white dwarf and massive star supernovae.

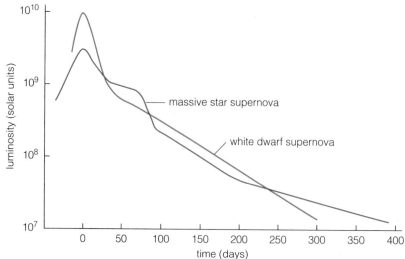

that have just reached the $1.4M_{Sun}$ limit. The light curves of all white dwarf supernovae therefore look amazingly similar, and their maximum luminosities are nearly identical. This fact is extremely useful: Once we know the true luminosity of one white dwarf supernova, we essentially know the luminosities of them all. Thus, whenever we discover a white dwarf supernova in a distant galaxy, we can determine the galaxy's distance by using the luminosity–distance formula [Section 15.2].

## 17.3 Neutron Stars

White dwarfs with densities of 5 tons per teaspoon may seem incredible, but neutron stars are stranger still. A **neutron star** is the ball of neutrons created by the collapse of the iron core in a massive star supernova (Figure 17.6). Typically just 10 kilometers across yet more massive than the Sun, neutron stars are essentially giant atomic nuclei, with two important differences: (1) They are made almost entirely of neutrons, and (2) gravity, not the strong force, is what binds them together.

The force of gravity at the surface of a neutron star is truly awe-inspiring. Escape velocity is about half the speed of light. The strong gravity causes photons to emerge with a *gravitational redshift* that increases their wavelengths by about 30%, just as predicted by Einstein's general theory of relativity [Section S3.5].

If you foolishly chose to visit a neutron star's surface, your body would be squashed immediately into a microscopically thin puddle of subatomic particles.

Things would be only slightly less troubling if a bit of neutron star came to visit you. A paper clip made from neutron star material would outweigh Mount Everest. If such a paper clip magically appeared in your hand, you could not prevent it from falling. Down it would plunge, passing through the Earth like a rock falling through space. It would gain speed until it reached the center of the Earth, and its momentum would carry it onward until it slowed to a stop on the other side of our planet. Then it would fall again. If it came in from space, each plunge of the neutron star material would drill a different hole through the rotating Earth. In the words of Carl Sagan, the inside of the Earth would "look briefly like Swiss cheese" (until the melted rock flowed to fill in the holes) by the time friction finally brought the piece of neutron star to rest at the center of the Earth.

In the unfortunate event that an *entire* neutron star came to visit you, it would not fall at all. Because it would be only about 10 kilometers across, the neutron star would probably fit in your hometown, but it would be 300,000 times more massive than the Earth. The neutron star's immense surface gravity would quickly destroy your hometown and the rest of civilization. By the time the dust settled, the former Earth would be a shell no thicker than your thumb on the surface of the neutron star.

**FIGURE 17.6** This composite image from the Hubble Space Telescope shows a neutron star streaking through our galaxy. The neutron star, created in a supernova explosion about a million years ago, glows in optical light because it is still very hot—about 600,000 K.

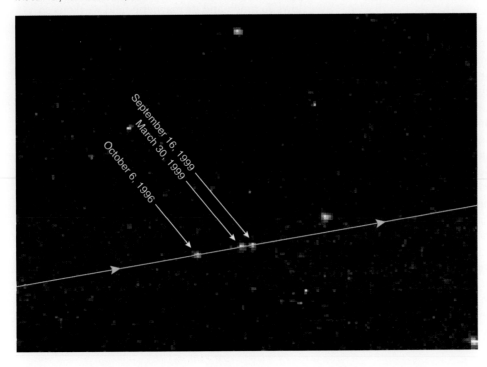

## Pulsars

Theorists first speculated about neutron stars in the 1930s. But until observational proof of their existence arrived in 1967, most astronomers assumed that neutron stars were too strange to exist. The proof came largely through the efforts of Jocelyn Bell, then a 24-year-old graduate student at Cambridge University. Bell had helped her adviser, Anthony Hewish, build a radio telescope ideal for discovering fluctuating sources of radio waves. She was busily trying to interpret the flood of data pouring out of this instrument in October 1967 when she noticed a peculiar signal. After ruling out other possibilities, she concluded that *pulses* of radio waves were arriving from somewhere near the direction of the constellation Cygnus at precise 1.337301-second intervals (Figure 17.7). No known astronomical object pulsated so regularly. In fact, the pulsations came at such precise intervals that they were nearly as reliable for measuring time as the most precise human-made clocks. For a while, the mysterious source of the radio waves was dubbed "LGM" for Little Green Men, only half-jokingly. Today we refer to such rapidly pulsing radio sources as **pulsars**.

The mystery of pulsars was soon resolved. By the end of 1968, astronomers had found two smoking guns: Pulsars sat at the centers of both the Crab Nebula and the Vela Nebula, the gaseous remnants of supernovae (Figure 17.8). The pulsars are neutron stars left behind by the supernova explosions.

The pulsations arise because the neutron star is spinning rapidly as a result of the conservation of angular momentum: As an iron core collapses into a neutron star, its rotation rate must increase as it shrinks in size. The collapse also bunches the magnetic field lines running through the core far more tightly, greatly amplifying the strength of the magnetic field. Shortly after the supernova event, the magnetic field of the remaining neutron star is a trillion times stronger than the Earth's. These intense magnetic fields somehow direct beams of radiation out along the magnetic poles, although we do not yet know exactly how the radiation is generated. If a neutron star's magnetic poles do not align with its rotation axis (just as the Earth's magnetic poles do not coincide with its geographic poles), the beams of radiation sweep round and round (Figure 17.9). Like lighthouses, these neutron stars actually emit a fairly steady beam of light, which we see as pulses of light each time the beam sweeps past Earth.

Pulsars are not quite perfect clocks, because each revolution of a pulsar takes slightly longer. This grad-

**FIGURE 17.7** About 20 seconds of data from the first pulsar discovered by Jocelyn Bell in 1967. Arrows mark the pulses, which come precisely 1.337301 seconds apart.

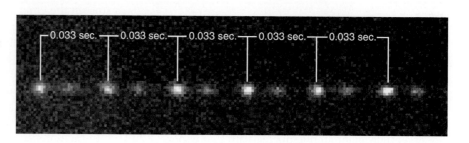

**FIGURE 17.8** This time-lapse image of the pulsar at the center of the Crab Nebula shows its main pulse recurring every 0.033 second. The fainter pulses are thought to come from the pulsar's other lighthouselike beam. (Photo from the Very Large Telescope of the European Southern Observatory.)

ual slowing of the neutron star's spin occurs because the continual twirling of the magnetic field generates electromagnetic radiation that carries away energy and angular momentum. The pulsar in the Crab Nebula, for example, currently spins about 30 times per second. Two thousand years from now, it will spin less than half as fast. Eventually, a pulsar's spin slows so much and its magnetic field weakens so much that we can no longer detect it. In addition, some spinning neutron stars may be oriented so that their beams do not sweep past our location. Thus, we have the following rule: All pulsars are neutron stars, but not all neutron stars are pulsars.

**TIME OUT TO THINK** *Suppose we do* not *see pulses from a particular neutron star and hence do not call it a pulsar. Is it possible that a civilization living in some other star system would see this neutron star as a pulsar? Explain.*

We know that pulsars must be neutron stars, because no other massive object could spin so fast. A white dwarf, for example, can spin no faster than about once per second; an increase in spin would tear it apart because its surface would be rotating faster than the escape velocity. Yet pulsars have been discovered that rotate as fast as 625 times per second. Only an object as extremely small and dense as a neutron star could spin so fast without breaking apart.

**a** A pulsar is a rapidly rotating neutron star that beams radiation along its magnetic axis.

**FIGURE 17.9** Radiation from a neutron star can appear to pulse if the neutron star is rotating.

**b** This artwork likens a pulsar (top) to a lighthouse (bottom). If a pulsar's radiation beams are not aligned with its rotation axis, they will sweep through space. Each time one of these beams sweeps across Earth, we see a pulse of radiation.

Interestingly, the first planets discovered outside our solar system orbit a pulsar. In 1992, the pulsar known as PSR B1257+12 was found to have a pulsation period that periodically becomes very slightly shorter or longer. A detailed analysis of the pulsation periods suggests that they can be explained by gravitational tugs of planetlike bodies on the pulsar. In fact, at least two planets appear to be orbiting PSR B1257+12, with orbital periods of about 67 and 98 days, respectively. This discovery came as an immense surprise to astronomers, because these planets are orbiting the remains of a star that exploded.

Why weren't the planets destroyed during their star's red supergiant stage? Why didn't they fly off into space when the supernova ejected most of the star's mass? Why didn't the supernova explosion kick the pulsar away from its planets? The planets probably formed *after* the explosion. It's likely that the pulsar once had a stellar companion that came too close. Tidal forces ripped the companion star apart, and the debris formed a protoplanetary disk that then coalesced into planets.

### Neutron Stars in Close Binary Systems

Like their white dwarf brethren, neutron stars in close binary systems can brilliantly burst back to life. As is the case with white dwarfs, gas overflowing from a companion star can create a hot, swirling accretion disk around the neutron star. However, in the neutron star's mighty gravitational field, infalling matter releases an amazing amount of gravitational potential energy. Dropping a brick onto a neutron star would liberate as much energy as an atomic bomb. Because the gravitational energies of accretion disks around neutron stars are so tremendous, they are much hotter and much more luminous than those around white dwarfs. The high temperatures in the inner regions of the accretion disk make it radiate powerfully in X rays. Some close binaries with neutron stars emit 100,000 times more energy in X rays than our Sun emits in all wavelengths of light combined. Due to this intense X-ray emission, close binaries that contain accreting neutron stars are often called **X-ray binaries**. Their existence confirms many of the strange properties of neutron stars.

Today we know of hundreds of X-ray binaries in the Milky Way. These neutron star systems are concentrated in the disk, just like most of our galaxy's stars, gas, and dust. X-ray sources are usually named by their constellation and order of discovery. For example, Sco X-1 was the first X-ray source discovered in the direction of the constellation Scorpio. Sco X-1 is now known to be an X-ray binary in which a low-mass star orbits a neutron star about every 19 hours.

The emission from most X-ray binaries pulsates rapidly, confirming the identification of the X-ray source as a neutron star. In contrast to radio pulsars, whose spins slow with time, the pulsation rates of X-ray binaries tend to accelerate. Matter accreting onto the neutron star adds angular momentum, speeding up the neutron star's rotation (Figure 17.10). By the time the companion star finally stops overflowing, the neutron star may be rotating hundreds of times per second. Because such pulsars spin every few thousandths of a second, they are sometimes called **millisecond pulsars**.

One of the strangest millisecond pulsars is known as the "black widow" because it appears to be destroying its companion. The companion star must once have had a reasonable mass, but almost all of it has spilled over onto the black widow pulsar. The result is that the pulsar now spins every 1.6 milliseconds, while the companion orbits it every 9 hours. The companion also eclipses the pulsar for about an hour of each orbit. Such a long eclipse means that the companion must still have an extended atmosphere despite the fact that its mass is a mere $0.02M_{Sun}$. Evidently, the pulsar's energy output gradually evaporates matter from the surface of its companion. In a few million years, the companion star will have vanished entirely, leaving behind a solitary millisecond pulsar.

Like accreting white dwarfs that occasionally erupt into novae, accreting neutron stars sporadically erupt with enormous luminosities. Hydrogen-rich material from the companion star builds up on the surface of the neutron star. Pressures at the bottom of this accreted hydrogen shell, only a meter thick, maintain steady fusion. Helium accumulates beneath the hydrogen-burning shell, and helium fusion suddenly ignites when the temperature builds to 100 million K. The helium burns rapidly to carbon and heavier elements, generating a burst of energy that flows from the neutron star in the form of X rays. These **X-ray bursters** typically flare every few hours to every few days. Each burst lasts only a few seconds, but during that short time the system radiates power equivalent to 100,000 Suns, all in X rays. Within a minute after a burst, the X-ray burster cools back down and resumes accreting.

## 17.4 Black Holes: Gravity's Ultimate Victory

We know that white dwarfs cannot exceed $1.4M_{Sun}$ because gravity overcomes electron degeneracy pressure above that mass. The mass of a neutron star has a similar limit. The precise *neutron star limit* is not known, but it certainly lies below $3M_{Sun}$. A

**FIGURE 17.10** Matter accreting onto a neutron star adds angular momentum, increasing the neutron star's rate of spin.

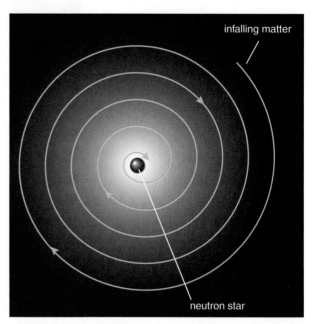

infalling matter

neutron star

collapsing stellar core that weighs more than $3M_{Sun}$ faces the ultimate oblivion: becoming a **black hole**.

A black hole originates in the collapse of the iron core that forms just prior to the supernova of a very high mass star. Any star born with more than about $8M_{Sun}$ dies in a supernova, but most of the star's mass is blown into space by the explosion. As a result, the collapsed cores left behind by most supernovae are neutron stars. However, theoretical models show that the most massive stars might not succeed in blowing away all their upper layers. If enough matter falls back onto the core, raising its mass above the neutron star limit, then neutron degeneracy pressure will not be able to fend off gravity.

A core whose mass exceeds the neutron star limit will continue to collapse catastrophically. Then, when the core has only a fraction of a second left, gravity plays its cruelest trick. Usually, the gravitational potential energy released as a star collapses boosts its temperature and pressure enough to fight off gravity. However, in a star destined to become a black hole, the enhanced temperature and pressure just make gravity stronger. According to Einstein's theory of relativity, energy is equivalent to mass ($E = mc^2$) and thus must exert some gravitational attraction. The gravity of pure energy usually is negligible, but not in a stellar core collapsing beyond the neutron star limit. Here the energy associated with the temperature and pressure concentrated in the tiny core acts like additional mass, hastening the collapse. To the best of our current understanding, *nothing* can halt the crush of gravity. The core collapses without end, forming a black hole. Gravity has achieved its ultimate triumph.

### A Hole in the Universe

The idea of a black hole was first suggested in the late 1700s by British philosopher John Mitchell and French physicist Pierre Laplace. It was already known from Newton's laws that the escape velocity from any object depends only on its mass and size: More compact objects of a particular mass have higher escape velocities [Section 5.6]. Mitchell and Laplace speculated about objects so compact that their escape velocity exceeded the speed of light. Because they worked in a time before it was known that light always travels at the same speed, they assumed that light emitted from such an object would behave like a rock thrown upward, slowing to a stop and falling back down.

Einstein's work showed that black holes are considerably more bizarre. He found that space and time are not distinct, as we usually think of them, but instead are bound up together as four-dimensional **spacetime** [Section S3.3]. Moreover, in his general theory of relativity, Einstein showed that what we perceive as gravity arises from *curvature of spacetime*. The concept "curvature of spacetime" is quite strange, because we cannot even visualize four dimensions, let alone visualize their curvature. However, as discussed in more detail in Chapter S3, we can draw an analogy to spacetime curvature with a "rubber sheet" diagram in which we show how different masses would affect a stretched rubber sheet. In this analogy, a black hole is a region in which spacetime is stretched so far that it becomes a bottomless pit (Figure 17.11). Keep in mind that a black hole is not really shaped like a funnel; the illustration is only a two-dimensional analogy. Black holes are actually spherical, and they are black because not even light can escape from them.

A black hole really is a *hole* in the observable universe, and the boundary between the inside of the black hole and the universe outside is called the **event horizon**. Within the event horizon, the escape velocity exceeds the speed of light, so nothing—not even light—can ever get out. The event horizon gets its name because information can never reach us from events that occur within it.

---

**FIGURE 17.11** Spacetime is strongly curved near a black hole.

**a** A two-dimensional representation of "flat" spacetime. The circumference of each circle is $2\pi$ times its radius.

**b** A two-dimensional representation of the "curved" spacetime around a black hole. The black hole's mass distorts spacetime, making the radial distance between two circles larger than it would be in "flat" spacetime.

A black hole has an event horizon because, according to general relativity, light always follows the *straightest possible path* through spacetime. If space happens to be curved, as it is near a black hole (or any other massive object), then the path of a light beam will also be curved. As the rubber-sheet analogy in Figure 17.11b shows, it is possible to draw a series of concentric circles around a black hole. However, it is not really possible to measure a *radius* for these circles. Because of the extreme curvature of spacetime near a black hole, their centers are within the event horizon and hence are not part of our observable universe. Thus, we define the radius of a circle around a black hole as the radius it *would* have if geometry were flat (Euclidean) as shown in Figure 17.11a. (That is, radius = circumference $\div 2\pi$.)

The radius of the event horizon is known as the **Schwarzschild radius**, named for Karl Schwarzschild (1873–1916), who computed it from Einstein's general theory of relativity in 1916. The Schwarzschild radius of a black hole depends only on its mass: The larger the mass, the larger the Schwarzschild radius. Schwarzschild computed his famous radius only a month after Einstein published his theory; he did the work while serving in the German Army on the Russian front during World War I. Sadly, he died less than a year later of an illness contracted during the war.

There is no way to tell what has fallen into a black hole in the past. A black hole that forms from the collapse of a stellar core has the mass of that core, but no recognizable material remains. Because stellar cores normally rotate, conservation of angular momentum dictates that black holes should be rotating rapidly when they form. Aside from mass and angular momentum, the only other measurable property of a black hole is its electrical charge, and most black holes are probably electrically neutral. Any other information carried by objects that plunge into a black hole is irrevocably lost from the universe.

### Voyage to a Black Hole

Imagine that you are a pioneer of the future, making the first visit to a black hole. You've selected a black hole with a mass of $10M_{Sun}$ and a Schwarzschild radius of 30 km. As your spaceship approaches the black hole, you fire its engines to put the ship on a circular orbit a few thousand kilometers above the event horizon. Note that this orbit will be perfectly stable—there is no need to worry about getting "sucked in."

Your first task is to test Einstein's general theory of relativity. As discussed in Chapter S3, this theory predicts that time should run more slowly as the force of gravity grows stronger. It also predicts that light coming out of a strong gravitational field should show a redshift, called a *gravitational redshift,* that is due to gravity rather than to the Doppler effect. You test these predictions with the aid of two identical clocks whose numerals glow with blue light. You keep one clock aboard the ship and push the other one, with a small rocket attached, directly toward the black hole (Figure 17.12). The small rocket automatically fires its engines just enough so that the clock falls only gradually toward the event horizon. Sure

---

## Mathematical Insight 17.1   The Schwarzschild Radius

The Schwarzschild radius ($R_S$) of a black hole is given by a simple formula:

$$\text{Schwarzschild radius} = R_S = \frac{2GM}{c^2}$$

where $M$ is the black hole's mass, $G = 6.67 \times 10^{-11}$ m³/ (kg $\times$ s²) is the gravitational constant, and $c = 3 \times 10^8$ m/s is the speed of light. With a bit of calculation, this formula can also be written as:

$$\text{Schwarzschild radius} = R_S = 3.0 \times \frac{M}{M_{Sun}} \text{ km}$$

*Example 1:* What is the Schwarzschild radius of a black hole with a mass of $10M_{Sun}$?

*Solution:* The latter version of the formula is easier to use in this case. We set $M = 10M_{Sun}$ to find:

$$R_S = 3 \times \frac{10M_{Sun}}{M_{Sun}} = 30 \text{ km}$$

The Schwarzschild radius of a $10M_{Sun}$ black hole is about 30 km.

*Example 2:* As far as we know, black holes in the present-day universe form only when an object's mass exceeds the roughly $3M_{Sun}$ neutron star limit. However, Stephen Hawking and others have speculated that much less massive *mini–black holes* might have formed during the Big Bang. Suppose a mini–black hole has the mass of the Earth (about $6 \times 10^{24}$ kg). What is its Schwarzschild radius?

*Solution:* In this case, the first version of the formula is more convenient:

$$R_S = \frac{2 \times \left(6.67 \times 10^{-11} \dfrac{m^3}{kg \times s^2}\right) \times (6 \times 10^{24} \text{ kg})}{\left(3 \times 10^8 \dfrac{m}{s}\right)^2}$$

$$\approx 0.009 \text{ m}$$

The mini–black hole would have a Schwarzschild radius of only 9 millimeters, making it small enough to fit on the tip of your finger. But don't try to hold it—it would weigh as much as the entire Earth!

enough, the clock on the rocket ticks slower as it heads toward the black hole, and its light becomes increasingly redshifted. When the clock reaches a distance of about 10 km above the event horizon, you see it ticking only half as fast as the clock on your spaceship, and its numerals are red instead of blue.

The rocket has to expend fuel rapidly to keep the clock hovering in the strong gravitational field, and it soon runs out of fuel. The clock plunges toward the black hole. From your safe vantage point inside the spaceship, you see the clock ticking slower and slower as it falls. However, you soon need a radio telescope to "see" it, as the light from the clock face shifts from the red part of the visible spectrum, through the infrared, and on into the radio. Finally, its light is so far redshifted that no conceivable telescope could detect it. Just as the clock vanishes from view, you see that the time on its face has frozen to a stop.

Curiosity overwhelms the better judgment of one of your colleagues. He hurriedly climbs into a space-suit, grabs the other clock, resets it, and jumps out of the airlock on a trajectory aimed straight for the black hole. Down he falls, clock in hand. He watches the clock, but because he and the clock are traveling together, its time seems to run normally and its numerals stay blue. From his point of view, time seems to neither speed up nor slow down. In fact, he'd say that *you* were the one with the strange time, as he would see your time running increasingly fast and your light becoming increasingly blueshifted. When the clock reads, say, 00:30, he and his clock pass through the event horizon. There is no barrier, no wall, no hard surface. The event horizon is a mathematical boundary, not a physical one. From his point of view, the clock keeps ticking. He is inside the event horizon, the first human being ever to leave our universe.

Back on the spaceship, you watch in horror as your overly curious friend plunges to his death. Yet, from your point of view, he will *never* cross the event horizon. You'll see time come to a stop for him and his clock just as he vanishes from view due to the huge gravitational redshift of light. When you return home, you can play a videotape for the judges at your trial, proving that your friend is still a part of our universe. Strange as it may seem, all of this is true according to Einstein's theory. From your point of view, your friend takes *forever* to cross the event horizon; from his point of view, it is but a moment's plunge before he leaves the universe.

## Common Misconceptions: Black Holes Don't Suck

What would happen if our Sun suddenly became a black hole? For some reason, it has become part of our popular culture for most people to believe that Earth and the other planets would inevitably be "sucked in" by the black hole. This is not true. Although the sudden disappearance of light and heat from the Sun would be bad news for life, the Earth's orbit would not change. Newton's law of gravity tells us that the allowed orbits in a gravitational field are ellipses, hyperbolas, and parabolas [Section 5.4]; note that "sucking" is not on the list! A spaceship would get into trouble only if it came so close to a black hole—within about three times its Schwarzschild radius—that gravity would deviate significantly from Newton's law. Otherwise, a spaceship passing near a black hole would simply swing around it on an ordinary orbit (ellipse, parabola, or hyperbola). In fact, because most black holes are so small—typical Schwarzschild radii are smaller than any star or planet, and smaller even than most asteroids—a black hole is actually one of the most difficult things in the universe to fall into by accident.

**FIGURE 17.12** Time runs slower on the clock nearer to the black hole, and gravitational redshift makes its glowing blue numerals appear red from your spaceship.

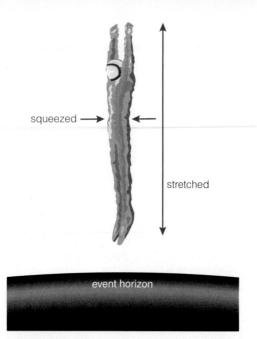

squeezed →          ← stretched

event horizon

**FIGURE 17.13** Tidal forces would be lethal near a black hole formed by the collapse of a star. The black hole would pull more strongly on the astronaut's feet than on his head, stretching him lengthwise and squeezing him from side to side.

The truly sad part of this story is that your friend did not live to experience the crossing of the event horizon. The force of gravity he felt as he approached the black hole grew so quickly that it actually pulled much harder on his feet than on his head, simultaneously stretching him lengthwise and squeezing him from side to side (Figure 17.13). In essence, your friend was stretched in the same way the oceans are stretched by the tides, except that the *tidal force* near the black hole is trillions of times stronger than the tidal force of the Moon on the Earth [Section 5.5]. No human could survive it.

If he had thought ahead, your friend might have waited to make his jump until you visited a much larger black hole, like one of the *supermassive black holes* thought to reside in the center of many galaxies [Section 20.5]. A 1 billion $M_{Sun}$ black hole has a Schwarzschild radius of 3 billion kilometers—about the distance from our Sun to Uranus. Although the gravitational forces at the event horizon of all black holes are equally great, the larger size of the supermassive black hole makes its tidal forces much weaker and hence nonlethal. Your friend could safely plunge through the event horizon. Again, from your point of view, the crossing would take forever, and you would see time come to a stop for him just as he vanished from sight because of the gravitational redshift. Again, he would experience time running normally, and he would see time in the outside universe running increasingly fast as he approached the event horizon. Unfortunately, anything he learned as he

watched the future of the universe unfold would do him little good as he plunged to oblivion inside the black hole.

### Singularity and the Limits to Knowledge

The center of a black hole is thought to be a place where gravity crushes all matter to an infinitely tiny and infinitely dense point called a **singularity**. This singularity is the point at which all the mass that created the black hole resides.

We can never know what really happens inside a black hole, because no information can ever emerge from within the event horizon. Nevertheless, we can use Einstein's theory of relativity to predict conditions inside the black hole, as long as we don't try to describe conditions too close to the singularity. The singularity itself is more puzzling, because the equations of modern physics yield conflicting predictions when we try to apply them to an infinitely compressed mass. General relativity predicts that spacetime should grow infinitely curved as it enters the pointlike singularity. Quantum physics predicts that, as a consequence of the uncertainty principle [Section S4.3], spacetime should fluctuate chaotically in regions smaller than $10^{-35}$ meter across. No current theory adequately accommodates these divergent claims. We will not fully understand how a singularity behaves until we have developed a quantum theory of gravity that encompasses both general relativity and quantum mechanics. This uncertainty in our current knowledge is a gold mine for science fiction writers, who speculate about using black holes for exotic forms of travel through spacetime [Section S3.6].

### Evidence for Black Holes

Have we discovered any black holes yet? We think so, but the evidence is indirect. Black holes emit no light. They are impossible to see, so we must look for their effects on surrounding matter. Black holes in close binaries should be among the easiest to identify. Gas overflowing a black hole's stellar companion will form a hot, X ray–emitting accretion disk similar to the disks that circle accreting neutron stars. The X rays can escape because the disk emits them from well outside the event horizon.

We strongly suspect that a few X-ray binaries contain black holes rather than neutron stars. The trick is to tell the difference, because the accretion disk is likely to be just as hot and to emit about as many X rays whether it circles a neutron star or a black hole. However, we can distinguish between the two possibilities if we can measure the mass of the accreting object. One of the most promising *black hole candidates* is in an X-ray binary called Cygnus

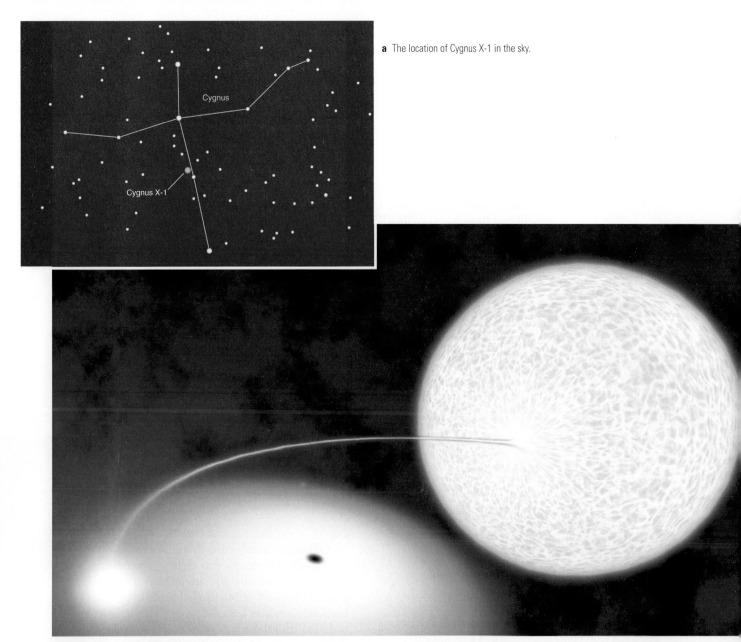

**b** Artist's conception of the Cygnus X-1 system. The X rays come from the high-temperature gas in the accretion disk surrounding the black hole. (The perspective in this painting is similar to that in Figure 17.3; see the inset in Figure 17.3.)

**FIGURE 17.14** Cygnus X-1, a binary system containing a black hole candidate.

X-1 (Figure 17.14). This system contains an extremely bright star with an estimated mass of $18M_{Sun}$; based on Doppler shifts of its spectral lines, this star orbits an unseen companion with a mass of about $10M_{Sun}$. Although there is some uncertainty in these mass estimates, the mass of the invisible accreting object clearly exceeds the $3M_{Sun}$ neutron star limit. Moreover, careful studies of variations in the system's X-ray emission indicate that this massive accreting object must be very small in size—far too small to be an ordinary star [Section 20.5]. Thus, based on our current knowledge, the accreting object in Cygnus X-1 cannot be anything other than a black hole.

**TIME OUT TO THINK** *As we discussed earlier, some X-ray binaries that contain neutron stars emit frequent X-ray bursts and are called X-ray bursters. Could an X-ray binary that contains a black hole exhibit the same type of X-ray bursts? Why or why not? (Hint: What is the source of the X-ray bursts from an X-ray binary with a neutron star, and where is it located? Does a similar location exist for a system containing a black hole?)*

### Too Strange to Be True?

Theoretical calculations predicted the existence of neutron stars and black holes long before their observational discovery, but many astronomers considered these theoretical results too strange to be true.

The story begins with Subrahmanyan Chandrasekhar, an astrophysicist from India. Chandrasekhar was only 19 when he completed the calculations showing that there is a white dwarf limit of $1.4M_{Sun}$, and he boldly predicted that a more massive white dwarf would collapse under the force of gravity. He did this work in 1931 while traveling by ship to England, where he hoped to impress the eminent British astrophysicist Sir Arthur Stanley Eddington. However, Eddington ridiculed Chandrasekhar for believing that white dwarfs could collapse. Neutrons had not yet been discovered, little was known about fusion, and no one had any idea what supernovae were. The idea of gravity achieving an ultimate victory seemed nonsensical to

Subrahmanyan Chandrasekhar

Eddington, who speculated that some type of force must prevent gravity from crushing any object.

A few more radical thinkers took collapsing stars more seriously. A Russian physicist, Lev Davidovich Landau, independently computed the white dwarf limit in 1932. Neutrons were discovered just a few months later, and Landau speculated that stellar corpses above the white dwarf limit might collapse until neutron degeneracy pressure halted the crush of gravity. Most astronomers found the idea of neutron stars to be unacceptably weird. But two European scientists who had emigrated to California, Fritz Zwicky and Walter Baade, were not so skeptical. Without knowing of Landau's ideas, they also concluded that neutron stars were possible. In 1934, they suggested

Sir Arthur Stanley Eddington

Lev Davidovich Landau

Of course, confirming that black holes are real with 100% certainty is very difficult. But our current theories successfully explain neutron stars, and the general theory of relativity that leads to the idea of black holes is also on solid ground. Unless something is dramatically wrong in our current theories about the mass limit of neutron stars or some other, unknown type of compact object can have a huge mass, black holes must be real.

## 17.5 The Mystery of Gamma-Ray Bursts

In the early 1960s, the United States began launching a series of top-secret satellites designed to look for gamma rays emitted by nuclear bomb tests. The satellites soon began detecting occasional bursts of gamma rays, typically lasting a few seconds (Figure 17.15). It took several years for military scientists to become convinced that these **gamma-ray bursts** were coming from space, not from some sinister human activity. They publicized the discovery in 1973.

An increasingly large armada of satellites launched over the next two decades detected hundreds of

**FIGURE 17.15** A typical gamma-ray burst light curve, showing dramatic fluctuations in gamma-ray intensity over a period of two minutes.

that a supernova might result when a stellar core collapses and forms a neutron star—an extraordinarily insightful guess. By 1938, physicist Robert Oppenheimer, working at Berkeley, was contemplating whether neutron stars had a limiting mass of their own. He and his coworkers concluded that the answer was yes and that neutron degeneracy pressure could not resist the crush of gravity when the mass rose above a few solar masses. Because no known force could keep such a star from collapsing indefinitely, Oppenheimer speculated that gravity would achieve ultimate victory, crushing the star into a black hole.

Astronomers gradually came to accept Chandrasekhar's $1.4M_{Sun}$ white dwarf limit, because observations found no white dwarfs more massive than this. However, most astronomers held to a belief that high-mass stars would inevitably shed enough mass late in life to prevent the formation of a more massive collapsed object. Jocelyn Bell's 1967 discovery of pulsars shattered this belief. Within a few months,

Jocelyn Bell

Thomas Gold of Cornell University correctly suggested that the pulsars were spinning neutron stars. These discoveries forced astronomers to admit that nature was far stranger than they had expected. The verification that neutron stars really did exist made the prospect of the still-stranger black holes much less difficult to accept.

Robert Oppenheimer

Chandrasekhar, who had long since moved to the University of Chicago, was awarded a Nobel Prize in 1984 for his lifelong contributions to astronomy. Landau won a Nobel Prize in 1962 for his work on condensed states of matter. Oppenheimer went on to lead the *Manhattan Project* that developed the atomic bomb in 1945. Eddington died in 1944, still convinced that white dwarf stars could not collapse.

other gamma-ray bursts. However, not only was their origin unknown, but it was very difficult to tell what direction the bursts came from. The problem is that gamma rays are very difficult to focus. A detector can record that it has been hit by a gamma ray but can provide little information on the direction of the gamma ray. With no specific proof, most astronomers assumed that gamma-ray bursts, like X-ray bursts, came from explosive events associated with neutron stars in X-ray binaries.

In 1991, NASA launched the *Compton Gamma Ray Observatory,* or *Compton* for short, which carried an array of eight detectors designed expressly to study gamma-ray bursts. By comparing the data recorded by all eight detectors, scientists could determine the direction of a gamma-ray burst within about 1°. The results were stunning. Compton detected gamma-ray bursts at a rate of about one per day and compiled a catalog of more than a thousand gamma-ray bursts within a few years. However, these bursts were *not* concentrated in the disk of the Milky Way like X-ray binaries and thus must not be associated with neutron stars in the disk of our galaxy.

So where do gamma-ray bursts come from? The very even distribution across the sky of gamma-ray bursts discovered by Compton ruled out the possibility that they come from anywhere in the Milky Way Galaxy. If the bursts came from objects distributed spherically about the Milky Way Galaxy, we would see a concentration of them in the direction of the galactic center. (Remember that we are located more than halfway out from the center of our galaxy.) Gamma-ray bursts must therefore originate far outside our own galaxy. Additional evidence for this conclusion came in 1997, when astronomers first observed the afterglow of a gamma-ray burst in other wavelengths. The higher resolution possible in these other wavelengths allowed astronomers to pinpoint the burst's origin in a distant galaxy. Since then, several other bursts have also been traced to explosions in distant galaxies (Figure 17.16).

We now know that gamma-ray bursts come from very distant explosions, but we still face a great mystery: How can something so distant be so bright? The afterglows of some gamma-ray bursts can be seen with binoculars, even though they are coming from galaxies billions of light-years away—making them by far the most powerful bursts of energy that ever occur in the universe. If these bursts shine their light equally in all directions, like a light bulb, then the total luminosity of a burst can briefly exceed the com-

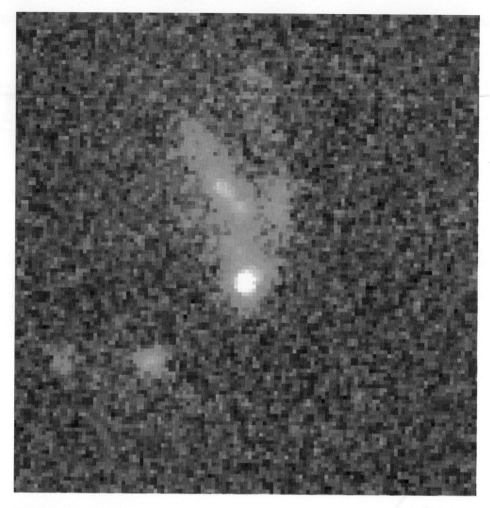

**FIGURE 17.16** The bright dot near the center of this image is the visible-light afterglow of a gamma-ray burst, as seen by the Hubble Space Telescope. The elongated blob extending above the dot is the distant galaxy in which the burst occurred.

bined luminosity of a million galaxies like our Milky Way! Because such a high luminosity is very difficult to explain, some scientists speculate that gamma-ray bursts channel their energy into narrow searchlight beams, like pulsars. A burst whose beam is pointed directly at Earth would look unusually bright, but even in this arrangement the burst's luminosity would still surpass that of many thousands of galaxies like our Milky Way.

Astronomers still do not know what causes such massive outbursts of energy. One hypothesis suggests that the bursts come from the collision of *two* neutron stars in a binary system. As discussed in Chapter S3, the neutron stars in such a system gradually spiral in toward each other (because they lose energy to *gravitational waves* [Section S3.5]) and must eventually be destroyed in some type of catastrophic collision resulting in a black hole. However, why a neutron star collision would produce the peculiar spectra

and light curves of gamma-ray bursts is not clear, and many scientists have raised theoretical objections to this model.

Another hypothesis, currently favored by many astronomers, is that gamma-ray bursts come from unusually powerful supernovae. An ordinary supernova that forms a neutron star does not release enough energy to power the luminosity of the brightest gamma-ray bursts. However, a supernova that forms a black hole crushes even more matter into an even smaller radius, releasing many times more gravitational potential energy than one that forms a neutron star. This kind of event, sometimes called a *hypernova,* might be powerful enough to explain the most extreme gamma-ray bursts. Some circumstantial evidence supports this idea. The extremely massive stars that lead to hypernovae are very short lived and should be found only in places where stars are actively forming. Indeed, all the distant galaxies known to have produced gamma-ray bursts also appear to be forming new stars. In addition, at least one relatively nearby gamma-ray burst appears to be linked to a supernova explosion. These observations have inspired many theoretical models that attempt to explain how hypernovae might generate gamma-ray bursts, but none has met with much success. Thus, we are left with one of the greatest mysteries in all of science: Gamma-ray bursts are the most powerful events in the universe, but we don't know what causes them.

## THE BIG PICTURE

We have now seen what happens to stars after they die. What a mind-bending experience! Nevertheless, try to keep these "big picture" ideas straight in your head:

- Despite the strange nature of stellar corpses, clear evidence exists for white dwarfs and neutron stars, and the case for black holes is very strong.

- White dwarfs, neutron stars, and black holes can all have close stellar companions from which they accrete matter. These binary systems produce some of the most spectacular events in the universe, including novae, white dwarf supernovae, and X-ray bursters.

- Black holes are truly holes in the observable universe that strongly warp space and time around them. The nature of black hole singularities remains beyond the frontier of current scientific understanding.

- Gamma-ray bursts were once thought to be related to neutron stars in our galaxy, but recent evidence indicates that this idea is wrong. Their origin is one of the greatest mysteries in the universe.

## Review Questions

1. What is the difference between *electron degeneracy pressure* and *neutron degeneracy pressure*? Which type supports a white dwarf? Why are neutron stars so much smaller in size than white dwarfs?

2. With degeneracy pressure, how are the speeds of electrons (or neutrons) related to the mass of the degenerate object? Explain why this relationship between speed and mass implies upper limits on the possible masses of white dwarfs and neutron stars. What is the *white dwarf limit?* What is the neutron star limit?

3. Explain why more massive white dwarfs are smaller in size. How does this idea explain why red giants become more luminous as they age?

4. What is an *accretion disk?* Under what conditions does an accretion disk form? Explain how the accretion disk provides a white dwarf with a new source of energy that we can detect from Earth.

5. Describe the process of a *nova*. Why do novae only occur in close binary star systems? Can the same star system undergo a nova event more than once? Explain.

6. Contrast the process of a *white dwarf supernova* with that of a *massive star supernova*. Observationally, how can we distinguish between these two types of supernovae?

7. What is a *pulsar?* Briefly describe how pulsars were discovered and how they get their name. How do we know that pulsars must be neutron stars?

8. Explain why neutron stars in close binary systems are often called *X-ray binaries*.

9. What is an *X-ray burster?* How is the process of an X-ray burst similar to that of a nova? How do X-ray bursts differ from novae observationally?

10. Briefly explain the process by which the core of a very high mass star can collapse to form a *black hole*.

11. What is the *event horizon* of a black hole? How does it get its name? How is it related to the *Schwarzschild radius?*

12. Suppose you are orbiting a black hole. Describe how you will see the passage of time on an object approaching the black hole. What will you notice about light from the object? Explain why an object falling toward the black hole will eventually fade from view yet never cross the event horizon from your point of view.

13. Suppose you are falling into a black hole. How will you perceive the passage of your own time? How will you perceive the passage of time in the universe around you? Briefly explain why your trip will be lethal if the black hole is relatively small in mass, and why you may survive to cross the event horizon of a supermassive black hole.

14. What do we mean by the *singularity* of a black hole? How do we know that our current theories are inadequate to explain what happens at the singularity?

15. Briefly describe the observational evidence supporting the idea that Cygnus X-1 contains a black hole.

16. What are *gamma-ray bursts?* Why are they so mysterious?

## Discussion Questions

1. *Too Strange to Be True?* Despite strong theoretical arguments for their existence, many scientists rejected the possibility that neutron stars or black holes could really exist until they were confronted with very strong observational evidence. Some people claim that this type of scientific skepticism demonstrates that scientists are too unwilling to give up their deeply held scientific beliefs. Others claim that this type of skepticism is necessary for scientific advancement. What do you think? Defend your opinion.

2. *Black Holes in Popular Culture.* Phrases such as "it disappeared into a black hole" are now common in popular culture. Give a few examples in which the term *black hole* is used in popular culture but is not meant to be taken literally. In what ways are these uses correct in their analogies to real black holes? In what ways are they incorrect? Why do you think such an esoteric scientific idea as that of a black hole has so captured the public imagination?

## Problems

*Sensible Statements?* For **problems 1–8**, decide whether the statement is sensible and explain why it is or is not.

1. Most white dwarf stars have masses close to that of our Sun, but a few white dwarf stars are up to three times more massive than the Sun.

2. The radii of white dwarf stars in close binary systems gradually increase as they accrete matter.

3. White dwarf supernovae are useful distance indicators.

4. Before pulsars were discovered, no one knew for sure whether neutron stars existed.

5. If you want to find a pulsar, you might want to look near the remnant of a supernova described by ancient Chinese astronomers.

6. If a black hole 10 times more massive than our Sun were lurking just beyond Pluto's orbit, we'd have no way of knowing it was there.

7. If the Sun suddenly became a $1\,M_{Sun}$ black hole, the orbits of the nine planets would not change at all.

8. We can detect black holes with X-ray telescopes because matter falling into a black hole emits X rays after it smashes into the event horizon.

*Life Stories of Stars.* Write a one- to two-page short story for the scenarios in **problems 9 and 10**. Each story should be detailed and scientifically correct, but also creative. That is, it should be entertaining while at the same time proving that you understand stellar evolution. Be sure to state whether "you" are a member of a binary system.

9. You are a white dwarf of $0.8\,M_{Sun}$. Tell your life story.

10. You are a neutron star of $1.5\,M_{Sun}$. Tell your life story.

*11. *Neutron Star Density.* A typical neutron star has a mass of about $1.5\,M_{Sun}$ and a radius of 10 km.

   a. Calculate the average density of a neutron star, in *kilograms per cubic centimeter.*

   b. Compare the mass of 1 $cm^3$ of neutron star material to the mass of Mount Everest ($\approx 5 \times 10^{10}$ kg).

*12. *A Black Hole?* You've just discovered a new X-ray binary, which we will call *Hyp-X1* ("Hyp" for hypothetical). The system Hyp-X1 contains a bright, B2 main-sequence star orbiting an unseen companion. The separation of the stars is estimated to be 20 million km, and the orbital period of the visible star is 4 days.

   a. Use Newton's version of Kepler's third law to calculate the sum of the masses of the two stars in the system. (*Hint:* See Mathematical Insight 15.4.) Give your answer in both kilograms and solar masses ($M_{Sun} = 2.0 \times 10^{30}$ kg).

   b. Determine the mass of the unseen companion. Is it a neutron star or a black hole? Explain. (*Hint:* A main-sequence star with spectral type B2 has a mass of about $10\,M_{Sun}$.)

*13. *Schwarzschild Radii.* Calculate the Schwarzschild radius (in km) for each of the following.

   a. A $10^8\,M_{Sun}$ black hole in the center of a quasar.

   b. A $5\,M_{Sun}$ black hole that formed in the supernova of a massive star.

   c. A mini–black hole with the mass of the Moon.

   d. A mini–black hole formed when a superadvanced civilization decides to punish you (unfairly) by squeezing you until you become so small that you disappear inside your own event horizon.

*14. *Challenge Problem: A Neutron Star Comes to Town.* Suppose a neutron star were suddenly to appear in your hometown. How thick a layer would the Earth form as it wraps around the neutron star's surface? To make the problem easier, you may assume that the layer formed by the Earth has the same average density as the neutron star. (*Hint:* Consider the mass of the Earth to be distributed in a spherical *shell* over the surface of the neutron star and then calculate the thickness of such a shell with the same mass as the Earth. The volume of a spherical shell is approximately its surface area times its thickness: $V_{shell} \approx 4\pi\,r^2 \times$ thickness. Because the shell will be thin, you can assume that its radius is the radius of the neutron star.)

## Web Projects

Find useful links for Web projects on the text Web site.

1. *Gamma-ray Bursts.* Go to the Web site for NASA's High Energy Transient Experiment (HETE) or another mission studying gamma-ray bursts and find the latest information about gamma-ray bursts. Write a one- to two-page essay on recent discoveries and how they may shed light on the mystery of gamma-ray bursts.

2. *White Dwarf Supernovae.* Learn more about how astronomers are using white dwarf supernovae to determine distances for distant galaxies. What have these observations taught us about the universe? What have they taught us about white dwarf supernovae?

# Galaxies and Beyond

*The infinitude of creation is great enough to make a world, or a Milky Way of worlds, look in comparison with it what a flower or an insect does in comparison with the Earth.*

IMMANUEL KANT

# CHAPTER 18

# Our Galaxy

In previous chapters, we saw how stars forge new elements and expel them into space. We also studied how interstellar gas clouds enriched with these stellar by-products form new stars and planetary systems. These processes do not occur in isolation. Instead, they are part of a dynamic system that acts throughout our Milky Way Galaxy.

You are probably familiar with the idea that all living species on Earth interact with one another and with the land, water, and air to form a large, interconnected ecosystem. In a similar way, but on a much larger scale, our galaxy is a nearly self-contained system that cycles matter from stars into interstellar space and back into stars again. The birth of our solar system and the evolution of life on Earth would not have been possible without this "galactic ecosystem."

In this chapter, we will study our Milky Way Galaxy. We will investigate the galactic processes that maintain an ongoing cycle of stellar life and death, examine the structure and motion of the galaxy, and explore the mysteries of the galactic center. Through it all, we will see that we are not only "star stuff" but "galaxy stuff"—the product of eons of complex recycling and reprocessing of matter and energy in the Milky Way Galaxy.

## 18.1 The Milky Way Revealed

On a dark night, you can see a faint band of light slicing across the sky through several constellations, including Sagittarius, Cygnus, Perseus, and Orion. This band of light looked like a flowing ribbon of milk to the ancient Greeks, and we now call it the *Milky Way*. In the early 1600s, Galileo used his telescope to prove that the light of the Milky Way comes from a myriad of individual stars. Together these stars make up the kind of stellar system we call a *galaxy*, echoing the Greek word for "milk," *galactos*.

Today we know that our Milky Way Galaxy holds over 100 billion stars and is just one among tens of billions of galaxies in the observable universe. If we could stand outside our galaxy, we would see it as a flat **disk** of stars with a bright central **bulge**, spectacular **spiral arms**, and a dimmer, rounder **halo** surrounding everything (Figure 18.1). A few hundred **globular clusters** of stars [Section 15.6] circle our galaxy's center in orbits extending tens of thousands of light-years into the halo. The Milky Way is a relatively large galaxy, so its gravity strongly influences smaller galaxies in its vicinity. Two small galaxies, known as the Large and Small Magellanic Clouds, orbit the Milky Way at distances of some 150,000 light-years (50 kpc).[1] (A third small galaxy, called the Sagittarius Dwarf Elliptical, lies even closer but is obscured from view by the Milky Way's galactic plane [Section 20.3].) Although the Magellanic Clouds are relatively small for galaxies (a few billion stars each), they are far larger than globular clusters (which typically contain a few hundred thousand stars). Both Magellanic Clouds are visible to the naked eye from the Southern Hemisphere.

Our knowledge of the Milky Way's true size and shape was long in coming. Clouds of interstellar gas and dust known collectively as the **interstellar medium** fill the galactic disk, obscuring our view when we try to peer directly through it. The smoggy nature of the interstellar medium hides most of our galaxy from us and long fooled astronomers into believing that we lived near our galaxy's center. Astronomer Harlow Shapley finally proved otherwise in the 1920s, when he demonstrated that the Milky Way's globular clusters orbit a point tens of thousands of light-years from our Sun. He concluded that this point, not our Sun, must be the center of the galaxy. We now know that our Sun lies near the outskirts of the galactic disk, about 28,000 light-years (8.5 kpc) from its center.

Our own galaxy can be difficult to study not only because it is dusty, but also because we see it from the inside. The Milky

**a** Artist's conception of the Milky Way viewed from its outskirts.

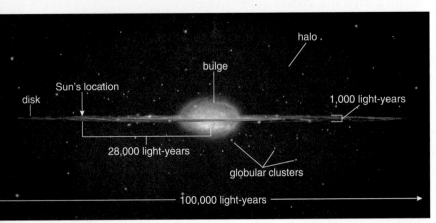

**b** Edge-on schematic view of the Milky Way.

**FIGURE 18.1** The Milky Way Galaxy

---

[1]Recall that 1 parsec (pc) ≈ 3.26 light-years, so 1 kiloparsec (kpc) ≈ 3,260 light-years and 1 megaparsec (Mpc) ≈ 3.26 million light-years.

### Discovering the Milky Way

The river of light in our sky that we call the Milky Way appears indistinct to our eyes. Galileo, looking through his telescope in 1610, was the first to realize that the Milky Way's light comes from innumerable faint stars. But the question of the size and shape of the Milky Way remained unanswered. In the late 1700s, British astronomers William and Caroline Herschel (brother and sister) tried to determine the shape of the Milky Way more accurately by counting how many stars lay in each direction. Their approach suggested that the Milky Way's width was five times its thickness. More than a century later, in the early 1900s, Dutch astronomer Jacobus Kapteyn and his colleagues used a more sophisticated star-counting method to gauge the size and shape of the Milky Way. Their results seemed to confirm the general picture found by the Herschels and suggested that the Sun lay very near the center of the galaxy.

Kapteyn's results made astronomers with a sense of history slightly nervous. Only four centuries earlier, before Copernicus challenged the Ptolemaic system, astronomers had believed the Earth to be the center of the universe. Kapteyn's placement of the Sun near the Milky Way's center seemed to be giving Earth a central place again. Kapteyn knew that obscuring material could deceive us by hiding the rest of the galaxy like some kind of interstellar fog, but he found no evidence for such a fog.

While Kapteyn was counting stars, American astronomer Harlow Shapley was studying globular clusters. He found that these clusters appeared to be centered around a point tens of thousands of light-years from the Sun. (His original estimate was that the center of the galaxy was 45,000 light-years from the Sun; today's accepted distance is 28,000 light-years.) Shapley concluded that this point marked the true center of our galaxy and that Kapteyn must be wrong.

Today we know that Shapley was right. The Milky Way's interstellar medium is the "fog" that misled Kapteyn. Robert Trumpler, working at California's Lick Observatory in the 1920s, established the existence of this dusty gas by studying open clusters of stars. By assuming that all open clusters had about the same diameter, he estimated their distances from their apparent sizes in the sky, much as you might estimate the distances of cars at night from the separation of their headlights. He found that stars in distant clusters appeared too dim, just as a car's headlights might appear in foggy weather. That is, the distant stars seemed to have lower luminosities than similar stars nearby. Trumpler concluded that light-absorbing material fills the spaces between the stars, partially obscuring the distant clusters and making them appear fainter than they would appear otherwise. Thus, we learned how interstellar material had been deceiving earlier astronomers, and that the stars visible in the night sky occupy a minuscule portion of the observable universe.

Way's dustiness is no longer such a hindrance, because technologies developed in the past few decades allow us to observe the Milky Way's radio and infrared light. These wavelengths penetrate the enshrouding interstellar medium, enabling us to see into regions of the galaxy previously obscured from view. Still, determining our galaxy's structure from our location within the galactic disk is somewhat like trying to draw a picture of your house without ever leaving your bedroom. Just as it is easier to draw pictures of other houses that you can see out the window, it is easier to measure the sizes and shapes of other galaxies than to measure our own. Nevertheless, the Milky Way is still the only galaxy whose inner workings we can examine up close.

We once thought of the Milky Way as a band of light, and later we saw it as a collection of stars. But now we see it revealed as a dynamic and complex system. In the rest of this chapter, we will see that our galaxy in many ways is like a forest of stars whose ecology is shaped by the cycle of stellar life and death and whose structure is determined by gravity and the majestic rotation of the galactic disk.

## 18.2 The Star–Gas–Star Cycle

Stars have formed, fused atomic nuclei, and exploded throughout the history of our galaxy. Generations of stars continually recycle the same galactic matter through their cores, gradually raising the overall abundance of elements made by fusion. Elements heavier than helium, usually called *heavy elements*[2] by astronomers, now constitute about 2% of the galaxy's gaseous content; the overall composition of the galaxy is about 70% hydrogen, 28% helium, and 2% heavy elements by mass. The process of adding to the abundance of heavy elements, called **chemical enrichment**, is an inevitable by-product of continual star formation. However, the synthesis of elements is only one part of the galactic ecocycle. If the galaxy did not reincorporate these elements into new stars and their accompanying planetary systems, the mineral riches fused in the bellies of stars would be wasted.

---

[2]Astronomers sometimes refer to elements heavier than helium as *metals*—a very different use of the term than that used in daily life, where *metal* refers to substances like copper, silver, and gold that shine when polished and often are good electrical conductors.

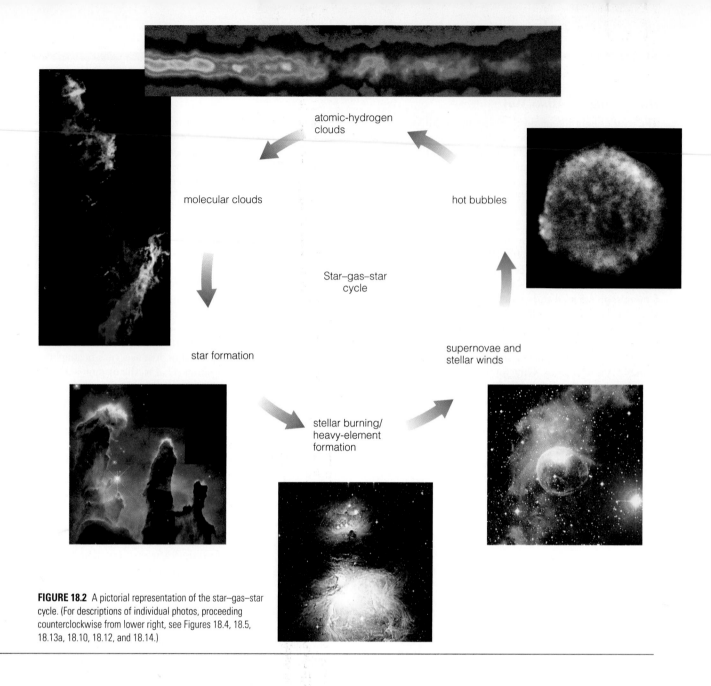

atomic-hydrogen
clouds

molecular clouds

hot bubbles

Star–gas–star
cycle

star formation

supernovae and
stellar winds

stellar burning/
heavy-element
formation

**FIGURE 18.2** A pictorial representation of the star–gas–star cycle. (For descriptions of individual photos, proceeding counterclockwise from lower right, see Figures 18.4, 18.5, 18.13a, 18.10, 18.12, and 18.14.)

**TIME OUT TO THINK** *Based on the idea of chemical enrichment, which types of stars must contain a higher proportion of heavy elements: stars in globular clusters or stars in open clusters? (Hint: Recall from Chapter 15 that stars in globular clusters are all very old, while stars in open clusters are relatively young.)*

Capturing the newly made elements released by stars is not an easy task. When a star explodes as a supernova, the ejected matter flies out at speeds of several thousand kilometers per second—far exceeding the escape velocity for the galaxy. Were it not for the interstellar medium, the new heavy elements released in the supernova would fly straight out of the Milky Way into intergalactic space. Instead, the blobs of matter expelled from the supernova collide with the interstellar medium, slow down, and eventually stop.

Supernovae of one star after another stir and heat the interstellar medium while feeding it new heavy elements. These elements eventually blend with the older, less chemically enriched hydrogen gas in the vicinity. However, before new stars can form, this gas must cool and form clouds. The hot gas cools first into clouds of atomic hydrogen (that is, neutral hydrogen atoms as opposed to ionized hydrogen or hydrogen molecules) and then into clouds of molecular hydrogen ($H_2$). The cooling of interstellar gas into clouds of molecular hydrogen takes millions of years. These clouds subsequently give birth to new stars more highly enriched in heavy elements, thus completing the star–gas–star cycle (Figure 18.2). Let's look at the stages of this cycle more closely.

### Gas from Stars

All stars return much of their original mass to interstellar space in two basic ways: through stellar winds that blow throughout their lives, and through "death events" of planetary nebulae (for low-mass stars) or supernovae (for high-mass stars). Low-mass stars generally have weak stellar winds while they are on the main sequence, but their winds grow stronger and carry more material into space when they become red giants. By the time a low-mass star like the Sun ends its life with the ejection of a planetary nebula [Section 16.3], it has returned almost half its original mass to the interstellar medium (Figure 18.3).

High-mass stars lose mass much more dynamically and explosively. The powerful winds from supergiants and massive O and B stars recycle large amounts of matter into the galaxy. At the ends of their lives, these stars explode as supernovae. The high-speed gas ejected into space by these winds and supernovae sweeps up surrounding interstellar material, excavating a **bubble** of hot, ionized gas around the exploding star. Although the bubble in Figure 18.4 looks much like a soap bubble, it is actually an expanding shell of hot gas. The glowing surface is the edge of the expanding bubble, where gas piles up as the bubble sweeps outward through the interstellar medium. These hot, tenuous bubbles are quite common, filling roughly 20–50% of the Milky Way's disk. How-

**FIGURE 18.4** This photo shows a bubble of hot, ionized gas blown by a wind from the hot star at its center.

ever, they are not always easy to detect. While some are hot enough to emit profuse amounts of X rays and others emit strongly in visible light, many others are evident only through radio emission from the shells of atomic hydrogen gas that surround them.

### Shock Waves and Supernova Remnants

Supernovae generate shock waves—waves of pressure created by gas that move faster than the speed of sound in the gas. A shock wave sweeps up surrounding gas as it travels, creating a "wall" of fast-moving gas on its leading edge. When we observe a *supernova remnant,* we are seeing the aftermath of its shock wave [Section 16.4]. Figure 18.5 shows a young supernova remnant whose shocked gas is hot enough to emit X rays. In contrast, older supernova remnants are cooler because their shock waves have swept up more material and must share their energy among more particles (Figure 18.6). Eventually, the shocked gas radiates away most of its original energy, and the expanding wall of gas slows to subsonic speeds. As the energy dissipates and the gas cools, the supernova's cargo of new elements merges with the surrounding interstellar medium.

In addition to their role as the movers and shakers of the interstellar medium, shock waves from supernovae can act as subatomic particle accelerators. Some of the electrons in supernova remnants accelerate to nearly the speed of light as they interact with the shock wave. These fast electrons emit radio waves as they spiral around magnetic field lines threading the supernova remnant (Figure 18.7). (This radio emission is sometimes called *synchrotron radiation.*)

Supernova remnants may also generate the **cosmic rays** that permeate the interstellar medium and bombard the Earth's atmosphere. Cosmic rays are

### Movie Madness: The Sound of Space

In many science fiction movies, a thunderous sound accompanies the demolition of a spaceship. If the moviemakers wanted to be more realistic, they would silence the explosion. On Earth, we perceive sound when sound waves—which are waves of alternately rising and falling pressure—cause trillions of gas atoms to push our eardrums back and forth. Although sound waves can and do travel through interstellar gas, the extremely low density of this gas means that only a handful of atoms per second would collide with something the size of a human eardrum. As a result, it would be impossible for a human ear (or a similar-size microphone) to register any sound. Despite the presence of sound waves and shock waves in space, the sound of space is silence.

made of electrons, protons, and atomic nuclei that zip through interstellar space at close to the speed of light. Some cosmic rays penetrate the Earth's atmosphere and reach the Earth's surface, and on average about one cosmic-ray particle strikes your body each second. At the altitudes at which jet planes fly, high above most of the Earth's protective atmosphere, the cosmic-ray bombardment rate is 100 times higher.

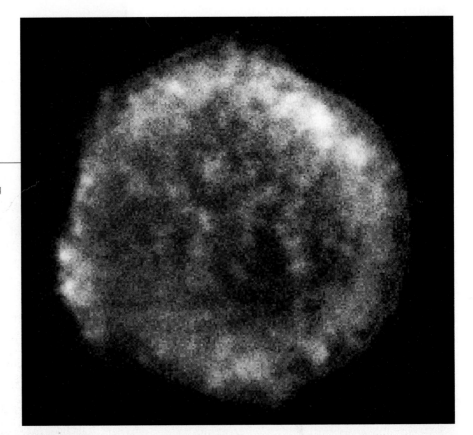

**FIGURE 18.5** This false-color image shows X-ray emission from hot electrons in a young supernova remnant—the remnant from the supernova observed by Tycho Brahe in 1572.

**a** This large-scale view shows the entire Cygnus Loop supernova remnant glowing in optical light. (The angular size of this remnant in our sky is six times that of the Moon.)

**b** The close-up view, from the Hubble Space Telescope, displays the fine filamentary structure of the remnant.

**c** An optical spectrum from the Cygnus Loop shows the strong emission lines that account for the distinct colors in the Hubble Space Telescope photo. Blue represents emission from singly ionized oxygen, green represents emission from atomic hydrogen, and red represents emission from singly ionized sulfur.

**FIGURE 18.6** The optical emission from a supernova remnant, the Cygnus Loop.

*Spectrum labels:* ionized oxygen; doubly ionized oxygen; doubly ionized oxygen; atomic hydrogen; doubly ionized neon; atomic hydrogen; ionized nitrogen; ionized sulfur

*Axes:* apparent brightness (vertical); wavelength (nanometers) 360 390 420 450 480 510 540 570 600 630 660 690 (horizontal)

**FIGURE 18.7** Supernova remnant Cassiopeia A.

**a** Radio emission caused by electrons spiraling around magnetic field lines in the young supernova remnant Cassiopeia A.

**b** False-color photograph of X-ray emission from the hot gas of Cassiopeia A, as seen by the Chandra X-ray Observatory. Red indicates the lowest-energy X rays; blue indicates the highest-energy X rays.

Superbubbles that grow
too large blow out of
the galactic disk.

Massive stars explode,
creating a superbubble
of hot gas.

young star cluster

cross-section of
the galactic plane

galactic disk

time

**FIGURE 18.8** Superbubbles can drive hot gas
into our galaxy's halo.

**a** Schematic sequence (bottom to top)
showing the development of a superbubble.

**b** Image from computer simulation of gas temperatures in a superbubble
blowout (blue = coldest gas; red = hottest gas).

Even more cosmic rays funnel along magnetic field
lines to the Earth's magnetic poles, so for safety reasons some airlines restrict how often their flight crews
cross the Earth's polar regions.

### Superbubbles and Fountains

The bubble associated with a single supernova remnant can grow to a size of about a hundred light-years
(30 pc), but in some areas of the Milky Way we see
cavities of hot gas over a thousand light-years (300 pc)
wide. These huge cavities arise because stars tend to
form in clusters. The hottest, most massive stars in
a cluster can end their lives and explode within a few
hundred thousand years of one another. The shock
waves from these individual supernovae soon overlap, combining their energy into one very powerful
shock wave. This extra-large shock wave forms an
enormous **superbubble** in the interstellar medium
(Figure 18.8). Subsequent supernovae from the
cluster explode inside the superbubble, adding even
more energy.

In many places in our galactic disk, we see what
appear to be elongated bubbles extending from young
clusters of stars to distances of 3,000 light-years
(1 kpc) or more above the disk. These probably are
places where superbubbles have grown so large that

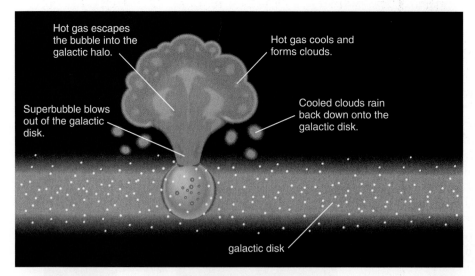

Hot gas escapes the bubble into the galactic halo.

Hot gas cools and forms clouds.

Superbubble blows out of the galactic disk.

Cooled clouds rain back down onto the galactic disk.

galactic disk

**FIGURE 18.9** Schematic picture of a galactic fountain. In the galactic fountain model for our interstellar medium, multiple supernovae create hot superbubbles that blow hot gas out into the galactic halo. The hot gas in the halo then cools into clouds that rain back down on the disk.

they cannot be contained within the disk of the Milky Way. Once the superbubble breaks out of the disk, where nearly all of the Milky Way's gas resides, nothing remains to slow its expansion except gravity. Such a *blowout* is in some ways similar to a volcanic eruption, but on a galactic scale: Hot plasma erupts from the disk and shoots high into the galactic halo.

In fact, there is growing evidence that processes like blowouts continually cycle gas between the Milky Way's disk and the halo, an idea summarized in a model known as the **galactic fountain**. According to this model, fountains of hot, ionized gas rise from the disk into the halo through the elongated bubbles carved by blowouts. The gravity of the galactic disk slows the rise of the gas, eventually pulling it back down. Near the top of its trajectory, the ejected gas starts to cool and form clouds of atomic hydrogen. These clouds cool further as they plunge back down, ultimately rejoining the layer of atomic hydrogen gas in the disk (Figure 18.9).

The galactic fountain model is plausible but difficult to verify. We do indeed see some hot gas high above the galaxy's disk. We also see cooler clouds that appear to be raining down from the halo. However, we can see this "rain" only directly above and below us, making it difficult to demonstrate beyond a doubt that galactic fountains circulate the products of supernovae throughout the Milky Way.

### Atomic Hydrogen Gas

The hot, ionized gas in bubbles, superbubbles, and fountains is dynamic and widespread, but it is a relatively small fraction of the gas in the Milky Way. Atomic hydrogen gas is much more common, and we can map its distribution in the Milky Way with radio observations. Atomic hydrogen emits a spectral line with a wavelength of 21 cm in the radio portion of the electromagnetic spectrum. We see the radio emission from this **21-cm line** coming from all directions, telling us that atomic hydrogen gas is distributed throughout the galactic disk. Based on the overall strength of the 21-cm emission, the amount of atomic hydrogen gas in our galaxy must be about 5 billion solar masses, which is a few percent of the galaxy's total mass.

Atomic hydrogen gas tends to be found in two distinct forms: large, tenuous clouds of warm (10,000 K) atomic hydrogen and smaller, denser clouds of cool (100 K) atomic hydrogen. If you were to take an interstellar voyage across the Milky Way, you would spend the majority of your time cruising through regions of warm atomic hydrogen interspersed with bubbles of hot, ionized gas. Every thousand light-years or so, you would encounter a cooler, denser cloud of atomic hydrogen. In the warm regions, you would detect about one atom per cubic centimeter and a weak magnetic field (weaker than Earth's magnetic field by a factor of about 100,000). In the cooler clouds, you would find a density of about 100 atoms per cubic centimeter and a stronger magnetic field.

Matter remains in the warm atomic hydrogen stage of the star–gas–star cycle for millions of years. Gravity slowly draws blobs of this gas together into tighter clumps, which radiate energy more efficiently as they grow denser. The blobs therefore cool and contract, forming the smaller clouds of cool atomic hydrogen. This process of shrinkage and coagulation takes a much longer time than the other steps in the journey from star death to star birth. The slowness of the transition from warm gas to cool clouds accounts for the large amount of gaseous matter in the atomic hydrogen stage of the star–gas–star cycle.

Remember that, although we speak of clouds of *hydrogen,* all interstellar material actually has a composition of about 70% hydrogen, 28% helium, and 2% heavy elements. Some of the heavy elements in regions of atomic hydrogen are in the form of tiny, solid **dust grains**: flecks of carbon and silicon minerals that resemble particles of smoke and form in the winds of red giant stars [Section 16.3]. Once formed, dust grains remain in the interstellar medium unless they are heated and destroyed by a passing shock wave or incorporated into a protostar. Although dust grains make up only about 1% of the mass of the atomic hydrogen clouds, they are responsible for the absorption of visible light that prevents us from seeing through the disk of the galaxy.

## Molecular Clouds

As the temperature drops further in the center of a cool cloud of atomic hydrogen, hydrogen atoms combine into molecules, making a **molecular cloud**. Molecular clouds are the coldest, densest collections of gas in the interstellar medium, and they often congregate into *giant molecular clouds* that hold up to a million solar masses of gas. The total mass of molecular clouds in the Milky Way is somewhat uncertain, but it is probably about the same as the total mass of atomic hydrogen gas—about 5 billion solar masses. Throughout much of this molecular gas, temperatures hover only a few degrees above absolute zero, and gas densities are a few hundred molecules per cubic centimeter.

Molecular hydrogen ($H_2$) is by far the most abundant molecule in molecular clouds, but it is difficult to detect because temperatures are usually too cold for the gas to produce $H_2$ emission lines. As a result, most of what we know about molecular clouds comes from observing spectral lines of molecules that make up only a tiny fraction of a cloud's mass. The most abundant of these molecules is carbon monoxide (CO, also a common ingredient in car exhaust), which produces strong emission lines in the radio portion of the spectrum at the 10–30 K temperatures of molecular clouds (Figure 18.10). Many other molecules also produce radio emission lines, and astronomers have used these lines to identify more than 80 different kinds of molecules in molecular clouds. Among the more familiar are water ($H_2O$), ammonia ($NH_3$), and alcohol ($CH_3OH$).

Molecular clouds are heavy and dense compared to the rest of the interstellar gas and therefore tend to settle toward the central layers of the Milky Way's disk. This tendency creates a phenomenon you can see with your own eyes: the dark fissures running through the luminous band of light in our sky that we call the Milky Way [Section 2.1].

Gravitational forces in molecular clouds gather molecules into the compact *cores* that eventually become protostars, and the final stages of star formation can be quite disruptive. Recall that protostars often have violent jets of gas spurting outward [Section 16.2]. The turbulence of these jets stirs up nearby regions of the molecular cloud, probably preventing other stars from forming in the vicinity of the growing protostar, at least for a while (Figure 18.11).

## Completing the Cycle

Once a few stars form in a cluster, their radiation begins to erode the surrounding gas in the molecular cloud. Ultraviolet photons from high-mass stars heat and ionize the gas, and winds and radiation pressure push the ionized gas away. This kind of feedback

**FIGURE 18.10** Image of a molecular cloud in the constellation Orion, showing its complex structure. The picture was made by measuring Doppler shifts of emission lines from carbon monoxide molecules in different locations. The colors indicate gas motions: Relative to the cloud as a whole, bluer parts are moving toward us and redder parts are moving away from us.

prevents much of the gas in a molecular cloud from turning into stars.

The process of molecular cloud erosion is sometimes spectacular. Figure 18.12 shows the *Eagle Nebula*, a complex of clouds where new stars are currently forming. The dark, lumpy columns are molecular clouds. Off to the upper right (outside the picture), newly formed massive stars glow with ultraviolet radiation. This radiation sears the surface of the molecular clouds, destroying molecules and stripping electrons from atoms. As a result, matter "evaporates" from the molecular clouds and joins the hotter ionized gas encircling them. Only the densest knots of gas resist evaporation. Stars are forming in some of these dense knots, which remain compact while the rest of the cloud erodes. These star-forming knots are the tips of the dark "whiskers" protruding from the columns of molecular gas in Figure 18.12.

We have arrived back where we started in the star–gas–star cycle. The most massive stars now forming in the Eagle Nebula will explode within a few million years, filling the region with hot gas and newly formed heavy elements. Farther in the future,

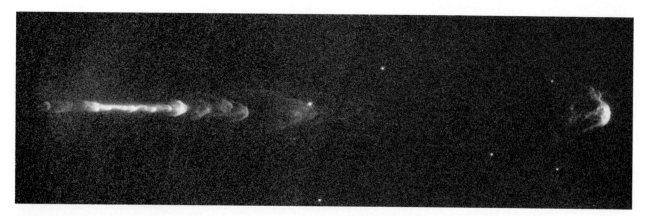

**FIGURE 18.11** Jets from protostars disrupt nearby regions of molecular clouds. This photo shows a jet emanating from the protostar on the left. All along the jet in the center and on the far right of the photo, gas shocked by the jet is glowing in optical light.

**FIGURE 18.12** A portion of the Eagle Nebula as seen by the Hubble Space Telescope.

**Table 18.1 Typical States of Gas in the Interstellar Medium**

| State of Gas | Primary Constituent | Approximate Temperature | Approximate Density (atoms per cm$^3$) | Description |
|---|---|---|---|---|
| Hot bubbles | Ionized hydrogen | 1,000,000 K | 0.01 | Pockets of gas heated by supernova shock waves |
| Warm atomic gas | Atomic hydrogen | 10,000 K | 1 | Fills much of galactic disk |
| Cool atomic clouds | Atomic hydrogen | 100 K | 100 | Intermediate stage of star–gas–star cycle |
| Molecular clouds | Molecular hydrogen | 30 K | 300 | Regions of star formation |
| Molecular cloud cores | Molecular hydrogen | 60 K | 10,000 | Star-forming clouds |

this gas will once again cool and coalesce into molecular clouds, forming new stars, new planets, and maybe even new civilizations.

Despite the recycling of matter from one generation of stars to the next, the star–gas–star cycle cannot go on forever. With each new generation, some of the galaxy's gas becomes permanently locked away in brown dwarfs that never return material to space and in stellar corpses left behind when stars die (white dwarfs, neutron stars, and black holes). The interstellar medium therefore is slowly running out of gas, and the rate of star formation will gradually taper off over the next 50 billion years or so. Eventually, star formation will cease.

### Putting It All Together: The Distribution of Gas in the Milky Way

As we look at different regions of the galaxy, we see various stages of the star–gas–star cycle playing themselves out. Because the cycle proceeds over such a long period of time compared to a human lifetime, each stage appears to us as a snapshot. We therefore see the interstellar medium in a wide variety of manifestations, ranging from the tenuous million-degree gas of bubbles to the cold, dense gas of molecular clouds. Table 18.1 summarizes the different states in which we see interstellar gas in the galactic disk.

Figure 18.13 shows seven views of the disk of the Milky Way Galaxy. Each view represents a panorama made by photographing the Milky Way's disk in every direction from Earth. You can visualize how one of these views corresponds to the sky by imagining cutting it out, bringing its ends together to form a circular band, and then lining up the band with the Milky Way on a model of the celestial sphere. Each view shows the Milky Way as it appears in a different set of wavelengths of light and thus reveals different features of the galactic disk.

- Figure 18.13a shows variations in the intensity of radio emission from the 21-cm line of atomic hydrogen. Thus, it maps the distribution of atomic hydrogen gas, demonstrating that this gas fills much of the galactic disk.

- Figure 18.13b shows variations in the intensity of radio emission lines from carbon monoxide (CO) and therefore maps the distribution of molecular clouds. Note that these cold, dense clouds are concentrated in a narrow layer near the midplane of the galactic disk.

- Figure 18.13c shows variations in the intensity of infrared emission (at wavelengths of 60–100 micrometers) from interstellar dust grains. Note that the regions of strongest emission from dust correspond to the locations of molecular clouds in Figure 18.13b.

- Figure 18.13d shows infrared light from stars at wavelengths that penetrate clouds of gas and dust (1–4 micrometers). Thus, this image shows how our galaxy would look if there were no dust blocking our view. The galactic bulge is clearly evident at the center.

- Figure 18.13e shows the galactic disk in visible light, just as it appears in the night sky. (Of course, only part of the Milky Way is above the horizon at any one time.) Because visible light cannot penetrate interstellar dust, the dark blotches correspond closely to the bright patches of molecular radio emission and infrared dust emission in Figure 18.13b and c.

- Figure 18.13f shows the distribution of X-ray light from the galactic disk. The pointlike blotches in this view are mostly X-ray binaries [Section 17.3], but the rest of the X-ray emission comes primarily

**a** 21-cm radio emission from atomic hydrogen gas.

**b** Radio emission from carbon monoxide reveals molecular clouds.

**c** Infrared (60–100 μm) emission from interstellar dust.

**d** Infrared (1–4 μm) emission from stars that penetrates most interstellar material.

**e** Visible light emitted by stars is scattered and absorbed by dust.

**f** X-ray emission from hot gas bubbles (diffuse blobs) and X-ray binaries (pointlike sources).

**g** Gamma-ray emission from collisions of cosmic rays with atomic nuclei in interstellar clouds.

**FIGURE 18.13** Panoramic views of the Milky Way in different bands of the spectrum. The center of the galaxy, which lies in the direction of the constellation Sagittarius, is in the center of each strip. The rest of each strip shows all other directions in the Milky Way disk as seen from Earth. (Imagine attaching the left and right ends of each strip to form a circular band that corresponds to the 360° band of the Milky Way in our sky.)

from hot gas bubbles. Note that hot gas tends to rise into the halo, so it is less concentrated toward the midplane than the atomic and molecular gas. (The prominent yellow blob on the lower right is the Vela supernova remnant.)

■ Figure 18.13g shows gamma-ray emission from the Milky Way. Most of the gamma-ray emission is produced by collisions between cosmic-ray particles and atomic nuclei in interstellar clouds. Such collisions happen most frequently where gas densities are highest, so the gamma-ray emission corresponds closely to the locations of molecular and atomic gas. (Gamma rays from the pulsar at the center of the Vela supernova remnant are prominent on the lower right.)

**TIME OUT TO THINK** *Carefully compare and contrast the different views of the Milky Way's disk in Figure 18.13. Why do regions that appear dark in some views appear bright in others? What kinds of general patterns do you notice?*

## 18.3 Galactic Environments

The star–gas–star cycle has operated continuously since the Milky Way's birth, yet new stars are not spread evenly across the galaxy. Some regions seem much more fertile than others. Galactic environments rich in molecular clouds tend to spawn new stars easily, while gas-poor environments do not. A quick tour of some characteristic galactic environments will help you spot where the action is.

### Out in the Halo

A census of stars in the Milky Way's *halo* would turn up many senior citizens and very few newborns. Most of the halo stars are old, red, and dim and much smaller in mass than our Sun. Halo stars also contain far fewer heavy elements than our Sun, sometimes having heavy-element proportions as low as 0.02% (in contrast to about 2% in the Sun). The relative lack of chemical enrichment in the halo indicates that its stars formed early in the galaxy's history— before many supernovae had exploded, adding heavy elements to star-forming clouds.

The halo's gas content corroborates this view. The halo is virtually gas-free compared to the disk, with very few detectable molecular clouds. Apparently, the bulk of the Milky Way's gas settled into the disk long ago. The halo environment is a place where lack of gas caused star formation to cease early in our galaxy's life. Now only very old stars still survive, and new stars are rarely born.

**TIME OUT TO THINK** *How does the halo of our galaxy resemble the distant future fate of the galactic disk? Why?*

### Our Neighborhood

Our own stellar neighborhood is more active than the halo and typifies much of the galactic disk. Within about 33 light-years (10 pc), we know of over 300 stars. Most are dim, red, spectral type M stars. A few, including Sirius, Vega, Altair, and Fomalhaut, are bright, white stars younger than our Sun. While stars of many different ages and different proportions of heavy elements are in our neighborhood, no very massive, short-lived stars (i.e., spectral type O or B) are present. We therefore infer that stars form periodically in our neighborhood but that no star clusters have formed here recently.

Our quiet suburb of the galaxy has not always been as calm as it is today. X-ray telescopes in space reveal hot, X ray–emitting gas coming from nearby in every direction. Surrounding this hot gas, at distances ranging up to a few hundred light-years (100 pc), lies a region of much cooler gas. Apparently, we and all our stellar neighbors live inside a hot bubble. The existence of this *Local Bubble* means that a number of supernovae must have detonated within our stellar neighborhood over the past several million years.

### Hot-Star Hangouts

The hot spots in our galaxy are the neighborhoods of high-mass stars. Because hot, massive stars live fast and die young, they never get a chance to move very far from their birthmates. Thus, we find them in star clusters close to the molecular clouds from which they formed. These environments are highly active and extraordinarily picturesque.

We find colorful, wispy blobs of glowing gas known as **ionization nebulae** throughout the galactic disk, particularly in the spiral arms. (Ionization nebulae are sometimes called *emission nebulae* or *H II regions;* H II is an abbreviation astronomers use for ionized hydrogen.) The energy that powers ionization nebulae comes from neighboring hot stars that irradiate them with ultraviolet photons. These photons ionize and excite the atoms in the nebulae, causing them to

The term *nebula* means *cloud,* but in astronomy it can refer to many different kinds of objects—a state of affairs that sometimes leads to misconceptions. Many astronomical objects look "cloudy" through small telescopes, and in past centuries astronomers called any such object a nebula as long as they were sure it wasn't a comet. For example, galaxies were called nebulae because they looked like either fuzzy round blobs or fuzzy spiral blobs. Using the term *nebula* to refer to a galaxy now sounds somewhat dated, given the enormous differences between these distant star systems and the much smaller clouds of gas that populate the interstellar medium. Nevertheless, some people still refer to spiral galaxies as "spiral nebulae." Today, we generally use the term *nebula* to refer to true interstellar clouds, but be aware that the term is still sometimes used in other ways.

emit light. The Orion Nebula, about 1,500 light-years away in the "sword" of the constellation Orion, is among the most famous. Few astronomical objects can match its spectacular beauty (Figure 18.14).

Most of the striking colors in an ionization nebula come from particular spectral lines produced by particular atomic transitions. For example, the transition in which an electron falls from energy level 3 to energy level 2 in a hydrogen atom generates a red photon with a wavelength of 656 nanometers [Section 6.4]. Ionization nebulae appear predominantly red in photographs because of all the red photons released by this particular transition. (Jumps from level 2 to level 1 are even more common, but they produce ultraviolet photons that can be studied only with ultraviolet telescopes in space.) Transitions in other elements produce other spectral lines of different colors (Figure 18.15).

The blue and black tints in some nebulae have a different origin. Starlight reflected from dust grains produces the blue colors, because interstellar dust grains scatter blue light much more readily than red light (Figure 18.16). These so-called *reflection nebulae* are always bluer in color than the stars supplying the light. (The effect is similar to the scattering of sunlight in our atmosphere that makes the sky blue [Section 10.2].) The black regions of nebulae are dark, dusty gas clouds that block our view of the stars beyond them. Figure 18.17 shows a multicolored nebula characteristic of a hot-star neighborhood.

**FIGURE 18.14** A photo of the Orion Nebula, an ionization nebula energized by ultraviolet photons from hot stars.

**FIGURE 18.15** Spectrum of an ionization nebula in blue and green light. The prominent emission lines in the spectrum reveal the atoms and ions that emit most of the light. Through careful modeling of these lines, we can determine the nebula's chemical composition.

FIGURE 18.16 The blue tints in this nebula in the constellation Orion are produced by reflected light.

FIGURE 18.17 A photo of the Horsehead Nebula and its surroundings.

**TIME OUT TO THINK** *In Figure 18.17, identify the red ionized regions, the blue reflecting regions, and the dark obscuring regions. Briefly explain the origin of the colors in each region.*

## 18.4 The Milky Way in Motion

The internal motions of the Milky Way range from the chaos of stars soaring on randomly oriented orbits through the halo to the stately rotation of the galactic disk. These motions, combined with the law of gravity, can tell us how mass is distributed within the Milky Way. When we decipher these movements, we find that the matter binding stars and gas to our galaxy extends far beyond its visible reaches and that the galaxy's spiral arms are propagating waves of new star formation. Let's investigate the motion of the Milky Way in more detail.

### Orbits in the Disk and Halo

If you could stand outside the Milky Way and watch it for a few billion years, the disk would resemble a huge merry-go-round. All the stars in the disk, in-

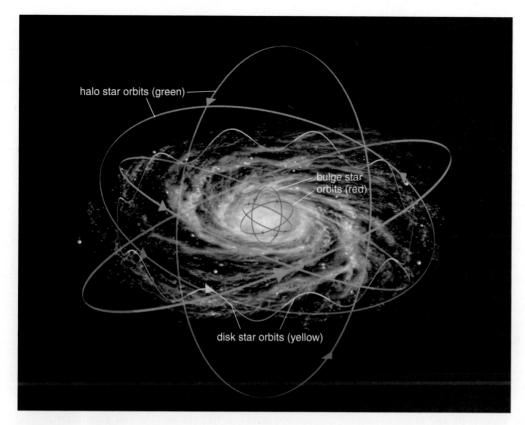

**FIGURE 18.18** Characteristic orbits of disk stars, bulge stars, and halo stars around the galaxy. The up-and-down motion of the disk star orbit is exaggerated compared to the radius of the orbit.

halo star orbits (green)

bulge star orbits (red)

disk star orbits (yellow)

cluding our Sun, orbit the center in the same direction. Moreover, like horses on a merry-go-round, individual stars bob up and down through the disk as they orbit. The general orbit of a star around the galaxy arises from its gravitational attraction toward the galactic center, while the bobbing arises from the localized pull of gravity within the disk itself (Figure 18.18): A star that is "too far" above the disk is pulled back into the disk by gravity; because the density of interstellar gas is too low to slow the star, it flies through the disk until it is "too far" below the disk on the other side. Gravity then pulls it back in the other direction. This ongoing process produces the bobbing of the stars. These up-and-down motions spread the disk stars over a thickness of about 1,000 light-years—quite thin in comparison to the 100,000-light-year diameter of the disk. Each orbit takes over 200 million years in the vicinity of our Sun, and each up-and-down "bob" takes a few tens of millions of years.

The orbits of stars in the halo and bulge are much less organized than the orbits of stars in the disk (see Figure 18.18). Individual bulge and halo stars travel around the galactic center on more or less elliptical paths, but the orientations of these paths are relatively random. Neighboring halo stars can circle the galactic center in opposite directions. They swoop from high above the disk to far below it and back again, plunging through the disk at velocities so high that the disk's gravity hardly alters their trajectories. Near the Sun, we see several fast-moving halo stars in the course of hasty excursions through the local region of the disk. One such star is Arcturus, the fourth-brightest star in the night sky.

**TIME OUT TO THINK** *Is there much danger that the Sun or Earth will someday be hit by a halo star swooping through the disk of the galaxy? Why or why not? (Hint: Think about the typical distances between stars, as illustrated by use of the 1-to-10-billion scale in Chapter 1.)*

The Sun's orbital path around the galaxy is called the **solar circle**, and its radius is our 28,000-light-year distance from the galactic center. By measuring the speeds of globular clusters relative to the Sun, we've determined that the Sun and its neighbors orbit the center of the Milky Way at a speed of about 220 km/s (about 800,000 km/hr [Section 1.3]). Even at

### Determining Stellar Orbits

Astronomers learned how stars orbit the Milky Way by measuring the motions of many different stars relative to the Sun. Although these measurements are easy in principle, they can be difficult in practice.

Determining a star's precise motion relative to the Sun requires knowing its true velocity through space. However, our primary means of measuring speeds in the universe—the Doppler effect—can tell us only a star's *radial velocity*, the component of its velocity directed toward or away from us. If we want to know the star's true velocity, we must also measure its *tangential velocity*, the component of its velocity directed across our line of sight.

Tangential velocity is difficult to measure because of the vast distances to stars. Over tens of thousands of years, the tangential velocities of stars cause their apparent positions in our sky to change, thereby changing the shapes of the constellations. These changes are far too small for human eyes to notice. However, we can measure tangential velocities for many stars by comparing telescopic photographs taken years or decades apart. For example, if photographs taken 10 years apart show that a star has moved across our sky by an angle of 1 arcsecond, we know the star is moving at an angular rate of 0.1 arcsecond per year. We can convert this angular rate of motion (often called the star's *proper motion*) to a tangential velocity if we also know the star's distance; for a given angular rate, the tangential velocity is greater for more distant stars (see Mathematical Insight 7.1).

Because the earliest telescopic photographs date only to the late-nineteenth century, we can measure tangential velocities only for objects that have moved noticeably since that time. In general, this limits us to stars within a few hundred light-years of Earth. Thus, we can determine precise stellar orbits only for relatively nearby stars. For more distant stars (and galaxies), we can usually measure only radial velocities, which is one reason why we have only limited knowledge of large-scale motion in the universe.

this speed, it takes the Sun about 230 million years to complete one orbit around the galactic center. Early dinosaurs ruled the Earth when it last visited this side of the galaxy.

### Orbits and Galactic Mass

Recall that Newton's law of gravity determines how quickly objects orbit one another. This fact, embodied in Newton's version of Kepler's third law, allows us to determine the mass of a relatively large object when we know the period and average distance of a much smaller object in orbit around it [Section 5.4]. A closely related law, which we will call the *orbital velocity law*, allows us to "weigh" the galaxy using the Sun's orbital velocity and its distance from the galactic center. If we call the Sun's orbital velocity $v$ and its distance (radius) from the galactic center $r$, the orbital velocity law tells us that the mass of the galaxy within the Sun's orbit ($M_r$) is:

$$M_r = \frac{r \times v^2}{G}$$

Note that the orbital velocity law tells us only how much mass lies *within* the Sun's orbit. It does not tell us the mass of the entire galaxy, because matter lying outside the solar circle (the Sun's orbit) has very little effect on the Sun's orbital velocity. Every part of the galaxy exerts gravitational forces on the Sun as it orbits, but the net force from matter outside the solar circle is relatively small because the pulls from opposite sides of the galaxy virtually cancel one another. In contrast, the net gravitational forces from mass within the solar circle all pull the Sun in the same direction—toward the galactic center. Thus, the Sun's orbital velocity responds almost exclusively to the gravitational pull of matter inside its orbit. Substituting the Sun's 28,000-light-year distance and 220-km/s orbital velocity into the orbital velocity law, we find that the total amount of mass within the solar circle is about $2 \times 10^{41}$ kilograms, or about 100 billion solar masses.

### The Distribution of Mass in the Milky Way

Just as we can use the orbit of the Sun to determine the mass of the galaxy within the solar circle, we can use the orbital motion of any other star to measure the mass of the Milky Way within the star's own orbital circle. In principle, we could determine the complete distribution of mass in the Milky Way by applying the orbital velocity law to the orbits of stars at every different distance from the galactic center. In practice, interstellar dust obscures our view of disk stars beyond a few thousand light-years, making it very difficult to measure stellar velocities. However, radio waves penetrate this dust, so we can see the 21-cm line from atomic hydrogen gas no matter where the gas is located in the galaxy. Such studies allow us to build a map of atomic hydrogen clouds. It is such maps that reveal our galaxy's large-scale spiral structure and also its overall pattern of rotation.

We can get a sense of the distribution of mass in the Milky Way by making a diagram called a **rotation curve**, which plots *rotational velocity* against distance from the center. As a simple example of the concept, let's construct a rotation curve for a merry-go-round. Every object on a merry-go-round goes around the center with the same rotational period, but objects farther from the center move in larger circles. Thus, objects farther from the center move at faster speeds, and the rotation curve for a merry-go-round is a straight line that rises steadily outward (Figure 18.19a). In contrast, the rotation curve for our solar system drops off with distance from the Sun because inner planets orbit at faster speeds than outer planets (Figure 18.19b). This drop-off in speed with distance occurs because virtually all the mass of the solar system is concentrated in the Sun. The gravitational force holding a planet in its orbit decreases with distance from the Sun, and a smaller force means a lower orbital speed. The rotation curve of any astronomical system whose mass is concentrated toward the center therefore drops steeply.

Figure 18.19c shows the rotation curve for the Milky Way Galaxy. Each individual dot represents the distance from the galactic center and the orbital speed of a particular star or cloud of atomic hydrogen. The curve running through the dots represents a "best fit" to the data. Note that, beyond the inner few thousand light-years, the orbital velocities remain approximately flat. This behavior contrasts sharply with the steeply declining rotation curve of the solar system. Thus, unlike the solar system, most of the mass of the Milky Way must *not* be concentrated at its center. Instead, the orbits of progressively more distant hydrogen clouds must encircle more and more mass. The solar circle encompasses about 100 billion solar masses, but a circle twice as large surrounds twice as much mass, and a larger circle surrounds even more mass. Because of the difficulty involved in finding clouds to measure on

## Mathematical Insight 18.1    The Orbital Velocity Law

As discussed in the text, the orbital velocity law allows us to use the orbital characteristics of a star or gas cloud to calculate the mass of the galaxy *within* the object's orbital circle. We can derive it by starting from Newton's version of Kepler's third law, using the version in which one object is much more massive than the other (see Mathematical Insight 5.2):

$$p^2 = \frac{4\pi^2}{G \times M} \times a^3$$

$M$ is the mass of the massive object, and $p$ and $a$ are the orbital period and semimajor axis of a smaller orbiting object, respectively. Solving for $M$, we find:

$$M = \frac{4\pi^2 \times a^3}{G \times p^2}$$

In Mathematical Insight 15.4, we found that the orbital speed of an object with a circular orbit is:

$$v = \frac{\text{distance traveled in one orbit}}{\text{period of one orbit}} = \frac{2\pi a}{p}$$

Solving for $p$, we find:

$$p = \frac{2\pi a}{v}$$

Substituting this expression for $p$ into Kepler's third law solved for the mass $M$, we find:

$$M = \frac{4\pi^2 \times a^3}{G \times p^2}$$

$$= \frac{4\pi^2 \times a^3}{G \times \left(\frac{2\pi a}{v}\right)^2}$$

$$= \frac{4\pi^2 \times a^3}{G \times \frac{4\pi^2 a^2}{v^2}} = \frac{a \times v^2}{G}$$

Because we are dealing with a circular orbit, we can replace $a$ with the radius $r$ and write this equation as:

$$M_r = \frac{r \times v^2}{G}$$

The subscript $r$ of $M_r$ reminds us that we have calculated the mass only within a distance $r$ of the galactic center.

*Example:* Calculate the mass of the Milky Way Galaxy within the solar circle.

*Solution:* The orbital velocity of the Sun around the center of the galaxy is $v = 220$ km/s $= 2.2 \times 10^5$ m/s. The radius of the solar circle is the Sun's 28,000-light-year distance from the galactic center. Using the fact that a light-year is about $9.46 \times 10^{15}$ meters, we find this radius to be equivalent to $r = 2.6 \times 10^{20}$ m. We can now find the mass within the solar circle by substituting these values for $v$ and $r$ into the orbital velocity law:

$$M_r = \frac{r \times v^2}{G}$$

$$= \frac{(2.6 \times 10^{20} \text{ m}) \times \left(2.2 \times 10^5 \, \frac{\text{m}}{\text{s}}\right)^2}{6.67 \times 10^{-11} \, \frac{\text{m}^3}{\text{kg} \times \text{s}^2}}$$

$$= 1.9 \times 10^{41} \text{ kg}$$

The mass of the Milky Way Galaxy within the solar circle is about $2 \times 10^{41}$ kg. Recall that the mass of the Sun is about $2 \times 10^{30}$ kg; thus, the mass within the solar circle is equivalent to about $10^{11}$, or 100 billion, solar masses.

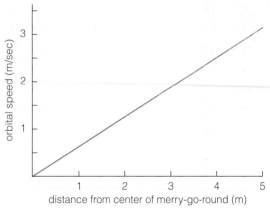

a A rotation curve for a merry-go-round.

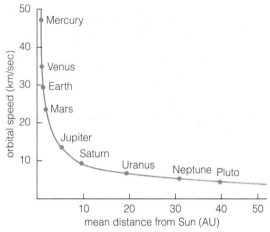

b The rotation curve for the planets in our solar system.

c The rotation curve for the Milky Way Galaxy.

**FIGURE 18.19** Rotation curves show how the orbital speed of a system depends on distance from its center. The solar system's rotation curve declines with radius because its mass is concentrated at the center. The Milky Way's rotation curve is flat, indicating that the Milky Way's mass extends well beyond the Sun's orbit.

the outskirts of the galaxy, we have not yet found the "edge" of this mass distribution.

The flatness of the Milky Way's rotation curve came as an immense surprise to astronomers because it implies that most of our galaxy's mass must lie well beyond our Sun, tens of thousands of light-years from the galactic center. In fact, a more detailed analysis suggests that most of this mass is distributed in the galactic halo and that the halo might outweigh all the disk stars *combined* by a factor of 10. However, aside from the light of the relatively small number of halo stars, we have detected very little other radiation coming from this enormous amount of mass. Because we see so little light coming from outside the Sun's orbit, most of the halo's huge mass cannot be in the form of orbiting stars. The nature of this mass remains unknown—which means that we do not know the nature of the vast majority of matter in our own galaxy. We call this mysterious mass **dark matter** because it does not emit any light that we have yet detected. The nature of this dark matter is one of the greatest mysteries in astronomy today. We will investigate it in much more depth in Chapter 21.

### Spiral Arms

The disks of spiral galaxies like the Milky Way display sweeping spiral arms that can stretch tens of thousands of light-years from their bulges. At first glance, spiral arms look as if they ought to rotate with the stars, like the fins of a giant pinwheel in space. However, because stars near the center of the galaxy take less time to complete an orbit than more distant stars, the arms would gradually wind themselves up if they really did rotate with the stars in the disk. By the time a spiral galaxy was a few billion years old, the spiral arms would look like a tightly wound coil. Because we do not see such tightly coiled spiral arms, the explanation for spiral structure must be more complex.

Detailed images show the spiral arms to be home to most of the young, bright, blue stars in a galaxy (Figure 18.20). Clusters of these hot, short-lived massive stars populate the spiral arms. Between the arms, we find many fewer hot stars. We also see enhanced amounts of molecular and atomic gas in the spiral arms, and streaks of interstellar dust often obscure the inner sides of the arms themselves (Figure 18.21). All these clues suggest that spiral arms result from waves of star formation that propagate through the disks of spiral galaxies.

Theoretical models suggest that disturbances called **spiral density waves** are probably the source of our galaxy's spiral arms. To visualize how these waves operate, think about waves in the ocean. If an earthquake in Alaska initiates a tidal wave (tsunami) that slams into the northern shore of Hawaii, the water pummeling the Hawaiian coastline does not travel all the way from Alaska. The water in any given location merely sloshes back and forth, but the wave carries energy across the ocean. The enhanced water pressure beneath the crest of a wave momentarily causes the water level to rise ahead of the wave. As the crest passes, the water level falls again, and the wave moves farther along.

Spiral density waves are like waves in the ocean in two respects: They need some sort of disturbance to generate them, and they do not carry stars or interstellar gas with them as they move through the disk. Tidal interactions with other galaxies passing nearby are one possible source of disturbance in a galaxy's

**FIGURE 18.21** The relationship of dust, gas, and new star clusters in a spiral arm.

Dust lane arises on inner edge of spiral arm where gas clouds crowd together.

Young blue stars are found on outer edge of spiral arm.

Ionization nebulae arise where newly forming blue stars are ionizing gas clouds.

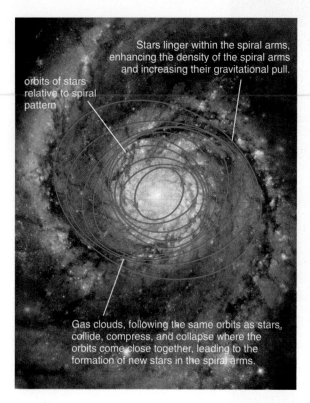

Stars linger within the spiral arms, enhancing the density of the spiral arms and increasing their gravitational pull.

orbits of stars relative to spiral pattern

Gas clouds, following the same orbits as stars, collide, compress, and collapse where the orbits come close together, leading to the formation of new stars in the spiral arms.

**FIGURE 18.22** Generation of spiral density waves in a two-armed spiral galaxy. Once spiral arms appear, they can strengthen themselves because their enhanced gravity pulls orbiting stars into elliptical orbits with greater elongation.

disk. Once such a disturbance starts a spiral density wave in motion, the wave will continue to propagate through the galaxy's disk, perhaps for billions of years.

Gravitational interactions between stars keep spiral density waves going. The spiral arms themselves are waves of enhanced density, so stars and gas at the location of any wave crest are packed slightly more densely than normal. Thus, the wave crest is also a location of enhanced gravitational attraction within the disk. This gravitational attraction pulls the stars ahead of the crest more closely together; after the crest passes, the stars move apart into looser groups.

Interstellar clouds react even more strongly to the gravitational attraction of the wave crest. Gas clouds collide with one another most frequently in the densest part of the wave, collecting into groups (Figure 18.22). Because gas clouds crowd so thickly into the crest of the wave, stars form more profusely in spiral arms than elsewhere in the disk. A froth of young stars and ionization nebulae thus marks the crests of spiral density waves.

**TIME OUT TO THINK** *Perhaps you have noticed what happens when the scene of an accident blocks one side of a highway. Curious drivers on the other side of the highway slow down to check out the accident, and traffic backs up behind them. After the drivers have passed by, they speed back up, and traffic thins out. How is this disturbance in the flow of traffic similar to a spiral density wave?*

The bluish hue of the spiral arms comes from their prolific star formation. Massive, short-lived, blue stars die out quickly as the wave crest passes by, long before the next spiral wave sweeps through. These luminous hot stars are therefore found close to the spiral arms in which they formed. Longer-lived yellow and red stars live through the passage of many spiral density waves and therefore are distributed relatively evenly throughout the galactic disk.

## 18.5 The Mysterious Galactic Center

The center of the Milky Way Galaxy lies in the direction of the constellation Sagittarius. This region of the sky does not look particularly special to our unaided eyes; however, if we could remove the interstellar dust that obscures our view, the elliptical shape of the galaxy's central bulge would fill Sagittarius, and its brilliance would be one of the night sky's most spectacular sights.

Because the Milky Way is relatively transparent to long-wavelength radiation, we can use radio and infrared telescopes to peer into its heart (Figure 18.23). Deep in the galactic center, we find swirling clouds of gas and a cluster of several million stars. Bright radio emission traces out the magnetic fields that thread this turbulent region. At the core of it all sits a source of bright radio emission named Sagittarius A* (pronounced "Sagittarius A-star"), or Sgr A* for short, that is quite unlike any other radio source in our galaxy.

The motions of the gas and stars in Sgr A* indicate that it contains a few million solar masses within a region no larger than about 3 light-years across (Figure 18.24). The star cluster in Sgr A* cannot account for all that mass. Many astronomers therefore suspect that Sgr A* contains a black hole weighing around 2.5 million solar masses.

However, the behavior of this suspected black hole is somewhat puzzling. The most plausible black-hole candidates in our galaxy—those in binary systems like Cygnus X-1 [Section 17.5]—accrete matter from their companions. The resulting accretion disks radiate brightly in X rays. If Sgr A* truly is a giant black hole, we might expect it to be accreting some of the surrounding gas from the galactic center. Because of its large mass, it would have a large accretion disk and would shine brightly in X rays. (Many other galaxies have tremendously luminous X-ray sources at their centers that most astronomers believe are accretion disks circling enormous black holes

**a** In visible light, dusty gas obscures our view of the galactic center, marked by the 0.65° green square.

**b** In this infrared image depicting a 2° by 4° region around the galactic center, we can see through the dust to the central star cluster.

**d** This false-color radio image of the galactic center shows ionized gas swirling around Sgr A*, which is the white dot near the center of the image.

**c** This radio image of the central square degree shows the strange environment of Sgr A*; the bright filaments trace magnetic field lines full of charged particles presumably energized by the central black hole.

**FIGURE 18.23** The galactic center at various wavelengths.

High speeds near Sgr A* suggest a very massive object in a small region.

**FIGURE 18.24** Star velocities near the galactic center.

[Section 20.5].) These X rays would shine through the dusty gas of our galaxy, and we would be able to detect them easily. Yet we detect only relatively faint X-ray emission from Sgr A*.

It is possible that Sgr A* contains a huge black hole that simply has run out of gas to accrete. Even more intriguingly, the black hole might be consuming the energy contained in the accreting matter before it has a chance to escape as radiation. In any case, if Sgr A* is indeed a black hole, it does not behave like other black holes whose accretion disks are more apparent. Because the black hole at the center of our galaxy is so well hidden from us, the nature of Sgr A* remains mysterious.

# THE BIG PICTURE

In this chapter, we have explored our galaxy, focusing on the recycling of gas that continually produces new stars and on the motions of the Milky Way that reveal its mass. When you review this chapter, pay attention to these "big picture" ideas:

■ The inability of visible light to penetrate deeply through interstellar gas and dust concealed the true nature of our galaxy until recent times. Modern astronomical instruments reveal the Milky Way to be a dynamic system of stars and gas that continually gives birth to new stars and planetary systems.

■ Stellar winds and explosions make interstellar space a violent place. Hot gas tears through the pervasive atomic hydrogen gas in the galactic disk, leaving expanding pockets of hot plasma and fast-moving clouds in its wake. All this violence might seem quite dangerous, but it performs the great service of mixing essential new elements throughout the Milky Way.

■ We can use the orbital speeds of stars and gas clouds around the center of the galaxy to determine the distribution of mass in the Milky Way. To our great surprise, we've discovered that most of the mass of the galaxy lies in the halo, not in the galactic disk where most of the stars are located. The nature of this *dark matter* is one of the greatest mysteries in astronomy today.

■ Although the elements from which we are made were forged in stars, we could not exist if stars were not organized into galaxies. The Milky Way Galaxy acts as a giant recycling plant, converting gas expelled from each generation of stars into the next and allowing some of the heavy elements to solidify into planets like our own.

## Review Questions

1. Draw simple sketches of our galaxy as it would appear face-on and edge-on, identifying the *disk, bulge, halo,* and *spiral arms.*

2. What do we mean by the *interstellar medium?* How does it affect our view of the galaxy?

3. What do we mean by *heavy elements?* How much of the Milky Way's gas is in the form of heavy elements? Where are heavy elements made?

4. What is the star–gas–star cycle, and how does it lead to *chemical enrichment?* Use the idea of chemical enrichment to explain why stars that formed early in the history of the galaxy contain a smaller proportion of heavy elements than stars that formed more recently.

5. Distinguish between the following forms of gas: ionized hydrogen, atomic hydrogen, and molecular hydrogen.

6. What are *cosmic rays?* Where do we think they come from?

7. What is a *superbubble?* How is it made? Describe what happens in a blowout in which a superbubble breaks out of the galactic disk.

8. Describe the *galactic fountain* model. What evidence supports this model?

9. What is the most common form of gas in the interstellar medium? What is the wavelength of the radio emission line characteristic of this gas?

10. What are *dust grains?* Where do they form?

11. How do *molecular clouds* form? How do we observe them? Why do molecular clouds tend to settle toward the central layers of the Milky Way's disk?

12. Will the star–gas–star cycle continue forever? Why or why not?

13. Describe the stars we find in the *halo* in terms of mass, luminosity, color, and proportion of heavy elements. Why do halo stars have these characteristics?

14. What is an *ionization nebula?* Why are such nebulae found near massive young stars? What produces their striking colors?

15. Contrast the general patterns of the orbits of stars in the disk with the orbits of stars in the halo.

16. At what speed does the Sun travel around the *solar circle?* About how long does one orbit take? Briefly explain how we can use the characteristics of the Sun's orbit to determine the mass of the Milky Way contained within the solar circle. What is the result?

17. What is a *rotation curve?* Describe the rotation curve of the Milky Way, and explain how it indicates that most of the Milky Way's mass lies outside the solar circle. What do we mean by *dark matter?*

18. How do we know that spiral arms are not simple "pinwheels" as they appear at first glance? What features do we see in images of spiral arms that suggest that they result from waves of star formation propagating through galaxies?

19. What is Sgr A*? What evidence suggests that it contains a massive black hole?

## Discussion Questions

1. *Galactic Ecosystem.* The introduction to this chapter likened the star–gas–star cycle in our Milky Way to the ecosystem that sustains life on Earth. Here on our planet, water molecules cycle from the sea to the sky to the ground and back to the sea. Our bodies convert atmospheric oxygen molecules into carbon dioxide, and plants convert the carbon dioxide back into oxygen molecules. How are the cycles of matter on Earth similar to the cycles of matter in the galaxy? How do they differ? Do you think the term *ecosystem* is appropriate to discussions of the galaxy?

2. *Galaxy Stuff.* In the chapters on stars, we learned why we are "star stuff." Based on what you've learned in this chapter, explain why we are also "galaxy stuff." Does the fact that the entire galaxy was involved in bringing forth life on Earth change your perspective on the Earth or on life in any way? If so, how? If not, why not?

## Problems

*Sensible Statements?* For **problems 1–7**, decide whether the statement is sensible and explain why it is or is not.

1. We did not understand the true size and shape of our galaxy until NASA satellites were launched into the galactic halo, enabling us to see what the Milky Way looks like from the outside.

2. Planets like Earth probably didn't form around the very first stars because there were so few heavy elements back then.

3. If I could see infrared light, the galactic center would look much more impressive.

4. Many spectacular ionization nebulae are seen throughout the Milky Way's halo.

5. The carbon in my diamond ring was once part of an interstellar dust grain.

6. The Sun's velocity around the Milky Way tells us that most of our galaxy's dark matter lies within the solar circle.

7. We know that a black hole lies at our galaxy's center because a few of the stars it is sucking in have vanished over the last several years.

8. *Unenriched Stars.* Suppose you discovered a star made purely of hydrogen and helium. How old do you think it would be? Explain your reasoning.

9. *Enrichment of Star Clusters.* The gravitational pull of an isolated globular cluster is rather weak—a single supernova explosion can blow all the interstellar gas out of a globular cluster. How might this fact be related to observations indicating that stars ceased to form in globular clusters long ago? How might it be related to the fact that globular clusters are deficient in elements heavier than hydrogen and helium? Summarize your answers in one or two paragraphs.

10. *High-velocity Star.* The average speed of stars *relative* to the Sun in the solar neighborhood is about 20 km/s (i.e., the speed at which we see stars moving toward or away from the Sun—*not* their orbital speed around the galaxy). Suppose you discover a star in the solar neighborhood that is moving relative to the Sun at a much higher speed, say 200 km/s. What kind of orbit does this star probably have around the Milky Way? In what part of the galaxy does it spend most of its time? Explain.

*11. *Mass from Rotation Curve.* Using velocities shown on the Milky Way's rotation curve in Figure 18.19c, along with the orbital velocity law (see Mathematical Insight 18.1), calculate the mass of the Milky Way Galaxy within each of the following distances. Give your answers in both kilograms and solar masses.

  a. 10,000 light-years.

  b. 30,000 light-years.

  c. 50,000 light-years.

12. *Research: Discovering the Milky Way.* Humans have been looking at the Milky Way since long before recorded history, but only in the past century did we verify the true shape of the galaxy and our location within it. Learn more about how conceptions of the Milky Way developed through history. What names did different cultures give the band of light they saw? What stories did they tell about it? How have ideas about the galaxy changed in the past few centuries? Try to locate diagrams that illustrate these changes. Write a two- to three-page summary of your findings.

## Web Projects

Find useful links to Web projects on the text Web site.

1. *Images of the Star–Gas–Star Cycle.* Explore the Web to find pictures of nebulae and other forms of interstellar gas in different stages of the star–gas–star cycle. Assemble the pictures into a sequence that tells the story of interstellar recycling, with a one-paragraph explanation accompanying each image.

2. *The Galactic Center.* Search the Web for recent images of the galactic center, along with information about whether the center hides a massive black hole. Present a two- to three-page report, with pictures, giving an update on current knowledge about the center of the Milky Way Galaxy.

*Thus the explorations of space end on a note of uncertainty. . . . Eventually, we reach the dim boundary—the utmost limits of our telescopes. There we measure shadows, and we search among ghostly errors of measurement for landmarks that are scarcely more susbtantial.*

EDWIN HUBBLE

# CHAPTER 19

# Galaxies
## From Here to the Horizon

Far beyond the Milky Way, we see many other galaxies—some similar to our own and some very different—scattered throughout space to the very limits of the observable universe. This fabulous sight inspires some fundamental questions: How far away are all these galaxies? How old is the universe? How big is it? Such questions might have seemed ridiculously speculative a century ago. Today, we believe we know the answers to all three questions with respectable accuracy.

Edwin Hubble, the man for whom the Hubble Space Telescope is named, provided the key discovery when he proved conclusively that galaxies exist beyond the Milky Way. The distances he measured revealed an astonishing fact: The more distant a galaxy is, the faster it moves away from us. Hubble's discovery dealt a mortal blow to the traditional belief in a static, eternal, and unchanging universe. The motions of the galaxies away from one another imply instead that the entire universe is expanding and that its age is finite.

This chapter follows the steps leading to this profound revelation as we acquaint ourselves with the different types of galaxies in the universe and then learn how to measure their distances. From the distances to other galaxies, we can infer the age of the universe and determine how large the observable universe really is.

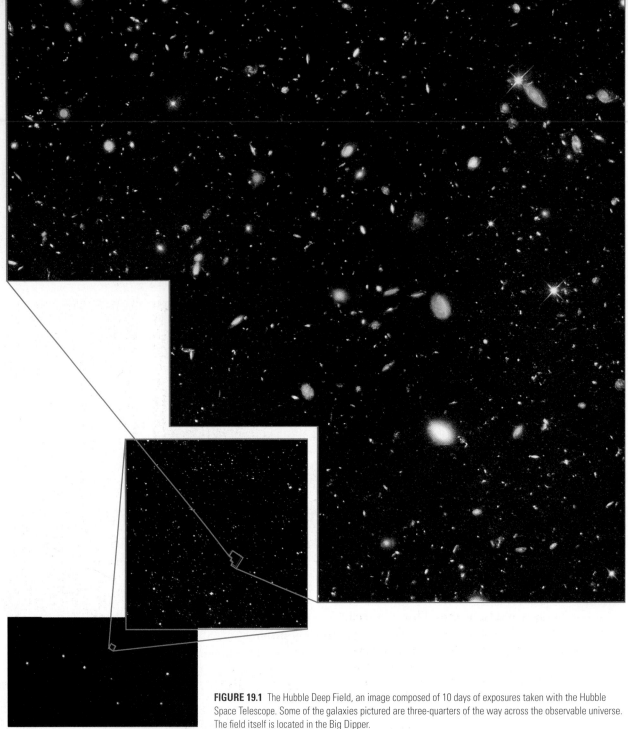

**FIGURE 19.1** The Hubble Deep Field, an image composed of 10 days of exposures taken with the Hubble Space Telescope. Some of the galaxies pictured are three-quarters of the way across the observable universe. The field itself is located in the Big Dipper.

## 19.1 Islands of Stars

Figure 19.1 shows an amazing image of a tiny slice of the sky taken by the Hubble Space Telescope. The telescope pointed toward a single direction in the sky, collecting all the light it could for 10 days. If you held a grain of sand at arm's length, the angular size of the grain would match the angular size of everything in this picture. This slice of the sky is jam-packed with galaxies of many sizes, colors, and shapes. Some look large, some small. Some are reddish, some whitish. Some appear round, and some appear flat. Small

galaxies greatly outnumber large ones, yet the large ones produce most of the light in the universe. Counting the galaxies in this slice of the sky and multiplying by the number of such slices it would take to make a montage of the entire sky, we find that the observable universe contains over 80 billion galaxies.

Each of these blobs of light is an island of stars bound together by gravity. Like our own Milky Way, each is a dynamic system that has cycled hydrogen gas through stars for billions of years, producing new elements for future generations of stars. Yet reconstructing the histories of these galaxies in more detail

**a** NGC 1232, a spiral galaxy similar to our Milky Way.

**b** M 83, a face-on spiral with a small bulge.

**FIGURE 19.2** Spiral galaxies (Objects carry "M" names if they are among the 110 objects in the *Messier Catalog*, published by Charles Messier in 1781. "NGC" stands for the *New General Catalog*, a listing of more than 7,000 objects published in 1888.)

**c** NGC 4414, a spiral galaxy somewhat tilted to our line of sight.

**d** NGC 891, an edge-on spiral considered to be very similar to the Milky Way—note the dusty disk.

poses a formidable challenge. Just as with stars, our observations capture only the briefest instant in any galaxy's life, leaving us to piece together the life story of a typical galaxy from pictures of different galaxies at various life stages. However, whereas stars of all ages can be found nearby in the Milky Way, young galaxies are found only at very great distances from Earth.

Because of the difficulty of studying how young galaxies form and develop, our understanding of galactic lives is less complete than our understanding of stellar lives. Nevertheless, we can proceed similarly in putting the story together. In the rest of this chapter we will study basic characteristics of galaxies, much as we began with basic characteristics of stars in Chapter 15. We will outline how astronomers classify galaxies and investigate how we measure their distances and estimate their ages. Along the way, we will learn how the first measurements of galaxy distances revolutionized the way we now look at the universe—as an expanding realm within which the story of creation still unfolds. With this understanding, we'll study the lives of galaxies in the next chapter.

## 19.2 Galaxy Types

Astronomers classify galaxies into three major categories. **Spiral galaxies** look like flat white disks with yellowish bulges at their centers (Figure 19.2). The disks are filled with cool gas and dust, interspersed

**e** NGC 4594, also known as the Sombrero Galaxy, an edge-on spiral with a large bulge and a dusty disk.

with hotter ionized gas as in the Milky Way, and usually display beautiful spiral arms. **Elliptical galaxies** are redder, more rounded, and often longer in one direction than in the other, like a football. Compared with spiral galaxies, elliptical galaxies contain very little cool gas and dust, though they often contain very hot, ionized gas. Galaxies that appear neither disklike nor rounded are classified as **irregular galaxies**.

The sizes of all three types of galaxy span a wide range, from *dwarf galaxies* containing as few as 100 million ($10^8$) stars to *giant galaxies* with more than 1 trillion ($10^{12}$) stars. The differing colors of galaxies arise from the different kinds of stars that populate them: Spiral and irregular galaxies look white because they contain stars of all different colors and ages; elliptical galaxies look redder because they contain very few young, blue stars.

**TIME OUT TO THINK** *Take a moment and try to classify the larger galaxies in Figure 19.1. How many appear spiral? Elliptical? Irregular? Do the colors of galaxies seem related to their shapes?*

### Spiral Galaxies

Like the Milky Way, other spiral galaxies also have a thin *disk* extending outward from a central *bulge* (Figure 19.2). The bulge itself merges smoothly into a *halo* that can extend to a radius of over 100,000 light-years. Together, the bulge and halo of a spiral galaxy make up its **spheroidal component**, so named because of its rounded shape. Although no clear boundary divides the pieces of the spheroidal component, astronomers usually consider stars within 10,000 light-years of the center to be members of the bulge and those outside this radius to be members of the halo.

The **disk component** of a spiral galaxy slices directly through the halo and bulge. The disk of a large spiral galaxy like the Milky Way can extend 50,000 light-years or more from the center. The disks of all spiral galaxies contain an *interstellar medium* of gas and dust, but the amounts and proportions of the interstellar medium in molecular, atomic, and ionized forms differ from one spiral galaxy to the next. Spiral galaxies with large bulges generally have less interstellar gas and dust than those with small bulges.

Not all galaxies with disks are standard spiral galaxies. Some spiral galaxies appear to have a straight bar of stars cutting across the center, with spiral arms curling away from the ends of the bar. Such galaxies are known as *barred spiral galaxies* (Figure 19.3).

Other galaxies have disks but appear to lack spiral arms (Figure 19.4). These are called *lenticular galaxies*, because they look lens-shaped when seen edge-on (*lenticular* means "lens-shaped"). Although they look like spiral galaxies without arms, lenticular galaxies

**FIGURE 19.3** NGC 1365, a barred spiral galaxy.

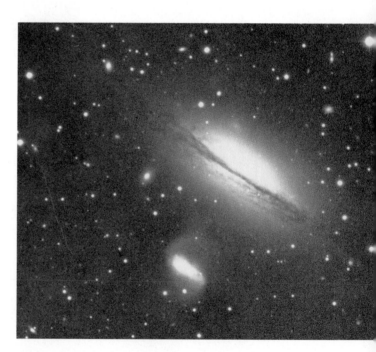

**FIGURE 19.4** NGC 5078, a lenticular galaxy. Most lenticular galaxies have less cool gas than this one, which displays a prominent black streak of interstellar dust.

**FIGURE 19.6** A portion of the Virgo cluster of galaxies, the nearest large galaxy cluster to the Milky Way.

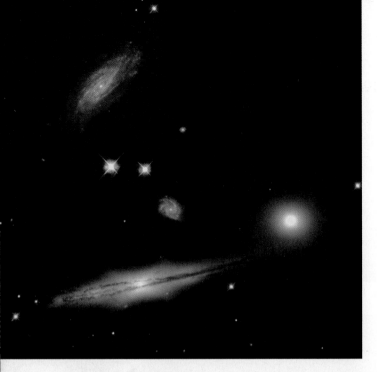

**FIGURE 19.5** Hickson Compact Group 87, a small group of galaxies consisting of a large edge-on spiral galaxy at the bottom of this photo, two smaller spiral galaxies at the center and upper left, and an elliptical galaxy to the right. (The other objects in this photograph are foreground stars in our own galaxy.)

might more appropriately be considered an intermediate class between spirals and ellipticals, because they tend to have less cool gas than normal spirals but more than ellipticals.

Among large galaxies in the universe, most (75–85%) are spiral or lenticular. (Spiral and lenticular galaxies are much rarer among small galaxies.) Spiral galaxies are often found in loose collections of several galaxies, called **groups**, that extend over a few million light-years (Figure 19.5). Our Local Group is one example, with two large spirals: the Milky Way and the Great Galaxy in Andromeda (M 31). Lenticular galaxies are particularly common in **clusters** of galaxies, which can contain hundreds and sometimes thousands of galaxies extending over more than 10 million light-years (Figure 19.6).

### Elliptical Galaxies

The major difference between elliptical and spiral galaxies is that ellipticals lack a significant disk component (Figure 19.7). Thus, an elliptical galaxy has only a spheroidal component and looks much like the bulge and halo of a spiral galaxy. (In fact, elliptical galaxies are sometimes called *spheroidal galaxies*.) Most of the interstellar medium in large elliptical galaxies consists of low-density, hot, X ray–emitting gas, making it much like the gas in bubbles and superbubbles in the Milky Way [Section 18.2]. Elliptical galaxies usually contain very little dust or cool gas, although they are not completely devoid of either. Some

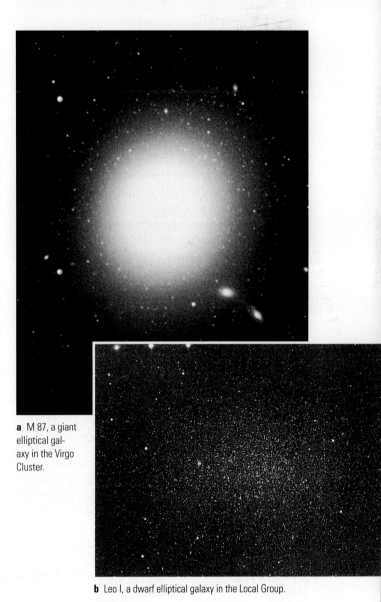

**a** M 87, a giant elliptical galaxy in the Virgo Cluster.

**b** Leo I, a dwarf elliptical galaxy in the Local Group.

**FIGURE 19.7** Elliptical galaxies.

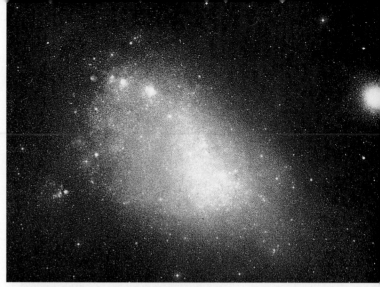

**b** The Small Magellanic Cloud, a smaller companion to the Milky Way.

**a** The Large Magellanic Cloud, a small companion to the Milky Way.

**FIGURE 19.8** Irregular galaxies.

**c** NGC 1313, an irregular galaxy with scattered patches of star formation.

have relatively small and cold gaseous disks rotating at their centers; these disks might be the remnants of a collision with a spiral galaxy [Section 20.3].

Elliptical galaxies appear to be more social than spiral galaxies: They are much more common in clusters of galaxies than outside clusters. Elliptical galaxies make up about half the large galaxies in the central regions of clusters, while they represent only a small minority (about 15%) of the large galaxies found outside clusters. However, ellipticals are more common among small galaxies. Particularly small elliptical galaxies with less than a billion stars, called **dwarf elliptical galaxies**, are often found near larger spiral galaxies. At least 10 dwarf elliptical galaxies belong to the Local Group.

### Irregular Galaxies

A small percentage of the large galaxies we see nearby fall into neither of the two major categories. This *irregular* class of galaxies is a miscellaneous class, encompassing small galaxies such as the Magellanic Clouds and "peculiar" galaxies that appear to be in disarray (Figure 19.8). These blobby star systems are usually white and dusty, like the disks of spirals. Telescopic observations probing deep into the universe show that distant galaxies are more likely to be irregular in shape than those nearby. Because the light of more distant galaxies was emitted longer ago in the

past, these observations tell us that irregular galaxies were more common when the universe was younger.

## 19.3 Measuring Cosmic Distances

To know more about galaxies than just their shape and color, we need to know how far away they are. However, measuring cosmic distances is one of the most challenging tasks we face when trying to understand galaxies and the universe as a whole. Our determinations of astronomical distances depend on a chain of methods that begins with knowing distances in our own solar system. At each link in this chain, we establish standards that help us forge the next link. Because each link depends on preceding links,

## Hubble's Galaxy Classes

Edwin Hubble invented a system for classifying galaxies that remains widely used. It assigns the letter *E*, followed by a number, to each elliptical galaxy. The larger the number, the flatter the galaxy. An E0 galaxy is round, and an E7 galaxy is highly elongated. A spiral galaxy is assigned an uppercase *S*, or *SB* if it has a bar, and a lowercase *a, b,* or *c*. The lowercase letter indicates the size of the bulge and the dustiness of the disk; the bulge size decreases from *a* to *c*, while the amount of dusty gas increases. For example, an Sa galaxy has a large bulge and a modest amount of dusty gas; an SBc galaxy has a bar, a small bulge, and lots of gas. The lenticular galaxies are designated S0, signifying their intermediate spot between spirals and ellipticals. Irregular galaxies are designated Irr.

Astronomers had once hoped that the classification of galaxies might yield deep insights, just as the classification of stars did in the early twentieth century. The Hubble classification scheme itself was suspected for a time to be an evolutionary sequence in which galaxies flattened and

spread out as they aged (see diagram). Unfortunately for astronomers, galaxies turn out to be far more complex than stars, and classification schemes like this one have not led to easy answers about the nature of galaxies.

The Hubble "tuning fork" diagram shows Hubble's galaxy classes. The arrangement was once suspected by astronomers to represent an evolutionary sequence, but that is no longer thought to be the case.

any inaccuracies accumulate as we move up the chain. Nevertheless, we now can measure the distances to the farthest galaxies to an accuracy of within 20%. The distance chain begins with radar measurements of the solar system's size. The second link involves parallax measurements of the distances to nearby stars [Section 15.2]. We will now follow the rest of this chain, link by link, to the outermost reaches of the observable universe.

## Standard Candles

We can usually measure an object's apparent brightness with a detector, so we can use the luminosity–distance formula [Section 15.2] to calculate the object's luminosity if we know its distance, or to calculate its distance if we know its luminosity. For example, suppose we see a distant street lamp and know that all street lamps of its type put out 1,000 watts of light. Then, once we measure the apparent brightness of

---

## Mathematical Insight 19.1    The Luminosity–Distance Relation Revisited

As we saw in Mathematical Insight 15.1, the luminosity–distance formula arises from the fact that apparent brightness decreases with the square of the distance to a light source. That is why we usually write it in the following form:

$$\text{apparent brightness} = \frac{\text{luminosity}}{4\pi \times (\text{distance})^2}$$

We can usually measure apparent brightness. Thus, we generally use this formula either to calculate luminosity when we know distance or to calculate distance when we know luminosity. We can solve the formula to find luminosity by multiplying both sides by $4\pi \times (\text{distance})^2$:

$$\text{luminosity} = 4\pi \times \text{apparent brightness} \times (\text{distance})^2$$

We can solve for the distance by dividing both sides of this version of the formula by ($4\pi \times$ apparent brightness) and then taking the square root of both sides:

$$\text{distance} = \sqrt{\frac{\text{luminosity}}{4\pi \times \text{apparent brightness}}}$$

*Example 1:* You measure the apparent brightness of a particular star to be $2.5 \times 10^{-10}$ watt/m². A parallax mea-

surement shows the star's distance to be 42 light-years, or about $4 \times 10^{17}$ meters. What is the luminosity of the star?

*Solution:* We simply substitute into the formula for the luminosity:

$$\text{luminosity} = 4\pi \times \left(2.5 \times 10^{-10} \frac{\text{watt}}{\text{m}^2}\right) \times (4 \times 10^{17} \text{ m})^2$$
$$= 5 \times 10^{26} \text{ watts}$$

The star's luminosity is $5 \times 10^{26}$ watts, or about 25% greater than the Sun's luminosity of $3.8 \times 10^{26}$ watts.

*Example 2:* Find the distance to a Sun-like star ($L = 3.8 \times 10^{26}$ watts) whose apparent brightness at Earth is $1.0 \times 10^{-10}$ watt/m².

*Solution:* We substitute into the formula for the distance:

$$\text{distance} = \sqrt{\frac{3.8 \times 10^{26} \text{ watts}}{4\pi \times \left(1.0 \times 10^{-10} \frac{\text{watt}}{\text{m}^2}\right)}} = 5.5 \times 10^{17} \text{ m}$$

The distance to the star is $5.5 \times 10^{17}$ meters, or about 59 light-years.

the street lamp (in units of watts/m$^2$), we can calculate its distance with the luminosity–distance formula.

An object such as a street lamp, for which we are likely to know the true luminosity, represents what astronomers call a **standard candle**. The term *standard candle* is meant to suggest a light source of a known, standard luminosity. Unlike light bulbs, astronomical objects do not come marked with wattage, so an astronomical object can serve as a standard candle only if we have some way of knowing its true luminosity without first measuring its apparent brightness and distance. Fortunately, many astronomical objects meet this requirement. For example, any star that is a twin of our Sun—that is, a main-sequence star with spectral type G2—should have about the same luminosity as the Sun. Thus, if we measure the apparent brightness of a Sun-like star, we can use the luminosity–distance formula to estimate its distance by assuming that it has the Sun's luminosity ($3.8 \times 10^{26}$ watts).

Beyond the few hundred light-years for which we can measure distances by parallax, standard candles are used in most cosmic distance measurements. These distance measurements always have some uncertainty, because no astronomical object is a perfect standard candle. The challenge of measuring astronomical distances comes down to the challenge of finding the objects that make the best standard candles. The more confidently we know an object's true luminosity, the less uncertain the distance we calculate with the luminosity–distance formula.

### Main-Sequence Fitting

We can use Sun-like stars as standard candles because we know that they are similar to the Sun and because we can measure the Sun's luminosity quite easily. However, Sun-like stars are relatively dim, and we cannot detect them at great distances. To measure distances beyond 1,000 light-years or so, we need brighter standard candles. An obvious first choice is to use brighter main-sequence stars. However, before we can use any main-sequence star as a standard candle, we must first have some way of knowing its true luminosity. Thus, we must follow two steps in order to use bright main-sequence stars as standard candles:

1. First, we identify a star cluster that is close enough for us to determine its distance by parallax and plot its H–R diagram. Because we know the distances to the cluster stars, we can use the luminosity–distance formula to establish their true luminosities from their apparent brightnesses.

2. Then we can look at stars in other clusters that are too far away for parallax measurements and measure their apparent brightnesses. If we assume that main-sequence stars in other clusters have the same true luminosities as their counterparts in the nearby cluster, we can calculate their distances with the luminosity–distance formula.

Twentieth-century astronomers laid the groundwork for this technique by calibrating the luminosities on a "standard" H–R diagram. This calibration relied largely on a single, nearby star cluster—the *Hyades Cluster* in the constellation Taurus. The Hyades distance is now known from its parallax, so the true luminosities of its stars can be calculated with the luminosity–distance formula. Astronomers find the distances to other star clusters by comparing the apparent brightnesses of their main-sequence stars with those in the Hyades Cluster and assuming that all main-sequence stars of the same color have the same luminosity (Figure 19.9). This technique of determining distances by comparing main sequences in different star clusters is called **main-sequence fitting.**

The Hyades Cluster does not contain stars of every spectral type, so building a complete, standard H–R diagram required that astronomers use main-sequence fitting to find the distances to many nearby star clusters until every spectral type was represented. Today, with the standard H–R diagram well understood, we can use main-sequence fitting to measure distances to any star cluster near enough for us to identify individual main-sequence stars.

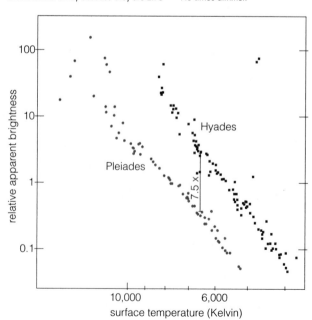

**FIGURE 19.9** Comparison of the apparent brightness of stars in the Hyades Cluster with those in the Pleiades Cluster shows that the Pleiades are 2.75 times farther away because they are $2.75^2 = 7.5$ times dimmer.

Note that, in principle, we need to measure the apparent brightness of only a single star in a cluster to determine the cluster's distance: Once we have determined the star's spectral type, we can use its expected true luminosity and the luminosity–distance formula to calculate its distance. This method is often used for measuring distances to isolated stars that are not members of clusters. The advantage of main-sequence fitting over using a single star in a cluster is that it reduces the uncertainty in the distance calculation. By comparing entire main sequences, we are essentially comparing many different luminosities at once and thus we achieve much more precise distance measurements.

### Cepheid Variables

Main-sequence fitting works well for measuring distances to star clusters throughout the Milky Way, but not for measuring distances to other galaxies. Most main-sequence stars are too faint to be seen in other galaxies, even with our largest telescopes. Instead, we need very bright stars to serve as standard candles for distance measurements beyond the Milky Way, and the most useful bright stars are the *Cepheid variables* [Section 15.5]. Recall that Cepheids are *pulsating variable stars* that follow a simple *period–luminosity relation:* The longer the time period between peaks in brightness, the greater the luminosity of the Cepheid variable star (Figure 19.10). All Cepheids of a particular period have very nearly the same luminosity (within about 10%), so Cepheids effectively scream out their true luminosities when we measure their periods. "Hey, everybody, my luminosity is 10,000 solar luminosities!" is how we would translate the message of a Cepheid variable whose brightness peaks every 30 days. Thus, Cepheid variables are the primary standard candles used to determine distances to nearby galaxies.

Cepheids also played a key role in the discovery that the Milky Way is only one of billions of galaxies in the universe. The only galaxies easily visible to the naked eye are the Andromeda Galaxy and the Large and Small Magellanic Clouds (which appear as little more than fuzzy, glowing blobs). By the mid-1700s, telescopes revealed that the Andromeda Galaxy was really a much larger spiral-shaped structure and that many similar spiral-shaped structures littered the sky. Many astronomers, who thought these spirals were spinning gas clouds inside our own galaxy, called them "spiral nebulae." Around the same time, some creative thinkers guessed the truth about "spiral nebulae"—that they are galaxies like the Milky Way. Here is a 1755 quote from German philosopher Immanuel Kant, as translated by Edwin Hubble in his book *The Realm of the Nebulae:*

> We see that scattered through space out to infinite distances, there exist similar systems of stars [i.e., galaxies], and that creation, in the whole extent of its infinite grandeur, is everywhere organized into systems whose members are in relation with one another. . . . A vast field lies open to discoveries and observation alone will give the key.

Following Kant, some later writers referred to galaxies as "island universes," because they appeared to be vast, self-contained communities of stars, isolated from one another by chasms of empty space. However, these views could not be conclusively established with the evidence available at the time. As

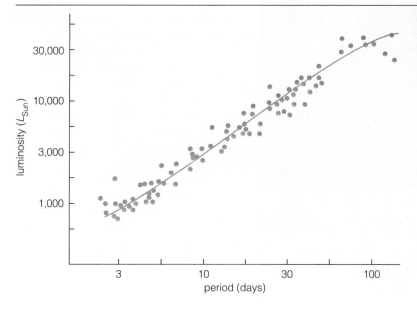

**FIGURE 19.10** Cepheid period–luminosity relation. Note that all Cepheids of a particular period have very nearly the same luminosity. (Cepheids actually come in two types with two different period–luminosity relations; the relation here is for Cepheids with heavy-element content similar to that of our Sun, or "Type I Cepheids.")

**b** The Hubble Space Telescope in orbit around Earth.

**a** Edwin Hubble at the Mount Wilson Observatory.

**FIGURE 19.11** Edwin Hubble and his namesake.

recently as the 1920s, many astronomers still held that the "spiral nebulae" were merely clouds of gas within the Milky Way—and therefore that the Milky Way represented the entire universe.

Edwin Hubble put this debate to rest in 1924 (Figure 19.11). Using the new, 100-inch telescope atop southern California's Mount Wilson (Figure 19.12)—the largest telescope in the world at the time—he discovered Cepheid variables in the Andromeda Galaxy by comparing photographs of the galaxy taken days apart. He used the period–luminosity relation to determine the luminosities of these stars and then used these luminosities in the luminosity–distance formula to compute their distances. (At the time, Hubble was unaware that there actually are two different types of Cepheids, depending on their heavy-element content, with each type obeying a different period–luminosity relation. As a result, he underestimated the true distance of the Cepheid variable stars in Andromeda by about half.)

Hubble's distance measurements proved that the Andromeda Galaxy sat far beyond the outer reaches of stars in the Milky Way, demonstrating that it is a separate galaxy. This single stroke of scientific discovery dramatically changed our view of the universe. Rather than inhabiting a universe that ended

**FIGURE 19.12** The 100-inch telescope on Mount Wilson, outside Los Angeles.

with the Milky Way, we suddenly knew that we live in just one among billions of galaxies.

## Hubble's Law

Hubble's determination of the distance to the Andromeda Galaxy assured him a permanent place in the history of astronomy, but he didn't stop there. Hubble proceeded to estimate the distances to many more galaxies. Within just a few years, Hubble made one of the most astonishing discoveries in the history of science: that the universe is expanding.

Astronomers had known since the 1910s that the spectra of most "spiral nebulae" tended to be *redshifted*. In other words, each of the emission and absorption lines in their spectra appeared at longer (redder) wavelengths than expected (Figure 19.13). Recall that redshifts occur when the object emitting the radiation is moving away from us [Section 6.5]. But, since Hubble had not yet proved that the "spiral nebulae" were distant galaxies, no one understood the true significance of their motions.

Following his discovery of Cepheids in Andromeda in 1924, Hubble and his coworkers spent the next few years busily measuring the redshifts of galaxies and estimating their distances. Because even Cepheids were too dim to be seen in most of these galaxies, Hubble needed brighter standard candles for his distance estimates. One of his favorite techniques was to assume that the brightest object in each galaxy—which he assumed to be a bright star—had about

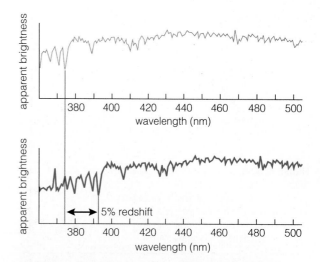

**FIGURE 19.13** Redshifted galaxy spectrum. The grey line shows the spectrum of light originally emitted by the galaxy. The blue line shows the spectrum we observe, which is shifted by 5% to longer (redder) wavelengths, indicating that this galaxy is moving away from ours at 5% of the speed of light.

the same luminosity, so he could use these objects as standard candles.

In 1929, Hubble announced his conclusion: The more distant a galaxy, the greater its redshift and hence the faster it moves away from us (Figure 19.14). Hubble's original assertion was based on an amazingly small sample of galaxies. Even more incredibly, he had grossly underestimated the luminosities of his

## Mathematical Insight 19.2   Redshift

The *redshift* of an object is the difference between the observed wavelength ($\lambda_{observed}$) of a line in the object's spectrum and the wavelength the line would have if the object were standing still ($\lambda_{rest}$). (The Greek letter $\lambda$ is usually used to stand for wavelength.) Redshifts are best expressed as fractional differences:

$$\text{redshift} = z = \frac{\lambda_{observed} - \lambda_{rest}}{\lambda_{rest}}$$

We use the letter $z$ to represent redshift. The value of $z$ for every line in a moving object's spectrum is the same.

For a relatively nearby galaxy, with a redshift $z$ that is much less than 1, we can find its velocity away from us with the following simple formula:

$$v = c \times z$$

where $c = 3.0 \times 10^5$ km/s is the speed of light. (A more complex formula can be used when the redshift is *not* much less than 1, but as we discuss later in this chapter, the idea of speed becomes hard to define for such distant galaxies.)

*Example:* Two emission lines from hydrogen in the visible spectrum have rest wavelengths of 656.3 nm and 486.1 nm. Suppose you see this pair of hydrogen emission lines at

662.9 nm and 491.0 nm in the spectrum of a distant galaxy. What is the redshift of the galaxy? How fast is it moving away from us?

*Solution:* For the two different lines, we find a redshift or $z$ of:

656.3-nm line:   $z = \dfrac{662.9 \text{ nm} - 656.3 \text{ nm}}{656.3 \text{ nm}} = 0.010$

486.1-nm line:   $z = \dfrac{491.0 \text{ nm} - 486.1 \text{ nm}}{486.1 \text{ nm}} = 0.010$

The redshift of the galaxy is $z = 0.010$. Note that, as we should expect, we find the same redshift from either line. (Astronomers generally try to measure the redshifts of at least two lines in any particular spectrum to make sure that they aren't mistaking a misidentified line for a shifted line.) Because this redshift is much less than 1, we can use the simple formula to find the galaxy's speed:

$$v = c \times z = (3.0 \times 10^5 \text{ km/s}) \times 0.01 = 3,000 \text{ km/s}$$

The galaxy is receding from us at 3,000 km/s, equivalent to 1% of the speed of light.

**FIGURE 19.14** Hubble's original velocity–distance diagram. Although Hubble underestimated the true galactic distances, he still discovered the general trend (represented by the straight lines) in which more distant galaxies move away from us at higher speeds. He determined the galaxy speeds by measuring redshifts in the galaxy spectra.

standard candles. The "brightest stars" he had been using as standard candles were really entire *clusters* of bright stars. Fortunately, Hubble was both bold and lucky. Subsequent studies of much larger samples of galaxies showed that they are indeed receding from us, but they are even farther away than Hubble thought.

We can express the idea that more distant galaxies move away from us faster with a very simple formula, now known as **Hubble's law**:

$$v = H_0 \times d$$

where *v* stands for velocity (sometimes called a *recession velocity*), *d* stands for distance, and $H_0$ (pronounced "H-naught") is a number called **Hubble's constant**. Astronomers generally quote the value of Hubble's constant in strange-sounding units of *kilometers per second per megaparsec* (km/s/Mpc). (Recall that 1 parsec [pc] ≈ 3.26 light-years, so 1 megaparsec [Mpc] ≈ 3.26 million light-years.)

To make sense of these units, suppose Hubble's constant had a value of $H_0 = 100$ km/s/Mpc. Then, according to Hubble's law, we would expect a galaxy located at distance *d* = 10 Mpc (32.6 million light-years) to be moving away from us at a speed of:

$$v = H_0 \times d = 100 \, \frac{km/s}{Mpc} \times 10 \, Mpc = 1{,}000 \text{ km/s}$$

Similarly, a galaxy located at a distance *d* = 11 Mpc (36 million light-years) would be moving away at a speed of:

$$v = H_0 \times d = 100 \, \frac{km/s}{Mpc} \times 11 \, Mpc = 1{,}100 \text{ km/s}$$

In other words, a value of $H_0 = 100$ km/s/Mpc would mean that, for each additional megaparsec of distance, a galaxy would be moving away from us at a speed that is greater by 100 km/s.

**TIME OUT TO THINK** *Suppose the value of $H_0$ is 50 km/s/Mpc (rather than 100 km/s/Mpc). In that case, what speed would Hubble's law predict for a galaxy located at a distance of 10 Mpc? Explain.*

Dividing both sides of Hubble's law by $H_0$ puts it into a form in which we can use a galaxy's velocity to determine its distance:

$$d = \frac{v}{H_0}$$

In principle, applying this law is one of the best ways to determine distances to galaxies. We find the velocity of a distant galaxy from its redshift; then we divide this velocity by $H_0$ to find its distance. However, we encounter two major practical difficulties in finding distances in this way:

1. Galaxies do not obey Hubble's law perfectly because they can have velocities relative to one another caused by gravitational tugs that Hubble's law does not take into account.

2. Even when galaxies do obey Hubble's law well, the distances we find with it are only as accurate as our best measurement of Hubble's constant.

The first problem makes Hubble's law difficult to use for nearby galaxies. Within the Local Group, for example, Hubble's law does not work at all: The galaxies in the Local Group are gravitationally bound together with the Milky Way and therefore are *not* moving away from us in accord with Hubble's law. However, Hubble's law works fairly well for more distant galaxies: The recession speeds of galaxies at large distances are so great that any motions caused by the gravitational tugs of neighboring galaxies are tiny in comparison.

The second problem means that, even for distant galaxies, we can know only *relative* distances until we pin down the true value of $H_0$. For example, Hubble's law tells us that a galaxy moving away from us at 20,000 km/s is twice as far away as one moving at 10,000 km/s, but we can determine the actual distances of the two galaxies only if we know $H_0$. The quest to measure $H_0$ accurately is one of the main missions of the Hubble Space Telescope.

**TIME OUT TO THINK** *Suppose a galaxy is moving away from us at 10,000 km/s. Use Hubble's law in the form* $d = v/H_0$ *to calculate its distance (in Mpc) if* $H_0 = 100$ *km/s/Mpc. What is its distance if* $H_0 = 50$ *km/s/Mpc?*

### Seeking Distant Standards

The process of measuring $H_0$ is rather like the process of calibrating a scale. We can calibrate a scale by, for example, making sure that it reads 10 pounds when we place a 10-pound weight on it, 20 pounds when we place a 20-pound weight on it, and so on. Once it is properly calibrated, we can use it to weigh objects whose weights are not known in advance. In a similar way, astronomers calibrate Hubble's law by making sure that it gives correct distances for galaxies whose distances we already know from applying some other method. However, until recently, telescopic technology was insufficient for measuring distances accurately by other methods: We simply were unable to detect good standard candles, such as Cepheids, in galaxies much beyond the Local Group.

The superior resolving power of the Hubble Space Telescope now enables us to measure the periods and apparent brightnesses of Cepheid variable stars in galaxies as distant as the Virgo Cluster of galaxies (Figure 19.15), about 55 million light-years away. This distance may sound quite far, but it is still near enough that gravitational tugs cause noticeable deviations from Hubble's law. Nevertheless, these Cepheids can help us by enabling us to calibrate even brighter standard candles, such as supernovae.

Recall that white dwarf supernovae are thought to represent exploding white dwarf stars that have reached the 1.4-solar-mass limit

and should all have nearly the same luminosity [Section 17.2]. Thus, white dwarf supernovae should be good standard candles—once we know their true luminosities. Although only a few supernovae have

**FIGURE 19.15** Images from the Hubble Space Telescope project to measure Hubble's constant.

**a** Galaxy M 100 in the Virgo Cluster.

**b** One of the Cepheid variable stars in M 100 varying in brightness over several weeks. Measurements of Cepheid variables place M 100 at about 56 million light-years from Earth.

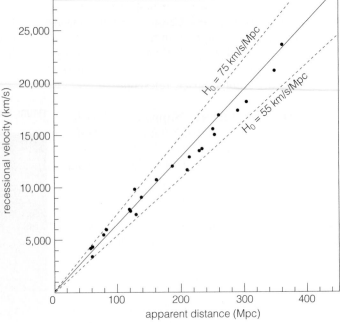

**FIGURE 19.16** White dwarf supernovae can be used as standard candles to establish Hubble's law out to very large distances. The points on this figure show the apparent distances of white dwarf supernovae and the recessional velocities of the galaxies in which they exploded. The fact that these points all fall close to the solid line demonstrates that these supernovae are good standard candles. Calibrating the luminosities of selected white dwarf supernovae using Cepheid variables indicates that Hubble's constant lies between 55 and 75 km/s/Mpc.

been detected during the past century in galaxies within about 50 million light-years of the Milky Way, astronomers have kept careful records of these events. Today, we can look back at the light curves for these events to determine which of these past supernovae were white dwarf supernovae (as opposed to massive star supernovae).

Once we have identified a white dwarf supernova in the historical records, we can look for Cepheids in the same galaxy. We then use the Cepheids as standard candles to determine the distance to the galaxy in which the supernova occurred. Once we know the galaxy's distance, we can use the luminosity–distance formula to determine the supernova's true luminosity. This technique has allowed researchers using the Hubble Space Telescope to determine the true luminosities of several white dwarf supernovae. As expected, they are all about the same, and we can now use them as reliable standard candles (Figure 19.16). Because white dwarf supernovae are so bright—about 10 billion solar luminosities at their peak—we can use them to measure distances to galaxies billions of light-years away (Figure 19.17).

Although white dwarf supernovae are excellent standard candles, most galaxies have not hosted supernovae during the time that humans have been watching them. Thus, it would be useful if we could use galaxies themselves as standard candles. Astronomers have discovered a close relationship between the total luminosities of spiral galaxies and the rotation speeds of their disks: The faster a spiral galaxy's rotation speed, the more luminous it is (Figure 19.18). This relationship, called the **Tully–Fisher relation** (after its discoverers), holds because both luminosity and rotation speed depend on the galaxy's mass. A galaxy's luminosity depends on the number of stars it contains, which is related to the total amount of matter within it, and the total amount of matter determines a galaxy's rotation speed [Section 18.4].

We can measure the rotation speed of a spiral galaxy's disk by, for example, comparing the Doppler shifts of the portion of the disk rotating toward us and the portion rotating away from us. Once we have

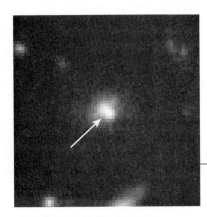

**FIGURE 19.17** Photo of a white dwarf supernova in a galaxy halfway across the observable universe, recorded in March 1996 by the Hubble Space Telescope.

measured the rotation speed of a spiral galaxy, the Tully–Fisher relation tells us its true luminosity, which makes the galaxy itself a standard candle that we can use to determine its distance.

Despite the new calibrations of Hubble's law made possible by the Hubble Space Telescope, some uncertainties remain. These uncertainties should decrease as we measure the distances to more and more galaxies. As of 2001, the true value of $H_0$ appears to be somewhere between 55 and 75 km/s/Mpc.

### Summary: The Distance Chain

Figure 19.19 summarizes the chain of measurements that allows us to determine ever-greater distances. Note that, with each link in the distance chain, uncertainties become somewhat greater. Thus, although

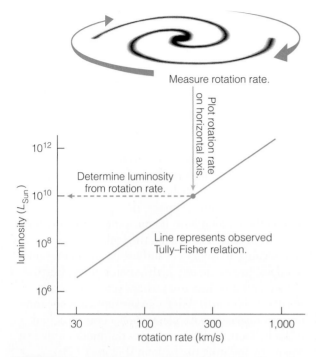

**FIGURE 19.18** A schematic diagram of the Tully–Fisher relation. (The precise relation differs among different subclasses of spiral galaxies.)

we know the Earth–Sun distance at the base of the chain extremely accurately, distances to the farthest reaches of the observable universe remain uncertain by about 20%.

- **Radar ranging**: We measure distances within the solar system by bouncing radio waves off planets. Then, with the aid of some geometry, we use these radar measurements to determine the Earth–Sun distance.

- **Parallax**: We measure the distances to nearby stars by observing how their positions change,

relative to the background stars, as the Earth moves around the Sun. These distances thus rely on our knowledge of the Earth–Sun distance.

- **Main-sequence fitting**: We know the distance to the Hyades Cluster in our Milky Way Galaxy through parallax. Comparing the observed intensities of its main-sequence stars to the intensities of those in other clusters gives us the distances to these other star clusters in our galaxy.

- **Cepheid variables**: By studying Cepheids in star clusters with distances measured by main-sequence fitting, we learn the precise period–luminosity relation for Cepheids. When we find a Cepheid in a more distant star cluster or galaxy, we can determine its true luminosity by measuring the period between its peaks in brightness and then use this true luminosity to determine the distance.

- **Distant standards**: By measuring distances to relatively nearby galaxies with Cepheids, we learn the true luminosities of white dwarf supernovae and the Tully–Fisher relation between the luminosities and rotation speeds of spiral galaxies. Thus, supernovae and entire galaxies become useful standard candles for measuring great distances in the universe.

- **Hubble's law**: Distances measured to galaxies with white dwarf supernovae and the Tully–Fisher relation allow us to calibrate Hubble's law and measure Hubble's constant, $H_0$. Once we know $H_0$, we can determine a galaxy's distance directly from its redshift.

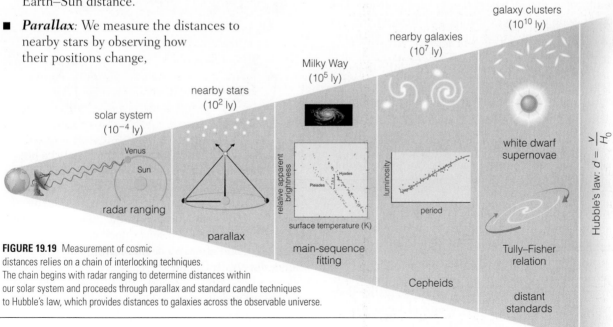

**FIGURE 19.19** Measurement of cosmic distances relies on a chain of interlocking techniques. The chain begins with radar ranging to determine distances within our solar system and proceeds through parallax and standard candle techniques to Hubble's law, which provides distances to galaxies across the observable universe.

## 19.4 Measuring Cosmic Ages

The ages of the galaxies we see in deep images of the universe, such as Figure 19.1, are directly related to their distances. Remember that light travels at a finite speed. Light from the most distant galaxies began its journey to Earth when the universe was a small fraction of its current age. We are therefore viewing these galaxies as they were when they were young, and the light we are detecting is ancient. Because a deep image records galaxies at many different distances, it contains information about galaxies of many different ages. For example, we see galaxies 1 billion light-years away as they were 1 billion years ago and galaxies 2 billion light-years away as they were two billion years ago. The history of galaxies across the universe is therefore encoded in such images, but to decipher the clues they hold we need to know how the universe's history is related to its expansion. The intimate relationship between the universe's expansion rate and its age helps us age-date galaxies throughout the observable universe.

### *Universal Expansion*

The fact that galaxies all across the universe are moving away from one another in accordance with Hubble's law implies that galaxies must have been closer together in the past. Tracing this convergence back in time, we reason that all the matter in the observable universe started very close together and that the entire universe came into being at a single moment. Ever since that moment the universe has been expanding, and all the while the gravitational pull of each galaxy on every other galaxy has been working to slow the expansion rate. In the densest regions of the universe, gravity has won out over expansion. The Local Group no longer expands, nor do other clusters of galaxies, but the expansion continues on all larger scales.

Visualizing this expansion requires a little thought. Upon first hearing about the expansion of the universe, most people are tempted to think of the universe as a ball of galaxies expanding into a void. This impression is mistaken. The universe expands, but as far as we can tell it is not expanding into empty space. Each point moves away from every other point, and no matter where you are located the distribution of galaxies around you will look more or less the same. (This idea, called the *Cosmological Principle*, states that matter in the universe is evenly distributed on scales much larger than superclusters of galaxies. It is impossible to prove that the Cosmological Principle holds outside the observable regions of the universe, but within the observable universe matter does appear to be distributed more evenly as we look on increasingly larger scales [Section 21.5].)

How can the universe be expanding if it's not expanding *into* anything? Back in Chapter 1, we likened the expanding universe to a baking raisin cake [Section 1.3], but a cake has a center and edges that grow into empty space as it bakes. A better analogy is something that can expand but that has no center and no edges. The surface of a balloon can fit the bill, as can an infinite surface like a flat sheet of rubber that extends to infinity in all directions. Because it's hard to visualize infinity, let's use a balloon as our model of the expanding universe. Such a model requires that we interpret the balloon's *surface* as representing all three dimensions of space; the spaces inside and outside the balloon have no meaning in this model. Aside from this mental leap, the balloon model works well because its spherical surface has no center and no edges, just as no city is the center of the Earth's surface and no edges exist where you could walk or sail off the Earth. We can represent clusters and groups of galaxies with plastic polka dots attached to the balloon, and we can make our model universe expand by inflating the balloon (Figure 19.20).

**FIGURE 19.20** As the balloon expands, dots uniformly move apart.

As the real universe expands, the distances between clusters of galaxies grow. However, the clusters themselves do not grow because gravity binds each cluster's galaxies together. In a similar way, as the surface of the balloon expands, the polka dots move apart, but the dots themselves don't grow. Suppose that, 1 second after you begin blowing into the balloon, dots A, B, C, and D are spaced 1 cm apart along a line. After 2 seconds, the distances between neighboring dots grow to 2 cm, and after 3 seconds to 3 cm. If you recorded the distances of the other dots from dot B once each second, your observations would look like this:

**Measuring Distances from Dot B**

| Time | Dot A Distance | Dot B Distance | Dot C Distance | Dot D Distance |
|---|---|---|---|---|
| 1 s | 1 cm | 0 cm | 1 cm | 2 cm |
| 2 s | 2 cm | 0 cm | 2 cm | 4 cm |
| 3 s | 3 cm | 0 cm | 3 cm | 6 cm |

Miniature scientists on dot B might be tempted to think that they are at the center of some explosion. After all, they see every other dot moving away from them, and the farthest dots move fastest. However, miniature scientists on dot C would record a very similar set of observations:

**Measuring Distances from Dot C**

| Time | Dot A Distance | Dot B Distance | Dot C Distance | Dot D Distance |
|---|---|---|---|---|
| 1 s | 2 cm | 1 cm | 0 cm | 1 cm |
| 2 s | 4 cm | 2 cm | 0 cm | 2 cm |
| 3 s | 6 cm | 3 cm | 0 cm | 3 cm |

The miniature scientists on dot C would also be tempted to think that they are at the center of some explosion. Eventually, the miniature scientists would realize that the balloon itself is expanding. Just as we cannot point to a single spot on a balloon's surface and say "the balloon is expanding from here," we cannot identify a single point in space from which the universe is expanding. Galaxies surround each point in the universe on all sides and move away from that point in exactly the same way.

## Hubble's Constant and Age

To see how the universe's expansion rate is related to its age, let's return to the miniature scientists living on dot B. Three seconds after the balloon began to expand, they would measure the following:

Dot A is 3 cm away and moving at 1 cm/s.

Dot C is 3 cm away and moving at 1 cm/s.

Dot D is 6 cm away and moving at 2 cm/s.

They could summarize these observations as follows: *Every dot is moving away from our home with a speed that is 1 cm/s for each 3 cm of distance.* And because the expansion of the balloon is uniform, scientists

living on any other dot would come to the same conclusion. Each scientist living on the balloon would determine that the following formula relates the distances and velocities of other dots on the balloon:

$$v = \left(\frac{1 \text{ cm/s}}{3 \text{ cm}}\right) \times d \quad \text{or} \quad v = \left(\frac{1}{3 \text{ s}}\right) \times d$$

where $v$ and $d$ are the velocity and distance of any dot, respectively.

**TIME OUT TO THINK** *Confirm that this formula gives the correct values for the speeds of dots C and D, as seen from dot B, 3 seconds after the balloon began expanding. How fast would a dot located 9 cm from dot B move, according to the scientists on dot B?*

If the miniature scientists think of their balloon as a bubble, they might call the number relating distance to velocity—the term $\frac{1}{3 \text{ s}}$ in the above formula—the "bubble constant." An especially insightful miniature scientist might flip over the "bubble constant" and find that it is exactly equal to the time since the balloon started expanding. That is, the "bubble constant" of $\frac{1}{3 \text{ s}}$ tells them that the balloon has been expanding for 3 seconds. Perhaps you see where we are heading.

Just as the inverse of the "bubble constant" tells the miniature scientists that their balloon has been expanding for 3 seconds, the inverse of the Hubble constant, or $1/H_0$, tells us something about how long our universe has been expanding. The "bubble constant" for the balloon depends on when it is measured, but it is always equal to 1/(time since balloon started expanding). Similarly, the Hubble constant actually changes with time but stays roughly equal to 1/(age of the universe). We call it a constant because it is the same at all locations in the universe. Moreover, its value does not change noticeably on the time scale of human civilization.

Current estimates based on the value of Hubble's constant put the age of the universe between about 12 and 18 billion years. To derive a more precise value for the universe's age, we need to know whether the expansion has been speeding up or slowing down over time, a question we will examine more closely in Chapter 21. If the gravitational pull of each galaxy on every other galaxy has significantly slowed the expansion rate, then the universe's age is somewhat less than $1/H_0$. If some mysterious force has accelerated the expansion rate, then the universe's age is somewhat more than $1/H_0$. Intriguingly, the oldest stars in globular clusters appear to be somewhere between 12 and 16 billion years old [Section 15.6]. These stars could not possibly have existed before the birth of the universe, so our age estimates based on Hubble's constant probably aren't far off the mark. The best available evidence as of 2001 suggests that the universe is indeed somewhere between 12 and 16 billion years old. If you are reading this book at a much later date, it is likely that the age of the universe is known within more tightly constrained limits.

### Lookback Time

All the galaxies we observe must be younger than the universe itself. Pictures of the farthest galaxies show us how galaxies looked when they were only a few billion years old; pictures of the closest show galaxies nearly as old as the universe. However, when we try to specify exactly how the distances of galaxies relate to their ages, we run into complications.

Imagine photons of light from a supernova in a distant galaxy traveling toward us at the speed of light. If the supernova occurred in a galaxy 400 million light-years away, we are seeing a supernova that

occurred 400 million years ago. But what do we mean by the distance of 400 million light-years? Because the universe is expanding, the distance between Earth and the supernova is greater today than it was at the time of the supernova event. Are we talking about the distance from the supernova to Earth when the supernova exploded, or are we referring to the distance between the supernova and Earth when the light arrived here? Do we mean that photons traveled through 400 million light-years of space? When we start trying to measure large distances through the universe, our everyday notions of space-only or time-only become inadequate. The path light takes from the supernova to us is really a trajectory through *both* space *and* time, so we must think in terms of *spacetime*.

Figure 19.21 shows a *spacetime diagram* for the supernova and our observation of it [Section S3.3]. The horizontal axis shows distance (through space) from the Milky Way, and the vertical axis shows time. Photons of light from the supernova travel toward us at the speed of light, starting at the place and time of the supernova explosion. By the time these photons reach us, the galaxy in which the supernova occurred has moved farther away from us. By looking along the time axis, we see that it has taken 400 million years for the photons of light to reach us. We call this the **lookback time** to the supernova. In other words, a distant object's lookback time is the difference between the current age of the universe and the age of the universe when the light left the object. This quantity, which essentially combines both space and

---

## Mathematical Insight 19.3
## Age from Hubble's Constant

As discussed in the text, the reciprocal of Hubble's constant, or $1/H_0$, is directly related to the age of the universe. In particular, it tells us what the age of the universe would be *if* the expansion rate has remained constant since the beginning. We can calculate this age from the measured value of $H_0$. The best current estimates put $H_0$ between 55 and 75 km/s/Mpc, so let's take the average and assume that $H_0 = 65$ km/s/Mpc.

The easiest way to find the reciprocal of $H_0$ is to first rewrite it in more convenient units. A megaparsec is about 3.26 million light-years, so we can write our value of Hubble's constant as:

$$H_0 = 65 \frac{\text{km/s}}{\text{Mpc}} = \frac{65 \text{ km/s}}{(3.26 \times 10^6 \text{ ly})}$$

Because a light-year is the speed of light ($c = 300{,}000$ km/s) times 1 year, we can further rewrite this value of Hubble's constant as:

$$H_0 = \frac{65 \text{ km/s}}{(3.26 \times 10^6) \times (3 \times 10^5 \text{ km/s}) \times 1 \text{ yr}}$$

Taking the reciprocal, we find:

$$\frac{1}{H_0} = \frac{(3.26 \times 10^6) \times (3 \times 10^5) \times 1 \text{ yr}}{65}$$

$$= \frac{9.78 \times 10^{11} \times 1 \text{ yr}}{65}$$

$$\approx 1.5 \times 10^{10} \text{ yr}$$

The reciprocal is $1.5 \times 10^{10}$ yr, or 15 billion years. In other words, if the expansion rate has never changed, a value of Hubble's constant of $H_0 = 65$ km/s/Mpc implies that the universe is 15 billion years old.

---

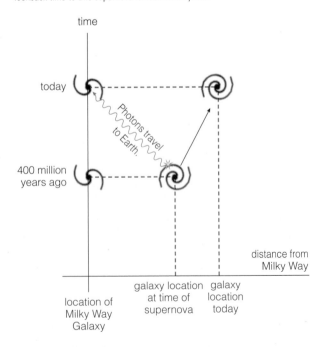

**FIGURE 19.21** A spacetime diagram for a supernova in a distant galaxy. The lookback time to this supernova is 400 million years.

**FIGURE 19.22** As the universe expands, photon wavelengths stretch like the wavy lines on this expanding balloon.

time, is much more meaningful than an actual distance when we discuss objects that are moving away from us with the expansion of the universe.

**TIME OUT TO THINK** *Explain why there is no question about meaning when we talk about distances to objects within the Local Group, but distances become difficult to define when we talk about objects much farther away.*

An object's lookback time is directly related to its redshift. We have seen that the redshifts of galaxies tell us how quickly they are moving away from us. In the context of an expanding universe, redshifts have an additional, more fundamental interpretation. Let's return one final time to the universe on the balloon. Suppose you draw wavy lines on the balloon's surface to represent light waves. As the balloon inflates, these wavy lines stretch out, and their wavelengths increase (Figure 19.22). This stretching closely resembles what happens to photons in an expanding universe. The expansion of the universe stretches out all the photons within it, shifting them to longer, redder wavelengths. We call this effect a **cosmological redshift**.

In a sense, we have a choice when we interpret the redshift of a distant galaxy: We can think of the redshift either as being caused by the Doppler effect as the galaxy moves away from us or as being caused by a photon-stretching, cosmological redshift. However, as we look to very distant galaxies, the ambiguity in the meaning of *distance* also makes it difficult to specify precisely what we mean by a galaxy's *speed*. Thus, it becomes preferable to interpret the redshift as being due to photon stretching in an expanding universe. From this perspective, it is better to think of space itself as expanding, carrying the galaxies along for the ride, than to think of the galaxies as projectiles flying through a static universe. The cosmological redshift of a galaxy thus tells us how much space has expanded during the lookback time to that galaxy.

---

## Common Misconceptions: Beyond the Horizon

Perhaps you're thinking there must be something beyond the cosmological horizon. After all, the horizon encircles more and more matter with each passing second. This new matter had to come from somewhere, didn't it? The problem with this reasoning is that the cosmological horizon, unlike a horizon on the Earth, is a boundary in *time*, not in space. At any one moment, in whatever direction we look, the cosmological horizon lies at the beginning of time and encompasses a certain volume of the universe. At the next moment, the cosmological horizon still lies at the beginning of time, but it encompasses a slightly larger volume. However, that does not mean that the matter at the outskirts of the observable universe used to lie "beyond the horizon." When we peer into the distant universe, we are looking back in both space and time. We cannot look "past the horizon" because we cannot look back to a time before the universe began.

### The Horizon of the Universe

What lies beyond the youngest, most distant galaxies? When we began our discussion of the expanding universe, we stressed that the universe does not have an edge. Yet the universe does have a horizon, a place beyond which we cannot see. This **cosmological horizon** is a boundary in time, not in space. It exists because we cannot see back to a time before the universe began. For example, if the universe is 14 billion years old, then no object can have lookback time greater than 14 billion years. Thus, the lookback time to the cosmological horizon is equal to the age of the universe.

For reasons we'll discuss in Chapter 22, we cannot see matter at the cosmological horizon, but if we could we would see it as it looked at the very beginning of time. One year from now, we would see this same matter as it looked 1 year after the beginning—which means the horizon will have moved somewhat farther from us. In fact, our horizon is continually expanding outward at the speed of light. Our observable universe therefore grows larger in radius by 1 light-year with each passing year.

Our quest to study galaxies and measure their distances has brought us to the very limits of the observable universe. The galaxies in Figure 19.1 at the beginning of this chapter extend from relatively nearby almost all the way to the horizon. Now it is time to examine what these galaxies have been doing for the past 10 billion or more years—the topic of our next chapter.

## THE BIG PICTURE

The picture could hardly get any bigger than it has in this chapter. We have reached the limits of the observable universe in both space and time. If your head hasn't already exploded, try to make sure that these "big picture" ideas fit inside:

- The universe is filled with galaxies that come in a variety of shapes and sizes. The most fundamental distinctions in galaxies are between *disk components*, with stars of many ages and abundant gas for new star formation, and *spheroidal components*, which contain old stars and little gas. Both components are present in spiral galaxies, while elliptical galaxies generally lack significant disks.

- Our measurements of the distances to faraway galaxies rely on a chain of distance measurements that begins with the Earth–Sun distance measured with the aid of radar ranging and continues with parallax and various standard-candle techniques. The distance chain allowed Hubble to measure distances to galaxies and thus to discover Hubble's law and the expansion of the universe.

- When we say that the universe is expanding, we mean that *space itself* is expanding. The universe is not expanding "into" anything.

- As the universe expands, it carries the galaxies within it along for the ride. From the current expansion rate and from estimates of the overall strength of gravity in the universe and the ages of the oldest stars, we infer that the universe is somewhere between about 12 and 16 billion years old. The galaxies themselves must be somewhat younger than this.

- When we look out into the universe, we are looking back in time. Just short of the cosmological horizon, we are seeing the universe shortly after the moment of creation. We can see no farther.

## Review Questions

1. Distinguish between *spiral galaxies* and *elliptical galaxies* in terms of their shapes and colors. What are *irregular galaxies*?

2. Distinguish between the *disk component* and the *spheroidal component* of a spiral galaxy. Which component includes the galaxy's spiral arms? Which includes its bulge? Which includes its halo?

3. How does a barred spiral galaxy differ from a normal spiral galaxy? How does a lenticular galaxy differ from a normal spiral galaxy?

4. What is a *group* of galaxies? What is a *cluster* of galaxies?

5. What is the major difference between an elliptical galaxy and a spiral galaxy? How is an elliptical galaxy similar to the halo of the Milky Way?

6. Among large galaxies in the universe, about what proportion are spiral or lenticular? Elliptical? What do we mean by a *dwarf elliptical galaxy*?

7. What do we mean by a *standard candle*? Briefly explain how, once we identify an object as a standard candle, we can use the luminosity–distance formula to find its distance.

8. Why are Cepheid variables good standard candles? Briefly explain how Edwin Hubble used his discovery of a Cepheid in Andromeda to prove that the "spiral nebulae" were actually entire galaxies.

9. Describe how we can use *Hubble's law* to determine the distance to a distant galaxy. What practical difficulties limit the use of Hubble's law for measuring distances?

10. What makes white dwarf supernovae good standard candles? Briefly describe how we have learned the true luminosities of white dwarf supernovae.

11. What is our current best estimate of *Hubble's constant*? Summarize all the links in the distance chain that allow us to estimate distances to the farthest reaches of the universe.

12. In what ways is the surface of an expanding balloon a good analogy to the universe? In what ways is this analogy limited? Explain why a miniature scientist living in a polka dot on the balloon would observe all other dots to be moving away, with more distant dots moving away faster.

13. What is a *lookback time*? Why does it make more sense to talk about a distant object in terms of its lookback time than in terms of its distance?

14. What do we mean by a *cosmological redshift*? How does our interpretation of a distant galaxy's redshift differ if we think of it as a cosmological redshift rather than as a Doppler shift?

15. What is the *cosmological horizon*? Why can't we see past it?

## Discussion Questions

1. *Cosmology and Philosophy.* One hundred years ago, many scientists believed that the universe was infinite and eternal, with no beginning and no end. When Einstein first developed his general theory of relativity, he found it predicted that the universe should be either expanding or contracting. He believed so strongly in an eternal and unchanging universe that he modified the theory, a modification he would later call his "greatest blunder." Why do you think Einstein and others assumed that the universe had no beginning? Do you think that a universe with a definite beginning in time, some 15 billion or so years ago, has any important philosophical implications? Explain.

2. *Tired Light.* Hubble's law relates the redshifts of galaxies directly to their distances. The overwhelming majority of astronomers believe that these redshifts arise from the Doppler effect, an easily measurable and well-understood phenomenon that can be measured in the laboratory. However, a few astronomers argue that there might be some other explanation for galaxy redshifts based on physical effects that occur only on vast scales. For example, perhaps photons somehow get "tired" and lose energy as they cross immense intergalactic distances. Which explanation for redshifts do you prefer? Why is considering alternative explanations important in science?

## Problems

*Sensible Statements?* For **problems 1–8**, decide whether the statement is sensible and explain why it is or is not.

1. If you want to find elliptical galaxies, you'll have better luck looking in clusters of galaxies than elsewhere in the universe.

2. Cepheid variables make good standard candles because they all have exactly the same luminosity.

3. If the standard candles you are using are less luminous than you think they are, then the distances you determine from them will be too small.

4. Galaxy A is moving away from me twice as fast as Galaxy B. That probably means it's twice as far away.

5. The lookback time to the Andromeda Galaxy is about 2.5 million years.

6. I'd love to live in one of the galaxies at the very edge of the universe, because I want to see the black void into which the universe is expanding.

7. We can't see galaxies beyond the cosmological horizon because they are moving away from us faster than the speed of light.

8. We see distant galaxies as they were when the universe was younger, and any people living in those galaxies today would see the Milky Way as it was when the universe was younger.

9. *Distance Measurements.* The techniques astronomers use to measure distances are not so different from the ones you use every day. Describe how parallax measurements are similar to your visual depth perception. Describe how standard-candle measurements are similar to the way you estimate the distance to an oncoming car at night.

10. *Cepheids as Standard Candles.* Suppose you are observing Cepheids in a nearby galaxy. You observe one Cepheid with a period of 8 days between peaks in brightness, and another with a period of 35 days. Estimate the luminosity of each star. Explain how you arrived at your estimate. (*Hint:* See Figure 19.10.)

*11. *Counting Galaxies.* Estimate how many galaxies are pictured in Figure 19.1. Explain the method you used to arrive at this estimate. This picture shows about 1/30,000,000 of the sky, so multiply your estimate by 30,000,000 to obtain an estimate of how many galaxies like these fill the entire sky.

*12. *Cepheids in M 100.* Scientists using the Hubble Space Telescope have observed Cepheids in the galaxy M 100. Here are actual data for three Cepheids in M 100:

- Cepheid 1: luminosity = $3.9 \times 10^{30}$ watts, brightness = $9.3 \times 10^{-19}$ watt/m$^2$.
- Cepheid 2: luminosity = $1.2 \times 10^{30}$ watts, brightness = $3.8 \times 10^{-19}$ watt/m$^2$.
- Cepheid 3: luminosity = $2.5 \times 10^{30}$ watts, brightness = $8.7 \times 10^{-19}$ watt/m$^2$.

Compute the distance to M 100 with data from each of the three Cepheids. Do all three distance computations agree? Based on your results, estimate the uncertainty in the distance you have found.

*13. *Redshift and Hubble's Law.* Imagine that you have obtained spectra for several galaxies and have measured the observed wavelength of a hydrogen emission line that has a rest wavelength of 656.3 nm. Here are your results:

- Galaxy 1: Observed wavelength of hydrogen line is 659.6 nm.
- Galaxy 2: Observed wavelength of hydrogen line is 664.7 nm.
- Galaxy 3: Observed wavelength of hydrogen line is 679.2 nm.

a. Calculate the redshift, $z$, for each of the three galaxies.

b. From their redshifts, calculate the speed at which each of the galaxies is moving away from us. Give your answers both in km/s and as a fraction of the speed of light.

c. Estimate the distance to each galaxy from Hubble's law. Assume that $H_0 = 65$ km/s/Mpc.

## Web Projects

Find useful links for Web projects on the text Web site.

1. *Galaxy Gallery.* Many fine images of galaxies are available on the Web. Collect several images of each major type and build a galaxy gallery of your own. Supply a descriptive paragraph about each galaxy.

2. *Hubble's Constant.* Measurements of Hubble's constant are rapidly growing more reliable. Find at least two measurements of $H_0$ determined in the past 2 years. Describe how these values were measured. What is the quoted uncertainty of each? By how much do they differ?

3. *Greatest Lookback Time.* Look for recent discoveries of objects with the largest lookback times (or redshifts). What is the current record for the most distant known object? What kind of object is it?

*Reality provides us with facts so romantic that imagination itself could add nothing to them.*

JULES VERNE

# CHAPTER 20
# Galaxy Evolution

The spectacle of galaxies strewn like beautiful islands across the universe invites us to ponder their origins. Some galaxies have majestic spiral arms, some are elliptical, and some are irregular. What processes sculpted them into their present shapes?

If we look closely, we see even more spectacular sights. A few nearby galaxies are engaged in titanic collisions with other galaxies. Many of these colliding galaxies are full of star-forming clouds in which new stars are born and massive stars explode 100 times more frequently than in the Milky Way. Other galaxies appear to harbor enormous black holes surrounded by gigantic accretion disks that generate extraordinary luminosities. Narrow streams of matter jet from a few of these galaxies into intergalactic space at nearly the speed of light.

The origins of galaxies and the incredible phenomena they sometimes display puzzled astronomers for much of the twentieth century, but today we are assembling a rudimentary understanding of how galaxies evolve. In this chapter, we will sift through the fascinating clues that hint at how galaxies formed and developed, pausing now and again to admire the fantastic spectacles that this search for our origins has uncovered.

## 20.1 Looking Back Through Time

In Chapter 19, we saw that galaxies come in a variety of shapes, colors, and sizes. This variety is interesting and beautiful to behold, but its significance goes much deeper. Remember that we would not be here if not for the recycling and reprocessing of matter and energy that take place in galaxies like our Milky Way. Thus, if we want to know our cosmic origins, we must learn how the great variety of galaxies we see today formed from the hydrogen and helium gas present in the early universe. The study of the formation and development of galaxies, or **galaxy evolution**, is now one of the most active research areas in astronomy, and each year brings new discoveries.

Our understanding of galaxy evolution is advancing rapidly, largely because modern telescopes enable us to look back through time. When we look at a galaxy a billion light-years away, we are seeing it at a time when the universe was a billion years younger than it is today. When we look at a galaxy halfway to the cosmological horizon [Section 19.4], we see it as it was when the universe was only half its present age. Even closer to the cosmological horizon, we see galaxies as they were within the first few billion years after the Big Bang.

The linkage between a galaxy's distance and its age gives us a remarkable ability: Simply by photographing galaxies at different distances, we can assemble "family albums" showing galaxies in different stages of development. Figure 20.1 shows partial family albums for elliptical, spiral, and irregular galaxies. Each individual photograph shows a single galaxy at a single stage in its life. Grouping these photographs by galaxy type allows us to see how galaxies of a particular type have changed through time. Pictures of the farthest galaxies show galaxies in their childhood, and pictures of the nearest show mature galaxies as they are today.

**TIME OUT TO THINK** *In the last sentence above, we use the term* today *in a very broad sense. For example, if we look at a relatively nearby galaxy—one located, say, 20 million light-years away— we see it as it was 20 million years ago. In what sense is this "today"? (Hint: How does 20 million years compare to the age of the universe? To the lifetime of a massive star?)*

We would like to tell the life stories of these galaxies from beginning to end as completely as we told the life stories of stars, but too many aspects of galaxy evolution remain mysterious. In broad terms, the story we seek should tell us how the hydrogen and helium gas in the early universe evolved into the galaxies we see today. As we'll discuss, even this general story still presents some puzzles, such as why

some galaxies turned out flattened and gas-rich while others did not. We also need to explain some of the stranger aspects of galaxies. For example, observations show that some galaxies, called *starburst galaxies,* are currently forming stars at a tremendous rate. Starbursts must be only a temporary phase in the lives of these galaxies, or they would have consumed all of the galaxies' gas long ago. We have also found that some galaxies have extremely bright centers, known as *active galactic nuclei,* that sometimes outshine all the stars in the galaxy combined. *Quasars,* the most luminous active galactic nuclei, can radiate more light than a thousand galaxies like our Milky Way. Because quasars are much more common in very distant galaxies than in nearby ones, we can conclude that they were much more common in the past than they are today. Perhaps all galaxies once harbored an active nucleus that shined brightly for a few hundred million years early in the universe's history. We simply don't yet know.

In this chapter, we'll discuss what is currently known about the lives of galaxies. We will first discuss how galaxies form and next examine why some galaxies end up as spirals while others end up as ellipticals. Then we will look in detail at the phenomena of starburst galaxies and active galactic nuclei and attempt to fit these dramatic stages into the overall puzzle of galaxy evolution. Finally, we will explore how very distant quasars are helping astronomers study galaxy evolution in a completely different way. The light from these distant quasars traverses billions of light-years on its way to Earth, and their spectra bear the signatures of many gaseous clouds that lie between the quasars and Earth. Some of these clouds probably represent galaxies in their most youthful state. Thus, the study of quasar spectra not only may teach us about some early phases in the evolution of galaxies, but also may soon help us understand the complete history of galaxy evolution.

## 20.2 Galaxy Formation

The photographs in Figure 20.1, taken by the Hubble Space Telescope, show galaxies extending back to ages of just 1 or 2 billion years, but the first stars and galaxies formed even earlier than this. Observing these first stars and galaxies is a challenge not even Hubble can meet. Detecting them will require extremely large telescopes that are extraordinarily sensitive to infrared light. Remember that the expansion of the universe shifts light from distant galaxies toward the red end of the spectrum [Section 19.3]. The redshifts of the most distant galaxies are so extreme that the visible and ultraviolet light they emitted comes to us in the form of infrared light. Ground-based telescopes can detect some of this infrared light, but the Earth's atmosphere greatly complicates such obser-

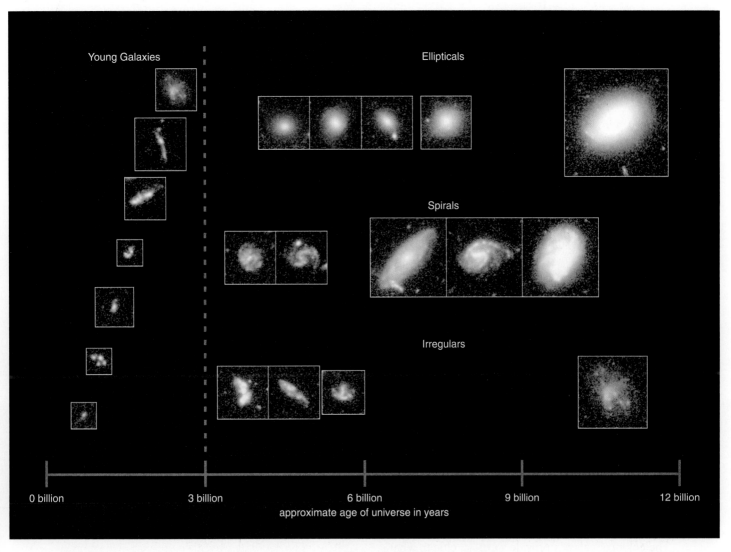

Young Galaxies

Ellipticals

Spirals

Irregulars

| 0 billion | 3 billion | 6 billion | 9 billion | 12 billion |

approximate age of universe in years

**FIGURE 20.1** Family albums for elliptical, spiral, and irregular galaxies at different ages along with some very young, distant galaxies. All of these galaxy photos have been drawn from the Hubble Space Telescope image in Figure 19.1. (Younger galaxies appear smaller because they are more distant.)

vations [Section 7.5]. Within a decade or so, NASA hopes to launch a much larger, infrared-sensitive successor to the Hubble Space Telescope (sometimes called the Next Generation Space Telescope), but for now we have little direct information about galaxy birth. Instead, we must try to weave several lines of less direct evidence into a single coherent story. In this section, we will discuss what astronomers have learned about galaxy formation from theoretical modeling, the properties of present-day galaxies, and the detailed structure of the Milky Way.

### Modeling Galaxy Birth

Because our telescopes cannot yet see back to the time when galaxies formed their first stars, we must use theoretical modeling to study the earliest stages

in galaxy evolution. The most successful models for galaxy formation assume the following:

■ Hydrogen and helium gas filled all of space more or less uniformly when the universe was very young—say, in the first million years after its birth.

■ This uniformity was not quite perfect, and certain regions of the universe were ever so slightly denser than others.

Beginning from these assumptions, which are supported by a mounting body of evidence (discussed in Chapter 22), we can model galaxy formation using well-established laws of physics to trace how the denser regions in the early universe grew into galaxies. The models show that the regions of enhanced density originally expanded along with the rest of the

a

center of galaxy

universe. However, the slightly greater pull of gravity in these regions gradually slowed their expansion. Within about a billion years, the expansion of these denser regions halted and reversed, and the material within them began to contract into **protogalactic clouds**, the clouds of matter that eventually formed galaxies.

According to the models, protogalactic clouds initially cooled as they contracted, radiating away their thermal energy, and the first generation of stars grew from the densest, coldest clumps of gas. The most massive of these stars lived and died within just a few million years, a short time compared to the time required for the collapse of a protogalactic cloud into a mature galaxy. The supernovae of these massive stars generated shock waves that heated the surrounding interstellar gas, slowing the collapse of young galaxies and the rate at which new stars formed within them.

### Old Spheroids, Young Disks

The colors of galaxies provide a crucial clue to what happened next. Recall that the disks of spiral galaxies appear whitish with flecks of blue [Section 19.2]. This indicates that the stars in the disks of spiral galaxies, sometimes referred to as the *disk population* (or *Population I*), include hot, blue stars as well as cool, red ones. Because only short-lived, massive stars look blue, we conclude that star formation must be an ongoing process in galactic disks—just as it is in the disk of the Milky Way. In contrast, the stars in elliptical galaxies and in the bulges and halos of spiral galaxies, called the *spheroidal population* (or *Population II*), look reddish in color. The absence of blue stars among the spheroidal population indicates that most of these stars are old and that their star formation must have ceased long ago—just as is the case in the halo of the Milky Way [Section 18.3].

The characteristic motions of stars in disks and spheroids provide another important clue to their nature (Figure 20.2). Disk stars generally orbit in orderly circles in the same direction; all galactic disks rotate much like the Milky Way's disk [Section 18.4]. Stars of spheroidal populations tend to orbit in ran-

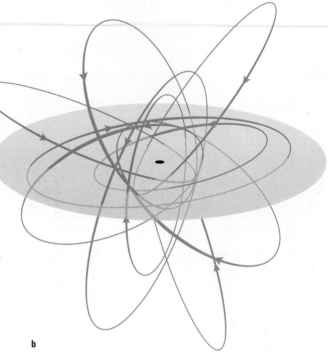

b

**FIGURE 20.2** Characteristic stellar orbits in (**a**) disk component and (**b**) spheroidal component. Stars in the disk tend to orbit in the same direction around the center of the galaxy, with a bit of up and down motion. Stars in the bulge and halo also orbit the center of the galaxy, but the orientations of their orbits are more random.

dom directions, much like stars in the bulge and halo of the Milky Way. Because the motions of stars in the populations are so different, disks and spheroids must have formed in very different ways.

According to the most basic model for galaxy formation from a protogalactic cloud, the stars of the spheroidal population formed first. Early on, the gravity associated with a protogalactic cloud drew in matter from all directions, creating a cloud that was blobby in shape and had little or no measurable rotation. The orbits of stars forming within such a cloud could have had any orientation, accounting for the randomly oriented orbits of spheroidal population stars.

Later, at least in spiral galaxies, conservation of angular momentum caused the remaining gas to flatten into a spinning disk as it contracted under the force of gravity (Figure 20.3). This process was much like the process that leads to protoplanetary disks around young stars [Section 8.3], but on a much larger scale: Collisions among gas particles tended to aver-

**a** A protogalactic cloud contains only hydrogen and helium gas.

**b** Halo stars begin to form as the protogalactic cloud collapses.

**c** Conservation of angular momentum ensures that the remaining gas flattens into a spinning disk.

**d** Billions of years later, the star–gas–star cycle supports ongoing star formation within the disk. The lack of gas in the halo precludes further star formation outside the disk.

**FIGURE 20.3** Schematic model of galaxy formation.

age out their random motions, leading them to acquire orbits in the same direction and in the same plane (see Figure 8.7). Stars that formed within this spinning disk were born on orbits moving at the same speed and in the same direction as their neighbors and thus became the disk population stars.

### Clues from the Milky Way

Because most spiral galaxies in today's universe look similar to our own Milky Way Galaxy, we can test our theories about the formation of spiral galaxies by studying the "fossil record" written within the stars of the Milky Way. The clues found to date support the basic picture but suggest that the full story of galaxy formation may be somewhat more complex.

All available evidence confirms that the stars in the Milky Way's halo are indeed old. The main-sequence turnoff points in H–R diagrams of globular clusters show that their stars were born at least 12 billion years ago [Section 15.6]. Individual halo stars (i.e., those not in globular clusters) and some of the bulge stars appear similarly old. Furthermore, the proportions of heavy elements in halo stars are much lower than in the Sun, indicating that they formed before

**FIGURE 20.4** Schematic illustration of how the Milky Way's halo may have formed. The characteristics of stars in the Milky Way's halo suggest that several smaller gas clouds, already bearing some stars and globular clusters, may have merged to form the Milky Way's protogalactic cloud. These stars and star clusters remained in the halo while the gas settled into the Milky Way's disk.

many generations of supernovae had a chance to enrich the Milky Way's interstellar medium [Section 18.2].

However, careful study of heavy-element proportions suggests that our galaxy formed from a few different gas clouds. If the Milky Way had formed from a single protogalactic cloud, it would have steadily accumulated heavy elements during its inward collapse as stars formed and exploded within it. In that case, the outermost stars in the halo would be the oldest and the most deficient in heavy elements. Halo stars in globular clusters do indeed differ in age and heavy-element content, but these variations do not seem to depend on the stars' distance from the galactic center. The easiest way to account for the variations is to suppose that the Milky Way's earliest stars formed in relatively small protogalactic clouds, each with a few globular clusters, and that these clouds later collided and combined to create the full protogalactic cloud that became the Milky Way (Figure 20.4).

**TIME OUT TO THINK** *If the preceding scenario is true, then the Milky Way suffered several collisions early in its history. Explain why we should not be surprised that galaxy collisions (or protogalactic cloud collisions) were rather common in the distant past. (Hint: How did the average separations of galaxies in the past compare to their average separations today?)*

Once the full protogalactic cloud was in place, its collapse and heavy-element enrichment should have continued in a more orderly fashion than previously. Support for this scenario comes from a layer of stars intermediate between the disk and the halo. The heavy-element content of stars and globular clusters in this intermediate layer does indeed depend on their distances from the galactic center. These stars are nearly as old as halo stars, but they formed before the spinning protogalactic cloud finished flattening

into a disk. Their proportions of heavy elements suggest that, at the time the disk formed, the Milky Way contained about 10% as much material in the form of heavy elements as it does today. After the disk formed, generations of stars lived and died in the star–gas–star cycle that gradually increased the abundance of heavy elements [Section 18.2]. Thus, the ages of stars in the Milky Way's disk range from newly born to 10 billion or more years old. New stars will continue to be born as long as enough gas remains in the disk.

### Loose Ends

We seem to be well on our way to understanding how and why protogalactic clouds evolve into galaxies. Nevertheless, a few puzzles remain. For example, while the oldest halo stars in our Milky Way have very low fractions of heavy elements, these fractions are not zero. Where did the heavy elements in these stars come from? They probably came from an even earlier generation of stars, but we have not yet discovered any examples of first-generation stars with no heavy elements. An even more fundamental question relates to the formation of the protogalactic clouds themselves. Our models assume that these clouds formed in regions of slightly enhanced density in the early universe, but where did these density enhancements come from? The question of the nature and origin of density enhancements in the early universe is one of the major puzzles in astronomy; we'll revisit it in Chapters 21 and 22.

## 20.3 Why Do Galaxies Differ?

The idea that galaxies grow from contracting protogalactic clouds and form their stars over billions of years is consistent with what we know from studying the Milky Way and from our limited observations of very young galaxies. However, this simple model does not explain why galaxies come in such a great variety of shapes and sizes. We now believe that both the initial conditions of the protogalactic clouds and later interactions with other galaxies affected the development of all types of galaxies, leading to the great variety we see today. To help differentiate the role of initial conditions and that of subsequent interactions, let us now consider a question about galaxy evolution that is still unanswered: Why do spiral galaxies have gas-rich disks, while elliptical galaxies do not?

### Destined from Birth?

Two potential explanations for the differences between spirals and ellipticals trace a galaxy's appearance back to the properties of the protogalactic cloud from which it formed. The first explanation concerns angular momentum differences among protogalactic clouds. If a protogalactic cloud has enough angular momentum, it will rotate quickly as it collapses, and the galaxy it produces will tend to form a disk. The resulting galaxy therefore would be a spiral galaxy. If a protogalactic cloud has little or no net angular momentum, its gas might not form a disk at all, and the resulting galaxy would be elliptical.

The second scenario hinges on the ability of protogalactic clouds to cool and form stars. Remember that large elliptical galaxies are most common in clusters of galaxies [Section 19.2]. Galaxy clusters are unusually dense regions of the universe. Thus, the preponderance of elliptical galaxies in clusters suggests that elliptical galaxies tended to form from protogalactic clouds denser than those from which spirals formed. The relatively higher gas densities in these protoelliptical clouds would have enabled them to radiate energy more efficiently and to cool more quickly. This cooling would have allowed gravity to collapse clumps of gas into stars more quickly, using up all the gas before the cloud had time to collapse into a disk. The resulting galaxy would therefore lack a disk, making it an elliptical galaxy. In contrast, the lower-density clouds that became spiral galaxies would have formed stars more slowly, leaving plenty of gas to form a disk as the cloud collapsed.

Some evidence for the latter scenario comes from a few giant elliptical galaxies at very great distances (Figure 20.5). These galaxies look very red even after we have accounted for their large redshifts. They apparently have no blue or white stars at all, indicating that new stars no longer form within these galaxies—even though we are seeing them as they were when the universe was only a few billion years old. This finding supports the idea that all the stars in these

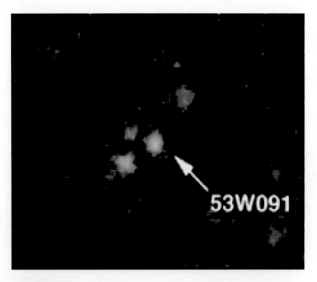

**FIGURE 20.5** The redness of this distant elliptical galaxy, LBDS 53W091, indicates that its stars all formed during the first billion years or so after the birth of the universe. Its two red companions to the left are probably also elliptical galaxies with similar star-formation histories.

galaxies formed almost simultaneously, leaving no time for a disk to develop.

### Shaped by Collisions?

The two previous scenarios, in which the formation of a gas-rich disk depends on the angular momentum or density of the protogalactic cloud, probably describe important parts of the overall story. However, they ignore one key fact: Galaxies rarely evolve in perfect isolation. Recall that, in our scale-model solar system in Chapter 1, we made the Sun the size of a grapefruit. On this scale, the nearest star was like another grapefruit a few thousand kilometers away. Because the average distances between stars are so huge compared to the sizes of stars, direct star–star collisions are extremely rare. However, if we rescale the universe so that our *galaxy* is the size of a grapefruit, the Andromeda Galaxy is like another grapefruit only about 3 meters away, and a few smaller galaxies lie considerably closer. Thus, the average distances between galaxies are not tremendously larger than the sizes of galaxies, and collisions between galaxies are inevitable. Even the Milky Way Galaxy is not immune. About 80,000 light-years away, directly behind the galactic bulge, a small elliptical galaxy (called the Sagittarius dwarf elliptical) is currently crashing through the Milky Way's disk.

Collisions between galaxies are spectacular events that unfold over hundreds of millions of years (Figure 20.6). In our short lifetimes, we can at best see a snapshot of a collision in progress, as evidenced by

**a** The Antennae, also known as NGC 4038/4039, are a pair of colliding spiral galaxies. The wide-field image taken from the ground reveals their vast tidal tails, and the close-up from the Hubble Space Telescope shows the fine details of the burst of star formation at the center of the collision.

**b** NGC 6240, a galaxy collision farther along than the Antennae, is still highly disturbed, but the two galaxies have almost merged into one.

**FIGURE 20.6** Galaxy collisions.

the distorted shape of the colliding galaxies. Galactic collisions must have been even more frequent when the universe was smaller and galaxies were even closer together. Photographs of galaxies at a variety of distances confirm that distorted-looking galaxies—probably galaxy collisions in progress—were more common in the early universe than they are today (Figure 20.7).

We can learn much more about galactic collisions with the aid of computer simulations that allow us to "watch" collisions that take hundreds of millions of years to unfold in nature. These computer models show that a collision between two spiral galaxies can create an elliptical galaxy (Figure 20.8). Tremendous tidal forces between the colliding galaxies tear apart the two disks, randomizing the orbits of their stars. Meanwhile, a large fraction of their gas sinks to the center of the collision and rapidly forms new stars. Supernovae and stellar winds eventually blow away the rest of the gas. When the cataclysm finally settles down, the merger of the two spirals has produced a single elliptical galaxy: Little gas is

Age of Universe: 2–4 billion years

Age of Universe: 5–7 billion years

**FIGURE 20.7** Hubble Space Telescope photos of distorted young galaxies.

left for a disk, and the orbits of the stars have random orientations.

Observations seem to confirm the idea that at least some elliptical galaxies result from collisions and subsequent mergers. The fact that elliptical galaxies dominate the galaxy populations at the cores of dense clusters of galaxies, where collisions should be most frequent, may mean that any spirals once present became ellipticals through collisions. Stronger evidence comes from structural details of elliptical galaxies, which often attest to a violent past. Some elliptical galaxies have stars and gas clouds in their cores that rotate in a different direction from the rest of the galaxy, suggesting that they are leftover pieces of galaxies that merged in a past collision. Other elliptical galaxies are surrounded by shells of stars, which probably formed when stars were stripped out of smaller galaxies that once strayed too close and were destroyed (Figure 20.9).

The most decisive evidence that collisions affect the evolution of elliptical galaxies comes from observations of the **central dominant galaxies** found at the centers of many dense clusters. Central dominant galaxies are gigantic elliptical galaxies that apparently grew to a huge size by consuming other galaxies through collisions. Central dominant galaxies frequently contain several tightly bound clumps of stars that probably were the centers of individual galaxies before being swallowed by the giant (Figure 20.10). This process of *galactic cannibalism* can create central dominant galaxies more than 10 times as massive as the Milky Way, making them the largest galaxies in the universe.

Two simulated spiral galaxies approach each other on a collision course.

The first encounter begins to disrupt the two galaxies and sends them into orbit around each other.

As the collision continues, much of the gas in the disk of each galaxy collapses toward the center.

Gravitational forces between the two galaxies tear out long streamers of stars called tidal tails.

The centers of the two galaxies approach each other and begin to merge.

The single galaxy resulting from the collision and merger is an elliptical galaxy surrounded by debris.

**FIGURE 20.9** Shells of stars around the elliptical galaxy NGC 3923.

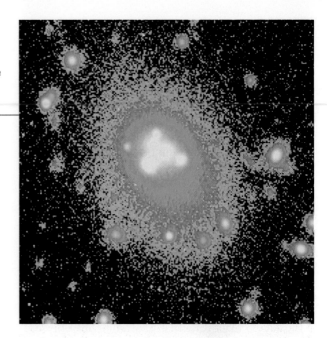

**FIGURE 20.10** The central dominant galaxy of the cluster Abell 3827, shown here in false color, has multiple clumps of stars that probably once were the centers of individual galaxies.

Clusters of galaxies might also turn spiral galaxies into ellipticals simply by pulling out their interstellar gas. Hot gas fills the centers of galaxy clusters [Section 21.3]. When a spiral galaxy cruises through the center of such a cluster, the intracluster gas exerts drag forces that slow the galaxy's gas but not its stars. The galaxy's stars continue to move freely along their way, but the gas is left behind. If the disk has not yet formed many stars, then the galaxy will evolve to look more like an elliptical galaxy as its massive stars die away. Its disk will fade, while its bulge and halo will remain prominent. In contrast, if the disk has already formed a large number of stars when its gas is stripped, the remaining galaxy is more likely to look *lenticular* in shape [Section 19.2].

### No Verdict Yet

We have identified several scenarios that may determine whether a galaxy becomes an elliptical or a spiral galaxy. Two of these scenarios depend on initial conditions: One suggests that elliptical galaxies form when protogalactic clouds have low angular momentum, and the other suggests that elliptical galaxies form as a result of rapid star formation in protogalactic clouds with relatively high density. But we have also found that interactions, such as galactic collisions or drag created by hot plasma in galaxy clusters, can drastically influence the lives of galaxies and very likely cause some spiral galaxies to become elliptical. Each of these mechanisms probably plays a role in galaxy evolution, but we do not yet know whether one is more important than the others. Irregular galaxies, which make up only a few percent of large galaxies, probably arise from a variety of different and unusual circumstances but are probably affected by the same processes that affect spirals and ellipticals.

### 20.4 Starburst Galaxies

We have discussed current ideas about galaxy formation and why galaxies come in different types. We now turn our attention to the incredible phenomena we see in some of our snapshots of galactic lives. We do not yet know how these phenomena fit into the overall story of galaxy evolution, but they are clearly important. We begin in this section by studying starburst galaxies; in the next section, we will look at quasars and other active galactic nuclei.

Most of the galaxies in the present-day universe appear comfortably settled, steadily forming new stars at modest rates. The Milky Way Galaxy produces an average of about one new star per year. At this rate, the Milky Way won't exhaust the interstellar gas in its disk until long after the Sun has died. **Starburst galaxies** are not so thrifty. Some form new stars at rates exceeding 100 stars per year, more than 100 times the star-formation rate in the Milky Way. These galaxies cannot possibly sustain such a torrid pace of star formation for long: At their current rates of star formation, they would consume *all* their interstellar gas in just a few hundred million years— a relatively short time compared to the 10 billion or more years since galaxies first formed. Starbursts are thus an important but temporary phase in the evolution of at least some galaxies.

Starburst galaxies are relatively new subjects of study. These voracious consumers of interstellar gas look peculiar at visible wavelengths because they are filled with star-forming molecular clouds, but these clouds conceal much of the action. Dust grains in the molecular clouds absorb most of the visible and ultraviolet radiation streaming from a starburst galaxy's many young stars. This radiation heats the dust grains to much higher temperatures than normal, and they ultimately reemit all the absorbed visible and ultraviolet energy as infrared light, with a peak

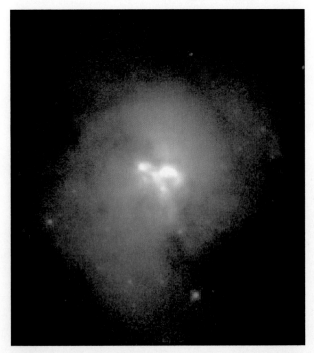

**a** Image of starburst galaxy Arp 220.

**FIGURE 20.11** Infrared observations of Arp 220, a large starburst galaxy.

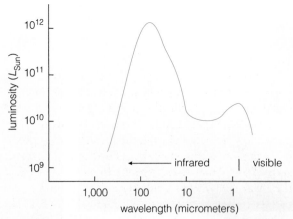

**b** The spectrum of Arp 220 shows that it emits most of its radiation as infrared light, rather than visible light.

wavelength of around 60,000 nanometers (60 micrometers). Because photons at these wavelengths cannot penetrate the Earth's atmosphere, the intensity of star-forming activity in starburst galaxies did not become fully apparent until the 1983 launching of the *Infrared Astronomy Satellite* (*IRAS*). Figure 20.11 shows an especially luminous starburst galaxy, along with its spectrum from radio through visible wavelengths. Note that the visible output of this galaxy is about 10 billion solar luminosities ($10^{10}L_{Sun}$), not very different from the total luminosity of the Milky Way. However, its infrared output is a trillion times that of our Sun ($10^{12}L_{Sun}$), making it 100 times brighter in infrared light than in visible light.

### Galactic Winds

A star-formation rate 100 times that of the Milky Way also means an occurrence of supernovae at 100 times the Milky Way's rate. Just as in the Milky Way, each supernova in a starburst galaxy generates a shock wave that creates a *bubble* of hot gas [Section 18.2]. The shock waves from several nearby supernovae quickly overlap and blend into a much larger *superbubble*. The story usually ends here in the Milky Way, but in a starburst galaxy the drama is just beginning. Supernovae continue to explode inside the superbubble, adding to its thermal and kinetic energy. When the

superbubble starts to break through the disrupted gaseous disk, it expands even faster. Hot gas erupts into intergalactic space, creating a **galactic wind**.

Galactic winds consist of low-density but extremely hot gas, typically with temperatures of 10–100 million Kelvin. They do not emit much visible light, but they do generate X rays. X-ray telescopes in orbit have detected pockets of X-ray emission surrounding the disks of some starburst galaxies, presumably coming from the outflowing galactic wind (Figure 20.12a). Sometimes we also see the glowing remnants of a punctured superbubble extending out into space (Figure 20.12b).

Supernova-driven galactic winds have an even more dramatic impact when they occur in small starburst galaxies (Figure 20.13). The winds can blow out of small galaxies on all sides, driving away virtually all their gas. As a result, star formation in these galaxies shuts down for billions of years. Some of the small elliptical galaxies in the Local Group apparently have burst like this at least twice during their lifetimes. In one example, about half the stars in the small galaxy were born more than about 12 billion years ago, and the rest only 5–8 billion years ago. Presumably, each of these bursts of star formation ejected all of the galaxy's gas. Star formation was put on hold for several billion years until enough gas could reaccumulate within the galaxy for a new starburst to ignite.

**a** This photographic image shows the visible light from the starburst galaxy NGC 253; the contour lines represent regions of strong X-ray emission. Note that the X rays appear on either side of the disk, suggesting that they come from hot gas blown out of the disk.

**FIGURE 20.12** Galactic winds can blow out the top and bottom of a starburst galaxy's disk.

**b** This photograph of the starburst galaxy M 82 shows violently disturbed gas (red) poking out from above and below the disk where hot gas is escaping.

**FIGURE 20.13** The small starburst galaxy NGC 1705 shows glowing gas (red) blown out on all sides by its supernova-driven galactic wind.

**TIME OUT TO THINK** *Dwarf galaxies that have undergone bursts of star formation tend to have fewer heavy elements than large galaxies. Why do you think that is? (Hint: What happens to the heavy elements produced by the burst of star formation?)*

### Causes of Starbursts

Many of the most luminous starburst galaxies look violently disturbed (see Figure 20.6). They are neither flat disks with symmetric spiral arms nor smoothly rounded balls of stars, like elliptical galaxies. Streamers of stars are strewn everywhere. Such galaxies are filled with dusty molecular clouds, and deep inside them we see two distinct clumps of stars that look like two different galactic centers. Their appearance suggests that such starbursts result from a collision between two gas-rich spiral galaxies. The collision apparently compresses the gas inside the colliding galaxies, leading to the burst of star formation.

The causes of smaller-scale starbursts are less clear. Some may result from direct collisions, while others may be caused by close encounters with other galaxies. The Large Magellanic Cloud is currently undergoing a period of rapid star formation, perhaps because of the tidal influence of the Milky Way. No matter what their exact causes turn out to be, starburst galaxies clearly represent an important piece in the overall puzzle of galaxy evolution.

## 20.5 Quasars and Other Active Galactic Nuclei

Starbursts may be spectacular, but some galaxies display even more incredible phenomena: extreme amounts of radiation, and sometimes powerful jets of material, emanating from deep in their centers (Figure 20.14). We generally refer to these unusually bright galactic centers as **active galactic nuclei** and reserve the term **quasar** for the very brightest of them. (Galaxies with active galactic nuclei are sometimes called *active galaxies*.) The brightest quasars shine more powerfully than 1,000 galaxies the size of the Milky Way.

The glory days of quasars are long past. We find quasars primarily at great distances, telling us that these blazingly luminous objects were most common billions of years ago, when galaxies were in their youth. Because we find no nearby quasars and relatively few nearby galaxies with any type of active galactic nucleus we conclude that the objects that shine as quasars in young galaxies must become dormant as the galaxies age. Thus, many nearby galaxies that now look quite normal—we don't yet know which ones—must have centers that once shone brilliantly as quasars.

What could possibly drive the incredible luminosities of quasars, and why did quasars fade away? A growing body of evidence points to a single answer:

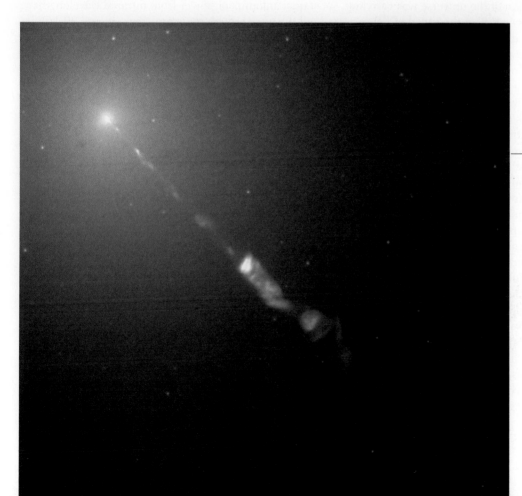

**FIGURE 20.14** The active galactic nucleus in the elliptical galaxy M 87. The bright yellow spot is the active nucleus, and the blue streak is a jet of particles shooting outward from the nucleus at nearly the speed of light.

The energy output of quasars comes from gigantic accretion disks surrounding **supermassive black holes**—black holes with masses millions to billions of times that of our Sun. But before we study how these incredible powerhouses work, let's investigate the evidence that points to their existence.

### The Discovery of Quasars

In the early 1960s, a young professor at the California Institute of Technology named Maarten Schmidt was busy identifying cosmic sources of radio-wave emission. Radio astronomers would tell him the coordinates of newly discovered radio sources, and he would try to match them with objects seen through visible-light telescopes. Usually the radio sources turned out to be normal-looking galaxies, but one day he discovered a major mystery. A radio source called 3C 273 looked like a blue star through a telescope but had strong emission lines at wavelengths that did not appear to correspond to any known chemical element. (The designation 3C 273 stands for 3rd Cambridge Radio Catalogue, object 273. A few other, similarly enigmatic radio sources were known at the time, but Schmidt's breakthrough came with 3C 273.) After months of puzzlement, Schmidt suddenly realized that the emission lines were not coming from an unfamiliar element at all. Instead, they were emission lines of hydrogen hugely redshifted from their normal wavelengths (Figure 20.15). Schmidt calculated that the expansion of the universe was carrying 3C 273 away from us at 17% of the speed of light.

Schmidt computed the distance to 3C 273 using Hubble's law; then he plugged this distance into the luminosity–distance formula [Section 15.2]. What he found was astonishing: 3C 273 has a luminosity of about $10^{39}$ watts, or well over a trillion ($10^{12}$) times that of our Sun—making it hundreds of times more powerful than the entire Milky Way Galaxy. Discoveries of similar but even more distant objects soon followed. Because the first few of these objects were strong sources of radio emission that looked like stars through visible-light telescopes, they were named "quasi-stellar radio sources," or *quasars* for short. Later, astronomers learned that most quasars are not such powerful radio emitters, but the name has stuck.

For many years, a debate raged among astronomers over whether Hubble's law could really be used to determine quasar distances. Some argued that quasars might have high redshifts for other reasons and therefore might be much nearer to us than Hubble's law would suggest. The vast majority of astronomers now consider this debate settled. Improved images show that quasars are indeed the centers of extremely distant galaxies and often are members of very distant galaxy clusters.

**FIGURE 20.15** Spectrum of the quasar 3C 273. The lines labeled H$\beta$, H$\gamma$, and H$\delta$ are hydrogen emission lines. Note their significant redshift in the quasar spectrum relative to the "comparison spectrum" that shows them at their rest wavelengths.

Most quasars lie more than halfway to the cosmological horizon. The lines in typical quasar spectra are shifted to more than three times their rest wavelengths, which tells us that the light from these quasars emerged when the universe was less than a third of its present age. The farthest known quasar as of 2001 has spectral lines shifted to 6.8 times their rest wavelengths. The light we see from this distant quasar began its journey when the universe was only about a tenth of its present age.

The extraordinary energy output of quasars emerges across an unusually wide swath of the electromagnetic spectrum. Quasars radiate approximately equal amounts of power from infrared wavelengths all the way through to gamma rays (Figure 20.16); they also produce strong emission lines. By comparison, most stars and galaxies emit primarily visible light. The wide spread of photon energies coming from quasars implies that they contain matter with a wide range of temperatures. How does this matter manage to radiate such a large luminosity?

### Evidence from Nearby Active Galactic Nuclei

Quasars are difficult to study in detail because they are so far away. Luckily, some quasarlike objects are much closer to home. About 1% of present-day galaxies—that is, galaxies we see nearby—have active galactic nuclei that look very much like quasars, except that they are less powerful. (These galaxies are often called *Seyfert galaxies* after astronomer Carl Seyfert, who in 1943 grouped galaxies with active galactic nuclei into a special class.) The spectra of these active nuclei range from infrared to gamma rays, just like those of quasars. The only real distinction between nearby active galactic nuclei and quasars is their luminosity. Generally, the power outputs of quasars swamp those of the galaxies that contain them, making the surrounding galaxies hard to detect (Figure 20.17). That is why quasars look "quasi-

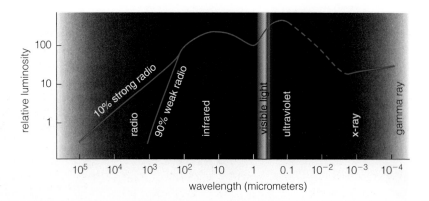

**FIGURE 20.16** This schematic spectrum, representing the average of many quasar spectra, shows that all quasars emit strongly across most of the electromagnetic spectrum. However, only about 10% of quasars show strong radio emission. Quasar spectra also have strong emission lines, not shown in this diagram.

stellar." The galaxies surrounding dimmer active galactic nuclei are much easier to see because their centers are not so overwhelmingly bright.

The light-emitting regions of active galactic nuclei are so small that even the sharpest images do not resolve them. Our best visible-light images show only that active galactic nuclei must be smaller than 100 light-years across. Radio-wave images made with the aid of *interferometry* [Section 7.5] show that these nuclei are even smaller: less than 3 light-years across. But rapid changes in the luminosities of some active galactic nuclei point to an even smaller size.

To understand how variations in luminosity give us clues about an object's size, imagine that you are a master of the universe and you want to signal one of your fellow masters a billion light-years away. An active galactic nucleus would make an excellent signal beacon, because it is so bright. However, suppose the smallest nucleus you can find is 1 light-year across. Each time you flash it on, the photons from the front end of the source reach your fellow master a full year before the photons from the back end. Thus, if you flash it on and off more than once a year, your signal will be smeared out. Similarly, if you find a source that is 1 light-day across, you can transmit signals that flash on and off no more than once a day. If you want to send signals just a few hours apart, you need a source no more than a few light-hours across.

Occasionally, the luminosity of an active galactic nucleus doubles in a matter of hours. The fact that we see a clear signal indicates that the source must be less than a few light-hours across. In other words, the incredible luminosities of active galactic nuclei and quasars are apparently being generated in a volume of space not much bigger than our solar system.

### Radio Galaxies and Jets

In the early 1950s, a decade before the discovery of quasars, radio astronomers noticed that certain galaxies emit unusually large quantities of radio waves.

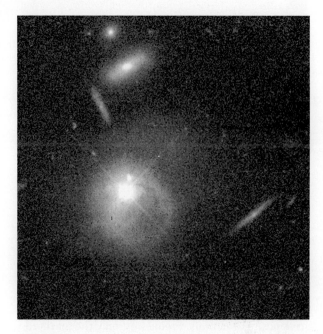

**FIGURE 20.17** The bright quasar in the nucleus of the galaxy just left of center outshines the rest of the galaxy, which appears disturbed, as if it has recently undergone a collision.

Today we believe that these **radio galaxies** are another class of celestial powerhouse that is closely related to quasars. Upon close inspection, we find that much of the radio emission comes not from the galaxies themselves but rather from pairs of huge *radio lobes,* one on either side of the galaxy (Figure 20.18).

The radio waves from the lobes are produced by electrons and protons spiraling around magnetic field lines at nearly the speed of light. Astronomers of the 1950s guessed that this might be the source of the radio emission, but the implied amounts of energy in the lobes seemed implausibly large until the discovery of quasars. British theoretician Martin Rees led the way in showing that radio galaxies contain active galactic nuclei. He argued in 1971 that radio galaxies

**FIGURE 20.18** Radio image of the radio galaxy Cygnus A recorded by the Very Large Array in New Mexico. The distance between the lobes is about 400,000 light-years, several times larger than the extent of the galaxy in visible light.

must have powerful **jets** spurting from their nuclei that transport energy to their lobes. That is, although the lobes lie far outside the visible galaxy, he asserted that the ultimate source of their energy would be found in the galaxy's tiny nucleus, which must therefore be as powerful as a quasar. A few years later, detailed radio images began to support his claims.

Today, radio telescopes resolve the structure of radio galaxies in vivid detail. At the center of a typical radio galaxy sits a tiny *radio core*—the active galactic nucleus of the radio galaxy—less than a few light-years across. Two jets of plasma shoot out of the core in opposite directions. Frequently, only the jet tilted

in our direction is visible. Using time-lapse radio images taken several years apart, we can track the motions of various plasma blobs in the jets. Some of these blobs move at close to the speed of light. The lobes lie at the ends of the jets, sometimes as much as a million light-years from the core. The relative prominence of these three elements—cores, jets, and lobes—varies from radio galaxy to radio galaxy. Thus, a gallery of typical radio galaxies exhibits a wide variety of sizes and shapes (Figure 20.19).

Quasars and radio galaxies may be much more similar than they appear. Indeed, many quasars, including 3C 273, have core–jet–lobe radio structures reminiscent of radio galaxies. For example, Fig-

**a** 3C 288

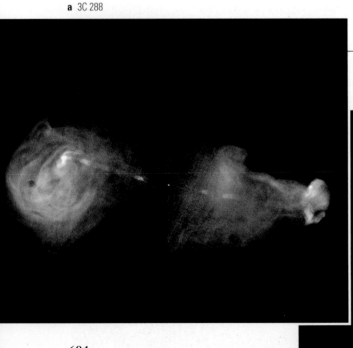

**FIGURE 20.19** Radio galaxy gallery. Note the double-lobe structure in all cases, but with very different shapes and sizes.

**b** 3C 219

ure 20.20 shows a series of pictures of a jet in which a blob of plasma is moving outward from a quasar at close to the speed of light. Moreover, the active galactic nuclei of many radio galaxies seem to be concealed beneath donut-shaped rings of dark molecular clouds (Figure 20.21). It may be that such structures look like quasars when they are oriented so that we can see the active galactic nucleus at the center and look like the cores of radio galaxies when the ring of dusty gas dims our view of the central object. (A subset of active galactic nuclei called *BL Lac objects* probably represent the centers of radio galaxies whose jets happen to point directly at us.)

### Supermassive Black Holes

Astronomers have worked hard to envision physical processes that might explain how radio galaxies, quasars, and other active galactic nuclei release so much energy within such small central volumes. Only one explanation seems to fit: The energy comes from matter falling into a supermassive black hole (Figure 20.22). Gravity converts the potential energy of the infalling matter into kinetic energy. Collisions between infalling particles convert the kinetic energy into thermal energy, and photons carry this thermal energy away. As in X-ray binaries, we expect that the infalling matter swirls through an accretion disk before it disappears beneath the event horizon of the black hole [Section 17.4].

This method of energy generation can be awesomely efficient. The gravitational potential energy lost by a chunk of matter falling into a black hole is equivalent to its mass-energy, $E = mc^2$. As much as 10–40% of this energy can emerge as radiation before the matter crosses the event horizon. Thus, ac-

cretion by black holes is far more efficient at producing light than is nuclear fusion, which converts less than 1% of mass-energy into photons. Note that, as with accretion into the black holes formed in supernovae, the light is coming not from the black hole itself but rather from the hot gas surrounding it.

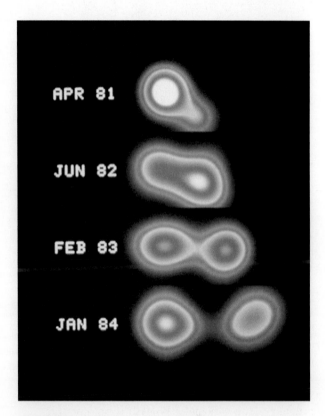

**FIGURE 20.20** These close-up images of the jet in the quasar 3C 345, taken over a period of several years, show a blob of plasma (right) moving away from the core (left) at close to the speed of light.

c 3C 31

d NGC 1265

**FIGURE 20.21** Artist's conception of the central region of a radio galaxy. The active galactic nucleus, obscured by a ring of dusty molecular clouds, lies at the point from which the jets emerge. If viewed along a direction closer to the jet axis, the active nucleus would not be obscured and would look more like a quasar.

**FIGURE 20.22** Artist's conception of an accretion disk surrounding a supermassive black hole. Note that this picture represents only the very center of an object like that shown in Figure 20.21.

A variety of mechanisms explain why quasars and other active galactic nuclei radiate energy across the electromagnetic spectrum. The hot gas in and above the accretion disk produces copious amounts of ultraviolet and X-ray photons. This radiation ionizes surrounding interstellar gas, energizing intense ionization nebulae that emit visible light. The emission lines produced by these nebulae are the same ones Maarten Schmidt used to measure the first quasar redshifts. The infrared light may come from rings of molecular clouds that encircle the active galactic nucleus (see Figure 20.21). As in starburst galaxies, dust grains in these molecular clouds absorb the high-energy light and reemit it as infrared light. This ring of dense clouds could well be the reservoir for the accretion disk, supplying the matter that the giant black hole eventually consumes. Finally, the radio emission from active galactic nuclei comes from the fast-moving electrons that we sometimes see jetting from these nuclei at nearly the speed of light.

Although it's easy to understand why matter swirls inward through the accretion disk toward the black hole, explaining the powerful jets emerging from active galactic nuclei is more challenging. One plausible model for jet production relies on the twisted magnetic fields thought to accompany accretion disks (Figure 20.23). As an accretion disk spins, it pulls the magnetic field lines that thread it around in circles. Charged particles start to fly outward along the field lines like beads on a twirling string. The

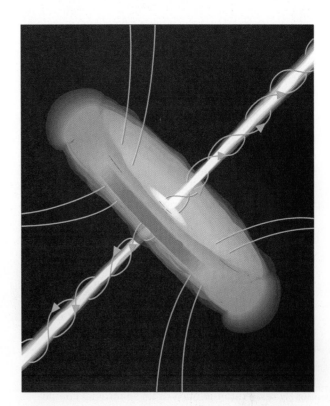

**FIGURE 20.23** This schematic drawing illustrates one theory that might explain how supermassive black holes create jets. The theory relies on the magnetic field lines thought to thread the accretion disk surrounding a black hole. As the accretion disk spins, it twists the magnetic field lines. Centrifugal forces then send charged particles at the disk's surface flying outward along the twisted magnetic field lines.

## Mathematical Insight 20.1    Feeding a Black Hole

As discussed in the text, 10–40% of the mass-energy of matter falling into a black hole can be radiated away as energy. (The precise value for a particular black hole depends on its rotation rate: Faster rotation allows more energy to be released.) Suppose 10% of the mass-energy is radiated away. Then the amount of energy radiated by mass $m$ falling into a black hole is $E = \frac{1}{10}mc^2$. Equivalently, if we know the energy $E$ radiated into space, then the amount of mass the black hole must accrete to radiate this energy is:

$$\text{accreted mass} = m = 10 \times \frac{E}{c^2}$$

*Example:* The most powerful quasars have luminosities of about $10^{40}$ watts. How much mass must the central black hole consume each second for its accretion disk to produce this luminosity? How many solar masses of material must it consume each year? Assume that 10% of the mass-energy of consumed mass is radiated away.

*Solution:* Recall that 1 watt = 1 joule/s, so the black hole must accrete enough mass to radiate $10^{40}$ joules each second. Thus, the amount of mass required to feed the black hole for 1 second is about:

$$m = 10 \times \frac{E}{c^2}$$

$$= 10 \times \frac{10^{40}\,\frac{\text{kg} \times \text{m}^2}{\text{s}^2}}{\left(3 \times 10^8\,\frac{\text{m}}{\text{s}}\right)^2}$$

$$= 1.1 \times 10^{24}\,\text{kg}$$

(Note that we replaced 1 joule with its equivalent units:

$$1\,\text{joule} = \frac{\text{kg} \times \text{m}^2}{\text{s}^2}.)$$

The black hole must accrete $1.1 \times 10^{24}$ kilograms of mass per second; we can convert this rate to solar masses per year as follows:

$$\frac{1.1 \times 10^{24}\,\text{kg}}{1\,\text{s}} \times \frac{1\,\text{solar mass}}{2.0 \times 10^{30}\,\text{kg}} \times \frac{3.1 \times 10^7\,\text{s}}{1\,\text{year}}$$

$$= \frac{17\,\text{solar masses}}{1\,\text{year}}$$

Thus, the central black hole in a luminous quasar must consume the equivalent of about 17 Suns every year!

particles careening along the field lines accelerate to speeds near the speed of light, forming a jet that shoots out into space. Some jets blast all the way through the galaxy's interstellar medium and penetrate into the much less dense intergalactic gas. The *hot spots* at the ends of the lobes in radio galaxies (see Figure 20.18) are the places where the jets are currently ramming into the intergalactic gas. When particles traveling down a jet hit the hot spot, they are deflected into the surrounding radio lobe like water from a firehose hitting a wall. The particles then fill the lobe with energy, generating powerful radio emission.

The supermassive black hole theory explains many of the observed features of quasars and other active galactic nuclei, but it is incomplete. We do not yet know what would create such giant black holes, nor do we know why quasars eventually run out of gas to accrete and stop shining. The preponderance of quasars during the first several billion years of the universe suggests that the formation of supermassive black holes is somehow linked to galaxy formation, a suggestion supported by recent observations showing that the mass of a galaxy's central black hole is closely related to the mass of its spheroidal component. Some scientists have suggested that clusters of neutron stars resulting from extremely dense starbursts at the centers of galaxies might somehow coalesce to form an enormous black hole, but these speculations are still unverified. The origins of supermassive black holes remain mysterious.

## Hunting for Monsters

Do supermassive black holes really drive the tremendous activity of radio galaxies, quasars, and other active galactic nuclei? The idea that such monsters even exist has been hard for some astronomers to swallow. Proving that we have found a black hole is tricky. Black holes themselves do not emit any light, so we need to infer their existence from the ways in which they alter their surroundings. In the vicinity of a black hole, matter should be orbiting at high speed around something invisible.

The case for supermassive black holes grew much stronger during the 1990s. The relatively nearby galaxy M 87 features a bright nucleus and a jet that emits both radio and visible light. Thus, it was already a prime black-hole suspect when astronomers pointed the Hubble Space Telescope at its core in 1994 (Figure 20.24). The spectra they gathered showed blueshifted emission lines on one side of the nucleus and redshifted emission lines on the other. This pattern of Doppler shifts is the characteristic signature of orbiting gas: On one side of the orbit the gas is coming toward us and hence is blueshifted, while on the other side it is moving away from us and is redshifted. The magnitude of these Doppler shifts shows that the gas, located up to 60 light-years from the center, is orbiting something invisible at a speed of hundreds of kilometers per second. This high-speed orbital motion indicates that the central object has a mass some 2–3 billion times that of our Sun. A

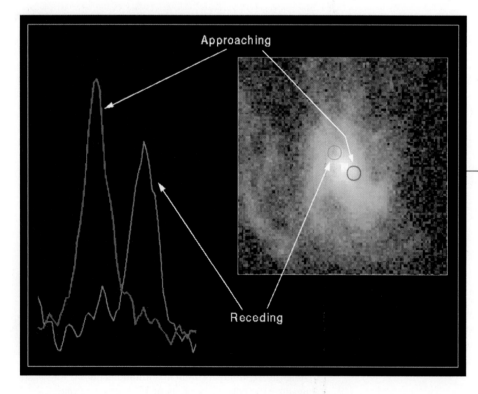

**FIGURE 20.24** Doppler shifts of the emission lines from the gas disk in the elliptical galaxy M 87 indicate a 2–3-billion-solar-mass black hole.

supermassive black hole is the only thing we know of that could be so massive while remaining unseen.

Observations of NGC 4258, another galaxy with a visible jet, delivered even more persuasive evidence just 1 year later. A ring of molecular clouds orbits the nucleus of this galaxy in a circle less than 1 light-year in radius. We can pinpoint these clouds because they amplify the microwave emission lines of water molecules, generating beams of microwaves very similar to laser beams. (The word *laser* stands for "light amplification by stimulated emission of radiation." These clouds contain *water masers*; the word *maser* stands for "microwave amplification by stimulated emission of radiation.") The Doppler shifts of these emission lines allow us to determine the orbits of the clouds very precisely. Their orbital motion tells us that the clouds are circling a single, invisible object—presumably a black hole—with a mass of 36 million solar masses.

We may never be 100% certain that we have discovered black holes in other galaxies. The best we can do is rule out all other possibilities. However, the hypothesis that gigantic black holes lie at the cores of quasars, nearby active galactic nuclei, and radio galaxies is so far withstanding the tests of time and thousands of observations.

## 20.6 Shedding Light on Protogalactic Clouds

The most mysterious part of galaxy evolution is the part we've never observed: the formation and development of protogalactic clouds. But in recent years, the study of quasars has begun to shed light on even this very early stage of galaxy evolution. The most distant quasars inhabit the outskirts of the observable universe. Photons from some of these quasars began journeying to Earth when the universe was only 1 or 2 billion years old. Along the way, these photons have passed through numerous intergalactic hydrogen clouds. The vast majority of these clouds are too diffuse and wispy ever to become galaxies, but a few have as much hydrogen as the disk of the Milky Way. The thickest of these clouds may well be protogalactic clouds in the process of becoming galaxies.

Quasar spectra therefore contain valuable information about the properties of hydrogen clouds in the early universe. Because atoms tend to absorb light at very specific wavelengths, every time a light beam from a quasar passes through an intergalactic or protogalactic cloud some of the atoms in the cloud absorb photons from the beam, creating an absorption line (Figure 20.25). Studies of these absorption lines in quasar spectra can tell us what happened in protogalactic clouds during the epoch of galaxy formation and thus provide clues about how galaxies evolve.

We are only beginning to learn how to read the clues that hydrogen absorption lines have etched into the spectra of quasars, but the evidence gathered so far supports our general picture of spiral-galaxy evolution. The extremely wide hydrogen absorption lines thought to be associated with newly forming galaxies are typically produced by the most distant clouds, indicating that the youngest galaxies are made mostly of gas. In fact, they contain about the same amount of mass in the form of hydrogen gas as older galaxies contain in the form of stars. The hydrogen lines from nearer clouds, which arise in more mature galaxies, are not nearly as wide, presumably because a greater fraction of the gas in these galaxies has already collected into stars.

---

**Mathematical Insight 20.2**
**Weighing Supermassive Black Holes**

We weigh supermassive black holes the same way we weigh almost everything else in the universe: by measuring the velocity $v$ and orbital radius $r$ of the matter circling the central black hole. Given these measurements, we can apply the orbital velocity law from Mathematical Insight 18.1 to find the mass $M_r$ within a distance $r$ of the galactic center:

$$M_r = \frac{r \times v^2}{G}$$

*Example:* Doppler shifts show that ionized gas in the nucleus of the active galaxy M 87 orbits at a speed of about 800 km/s at a radius of 60 light-years $\approx 5.6 \times 10^{17}$ meters. Use these values to calculate the mass within 60 light-years of the galactic center.

*Solution:* Substituting the given values into the orbital velocity law, we find:

$$M_r = \frac{(5.6 \times 10^{17} \text{ m}) \times \left(8.0 \times 10^5 \, \frac{\text{m}}{\text{s}}\right)^2}{6.67 \times 10^{-11} \, \frac{\text{m}^3}{\text{kg} \times \text{s}^2}}$$

$$= 5.3 \times 10^{39} \text{ kg}$$

Converting kilograms to solar masses, we find:

$$M_r = (5.3 \times 10^{39} \text{ kg}) \times \frac{1 \text{ solar mass}}{2.0 \times 10^{30} \text{ kg}}$$

$$= 2.7 \times 10^9 \text{ solar masses}$$

The ionized gas is orbiting around a mass of about 2.7 billion solar masses. Presumably, nearly all of this mass is in the central black hole.

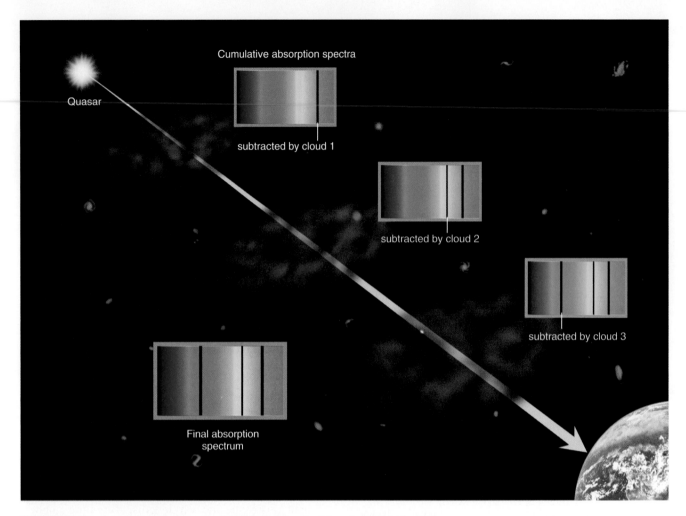

**FIGURE 20.25** This schematic illustration shows how interstellar hydrogen clouds leave their mark on the spectra of quasars. As light travels from a distant quasar to Earth, it passes through many different clouds of hydrogen gas. Hydrogen atoms within each cloud absorb light of a very specific wavelength. Because these clouds are at different distances and therefore have different redshifts, we observe the wavelength corresponding to hydrogen atoms in a different place for each cloud. Thus, each line in the final spectrum tells us about a unique hydrogen cloud along the line of sight; as we study progressively redder lines, we learn about progressively younger clouds.

Absorption lines from elements other than hydrogen corroborate this picture. The lines from these heavy elements are more prominent in the mature galaxies than in the youngest galaxies, implying that the mature galaxies have experienced more supernovae, which have added heavy elements to their interstellar gas. This overall pattern of gradual heavy-element enrichment accompanied by the gradual diminishing of interstellar hydrogen agrees well with what we know about the Milky Way. All across the universe, stars in the gaseous disks of galaxies appear to have been forming steadily for over 10 billion years.

With every new study of a quasar spectrum, we learn more about the galaxies and intergalactic clouds that have left their mark on the light we observe from quasars. Perhaps someday soon these observations will help us fit together all the pieces of the galaxy evolution puzzle, and we at last will understand the whole glorious history of galaxy evolution in our universe. Until that time, we will keep peering deep into space and back into time, searching for the clues that will unlock the mysteries of cosmic evolution.

## THE BIG PICTURE

We have not yet solved the whole puzzle of galaxy evolution, but in this chapter we have described some of its crucial pieces. As you look back, keep sight of these "big picture" ideas:

■ Although we do not yet know the complete story of galaxy evolution, we are rapidly learning more. We know that galaxies grow from protogalactic clouds of gas, but collisions with neighboring galaxies have probably affected many galaxies.

■ Galaxies in the present-day universe do not always evolve peacefully—many undergo temporary starbursts that can eject large fractions of their interstellar gas.

■ The tremendous energy outputs of quasars and other active galactic nuclei, including those of radio galaxies, are probably powered by gas accreting onto supermassive black holes. The centers of many present-day galaxies must still contain the supermassive black holes that once enabled them to shine as quasars.

■ Quasars are brilliant beacons whose light has crossed billions of light-years of space to reach us, passing through numerous intergalactic clouds and perhaps some newly forming galaxies on the way. These clouds and galaxies leave their mark on quasar spectra, revealing how protogalactic clouds were behaving before they formed most of their stars.

### Review Questions

1. What do we mean by *galaxy evolution?* Briefly describe three unanswered questions about galaxy evolution.

2. How do theoretical models help us study galaxy birth? What two assumptions underlie theoretical models of galaxy formation?

3. How do disk population stars differ from spheroidal population stars? Briefly explain how the collapse of a *protogalactic cloud* is thought to lead to these two distinct populations of stars. How does this explain why the halo of our galaxy looks so much like an elliptical galaxy?

4. What evidence suggests that the protogalactic cloud that formed our own Milky Way resulted from several collisions among smaller clouds?

5. Describe the two scenarios in which the properties of a protogalactic cloud determine whether a galaxy becomes elliptical or spiral. What evidence supports these scenarios?

6. Briefly explain why we expect that collisions between galaxies should be relatively common, while collisions between stars are extremely rare. Why should galaxy collisions have been more common in the past than they are today?

7. Briefly describe how a collision between two spiral galaxies might lead to the creation of a single elliptical galaxy. What evidence supports this scenario for the formation of elliptical galaxies?

8. What are *central dominant galaxies?* How do we think they formed?

9. Briefly explain why *starburst galaxies* often appear ordinary when they are observed in visible light but extraordinary when they are observed in infrared light.

10. What is a *galactic wind?* What causes it? How is it similar to a superbubble in the Milky Way, and how is it different?

11. Why must starbursts cease after a relatively short time? What evidence suggests that small galaxies in our Local Group have undergone two or more starbursts in the past?

12. Briefly describe the discovery of *quasars.* What evidence convinced astronomers that the high redshifts of quasars really do imply great distances? Why can we learn more about quasars by studying nearby *active galactic nuclei?*

13. Briefly explain how we can use variations in luminosity to set limits on the size of an object's emitting region. For example, if an object doubles its luminosity in 1 hour, how big can it be?

14. What is a *radio galaxy?* Describe *jets* and radio lobes. Why do we think that the ultimate energy sources of radio galaxies lie in quasarlike galactic nuclei?

15. Briefly explain the general picture of how *supermassive black holes* enable quasars to produce their huge luminosities. Summarize the evidence supporting the idea that supermassive black holes lie at the center of radio galaxies, quasars, and other active galactic nuclei.

16. Briefly explain how intergalactic clouds between a distant quasar and Earth leave distinctive marks in the quasar's spectrum.

### Discussion Questions

1. *The Case for Supermassive Black Holes.* The evidence for supermassive black holes at the center of galaxies is strong. However, it is very difficult to prove absolutely that they exist because the black holes themselves emit no light. We can only infer their existence from their powerful gravitational influences on surrounding matter. How compelling do you find the evidence? Do you think astronomers have proved the case for black holes beyond a reasonable doubt? Defend your opinion.

2. *Life in Colliding Galaxies.* Suppose the Milky Way were currently undergoing a collision with another large spiral galaxy. Do you think this collision would affect life on Earth? Why or why not? How different would the night sky look if our galaxy was in the midst of such a collision?

## Problems

*True Statements?* For **problems 1–7**, decide whether the statement is true and explain why it is or is not.

1. Galaxies that are more than 10 billion years old are too far away to see even with our most powerful telescopes.

2. Heavy elements ought to be much more common near the Milky Way's center than at its outskirts.

3. If the Andromeda Galaxy someday collides and merges with the Milky Way, then the resulting galaxy would probably be elliptical.

4. Starburst galaxies have been forming stars at the same furious pace ever since the universe was about a billion years old.

5. We know that some galaxies contain supermassive black holes because their centers are completely dark.

6. The black hole at the center of our own galaxy may once have powered an active galactic nucleus.

7. Analyses of quasar light can tell us about intergalactic clouds that might otherwise remain invisible.

8. *Life Story of a Spiral.* Imagine that you are a spiral galaxy. Describe your life history from birth to the present day. Your story should be detailed and scientifically consistent, but also creative. That is, it should be entertaining while at the same time incorporating current scientific ideas about the formation of spiral galaxies.

9. *Life Story of an Elliptical.* Imagine that you are an elliptical galaxy. Describe your life history from birth to the present. There are several possible scenarios for the formation of elliptical galaxies, so choose one and stick to it. Be creative while also incorporating scientific ideas that demonstrate your understanding.

*10. *Your Last Hurrah.* Suppose you fell into an accretion disk that swept you into a supermassive black hole. Assume that, on your way down, the disk will radiate 10% of your mass energy, $E = mc^2$. (*Hint:* See Mathematical Insight 20.1.)

a. What is your mass in kilograms? (*Hint:* Use the conversion 1 kg = 2.2 pounds.)

b. Calculate how much radiative energy will be produced by the accretion disk as a result of your fall into the black hole.

c. Calculate approximately how long a 100-watt light bulb would have to burn to radiate this same amount of energy.

*11. *The Black Hole in NGC 4258.* The molecular clouds circling the center of the active galaxy NGC 4258 orbit at a speed of about 1,000 km/s, with an orbital radius of 0.49 light-year = $4.8 \times 10^{15}$ meters. Use the orbital velocity law (see Mathematical Insight 20.2) to calculate the mass of the central black hole. Give your answer both in kilograms and in solar masses ($1M_{Sun} = 2.0 \times 10^{30}$ kg).

## Web Projects

Find useful links for Web projects on the text Web site.

1. *Future Missions.* The subject of galaxy evolution is a very active area of research. Look for information on current and future NASA missions involved in investigating galaxy evolution (such as the Next Generation Space Telescope). How big are the planned telescopes? What wavelengths will they look at? When will they be launched? Write a short summary of a proposed mission.

2. *Greatest Redshift.* As of early 2001, the most distant quasar known has a redshift $z = 5.8$, meaning that the wavelengths of its light are 1 + 5.8 = 6.8 longer than normal. Find the current record holder for the largest redshift. Write a one-page report describing the object and its discovery.

3. *The Quasar Controversy.* For many years, some astronomers argued that quasars were not really as distant as Hubble's law indicates. Research the history of the discovery of quasars and the debates that followed. What evidence led some astronomers to think quasars might be nearer than Hubble's law suggested? Why did most astronomers eventually conclude that quasars really are far away? Write a one- to two-page report summarizing your findings.

*It is difficult beyond description to conceive that space can have no end; but it is more difficult to conceive an end. It is difficult beyond the power of man to conceive an eternal duration of what we call time; but it is more impossible to conceive a time when there shall be no time.*

THOMAS PAINE, *THE AGE OF REASON* (1796)

# CHAPTER 21

# Dark Matter and the Fate of the Universe

The majority of the matter in the universe, the stuff that binds galaxies together with the force of its own gravity, is too dark to see. We know that this matter exists because we can detect its gravitational influence on other things, but what is this so-called *dark matter*? Do armies of Jupiter-size bodies, too dim for us to see at a distance, populate the voids between the stars? Could black holes be responsible? Or is dark matter an entirely new form of matter, still undiscovered here on Earth? We don't yet know the answer. Incredibly, we still haven't identified the most common form of matter in the universe, making dark matter one of the greatest cosmic mysteries.

In this chapter, we will investigate why most astronomers believe that dark matter exists. We'll see how it affects structures the size of galaxies and larger. We'll investigate current hypotheses about the nature of dark matter. We'll see how the fate of the universe relates to the question of just how much dark matter there is. And we'll explore recent evidence suggesting that the universe's expansion may be accelerating.

## 21.1 The Mystery of Dark Matter

We first encountered dark matter when we studied the Milky Way's rotation in Chapter 18. We saw that atomic hydrogen clouds lying farther from the galactic center than our Sun orbit the galaxy at unexpectedly high speeds. We concluded that much of our galaxy's mass must lie beyond the distance of the Sun's orbit around the galactic center, distributed throughout the galaxy's spherical halo [Section 18.4]. Yet most of the Milky Way's *light* comes from stars lying closer to the galaxy's center than does our Sun. Together, these facts imply that the halo contains large amounts of matter but this matter emits so little light that we cannot see it. Thus, we call it *dark matter.*

Does dark matter really exist? To claim that the galaxy is filled with a form of matter that we cannot yet identify may seem strange, but there are only two possible explanations for the high orbital velocities of the atomic hydrogen clouds: Either their velocities are caused by the gravitational attraction of unseen matter, or we are doing something wrong when we apply the law of gravity to understand their orbits. The latter possibility would imply that we do not understand how gravity operates on galaxy-size scales, but our theories of gravity successfully account for many cosmic phenomena. Thus, the vast majority of astronomers believe that we correctly understand gravity and that dark matter must really exist.

The evidence that the Milky Way contains dark matter qualifies as an interesting surprise on its own, but it is also a glimpse into a more profound mystery. If our suspicions about dark matter are correct, then the luminous part of the Milky Way's disk must be rather like the tip of an iceberg, marking only the center of a much larger clump of mass (Figure 21.1). A more detailed analysis involving the motions of nearby dwarf galaxies shows that the total mass of dark matter in the Milky Way might be 10 times greater than the mass of visible stars. Each galaxy in the universe is similar to our own in this respect, meaning that we probably cannot see most of the matter in the universe. This matter's darkness makes it challenging to study, but its overwhelming dominance of the universe makes it extremely important. Dark matter, by virtue of its mighty gravitational pull, seems to be the glue that holds galaxies and clusters of galaxies together.

Dark matter has even more profound implications for the fate of the universe. The universe ultimately has two possible fates: It might continue to expand forever, or it might someday stop expanding and begin to collapse. We do not yet know which fate awaits our universe because the answer depends on the overall density of matter in the universe—and we cannot determine the overall density until we first determine how much dark matter is out there. Thus, the very fate of the universe hinges on the total amount of dark matter.

In this chapter, we will presume that we understand gravity correctly and consequently that dark matter pervades the universe. If our understanding of gravity is correct, then we already know quite a lot about dark matter, despite the fact that its composition remains a mystery. We do not know the total amount of dark matter in the universe, but we can measure the amounts in individual galaxies and clusters of galaxies from its gravitational effects. We can even make some reasonable guesses as to what it will turn out to be. We'll begin by discussing how we "discover" dark matter and conclude by discussing what our current knowledge predicts about the ultimate fate of the universe.

**FIGURE 21.1** Dark matter distribution relative to luminous matter in a spiral galaxy.

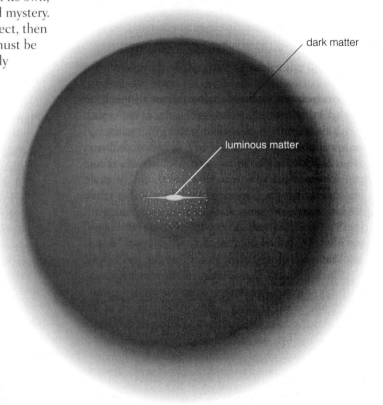

dark matter

luminous matter

## 21.2  Dark Matter in Galaxies

The claim that dark matter far outweighs the visible matter in the universe might seem farfetched, but it rests on fundamental physical laws. Newton's laws of motion and gravity are among the most trustworthy tools in science. We have used them time and again to measure masses of celestial objects. We found the masses of the Earth and the Sun by applying Newton's version of Kepler's third law [Section 5.4]. We used this same law to calculate the masses of stars in binary star systems, revealing the general relationships between the masses of stars and their outward appearances. Newton's laws have also told us the masses of things we can't see directly, such as the masses of neutron stars in X-ray binaries and of black holes in active galactic nuclei. These laws have proved extremely reliable in many different applications. Thus, when Newton's laws tell us that dark matter exists, we are not inclined to ignore them.

We determine the amount of dark matter in a galaxy from the galaxy's mass and luminosity: We can infer the total mass in stars from the galaxy's luminosity, so whatever additional mass remains unaccounted for must be dark. Measuring a galaxy's luminosity is relatively easy. We simply point a telescope at the galaxy in question, measure its apparent brightness, and calculate its luminosity from the luminosity–distance formula [Section 15.2]. Measuring the mass is more complicated. We would like to apply Newton's laws in the form of the orbital velocity law from Chapter 18 to matter orbiting as far from the galaxy's center as possible. However, the matter farthest from the center of a galaxy is extremely dim. For all we know, the matter at the edge of a galaxy might be completely dark.

### *Weighing Spiral Galaxies*

We can weigh a spiral galaxy by measuring the gravitational effects of the galaxy's mass on the orbits of objects in its disk. Even beyond the point in the disk at which starlight fades into the blackness of intergalactic space, we can still see radio waves from atomic hydrogen gas. We can therefore use Doppler shifts of the 21-cm emission line of atomic hydrogen [Section 18.2] to determine how quickly this gas moves toward us or away from us (Figure 21.2). Galaxies beyond the Local Group have cosmological redshifts affecting all their spectral lines. However, on one side of a spiral galaxy the gas is rotating away from us, so its 21-cm line is redshifted a little more than the redshift of the galaxy as a whole. On the other side, the 21-cm line is blueshifted relative to the redshift of the galaxy as a whole because the gas is rotating toward us. From the Doppler shifts of these clouds, we can construct a *rotation curve*—a plot

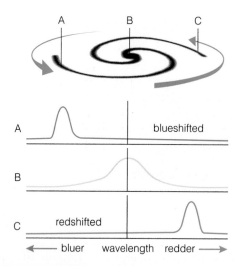

**FIGURE 21.2** Measuring the rotation of a spiral galaxy with the 21-cm line of atomic hydrogen. Blueshifted lines on the left side of the disk show how fast that side is rotating toward us. Redshifted lines on the right side show how fast that side is rotating away from us.

showing orbital velocities of gas clouds and stars—just as we did for the Milky Way (Figure 21.3) [Section 18.4]. A rotation curve contains all the information we need to measure the mass contained within the orbits of the outermost gas clouds. (Because the Doppler effect tells us only about the velocity of material directly toward or away from us, we must also take into account the tilt of the galaxy before we construct the rotation curve.)

**TIME OUT TO THINK** *As a brief review, draw a rotation curve for our solar system. How does the solar system rotation curve differ from the rotation curve of the Milky Way? What does that tell us about the distribution of matter in the Milky Way? Why? (Hint: See Chapter 18 for review.)*

The rotation curves of most spiral galaxies turn out to be remarkably flat as far out as we can see, which means that the orbital speeds of gas clouds remain roughly constant with increasing distance from the galactic center (Figure 21.4). We saw in Chapter 18 that our Milky Way's rotation curve remains more or less flat from well within the radius of the Sun's orbit (28,000 light-years) to beyond twice that radius. The rotation curves of some other spiral galaxies are flat to well beyond 150,000 light-years.

Because the orbital speeds of gas clouds tell us the amount of mass contained within their orbital paths, the flat rotation curves imply that a great deal of matter lies far from the galactic center [Section 18.4]. In particular, if we imagine drawing bigger and bigger circles around a galaxy, the flat rotation curves imply that we must keep encircling more and more matter.

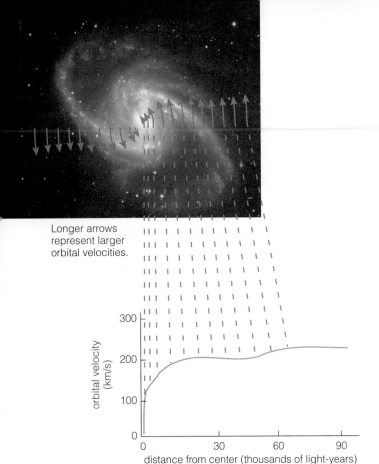

Longer arrows represent larger orbital velocities.

**FIGURE 21.3** A rotation curve shows the orbital velocities of stars or gas clouds at different distances from a galaxy's center.

The mass of a spiral galaxy with gas clouds orbiting at 200 km/s at a distance of 150,000 light-years from its center must be at least 500 billion ($5 \times 10^{11}$) solar masses.

### Weighing Elliptical Galaxies

We must use a different technique to weigh elliptical galaxies, because most of them contain very little atomic hydrogen gas and hence do not produce detectable 21-cm radiation. Instead, we generally weigh the inner parts of elliptical galaxies by observing the motions of the stars themselves.

The motions of stars in an elliptical galaxy are disorganized, so we cannot assemble their velocities into a sensible rotation curve. Nevertheless, the velocity of each individual star still responds to the mass inside the star's orbit. At any particular distance from an elliptical galaxy's center, some stars are moving toward us and some are moving away from us. Thus, the spectral lines from the galaxy as a whole tend to be smeared out: Instead of a nice sharp line at a particular wavelength, we see a *broadened* line spanning a range of wavelengths reflecting the various Doppler shifts of the individual stars (Figure 21.5). The greater the broadening of the spectral line, the faster the stars must be moving.

When we compare spectral lines from different regions of an elliptical galaxy, we find that the speeds of the stars remain fairly constant as we look farther from the galactic center. Thus, just as in spirals, most of the matter in elliptical galaxies must lie beyond the distance where the light trails off and hence must be dark matter. However, we cannot determine the *total* amount of dark matter in elliptical galaxies as well as we can in spirals, because we cannot measure their masses as far from their centers. In ellipticals we can study only the motions of stars, while in spirals we are able to detect the 21-cm radiation from gas clouds well beyond the radii at which we no longer see individual stars.

### Mass-to-Light Ratio

We can determine how much dark matter a galaxy contains by comparing the galaxy's measured mass to its luminosity. For example, the Milky Way contains about 90 billion ($9 \times 10^{10}$) solar masses of material within the Sun's orbit. However, the total luminosity of stars within this region is only about 15 billion ($1.5 \times 10^{10}$) solar luminosities. Thus, on average, it takes 6 solar masses of matter to produce 1 solar luminosity of light in this region of the galaxy (15 billion × 6 = 90 billion). We therefore say that

**FIGURE 21.4** Actual rotation curves of four spiral galaxies.

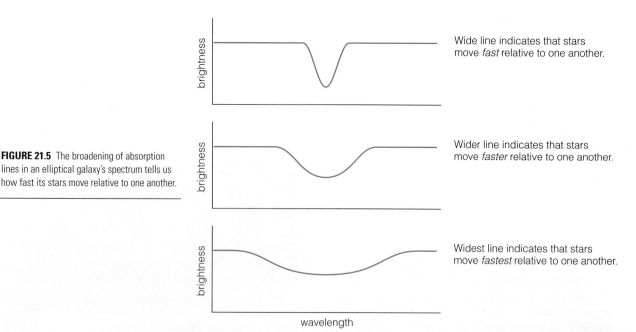

Wide line indicates that stars move *fast* relative to one another.

Wider line indicates that stars move *faster* relative to one another.

Widest line indicates that stars move *fastest* relative to one another.

wavelength

**FIGURE 21.5** The broadening of absorption lines in an elliptical galaxy's spectrum tells us how fast its stars move relative to one another.

the Milky Way's **mass-to-light ratio** within the Sun's orbit is about 6 solar masses per solar luminosity. This fact tells us that most matter is dimmer than our Sun, which is not surprising since we know that most stars are smaller and dimmer than our Sun. We find similar mass-to-light ratios for the inner regions of most other spiral galaxies.

**TIME OUT TO THINK** *Because the Sun's mass is $1M_{Sun}$ and its luminosity is $1L_{Sun}$, its mass-to-light ratio is $1M_{Sun}/1L_{Sun}$ = 1 solar mass per solar luminosity. What is the mass-to-light ratio of a $1M_{Sun}$ red giant with luminosity $100L_{Sun}$? What is the mass-to-light ratio of a $1M_{Sun}$ white dwarf with luminosity $0.001L_{Sun}$?*

Elliptical galaxies contain virtually no luminous high-mass stars, so their stars are less bright on average than the stars in a spiral galaxy. In the inner regions of elliptical galaxies, the orbits of stars indicate a mass-to-light ratio of about 10 solar masses per solar luminosity—nearly double the mass-to-light ratio in the central region of the Milky Way. This is not surprising given the fact that elliptical galaxies have dimmer stars.

The surprise in mass-to-light ratios—and one of the key pieces of evidence for the existence of dark matter—comes when we look to the outer reaches of galaxies. As we look farther from a galaxy's center, we find a lot more mass but not much more light. The mass-to-light ratios for entire spiral galaxies can be as high as 50 solar masses per solar luminosity, and the overall ratios in some dwarf galaxies can be even higher. We are forced to conclude that stars alone cannot account for the amount of mass pres-

## Mathematical Insight 21.1    Mass-to-Light Ratio

Mathematically, an object's mass-to-light ratio is defined as its total mass in units of solar masses divided by its total luminosity in units of solar luminosities. Thus, by definition, the mass-to-light ratio of the Sun is:

$$\frac{1 \text{ solar mass}}{1 \text{ solar luminosity}} = 1 \text{ solar mass per solar luminosity}$$

A galaxy made entirely of stars just like the Sun would have a mass-to-light ratio identical to that of the Sun.

*Example 1:* What is the mass-to-light ratio of the matter inside the solar circle of the Milky Way?

*Solution:* To answer this question, we divide the 90 billion solar masses inside the solar circle by the 15 billion solar luminosities of the stars in the same region:

$$\frac{9 \times 10^{10} \text{ solar masses}}{1.5 \times 10^{10} \text{ solar luminosities}} = 6 \text{ solar masses per solar luminosity}$$

Because this mass-to-light ratio is larger than the Sun's ratio of 1, the average luminosity of objects in this region of the Milky Way must be less than that of the Sun.

*Example 2:* Suppose a galaxy contains $5 \times 10^{11}$ solar masses within a radius of 150,000 light-years of its center, but its total luminosity is only $1.5 \times 10^{10}$ solar luminosities. What is its mass-to-light ratio? What does this imply?

*Solution:* Again we divide the total mass by the total luminosity. The mass-to-light ratio within 150,000 light-years of this galaxy's center is:

$$\frac{5 \times 10^{11} \text{ solar masses}}{1.5 \times 10^{10} \text{ solar luminosities}} = 33 \text{ solar masses per solar luminosity}$$

Taken as a whole, the mass in this galaxy is far darker, on average, than the Sun or than the objects in the inner region of the Milky Way.

ent in galaxies. For example, if a galaxy's overall mass-to-light ratio is 60 solar masses per solar luminosity and its stars account for only 6 solar masses per solar luminosity, then the remaining 90% of the galaxy's mass must be dark.

## 21.3 Dark Matter in Clusters

The problem of dark matter in astronomy is not particularly new. In the 1930s, astronomer Fritz Zwicky was already arguing that clusters of galaxies held enormous amounts of this mysterious stuff (Figure 21.6). Few of his colleagues paid attention, but later observations supported Zwicky's claims. We can now weigh clusters of galaxies in three different ways: by measuring the speeds of galaxies orbiting the center of the cluster, by studying the X-ray emission from hot gas between the cluster galaxies, and by observing how the clusters bend light as *gravitational lenses* [Section S3.5]. All three techniques indicate that clusters contain huge amounts of dark matter. Let's investigate each of these techniques more closely.

**FIGURE 21.6** Fritz Zwicky.

### Orbiting Galaxies

Zwicky was one of the first astronomers to think of galaxy clusters as huge swarms of galaxies bound together by gravity. It seemed natural to him that galaxies clumped closely in space should all be orbiting one another, just like the stars in a star cluster. He therefore assumed that he could measure cluster masses by observing galaxy motions and applying the orbital velocity law.

Armed with a spectrograph, Zwicky measured the redshifts of the galaxies in a particular cluster and used these redshifts to calculate the speeds at which the individual galaxies are moving away from us. He determined the velocity of the cluster as a whole by averaging the velocities of its individual galaxies. He then estimated the speed of a galaxy around the cluster— that is, its orbital speed—by subtracting this average velocity from the individual galaxy's velocity. Finally, he plugged these orbital speeds into an appropriate form of the orbital velocity law [Section 18.4] to estimate the cluster's mass and compared this mass to the luminosity of the cluster. To his surprise, Zwicky found that clusters of galaxies have huge mass-to-light ratios: They contain hundreds of solar masses for each solar luminosity of radiation they emit. He concluded that most of the matter within these clusters must be

almost entirely dark. Many astronomers disregarded Zwicky's result, believing that he must have done something wrong to arrive at such a strange answer.

Today, far more sophisticated measurements of galaxy orbits in clusters confirm Zwicky's original finding. We cannot measure the actual orbital velocity and position of a single galaxy; we can measure only its *radial velocity* along our line of sight (Figure 21.7).

**FIGURE 21.7** A galaxy's true velocity can be broken into a radial component along our line of sight and a tangential component across our line of sight. Doppler shifts tell us only the radial component; we cannot measure the tangential component for distant galaxies.

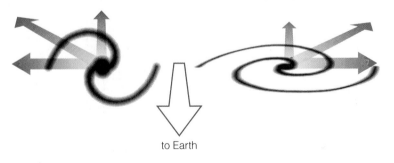

to Earth

→ radial velocity (along our line of sight)

→ tangential velocity (across our line of sight)

→ true (total) velocity

## Pioneers of Science

Scientists always take a risk when they publish what they think are ground-breaking results. If their results turn out to be in error, their reputations may suffer. In the case of dark matter, the pioneers in its discovery risked their entire careers. A case in point is Fritz Zwicky, with his proclamations in the 1930s about dark matter in clusters of galaxies. Most of his colleagues considered him an eccentric who leapt to premature conclusions.

Another pioneer in the discovery of dark matter was Vera Rubin, an astronomer at the Carnegie Institute. Working in the 1960s, she became the first woman to observe under her own name at California's Palomar Observatory, then the largest telescope in the world. (Another woman, Margaret Burbidge, was permitted to observe at Palomar earlier but was required to apply for time under the name of her husband, also an astronomer.) Rubin first saw the gravitational signature of dark matter in spectra she recorded of stars in the Andromeda Galaxy. She noticed that stars in the outskirts of Andromeda moved at suprisingly high speeds, suggesting a stronger gravitational attraction than could be explained by the mass of the galaxy's stars

alone. In other words, she found that the rotation curve for Andromeda is relatively flat to great distances from the center, just as we now know is also the case for the Milky Way. Working with a colleague, Kent Ford, she constructed rotation curves for the hydrogen gas in many other spiral galaxies (by studying Doppler shifts in the spectra of hydrogen gas) and discovered that flat rotation curves are common. Although Rubin and Ford did not immediately recognize the significance of the results, they were soon arguing that the universe must contain substantial quantities of dark matter.

For a while, other astronomers had trouble believing the results. Some astronomers suspected that the bright galaxies studied by Rubin and Ford were unusual for some reason. So Rubin and Ford went back to work, obtaining rotation curves for fainter galaxies. They found flat rotation curves—a signature of dark matter—even in these galaxies. By the 1980s, the evidence compiled by Rubin and Ford was so overwhelming that even their early critics came around. Either the theory of gravity was wrong, or they had discovered dark matter in spiral galaxies.

a

b

**FIGURE 21.8** (**a**) The Coma Cluster of galaxies seen in visible light. Virtually every pictured object here is a galaxy. (**b**) A map of X-ray emission from the Coma Cluster. Hot, X ray–emitting gas (the intracluster medium) bound to the cluster by gravity fills the spaces between the galaxies.

However, if we measure the radial velocities of many galaxies in a cluster, we can estimate the average orbital velocity of all the cluster's galaxies. Cluster masses found in this way imply lots of dark matter. The visible portions of a cluster's galaxies represent less than 10% of the cluster's mass.

### Intracluster Medium

A second method for weighing a cluster of galaxies relies on X-ray observations of the hot gas that fills the space between the galaxies in the cluster (Figure 21.8). This gas, also known as the **intracluster medium** (*intra* means "within"), is so hot that it emits primarily X rays and therefore went undetected until the 1960s, when X-ray telescopes were finally launched above the Earth's atmosphere. The temperature of this gas is tens of millions of degrees in many clusters and can exceed 100 million degrees in the largest clusters. Even though the intracluster medium is invisible in optical light, its mass often exceeds the mass of all the visible stars in all the cluster's galaxies combined. The largest clusters of galaxies contain up to five times more matter in the form of hot gas than in the form of stars.

The temperature of the hot intracluster gas depends on the mass of the cluster itself, enabling us to use X-ray telescopes to measure the masses of galaxy clusters. The intracluster medium in most clusters is nearly in a state of *gravitational equilibrium*—that is, the outward gas pressure balances gravity's inward pull [Section 14.1]. In this state of balance, the average kinetic energies of the gas particles are determined primarily by the strength of gravity and hence by the amount of mass within the cluster. Because the temperature of a gas reflects the average kinetic energies of its particles, the gas temperatures we measure with X-ray telescopes tell us the average speeds of the X ray–emitting particles. We can then use these speeds and the orbital velocity law to weigh the cluster.

The results obtained with this method agree well with the results found by studying the orbital motions of the cluster's galaxies. Again, we find that mass-to-light ratios in clusters of galaxies generally exceed 100 solar masses per solar luminosity. Even after accounting for the hot intracluster gas, it is clear that clusters must contain huge quantities of dark matter binding all the galaxies together.

### Gravitational Lensing

We have so far relied exclusively on methods derived from Newton's laws, such as the orbital velocity law, to measure galaxy and cluster masses. These laws

---

### Mathematical Insight 21.2    Masses of Clusters

The first two of the three ways described in the text for measuring the masses of galaxy clusters rely on the orbital velocity law from Mathematical Insight 18.1 to find the mass $M_r$ within a distance $r$ of the galactic center:

$$M_r = \frac{r \times v^2}{G}$$

where $v$ is the velocity of objects moving under the influence of gravity. This formula can also be applied to clusters of galaxies.

In the case where we measure the orbital speeds of galaxies directly, we simply use the average speed of the galaxies and the cluster radius in the orbital velocity law. In the case where we measure the temperature of hot, intracluster gas from its X-ray emission, we must first convert the gas temperature into an average speed for the gas particles. Although we will not present a derivation here, we can make this conversion with the following formula, which gives the approximate average speeds of the hydrogen nuclei in a gas of temperature $T$:

$$\text{average speed of hydrogen nuclei} \approx 100 \, \frac{m}{s} \times \sqrt{T} \quad (T \text{ in Kelvin})$$

Once we find this speed, we can use it as $v$ in the orbital velocity law.

*Example:* Suppose a cluster has a radius of 3.3 million light-years ($3.1 \times 10^{22}$ meters). Its galaxies orbit with an average speed of approximately 1,000 km/s ($1 \times 10^6$ m/s), and its intracluster gas has a temperature of $9 \times 10^7$ K. Find the cluster's mass from both the galaxy speeds and the gas temperature. Do the results agree?

*Solution:* First, we find the mass from the galaxy speeds. We set $r = 3.1 \times 10^{22}$ m for the cluster radius, set $v \approx 1 \times 10^6$ m/s for the average speed of the galaxies, and assign the gravitational constant $G$ its usual value. Plugging these values into the orbital velocity law, we find:

$$\text{cluster mass} = M_r \approx \frac{(3.1 \times 10^{22} \, m) \times \left(1 \times 10^6 \, \frac{m}{s}\right)^2}{6.67 \times 10^{-11} \, \frac{m^3}{kg \times s^2}}$$

$$= 4.6 \times 10^{44} \, kg$$

To find the mass from the temperature of the X ray–emitting gas, we first use the given formula to find the average speeds of the hydrogen nuclei in the gas:

$$\text{average speed} \approx 100 \, \frac{m}{s} \times \sqrt{T} = 100 \, \frac{m}{s} \times \sqrt{9 \times 10^7}$$

$$= 9.5 \times 10^5 \, \frac{m}{s}$$

Plugging this velocity into the orbital velocity law, we find:

$$\text{cluster mass} = M_r \approx \frac{(3.1 \times 10^{22} \, m) \times \left(9.5 \times 10^5 \, \frac{m}{s}\right)^2}{6.67 \times 10^{-11} \, \frac{m^3}{kg \times s^2}}$$

$$= 4.2 \times 10^{44} \, kg$$

Note that the two methods have given two results that agree fairly well: $4.6 \times 10^{44}$ kg and $4.2 \times 10^{44}$ kg. Thus, we can be confident that we are in the correct range for the actual mass of the cluster. Taking $4.4 \times 10^{44}$ kg as an intermediate value and recalling that the Sun's mass is $2.0 \times 10^{30}$ kg, we find:

$$\text{cluster mass} \approx (4.4 \times 10^{44} \, kg) \times \frac{1 \text{ solar mass}}{2.0 \times 10^{30} \, kg}$$

$$= 2.2 \times 10^{14} \text{ solar masses}$$

**FIGURE 21.9** Hubble Space Telescope picture of a galaxy cluster acting as a gravitational lens. The yellow elliptical galaxies are cluster members, and the odd, blue ovals are multiple images of a single galaxy that lies almost directly behind the cluster's center.

keep telling us that the universe holds far more matter than we can see. Can we trust these laws? Today, we have another tool for measuring masses: *gravitational lensing.*

Gravitational lensing occurs because masses distort spacetime—the "fabric" of the universe [Section S3.3]. Massive objects can therefore act as **gravitational lenses** that bend light beams passing nearby. This prediction of Einstein's theory of general relativity was first verified in 1919 during an eclipse of the Sun [Section S3.5]. Because the light-bending angle of a gravitational lens depends on the mass of the object doing the bending, we can measure the masses of objects by observing how strongly they distort light paths.

Figure 21.9 shows a striking example of how a cluster of galaxies can act as a gravitational lens. Many of the yellow elliptical galaxies concentrated toward the center of the picture belong to the cluster, but at least one of the galaxies pictured does not. At several positions on various sides of the central clump of yellow galaxies you will notice multiple images of the same blue galaxy. Each one of these images, whose sizes differ, looks like a distorted oval with an off-center smudge.

The blue galaxy seen in these multiple images lies almost directly behind the center of the cluster, at a much greater distance. Multiple images arise because photons traveling from this blue galaxy to Earth do not follow straight paths. Instead, the cluster's gravity bends their paths as they pass through the cluster, enabling light from this galaxy to arrive at Earth from a few slightly different directions. Each alternative path produces a separate, distorted image of the blue galaxy, making this one galaxy look like several galaxies (Figure 21.10).

Multiple images of a gravitationally lensed galaxy are rare, occurring only when a distant galaxy lies

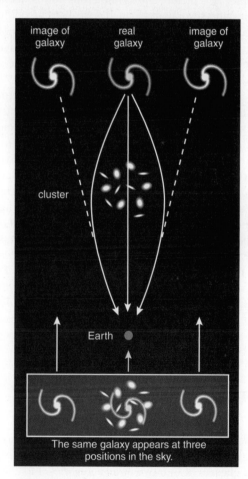

**FIGURE 21.10** A cluster's powerful gravity bends light paths from background galaxies to Earth. If light can arrive from several different directions, we see multiple images of the same galaxy.

directly behind the lensing cluster, but single images of gravitationally lensed galaxies behind clusters are quite common. Figure 21.11 shows a more typical example. This picture shows numerous normal-looking galaxies and several arc-shaped galaxies. The oddly curved galaxies are not members of the cluster, nor are they really curved. They are normal galaxies lying far beyond the cluster whose images have been distorted by the cluster's gravity.

Careful analyses of the distorted images in pictures of clusters like these enable us to weigh the clusters without resorting to the orbital velocity law. Instead, Einstein's theory of general relativity tells us how massive these clusters must be to generate the observed distortions. It is reassuring that cluster masses derived in this way generally agree with those derived from galaxy velocities and X-ray temperatures. The three different methods all indicate that clusters of galaxies hold very substantial amounts of dark matter.

**TIME OUT TO THINK** *Should the fact that we have three different ways of measuring cluster masses give us greater confidence that we really do understand gravity and that dark matter really does exist? Why or why not?*

## 21.4 Dark Matter: Ordinary or Extraordinary?

We do not yet know what the dark matter in galaxies and clusters of galaxies is composed of, but our educated guesses fit into two basic categories. First, some or all of the dark matter could be *ordinary,* made of protons, neutrons, and electrons. In that case, the only unusual thing about dark matter is that it is dim; other-wise it is made of the same stuff as all the "bright matter" that we can see. The second possibility is that some or all of the dark matter is *extraordinary,* made of particles that we have yet to discover. A bit more terminology will be useful. Protons and neutrons belong to a category of particles called **baryons**, so ordinary matter is sometimes called **baryonic matter**. (Technically, a baryon is a particle made from three quarks [Section S4.2].) By extension, extraordinary matter is called **nonbaryonic matter**.

### Ordinary Dark Matter: MACHOs

Matter need not be extraordinary to be dark. In astronomy, "dark" merely means not as bright as a normal star and therefore not visible across vast distances of space. Your body is dark matter. Everything you own is dark matter. Earth and the planets are also dark matter. The process of star formation itself leaves behind dark matter in the form of *brown dwarfs,* those dim "failed stars" that are not quite massive enough to sustain nuclear fusion [Section 16.2]. Some scientists believe that trillions of faint red stars, brown dwarfs, and Jupiter-size objects left over from the Milky Way's formation still roam our galaxy's halo, providing much of its mass. They fancifully term these objects **MACHOs**, for *massive compact halo objects.*

Because MACHOs are too faint for us to see directly, astronomers who wish to detect them must resort to clever techniques. One innovative way to detect faint starlike objects in the Milky Way's halo takes advantage of gravitational lensing. If trillions of these MACHOs really exist, every once in a while a MACHO should drift across our line of sight to a more distant star. When a MACHO lies almost directly between us and the farther star, the MACHO's gravity will focus the star's light directly toward the Earth. The distant star will appear much brighter

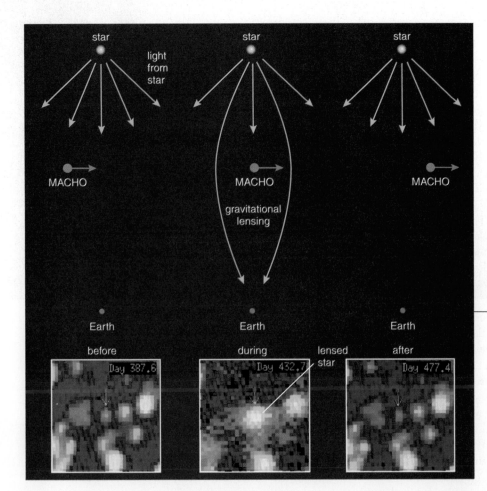

**FIGURE 21.12** A lensing event in which a MACHO passing in front of a more distant star temporarily makes the star appear brighter, revealing the presence of the dark MACHO. Multiple images of the star are possible, but they are too close together to resolve with current telescopes.

than usual for several days or weeks as the MACHO passes in front of it (Figure 21.12). We cannot see the MACHO itself, but the duration of the lensing event reveals its mass.

Gravitational lensing events such as these are rare; they happen to about one star in a million each year. To detect MACHO lensing events, we therefore must monitor huge numbers of stars. Current large-scale monitoring projects now record numerous lensing events annually. These events demonstrate that MACHOs do indeed populate our galaxy's halo, but probably not in large enough numbers to account for all the Milky Way's dark matter. Something else lurks unseen in the outer reaches of our galaxy. Maybe it is also normal matter made from baryons, but maybe not.

### Extraordinary Dark Matter: WIMPs

A more exotic possibility is that most of the dark matter in galaxies and clusters of galaxies is not made of ordinary, baryonic matter at all. Let's begin to explore this possibility by taking another look at those non-baryonic particles we discussed in Section 14.3: neutrinos. These unusual particles are dark by their very nature, because they have no electrical charge and hence cannot emit electromagnetic radiation of any kind. Moreover, they are never bound together with

charged particles in the way that neutrons are bound in atomic nuclei, so their presence cannot be revealed by associated light-emitting particles. In fact, particles like neutrinos interact with other forms of matter through only two of the four forces: gravity and the *weak force* [Section S4.2]. For this reason, they are said to be *weakly interacting particles*. If you recall that trillions of neutrinos from the Sun are passing through your body at this very moment without doing any damage, you'll see why the name *weakly interacting* fits well.

The dark matter in galaxies cannot be made of neutrinos, because these tiny particles travel through the universe at enormous speeds and can easily escape a galaxy's gravitational pull. (However, as we'll discuss shortly, neutrinos might contribute to the amount of dark matter outside galaxies.) But what if other weakly interacting particles exist that are similar to neutrinos but considerably heavier? They too would evade direct detection, but they would move more slowly and could collect into galaxies, adding mass without adding light. Such hypothetical particles are called **WIMPs**, for *weakly interacting massive particles*. (Weakly interacting particles that are slow-moving enough to collect into galaxies are sometimes called *cold dark matter* to set them apart from faster-moving *hot dark matter* particles such as neutrinos.) WIMPs could make up most of our galaxy's mass, but they would be completely invisible in all wavelengths of light.

It might surprise you that scientists would suspect the universe to be filled with particles they haven't yet discovered. However, WIMPs could also explain why dark matter doesn't behave like the visible matter in galaxies. During the early stages of the Milky Way's formation, the ordinary (baryonic) matter settled toward our galaxy's center and then flattened into a disk. Meanwhile, the dark matter stayed where it was, out in the galaxy's halo. This resistance of the dark matter to settling is exactly what we would expect from weakly interacting particles. Because WIMPs do not emit electromagnetic radiation, they cannot radiate away their energy. They are therefore stuck orbiting out at large distances and cannot collapse with the rest of the protogalactic cloud. By itself, the inability of dark matter to settle into the luminous regions of galaxies does not prove that dark matter is extraordinary and nonbaryonic. However, as we'll discuss in the next chapter, some other reasons lead us to believe that baryons represent only a minority of the universe's mass and hence that WIMPs really exist.

**TIME OUT TO THINK** *What do you think of the idea that much of the universe is made of as-yet-undiscovered particles? Can you think of other instances in the history of science in which the existence of something was predicted before it was discovered?*

## 21.5 Structure Formation

Dark matter remains enigmatic, but every year we are learning more about its role in the universe. Because galaxies and clusters of galaxies seem to contain much more dark matter than luminous matter, we believe that dark matter's gravitational pull must be the primary force holding these structures together. Thus, we strongly suspect that the gravitational attraction of dark matter is what pulled galaxies and clusters together in the first place.

### Growth of Structure

Stars, galaxies, and clusters of galaxies are all *gravitationally bound systems,* meaning that their gravity is strong enough to hold them together. In most of the gravitationally bound systems we have discussed so far, gravity has completely overwhelmed the expansion of the universe. That is, while the universe as a whole is expanding, space is *not* expanding within

our solar system, our galaxy, or our Local Group of galaxies.

Our best guess at how galaxies formed, briefly outlined in Section 20.2, envisions them growing from slight density enhancements that were present in the very early universe. During the first few million years after the Big Bang, the universe expanded everywhere. But the stronger gravity in regions of enhanced density gradually pulled in matter until these regions stopped expanding and became protogalactic clouds—even as the universe as a whole continued (and still continues) to expand. If dark matter is indeed the most common form of mass in galaxies, it must have provided most of the gravitational attraction responsible for creating the protogalactic clouds. The hydrogen and helium gas in the protogalactic clouds collapsed inward and gave birth to stars, while weakly interacting dark matter remained in the outskirts because of its inability to radiate away its orbital energy. According to this model, the luminous matter in each galaxy must still be nestled inside the larger cocoon of dark matter that initiated the galaxy's formation, just as observational evidence seems to suggest.

The formation of galaxy clusters probably echoes the formation of galaxies. Early on, all the galaxies that will eventually constitute a cluster are flying apart with the expansion of the universe. But the gravity of the dark matter associated with the cluster eventually reverses the trajectories of these galaxies. The galaxies ultimately fall back inward and start orbiting each other randomly, like the stars in the halo of our galaxy.

Some clusters of galaxies apparently have not yet finished forming: Their immense gravity continues to draw in new members. For example, the nearby Virgo Cluster of galaxies appears to be tugging on our own Local Group. Right now the Local Group is still moving away from the Virgo Cluster, but not as quickly as a simple application of Hubble's law would predict. Hubble's law lets us calculate the speed at which universal expansion carries us away from the Virgo Cluster [Section 19.4], but it does not account for any gravitational effects. The discrepancy between a straight application of Hubble's law and our actual velocity away from the Virgo Cluster is about 400 km/s. That is, we are moving away from the Virgo Cluster 400 km/s more slowly than we would be as a result of the expansion of the universe alone. Astronomers call this 400-km/s deviation from Hubble's law a **peculiar velocity**, but it's really not so peculiar. It is simply the effect of the gravitational attraction pulling us back toward Virgo against the flow of universal expansion. The overall effect is rather like that of swimming upstream against a strong current: You move "upstream" relative to other objects floating in the current, but you're still headed "downstream" relative to the shore because of the strong current. The speed of the current is like the speed of expansion of the universe, and your swimming speed "upstream" is your peculiar velocity.

Just as the Earth's gravity slows a rising baseball and eventually turns it around and pulls it back toward the ground, the gravitational tug of the Virgo Cluster may eventually turn the galaxies of our Local Group around and pull them into the cluster. Similar processes are taking place on the outskirts of other large clusters of galaxies, where we see many galaxies with large peculiar velocities pointing in the direction of the cluster. Their peculiar velocities indicate that the cluster's gravity is pulling on them. Eventually, some or perhaps all of these galaxies will fall into the cluster. Thus, many clusters are still attracting galaxies, adding to the hundreds they already contain. On even larger scales, clusters themselves have surprisingly large peculiar velocities, hinting that they are parts of even bigger gravitationally bound systems, called **superclusters**, that are just beginning to form (Figure 21.13).

### Large-Scale Structures

Beyond about 300 million light-years, we can no longer measure distances accurately enough to determine peculiar velocities. We can estimate the distances to faraway galaxies only by measuring their redshifts and applying Hubble's law. Today we have redshift measurements for many thousands of distant galaxies. When we convert the redshifts to distance estimates, we can create three-dimensional maps of the universe. Such maps have been made for only a few "slices" of the sky so far, but they are already revealing **large-scale structures** much vaster than clusters of galaxies.

One of the most famous depictions of large-scale structure is the "slice of the universe" pictured in Figure 21.14a. Many astronomers collaborated to measure the redshifts of all the galaxies they could find in this particular slice of the sky. This project dramatically revealed the complex structure of our corner of the universe. Each dot in such pictures represents an entire galaxy of stars. The arrangement of the dots reveals huge sheets of galaxies spanning many millions of light-years (Figure 21.14b,c). Clusters of galaxies are located at the intersections of these sheets. Between the sheets of galaxies lie giant empty regions called **voids**.

Some of the structures we see in the universe are amazingly large. The so-called *Great Wall* of galaxies stretches across an expanse measuring some 180 million light-years side to side. Immense structures such

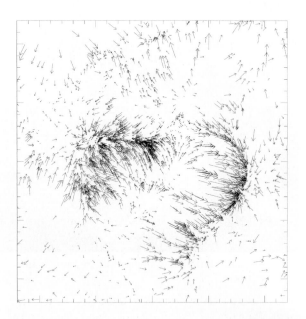

**FIGURE 21.13** Peculiar velocities of galaxies flowing into superclusters. Each arrow shows the peculiar velocity of a galaxy inferred from a combination of observations and modeling. The Milky Way is at the center of the picture, and not all galaxies are shown. The area pictured is about 600 million light-years from side to side. Note how the galaxies tend to flow into regions where the density of galaxies is already high. These vast, high-density regions are probably superclusters in the process of formation.

as these apparently have not yet collapsed into randomly orbiting, gravitationally bound systems. They haven't had enough time. The universe may still be growing structures on ever larger scales even though it is billions of years old (Figure 21.15).

Most astronomers believe that all these large-scale structures grew from slight density enhancements in the early universe, just as galaxies did. Galaxies, clusters, superclusters, and the Great Wall probably all started as mildly high-density regions of different sizes. The voids in the distribution of galaxies probably started as mildly low-density regions.

If this picture of structure formation is correct, then the structures we see in today's universe mirror the original distribution of dark matter very early in time. Supercomputer models of structure formation in the universe can now simulate the growth of galaxies, clusters, and larger structures from tiny density enhancements as the universe evolves (Figure 21.16a). The results of these models look remarkably similar to the slices of the universe in Figure 21.14, bolstering our confidence in this scenario (Figure 21.16b). However, the models do not tell us *why* the universe started with these slight density enhancements— that is a topic for the next chapter. Nevertheless, it seems increasingly clear that these "lumps" in the early universe were the seeds of all the marvelous structures we see today.

**a** The "Great Wall" is the sheet of galaxies that forms the arms of the stick figure at the center.

**FIGURE 21.14** These "slices" show galaxies in very thin, fanlike swaths extending outward from the Earth. Each dot represents a galaxy. Note that galaxies are not scattered randomly but instead seem to lie along sheets and strings interspersed with voids that contain very few galaxies.

**b** The upper swath is similar to (a) but thicker and thus contains more galaxies; the lower swath points in a different direction.

**c** The galaxies in these slices of the sky extend much deeper into space. Many voids, walls, and filaments of galaxies are evident, and the distribution of galaxies on scales larger than a billion light-years is nearly uniform.

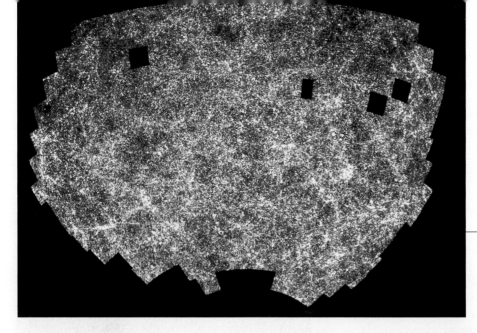

FIGURE 21.15 This picture shows the positions of over 3 million galaxies spread across 15% of the sky. Brighter areas contain more galaxies than darker areas, and the black rectangles are regions for which there is no data. Note that the universe is more uniform on large scales than on small scales.

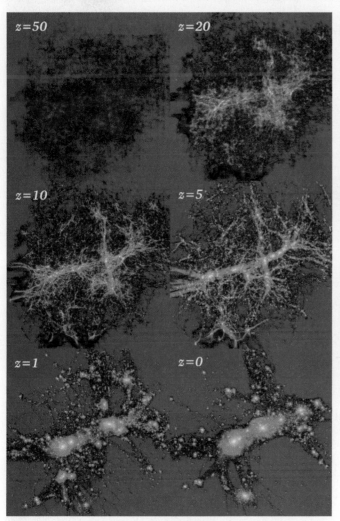

z=50    z=20

z=10    z=5

z=1    z=0

b This frame shows how the present-day universe appears in a large-scale simulation. Note the similarity of the filamentary structures in this simulation to the slices of the universe in Figure 21.14.

a These six frames depict the development of a region the size of our Local Group. As the age of the universe progresses from about 60 million years (cosmological redshift $z = 50$) to the present ($z = 0$), the high-density portions of the universe, shown in orange, continue to attract more and more matter.

FIGURE 21.16 Frames from supercomputer simulations of structure formation.

## 21.6 Fire or Ice?

*Some say the world will end in fire,*
*Some say in ice.*
*From what I've tasted of desire*
*I hold with those who favor fire.*
*But if it had to perish twice,*
*I think I know enough of hate*
*To say that for destruction ice*
*Is also great*
*And would suffice.*
　　ROBERT FROST

We now arrive at one of the ultimate questions in astronomy: How will the universe end? Edwin Hubble's work established that the galaxies in the universe are rapidly flying away from one another [Section 19.3], but the gravitational pull of each galaxy on every other galaxy acts to slow the expansion. These facts suggest two possible fates for the universe. If gravity is strong enough, the expansion will someday halt and the universe will begin collapsing, eventually ending in a cataclysmic crunch. Alternatively, if the expansion can overcome the pull of gravity, the universe will continue to expand forever, growing ever colder as its galaxies grow ever farther apart. The fate of the universe thus boils down to a simple question: Does the expanding universe have enough kinetic energy to escape its own gravitational pull?

### Density: Not Quite Critical

Hubble's constant essentially tells us the current kinetic energy of the universe, but we do not yet know the overall strength of the universe's gravitational pull. The strength of this pull depends on the density of matter in the universe: The greater the density, the greater the overall strength of gravity and the higher the likelihood that gravity will someday halt the expansion. Precise calculations show that gravity can win out over expansion if the current density of the universe exceeds a seemingly minuscule $10^{-29}$ gram per cubic centimeter, which is roughly equivalent to a few hydrogen atoms in a volume the size of a closet. The precise density marking the dividing line between eternal expansion and eventual collapse is called the **critical density**.

Observations of the luminous matter in galaxies show that the mass contained in stars falls far short of the critical density. The visible parts of galaxies contribute less than 1% of the matter density needed to half the universe's expansion. The fate of the universe thus rests with the dark matter. Is there enough dark matter to halt the expansion of the universe?

Recall that we can estimate the amount of dark matter by looking at the mass-to-light ratio. For dark matter to contribute enough mass for the universe to have the critical density, the average mass-to-light ratio throughout the universe would have to be approximately 1,000 solar masses per solar luminosity. Clusters of galaxies have mass-to-light ratios of a few hundred solar masses per solar luminosity, still a few times less than the ratio needed to halt the expansion. Thus, if the proportion of dark matter in the universe at large is similar to that in clusters, the universe will expand forever. For gravity to reverse the expansion and pull the universe back together, even more dark matter would have to lie beyond the boundaries of clusters.

Amazingly, tiny ghostlike neutrinos might supply some of the mass needed to raise the universe's density to the critical density. The masses of individual neutrinos are so small that they have not yet been measured, but what neutrinos lack in mass they might make up in sheer numbers—neutrinos are thought to be more common than any other particles in the universe except photons. Because neutrinos zip through the universe at such high speeds, they do not necessarily collect into clusters of galaxies. However, they might gravitate into larger-scale structures, where in principle their influence can be measured.

If large-scale structures really do contain a higher proportion of dark matter than do clusters, the influence of that extra dark matter should show up in the velocities of galaxies near those large-scale structures: Larger amounts of dark matter should cause greater deviations from Hubble's law. To date, studies of these galaxy velocities remain inconclusive. Some researchers claim to find evidence that large-scale structures have significantly higher mass-to-light ratios than do clusters of galaxies, in which case the universe's matter density could be close to the critical value. As of 2001, however, most studies hold the line near the value we infer from clusters, which is about 25% of the critical density required to reverse the expansion. If that is the case, the universe will continue to expand forever.

### Mysterious Acceleration

In the past few years, observations of distant white dwarf supernovae have enabled us to probe the fate of the universe in an entirely new way. Because white dwarf supernovae are such good standard candles [Section 19.3], we can use them to determine whether gravity has been slowing the universe's expansion, as it must if the universe is destined to end in a cataclysmic crunch. However, the astronomers who set out to measure gravity's influence over the universe by observing supernovae discovered something completely unexpected. Instead of slowing because of gravity, the expansion of the universe appears to be speeding up, suggesting that some mysterious repulsive force is pushing all the universe's galaxies apart. This discovery, if it holds up to further scrutiny, has far-reaching implications for both the fate of the universe and our understanding of the forces that govern its behavior on large scales. Before examining the evidence for an accelerating expansion, we must further explore the possible fates of the universe.

Astronomers subdivide the two general possibilities for the fate of the universe, expanding forever or someday collapsing, into four broad categories, each representing a particular pattern of change in the future expansion rate. We will call these four possible expansion patterns *recollapsing, critical, coasting,* and *accelerating.* The first three possibilities assume that gravity is the only force that affects the expansion rate of the universe:

- If the matter density of the universe is *larger* than the critical density, the collective gravity of all its matter will eventually halt the universe's expansion and reverse it. The galaxies will come crashing back together, and the entire universe will end in a fiery "Big Crunch." If this is the fate of our universe, then we live in a **recollapsing universe**. (The overall geometry of a recollapsing universe closes upon itself like the surface of a sphere [Section S3.4], which is why this type of universe is sometimes called a *closed universe.*)

- If the matter density of the universe *equals* the critical density, the collective gravity of all its matter is exactly the amount needed to balance the expansion. The universe will never collapse but will expand more and more slowly as time progresses. If this is the fate of our universe, then we live in a **critical universe**. (Mathematically speaking, a critical universe stops expanding after infinite time, and its overall geometry is flat like the surface of a table [Section S3.4]; thus, a critical universe is one example of what astronomers call a *flat universe.*)

- If the matter density of the universe is *smaller* than the critical density, the collective gravity of all its matter cannot halt the expansion. The universe will keep expanding forever, with little change in its rate of expansion. If this is the fate of our universe, then we live in a **coasting universe**. (A coasting universe is sometimes called an *open universe,* because its overall geometry is more like the open surface of a saddle than like the closed surface of a sphere [Section S3.4].)

Because observations of distant supernovae suggest that a repulsive force opposes gravity on very large scales, astronomers are now seriously considering a fourth possibility:

- If a repulsive force causes the expansion of the universe to accelerate with time, then we

live in an **accelerating universe**. Its galaxies will recede from one another increasingly faster, and it will become cold and dark more quickly than a coasting universe. (Depending on the strength of gravity relative to the repulsive force, the overall geometry of an accelerating universe could be flat, open, or closed; however, most astronomers favor a flat geometry for this case.)

**TIME OUT TO THINK** *Do you think that one of the potential fates of the universe is preferable to the others? If so, why? If not, why not?*

Figure 21.17 illustrates how the average distance between galaxies changes with time for each possibility. The lines for the accelerating, coasting, and critical universes always continue upward as time increases, because in these cases the universe is always expanding; the steeper the slope, the faster the expansion. In the recollapsing case, the line begins on an upward slope but eventually turns around and declines as the universe contracts. All the lines pass through the same point and have the same slope at the moment labeled "now," because the current separation between galaxies and the current expansion

---

**FIGURE 21.17** Four different models for the expansion of the universe. Each curve shows how the average distance between galaxies changes with time. A rising curve means that the universe is expanding, and a falling curve means that the universe is contracting. All the curves are aligned at the time labeled "now," where the expansion rate and average distance between galaxies are the same for all the models. Note that the lookback time to the birth of the universe, which is the moment at which the average distance between galaxies is essentially zero, depends on how strongly gravity affects the expansion rate. If gravity is strong enough to slow the universe's expansion, as in the critical and recollapsing universe models, the lookback time is relatively short—10 billion years or less. In the coasting and accelerating universe models, the pull of gravity is relatively weak, and the lookback time to the birth of the universe is closer to 16 billion years. Observations of distant white dwarf supernovae suggest that the universe is indeed accelerating and is destined to expand forever.

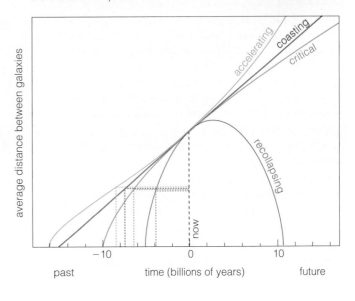

rate in each case must agree with observations of the present-day universe.

Note that the age for the universe that we infer from its expansion rate differs in each case. A recollapsing universe requires the least amount of time to arrive at the current separation between galaxies—the example in Figure 21.17 goes from zero separation to the current separation in only about 5 billion years. The cases for which gravity is less important require more time to achieve the current separation between galaxies. The ages we would infer from the examples in Figure 21.17 are 10 billion years for a critical universe, 15 billion years for a coasting universe, and around 16 billion years for an accelerating universe.

This relationship between the age of the universe and its expansion pattern enables us to determine the expansion pattern from supernova observations. To understand how, imagine observing a distant white dwarf supernova with spectral lines redshifted to twice their normal wavelengths. Recall that the expansion of the universe stretches light waves by the same amount that it increases the average distance between galaxies [Section 19.4], so the light we are observing from that supernova must have left when the average distance between galaxies was only half its current value. Because white dwarf supernovae are such excellent standard candles, we can also determine the actual distance—and thus the lookback time [Section 19.4]—to the supernova from its apparent brightness.

In principle, knowing both the supernova's redshift and its lookback time enables us to determine the universe's past expansion rate. The horizontal dotted lines in Figure 21.17 indicate the average distance between galaxies at the time of the supernova, and the vertical dotted lines indicate the corresponding lookback time for each of the illustrated expansion patterns. Note that the lookback times are smallest for models in which the universe grows most quickly to its present size. Thus, we expect a supernova with a given redshift to be somewhat closer, and therefore somewhat brighter, if the universe is recollapsing or critical than if it is coasting. Conversely, if the supernova turns out to be somewhat farther and dimmer than we would expect in a coasting universe, then we would conclude that the expansion is accelerating.

In practice, observations of such distant supernovae are still very difficult, but the results to date favor an accelerating universe: White dwarf supernovae with large redshifts appear to be somewhat dimmer than we would expect if the universe were coasting. These observations are consistent with an accelerating universe and highly inconsistent with either a critical or a recollapsing universe.

Exactly why the universe might be accelerating remains a deep mystery, because no known force would act to push the universe's galaxies apart. Some speculative ideas for what might generate such a force go by the names *dark energy, quintessence,* and *cosmological constant*. No matter what the mechanism turns out to be, it now seems likely that the universe is indeed doomed to expand forever, its galaxies receding ever more quickly into an icy, empty future.

*This is the way the world ends*
*This is the way the world ends*
*This is the way the world ends*
*Not with a bang but a whimper.*
FROM *The Hollow Men* BY T. S. ELIOT

## THE BIG PICTURE

In this chapter, we have found that there may be much more to the universe than meets the eye. Dark matter too dim for us to see seems to far outweigh the stars. Here are some key "big picture" points to remember about this mysterious matter:

- Either dark matter exists, or we do not understand how gravity operates across galaxy-size distances. We have many reasons to have confidence in our understanding of gravity, so the majority of astronomers believe that dark matter is real.

- Measurements of the mass and luminosity of galaxies and galaxy clusters indicate that they contain far more mass in dark matter than in stars.

- Despite the fact that dark matter is by far the most abundant form of mass in the universe, we still have little idea what it is.

- Superclusters, walls, and voids much larger than clusters of galaxies extend many millions of light-years across the universe. Each of these structures probably began as a very slight enhancement in the density of dark matter early in time, and these enormous structures are still in the process of forming.

- Dark matter holds the key to the fate of the universe. If there is enough of it, its gravity will cause the expansion of the universe to halt and reverse someday. Current indications are that there is not enough dark matter to halt the expansion, in which case the universe will continue to expand forever. Recent observations of an accelerating expansion only reinforce the suggestion that the expansion will never cease.

## Review Questions

1. In what sense is dark matter "dark"?

2. What evidence suggests that the Milky Way contains dark matter?

3. Briefly describe how we construct rotation curves for spiral galaxies and how these curves lead us to conclude that spiral galaxies contain dark matter.

4. Briefly describe how we can infer the average orbital speeds of stars in an elliptical galaxy from the widths of its spectral lines and how this allows us to weigh elliptical glaxies.

5. What is a *mass-to-light ratio*? Explain why higher mass-to-light ratios imply more dark matter.

6. What are typical mass-to-light ratios for inner regions of spiral galaxies? For inner regions of elliptical galaxies? How do these mass-to-light ratios compare to the mass-to-light ratios we find when we look farther from a galaxy's center? What does this tell us about dark matter in galaxies?

7. Briefly describe the three different ways of measuring the mass of a cluster of galaxies. Do the results from the different methods agree? What do they tell us about dark matter in galaxy clusters?

8. What is gravitational lensing? Why does it occur? How can we use it to estimate the masses of lensing objects?

9. Briefly explain what we mean by *baryonic* and *non-baryonic matter*. Which type are you made of?

10. What do we mean by *MACHOs*? Describe several possibilities for the nature of MACHOs. Based on evidence from gravitational lensing events, can MACHOs explain all the dark matter in the Milky Way? Why or why not?

11. Explain what we mean when we say that a neutrino is a weakly interacting particle. Why can't the dark matter in galaxies be made of neutrinos?

12. What do we mean by *WIMPs*? Why do many astronomers believe that dark matter consists largely of WIMPs?

13. What do we mean by gravitationally bound systems? How did such structures come to exist in an expanding universe?

14. What are *peculiar velocities*? What causes them, and what do they tell us about the formation of clusters and *superclusters*?

15. Briefly describe the appearance of the universe on the largest scales. What is the Great Wall of galaxies?

16. Explain how the total amount of dark matter in the universe holds the key to its final fate. According to current evidence about the amount of dark matter, what is the fate of the universe?

17. Briefly describe the four possible patterns for the expansion of the universe. What is the fate of the universe in each case? How does the current age of the universe differ among the four cases?

18. Briefly describe the recent evidence suggesting that the expansion of the universe is accelerating.

## Discussion Questions

1. *Dark Matter or Revised Gravity.* One possible explanation for the large mass-to-light ratios we measure in galaxies and clusters is that we are currently using the wrong law of gravity to measure the masses of very large objects. If we really do misunderstand gravity, then many fundamental theories of physics, including Einstein's theory of general relativity, will need to be revised. Which explanation for these mass-to-light ratios do you find more appealing, dark matter or revised gravity? Explain why. Why do you suppose most astronomers find dark matter more appealing?

2. *Our Fate.* Scientists, philosophers, and poets alike have speculated on the fate of the universe. How would you prefer the universe as we know it to end, in a big crunch or through eternal expansion? Explain the reasons behind your preference.

## Problems

*True Statements?* For **problems 1–6**, decide whether the statement is true and explain why it is or is not.

1. Astronomers now believe that most of any galaxy's mass lies beyond the portions of the galaxy that we can see.

2. If our galaxy had less dark matter, its mass-to-light ratio would be lower.

3. A cluster of galaxies is held together by the mutual gravitational attraction of all the stars in the cluster's galaxies.

4. We can estimate the total mass of a cluster of galaxies by studying the distorted images of galaxies whose light passes through the cluster.

5. Clusters of galaxies are the largest structures that we have so far detected in the universe.

6. There is no doubt remaining among astronomers that the fate of the universe is to expand forever.

7. *Strange Repulsive Force.* The idea that a strange repulsive force may be accelerating the universe's expansion is quite recent. What do we mean by an accelerating expansion, and what evidence suggests that such an acceleration may be occurring? If the acceleration is real, what is the fate of the universe? Explain.

8. *Mass-to-Light Ratio.* Suppose you discovered a galaxy with a mass-to-light ratio of 0.1 solar mass per solar luminosity. Would you be surprised? Explain why or why not. What would this measurement say about the nature of the stars in this galaxy?

*9. *Weighing a Spiral Galaxy.* Figure 21.4 shows the rotation curve for a spiral galaxy called NGC 7541.

   a. Use the orbital velocity law to determine the mass (in solar masses) of NGC 7541 enclosed within a radius of 30,000 light-years from its center. (*Hint:* 1 light-year = $9.461 \times 10^{15}$ m.)

   b. Use the orbital velocity law to determine the mass of NGC 7541 enclosed within a radius of 60,000 light-years from its center.

   c. Based on your answers to parts (a) and (b), what can you conclude about the distribution of mass in this galaxy?

*10. *Weigh a Cluster of Galaxies.* Suppose a cluster of galaxies has a radius of about 6.7 million light-years ($6.2 \times 10^{22}$ m) and an intracluster medium with a temperature of $8 \times 10^7$ K. Estimate the mass of the cluster. Give your answer in both kilograms and solar masses.

*11. *How Many MACHOs?* Suppose the rotation of a highly simplified galaxy whose stars are all identical to the Sun (1 solar mass per solar luminosity) shows that its overall mass-to-light ratio is equal to 30 solar masses per solar luminosity.

   a. What is the ratio of dark matter to luminous matter in this galaxy?

   b. Suppose all the dark matter consists of MACHOs similar to Jupiter, each with a mass of 0.001 solar mass. How many of these MACHOs must the galaxy contain for each ordinary star? Explain.

## Web Projects

Find useful links for Web projects on the text Web site.

1. *Gravitational Lenses.* Gravitational lensing occurs in numerous astronomical situations. Compile a catalog of examples from the Web. Try to find pictures of lensed stars, quasars, and galaxies. Supply a one-paragraph explanation of what is going on in each picture.

2. *Accelerating Universe.* Search for the most recent information about possible acceleration of the expansion of the universe. Write a one- to three-page report on your findings.

3. *The Nature of Dark Matter.* Find and study recent reports on new ideas about the possible nature of dark matter. Write a one- to three-page report that summarizes the latest ideas about what dark matter is made of.

*Somewhere, something incredible is waiting to be known.*

CARL SAGAN

# CHAPTER 22

# The Beginning of Time

The universe has been expanding for over 10 billion years. During that time, matter collected into galaxies. Stars formed in those galaxies, producing heavy elements that were recycled into later generations of stars. One of these late-coming stars formed about 4.6 billion years ago, in a remote corner of a galaxy called the Milky Way. This star was born with a host of planets that formed in a flattened disk surrounding it. One of these planets soon became covered with life that gradually evolved into more and more complex forms. Today, the most advanced life-form on this planet, human beings, can look back on this series of events and marvel at how the universe created conditions suitable for life.

To this point in the book, we have discussed how the matter in the early universe collected into galaxies, stars, planets, and ultimately people. We have seen that we are star stuff, and galaxy stuff as well. More to the point, we now recognize that we are the product of more than 10 billion years of cosmic evolution. We have one question left to address: Where did the *matter itself* come from?

To answer this ultimate question, we must go beyond the most distant galaxies and even beyond what we can see near the horizon of the universe. We must go back not only to the origins of matter and energy but to the beginning of time itself.

## 22.1 Running the Expansion Backward

Is it really possible to study the origin of the entire universe? Not long ago, questions about creation were considered unfit for scientific study. But that attitude began to change with Hubble's discovery that the universe is expanding. This discovery led to the insight that all things very likely sprang into being at a single moment in time, in an event that we have come to call the *Big Bang*. Today, powerful telescopes allow us to view how galaxies have changed over the last 10 billion years, and at great distances we see young galaxies still in the process of forming [Section 20.1]. These observations confirm that the universe is gradually aging, just as we should expect if the entire universe really was born some 10–16 billion years ago.

Unfortunately, we cannot see back to the very beginning of time. Light from the most distant galaxies shows us what the universe looked like when it was a few billion years old. Beyond these galaxies, we have not yet found any objects shining brightly enough for us to see them. But we face an even more fundamental problem. The universe is filled with a faint glow of radiation that appears to be the remnant heat of the Big Bang. This faint glow comes from a time when the universe was about 500,000 years old, and it prevents us from seeing directly to earlier times. Thus, just as we must rely on theoretical modeling to determine what the Earth or the Sun is like on the inside, we must use modeling to investigate what happened in the universe in its first 500,000 years.

Fortunately, calculating conditions in the early universe is straightforward if we consider some fundamental principles. We know that the expanding universe is cooling and becoming less dense as it grows. Therefore, the universe must have been hotter and denser in the past. Calculating exactly how hot and dense the universe must have been when it was more compressed is similar to calculating the temperatures and densities in a car engine as the pistons compress the fuel mix, except that the conditions become much more extreme. Figure 22.1 shows just how hot the universe was during its earliest moments, according to such calculations. To understand these early moments, we need to know how matter and energy behave under such extraordinarily hot conditions.

Recent advances in physics have enabled us to predict the behavior of matter and energy under conditions far more extreme than in the centers of the hottest stars. When we apply our understanding of modern physics to the early universe, we find something so astonishing that it almost sounds preposterous: Today, we may understand the behavior of matter and energy well enough to describe what was happening in the universe just *one ten-billionth*

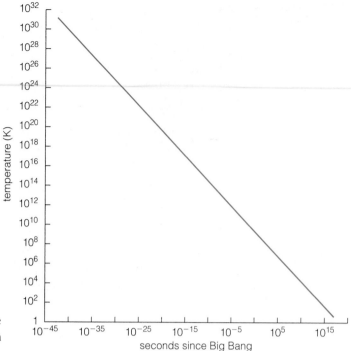

**FIGURE 22.1** Temperature of the universe from the Big Bang to the present ($10^{10}$ years $\approx 3 \times 10^{17}$ seconds).

($10^{-10}$) of a second after the Big Bang. And that's not all. While our understanding of physics is less certain under the more extreme conditions that prevailed even earlier, we have some ideas about what the universe was like when it was a mere $10^{-38}$ second old, and perhaps a glimmer of what it was like at the age of just $10^{-43}$ second. These tiny fractions of a second are so small that, for all practical purposes, we are studying the very moment of creation.

## 22.2 A Scientific History of the Universe

The **Big Bang theory**—the scientific theory of the universe's earliest moments—presumes that all we see today, from Earth to the cosmic horizon, began as an incredibly tiny, hot, and dense collection of matter and radiation. It describes how expansion and cooling of this unimaginably intense mixture of particles and photons could have led to the present universe of stars and galaxies, and it explains several aspects of today's universe with impressive accuracy. Our ideas about the earliest moments of the universe are quite speculative because they depend on aspects of physics that we do not yet fully comprehend. However, the evidence supporting this theory grows stronger and stronger as we focus on progressively

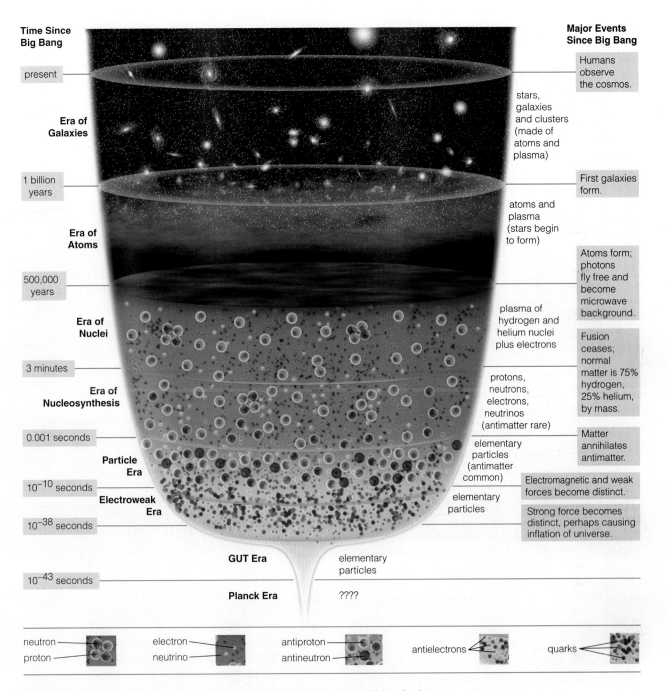

**Time Since Big Bang**

present

Era of Galaxies

1 billion years

Era of Atoms

500,000 years

Era of Nuclei

3 minutes

Era of Nucleosynthesis

0.001 seconds

Particle Era

$10^{-10}$ seconds

Electroweak Era

$10^{-38}$ seconds

GUT Era

$10^{-43}$ seconds

Planck Era

**Major Events Since Big Bang**

Humans observe the cosmos.

stars, galaxies and clusters (made of atoms and plasma)

First galaxies form.

atoms and plasma (stars begin to form)

Atoms form; photons fly free and become microwave background.

plasma of hydrogen and helium nuclei plus electrons

Fusion ceases; normal matter is 75% hydrogen, 25% helium, by mass.

protons, neutrons, electrons, neutrinos (antimatter rare)

elementary particles (antimatter common)

Matter annihilates antimatter.

Electromagnetic and weak forces become distinct.

elementary particles

Strong force becomes distinct, perhaps causing inflation of universe.

elementary particles

????

neutron
proton
electron
neutrino
antiproton
antineutron
antielectrons
quarks

**FIGURE 22.2** This diagram summarizes the eras of the universe. The names of the eras and their ending times are indicated on the left, and the state of matter during each era and the events marking the end of each era are indicated on the right.

later moments in time. We will discuss the evidence supporting the Big Bang theory later in this chapter. First, in order to help you understand the significance of the evidence, let's examine the story of creation according to this theory.

Figure 22.2 summarizes the story by dividing the overall history of the universe into a series of *eras*, or time periods. Each era is distinguished from the next

by some major change in the conditions of the universe. You'll find it easiest to keep track of the various eras if you refer back to this figure as we discuss each era in detail. (In more specialized books on cosmology, these eras are subdivided into many more eras, providing additional details about the early universe not covered here.)

Before we delve into the story of creation, it's important to be aware of a key aspect of the early universe: it was so hot that photons could transform themselves into matter, and vice versa, in accordance with Einstein's formula $E = mc^2$ [Section 4.2]. Today, physicists can study many such reactions by reproducing them in their laboratories, but reactions that create and destroy matter are now relatively rare in the universe at large.

One example of such a reaction is the creation or destruction of an *electron–antielectron pair* [Section S4.5]. When two photons collide with a total energy greater than twice the mass-energy of an electron (i.e., the electron's mass times $c^2$), they can create two brand-new particles: a negatively charged electron and its positively charged twin, the *antielectron,* also known as a *positron* (Figure 22.3). The electron is a particle of **matter**, and the antielectron is a particle of **antimatter**. The reaction that creates an electron–antielectron pair also runs in reverse: When an electron and an antielectron meet, they *annihilate* each other totally, transforming all their mass-energy back into photon energy.

**FIGURE 22.3** Electron–antielectron creation and annihilation.

Particle creation

Particle annihilation

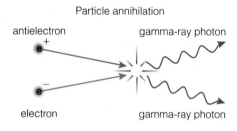

Similar reactions can produce or destroy any particle–antiparticle pair, such as a proton and antiproton or neutron and antineutron. The early universe was therefore filled with an extremely dynamic blend of photons, matter, and antimatter, converting furiously back and forth. Despite all these vigorous reactions, describing conditions in the early universe is straightforward, because we can calculate the proportions of the various forms of radiation and matter from the universe's temperature and density at any time.

### The First Instant

The scientific story of creation begins when the universe was an incomprehensibly tiny $10^{-43}$ second old. This instant in time is called the **Planck time** after physicist Max Planck, one of the founders of the science of quantum mechanics. According to the laws of quantum mechanics, there must have been substantial energy fluctuations from point to point in the very early universe. Because energy and mass are equivalent, Einstein's theory of general relativity tells us that these energy fluctuations must have generated a rapidly changing gravitational field that randomly warped space and time.

Prior to the Planck time, in the **Planck era**, these random energy fluctuations were so large that our current theories are powerless to describe what might have been happening. The problem is that we do not yet have a theory that links quantum mechanics and general relativity. In a sense, quantum mechanics is our successful theory of the very small (subatomic particles), and general relativity is our successful theory of the very big (the large-scale structure of spacetime). Perhaps someday we will be able to merge these theories of the very small and the very big into a single "theory of everything." Until that happens, science cannot describe the universe before the Planck time.

### The GUT Era

Understanding the transition that marked the beginning of the next era requires thinking in terms of the *forces* that operate in the universe. Everything that happens in the universe today is governed by four distinct forces: *gravity, electromagnetism,* the *strong force,* and the *weak force* [Section S4.2]. Gravity dominates large-scale action, and electromagnetism dominates chemical and biological reactions. The strong and weak forces determine what happens within atomic nuclei: The strong force binds nuclei together, and the weak force mediates nuclear reactions such as fission or fusion.

These forces were not so distinct in the early universe. The four forces that act so differently today turn out to be separate aspects of a smaller number of more fundamental forces, probably only one or two (Figure 22.4). As an analogy, think about ice, liquid water, and water vapor. These three substances are quite different from one another in appearance and behavior, yet they are just different phases of the single substance $H_2O$. In a similar way, physicists have shown that the electromagnetic and weak forces lose their separate identities under conditions of very high temperature or energy and merge together into a single *electroweak force.* Physicists also believe that the electroweak force and the strong force ultimately

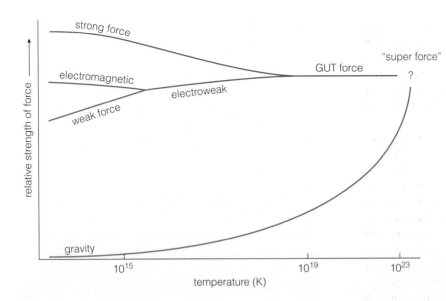

**FIGURE 22.4** The four forces are distinct at low temperatures but may merge at very high temperatures.

lose their separate identities at even higher energies. The theories that predict this merger of the electroweak and strong forces are called **grand unified theories**, or **GUTs** for short; their merger is usually referred to as the *GUT force*. Many physicists believe that at even higher energies the GUT force and gravity merge into a single "super force" that governs the behavior of everything. (Among the names you may hear for theories linking all four forces are *supersymmetry, superstrings,* and *supergravity*.)

Calculations from general relativity and quantum mechanics suggest that this unified "super force" may have reigned in the universe during the Planck era. If so, the Planck time ($10^{-43}$ s) marks the instant when gravity became distinct from the other three forces, which were still merged as the GUT force. By analogy to ice crystals forming as a liquid cools, we say that gravity "froze out" at the Planck time. The universe subsequently entered the **GUT era**, when two forces operated in the universe: gravity and the GUT force.

The GUT era lasted but a tiny fraction of a second, coming to an end when the universe had cooled to $10^{29}$ K at an age of $10^{-38}$ second. Grand unified theories predict that the strong force froze out from the GUT force at this point, leaving three forces operating in the universe: gravity, the strong force, and the electroweak force. As we will discuss later, it now seems possible that this freezing out of the strong force released an enormous amount of energy. This energy release would have caused the universe to undergo a sudden and dramatic expansion that we call **inflation**. In the space of a mere $10^{-36}$ second, pieces of the universe the size of an atomic nucleus may have grown to the size of our solar system.

Inflation sounds bizarre, but it might actually explain some puzzling features of today's universe.

### The Electroweak Era

The end of the GUT era marks the beginning of the **electroweak era**, so named because the electromagnetic and weak forces were still unified into the electroweak force. Intense radiation filled all of space, as it had since the Planck era, spontaneously producing matter and antimatter particles of many different sorts that immediately reverted back to energy. The universe continued to expand and cool throughout the electroweak era, dropping to a temperature of $10^{15}$ K when it reached an age of $10^{-10}$ second. This temperature is still 100 million times hotter than the temperature in the core of the Sun, but it was low enough for the electromagnetic and weak forces to freeze out from the electroweak force. After this instant ($10^{-10}$ s), all four forces were forever distinct in the universe.

The end of the electroweak era marks an important transition not only in the universe, but also in human understanding of the universe. The theory that unified the weak and electromagnetic forces, developed in the 1970s, predicted the emergence of new types of particles (called the W and Z bosons, or *weak bosons*) when temperatures rose above the $10^{15}$ K that pervaded the universe when it was $10^{-10}$ second old. In 1983, experiments performed in a huge particle accelerator near the French/Swiss border (CERN [Section S4.2]) reached energies equivalent to such high temperatures for the first time. The new particles showed up just as predicted, produced from the extremely high energy in accord with $E = mc^2$. Thus, we have direct experimental evidence con-

### Einstein's Greatest Blunder

Shortly after Einstein completed his general theory of relativity in 1915, he found that it predicted that the universe could not be standing still: The mutual gravitational attraction of all the matter would make the universe collapse. Because Einstein thought at the time that the universe should be eternal and static, he decided to alter his equations. In essence, he inserted a "fudge factor" called the *cosmological constant* that acted as a repulsive force to counteract the attractive force of gravity. Had he not been so convinced that the universe should be standing still, he might instead have come up with the correct explanation for why the universe is not collapsing: because it is still expanding from the event of its birth. After Hubble discovered that the universe is expanding, Einstein called his invention of the cosmological constant the greatest blunder of his career.

Despite Einstein's disavowal, variations both on the idea of an eternal universe and on the cosmological constant continued to crop up over the years. One of the cleverest ideas, developed in the late 1940s, was called the *steady state theory* of the universe. This theory accepted the fact that the universe is expanding but rejected the idea of a Big Bang and instead postulated that the universe is infinitely old. This idea may seem paradoxical at first: If the universe has been expanding forever, shouldn't every galaxy be infinitely far away from every other galaxy? The steady state theory suggested that new galaxies continually form in the gaps that open up as the universe expands, thereby keeping the same average distance between galaxies at all times. In a sense, the steady state theory said that the creation of the universe is an ongoing and eternal process rather than having happened all at once with a Big Bang.

Two key discoveries caused the steady state theory to lose favor. First, the 1965 discovery of the cosmic microwave background matched a prediction of the Big Bang theory but could not be adequately explained by the steady state theory. Second, the steady state theory predicts that the universe looks about the same at all times, which is inconsistent with observations showing that galaxies at great distances look younger than nearby galaxies. As a result of these predictive failures, the steady state theory is no longer taken seriously by most astronomers.

More recently, astronomers have begun to take the idea of a cosmological constant more seriously. In the mid-1990s, a few observations suggested that the ages of the oldest stars are slightly older than the age of the universe derived from Hubble's constant under the assumption that gravity is the only force affecting the universe's expansion. Clearly, stars cannot be older than the universe. If these observations were being interpreted correctly, the universe had to be older than Hubble's constant implies. Recall that we estimate the age of the universe by running the expansion backward while accounting for how gravity and other forces have modified the expansion rate [Section 21.6]. If the expansion rate has accelerated, so that the universe is expanding faster today than it was in the past, then the age of the universe would be greater than that ordinarily found from Hubble's constant. What could cause the expansion of the universe to accelerate over time? The repulsive force represented by a cosmological constant, of course.

Further study of the troubling observations has shown that the oldest stars probably are *not* older than the age of the universe derived from Hubble's constant. However, other observations still suggest that a cosmological constant is necessary. As we discussed in Chapter 21, measurements of distances to high-redshift galaxies using white dwarf supernovae as standard candles now suggest that the expansion *is* accelerating. A cosmological constant could account for this startling finding, but we'll need many more observations before we'll know whether it is correct. Einstein's greatest blunder, it seems, just won't go away.

---

cerning the conditions in the universe at the end of the electroweak era. Prior to that time, we do not have any direct experimental evidence. Our theories concerning the earlier parts of the electroweak era and the GUT era consequently are much more speculative than our theories describing the universe from the end of the electroweak era to the present.

### The Particle Era

Spontaneous creation and annihilation of particles continued throughout the next era, which we call the **particle era** because tiny particles of matter were as numerous as photons. These particles included electrons, neutrinos, and *quarks*—the building blocks of heavier particles such as protons, antiprotons, neutrons, and antineutrons [Section S4.2]. Near the end of the particle era, when the universe was about 0.0001 second old, the temperature grew too cool for quarks to exist on their own, and quarks combined in groups of three to form protons and neutrons. The particle era came to an end when the universe reached an age of 1 millisecond (0.001 s) and the temperature had fallen to $10^{12}$ K. At this point, it was no longer hot enough to spontaneously produce protons and antiprotons (or neutrons and antineutrons) from pure energy.

If the universe had contained equal numbers of protons and antiprotons (or neutrons and antineutrons) at the end of the particle era, all of the pairs would have annihilated each other, creating photons and leaving essentially no matter in the universe. In today's universe, photons outnumber protons by over a billion to one. We conclude that protons must have slightly outnumbered antiprotons at the end of the particle era: For every billion antiprotons, there were about a billion and one protons. Thus, for each 1 billion protons and antiprotons that annihilated each other, creating photons, a single proton was left over. This seemingly slight excess of ordinary matter over antimatter makes up all the matter in the present-day universe. That is, the protons (and neutrons) left over from when the universe was 0.001 second old are the very ones that make up our bodies.

### The Era of Nucleosynthesis

So far, everything we have discussed occurred within the first 0.001 second of the universe's existence—a time span shorter than the time it takes you to blink an eye. At this point, the protons and neutrons left over after the annihilation of antimatter attempted to fuse into heavier nuclei. However, the heat of the universe remained so high that most nuclei broke apart as fast as they formed. This dance of fusion and breakup marked the **era of nucleosynthesis**.

The era of nucleosynthesis ended when the universe was about 3 minutes old. By this time, the density in the expanding universe had dropped so much that fusion no longer occurred, even though the temperature was still about a billion Kelvin ($10^9$ K)—much hotter than the temperature at the center of the Sun today. When fusion ceased, about 75% of the mass of the ordinary (baryonic) matter in the universe remained as individual protons, or hydrogen nuclei. The other 25% of this mass had fused into helium nuclei, with trace amounts of deuterium (hydrogen with a neutron) and lithium. Except for the relatively small amount of matter that stars later forged into heavier elements, the chemical composition of the universe remains unchanged today.

### The Era of Nuclei

At the end of the era of nucleosynthesis, the universe consisted of a very hot plasma of hydrogen nuclei, helium nuclei, and free electrons. This basic picture held for about the next 500,000 years as the universe continued to expand and cool. The fully ionized nuclei moved independently of electrons during this period (rather than being bound with electrons in neutral atoms), which we call the **era of nuclei**. Throughout this era, photons bounced rapidly from one electron to the next, just as they do deep inside the Sun today, never managing to travel far between collisions. Any time a nucleus managed to capture an electron to form a complete atom, one of the photons quickly ionized it.

The era of nuclei came to an end when the expanding universe was about 500,000 years old, at which point the temperature had fallen to about 3,000 K—roughly half the temperature of the Sun's surface today. Hydrogen and helium nuclei finally captured electrons for good, forming stable, neutral atoms for the first time. With electrons now bound into atoms, the universe suddenly became transparent. Photons, formerly trapped among the electrons, began to stream freely across the universe. We still see these photons today as the *cosmic microwave background,* which we will discuss shortly.

### The Era of Atoms and the Era of Galaxies

We've already discussed the rest of the story in earlier chapters. The end of the era of nuclei marked the beginning of the **era of atoms**, when the universe consisted of a mixture of neutral atoms and plasma. Thanks to the slight density enhancements present in the universe at this time and the gravitational attraction of dark matter, the atoms and plasma slowly assembled into protogalactic clouds [Section 21.5]. Stars formed in these clouds, transforming the gas clouds into galaxies. The first full-fledged galaxies had formed by the time the universe was about 1 billion years old, beginning what we call the **era of galaxies**.

The era of galaxies continues to this day. Generation after generation of star formation in galaxies steadily builds elements heavier than helium and incorporates them into new star systems. Some of these star systems develop planets, and on at least one of these planets life burst into being a few billion years ago. And here we are, thinking about it all. Describing both the follies and the achievements of the human race, Carl Sagan once said, "These are the things that hydrogen atoms do—given 15 billion years of cosmic evolution."

## 22.3 Evidence for the Big Bang

Like any scientific theory, the Big Bang theory is a model designed to explain a set of facts. If it is close to the truth, it should be able to make predictions about the real universe that we can verify through observations or experiments. The Big Bang model has gained wide scientific acceptance for two key reasons:

■ The Big Bang model predicts that the radiation that began to stream across the universe at the end of the era of nuclei should still be present today. Sure enough, we find that the universe is filled with what we call the **cosmic microwave background**. Its characteristics precisely match what we expect according to the Big Bang model.

- The Big Bang model predicts that some of the original hydrogen in the universe should have fused into helium during the era of nucleosynthesis. Observations of the actual helium content of the universe closely match the amount of helium predicted by the Big Bang model. Fusion of hydrogen to helium in stars could have produced only about 10% of the observed helium.

### The Cosmic Microwave Background

The first major piece of evidence supporting the Big Bang theory arrived in 1965. Arno Penzias and Robert Wilson, two physicists working at Bell Laboratories in New Jersey, were calibrating a sensitive microwave antenna designed for satellite communications (Figure 22.5). (*Microwaves* fall within the radio portion of the electromagnetic spectrum.) Much to their chagrin, they kept finding unexpected "noise" in every measurement they made with the antenna. Fearing that they were doing something wrong, they worked frantically to discover and eliminate all possible sources of background noise. They even climbed up on their antenna to scrape off pigeon droppings, on the off-chance that these were somehow causing the noise. No matter what they did, the microwave noise wouldn't go away. The noise was the same no matter where they pointed their antenna, indicating that it came from all directions in the sky and ruling out the possibility that it came from any particular astronomical object or from any place on the Earth. Embarrassed by their inability to explain the noise, Penzias and Wilson prepared to "bury" their discovery at the end of a long scientific paper about their antenna.

Meanwhile, physicists at nearby Princeton University were busy calculating the expected characteristics of the radiation left over from the heat of the Big Bang. They concluded that, if the Big Bang had really occurred, this radiation should be permeating the entire universe and should be detectable with a microwave antenna. On a fateful airline trip home from an astronomical meeting, Penzias sat next to an astronomer who told him of the Princeton calculations. The Princeton group soon met with Penzias and Wilson to compare notes. The "noise" in the Bell Labs antenna was not an embarrassment after all. Instead, it was the cosmic microwave background—and the first strong evidence that the Big Bang had really happened. Penzias and Wilson received the 1978 Nobel Prize in physics for their discovery of the cosmic microwave background.[1]

---

[1]The dramatic story of the discovery of the cosmic microwave background is told in greater detail, along with much more scientific history, in Timothy Ferris, *The Red Limit* (New York: Quill, 1983).

**FIGURE 22.5** Arno Penzias and Robert Wilson with the Bell Labs microwave antenna.

The cosmic microwave background radiation consists of photons arriving at Earth directly from the end of the era of nuclei, when the universe was about 500,000 years old. Because neutral atoms could remain stable for the first time, they captured most of the electrons in the universe. With no more free electrons to block them, the photons from that epoch have flown unobstructed through the universe ever since (Figure 22.6). When we observe the cosmic microwave background, we essentially are seeing back to a time when the universe was only 500,000 years old. In that sense, we are seeing light from the most distant regions of the observable universe— only 500,000 light-years from our cosmological horizon [Section 19.4]. Surprisingly, it does not take a particularly powerful telescope to "see" this radiation. In fact, you can pick it up with an ordinary television antenna. If you set an antenna-fed television (i.e., *not* cable or satellite TV) to a channel for which there is no local station, you will see a screen full of static "snow." About 1% of this static is due to photons in the cosmic microwave background. Try it. If your friends ask why you are watching nothing, tell them that you are actually watching the most incredible sight ever seen on a television screen: the Big Bang, or at least as close to it as we'll ever get.

The cosmic microwave background came from the heat of the universe itself and therefore should have an essentially perfect thermal radiation spectrum [Section 6.4]. When this radiation first broke free 500,000 years after the Big Bang, the temperature of the universe was about 3,000 K, not too different from that of a red giant star's surface. Thus, the spectrum of the cosmic microwave background originally peaked in visible light, just like the thermal radiation

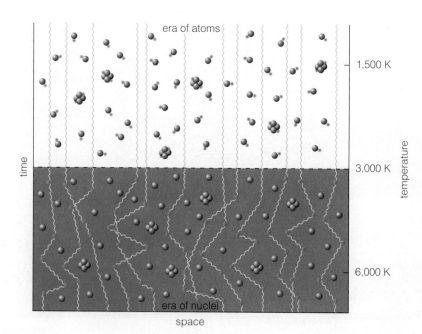

era of atoms

time

space

era of nuclei

temperature

1,500 K

3,000 K

6,000 K

**FIGURE 22.6** Photons frequently collided with free electrons during the era of nuclei and thus could travel freely only after electrons became bound into atoms. The photons released at the end of the era of nuclei make up the cosmic microwave background.

from a red star, with wavelengths of a few hundred nanometers. However, the universe has expanded by a factor of about 1,000 since that time, stretching the wavelengths of these photons by the same amount [Section 19.4]. Their wavelengths should therefore have shifted to about a millimeter, squarely in the microwave portion of the spectrum and corresponding to a temperature of a few degrees above absolute zero. In the early 1990s, a NASA satellite called the *Cosmic Background Explorer (COBE)* was launched to test these ideas about the cosmic microwave background. The results were a stunning success for the Big Bang theory. As shown in Figure 22.7, the cosmic microwave background does indeed have a perfect thermal radiation spectrum, with a peak corresponding to a

temperature of 2.73 K. In a very real sense, the temperature of the night sky is a frigid 3 degrees above absolute zero.

**TIME OUT TO THINK** *Suppose the cosmic microwave background did not really come from the heat of the universe itself but instead came from many individual stars and galaxies. Explain why, in that case, we would not expect it to have a perfect thermal radiation spectrum. How does the spectrum of the cosmic microwave background lend support to the Big Bang theory?*

COBE achieved an even greater success mapping the temperature of the cosmic microwave background in all directions. It was already known that the cosmic microwave background is extraordinarily uniform throughout the universe. Conditions in the early universe must have been extremely uniform to produce such a smooth radiation field. For a time, this uniformity was considered a strike against the Big Bang theory because, as we discussed in Chapters 20 and 21, the universe must have contained

relative intensity

wavelength (mm)

**FIGURE 22.7** Spectrum of the cosmic microwave background from COBE. A theoretically calculated thermal radiation spectrum (smooth curve) for a temperature of 2.73 K perfectly fits the data (dots).

**FIGURE 22.8** This all-sky map shows temperature differences in the cosmic microwave background measured by COBE. The background temperature is about 2.73 K everywhere, but the brighter regions of this picture are slightly less than 0.0001 K hotter than the darker regions—indicating that the early universe was very slightly lumpy. We are essentially seeing what the universe was like at the surface marked "500,000 years" in Figure 22.2. (The central strip of this map, which corresponds to the disk of the Milky Way, has been masked out because the brightness differences there stem primarily from radio noise in the Milky Way.

some regions of enhanced density in order to explain the formation of galaxies. The COBE measurements restored confidence in the Big Bang theory because they showed that the cosmic microwave background is *not quite* perfectly uniform. Instead, its temperature varies very slightly from one place to another by a few parts in 100,000 (Figure 22.8).[2] These variations in temperature indicate that the density of the early universe really did differ slightly from place to place—the seeds of structure formation were indeed present during the era of nuclei.

COBE's discovery of density enhancements bolstered the idea that some of the dark matter consists of WIMPs (weakly interacting massive particles [Section 21.4]) that we have not yet identified and that the gravity of this dark matter drove the formation of structure in the universe. Regions of enhanced density can grow into galaxies because the extra gravity in these regions draws matter together even while the rest of the universe expands. The greater the density enhancements, the faster matter should have

collected into galaxies. Detailed calculations show that, to explain the fact that galaxies formed within a few billion years, the density enhancements at the end of the era of nuclei must have been significantly greater than the few parts in 100,000 suggested by the temperature variations in the cosmic microwave background. Because WIMPs are weakly interacting and do not interact with photons, we do not expect them to influence the temperature of the cosmic microwave background directly. However, the gravity of the WIMPs can collect ordinary baryonic matter into clumps that *do* interact with photons. Thus, the small density enhancements detected by COBE may actually echo the much larger density enhancements made up of WIMPs. Careful modeling of the COBE temperature variations shows that they are consistent with dark-matter density enhancements large enough to account for the structure we see in the universe today.

### Synthesis of Helium

The discovery of the cosmic microwave background in 1965 quickly solved another long-standing astronomical problem: the origin of cosmic helium. Everywhere in the universe, about one-quarter of the mass of ordinary matter (i.e., not dark matter) is helium. The Milky Way's helium fraction is about 28%, and

---

[2]The Earth's motion (e.g., orbit of Sun, rotation of galaxy, etc.) means that we are moving relative to the cosmic background radiation. Thus, we see a slight blueshift (about 0.12%) in the direction we're moving, and a slight redshift in the opposite direction. We must first subtract these effects before analyzing the temperature of the background radiation.

no galaxy has a helium fraction lower than 25%. A small proportion of this helium comes from hydrogen fusion in stars, but most does not. The majority of the helium in the universe must already have been present in the protogalactic clouds that preceded the formation of galaxies. In other words, the universe itself must once have been hot enough to fuse hydrogen into helium. The current microwave background temperature of 2.73 K tells us precisely how hot the universe was in the distant past and exactly how much helium it should have made. The result—25% helium—is another impressive success of the Big Bang theory.

A helium nucleus contains two protons and two neutrons, so we need to understand what protons and neutrons were doing during the era of nucleosynthesis in order to see why the primordial fraction of helium was 25%. Early in this era, when the universe's temperature was $10^{11}$ K, nuclear reactions could convert protons into neutrons, and vice versa. For example, a proton and an electron could combine to form a neutron and a neutrino. This reaction is one of several that change protons into neutrons. All such proton–neutron conversion reactions involve neutrinos or antineutrinos, which experience only the weak force. As long as the universe remained hotter than $10^{11}$ K, these reactions kept the numbers of protons and neutrons nearly equal.

As the universe cooled from $10^{11}$ K to $10^{10}$ K, neutron–proton conversion reactions began to favor protons. Neutrons are slightly heavier than protons, and therefore reactions that convert protons to neutrons require energy to proceed (in accordance with $E = mc^2$). Below $10^{11}$ K, the required energy for neutron production was no longer readily available, so the rate of these reactions slowed. In contrast, reactions that convert neutrons into protons release energy and thus are unhindered by cooler temperatures. At the time the temperature of the universe fell to $10^{10}$ K, protons began to outnumber neutrons because the conversion reactions ran only in one direction: Neutrons changed into protons, but the protons didn't change back.

At $10^{10}$ K, the universe was still hot and dense enough for nuclear fusion to operate. Protons and neutrons constantly combined to form *deuterium*—the rare form of hydrogen nuclei that contains a neutron in addition to a proton—and deuterium nuclei fused to form helium. However, during the early parts of the era of nucleosynthesis, the helium nuclei were almost immediately blasted apart by one of the many gamma rays that filled the universe.

Fusion finally created long-lasting helium nuclei when the universe was about 1 minute old, at which time the destructive gamma rays were gone (Figure 22.9). Calculations show that the proton-to-neutron ratio at this time should have been about 7 to 1. Moreover, virtually all the available neutrons should have become incorporated into nuclei of helium-4. Figure 22.10 shows that, based on the 7-to-1 ratio of protons to neutrons, the universe should have had a composition of 75% hydrogen and 25% helium by mass at the end of the era of nucleosynthesis.

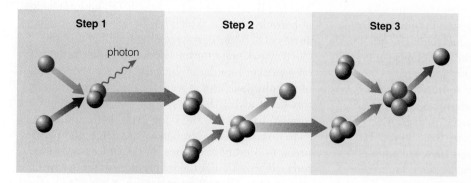

**FIGURE 22.9** During the era of nucleosynthesis, virtually all the neutrons in the universe fused with protons to form helium-4. This figure illustrates one of several possible reaction pathways. In step 1, a neutron and a proton fuse to form a deuterium nucleus, releasing a photon. In step 2, two deuterium nuclei fuse to make hydrogen-3, releasing a proton. In step 3, the hydrogen-3 nucleus fuses with deuterium to create helium-4, releasing one of the neutrons.

**FIGURE 22.10** During helium synthesis, protons outnumbered neutrons 7 to 1, which is the same as 14 to 2. The result was 12 hydrogen nuclei (individual protons) for each helium nucleus. Thus, the hydrogen-to-helium mass ratio is 12 to 4, which is the same as 75% to 25%.

Thus, the Big Bang theory makes a very concrete prediction about the chemical composition of the universe: It should be 75% hydrogen and 25% helium by mass. The fact that observations confirm this predicted ratio of hydrogen to helium is another striking success of the Big Bang theory.

**TIME OUT TO THINK** *Briefly explain why it should not be surprising that some galaxies contain a little more than 25% helium, but it would be very surprising if some galaxies contained less. (Hint: Think about how the relative amounts of hydrogen and helium in the universe can be affected by fusion in stars.)*

### Synthesis of Other Light Nuclei

Why didn't the Big Bang produce heavier elements? By the time stable helium nuclei formed, when the universe was about a minute old, the temperature and density of the rapidly expanding universe had already dropped too far for a process like carbon production (three helium nuclei fusing into carbon [Section 16.3]). to occur. Reactions between protons, deuterium nuclei, and helium were still possible, but most of these led nowhere. In particular, fusing two helium-4 nuclei together results in a nucleus that is unstable and falls apart in a fraction of a second, as does fusing a proton to a helium-4 nucleus.

A few reactions involving hydrogen-3 (also known as *tritium*) or helium-3 can create long-lasting nuclei. For example, fusing helium-4 and hydrogen-3 produces lithium-7. However, the contributions of these reactions to the overall composition of the universe were minor because hydrogen-3 and helium-3 were so rare. Models of element production in the early universe show that, before the cooling of the universe shut off fusion entirely, such reactions generated only trace amounts of lithium, the next lightest element after helium. Thus, aside from hydrogen, helium, and lithium, all other elements were forged much later in the nuclear furnaces of stars. (Beryllium and boron, which are heavier than lithium but lighter than carbon, were created later when high-energy particles broke apart heavier nuclei that formed in stars.)

### The Density of Ordinary Matter

Calculations made with the Big Bang model allow scientists to estimate the density of ordinary (baryonic) matter in the universe from the observed amount of deuterium in the universe today. The fact that some deuterium nuclei still exist in the universe indicates that the fusing of neutrons into helium nuclei in the early universe was incomplete. The amount of deuterium—roughly one hydrogen atom in 100,000 contains a deuterium nucleus—tells us about the density of protons and neutrons (baryons) during the era of nucleosynthesis. If this density had been higher in the early universe, protons and neutrons would have fused more efficiently into helium, and less deuterium would have been left over.

The results of such calculations show that the density of ordinary (baryonic) matter in the universe is somewhere between 1% and 10% of the critical density. (Recall that the critical density is the density required if the expansion of the universe is to stop and reverse someday [Section 21.6].) Similar calculations based on the observed abundance of lithium lead to the same conclusion, adding to our confidence in the Big Bang model and implying something very interesting about the fate of the universe: Unless extraordinary (nonbaryonic) matter outweighs ordinary matter by at least a factor of 10, the universe cannot recollapse. Moreover, if the universe's density is greater than 10% of the critical density—as appears to be the case—then extraordinary (nonbaryonic) matter may constitute the majority of the universe's mass.

**TIME OUT TO THINK** *The ideas discussed above point to a rather amazing fact: Although we have yet to discover any WIMPs, we suspect that they dominate the total mass of the universe. Briefly explain how this is possible, and comment on how confident we can be that weakly interacting particles make up the bulk of dark matter.*

## 22.4 Inflation

The Big Bang model relies heavily on our knowledge of particle physics, which has been tested to temperatures of $10^{15}$ K, corresponding to the end of the electroweak era. Our knowledge of earlier times rests on a weaker foundation because we are less certain of the physical laws at work. In fact, the best laboratory for studying the laws of physics at such high temperatures is the Big Bang itself. Different guesses as to how matter might behave at such high energies predict different outcomes for the universe we see today. If a particular model predicts that our universe should look different from the way it really does, then that model must be wrong. On the other hand, if a new model of particle physics explains some previously unexplained aspects of the universe, then it may be on the right track. The grand unified theories of particle physics discussed in Section 22.2 have not yet been proved, but many scientists believe these theories are on the right track for just this reason.

Prior to the early 1980s, scientists had identified several major aspects of our actual universe that were unexplained by the Big Bang model. Three of the most pressing unanswered questions were the following:

- *Where does structure come from?* According to the Big Bang theory, the process of galaxy formation required the density of the early universe to differ slightly from place to place. Otherwise, the pull of gravity would have been equally balanced everywhere, prohibiting the collapse of protogalactic clouds. The subtle temperature differences seen in the cosmic microwave background tell us that regions of enhanced density did indeed exist at the end of the era of nuclei, when the universe was 500,000 years old. However, the Big Bang theory cannot explain where these density enhancements came from.

- *Why is the large-scale universe so smooth?* Not only is the slight lumpiness of the early universe a problem, but its large-scale smoothness is also a problem. Observations of the cosmic microwave background show that, overall, the density of the universe at the end of the era of nuclei varied from place to place by no more than about 0.01%. The standard Big Bang theory does not explain why distant reaches of the universe look so similar.

- *Why is the density almost critical?* The density of matter in the universe is somewhere around 20–100% of the critical density [Section 21.6]—remarkably close to the critical density considering that the standard Big Bang theory doesn't say anything about what the density should be. Why isn't it 1,000 times the critical density, or 0.0000001 the critical density?

Physicist Alan Guth realized in 1981 that grand unified theories could potentially answer all three questions. These theories predict that the separation of the strong force from the GUT force should have released enormous energy, causing the universe to expand dramatically, perhaps by as much as $10^{30}$ times in less than $10^{-36}$ second. This dramatic expansion is what we call *inflation,* and while it sounds outrageous, it may have shaped the way the universe looks today.

### Giant Quantum Fluctuations

To understand how inflation solves the structure problem, we need to recognize a special feature of energy fields. Laboratory-tested principles of quantum mechanics (especially the uncertainty principle [Section S4.3]) require that the energy fields at any point in space be always fluctuating. Thus, the distribution of energy through space on very small scales is slightly irregular, even in a complete vacuum. These tiny quantum "ripples" can be characterized by a wavelength that corresponds roughly to their size. In principle, quantum ripples in the very early universe

could have been the seeds for density enhancements that later grew into galaxies. However, the wavelengths of the original ripples were far too small to explain density enhancements like those we see imprinted on the cosmic microwave background.

Inflation would have dramatically altered these quantum fluctuations. The fantastic growth of the universe during the period of inflation would have stretched tiny ripples in space to enormous wavelengths (Figure 22.11). Ultimately, inflation could have caused these quantum ripples to grow large enough to become the density enhancements that later formed large structures in the universe. Amazingly, all the structure we see today in the universe may have started as tiny quantum fluctuations just before the period of inflation.

**FIGURE 22.11** During inflation, ripples in spacetime would have stretched by a factor of perhaps $10^{30}$.

size of ripple before inflation = size of atomic nucleus

size of ripple after inflation = size of solar system

Inflation goes a long way toward solving the structure problem. However, it is important to note that the models invoking inflation do not entirely solve the structure problem. Although these models make reasonable predictions for the wavelengths of the quantum ripples, they do not predict their amplitudes. This problem underscores the speculative nature of the idea of inflation. Many scientists are working hard to improve models of inflation in hopes that they will soon be able to make more definitive predictions that can be tested observationally.

### Equalizing Temperatures and Densities

The idea that different parts of the universe should be very similar shortly after the Big Bang may seem

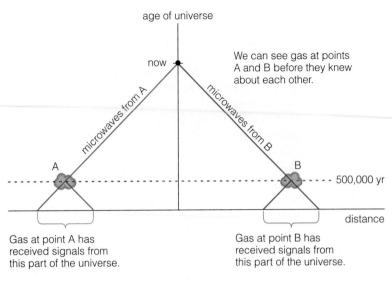

age of universe

now

We can see gas at points A and B before they knew about each other.

microwaves from A

microwaves from B

A

B

————————————————————— 500,000 yr

distance

Gas at point A has received signals from this part of the universe.

Gas at point B has received signals from this part of the universe.

**FIGURE 22.12** Light left the microwave-emitting regions we see on opposite sides of the universe long before they could have communicated with each other and equalized their temperatures, yet their temperatures are virtually identical.

quite natural at first, but on further inspection the smoothness of the universe becomes difficult to explain. Imagine observing the cosmic microwave background in a certain part of the sky. You are seeing that region as it was only 500,000 years after it formed. The microwaves coming from it have taken some 12 billion years or more—almost the entire age of the universe—to travel all the way to Earth. Now imagine turning around and looking at the background

radiation coming from the opposite direction. You are also seeing this region at an age of 500,000 years, and it looks virtually identical. The two microwave-emitting regions are billions of light-years apart, but we are seeing them as they were when they were only 500,000 years old. They can't possibly have had communication with each other then (Figure 22.12). A signal traveling at the speed of light from one to the other would barely have started its journey. So how do they come to be exactly the same temperature?

The idea of inflation solves this problem because it says that the entire observable universe was less than $10^{-38}$ light-second across before the episode of enormous expansion. Radiation signals traveling at the speed of light would have had time to equalize all the temperatures and densities in this region. Inflation then pushed these equalized regions to much greater distances, far out of contact with one another (Figure 22.13). Like criminals getting their stories straight before being locked in separate jail cells, all parts of the observable universe came to the same temperature and density before inflation spread them far apart. Thus, inflation accounts for how vastly separated regions can look so similar.

This explanation of why the universe appears so uniform at first appears paradoxical. It seems to re-

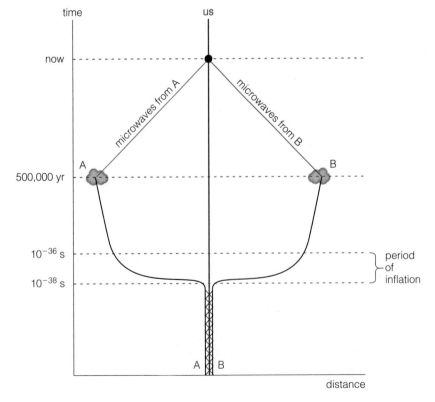

time

us

now

microwaves from A

microwaves from B

A

B

500,000 yr

$10^{-36}$ s

$10^{-38}$ s

period of inflation

A B

distance

**FIGURE 22.13** Before inflation, regions A and B were near enough to communicate and equalize their temperatures. Inflation pushed them far apart. Today, we can see both A and B, but they are too far apart to see each other.

quire pieces of the observable universe to move faster than the speed of light during inflation. Yet we know that nothing can move faster than the speed of light [Section S2.2]. To understand why inflation does not violate this universal speed limit, remember that the expansion of the universe is really the expansion of *space itself.* Objects with large cosmological redshifts aren't moving at high speed so much as they are riding along with the expansion of the universe. The gap between two objects thus increases because the space between them is expanding. Photons can easily cross this gap before inflation, but during inflation the gaps expand much faster than photons can cross them, and communication between the two objects ceases. One object never detects the other moving faster than light speed. Communication between these objects can resume only long after inflation, when photons have had time to cross the huge chasm in space that has opened.

### Balancing the Universe

The third question answered by inflation asks why the matter density of the universe is so close to the critical density. Another way to say that the universe's density is close to critical is to say that the overall geometry of the universe is remarkably "flat" [Section 21.6]. If the density of the universe exactly equals the critical density, then the kinetic energy of expansion precisely balances the universe's overall gravitational pull. According to Einstein's theory of general relativity, an imbalance in these energies causes curvature of spacetime, and deviations from precise balance grow more severe as the universe evolves. For example, if the universe had been 10% denser at the end of the era of nuclei, it would have collapsed long ago. On the other hand, if it had been 10% less dense at that time, galaxies would never have formed before expansion spread all the matter too thin. Thus, the universe had to start out remarkably balanced to be even remotely close to flat today.

Inflation balances the universe by ensuring that the mass-energy providing the universe's gravity precisely matches its kinetic energy of expansion. Once this balance is set, it should never waver. In terms of Einstein's theory, the effect of inflation on spacetime curvature is similar to the flattening of a balloon's surface when you blow into it (Figure 22.14). The flattening of space during the period of inflation would have been so enormous that it would virtually have eliminated any curvature the universe might have had previously.

The fine balance created by inflation turns out to be both a success and a potential pitfall of the inflation theory. On one hand, it explains how the universe managed to stay balanced long enough to bring forth galaxies. However, our studies of dark matter suggest

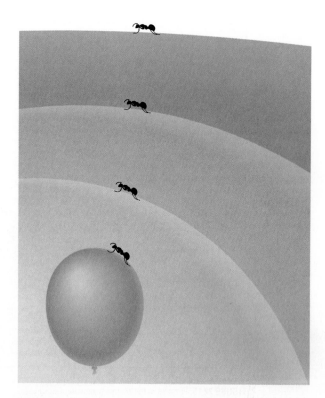

**FIGURE 22.14** As a balloon expands, its surface seems increasingly flat to an ant crawling along it.

that the current universe might be slightly out of balance: The best current estimates put the actual density of the universe at only about 25% of the critical density [Section 21.6], in which case the universe has about four times more kinetic energy than gravity can overcome.

Inflation theory has difficulty explaining this imbalance, but a loophole in Einstein's theory may solve the problem: Energy associated with a large-scale repulsive force can compensate for the shortfall in the matter density, making the present-day universe flatter than it would otherwise be. Remarkably, the supernova measurements indicating that our universe's expansion is accelerating [Section 21.6] also show that the strength of the implied repulsive force is about right to render the universe perfectly flat, just as inflation predicts.

### Testing for Inflation

Verifying that the universe underwent an episode of inflation is difficult, because this inflationary episode would have happened extremely early in the history of the universe—much earlier than we can observe directly. Nevertheless, we can test the idea of inflation by exploring whether its predictions are consistent with our observations of the universe at later

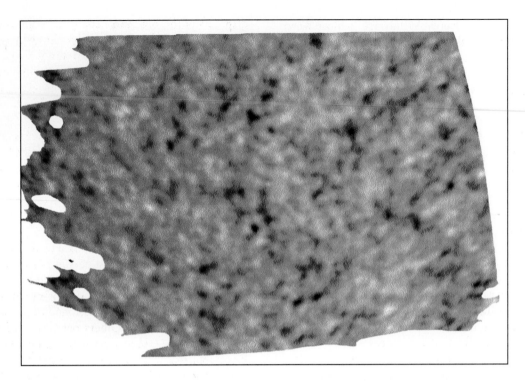

**FIGURE 22.15** Patterns in the cosmic microwave background. This microwave image showing about 2.5% of the sky was created by the BOOMERanG telescope, which flew above Antarctica on a balloon for $10\frac{1}{2}$ days in 1998. The shades of color represent tiny differences in temperature created by sound waves propagating through the universe when it was about 500,000 years old. Because these waves were stimulated by the density enhancements that later turned into galaxies, clusters, and larger-scale structures, careful study of the patterns they generated in the microwave sky tells us about the "genetic code" imprinted on the universe during its earliest moments. Observations to date are consistent with the idea of inflation and also indicate that the overall geometry of the universe is flat.

times. Such observations cannot prove the theory of inflation, but if they are inconsistent with the theory, then inflation probably never happened. Scientists are only beginning to make observations that test inflation, but to date the findings are consistent with the idea that an early inflationary episode smoothed and flattened the universe while planting the seeds of structure formation.

The earliest moment we can directly observe is the end of the era of nuclei, when photons began to stream freely across the universe, ultimately becoming the cosmic microwave background. COBE was the first telescope to reveal the density enhancements present at that moment in time, but many telescopes are following in COBE's footsteps and further refining our view of the microwave background (Figure 22.15). Because physical models of inflation make specific predictions about the nature of the density enhancements that ought to have been present in the early universe, measurements of the cosmic microwave background offer a way to test those models.

In a certain sense, cosmic microwave observations are recording the "genetic code" of the universe, be-cause the characteristics of the density enhancements present in the early universe governed the subsequent growth of galaxies, clusters, and larger-scale structures. To the extent that we have been able to read this code, it is quite similar to what we expect from inflation. These observations also indicate that the universe has a flat geometry, again in accord with inflation. More stringent tests are under way, and others are planned for the near future. Instruments like NASA's Microwave Anisotropy Probe (MAP) will be delivering details about the universe's genetic code over the next several years so keep listening for the latest news about inflation.

### The Bottom Line

All things considered, inflation does a remarkable job of addressing the problems inherent in the standard Big Bang theory. Many astronomers and physicists believe that some process akin to inflation did affect the early universe, but the details of the interaction between high-energy particle physics and the evolving universe remain unclear. If these details can be worked out successfully, we face an amazing prospect—a breakthrough in our understanding of the very smallest particles achieved by studying the universe on the largest observable scales.

## 22.5 Did the Big Bang Really Happen?

You might occasionally read an article in a newspaper or a magazine questioning whether the Big Bang really happened. We may never be able to prove with absolute certainty that the Big Bang theory is correct. However, no one has come up with any other model of the universe that so successfully explains so much of what we see. As we have discussed, the Big Bang model makes at least two specific predictions that we have observationally verified: the characteristics of the cosmic microwave background and the composition of the universe. It also explains quite naturally many other features of the universe. And, at least so far, we know of nothing that is absolutely inconsistent with the Big Bang model.

The Big Bang theory's very success has also made it a target for respected scientists, skeptical nonscientists, and crackpots alike. The nature of scientific work requires that we test established wisdom to make sure it is valid. A sound scientific disproof of the Big Bang theory would be a discovery of great importance. However, stories touted in the news media as

disproofs of the Big Bang usually turn out to be disagreements over details rather than fundamental problems that threaten to bring down the whole edifice. Nevertheless, scientists must keep refining the theory and tracking down the disagreements, because every once in a while a small disagreement blossoms into a full-blown scientific revolution.

You don't need to believe all you have read without question. The next time you are musing on the universe's origins, try an experiment for yourself. Go outside on a clear night and look at the sky. Notice how dark it is, and then ask yourself *why* it is dark. If the universe were infinite, unchanging, and everywhere the same, then the entire night sky would blaze as brightly as the Sun. Johannes Kepler [Section 5.3] was perhaps the first person to realize that the night sky in such a universe should be bright, but this realization is now called **Olbers' paradox** after Heinrich Olbers, a German astronomer of the 1800s.

To understand how Olbers' paradox comes about, imagine that you are in a dense forest on a flat plain. If you look in any given direction, you'll likely see a tree. If the forest is small, you might be able to see through some gaps in the trees to the open plains, but larger forests have fewer gaps (Figure 22.16). An infinite forest would have no gaps at all—a tree trunk would block your view along any direction.

**FIGURE 22.16** In a large forest (left) you'll see trees no matter where you look. In a small forest (below), you can see open spaces beyond the trees.

The universe is like a forest of stars in this respect. In an unchanging universe with an infinite number of stars, we would see a star in every direction, making every point in the sky as bright as the Sun's surface. Obscuring dust doesn't change this conclusion. The intense starlight would heat the dust over time until it too glowed like the Sun or evaporated away.

There are only two ways out of this dilemma: Either the universe has a finite number of stars, in which case we would not see a star in every direction, or it changes over time in some way that prevents us from seeing an infinite number of stars. For several centuries after Kepler first recognized the dilemma, astronomers leaned toward the first option.

Kepler himself preferred to believe that the universe had a finite number of stars because he thought it had to be finite in space, with some kind of dark wall surrounding everything. Astronomers in the early twentieth century preferred to believe that the universe was infinite in space but that we lived inside a finite collection of stars; they thought of the Milky Way as an island floating in a vast black void. However, subsequent observations showed that galaxies fill all of space more or less uniformly. We are therefore left with the second option: The universe changes in time.

The Big Bang theory solves Olbers' paradox in a particularly simple way: It tells us that we can see only

### The End of Time

According to the Big Bang theory, time and space have a beginning in the Big Bang. Do they also have an end? If we live in a recollapsing universe, the answer seems to be a clear yes: Sometime in the distant future, the universal expansion will cease and reverse, and the universe will eventually come to an end in a fiery *Big Crunch*. But it appears more likely that the universe will continue to expand forever.

In a critical, coasting, or accelerating universe, the end will come much more gradually. The star–gas–star cycle in galaxies cannot continue forever, because not all the material is recycled: With each generation of stars, more mass becomes locked up in planets, brown dwarfs, white dwarfs, neutron stars, and black holes. Eventually, about a trillion years from now, even the longest-lived stars will burn out, and the galaxies will fade into darkness.

At this point, the only new action in the universe will occur on the rare occasions when two objects—such as two brown dwarfs or two white dwarfs—collide within a galaxy. The vast distances separating star systems in galaxies make such collisions extremely rare. For example, the probability of our Sun (or the white dwarf that it will become) colliding with another star is so small that it would be expected to happen only once in a quadrillion ($10^{15}$) years. But forever is a long time, and even low-probability events will eventually happen many times. If a star system experiences a collision once in a quadrillion years, it will experience about 100 collisions in 100 quadrillion ($10^{17}$) years. By the time the universe reaches an age of $10^{20}$ years, star systems will have suffered an average of 100,000 collisions each, making a time-lapse history of any galaxy look like a cosmic game of pinball.

These multiple collisions will severely disrupt galaxies. As in any gravitational encounter, some objects lose energy and some gain energy. Objects that gain enough energy will be flung into intergalactic space, where they will drift ever farther from all other objects with the expansion of the universe. Objects that lose energy will eventually fall to the galactic center, forming a gigantic black hole.

The remains of the universe will consist of black holes with masses as great as a trillion solar masses widely separated from a few scattered planets, brown dwarfs, and stellar corpses. If the Earth somehow survives, it will be a frozen chunk of rock in the darkness of the expanding universe, billions of light-years from any other solid object.

If grand unified theories are correct, the Earth still cannot last forever. These theories predict that protons will eventually fall apart. The predicted lifetime of protons is extremely long: a half-life of at least $10^{32}$ years. However, if protons really do decay, then by the time the universe is $10^{40}$ years old the Earth and all other atomic matter will have disintegrated into radiation and subatomic particles, such as electrons and neutrinos.

The final phase is predicted to come with the disintegration of the giant, black-hole corpses of galaxies. Black holes are predicted to slowly evaporate through the process of *Hawking radiation,* finally disappearing in brilliant bursts of radiation [Section S4.5]. The largest black holes last longest, but even trillion-solar-mass black holes will evaporate sometime after the universe reaches an age of $10^{100}$ years. From then on, the universe will consist only of individual photons and subatomic particles, each separated by enormous distances from the others. Nothing new will ever happen, and no events will ever occur that would allow an omniscient observer to distinguish past from future. In a sense, the universe will finally have reached the end of time.

Lest any of this sound depressing, keep in mind that $10^{100}$ years is an indescribably long time. As an example, imagine that you wanted to write on a piece of paper a number that consisted of a 1 followed by $10^{100}$ zeros (i.e., the number $10^{10^{100}}$). It sounds easy, but a piece of paper large enough to fit all those zeros *would not fit in the observable universe* today. And, if that still does not alleviate your concerns, you may be glad to know that a few creative thinkers speculate about ways in which the universe might undergo rebirth, even after the end of time.

a finite number of stars because the universe began at a particular moment. While the universe may contain an infinite number of stars, we can see only those that lie within our cosmological horizon [Section 19.4]. There are other ways in which the universe could change in time and prevent us from seeing an infinite number of stars, so Olbers' paradox does not *prove* that the universe began with a Big Bang. But we must have some explanation for why the sky is dark at night, and no explanation besides the Big Bang also explains so many other observed properties of the universe so well.

## THE BIG PICTURE

Our "big picture" is now about as complete as it gets. We've discussed the universe from the Earth outward, and from the beginning to the end. When you think back on this chapter, keep in mind the following ideas:

- Predicting conditions in the early universe is straightforward. The only real question is how matter and energy behave under such extreme conditions.

- Our current understanding of physics allows us to reconstruct the conditions that prevailed in the universe all the way back to the first $10^{-10}$ second. Our understanding is less certain back to $10^{-38}$ second. Beyond $10^{-43}$ second, we run up against the present limits of human knowledge.

- Although it may sound strange to talk about the universe during its first fraction of a second, our ideas about the Big Bang rest on a solid foundation of observational, experimental, and theoretical evidence. We cannot say with absolute certainty that the Big Bang really happened, but no other model ever proposed has so successfully explained how our universe came to be as it is.

### Review Questions

1. Briefly explain why the early universe must have been much hotter and denser than the universe is today.

2. What do we mean by the *Big Bang theory?*

3. What is *antimatter?* How were particle–antiparticle pairs created in the early universe? How were they destroyed?

4. Briefly summarize the characteristics marking each of the various eras shown in Figure 22.2.

5. What are the *Planck era* and the *Planck time?* Why can't our current theories describe the history of the universe during the Planck era?

6. What are *grand unified theories?* According to these theories, how many forces operated in the universe during the *GUT era?* Why?

7. What do we mean by *inflation?* Briefly describe why inflation might have occurred at the end of the GUT era.

8. What characterized the universe during the *electroweak era?* What evidence from particle accelerators supports the idea that the weak and electromagnetic forces were once unified as a single electroweak force?

9. What characterized the universe during the *particle era?* What happened to the quarks that existed freely in the universe early in the particle era?

10. How long did the *era of nucleosynthesis* last? Why was this era so important in determining the chemical composition of the universe forever after?

11. Briefly explain why radiation was trapped for 500,000 years during the *era of nuclei* and why the cosmic microwave background broke free at the end of this era.

12. What do we mean by the *era of atoms* and the *era of galaxies?* What era do we live in? Explain.

13. Briefly describe the two key pieces of evidence that support the Big Bang theory.

14. Briefly describe how the *cosmic microwave background* was discovered.

15. Why does the Big Bang theory predict that the cosmic microwave background should have a perfect thermal radiation spectrum? How did the Cosmic Background Explorer (COBE) support this prediction of the Big Bang theory? What is the temperature of the cosmic microwave background?

16. Briefly describe how theoretical calculations allow us to predict the fraction of ordinary matter in the universe that should consist of helium as opposed to hydrogen.

17. How do measurements of the abundance of deuterium in today's universe allow us to estimate the density of ordinary matter during the era of nucleosynthesis? Explain why these measurements suggest that at least some of the dark matter in the universe must be extraordinary.

18. Why do we think that tiny quantum ripples should have been present in the early universe? How might inflation have caused these tiny ripples to become the seeds that later grew into galaxies?

19. How does inflation explain why the universe appears so uniform?

20. Briefly explain why the theory of inflation predicts that the universe ought to be flat. How is inflation being tested by astronomers?

21. What is *Olbers' paradox*? Explain how this simple paradox provides at least some support for the idea that the universe began in a Big Bang.

## Discussion Questions

1. *The Moment of Creation.* You've probably noticed that, in discussing the Big Bang theory, we never quite talk about the first instant. Even our most speculative theories at present take us back only to within $10^{-43}$ second of creation. Do you think it will *ever* be possible for science to consider the moment of creation itself? Will we ever be able to answer questions such as *why* the Big Bang happened? Defend your opinions.

2. *The Big Bang.* How convincing do you find the evidence for the Big Bang model of the universe's origin? What are the strengths of the theory? What does it fail to explain? Overall, do *you* think the Big Bang really happened? Defend your opinion.

3. *The End of Time.* According to our current understanding, the universe as we know it will eventually come to an end—either in a fiery Big Crunch or in a slow death as all the stars eventually die. However, some people speculate that the universe might then undergo some type of rebirth. In the case of a recollapsing universe, the rebirth might consist of a new Big Bang; some people even speculate that the universe might repeatedly oscillate through cycles of Big Bangs and Big Crunches. Discuss some ideas about how the universe might undergo rebirth if it continues to expand forever. (*Note:* You may wish to read Isaac Asimov's short story *The Last Question,* published in 1956.)

4. *Forever.* If you could live forever, would you choose to do so? Suppose the universe will keep expanding forever, as the bulk of observations currently suggest. How would you satisfy your energy needs as time goes on? How would you grow food? What would you do with all that time?

## Problems

*True Statements?* For **problems 1–8**, decide whether the statement is true and explain why it is or is not.

1. According to the Big Bang theory, the universe's temperature was greater than 10 billion ($10^{10}$) K when the universe was less than one ten-billionth ($10^{-10}$) of a second old.

2. Although the universe today appears to be made mostly of matter and not antimatter, the Big Bang theory suggests that the early universe had nearly equal amounts of matter and antimatter.

3. According to the Big Bang theory, the cosmic microwave background was created when energetic photons ionized the neutral hydrogen atoms that originally filled the universe.

4. While the existence of the cosmic microwave background is consistent with the Big Bang theory, it is also easily explained by assuming that it comes from individual stars and galaxies.

5. According to the Big Bang theory, most of the helium in the universe was created by nuclear fusion in the cores of stars.

6. The theory of inflation suggests that the structure in the universe today may have originated as tiny quantum fluctuations.

7. Within the next decade, observations of the cosmic microwave background will prove definitively whether inflation really occurred in the early universe.

8. The fact that the night sky is dark tells us that the universe cannot be infinite, unchanging, and everywhere the same.

9. *Life Story of a Proton.* Tell the life story of a proton from its formation shortly after the Big Bang to its presence in the nucleus of an oxygen atom you have just inhaled. Your story should be creative and imaginative, but it also should demonstrate your scientific understanding of as many stages in the proton's life as possible. You can draw on material from the entire book, and your story should be three to five pages long.

*10. *The Cosmic Microwave Background.* The cosmic microwave background first began to stream freely across the universe at the end of the era of nuclei, when the universe was 500,000 years old and its temperature was about 3,000 K. Since that time, the universe has expanded by a factor of about 1,000.

    a. Using Wien's law (see Mathematical Insight 7.2), calculate the wavelength of maximum intensity for thermal radiation with a temperature of 3,000 K.

    b. The observed temperature of the cosmic microwave background today is about 2.73 K. Use Wien's law to calculate the wavelength of maximum intensity for the cosmic microwave background today.

    c. How much longer are the wavelengths of the cosmic microwave background today than they were at the time the radiation was first released? Is this change in wavelength consistent with the idea that the universe has expanded by a factor of about 1,000 since the end of the era of nuclei? Explain. (*Hint:* Look back at the discussion of cosmological redshifts in Chapter 19.)

*11. $10^{100}$ *Years.* In the box Thinking About . . . The End of Time, we found that the final stage in the history of a critical, coasting, or accelerating universe will come about $10^{100}$ years from now. Such a large number is easy to write but difficult to understand. In this problem, we investigate some of the incredible properties of very large numbers.

a. The current age of the universe is around $10^{10}$ years. How much longer is a trillion years than this current age? How much longer is $10^{15}$ years? $10^{20}$ years?

b. Suppose protons decay with a half-life of $10^{32}$ years. When will the number of remaining protons be half the current amount? When will it be a quarter of its current amount? How many half-lives will have gone by when the universe reaches an age of $10^{34}$ years? What fraction of the original protons will remain at this time? Based on your answers, is it reasonable to conclude that *all* protons in today's universe will be gone by the time the universe is $10^{40}$ years old? Explain.

c. Suppose you were trying to write $10^{100}$ zeros on a piece of paper and could write microscopically, so that each zero (including the thickness of the pencil mark) occupied a volume of 1 cubic micrometer—about the size of a bacterium. Could $10^{100}$ zeros of this size fit in the observable universe? Explain. (*Hints:* Calculate the volume of the observable universe in cubic micrometers by assuming it is a sphere with a radius of 15 billion light-years. The volume of a sphere is $4/3 \times \pi \times$ (radius)$^3$; 1 light-year $\approx 10^{15}$ meters; 1 cubic meter = $10^{18}$ cubic micrometers.)

## Web Projects

Find useful links for Web projects on the text Web site.

1. *New Tests of the Big Bang Theory.* The Cosmic Background Explorer (COBE) satellite provided striking confirmation of several predictions of the Big Bang theory. But new satellites are already being designed that will test the Big Bang theory further, primarily by observing the subtle variations in the cosmic microwave background with a much higher sensitivity than COBE. Use the Web to gather pictures and information about the COBE mission and its planned successors, such as MAP or Planck. Write a one- to two-page report about the strength of the evidence compiled by COBE and how much more we might learn from the upcoming missions.

2. *Decay of the Proton.* One of the most startling predictions of grand unified theories is that protons will eventually decay, albeit with a half-life of more than $10^{32}$ years. If this is true, it may be possible to observe an occasional proton decay, despite the extraordinarily long half-life. Several experiments to look for proton decay are under way or being planned. Find out about one or more of these experiments, and write a one- to two-page summary in which you describe the experiment(s), any results to date, and what these results (or potential results) mean to the grand unified theories.

3. *New Ideas in Inflation.* The idea of inflation solves many of the puzzles associated with the standard Big Bang theory, but we are still a long way from finding strong evidence that inflation really occurred. Find recent articles that discuss some of the latest ideas about inflation and how we might test these ideas. Write a two- to three-page summary of your findings.

*We, this people, on a small and lonely planet*
*Travelling through casual space*
*Past aloof stars, across the way of indifferent suns*
*To a destination where all signs tell us*
*It is possible and imperative that we learn*
*A brave and startling truth.*

MAYA ANGELOU, EXCERPTED FROM
*A BRAVE AND STARTLING TRUTH*

# CHAPTER S5

# Interstellar Travel
## and the Search for
## Extraterrestrial Civilizations

According to science fiction, our descendants will soon travel among the stars as routinely as we jet about the Earth in airplanes. They'll race around the galaxy in starships of all sizes and shapes, circumventing nature's prohibition on faster-than-light travel by entering hyperspace, wormholes, or warp drive. They'll witness incredible cosmic phenomena firsthand, including stars and planets in all stages of development, accretion disks around white dwarfs and neutron stars, and the distortion of spacetime near black holes. Along the way, they'll encounter numerous alien species, most of which will look a lot like us and share virtually the same level of technological advancement.

Real interstellar travel is likely to be limited by the speed of light. More-over, given the billions of years over which the galaxy has existed, finding an alien species that shares our level of technological development would be an extraordinary coincidence; more likely, any other species we encounter will be either far ahead of us or far behind us.

Nevertheless, if our civilization survives long enough, it seems almost inevitable that our descendants will leave the confines of our solar system. In this final chapter, we will explore how that might happen. We will also consider whether other species might already have progressed beyond this point and, if so, how we might contact them.

## S5.1 Starships: Distant Dream or Near-Reality?

Before our ancestors domesticated camels and horses, and before the invention of the wheel, the fastest way to travel was on foot. Traveling on foot, our ancestors could sustain speeds of no more than a few kilometers per hour. Today, our fastest interplanetary spacecraft travel through the solar system at speeds of a few *tens of thousands* of kilometers per hour—a factor of 10,000 faster than our ancestors traveled on foot. But we will need to go much faster to travel among the stars (at least if we are interested in making round-trip journeys within human lifetimes). At the speeds of our current interplanetary spacecraft, the journey to even the nearest stars (besides the Sun) would take more than 50,000 years.

The vast distances between the stars mean that practical starships would have to travel near the speed of light in order to complete a journey within a human lifetime. Today's seemingly fast interplanetary spacecraft travel less than 1/10,000 the speed of light—meaning that starships will need to go 10,000 times faster. From this standpoint, we are as far from interstellar flight as cavemen were from the space age.

From another standpoint, however, starflight might be just around the corner. Nearly all of the increase in speed we have achieved over our ancestors occurred within the past century or so, with the advent of flight and the dawn of the space age. If we can achieve a comparable speed advancement in the next century, our great-grandchildren may be building starships.

Regardless of how far in the future interstellar travel might be, we will have to overcome huge technological and social hurdles to achieve it. On the technological side, we will need entirely new types of engines to reach speeds close to the speed of light. We'll also need new types of shielding to protect crew members from instant death: When a starship travels through interstellar gas at near–light speed, ordinary atoms and ions will hit it like a flood of high-energy cosmic rays.

The social hurdles may be even more difficult to overcome. Building starships will almost certainly require construction facilities in space and probably cannot be achieved until we first learn to mine materials from the Moon or nearby asteroids. Thus, at least a few major space stations and outposts on the Moon are probably prerequisites to any era of starship exploration. Given global political realities, such colonization of space will probably not occur without far greater international trust and cooperation than we enjoy today.

Even if we overcome the technological and social hurdles, interstellar travel will pose further difficulties for starship crews. Einstein's theory of relativity offers high-speed travelers a "ticket to the stars": Time will run slow for the travelers, enabling them to make journeys across many light-years of space in relatively short amounts of time. For example, in a ship traveling at an average speed of 99.9% of the speed of light, the 50 light-year round-trip to Vega would take the travelers only about 2 years [Section S2.6]. But more than 50 years would pass on Earth while they were gone, which would make their lives very difficult when they returned. Family and friends would be older or gone, new technologies might have made their knowledge and skills obsolete, and it might take them many years just to understand the political and social changes that occurred in their absence.

Despite all these hurdles, the human race is progressing toward the achievement of interstellar travel. Technology continues to advance rapidly, and the potential for international cooperation is much greater today than it was just a couple of decades ago, when the United States and the Soviet Union seemed poised for World War III. Even the difficulties posed by long trips may not be insurmountable. Perhaps the trips will be one-way, with the travelers discovering and colonizing new planets. Or perhaps advances in medicine will extend human life spans to hundreds or even thousands of years, in which case being away from Earth for a few decades may be no more traumatic than going off to college is today.

All things considered, we seem bound to become interstellar travelers unless we *choose* otherwise. Such a choice might be deliberate: Many people argue that money for space exploration would be better spent here on Earth, and others argue against space colonization on philosophical grounds. Or it might be the consequence of a catastrophe: Despite the lessening of international tensions since the end of the Cold War, more than 10,000 nuclear weapons remain in the global arsenal, and many nations possess the technology to build chemical and biological weapons of mass destruction. Our civilization might also succumb to disasters brought on by human activity, such as overpopulation, epidemic disease, or global warming.

If an alien civilization were watching us, they might well conclude that we are poised on the brink of the most significant turning point in human history. If we destroy ourselves, all our achievements in science, art, and philosophy will be lost forever. But if we survive and choose to continue the exploration of space, we may be embarking on a path that will take us to the stars.

**TIME OUT TO THINK** *While we could certainly destroy our civilization today, some people argue that a civilization with colonies spread among many different star systems would be essentially*

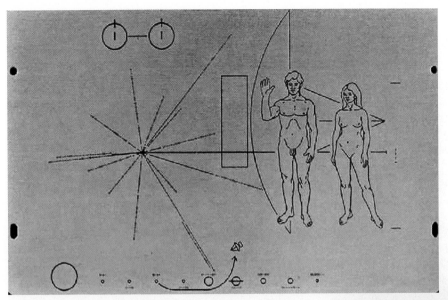

**a** *Pioneers 10* and *11* carry a copy of this etching as a greeting to anyone who might find them.

**b** *Voyagers 1* and *2* carry a phonograph record—a 12-inch gold-plated copper disk containing music, greetings, and images from Earth.

**FIGURE S5.1** Messages aboard the Pioneer and Voyager spacecraft, which are bound for the stars.

*"extinction-proof." Because of the long travel times between star systems, no single event (such as war, disease, or environmental damage) could wipe out all the colonies. Do you agree that attaining large-scale interstellar travel would assure the long-term survival of the human species? Defend your opinion.*

## S5.2 Starship Design

So far we have spoken of starships that could carry humans across vast interstellar distances. But if we expand the definition to include robotic spacecraft, then we have already launched our first starships. Four interplanetary probes—*Pioneers 10* and *11*, and *Voyagers 1* and *2*—are traveling fast enough to escape the solar system. It will take them more than 10,000 years to cover each light-year of distance, and their trajectories will not take them on close passes of any nearby stars. Nevertheless, these spacecraft should

suffer little damage during their journeys and are likely to look almost as good as new for millions of years. Each carries a greeting from Earth, in case someone comes across one of them someday (Figure S5.1).

Current spacecraft, including both robotic probes like Pioneer and Voyager and crew-carrying spacecraft such as the Space Shuttle, are launched by *chemical rockets*. Their engines use energy from chemical reactions to drive hot gas out the back of the rocket, which causes the rocket to accelerate forward. Chemical rockets will never be practical for interstellar travel because a limiting process prevents them from reaching very high speeds: Achieving higher speeds requires more fuel, but the added weight of additional fuel makes it more difficult to increase the rocket's speed. Detailed calculations of this limiting process show that chemical rockets, even as propulsion systems for relatively small robotic spacecraft, cannot exceed speeds of about $0.001c$—in which case the journey to Alpha Centauri would take more than 4,000 years. For the much larger starships

**FIGURE S5.2** Artist's conception of the Project Orion starship, showing one of the small H-bomb detonations that propel it. Debris from the detonation impacts the flat disk, called the pusher plate, at the back of the spaceship. The central sections (enclosed in lattice) hold the bombs, and the crew lives in the front sections.

needed to support human crews, chemical rockets are completely out of the question. Fortunately, other technologies may allow much faster travel.

### Nuclear Rocket Propulsion

Rockets would be far more powerful if their engines used nuclear power rather than chemical power. Nuclear reactions generate far more power than chemical reactions because they convert some of the mass in atomic nuclei into energy in accord with $E = mc^2$. Fusing a kilogram of hydrogen, for example, generates more than a million times more energy than chemical reactions in a kilogram of hydrogen and oxygen.

One way to realize the benefits of fusion power would be to power starships with nuclear bombs. This idea, called *nuclear pulse propulsion*, involves generating energy with repeated detonations of relatively small H-bombs. One design, created under the name Project Orion, envisions the explosions taking place a few tens of meters behind the space ship (Figure S5.2). (Project Orion lasted from 1958 to

1965 and involved about 40 engineers and scientists.) The vaporized debris from each explosion would impact a "pusher plate" on the back of the spacecraft, propelling the ship forward. In principle, we could build an Orion spacecraft with existing technology, although it would be very expensive and would require an exception to the international treaty banning nuclear detonations in space.

Another design for a fusion-powered rocket, called Project Daedalus, (designed in the 1970s by members of the British Interplanetary Society), relies on generation of a continuous stream of energy from an on-board controlled nuclear fusion reactor (Figure S5.3). Because we have not yet achieved controlled nuclear fusion (as opposed to "uncontrolled" bombs), Daedalus remains beyond our current technological capabilities.

Fusion-powered starships such as Orion or Daedalus could probably achieve speeds of about 10% of the speed of light, completing journeys to nearby stars in a few decades. Such speeds are certainly sufficient for sending colonists on one-way voyages, particularly if the crew can be put into some sort of hibernation that prevents them from aging during the trip.

**FIGURE S5.3** Artist's conception of a robotic Project Daedalus starship. The front section (right) holds the scientific instruments. The large spheres hold the hydrogen for the central fusion reactor.

**TIME OUT TO THINK** *From the sixteenth to the nineteenth century, many people left their homes in Europe on one-way journeys to the "new world" of America. In the future, similar one-way trips to colonies on Earth-like planets around other stars may be possible. If offered the opportunity, would you go? Do you know anyone who would? Why or why not?*

### Matter–Antimatter Rocket Engines

In principle, there is an even more powerful energy source for rocket engines than fusion: matter–antimatter annihilation [Section S4.2]. Whereas fusion converts less than 1% of the mass of atomic nuclei into energy, matter–antimatter annihilation converts *all* the annihilated mass into energy. Starships with matter–antimatter engines could probably reach 90% or more of the speed of light. At these speeds, the slowing of time predicted by relativity becomes noticeable, putting many nearby stars within a few years' journey for the crew members.

However, while matter–antimatter engines may someday be the propulsion systems of choice for starships, this technology appears to be far in the future. The two major technological challenges to developing matter–antimatter engines are finding a way to produce sufficient quantities of antimatter to be used in the engines and finding a way to safely store the antimatter until it is needed.

Neither challenge seems likely to be met soon. At present, we can produce antimatter only in huge particle accelerators that cost billions of dollars to build and require enormous amounts of energy to operate. With present technology, making just a single kilogram of antimatter would take more energy than the current annual energy use of all of humanity. Moreover, even if we could produce the antimatter, we do not yet have the technology to store it safely. We could not put it in a normal container, because it would instantly annihilate with the matter in the container walls. We could potentially use a *magnetic container*—which uses magnetic fields to keep charged particles confined inside—but the container would have to be completely empty of ordinary matter in order to prevent annihilation.

### Sails and Beamed Energy Propulsion

In principle, spacecraft with large, lightweight sails could be propelled by the solar wind and the radiation pressure of sunlight. Solar sailing may well prove to be a fairly inexpensive way of navigating within the solar system (Figure S5.4). Surprisingly, it may even be useful for interstellar travel. Energy flowing from the Sun would give an optimally designed sailing starship a small but continuous acceleration as it headed out of the solar system. By the time the ship reached the distance at which the solar wind could no longer provide acceleration, it might already be traveling at speeds of a few percent of the speed of light.

We might achieve even higher velocities by shining powerful lasers at the spacecraft sails. Such *beamed energy propulsion* theoretically could accelerate ships to substantial fractions of the speed of light—but only if we could build enormous lasers. For example, accelerating a ship to half the speed of light within a few years would require a laser that uses 1,000 times more power than all current human power consumption. As a result, starships propelled by beamed energy probably remain far in the future. (Another challenge for beamed energy propulsion is figuring out how to slow down the ship when it reaches its destination.)

### Interstellar Ramjets

All the propulsion systems we've discussed so far have limited capabilities: Rockets can carry only a limited amount of fuel no matter what their fuel source, and beamed energy becomes too weak to accelerate starships when they get very far from home. One way around these difficulties would be to build a starship that collects fuel as it goes, using a giant scoop to gather interstellar hydrogen as fuel for a fusion engine. Such ships are known as *interstellar ramjets* (Figure S5.5); in principle, they can accelerate continuously by collecting and using fuel continuously.

Imagine an interstellar ramjet that accelerates at 1g for half the voyage to its destination and then turns around and decelerates at 1g until it arrives. The crew would find the trip quite comfortable, experiencing Earth-like gravity the entire way. During most of the journey, the ship would be traveling relative to Earth (and its destination) at a speed very

**FIGURE S5.4** Artist's conception of a spaceship propelled by a solar sail, shown as it approaches a forming planet in a young solar system. The sail is many kilometers across; the scientific payload is at the central meeting point of the four scaffoldlike structures.

**FIGURE S5.5** Artist's conception of a spaceship powered by an interstellar ramjet. The giant scoop in the front (left) collects interstellar hydrogen for use as fusion fuel.

close to the speed of light, so time on the ship would pass very slowly compared to time on Earth. Longer trips would mean reaching top speeds closer to the speed of light and therefore more extreme effects on time. For example, such a ship could make a trip to a star 500 light-years away in only about 12 years of ship time. (You can calculate this and the other travel times for the crew using the formula given in problem 9 of Chapter S3.) It could travel the 28,000 light-years to the center of the Milky Way Galaxy, where it could observe firsthand the mysterious galactic center [Section 18.5], in only about 21 years of ship time. It could make the trip to a star system in the Andromeda Galaxy in only about 29 years of ship time. Thus, the crew could travel to the Andromeda Galaxy, spend 2 years studying one of its star systems and taking pictures of the Milky Way Galaxy to bring home, and return in just 60 years of ship time. However, because the Andromeda Galaxy is about 2.5 million light-years away, the crew would find that about 5 million years had passed on Earth by the time they returned home.

### Science Fiction

If you are a science fiction fan, this discussion of interstellar travel may be depressing. Interstellar tourism and commerce seem out of the question, even with interstellar ramjets that reach speeds very close to the speed of light. If we are ever to travel about the galaxy the way we now travel about the Earth, we will need spacecraft that can get us from here to there much faster than the speed of light.

Einstein's theory of relativity leaves little hope that we can ever find a way to travel *through* space faster than the speed of light, but science fiction writers have imagined all kinds of novel shortcuts that don't necessarily violate relativity or any other known laws of physics. We discussed some of these ideas (hyperspace, wormholes, and warp drive) in Chapter S3. The bottom line is that our present knowledge does not allow us to say one way or the other whether any of these technologies are possible.

## S5.3 Radio Communication: Virtual Interstellar Travel

We cannot travel at the speed of light, but we can send information at the speed of light using radio waves, lasers, or other forms of light. Because radio waves penetrate interstellar gas and dust fairly easily, they probably will prove to be the most useful form of interstellar communication. Although we usually think of radio communication as a way of sending and receiving fairly simple messages, there is really no limit to how much information we could transmit or receive. In principle, we could become *virtual* interstellar travelers. Imagine, for example, that we sent a robotic probe to Alpha Centauri at 10% of the speed of light. The probe would take 40 years to get there, but it could send data back to Earth via radio in just 4 years. Nearby stars, at least, could be explored with robotic spacecraft in the same way we now explore the planets of our own solar system.

An even better way to gather data about distant worlds would be to receive signals from civilizations in other star systems. If such civilizations exist, they may already be broadcasting messages to us. The **search for extraterrestrial intelligence**, or **SETI**, is a project in which scientists use large radio telescopes to scan the skies for signals from other civilizations (Figure S5.6). With enough data and the computer technology known as virtual reality, we could actually experience what it would be like to walk among the cities of an alien civilization.

The more immediate hope of SETI efforts is simply to learn whether anyone else is out there—and happens to be broadcasting messages. But how could we interpret these messages? After all, we could hardly expect alien civilizations to share any of our social customs, let alone to speak English. Fortunately, we know that all civilizations must share some things in common: the laws of mathematics and science that are the same everywhere. Imagine that we wanted to send a message to a distant civilization. As popularized in the movie *Contact,* we might begin by broadcasting radio pulses in the order of the prime numbers (1, 2, 3, 5, 7, 11, . . .)—clearly identifying the message as something sent by an intelligent species, since no known natural process can broadcast prime numbers. We could then represent the prime numbers with a binary code and use this same code to begin representing some of the laws of mathematics. Because alien civilizations would know these laws already, they could learn the intricacies of our code. Once they knew the full code, they could receive as much additional information about Earth and our civilization as we wished to send them.

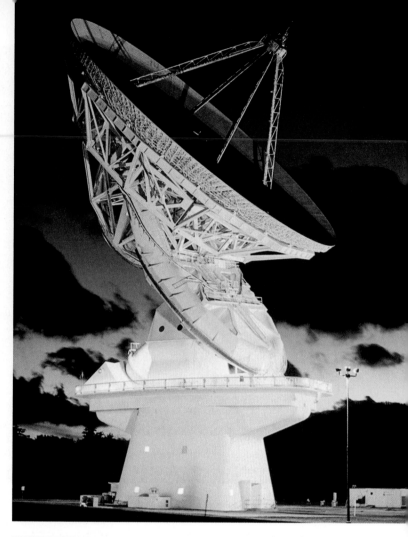

**FIGURE S5.6** This 210-foot radio telescope in New South Wales, Australia, is being used for Project Phoenix, a project to search nearby, Sun-like star systems for signals from extraterrestrial civilizations. Project Phoenix is sustained by private funding.

Scientists working on SETI hope that someone out there is already broadcasting similar coded messages to Earth. Even if such messages are being continually broadcast to Earth, finding them may be rather like finding the proverbial needle in a haystack: There are billions of stars to search, and we don't know the radio frequencies at which other civilizations might choose to broadcast their messages. Nevertheless, we can make some guesses. For example, we might focus our attention on Sun-like stars and assume that the aliens would broadcast near some "natural" frequency, such as the frequency of 21-cm radio waves from hydrogen. In addition, new technologies allow us to search many frequencies simultaneously, increasing the odds of success. However, SETI efforts remain controversial because they require extensive time on powerful and expensive radio telescopes when we have no way of knowing whether anyone is even out there.

**TIME OUT TO THINK** *SETI supporters argue that, despite the costs and the unknowns, the efforts are justified because contact with an extraterrestrial intelligence would be one of the most dramatic discoveries in human history. Do you agree? Defend your opinion.*

## S5.4 Civilizations

Whether we consider the virtual travel of radio communication or actual ships bound for the stars, a recurrent theme of interstellar travel is contact with other civilizations. Thus, we are led to one of the most exciting questions in science: Is anyone else out there?

Unfortunately, we simply don't yet know. But we can speculate—and perhaps even learn something important in the process. Let's try a systematic approach to guessing the number of alien civilizations that exist. We'll concentrate on the Milky Way Galaxy and then extend our results to the entire observable universe. For simplicity's sake, we'll also assume that alien life, like life on Earth, will need liquid water and therefore that it must evolve on a planet that lies within the *habitable zone* around a star [Section 13.6].

### How Many Civilizations Are Out There?

In principle, we could calculate the number of civilizations in the Milky Way Galaxy if we knew just a few basic facts. We would start with the number of planets that lie within habitable zones, which we'll call $N_P$ (for "number of planets"). Then we would determine the fraction of those planets that actually have life; let's use $f_{life}$ to stand for this fraction. Multiplying $N_P$ by $f_{life}$ would tell us the number of life-bearing planets in the Milky Way. Next, we'd multiply this number by the fraction of life-bearing planets on which intelligent beings evolve and develop a civilization, which we'll call $f_{civ}$. Finally, we'd multiply by the fraction of planets with civilizations that have those civilizations *now* (as opposed to the distant past or future), which we'll call $f_{now}$. Putting all these ideas together gives us the following simple equation (a variation on what is called the Drake equation) for the number of civilizations now inhabiting the Milky Way Galaxy:

$$\text{Number of civilizations} = N_P \times f_{life} \times f_{civ} \times f_{now}$$

The only difficulty in using this equation is that we don't know the value of any of its terms! In fact, the only term for which we can even make a reasonable guess is the number of planets, $N_P$. Our theories of star formation tell us that planetary systems ought to be common, and recent discoveries of extrasolar planets support this idea [Sections 8.8 and 16.2]. Studies of our own solar system suggest that both

Earth and Mars lie within the Sun's habitable zone [Section 13.6], and Venus is probably close to this zone. If other planetary systems are similar, we might expect the typical number of planets within the habitable zone to be between one and three. In that case, it seems likely that many, and perhaps even most, of the several hundred billion stars in the Milky Way have at least one planet within their habitability zone. The technology for detecting planets beyond our solar system is rapidly advancing, so we may be able to improve or confirm this estimate within the next couple of decades.

For the moment, we have no rational way to guess the fraction $f_{life}$ of planets on which life actually arose. The fact that life arose quickly on Earth [Section 13.4] suggests that life develops fairly easily under the right conditions, but it is by no means conclusive. As far as we know today, $f_{life}$ could be anywhere between about 1 in 100 billion (within the Milky Way Galaxy, it happened only on Earth) and 1 (it happened on all planets suitable for life).

**TIME OUT TO THINK** *Suppose we discover life on Mars. Would this give us any greater insight into the value of $f_{life}$? Explain. Also explain what we would learn about $f_{life}$ if we discovered that life had never existed on Mars.*

Similarly, we have little basis on which to guess the fraction $f_{civ}$ of life-bearing planets that develop a civilization. However, the fact that life flourished on Earth for some 4 billion years before the rise of humans suggests that developing intelligent life is much more difficult than developing microbial life. The question is *how much* more difficult. Roughly half the stars in the Milky Way are older than our Sun, so if 4 billion years is a typical time for a civilization to develop then it should have happened already on about half the planets with life. On the other hand, if the Earth was "fast" and the typical time needed for intelligent life to develop is much longer, then most life-bearing planets may be covered with nothing more advanced than bacteria.

The huge uncertainties in $f_{life}$ and $f_{civ}$ make it impossible for us to determine the number of civilizations that have arisen in the Milky Way's history. If 1 in 1,000 suitable planets ends up with a civilization, then we are newcomers among a billion civilizations in the Milky Way. If 1 in 1 million develops a civilization, there would still have been some 100,000 civilizations out there in the Milky Way Galaxy alone. But if only 1 in 1 trillion planets ends up with a civilization, then we may be the first in the Milky Way—and the only civilization within millions of light-years.

*Recall that the total number of stars in the observable universe is greater than the number of grains of sand on all the beaches on Earth* [Section 2.4]. *Do you think it's possible that we are actually alone in the* universe? *Defend your opinion.*

The final step in our calculation, determining the number of civilizations that exist *now,* requires knowing how long a civilization typically lasts in a planet's history. Here we must define what we mean by *civilization;* let's use a definition that presumes a civilization advanced enough to travel in space. On the nearly 5-billion-year-old planet Earth, the space age began only about 50 years ago. Thus, the fraction of Earth's history during which it has had a space-faring civilization is about 50 in 5 billion, or about 1 in 100 million. If this fraction is typical, there would have to be some 100 million civilization-bearing planets in the Milky Way in order for us to have good odds of finding another civilization out there *now.* However, we'd expect this fraction to be typical only if we are on the brink of self-destruction, since the fraction will grow larger as long as our civilization continues to thrive. Thus, if civilizations are at all common, the key factor in whether any are out there now is their survivability. If most civilizations self-destruct shortly after achieving the technology for space travel, then we probably are alone in the galaxy at present. But if most survive and become interstellar travelers, the Milky Way may be brimming with civilizations— most far more advanced than ours.

**TIME OUT TO THINK** *What do you think is the likelihood that our civilization will survive to become interstellar travelers? Explain.*

### A Paradox: Where Are the Aliens?

Imagine that we survive and become interstellar travelers and that we begin colonizing habitable planets around nearby stars. As the colonies grow at each new location, some of the people may decide to set out for other star systems. Even if our starships traveled at relatively low speeds—say, a few percent of the speed of light—we could have dozens of outposts around nearby stars within a few centuries. In 10,000 years, our descendants would be spread among stars within a few hundred light-years of Earth. In a few million years, we could have outposts scattered throughout the Milky Way and would likely have explored nearly every star system in the galaxy. We would have become a true galactic civilization.

Now, if we take the idea that *we* could develop a galactic civilization within a few million years and combine it with the reasonable (though unproved) idea that civilizations ought to be common, we are

led to an astonishing conclusion: Someone else should already have created a galactic civilization. In fact, someone should have done it a long time ago. For argument's sake, let's suppose that civilizations arise around 1 in a million stars, in which case some 100,000 civilizations should have arisen in the Milky Way. Further, let's suppose that civilizations typically arise when their stars are 5 billion years old. Given that the galaxy is at least 10 billion years old, the first of these 100,000 civilizations would have arisen at least 5 billion years ago, and others would have arisen, on average, every 50,000 years. Under these assumptions, the youngest civilization besides ours would be some 50,000 years ahead of us technologically, and most would be millions or billions of years ahead of us.

Thus, we encounter a strange paradox: Plausible arguments suggest that a galactic civilization should already exist, yet we have so far found no evidence of such a civilization. (This paradox is often called *Fermi's paradox,* because during a conversation about extraterrestrial life in 1948 the scientist Enrico Fermi supposedly blurted out, "Where are they?") There are many possible solutions to this paradox, but most fall into one of three basic categories:

1. There is no galactic civilization because civilizations are not common. Perhaps we are the first, or perhaps civilizations are so rare that many star systems, including ours, remain unexplored.

2. There is no galactic civilization because civilizations do not leave their home worlds—either because they are uninterested in interstellar travel or because they destroy themselves before achieving it.

3. There *is* a galactic civilization, but it has deliberately avoided revealing its existence to us.

We do not know which, if any, of these three explanations is the correct solution to the paradox, but each leads to intriguing possibilities. If the first is correct, then our civilization is an astonishing achievement—something that few if any other species have ever accomplished. From this point of view, humanity becomes all the more precious, and the collapse of our civilization would be all the more tragic. The second possible explanation is much less satisfying. Unless we "think differently" from other civilizations, it says that we will soon either lose our interest in interstellar travel or destroy ourselves—hardly a comforting thought. The third possibility is perhaps the most intriguing. It says that we are newcomers on the scene of a galactic civilization that has existed for millions or billions of years before us. Perhaps members of this civilization are deliberately leaving us alone for the time being and will invite us to join them when we prove ourselves worthy. If so, our entire species may be on the verge of beginning a journey every bit as incredible as that of a baby emerging from the womb and coming into the world.

## THE BIG PICTURE

Throughout our study of astronomy, we have taken the "big picture" view of trying to understand how we fit into the universe. Here, at last, we have returned to Earth and examined the role of our own generation in the big picture of human history. Tens of thousands of past human generations have walked this Earth, but ours is the first generation with the technology to study the far reaches of our universe and to travel beyond the Earth. It is up to us to decide whether we will use this technology to advance our species or to destroy it.

Take a long view, a view down the centuries and millennia from this moment. Imagine our descendants living among the stars, having created or joined a great galactic civilization. They will have the privilege of experiencing ideas, worlds, and discoveries far beyond our wildest imagination. Perhaps, in their history lessons, they will learn of our generation—the generation that history placed at the turning point and that chose life over death and destruction.

## Review Questions

1. How do speeds of current spacecraft compare to the speed of light?

2. Describe several hurdles, both technological and social, that we must overcome in order to achieve interstellar flight.

3. Why do we say that *Pioneers 10* and *11* and *Voyagers 1* and *2* are our first interstellar spacecraft? How long will it take them to reach nearby stars?

4. Why are chemical rockets inadequate for interstellar travel?

5. Briefly describe the prospects and limitations for each of the following alternative starship designs: nuclear propulsion, matter–antimatter engines, sails and beamed energy propulsion, and interstellar ramjets.

6. What is *SETI*? Outline how we might recognize a signal from another civilization.

7. Briefly describe and interpret the equation given in the text that allows us to estimate the number of civilizations in the Milky Way Galaxy. Why is the term $f_{now}$ particularly important?

8. Describe several potential solutions to the paradox of "where are the aliens?"

## Discussion Questions

1. *Distant Dream or Near-Reality?* Considering all the issues surrounding interstellar flight, when (if ever) do you think we are likely to begin traveling among the stars? Why?

2. *Where Are the Aliens?* Consider the paradox that arises from the fact that we do not yet have evidence of a galactic civilization. What do *you* think is the solution to this paradox? Why?

3. *Aliens in the Movies.* Choose a science fiction movie (or television show) that involves alien species, and discuss what aspects of it are realistic and what aspects are not. Pay particular attention to the depiction of alien species and encounters between different species. Do you think such encounters are portrayed realistically?

## Problems

*Fantasy or Science Fiction?* Each of **problems 1–6** describes some futuristic device or discovery. In each case, decide whether the device or discovery is plausible according to our present understanding of science or whether it is unlikely to be possible. Explain your reasoning.

1. A brilliant teenager discovers a way to build a rocket that burns coal as its fuel and can travel at half the speed of light.

2. Using beamed energy propulsion from a laser powered by energy produced at a windmill farm in the California desert, NASA engineers are able to send a solar sailing ship on a journey to Alpha Centauri that will take only 50 years.

3. Future human colonization of the moons of Saturn occurs using spaceships powered by nuclear pulse propulsion.

4. In the year 2750, we receive a signal from a civilization around a nearby star telling us that the *Voyager 2* spacecraft recently crash-landed on their planet.

5. Upon receiving our first clear sign of extraterrestrial intelligence from the SETI project, we learn that the broadcasting civilization is at precisely the same level of technological development as we are.

6. In the year 2047, we receive a greeting from a galactic civilization that has already existed for more than a billion years.

7. *Research: Pioneers of Flight.* Write a one- to two-page biography of one of the following pioneers of flight: Otto Lilienthal, the Wright brothers, Charles Lindbergh, Amelia Earhart.

8. *Research: Development of Rocketry.* Write a one- to two-page paper about the development of rocketry. Be sure to include the roles of Konstantin Tsiolkovsky and Robert Goddard.

9. *Research: Starship Design.* Find more details about one of the proposals for starship propulsion and design discussed in this chapter. How would the starship actually be built? What new technologies would be needed, and what existing technologies could be used? Summarize your findings in a one- to two-page research report.

## Web Projects

Find useful links for Web projects on the text Web site.

1. *SETI.* Visit the Web site for the SETI Institute and learn more about the search for other civilizations. Choose some aspect of this issue that interests you, and write a one- to two-page report on what you learn.

2. *Advance Spaceship Design.* NASA supports many efforts to incorporate new technologies into space-ships. Although few of these technologies reach the level of being suitable for interstellar colonization, most are innovative and fascinating. Learn about one such NASA project and write a short summary of your findings.

# APPENDIXES

# APPENDIX A

# USEFUL NUMBERS

## Astronomical Distances

1 AU $\approx 1.496 \times 10^8$ km  [p. 27]

1 light-year $\approx 9.46 \times 10^{12}$ km  [p. 8]

1 parsec (pc) $\approx 3.09 \times 10^{13}$ km $\approx 3.26$ light-years  [p. 475]

1 kiloparsec (kpc) = 1,000 pc $\approx 3.26 \times 10^3$ light-years

1 megaparsec (Mpc) = $10^6$ pc $\approx 3.26 \times 10^6$ light-years

## Astronomical Times

1 solar day (average) = $24^h$  [p. 66]

1 sidereal day $\approx 23^h\,56^m\,4.09^s$  [p. 66]

1 synodic month (average) $\approx 29.53$ solar days  [p. 67]

1 sidereal month (average) $\approx 27.32$ solar days  [p. 67]

1 tropical year $\approx 365.242$ solar days  [p. 67]

1 sidereal year $\approx 365.256$ solar days  [p. 67]

## Universal Constants

Speed of light [p. 8]: $\qquad c = 3 \times 10^5$ km/s = $3 \times 10^8$ m/s

Gravitational constant [p. 140]: $\qquad G = 6.67 \times 10^{-11}\ \dfrac{m^3}{kg \times s^2}$

Planck's constant [p. 156]: $\qquad h = 6.626 \times 10^{-34}$ joule $\times$ s

Stefan–Boltzmann constant [p. 162]: $\qquad \sigma = 5.7 \times 10^{-8}\ \dfrac{watt}{m^2 \times Kelvin^4}$

mass of a proton: $\qquad m_p = 1.67 \times 10^{-27}$ kg

mass of an electron: $\qquad m_e = 9.1 \times 10^{-31}$ kg

## Useful Sun and Earth Reference Values

Mass of the Sun: $1M_{Sun} \approx 2 \times 10^{30}$ kg

Radius of the Sun: $1R_{Sun} \approx 696,000$ km

Luminosity of the Sun: $1L_{Sun} \approx 3.8 \times 10^{26}$ watts

Mass of the Earth: $1M_{Earth} \approx 5.97 \times 10^{24}$ kg

Radius (equatorial) of the Earth: $1R_{Earth} \approx 6,378$ km

Acceleration of gravity on Earth: $g = 9.8$ m/s$^2$

Escape velocity from surface of Earth: $v_{escape} = 11$ km/s = 11,000 m/s

## Energy and Power Units

Basic unit of energy [p. 114]: 1 joule = $1\ \dfrac{kg \times m^2}{s^2}$

Basic unit of power [p. 114]: 1 watt = 1 joule/s

Electron-volt [p. 121]: 1 eV = $1.60 \times 10^{-19}$ joule

# USEFUL FORMULAS

- Universal law of gravitation for the force between objects of mass $M_1$ and $M_2$, distance $d$ between their centers [p. 140]:

$$F = G\frac{M_1 M_2}{d^2}$$

- Newton's version of Kepler's third law; $p$ and $a$ are period and semimajor axis, respectively, of either orbiting mass [p. 141]:

$$p^2 = \frac{4\pi^2}{G(M_1 + M_2)a^3}$$

- Escape velocity at distance $R$ from center of object of mass $M$ [p. 146]:

$$v_{\text{escape}} = \sqrt{\frac{2GM}{R}}$$

- Relationship between a photon's wavelength ($\lambda$), frequency ($f$), and the speed of light ($c$) [p. 156]:

$$\lambda \times f = c$$

- Energy of a photon of wavelength $\lambda$ or frequency $f$ [p. 156]:

$$E = hf = \frac{hc}{\lambda}$$

- Stefan–Boltzmann law for thermal radiation at temperature $T$ (in Kelvin) [p. 162]:

$$\text{emitted power per unit area} = \sigma T^4$$

- Wien's law for the peak wavelength ($\lambda_{\text{max}}$) thermal radiation at temperature $T$ (in Kelvin) [p. 162]:

$$\lambda_{\text{max}} = \frac{2,900,000}{T}\,\text{nm}$$

- Doppler shift (radial velocity is positive if the object is moving away from us and negative if it is moving toward us) [p. 167]:

$$\frac{\text{radial velocity}}{\text{speed of light}} = \frac{\text{shifted wavelength} - \text{rest wavelength}}{\text{rest wavelength}}$$

- Angular separation ($\alpha$) of two points with an actual separation $s$, viewed from a distance $d$ (assuming $d$ is much larger than $s$) [p. 174]:

$$\alpha = \frac{s}{2\pi d} \times 360°$$

- Luminosity–distance formula [p. 473]:

$$\text{apparent brightness} = \frac{\text{luminosity}}{4\pi d^2}$$

(where $d$ is the distance to the object)

- Parallax formula (distance $d$ to a star with parallax angle $p$ in arcseconds) [p. 475]:

$$d \text{ (in parsecs)} = \frac{1}{p \text{ (in arcseconds)}}$$

- The orbital velocity law [p. 542], to find the mass $M_r$ contained within the circular orbit of radius $r$ for an object moving at speed $v$:

$$M_r = \frac{r \times v^2}{G}$$

# APPENDIX C

# A FEW MATHEMATICAL SKILLS

This appendix reviews the following mathematical skills: powers of 10, scientific notation, working with units, the metric system, and finding a ratio. You should refer to this appendix as needed while studying the textbook, particularly if you are having difficulty with the Mathematical Insights.

## C.1 Powers of 10

Powers of 10 simply indicate how many times to multiply 10 by itself. For example:

$$10^2 = 10 \times 10 = 100$$

$$10^6 = 10 \times 10 \times 10 \times 10 \times 10 \times 10 = 1,000,000$$

Negative powers are the reciprocals of the corresponding positive powers. For example:

$$10^{-2} = \frac{1}{10^2} = \frac{1}{100} = 0.01$$

$$10^{-6} = \frac{1}{10^6} = \frac{1}{1,000,000} = 0.000001$$

Table C.1 lists powers of 10 from $10^{-12}$ to $10^{12}$. Note that powers of 10 follow two basic rules:

1. A positive exponent tells how many zeros follow the 1. For example, $10^0$ is a 1 followed by no zeros, and $10^8$ is a 1 followed by eight zeros.

2. A negative exponent tells how many places are to the right of the decimal point, including the 1. For example, $10^{-1} = 0.1$ has one place to the right of the decimal point; $10^{-6} = 0.000001$ has six places to the right of the decimal point.

**Table C.1  Powers of 10**

| Zero and Positive Powers | | | Negative Powers | | |
|---|---|---|---|---|---|
| Power | Value | Name | Power | Value | Name |
| $10^0$ | 1 | One | | | |
| $10^1$ | 10 | Ten | $10^{-1}$ | 0.1 | Tenth |
| $10^2$ | 100 | Hundred | $10^{-2}$ | 0.01 | Hundredth |
| $10^3$ | 1,000 | Thousand | $10^{-3}$ | 0.001 | Thousandth |
| $10^4$ | 10,000 | Ten thousand | $10^{-4}$ | 0.0001 | Ten thousandth |
| $10^5$ | 100,000 | Hundred thousand | $10^{-5}$ | 0.00001 | Hundred thousandth |
| $10^6$ | 1,000,000 | Million | $10^{-6}$ | 0.000001 | Millionth |
| $10^7$ | 10,000,000 | Ten million | $10^{-7}$ | 0.0000001 | Ten millionth |
| $10^8$ | 100,000,000 | Hundred million | $10^{-8}$ | 0.00000001 | Hundred millionth |
| $10^9$ | 1,000,000,000 | Billion | $10^{-9}$ | 0.000000001 | Billionth |
| $10^{10}$ | 10,000,000,000 | Ten billion | $10^{-10}$ | 0.0000000001 | Ten billionth |
| $10^{11}$ | 100,000,000,000 | Hundred billion | $10^{-11}$ | 0.00000000001 | Hundred billionth |
| $10^{12}$ | 1,000,000,000,000 | Trillion | $10^{-12}$ | 0.000000000001 | Trillionth |

## Multiplying and Dividing Powers of 10

Multiplying powers of 10 simply requires adding exponents, as the following examples show:

$$10^4 \times 10^7 = \underbrace{10,000}_{10^4} \times \underbrace{10,000,000}_{10^7} = \underbrace{100,000,000,000}_{10^{4+7} = 10^{11}} = 10^{11}$$

$$10^5 \times 10^{-3} = \underbrace{100,000}_{10^5} \times \underbrace{0.001}_{10^{-3}} = \underbrace{100}_{10^{5+(-3)} = 10^2} = 10^2$$

$$10^{-8} \times 10^{-5} = \underbrace{0.00000001}_{10^{-8}} \times \underbrace{0.00001}_{10^{-5}} = \underbrace{0.0000000000001}_{10^{-8+(-5)} = 10^{-13}} = 10^{-13}$$

Dividing powers of 10 requires subtracting exponents, as in the following examples:

$$\frac{10^5}{10^3} = \underbrace{100,000}_{10^5} \div \underbrace{1,000}_{10^3} = \underbrace{100}_{10^{5-3} = 10^2} = 10^2$$

$$\frac{10^3}{10^7} = \underbrace{1,000}_{10^3} \div \underbrace{10,000,000}_{10^7} = \underbrace{0.0001}_{10^{3-7} = 10^{-4}} = 10^{-4}$$

$$\frac{10^{-4}}{10^{-6}} = \underbrace{0.0001}_{10^{-4}} \div \underbrace{0.000001}_{10^{-6}} = \underbrace{100}_{10^{-4-(-6)} = 10^2} = 10^2$$

## Powers of Powers of 10

We can use the multiplication and division rules to raise powers of 10 to other powers or to take roots. For example:

$$(10^4)^3 = 10^4 \times 10^4 \times 10^4 = 10^{4+4+4} = 10^{12}$$

Note that we can get the same end result by simply multiplying the two powers:

$$(10^4)^3 = 10^{4 \times 3} = 10^{12}$$

Because taking a root is the same as raising to a fractional power (e.g., the square root is the same as the 1/2 power, the cube root is the same as the 1/3 power, etc.), we can use the same procedure for roots, as in the following example:

$$\sqrt{10^4} = (10^4)^{1/2} = 10^{4 \times (1/2)} = 10^2$$

### Adding and Subtracting Powers of 10

Unlike with multiplication and division, there is no shortcut for adding or subtracting powers of 10. The values must be written in longhand notation. For example:

$$10^6 + 10^2 = 1,000,000 + 100 = 1,000,100$$

$$10^8 + 10^{-3} = 100,000,000 + 0.001 = 100,000,000.001$$

$$10^7 - 10^3 = 10,000,000 - 1,000 = 9,999,000$$

### Summary

We can summarize our findings using $n$ and $m$ to represent any numbers:

- To *multiply* powers of 10, *add* exponents: $10^n \times 10^m = 10^{n+m}$

- To *divide* powers of 10, *subtract* exponents: $\dfrac{10^n}{10^m} = 10^{n-m}$

- To *raise* powers of 10 to other powers, multiply exponents: $(10^n)^m = 10^{n \times m}$

## C.2 Scientific Notation

When we are dealing with large or small numbers, it's generally easier to write them with powers of 10. For example, it's much easier to write the number 6,000,000,000,000 as $6 \times 10^{12}$. This format, in which a number *between* 1 and 10 is multiplied by a power of 10, is called **scientific notation**.

### Converting a Number to Scientific Notation

We can convert numbers written in ordinary notation to scientific notation with a simple two-step process:

1. Move the decimal point to come after the *first* nonzero digit.

2. The number of places the decimal point moves tells you the power of 10; the power is *positive* if the decimal point moves to the left and *negative* if it moves to the right.

   *Examples:*

   $$3,042 \xrightarrow[\text{3 places to left}]{\text{decimal needs to move}} 3.042 \times 10^3$$

   $$0.00012 \xrightarrow[\text{4 places to right}]{\text{decimal needs to move}} 1.2 \times 10^{-4}$$

   $$226 \times 10^2 \xrightarrow[\text{2 places to left}]{\text{decimal needs to move}} (2.26 \times 10^2) \times 10^2 = 2.26 \times 10^4$$

### Converting a Number from Scientific Notation

We can convert numbers written in scientific notation to ordinary notation by the reverse process:

1. The power of 10 indicates how many places to move the decimal point; move it to the *right* if the power of 10 is positive and to the *left* if it is negative.

2. If moving the decimal point creates any open places, fill them with zeros.

   *Examples:*

$$4.01 \times 10^2 \xrightarrow[\text{2 places to right}]{\text{move decimal}} 401$$

$$3.6 \times 10^6 \xrightarrow[\text{6 places to right}]{\text{move decimal}} 3{,}600{,}000$$

$$5.7 \times 10^{-3} \xrightarrow[\text{3 places to left}]{\text{move decimal}} 0.0057$$

### Multiplying or Dividing Numbers in Scientific Notation

Multiplying or dividing numbers in scientific notation simply requires operating on the powers of 10 and the other parts of the number separately.

   *Examples:*

$$(6 \times 10^2) \times (4 \times 10^5) = (6 \times 4) \times (10^2 \times 10^5) = 24 \times 10^7 = (2.4 \times 10^1) \times 10^7 = 2.4 \times 10^8$$

$$\frac{4.2 \times 10^{-2}}{8.4 \times 10^{-5}} = \frac{4.2}{8.4} \times \frac{10^{-2}}{10^{-5}} = 0.5 \times 10^{-2-(-5)} = 0.5 \times 10^3 = (5 \times 10^{-1}) \times 10^3 = 5 \times 10^2$$

Note that, in both these examples, we first found an answer in which the number multiplied by a power of 10 was *not* between 1 and 10. We therefore followed the procedure for converting the final answer to scientific notation.

### Addition and Subtraction with Scientific Notation

In general, we must write numbers in ordinary notation before adding or subtracting.

   *Examples:*

$$(3 \times 10^6) + (5 \times 10^2) = 3{,}000{,}000 + 500 = 3{,}000{,}500 = 3.0005 \times 10^6$$

$$(4.6 \times 10^9) - (5 \times 10^8) = 4{,}600{,}000{,}000 - 500{,}000{,}000 = 4{,}100{,}000{,}000 = 4.1 \times 10^9$$

When both numbers have the *same* power of 10, we can factor out the power of 10 first.

   *Examples:*

$$(7 \times 10^{10}) + (4 \times 10^{10}) = (7 + 4) \times 10^{10} = 11 \times 10^{10} = 1.1 \times 10^{11}$$

$$(2.3 \times 10^{-22}) - (1.6 \times 10^{-22}) = (2.3 - 1.6) \times 10^{-22} = 0.7 \times 10^{-22} = 7.0 \times 10^{-23}$$

## C.3  Working with Units

Showing the units of a problem as you solve it usually makes the work much easier and also provides a useful way of checking your work. If an answer does not come out with the units you expect, you probably did something wrong. In general, working with units is very similar to working with numbers, as the following guidelines and examples show.

### Five Guidelines for Working with Units

Before you begin any problem, think ahead and identify the units you expect for the final answer. Then operate on the units along with the numbers as you solve the problem. The following five guidelines may be helpful when you are working with units:

1. Mathematically, it doesn't matter whether a unit is singular (e.g., meter) or plural (e.g., meters); we can use the same abbreviation (e.g., m) for both.

2. You cannot add or subtract numbers unless they have the *same* units. For example, 5 apples + 3 apples = 8 apples, but the expression 5 apples + 3 oranges cannot be simplified further.

3. You *can* multiply units, divide units, or raise units to powers. Look for key words that tell you what to do.

   ■ *Per* suggests division. For example, we write a speed of 100 kilometers per hour as:

   $$100 \frac{km}{hr} \quad \text{or} \quad 100 \frac{km}{1 \, hr}$$

   ■ *Of* suggests multiplication. For example, if you launch a 50-kg space probe at a launch cost *of* $10,000 per kilogram, the total cost is:

   $$50 \, \cancel{kg} \times \frac{\$10,000}{\cancel{kg}} = \$500,000$$

   ■ *Square* suggests raising to the second power. For example, we write an area of 75 square meters as 75 $m^2$.

   ■ *Cube* suggests raising to the third power. For example, we write a volume of 12 cubic centimeters as 12 $cm^3$.

4. Often the number you are given is not in the units you wish to work with. For example, you may be given that the speed of light is 300,000 km/s but need it in units of m/s for a particular problem. To convert the units, simply multiply the given number by a *conversion factor*: a fraction in which the numerator (top of the fraction) and denominator (bottom of the fraction) are equal, so that the value of the fraction is 1; the number in the denominator must have the units that you wish to change. In the case of changing the speed of light from units of km/s to m/s, you need a conversion factor for kilometers to meters. Thus, the conversion factor is:

   $$\frac{1,000 \, m}{1 \, km}$$

   Note that this conversion factor is equal to 1, since 1,000 meters and 1 kilometer are equal, and that the units to be changed (km) appear in the denominator. We can now convert the speed of light from units of km/s to m/s simply by multiplying by this conversion factor:

   $$\underbrace{300,000 \frac{\cancel{km}}{s}}_{\substack{\text{speed of light} \\ \text{in km/s}}} \times \underbrace{\frac{1,000 \, m}{1 \, \cancel{km}}}_{\substack{\text{conversion from} \\ \text{km to m}}} = \underbrace{3 \times 10^8 \frac{m}{s}}_{\substack{\text{speed of light} \\ \text{in m/s}}}$$

   Note that the units of km cancel, leaving the answer in units of m/s.

5. It's easier to work with units if you replace division with multiplication by the reciprocal. For example, suppose you want to know how many minutes are represented by 300 seconds. We can find the answer by dividing 300 seconds by 60 seconds per minute:

   $$300 \, s \div 60 \frac{s}{min}$$

   However, it is easier to see the unit cancellations if we rewrite this expression by replacing the division with multiplication by the reciprocal (this process is easy to remember as "invert and multiply"):

   $$300 \, s \div 60 \frac{s}{min} = 300 \, \cancel{s} \times \underbrace{\frac{1 \, min}{60 \, \cancel{s}}}_{\substack{\text{invert} \\ \text{and multiply}}} = 5 \, min$$

We now see that the units of seconds (s) cancel in the numerator of the first term and the denominator of the second term, leaving the answer in units of minutes.

### More Examples of Working with Units

**Example 1.** How many seconds are there in 1 day?

**Solution**: We can answer the question by setting up a *chain* of unit conversions in which we start with 1 *day* and end up with *seconds*. We use the facts that there are 24 hours per day (24 hr/day), 60 minutes per hour (60 min/hr), and 60 seconds per minute (60 s/min):

$$1 \, \text{day} \times \frac{24 \, \text{hr}}{\text{day}} \times \frac{60 \, \text{min}}{\text{hr}} \times \frac{60 \, \text{s}}{\text{min}} = 86{,}400 \, \text{s}$$

starting value — conversion from day to hr — conversion from hr to min — conversion from min to s

Note that all the units cancel except *seconds*, which is what we want for the answer. There are 86,400 seconds in 1 day.

**Example 2.** Convert a distance of $10^8$ cm to km.

**Solution**: The easiest way to make this conversion is in two steps, since we know that there are 100 centimeters per meter (100 cm/m) and 1,000 meters per kilometer (1,000 m/km):

$$10^8 \, \text{cm} \times \frac{1 \, \text{m}}{100 \, \text{cm}} \times \frac{1 \, \text{km}}{1{,}000 \, \text{m}} = 10^8 \, \text{cm} \times \frac{1 \, \text{m}}{10^2 \, \text{cm}} \times \frac{1 \, \text{km}}{10^3 \, \text{m}} = 10^3 \, \text{km}$$

starting value — conversion from cm to m — conversion from m to km

Alternatively, if we recognize that the number of kilometers should be smaller than the number of centimeters (because kilometers are larger), we might decide to do this conversion by dividing as follows:

$$10^8 \, \text{cm} \div \frac{100 \, \text{cm}}{\text{m}} \div \frac{1{,}000 \, \text{m}}{\text{km}}$$

In this case, before carrying out the calculation, we replace each division with multiplication by the reciprocal:

$$10^8 \, \text{cm} \div \frac{100 \, \text{cm}}{\text{m}} \div \frac{1{,}000 \, \text{m}}{\text{km}} = 10^8 \text{cm} \times \frac{1 \, \text{m}}{100 \, \text{cm}} \times \frac{1 \, \text{km}}{1{,}000 \, \text{m}}$$

$$= 10^8 \, \text{cm} \times \frac{1 \, \text{m}}{10^2 \, \text{cm}} \times \frac{1 \, \text{km}}{10^3 \, \text{m}}$$

$$= 10^3 \, \text{km}$$

Note that we again get the answer that $10^8$ cm is the same as $10^3$ km, or 1,000 km.

**Example 3.** Suppose you accelerate at 9.8 m/s² for 4 seconds, starting from rest. How fast will you be going?

**Solution**: The question asked "how fast?" so we expect to end up with a speed. Therefore, we multiply the acceleration by the amount of time you accelerated:

$$9.8 \, \frac{\text{m}}{\text{s}^2} \times 4 \, \text{s} = (9.8 \times 4) \, \frac{\text{m} \times \text{s}}{\text{s}^2} = 39.2 \, \frac{\text{m}}{\text{s}}$$

Note that the units end up as a speed, showing that you will be traveling 39.2 m/s after 4 seconds of acceleration at 9.8 m/s².

**Example 4**. A reservoir is 2 km long and 3 km wide. Calculate its area, in both square kilometers and square meters.

**Solution**: We find its area by multiplying its length and width:

$$2 \text{ km} \times 3 \text{ km} = 6 \text{ km}^2$$

Next we need to convert this area of 6 km² to square meters, using the fact that there are 1,000 meters per kilometer (1,000 m/km). Note that we must square the term 1,000 m/km when converting from km² to m²:

$$6 \text{ km}^2 \times \left(1{,}000 \, \frac{\text{m}}{\text{km}}\right)^2 = 6 \text{ km}^2 \times 1{,}000^2 \, \frac{\text{m}^2}{\text{km}^2} = 6 \, \cancel{\text{km}^2} \times 1{,}000{,}000 \, \frac{\text{m}^2}{\cancel{\text{km}^2}}$$

$$= 6{,}000{,}000 \text{ m}^2$$

The reservoir area is 6 km², which is the same as 6 million m².

## C.4 The Metric System (SI)

The modern version of the metric system, known as *Système Internationale d'Unites* (French for "International System of Units") or **SI**, was formally established in 1960. Today, it is the primary measurement system in nearly every country in the world with the exception of the United States. Even in the United States, it is the system of choice for science and international commerce.

The basic units of length, mass, and time in the SI are:

- The **meter** for length, abbreviated m

- The **kilogram** for mass, abbreviated kg

- The **second** for time, abbreviated s

Multiples of metric units are formed by powers of 10, using a prefix to indicate the power. For example, *kilo* means $10^3$ (1,000), so a kilometer is 1,000 meters; a microgram is 0.000001 gram, because *micro* means $10^{-6}$, or one millionth. Some of the more common prefixes are listed in Table C.2.

### Metric Conversions

Table C.3 lists conversions between metric units and units used commonly in the United States. Note that the conversions between kilograms and pounds are valid only on Earth, because they depend on the strength of gravity.

**Example 1**. International athletic competitions generally use metric distances. Compare the length of a 100-meter race to that of a 100-yard race.

**Table C.2  SI (Metric) Prefixes**

| | Small Values | | | Large Values | |
|---|---|---|---|---|---|
| Prefix | Abbreviation | Value | Prefix | Abbreviation | Value |
| Deci | d | $10^{-1}$ | Deca | da | $10^1$ |
| Centi | c | $10^{-2}$ | Hecto | h | $10^2$ |
| Milli | m | $10^{-3}$ | Kilo | k | $10^3$ |
| Micro | μ | $10^{-6}$ | Mega | M | $10^6$ |
| Nano | n | $10^{-9}$ | Giga | G | $10^9$ |
| Pico | p | $10^{-12}$ | Tera | T | $10^{12}$ |

**Table C.3  Metric Conversions**

| To Metric | From Metric |
|---|---|
| 1 inch = 2.540 cm | 1 cm = 0.3937 inch |
| 1 foot = 0.3048 m | 1 m = 3.28 feet |
| 1 yard = 0.9144 m | 1 m = 1.094 yards |
| 1 mile = 1.6093 km | 1 km = 0.6214 mile |
| 1 pound = 0.4536 kg | 1 kg = 2.205 pounds |

**Solution**: Table C.3 shows that 1 m = 1.094 yd, so 100 m is 109.4 yd. Note that 100 meters is almost 110 yards; a good "rule of thumb" to remember is that distances in meters are about 10% longer than the corresponding number of yards.

**Example 2**. How many square kilometers are in 1 square mile?

**Solution**: We use the square of the miles-to-kilometers conversion factor:

$$(1 \text{ mi}^2) \times \left( \frac{1.6093 \text{ km}}{1 \text{ mi}} \right)^2 = (1 \text{ mi}^2) \times \left( 1.6093^2 \frac{\text{km}^2}{\text{mi}^2} \right) = 2.5898 \text{ km}^2$$

Therefore, 1 square mile is 2.5898 square kilometers.

## C.5 Finding a Ratio

Suppose you want to compare two quantities, such as the average density of the Earth and the average density of Jupiter. The way we do such a comparison is by dividing, which tells us the *ratio* of the two quantities. In this case, the Earth's average density is 5.52 grams/cm$^3$ and Jupiter's average density is 1.33 grams/cm$^3$ (see Table 11.1), so the ratio is:

$$\frac{\text{average density of Earth}}{\text{average density of Jupiter}} = \frac{5.52 \text{ g/cm}^3}{1.33 \text{ g/cm}^3} = 4.15$$

Notice how the units cancel on both the top and bottom of the fraction. We can state our result in two equivalent ways:

■ The ratio of the Earth's average density to Jupiter's average density is 4.15.

■ The Earth's average density is 4.15 times Jupiter's average density.

Sometimes, the quantities that you want to compare may each involve an equation. In such cases, you could, of course, find the ratio by first calculating each of the two quantities individually and then dividing. However, it is much easier if you first express the ratio as a fraction, putting the equation for one quantity on top and the other on the bottom. Some of the terms in the equation may then cancel out, making any calculations much easier.

**Example 1**. Compare the kinetic energy of a car traveling at 100 km/hr to that of a car traveling at 50 km/hr.

**Solution**: We do the comparison by finding the ratio of the two kinetic energies, recalling that the formula for kinetic energy is $\frac{1}{2} mv^2$. Since we are not told the mass of the car, you might at first think that we don't have enough information to find the ratio. However, notice what happens when we put the equations for each kinetic energy into the ratio, calling the two speeds $v_1$ and $v_2$:

$$\frac{\text{K.E. car at } v_1}{\text{K.E. car at } v_2} = \frac{\frac{1}{2} m_{\text{car}} v_1^2}{\frac{1}{2} m_{\text{car}} v_2^2} = \frac{v_1^2}{v_2^2} = \left( \frac{v_1}{v_2} \right)^2$$

All the terms cancel except those with the two speeds, leaving us with a very simple formula for the ratio. Now we put in 100 km/hr for $v_1$ and 50 km/hr for $v_2$:

$$\frac{\text{K.E. car at 100 km/hr}}{\text{K.E. car at 50 km/hr}} = \left( \frac{100 \text{ km/hr}}{50 \text{ km/hr}} \right)^2 = 2^2 = 4$$

The ratio of the car's kinetic energies at 100 km/hr and 50 km/hr is 4. That is, the car has four times as much kinetic energy at 100 km/hr as it has at 50 km/hr.

**Example 2**. Compare the strength of gravity between the Earth and the Sun to the strength of gravity between the Earth and the Moon.

**Solution**: We do the comparison by taking the ratio of the Earth–Sun gravity to the Earth–Moon gravity. In this case, each quantity is found from the equation of Newton's law of gravity. (See Section 5.4.) Thus, the ratio is:

$$\frac{\text{Earth–Sun gravity}}{\text{Earth–Moon gravity}} = \frac{\cancel{G}\frac{\cancel{M_{\text{Earth}}}M_{\text{Sun}}}{(d_{\text{Earth–Sun}})^2}}{\cancel{G}\frac{\cancel{M_{\text{Earth}}}M_{\text{Moon}}}{(d_{\text{Earth–Moon}})^2}} = \frac{M_{\text{Sun}}}{(d_{\text{Earth–Sun}})^2} \times \frac{(d_{\text{Earth–Moon}})^2}{M_{\text{Moon}}}$$

Note how all but four of the terms cancel; the last step comes from replacing the division with multiplication by the reciprocal (the "invert and multiply" rule for division). We can simplify the work further by rearranging the terms so that we have the masses and distances together:

$$\frac{\text{Earth–Sun gravity}}{\text{Earth–Moon gravity}} = \frac{M_{\text{Sun}}}{M_{\text{Moon}}} \times \frac{(d_{\text{Earth–Moon}})^2}{(d_{\text{Earth–Sun}})^2}$$

Now it is just a matter of looking up the numbers (see Appendix E) and calculating:

$$\frac{\text{Earth–Sun gravity}}{\text{Earth–Moon gravity}} = \frac{1.99 \times 10^{30} \cancel{\text{kg}}}{7.35 \times 10^{22} \cancel{\text{kg}}} \times \frac{(384.4 \times 10^3 \cancel{\text{km}})^2}{(149.6 \times 10^6 \cancel{\text{km}})^2} = 179$$

In other words, the Earth–Sun gravity is 179 times stronger than the Earth–Moon gravity.

# THE PERIODIC TABLE OF THE ELEMENTS

**Key**

12 — Atomic number
**Mg** — Element's symbol
Magnesium — Element's name
24.305 — Atomic mass*

*Atomic masses are fractions because they represent a
weighted average of atomic masses of different isotopes—
in proportion to the abundance of each isotope on Earth.

| 1 H Hydrogen 1.00794 | | | | | | | | | | | | | | | | | 2 He Helium 4.003 |
|---|---|---|---|---|---|---|---|---|---|---|---|---|---|---|---|---|---|
| 3 Li Lithium 6.941 | 4 Be Beryllium 9.01218 | | | | | | | | | | | 5 B Boron 10.81 | 6 C Carbon 12.011 | 7 N Nitrogen 14.007 | 8 O Oxygen 15.999 | 9 F Fluorine 18.988 | 10 Ne Neon 20.179 |
| 11 Na Sodium 22.990 | 12 Mg Magnesium 24.305 | | | | | | | | | | | 13 Al Aluminum 26.98 | 14 Si Silicon 28.086 | 15 P Phosphorus 30.974 | 16 S Sulfur 32.06 | 17 Cl Chlorine 35.453 | 18 Ar Argon 39.948 |
| 19 K Potassium 39.098 | 20 Ca Calcium 40.08 | 21 Sc Scandium 44.956 | 22 Ti Titanium 47.88 | 23 V Vanadium 50.94 | 24 Cr Chromium 51.996 | 25 Mn Manganese 54.938 | 26 Fe Iron 55.847 | 27 Co Cobalt 58.9332 | 28 Ni Nickel 58.69 | 29 Cu Copper 63.546 | 30 Zn Zinc 65.39 | 31 Ga Gallium 69.72 | 32 Ge Germanium 72.59 | 33 As Arsenic 74.922 | 34 Se Selenium 78.96 | 35 Br Bromine 79.904 | 36 Fr Krypton 83.80 |
| 37 Rb Rubidium 85.468 | 38 Sr Strontium 87.62 | 39 Y Yttrium 88.9059 | 40 Zr Zirconium 91.224 | 41 Nb Niobium 92.91 | 42 Mo Molybdenum 95.94 | 43 Tc Technetium (98) | 44 Ru Ruthenium 101.07 | 45 Rh Rhodium 102.906 | 46 Pd Palladium 106.42 | 47 Ag Silver 107.868 | 48 Cd Cadmium 112.41 | 49 In Indium 114.82 | 50 Sn Tin 118.71 | 51 Sb Antimony 121.75 | 52 Te Tellurium 127.60 | 53 I Iodine 126.905 | 54 Xe Xenon 131.29 |
| 55 Cs Cesium 132.91 | 56 Ba Barium 137.34 | | 72 Hf Hafnium 178.49 | 73 Ta Tantalum 180.95 | 74 W Tungsten 183.85 | 75 Re Rhenium 186.207 | 76 Os Osmium 190.2 | 77 Ir Iridium 192.22 | 78 Pt Platinum 195.08 | 79 Au Gold 196.967 | 80 Hg Mercury 200.59 | 81 Ti Thallium 204.383 | 82 Pb Lead 207.2 | 83 Bi Bismuth 208.98 | 84 Po Polonium (209) | 85 At Astatine (210) | 86 Rn Radon (222) |
| 87 Fr Francium (223) | 88 Ra Radium 226.0254 | | 104 Rf Rutherfordium (261) | 105 Db Dubnium (262) | 106 Sg Seaborgium (263) | 107 Bh Bohrium (262) | 108 Hs Hassium (265) | 109 Mt Meitnerium (266) | 110 Uun Ununnilium (269) | 111 Uuu Unununium (272) | 112 Uub Ununbium (277) | | | | | | |

**Lanthanide Series**

| 57 La Lanthanum 138.906 | 58 Ce Cerium 140.12 | 59 Pr Praseodymium 140.908 | 60 Nd Neodymium 144.24 | 61 Pm Promethium (145) | 62 Sm Samarium 150.36 | 63 Eu Europium 151.96 | 64 Gd Gadolinium 157.25 | 65 Tb Terbium 158.925 | 66 Dy Dysprosium 162.50 | 67 Ho Holmium 164.93 | 68 Er Erbium 167.26 | 69 Tm Thulium 168.934 | 70 Yb Ytterbium 173.04 | 71 Lu Lutetium 174.967 |
|---|---|---|---|---|---|---|---|---|---|---|---|---|---|---|

**Actinide Series**

| 89 Ac Actinium 227.028 | 90 Th Thorium 232.038 | 91 Pa Protactinium 231.036 | 92 U Uranium 238.029 | 93 Np Neptunium 237.048 | 94 Pu Plutonium (244) | 95 Am Americium (243) | 96 Cm Curium (247) | 97 Bk Berkelium (247) | 98 Cf Californium (251) | 99 Es Einsteinium (252) | 100 Fm Fermium (257) | 101 Md Mendelevium (258) | 102 No Nobelium (259) | 103 Lr Lawrencium (260) |
|---|---|---|---|---|---|---|---|---|---|---|---|---|---|---|

# PLANETARY DATA

## Table E.1  Physical Properties of the Sun and Planets

| Name | Radius (Eq[a]) (km) | Radius (Eq) (Earth units) | Mass (kg) | Mass (Earth units) | Average Density (g/cm$^3$) | Surface Gravity (Earth = 1) |
|---|---|---|---|---|---|---|
| Sun | 695,000 | 109 | $1.99 \times 10^{30}$ | 333,000 | 1.41 | 27.5 |
| Mercury | 2,440 | 0.382 | $3.30 \times 10^{23}$ | 0.055 | 5.43 | 0.38 |
| Venus | 6,051 | 0.949 | $4.87 \times 10^{24}$ | 0.815 | 5.25 | 0.91 |
| Earth | 6,378 | 1.00 | $5.97 \times 10^{24}$ | 1.00 | 5.52 | 1.00 |
| Mars | 3,397 | 0.533 | $6.42 \times 10^{23}$ | 0.107 | 3.93 | 0.38 |
| Jupiter | 71,492 | 11.19 | $1.90 \times 10^{27}$ | 317.9 | 1.33 | 2.53 |
| Saturn | 60,268 | 9.46 | $5.69 \times 10^{26}$ | 95.18 | 0.71 | 1.07 |
| Uranus | 25,559 | 3.98 | $8.66 \times 10^{25}$ | 14.54 | 1.24 | 0.91 |
| Neptune | 24,764 | 3.81 | $1.03 \times 10^{26}$ | 17.13 | 1.67 | 1.14 |
| Pluto | 1,160 | 0.181 | $1.31 \times 10^{22}$ | 0.0022 | 2.05 | 0.07 |

[a]Eq = equatorial.

## Table E.2  Orbital Properties of the Sun and Planets

| Name | Distance from Sun[a] (AU) | (10$^6$ km) | Orbital Period (years) | Orbital Inclination[b] (degrees) | Orbital Eccentricity | Sidereal Rotation Period (Earth days)[c] | Axis Tilt (degrees) |
|---|---|---|---|---|---|---|---|
| Sun | — | — | — | — | — | 25.4 | 7.25 |
| Mercury | 0.387 | 57.9 | 0.2409 | 7.00 | 0.206 | 58.6 | 0.0 |
| Venus | 0.723 | 108.2 | 0.6152 | 3.39 | 0.007 | −243.0 | 177.4 |
| Earth | 1.00 | 149.6 | 1.0 | 0.00 | 0.017 | 0.9973 | 23.45 |
| Mars | 1.524 | 227.9 | 1.881 | 1.85 | 0.093 | 1.026 | 23.98 |
| Jupiter | 5.203 | 778.3 | 11.86 | 1.31 | 0.048 | 0.41 | 3.08 |
| Saturn | 9.539 | 1,427 | 29.46 | 2.49 | 0.056 | 0.44 | 26.73 |
| Uranus | 19.19 | 2,870 | 84.01 | 0.77 | 0.046 | −0.72 | 97.92 |
| Neptune | 30.06 | 4,497 | 164.8 | 1.77 | 0.010 | 0.67 | 29.6 |
| Pluto | 39.54 | 5,916 | 248.0 | 17.15 | 0.248 | −6.39 | 118 |

[a]Semimajor axis of the orbit.

[b]With respect to the ecliptic.

[c]A negative sign indicates rotation relative to other planets.

**Table E.3  Satellites of the Solar System[a]**

| Planet Satellite | Radius or Dimensions[b] (km) | Distance from Planet[c] ($10^3$ km) | Orbital Period[c] (Earth days) | Mass[d] (kg) | Density[d] ($g/cm^3$) | Notes About the Satellites |
|---|---|---|---|---|---|---|
| **Earth** | | | | | | **Earth** |
| Moon | 1,738 | 384.4 | 27.322 | $7.349 \times 10^{22}$ | 3.34 | *Moon:* Probably formed in giant impact. |
| **Mars** | | | | | | **Mars** |
| Phobos | 13×11×9 | 9.38 | 0.319 | $1.3 \times 10^{16}$ | 2.2 | *Phobos, Deimos:* Probable captured asteroids. |
| Deimos | 8×6×5 | 23.5 | 1.263 | $1.8 \times 10^{15}$ | 1.7 | |
| **Jupiter** | | | | | | **Jupiter** |
| Small inner moons (5 moons) | 10 to 135×82×75 | 128–222 | 0.295–0.6745 | — | — | *Metis, Adrastea, Amalthea, Thebe, 1999 J1:* Small moonlets within and near Jupiter's ring system. |
| Io | 1,821 | 421.6 | 1.769 | $8.933 \times 10^{22}$ | 3.57 | *Io:* Most volcanically active object in the solar system. |
| Europa | 1,565 | 670.9 | 3.551 | $4.797 \times 10^{22}$ | 2.97 | *Europa:* Possible oceans under icy crust. |
| Ganymede | 2,634 | 1,070.0 | 7.155 | $1.482 \times 10^{23}$ | 1.94 | *Ganymede:* .Largest satellite in solar system; unusual ice geology. |
| Callisto | 2,403 | 1,883.0 | 16.689 | $1.076 \times 10^{23}$ | 1.86 | *Callisto:* Cratered iceball. |
| Irregular group 1 (5 moons) | 7–22 | 11,400–17,100 | 453–829 | — | — | *Leda, Himalia, Elara, Lysithea, 2000 J11:* Probable captured moons with inclined orbits. |
| Irregular group 2 (14 moons) | 5–15 | 17,400–18,000 | −854 to −901 | — | — | *Ananke, Carme, Pasiphae, Sinope, 2000 J1–J10:* Probable captured moons in inclined backward orbits. |
| **Saturn** | | | | | | **Saturn** |
| Small inner moons (6) | 10 to 97×95×77 | 134–151 | 0.574–0.695 | — | — | *Pan, Atlas, Prometheus, Pandora, Epimetheus, Janus:* Small moonlets within and near Saturn's ring system. |
| Mimas | 199 | 185.52 | 0.942 | $3.70 \times 10^{19}$ | 1.17 | *Mimas, Enceladus, Tethys:* Small and medium-size iceballs, many with interesting geology. |
| Enceladus | 249 | 238.02 | 1.370 | $1.2 \times 10^{20}$ | 1.24 | |
| Tethys | 530 | 294.66 | 1.888 | $6.17 \times 10^{20}$ | 1.26 | |
| Calypso | 15×8×8 | 294.66 | 1.888 | $4 \times 10^{15}$ | — | *Calypso, Telesto:* Small moonlets sharing Tethys's orbit. |
| Telesto | 15×13×8 | 294.67 | 1.888 | $6 \times 10^{15}$ | — | |
| Dione | 559 | 377.4 | 2.737 | $1.08 \times 10^{21}$ | 1.44 | *Dione:* Medium-size iceball, with interesting geology. |
| Helene | 18×?×15 | 377.4 | 2.737 | $1.6 \times 10^{16}$ | — | *Helene:* Small moonlet sharing Dione's orbit. |
| Rhea | 764 | 527.04 | 4.518 | $2.31 \times 10^{21}$ | 1.33 | *Rhea:* Medium-size iceball, with interesting geology. |
| Titan | 2,575 | 1,221.85 | 15.945 | $1.3455 \times 10^{23}$ | 1.88 | *Titan:* Dense atmosphere shrouds surface; ongoing geological activity possible. |
| Hyperion | 180×140×112 | 1,481.1 | 21.277 | $2.8 \times 10^{19}$ | — | *Hyperion:* Only satellite known not to rotate synchronously. |

| Moon | Radius (km) | Distance (10³ km) | Period (days) | Mass (kg) | Density | Comments |
|---|---|---|---|---|---|---|
| Iapetus | 718 | 3,561.3 | 79.331 | $1.59 \times 10^{21}$ | 1.21 | *Iapetus:* Bright and dark hemispheres show greatest contrast in the solar system. |
| Phoebe | 110 | 12,952 | −550.4 | $1 \times 10^{19}$ | — | *Phoebe:* Very dark; material ejected from Phoebe may coat one side of Iapetus. |
| Irregular group 1 (4 moons) | 7–22 | 11,400–17,100 | 453–829 | — | — | *2000 S2, S3, S5, S6:* Probable captured moons with highly inclined orbits. |
| Irregular group 2 (3 moons) | 5–15 | 17,400–18,000 | 854–901 | — | — | *2000 S4, S10, S11:* Probable captured moons in inclined orbits. |
| Irregular group 3 (5 moons) | 4–10 | 15,600–23,400 | −723 to −1,325 | — | — | *2000 S1, S7, S8, S9, S12:* Probable captured moons in inclined backward orbits. |
| **Uranus** | | | | | | |
| Small inner moons (11 moons) | 10 to 97×95×77 | 134–151 | 0.574–0.695 | — | — | *Cordelia, Ophelia, Bianca, Cressida, Desdemona, Juliet, Portia, Rosalind, Belinda, Puck, 1986 U10:* Small moonlets within and near Uranus's ring system. |
| Miranda | 236 | 129.8 | 1.413 | $6.6 \times 10^{19}$ | 1.26 | *Miranda, Ariel, Umbriel, Titania, Oberon:* Small and medium-size iceballs, with some interesting geology. |
| Ariel | 579 | 191.2 | 2.520 | $1.35 \times 10^{21}$ | 1.65 | |
| Umbriel | 584.7 | 266.0 | 4.144 | $1.17 \times 10^{21}$ | 1.44 | |
| Titania | 788.9 | 435.8 | 8.706 | $3.52 \times 10^{21}$ | 1.59 | |
| Oberon | 761.4 | 582.6 | 13.463 | $3.01 \times 10^{21}$ | 1.50 | |
| Irregular group (5 moons) | ???–60 | 7,170–25,000 | 580–2,280 | — | — | *Caliban, Sycorax, Stephano, Prospero, Setebos:* Too recently discovered for accurate determination of their properties; several in backward orbits. |
| **Neptune** | | | | | | |
| Small inner moons (5 moons) | 29 to 104×?×89 | 48–74 | 0.296–0.554 | — | — | *Naiad, Thalassa, Despina, Galatea, Larissa:* Small moonlets within and near Neptune's ring system. |
| Proteus | 218×208×201 | 117.6 | 1.121 | $6 \times 10^{19}$ | — | |
| Triton | 1,352.6 | 354.59 | −5.875 | $2.14 \times 10^{22}$ | 2.0 | *Triton:* Probable captured Kuiper belt object—largest captured object in solar system. |
| Nereid | 170 | 5,588.6 | 360.125 | $3.1 \times 10^{19}$ | — | *Nereid:* Small, icy moon; very little known. |
| **Pluto** | | | | | | |
| Charon | 635 | 19.6 | 6.38718 | $1.56 \times 10^{21}$ | 1.6 | *Charon:* Unusually large compared to its planet; may have formed in giant impact. |

[a] *Note:* Authorities differ substantially on many of the values in this table.

[b] a × b × c values for the Dimensions are the approximate lengths of the axes for irregular moons.

[c] Negative sign indicates backward orbit.

[d] Masses and densities are most accurate for those satellites visited by a spacecraft on a flyby. Masses for the smallest moons have not been measured but can be estimated from the radius and an assumed density.

# STELLAR DATA

### Table F.1  Stars Within 12 Light-Years

| Star | Distance (ly) | Spectral Type | | RA h | RA m | Dec ° | Dec ′ | Luminosity $(L/L_{Sun})$ |
|---|---|---|---|---|---|---|---|---|
| Sun | 0.000016 | G2 | V | — | — | — | — | 1.0 |
| Proxima Centauri | 4.2 | M5.5 | V | 14 | 30 | −62 | 41 | 0.0006 |
| α Centauri A | 4.4 | G2 | V | 14 | 40 | −60 | 50 | 1.6 |
| α Centauri B | 4.4 | K0 | V | 14 | 40 | −60 | 50 | 0.53 |
| Barnard's Star | 6.0 | M4 | V | 17 | 58 | +04 | 42 | 0.005 |
| Wolf 359 | 7.8 | M6 | V | 10 | 56 | +07 | 01 | 0.0008 |
| Lalande 21185 | 8.3 | M2 | V | 11 | 03 | +35 | 58 | 0.03 |
| Sirius A | 8.6 | A1 | V | 06 | 45 | −16 | 42 | 26.0 |
| Sirius B | 8.6 | DA2 | — | 06 | 45 | −16 | 42 | 0.002 |
| Luyten 726-8A | 8.7 | M5.5 | V | 01 | 39 | −17 | 57 | 0.0009 |
| Luyten 726-8B | 8.7 | M6 | V | 01 | 39 | −17 | 57 | 0.0006 |
| Ross 154 | 9.7 | M3.5 | V | 18 | 50 | −23 | 50 | 0.004 |
| Ross 248 | 10.3 | M5.5 | V | 23 | 42 | +44 | 11 | 0.001 |
| ε Eridani | 10.5 | K2 | V | 03 | 33 | −09 | 28 | 0.37 |
| Lacaille 9352 | 10.7 | M1.5 | V | 23 | 06 | −35 | 51 | 0.05 |
| Ross 128 | 10.9 | M4 | V | 11 | 48 | +00 | 49 | 0.003 |
| EZ Aquarii A | 11.3 | M5 | V | 22 | 39 | −15 | 18 | 0.0006 |
| EZ Aquarii B | 11.3 | M6 | V | 22 | 39 | −15 | 18 | 0.0004 |
| EZ Aquarii C | 11.3 | M6.5 | V | 22 | 39 | −15 | 18 | 0.0003 |
| 61 Cygni A | 11.4 | K5 | V | 21 | 07 | +38 | 42 | 0.15 |
| 61 Cygni B | 11.4 | K7 | V | 21 | 07 | +38 | 42 | 0.09 |
| Procyon A | 11.4 | F5 | IV–V | 07 | 39 | +05 | 14 | 7.4 |
| Procyon B | 11.4 | DA | — | 07 | 39 | +05 | 14 | 0.0005 |
| Gliese 725 A | 11.4 | M3 | V | 18 | 43 | +59 | 38 | 0.02 |
| Gliese 725 B | 11.4 | M3.5 | V | 18 | 43 | +59 | 38 | 0.01 |
| Gliese 15 A | 11.6 | M1.5 | V | 00 | 18 | +44 | 01 | 0.03 |
| Gliese 15 B | 11.6 | M3.5 | V | 00 | 18 | +44 | 01 | 0.003 |
| DX Cancri | 11.8 | M6.5 | V | 08 | 30 | +26 | 47 | 0.0003 |
| ε Indi | 11.8 | K5 | V | 22 | 03 | −56 | 45 | 0.26 |
| τ Ceti | 11.9 | G8 | V | 01 | 44 | −15 | 57 | 0.59 |
| GJ 1061 | 11.9 | M5.5 | V | 03 | 36 | −44 | 31 | 0.0009 |

*Note:* These data were provided by the RECONS project, courtesy of Dr. Todd Henry. The luminosities are all total (bolometric) luminosities. The DA stellar types are white dwarfs. The coordinates are for the year 2000.

## Table F.2  Twenty Brightest Stars

| Star | Constellation | RA h | RA m | Dec ° | Dec ′ | Distance (ly) | Spectral Type | | Apparent Magnitude | Luminosity ($L/L_{Sun}$) |
|---|---|---|---|---|---|---|---|---|---|---|
| Sirius | Canis Major | 6 | 45 | −16 | 42 | 8.6 | A1 | V | −1.46 | 26 |
| Canopus | Carina | 6 | 24 | −52 | 41 | 313 | F0 | Ib–II | −0.72 | 13,000 |
| α Centauri | Centaurus | 14 | 40 | −60 | 50 | 4.4 | G2 | V | −0.01 | 1.6 |
| | | | | | | | K0 | V | 1.3 | 0.53 |
| Arcturus | Boötes | 14 | 16 | +19 | 11 | 37 | K2 | III | −0.06 | 170 |
| Vega | Lyra | 18 | 37 | +38 | 47 | 25 | A0 | V | 0.04 | 60 |
| Capella | Auriga | 5 | 17 | +46 | 00 | 42 | G0 | III | 0.75 | 70 |
| | | | | | | | G8 | III | 0.85 | 77 |
| Rigel | Orion | 5 | 15 | −08 | 12 | 772 | B8 | Ia | 0.14 | 70,000 |
| Procyon | Canis Minor | 7 | 39 | +05 | 14 | 11.4 | F5 | IV–V | 0.37 | 7.4 |
| Betelgeuse | Orion | 5 | 55 | +07 | 24 | 427 | M2 | Iab | 0.41 | 38,000 |
| Achernar | Eridanus | 1 | 38 | −57 | 15 | 144 | B5 | V | 0.51 | 3,600 |
| Hadar | Centaurus | 14 | 04 | −60 | 22 | 525 | B1 | III | 0.63 | 100,000 |
| Altair | Aquila | 19 | 51 | +08 | 52 | 17 | A7 | IV–V | 0.77 | 10.5 |
| Acrux | Crux | 12 | 27 | −63 | 06 | 321 | B1 | IV | 1.39 | 22,000 |
| | | | | | | | B3 | V | 1.9 | 7,500 |
| Aldebaran | Taurus | 4 | 36 | +16 | 30 | 65 | K5 | III | 0.86 | 350 |
| Spica | Virgo | 13 | 25 | −11 | 09 | 260 | B1 | V | 0.91 | 23,000 |
| Antares | Scorpio | 16 | 29 | −26 | 26 | 604 | M1 | Ib | 0.92 | 38,000 |
| Pollux | Gemini | 7 | 45 | +28 | 01 | 34 | K0 | III | 1.16 | 45 |
| Fomalhaut | Piscis Austrinus | 22 | 58 | −29 | 37 | 25 | A3 | V | 1.19 | 18 |
| Deneb | Cygnus | 20 | 41 | +45 | 16 | 2,500 | A2 | Ia | 1.26 | 170,000 |
| β Crucis | Crux | 12 | 48 | −59 | 40 | 352 | B0.5 | IV | 1.28 | 37,000 |

*Note:* Three of the stars on this list, Capella, α Centauri, and Acrux, are binary systems with members of comparable brightness. They are counted as single stars because that is how they appear to the naked eye. All the luminosities given are total (bolometric) luminosities. The coordinates are for the year 2000.

# GALAXY DATA

## Table G.1  Galaxies of the Local Group

| Galaxy Name | Distance (millions of ly) | Type[a] | RA h | RA m | Dec ° | Dec ′ | Luminosity (millions of $L_{Sun}$) |
|---|---|---|---|---|---|---|---|
| Milky Way | — | Sbc | — | — | — | — | 15,000 |
| WLM | 3.0 | Irr | 00 | 02 | −15 | 30 | 50 |
| NGC 55 | 4.8 | Irr | 00 | 15 | −39 | 13 | 1,300 |
| IC 10 | 2.7 | dIrr | 00 | 20 | +59 | 18 | 160 |
| NGC 147 | 2.4 | dE | 00 | 33 | +48 | 30 | 131 |
| And III | 2.5 | dE | 00 | 35 | +36 | 30 | 1.1 |
| NGC 185 | 2.0 | dE | 00 | 39 | +48 | 20 | 120 |
| NGC 205 | 2.7 | E | 00 | 40 | +41 | 41 | 370 |
| M 32 | 2.6 | E | 00 | 43 | +40 | 52 | 380 |
| M 31 | 2.5 | Sb | 00 | 43 | +41 | 16 | 21,000 |
| And I | 2.6 | dE | 00 | 46 | +38 | 00 | 4.7 |
| SMC | 0.19 | Irr | 00 | 53 | −72 | 50 | 230 |
| Sculptor | 0.26 | dE | 01 | 00 | −33 | 42 | 2.2 |
| LGS 3 | 2.6 | dIrr | 01 | 04 | +21 | 53 | 1.3 |
| IC 1613 | 2.3 | Irr | 01 | 05 | +02 | 08 | 64 |
| And II | 1.7 | dE | 01 | 16 | +33 | 26 | 2.4 |
| M 33 | 2.7 | Sc | 01 | 34 | +30 | 40 | 2,800 |
| Phoenix | 1.5 | dIrr | 01 | 51 | −44 | 27 | 0.9 |
| Fornax | 0.45 | dE | 02 | 40 | −34 | 27 | 15.5 |
| EGB0427+63 | 4.3 | dIrr | 04 | 32 | +63 | 36 | 9.1 |
| LMC | 0.16 | Irr | 05 | 24 | −69 | 45 | 1,300 |
| Carina | 0.33 | dE | 06 | 42 | −50 | 58 | 0.4 |
| Leo A | 2.2 | dIrr | 09 | 59 | +30 | 45 | 3.0 |
| Sextans B | 4.4 | dIrr | 10 | 00 | +05 | 20 | 41 |
| NGC 3109 | 4.1 | Irr | 10 | 03 | −26 | 09 | 160 |
| Antlia | 4.0 | dIrr | 10 | 04 | −27 | 19 | 1.7 |
| Leo I | 0.82 | dE | 10 | 08 | +12 | 18 | 4.8 |
| Sextans A | 4.7 | dIrr | 10 | 11 | −04 | 42 | 56 |
| Sextans | 0.28 | dE | 10 | 13 | −01 | 37 | 0.5 |
| Leo II | 0.67 | dE | 11 | 13 | +22 | 09 | 0.6 |
| GR 8 | 5.2 | dIrr | 12 | 59 | +14 | 13 | 3.4 |
| Ursa Minor | 0.22 | dE | 15 | 09 | +67 | 13 | 0.3 |
| Draco | 2.7 | dE | 17 | 20 | +57 | 55 | 0.3 |
| Sagittarius | 0.08 | dE | 18 | 55 | −30 | 29 | 18 |
| SagDIG | 3.5 | dIrr | 19 | 30 | −17 | 41 | 6.8 |
| NGC 6822 | 1.6 | Irr | 19 | 45 | −14 | 48 | 94 |
| DDO 210 | 2.6 | dIrr | 20 | 47 | −12 | 51 | 0.8 |
| IC 5152 | 5.2 | dIrr | 22 | 03 | −51 | 18 | 70 |
| Tucana | 2.9 | dE | 22 | 42 | −64 | 25 | 0.5 |
| UKS2323-326 | 4.3 | dE | 23 | 26 | −32 | 23 | 5.2 |
| Pegasus | 3.1 | dIrr | 23 | 29 | +14 | 45 | 12 |

[a]Types beginning with S are spiral galaxies classified according to Hubble's system (see Chapter 19). Type E galaxies are elliptical or spheroidal. Type Irr galaxies are irregular. The prefix d denotes a dwarf galaxy.

## Table G.2 Nearby Galaxies in the Messier Catalog[a,b]

| Galaxy Name (M / NGC)[c] | RA h | RA m | Dec ° | Dec ′ | RV$_{hel}$[d] | RV$_{gal}$[e] | Type[f] | Nickname |
|---|---|---|---|---|---|---|---|---|
| M 31 / NGC 224 | 00 | 43 | +41 | 16 | −300 ± 4 | −122 | Spiral | Andromeda |
| M 32 / NGC 221 | 00 | 43 | +40 | 52 | −145 ± 2 | 32 | Elliptical | |
| M 33 / NGC 598 | 01 | 34 | +30 | 40 | −179 ± 3 | −44 | Spiral | Triangulum |
| M 49 / NGC 4472 | 12 | 30 | +08 | 00 | 997 ± 7 | 929 | Elliptical/ Lenticular/Seyfert | |
| M 51 / NGC 5194 | 13 | 30 | +47 | 12 | 463 ± 3 | 550 | Spiral/Interacting | Whirlpool |
| M 58 / NGC 4579 | 12 | 38 | +11 | 49 | 1,519 ± 6 | 1,468 | Spiral/Seyfert | |
| M 59 / NGC 4621 | 12 | 42 | +11 | 39 | 410 ± 6 | 361 | Elliptical | |
| M 60 / NGC 4649 | 12 | 44 | +11 | 33 | 1,117 ± 6 | 1,068 | Elliptical | |
| M 61 / NGC 4303 | 12 | 22 | +04 | 28 | 1,566 ± 2 | 1,483 | Spiral/Seyfert | |
| M 63 / NGC 5055 | 13 | 16 | +42 | 02 | 504 ± 4 | 570 | Spiral | Sunflower |
| M 64 / NGC 4826 | 12 | 57 | +21 | 41 | 408 ± 4 | 400 | Spiral/Seyfert | Black Eye |
| M 65 / NGC 3623 | 11 | 19 | +13 | 06 | 807 ± 3 | 723 | Spiral | |
| M 66 / NGC 3627 | 11 | 20 | +12 | 59 | 727 ± 3 | 643 | Spiral/Seyfert | |
| M 74 / NGC 628 | 01 | 37 | +15 | 47 | 657 ± 1 | 754 | Spiral | |
| M 77 / NGC 1068 | 02 | 43 | −00 | 01 | 1,137 ± 3 | 1,146 | Spiral/Seyfert | |
| M 81 / NGC 3031 | 09 | 56 | +69 | 04 | −34 ± 4 | 73 | Spiral/Seyfert | |
| M 82 / NGC 3034 | 09 | 56 | +69 | 41 | 203 ± 4 | 312 | Irregular/Starburst | |
| M 83 / NGC 5236 | 13 | 37 | −29 | 52 | 516 ± 4 | 385 | Spiral/Starburst | |
| M 84 / NGC 4374 | 12 | 25 | +12 | 53 | 1,060 ± 6 | 1,005 | Elliptical | |
| M 85 / NGC 4382 | 12 | 25 | +18 | 11 | 729 ± 2 | 692 | Spiral | |
| M 86 / NGC 4406 | 12 | 26 | +12 | 57 | −244 ± 5 | −298 | Elliptical/ Lenticular | |
| M 87 / NGC 4486 | 12 | 30 | +12 | 23 | 1,307 ± 7 | 1,254 | Elliptical/Central Dominant/Seyfert | Virgo A |
| M 88 / NGC 4501 | 12 | 32 | +14 | 25 | 2,281 ± 3 | 2,235 | Spiral/Seyfert | |
| M 89 / NGC 4552 | 12 | 36 | +12 | 33 | 340 ± 4 | 290 | Elliptical | |
| M 90 / NGC 4569 | 12 | 37 | +13 | 10 | −235 ± 4 | −282 | Spiral/Seyfert | |
| M 91 / NGC 4548 | 12 | 35 | +14 | 30 | 486 ± 4 | 442 | Spiral/Seyfert | |
| M 94 / NGC 4736 | 12 | 51 | +41 | 07 | 308 ± 1 | 360 | Spiral | |
| M 95 / NGC 3351 | 10 | 44 | +11 | 42 | 778 ± 4 | 677 | Spiral/Starburst | |
| M 96 / NGC 3368 | 10 | 47 | +11 | 49 | 897 ± 4 | 797 | Spiral/Seyfert | |
| M 98 / NGC 4192 | 12 | 14 | +14 | 54 | −142 ± 4 | −195 | Spiral/Seyfert | |
| M 99 / NGC 4254 | 12 | 19 | +14 | 25 | 2,407 ± 3 | 2,354 | Spiral | |
| M 100 / NGC 4321 | 12 | 23 | +15 | 49 | 1,571 ± 1 | 1,525 | Spiral | |
| M 101 / NGC 5457 | 14 | 03 | +54 | 21 | 241 ± 2 | 360 | Spiral | |
| M 104 / NGC 4594 | 12 | 40 | −11 | 37 | 1,024 ± 5 | 904 | Spiral/Seyfert | Sombrero |
| M 105 / NGC 3379 | 10 | 48 | +12 | 35 | 911 ± 2 | 814 | Elliptical | |
| M 106 / NGC 4258 | 12 | 19 | +47 | 18 | 448 ± 3 | 507 | Spiral/Seyfert | |
| M 108 / NGC 3556 | 11 | 09 | +55 | 57 | 695 ± 3 | 765 | Spiral | |
| M 109 / NGC 3992 | 11 | 55 | +53 | 39 | 1,048 ± 4 | 1,121 | Spiral | |
| M 110 / NGC 205 | 00 | 38 | +41 | 25 | −241 ± 3 | −61 | Elliptical | |

[a]Galaxies identified in the catalog published by Charles Messier in 1781; these galaxies are relatively easy to observe with small telescopes.

[b]Data obtained from NED: NASA/IPAC Extragalactic Database (http://ned.ipac.caltech.edu). The original Messier list of galaxies was obtained from SED, and the list data were updated to 2001 and M 102 was dropped.

[c]The galaxies are identified by the Messier number (M followed by a number) and by their NGC numbers, which come from the *New General Catalog* published in 1888.

[d]Radial velocity in km/s, with respect to the Sun (heliocentric). Positive values mean motion away from the Sun, and negative values are toward the Sun.

[e]Radial velocity in km/s, with respect to the Milky Way Galaxy, calculated from the RV$_{hel}$ values with a correction for the Sun's motion around the galactic center.

[f]Galaxies are first listed by their primary type (spiral, elliptical, or irregular) and then by any other special categories that apply (see Chapters 19 and 20).

## Table G.3 Nearby, X-ray Bright Clusters of Galaxies

| Cluster Name | Redshift | Distance[a] (billions of ly) | Temperature of Intracluster Medium (millions of K) | Average Orbital Velocity of Galaxies[b] (km/sec) | Cluster Mass[c] ($10^{15} M_{Sun}$) |
|---|---|---|---|---|---|
| Abell 2142 | 0.0907 | 1.20 | 101. ± 2 | 1,132 ± 110 | 1.8 |
| Abell 2029 | 0.0766 | 1.07 | 100. ± 3 | 1,164 ± 98 | 1.8 |
| Abell 401 | 0.0737 | 1.03 | 95.2 ± 5 | 1,152 ± 86 | 1.6 |
| Coma | 0.0233 | 0.34 | 95.1 ± 1 | 821 ± 49 | 1.6 |
| Abell 754 | 0.0539 | 0.77 | 93.3 ± 3 | 662 ± 77 | 1.6 |
| Abell 2256 | 0.0589 | 0.83 | 87.0 ± 2 | 1,348 ± 86 | 1.4 |
| Abell 399 | 0.0718 | 1.01 | 81.7 ± 7 | 1,116 ± 89 | 1.3 |
| Abell 3571 | 0.0395 | 0.57 | 81.1 ± 3 | 1,045 ± 109 | 1.3 |
| Abell 478 | 0.0882 | 1.22 | 78.9 ± 2 | 904 ± 281 | 1.2 |
| Abell 3667 | 0.0566 | 0.80 | 78.5 ± 6 | 971 ± 62 | 1.2 |
| Abell 3266 | 0.0599 | 0.85 | 78.2 ± 5 | 1,107 ± 82 | 1.2 |
| Abell 1651a | 0.0846 | 1.17 | 73.1 ± 6 | 685 ± 129 | 1.2 |
| Abell 85 | 0.0560 | 0.80 | 70.9 ± 2 | 969 ± 95 | 1.2 |
| Abell 119 | 0.0438 | 0.63 | 65.6 ± 5 | 679 ± 106 | 0.94 |
| Abell 3558 | 0.0480 | 0.69 | 65.3 ± 2 | 977 ± 39 | 0.94 |
| Abell 1795 | 0.0632 | 0.89 | 62.9 ± 2 | 834 ± 85 | 0.88 |
| Abell 2199 | 0.0314 | 0.46 | 52.7 ± 1 | 801 ± 92 | 0.68 |
| Abell 2147 | 0.0353 | 0.51 | 51.1 ± 4 | 821 ± 68 | 0.65 |
| Abell 3562 | 0.0478 | 0.68 | 45.7 ± 8 | 736 ± 49 | 0.55 |
| Abell 496 | 0.0325 | 0.47 | 45.3 ± 1 | 687 ± 89 | 0.54 |
| Centaurus | 0.0103 | 0.15 | 42.2 ± 1 | 863 ± 34 | 0.49 |
| Abell 1367 | 0.0213 | 0.31 | 41.3 ± 2 | 822 ± 69 | 0.47 |
| Hydra | 0.0126 | 0.19 | 38.0 ± 1 | 610 ± 52 | 0.42 |
| C0336 | 0.0349 | 0.50 | 37.4 ± 1 | 650 ± 170 | 0.41 |
| Virgo | 0.0038 | 0.06 | 25.7 ± 0.5 | 632 ± 41 | 0.23 |

*Note:* This table lists the 25 brightest clusters of galaxies in the X-ray sky from a catalog by J. P. Henry (2000).

[a]Cluster distances were computed using a value for Hubble's constant of 65 km/sec/Mpc.

[b]The average orbital velocities of galaxies given in this column are the velocity dispersions of the clusters' galaxies.

[c]This column gives each cluster's mass within the largest radius at which the intracluster medium can be in gravitational equilibrium. Because our estimates of that radius depend on Hubble's constant, these masses are inversely proportional to Hubble's constant, which we have assumed to be 65 km/s/Mpc.

# APPENDIX H

## SELECTED ASTRONOMICAL WEB SITES

The Web contains a vast amount of astronomical information. For all your astronomical Web surfing, the best starting point is the Web site for this textbook:

The Astronomy Place
**www.astronomyplace.com**

The following are some other sites that may be of particular use. In case any of the links change, you can always find live links to these sites, and many more, on The Astronomy Place.

### Key Mission Sites

The following table lists the Web pages for major current astronomy missions.

| Site | Description | Web Address |
|---|---|---|
| NASA's Office of Space Science Missions Page | Direct links to all past, present, and planned NASA space science missions | http://spacescience.nasa.gov/missions |
| Cassini/Huygens | Mission scheduled to arrive at Saturn in 2004 | http://www.jpl.nasa.gov/cassini |
| Chandra X-Ray Observatory | Latest discoveries, educational activities, and other information from the Chandra X-Ray Observatory | http://chandra.harvard.edu |
| Far Ultraviolet Spectroscopic Explorer (FUSE) | Ultraviolet observatory in space | http://fuse.pha.jhu.edu |
| Galileo | Mission orbiting Jupiter | http://www.jpl.nasa.gov/galileo |
| Hubble Space Telescope | Latest discoveries, educational activities, and other information from the Hubble Space Telescope | http://hubble.stsci.edu |
| Mars Exploration Program | Information on current and planned Mars missions | http://mars.jpl.nasa.gov |
| Microwave Anisotropy Probe (MAP) | Mission to study the cosmic microwave background | http://map.gsfc.nasa.gov |
| Space Infrared Telescope Facility (SIRTF) | Infrared observatory scheduled for launch in 2002 | http://sirtf.jpl.nasa.gov |
| Stratospheric Observatory for Infrared Astronomy (SOFIA) | Airborne observatory scheduled to begin flights in 2002 | http://sofia.arc.nasa.gov |

# Key Observatory Sites

The following table lists the Web pages leading to major ground-based observatories.

| Site | Description | Web Address |
|---|---|---|
| World's Largest Optical Telescopes | Direct links to most of the world's major optical observatories | http://www.seds.org/billa/bigeyes.html |
| Arecibo Observatory (Puerto Rico) | World's largest single-dish radio telescope | http://www.naic.edu |
| Cerro Tololo Inter-American Observatory | Links to major observatories on site in Cerro Tololo, Chile | http://www.ctio.noao.edu |
| European Southern Observatory | Links to European telescope projects in Chile, including the Very Large Telescope | http://www.eso.org |
| Mauna Kea Observatories | Links to major observatories in Hawaii, including Keck, Gemini, Subaru, CFHT, and others | http://www.ifa.hawaii.edu/mko |
| Mt. Palomar Observatory | Powerful telescope near San Diego | http://www.astro.caltech.edu/palomarpublic |
| National Optical Astronomy Observatory | Home page for United States national observatories in Arizona, Hawaii, and Chile | http://www.noao.edu |
| National Radio Astronomy Observatory | Home page for United States national radio observatories, including the Very Large Array (VLA) | http://www.nrao.edu |

## More Astronomical Web Sites

The following Web sites are some of the authors' favorites among many other non-commercial resources for astronomy.

| Site | Description | Web Address |
|---|---|---|
| **The Astronomy Place** | **Don't forget to start here for all your astronomical Web surfing.** | **http://www.astronomyplace.com** |
| American Association of Variable Star Observers (AAVSO) | One of the largest organizations of amateur astronomers in the world. Check this site if you are interested in serious amateur astronomy. | http://www.aavso.org |
| Astronomical Society of the Pacific | An organization for both professional astronomers and the general public, devoted largely to astronomy education. | http://www.aspsky.org |
| Astronomy Picture of the Day | An archive of beautiful pictures, updated daily. | http://antwrp.gsfc.nasa.gov/apod |
| AstroWeb | Listing of major resources for astronomy on the Web. | http://www.cv.nrao.edu/fits/www/astronomy.html |
| Canadian Space Agency | Home page for Canada's space program. | http://www.space.gc.ca |
| European Space Agency (ESA) | Home page for this international agency. | http://www.esa.int |
| The Extrasolar Planets Encyclopedia | Information about the search for and discoveries of extrasolar planets. | http://cfa-www.harvard.edu/planets |
| NASA Home Page | Learn almost anything you want about NASA. | http://www.nasa.gov |
| NASA Science News | Read the latest news from NASA; has option to subscribe to e-mail notices of news releases. | http://science.nasa.gov |
| The Nine Planets (University of Arizona) | A multimedia tour of the solar system. | http://seds.lpl.arizona.edu/nineplanets/nineplanets/nineplanets.html |
| The Planetary Society | Has more than 100,000 members who are interested in planetary exploration and the search for life in the universe. | http://planetary.org |
| The SETI Institute | Devoted to the search for other civilizations. | http://www.seti.org |
| Voyage Scale Model Solar System | Take a virtual tour of the Voyage Scale Model Solar System. | http://www.voyageonline.org |

# THE 88 CONSTELLATIONS

## Constellation Names (English equivalent in parentheses)

Andromeda (The Chained
  Princess)
Antlia (The Air Pump)
Apus (The Bird of Paradise)
Aquarius (The Water Bearer)
Aquila (The Eagle)
Ara (The Altar)
Aries (The Ram)
Auriga (The Charioteer)
Boötes (The Herdsman)
Caelum (The Chisel)
Camelopardalis (The Giraffe)
Cancer (The Crab)
Canes Venatici (The Hunting Dogs)

Canis Major (The Great Dog)
Canis Minor (The Little Dog)
Capricornus (The Sea Goat)
Carina (The Keel)
Cassiopeia (The Queen)
Centaurus (The Centaur)
Cepheus (The King)
Cetus (The Whale)
Chamaeleon (The Chameleon)
Circinus (The Drawing Compass)
Columba (The Dove)
Coma Berenices (Berenice's Hair)
Corona Australis (The Southern
  Crown)

Corona Borealis (The Northern
  Crown)
Corvus (The Crow)
Crater (The Cup)
Crux (The Southern Cross)
Cygnus (The Swan)
Delphinus (The Dolphin)
Dorado (The Goldfish)
Draco (The Dragon)
Equuleus (The Little Horse)
Eridanus (The River)
Fornax (The Furnace)
Gemini (The Twins)
Grus (The Crane)

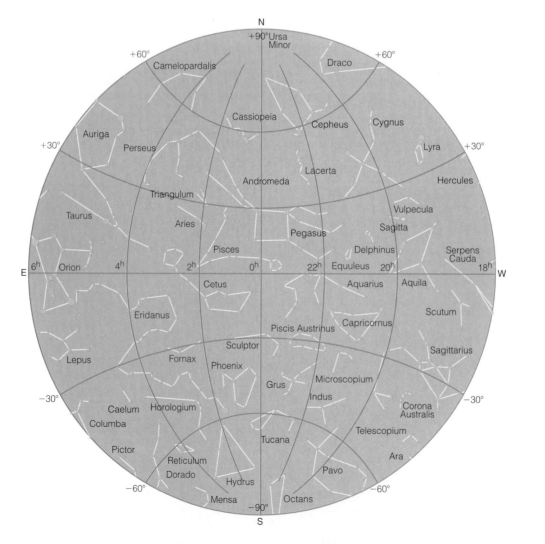

Hercules
Horologium (The Clock)
Hydra (The Sea Serpent)
Hydrus (The Water Snake)
Indus (The Indian)
Lacerta (The Lizard)
Leo (The Lion)
Leo Minor (The Little Lion)
Lepus (The Hare)
Libra (The Scales)
Lupus (The Wolf)
Lynx (The Lynx)
Lyra (The Lyre)
Mensa (The Table)
Microscopium (The Microscope)
Monoceros (The Unicorn)
Musca (The Fly)
Norma (The Level)
Octans (The Octant)
Ophiuchus (The Serpent Bearer)
Orion (The Hunter)
Pavo (The Peacock)

Pegasus (The Winged Horse)
Perseus (The Hero)
Phoenix (The Phoenix)
Pictor (The Painter's Easel)
Pisces (The Fish)
Piscis Austrinus (The Southern Fish)
Puppis (The Stern)
Pyxis (The Compass)
Reticulum (The Reticle)
Sagitta (The Arrow)
Sagittarius (The Archer)
Scorpius (The Scorpion)
Sculptor (The Sculptor)
Scutum (The Shield)
Serpens (The Serpent)
Sextans (The Sextant)
Taurus (The Bull)
Telescopium (The Telescope)
Triangulum (The Triangle)
Triangulum Australe (Southern Triangle)

Tucana (The Toucan)
Ursa Major (The Great Bear)
Ursa Minor (The Little Bear)
Vela (The Sail)
Virgo (The Virgin)
Volans (The Flying Fish)
Vulpecula (The Fox)

## Constellation Locations

Each of the charts on these pages shows half of the celestial sphere in projection, so you can use them to learn the approximate locations of the constellations. The grid lines are marked by right ascension and declination [Section S1.4].

# STAR CHARTS

How to use the star charts:

Check the times and dates under each chart to find the best one for you. Take it outdoors within an hour or so of the time listed for your date. Bring a dim flashlight to help you read it.

On each chart, the round outside edge represents the horizon all around you. Compass directions around the horizon are marked in yellow. Turn the chart around so the edge marked with the direction you're facing (for example, north, southeast) is down. The stars above this horizon now match the stars you are facing. Ignore the rest until you turn to look in a different direction.

The center of the chart represents the sky overhead, so a star plotted on the chart halfway from the edge to the center can be found in the sky halfway from the horizon to straight up.

The charts are drawn for 40°N latitude (for example, Denver, New York, Madrid). If you live far south of there, stars in the southern part of your sky will appear higher than on the chart and stars in the north will be lower. If you live far north of there, the reverse is true.

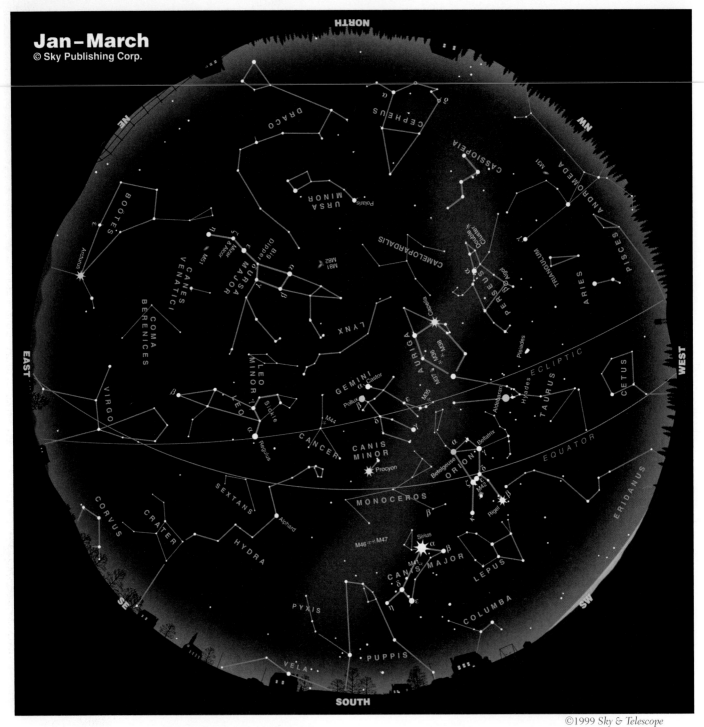

©1999 *Sky & Telescope*

***Use this chart January, February, and March.***

| | | |
|---|---|---|
| Early January — 1 A.M. | Early February — 11 P.M. | Early March — 9 P.M. |
| Late January — Midnight | Late February — 10 P.M. | Late March — Dusk |

©1999 *Sky & Telescope*

*Use this chart April, May, and June.*

| | | |
|---|---|---|
| Early April — 3 A.M.* | Early May — 1 A.M.* | Early June — 11 P.M.* |
| Late April — 2 A.M.* | Late May — Midnight* | Late June — Dusk |

*Daylight Saving Time

**Use this chart July, August, and September.**

Early July — 1 A.M.*      Early August — 11 P.M.*      Early September — 9 P.M.*
Late July — Midnight*      Late August — 10 P.M.*      Late September — Dusk

*Daylight Saving Time

# Oct.–Dec.
©Sky Publishing Corp.

©1999 *Sky & Telescope*

**Use this chart October, November, and December.**

Early October — 1 A.M.*        Early November — 10 P.M.        Early December — 8 P.M.
Late October — Midnight*      Late November — 9 P.M.          Late December — 7 P.M.

*Daylight Saving Time

# GLOSSARY

**21-cm line** A spectral line from atomic hydrogen with wavelength 21 cm (in the radio portion of the spectrum).

**absolute magnitude** A measure of an object's luminosity; defined to be the apparent magnitude the object would have if it were located exactly 10 parsecs away.

**absolute zero** The coldest possible temperature, which is 0 K.

**absorption** (of light) The process by which matter absorbs radiative energy.

**absorption-line spectrum** A spectrum that contains absorption lines.

**accelerating universe** The possible fate of our universe in which a repulsive force (*see* cosmological constant) causes the expansion of the universe to accelerate with time. Its galaxies will recede from one another increasingly faster, and it will become cold and dark more quickly than a coasting universe.

**acceleration** The rate at which an object's velocity changes. Its standard units are m/s².

**acceleration of gravity** The acceleration of a falling object. On Earth, the acceleration of gravity, designated by g, is 9.8 m/s².

**accretion** The process by which small objects gather together to make larger objects.

**accretion disk** A rapidly rotating disk of material that gradually falls inward as it orbits a starlike object (e.g., white dwarf, neutron star, or black hole).

**active galactic nuclei** The unusually luminous centers of some galaxies, thought to be powered by accretion onto supermassive black holes. Quasars are the brightest type of active galactic nuclei; radio galaxies also contain active galactic nuclei.

**adaptive optics** A technique in which telescope mirrors flex rapidly to compensate for the bending of starlight caused by atmospheric turbulence.

**albedo** Describes the fraction of sunlight reflected by a surface; albedo = 0 means no reflection at all (a perfectly black surface); albedo = 1 means all light is reflected (a perfectly white surface).

**altitude** (above horizon) The angular distance between the horizon and an object in the sky.

**amino acids** The building blocks of proteins.

**analemma** The figure-8 path traced by the Sun over the course of a year when viewed at the same place and the same time each day; represents the discrepancies between apparent and mean solar time.

**Andromeda Galaxy** (M 31; the Great Galaxy in Andromeda) The nearest large spiral galaxy to the Milky Way.

**angular momentum** Momentum attributable to rotation or revolution. The angular momentum of an object moving in a circle of radius r is the product $m \times v \times r$.

**angular resolution** (of a telescope) The smallest angular separation that two point-like objects can have and still be seen as distinct points of light (rather than as a single point of light).

**angular size** (or **angular distance**) A measure of the angle formed by extending imaginary lines outward from our eyes to span an object (or between two objects).

**annihilation** *See* matter–antimatter annihilation

**annular solar eclipse** A solar eclipse during which the Moon is directly in front of the Sun but its angular size is not large enough to fully block the Sun; thus, a ring (or *annulus*) of sunlight is still visible around the Moon's disk.

**Antarctic Circle** The circle on the Earth with latitude 66.5°S.

**antimatter** Refers to any particle with the same mass as a particle of ordinary matter but whose other basic properties, such as electrical charge, are precisely opposite.

**aphelion** The point at which an object orbiting the Sun is farthest from the Sun.

**apogee** The point at which an object orbiting the Earth is farthest from the Earth.

**apparent brightness** The amount of light reaching us *per unit area* from a luminous object; often measured in units of watts/m².

**apparent magnitude** A measure of the apparent brightness of an object in the sky, based on the ancient system developed by Hipparchus.

**apparent retrograde motion** Refers to the apparent motion of a planet, as viewed from Earth, during the period of a few weeks or months when it moves westward relative to the stars in our sky.

**apparent solar time** Time measured by the actual position of the Sun in your local sky; defined so that noon is when the Sun is *on* the meridian.

**arcminutes** (or **minutes of arc**) One arcminute is 1/60 of 1°.

**arcseconds** (or **seconds of arc**) One arcsecond is 1/60 of an arcminute, or 1/3,600 of 1°.

**Arctic Circle** The circle on the Earth with latitude 66.5°N.

**asteroid** A relatively small and rocky object that orbits a star; asteroids are sometimes called *minor planets* because they are similar to planets but smaller.

**asteroid belt** The region of our solar system between the orbits of Mars and Jupiter in which asteroids are heavily concentrated.

**astrobiology** The study of life on Earth and beyond; emphasizes research into questions of the origin of life, the conditions under which life can survive, and the search for life beyond Earth.

**astronomical unit (AU)** The average distance (semimajor axis) of the Earth from the Sun, which is about 150 million km.

**atmospheric pressure** The surface pressure resulting from the overlying weight of an atmosphere.

**atomic mass** The combined number of protons and neutrons in an atom.

**atomic number** The number of protons in an atom.

**atoms** Consist of a nucleus made from protons and neutrons surrounded by a cloud of electrons.

**aurora** Dancing lights in the sky caused by charged particles entering our atmosphere; called the *aurora borealis* in the Northern Hemisphere and the *aurora australis* in the Southern Hemisphere.

**azimuth** (usually called *direction* in this book) Direction around the horizon from due north, measured clockwise in degrees. E.g., the azimuth of due north is 0°, due east is 90°, due south is 180°, and due west is 270°.

**bar** The standard unit of pressure, approximately equal to the Earth's atmospheric pressure at sea level.

**baryonic matter** Refers to ordinary matter made from atoms (because the nuclei of atoms contain protons and neutrons, which are both baryons).

**baryons** Particles, including protons and neutrons, that are made from three quarks.

**basalt** A type of volcanic rock that makes a low-viscosity lava when molten.

**belts** (on a jovian planet) Dark bands of sinking air that encircle a jovian planet at a particular set of latitudes.

**Big Bang** The event that gave birth to the universe.

**Big Crunch** If gravity ever reverses the universal expansion, the universe will someday begin to collapse and presumably end in a Big Crunch.

**binary star system** A star system that contains two stars.

**biosphere** Refers to the "layer" of life on Earth.

**black hole** A bottomless pit in spacetime. Nothing can escape from within a black hole, and we can never again detect or observe an object that falls into a black hole.

**black smokers** Structures around seafloor volcanic vents that support a wide variety of life.

**blueshift** A Doppler shift in which spectral features are shifted to shorter wavelengths, caused when an object is moving toward the observer.

**bosons** Particles, such as photons, to which the exclusion principle does not apply.

**bound orbits** Orbits on which an object travels repeatedly around another object; bound orbits are elliptical in shape.

**brown dwarf** An object too small to become an ordinary star because electron degeneracy pressure halts its gravitational collapse before fusion becomes self-sustaining; brown dwarfs have mass less than $0.08 M_{Sun}$.

**bubble** (interstellar) The surface of a bubble is an expanding shell of hot, ionized gas driven by stellar winds or supernovae; inside the bubble, the gas is very hot and has very low density.

**bulge** (of a spiral galaxy) The central portion of a spiral galaxy that is roughly spherical (or football shaped) and bulges above and below the plane of the galactic disk.

**Cambrian explosion** The dramatic diversification of life on Earth that occurred between about 540 and 500 million years ago.

**carbon stars** Stars whose atmospheres are especially carbon-rich, thought to be near the ends of their lives; carbon stars are the primary sources of carbon in the universe.

**carbonate rock** A carbon-rich rock, such as limestone, that forms underwater from chemical reactions between sediments and carbon dioxide. On Earth, most of the outgassed carbon dioxide currently resides in carbonate rocks.

**carbonate–silicate cycle** The process that cycles carbon dioxide between the Earth's atmosphere and surface rocks.

**CCD (charge coupled device)** A type of electronic light detector that has largely replaced photographic film in astronomical research.

**celestial coordinates** The coordinates of right ascension and declination that fix an object's position on the celestial sphere.

**celestial equator (CE)** The extension of the Earth's equator onto the celestial sphere.

**celestial navigation** Navigation on the surface of the Earth accomplished by observations of the Sun and stars.

**celestial sphere** The imaginary sphere on which objects in the sky appear to reside when observed from Earth.

**Celsius** (temperature scale) The temperature scale commonly used in daily activity internationally. Defined so that, on Earth's surface, water freezes at 0°C and boils at 100°C.

**central dominant galaxy** A giant elliptical galaxy found at the center of a dense cluster of galaxies, apparently formed by the merger of several individual galaxies.

**Cepheid** See Cepheid variable

**Cepheid variable** A particularly luminous type of pulsating variable star that follows a period–luminosity relation and hence is very useful for measuring cosmic distances.

**charged particle belts** Zones in which ions and electrons accumulate and encircle a planet.

**chemical enrichment** The process by which the abundance of heavy elements (heavier than helium) in the interstellar medium gradually increases over time as these elements are produced by stars and released into space.

**chromosphere** The layer of the Sun's atmosphere below the corona; most of the Sun's ultraviolet light is emitted from this region, in which the temperature is about 10,000 K.

**circulation cells** (also called *Hadley cells*) Large-scale cells (similar to convection cells) in a planet's atmosphere that transport heat between the equator and the poles.

**circumpolar star** A star that always remains above the horizon for a particular latitude.

**climate** Describes the long-term average of weather.

**close binary** A binary star system in which the two stars are very close together.

**closed universe** The universe is closed if its average density is greater than the critical density, in which case spacetime must curve back on itself to the point where its overall shape is analogous to that of the surface of a sphere. In the absence of a repulsive force (*see* cosmological constant), a closed universe would someday stop expanding and begin to contract.

**cluster of galaxies** A collection of a few dozen or more galaxies bound together by gravity; smaller collections of galaxies are simply called *groups*.

**cluster of stars** A group of anywhere from several hundred to a million or so stars; star clusters come in two types—open clusters and globular clusters.

**CNO cycle** The cycle of reactions by which intermediate- and high-mass stars fuse hydrogen into helium.

**coasting universe** The possible fate of our universe in which the mass density of the universe is *smaller* than the critical density, so that the collective gravity of all matter cannot halt the expansion. In the absence of a repulsive force (*see* cosmological constant), such a universe would keep expanding forever with little change in its rate of expansion.

**coma** (of a comet) The dusty atmosphere of a comet created by sublimation of ices in the nucleus when the comet is near the Sun.

**comet** A relatively small, icy object that orbits a star.

**comparative planetology** The study of the solar system by examining and understanding the similarities and differences among worlds.

**compound** (chemical) A substance made from molecules consisting of two or more atoms with different atomic number.

**condensates** Solid or liquid particles that condense from a cloud of gas.

**condensation** The formation of solid or liquid particles from a cloud of gas.

**conduction** (of energy) The process by which thermal energy is transferred by direct contact from warm material to cooler material.

**conjunction** (of a planet with the Sun) When a planet and the Sun line up in the sky.

**conservation of angular momentum** (law of) The principle that, in the absence of net torque (twisting force), the total angular momentum of a system remains constant.

**conservation of energy** (law of) The principle that energy (including mass-energy) can be neither created nor destroyed, but can only change from one form to another.

**conservation of momentum** (law of) The principle that, in the absence of net force, the total momentum of a system remains constant.

**constellation** A region of the sky; 88 official constellations cover the celestial sphere.

**convection** The energy transport process in which warm material expands and rises, while cooler material contracts and falls.

**convection cell** An individual small region of convecting material.

**convection zone** (of a star) A region in which energy is transported outward by convection.

**core** (of a planet) The dense central region of a planet that has undergone differentiation.

**core** (of a star) The central region of a star, in which nuclear fusion can occur.

**Coriolis effect** Causes air or objects moving on a rotating planet to deviate from straight-line trajectories.

**corona** (solar) The tenuous uppermost layer of the Sun's atmosphere; most of the Sun's X rays are emitted from this region, in which the temperature is about 1 million K.

**coronal holes** Regions of the corona that barely show up in X-ray images because they are nearly devoid of hot coronal gas.

**cosmic microwave background** The remnant radiation from the Big Bang, which we detect using radio telescopes sensitive to microwaves (which are short-wavelength radio waves).

**cosmic rays** Particles such as electrons, protons, and atomic nuclei that zip through interstellar space at close to the speed of light.

**cosmological constant** The name given to a term in Einstein's equations of general relativity. If it is not zero, then it represents a repulsive force or a type of energy (sometimes called *dark energy* or *quintessence*) that might cause the expansion of the universe to accelerate with time.

**cosmological horizon** The boundary of our observable universe, which is where the lookback time is equal to the age of the universe. Beyond this boundary in spacetime, we cannot see anything at all.

**cosmological redshift** Refers to the redshifts we see from distant galaxies, caused by the fact that expansion of the universe stretches all the photons within it to longer, redder wavelengths.

**critical density** The precise average density for the entire universe that marks the dividing line between a recollapsing universe and one that will expand forever.

**critical universe** The possible fate of our universe in which the mass density of the universe *equals* the critical density. The universe will never collapse, but in the absence of a repulsive force it will expand more and more slowly as time progresses. *See* cosmological constant

**crust** (of a planet) The low-density surface layer of a planet that has undergone differentiation.

**cycles per second** Units of frequency for a wave; describes the number of peaks (or troughs) of a wave that pass by a given point each second. Equivalent to *hertz.*

**dark energy** Name sometimes given to energy that could be causing the expansion of the universe to accelerate. *See* cosmological constant.

**dark matter** Matter that we infer to exist from its gravitational effects but from which we have not detected any light; dark matter apparently dominates the total mass of the universe.

**daylight saving time** Standard time plus 1 hour, so that the Sun appears on the meridian around 1 P.M. rather than around noon.

**declination (dec)** Analogous to latitude, but on the celestial sphere; it is the angular north-south distance between the celestial equator and a location on the celestial sphere.

**degeneracy pressure** A type of pressure unrelated to an object's temperature, which arises when electrons (electron degeneracy pressure) or neutrons (neutron degeneracy pressure) are packed so tightly that the exclusion and uncertainty principles come into play.

**degenerate object** An object in which degeneracy pressure is the primary pressure pushing back against gravity, such as a brown dwarf, white dwarf, or neutron star.

**deuterium** A form of hydrogen in which the nucleus contains a proton and a neutron, rather than only a proton (as is the case for most hydrogen nuclei).

**differential rotation** Describes the rotation of an object in which the equator rotates at a different rate than the poles.

**differentiation** The process in which gravity separates materials according to density, with high-density materials sinking and low-density materials rising.

**diffraction grating** A finely etched surface that can split light into a spectrum.

**diffraction limit** The angular resolution that a telescope could achieve if it were limited only by the interference of light waves; it is smaller (i.e., better angular resolution) for larger telescopes.

**dimension** (mathematical) Describes the number of independent directions in which movement is possible; e.g., the surface of the Earth is two-dimensional because only two independent directions of motion are possible (north-south and east-west).

**direction** (in local sky) One of the two coordinates (the other is altitude) needed to pinpoint an object in the local sky. It is the direction, such as north, south, east, or west, in which you must face to see the object. *See also* azimuth

**disk component** (of a galaxy) The portion of a spiral galaxy that looks like a disk and contains an interstellar medium with cool gas and dust; stars of many ages are found in the disk component.

**Doppler effect (shift)** The effect that shifts the wavelengths of spectral features in objects that are moving toward or away from the observer.

**down quark** One of the two quark types (the other is the up quark) found in ordinary protons and neutrons. Has a charge of $-\frac{1}{3}$.

**dust** (or **dust grains**) Tiny solid flecks of material; in astronomy, we often discuss interplanetary dust (found within a star system) or interstellar dust (found between the stars in a galaxy). *See also* interstellar dust grains

**dust tail** (of a comet) One of two tails seen when a comet passes near the Sun (the other is the plasma tail); composed of small solid particles pushed away from the Sun by the radiation pressure of sunlight.

**dwarf elliptical galaxy** A small elliptical galaxy with less than about a billion stars.

**Earth-orbiters** (spacecraft) Spacecraft designed to study the Earth or the universe from Earth orbit.

**eccentricity** A measure of how much an ellipse deviates from a perfect circle; defined as the center-to-focus distance divided by the length of the semimajor axis.

**eclipse** Occurs when one astronomical object casts a shadow on another or crosses our line of sight to the other object.

**eclipse seasons** Periods during which lunar and solar eclipses can occur because the nodes of the Moon's orbit are nearly aligned with the Earth and Sun.

**eclipsing binary** A binary star system in which the two stars happen to be orbiting in the plane of our line of sight, so that each star will periodically eclipse the other.

**ecliptic** The Sun's apparent annual path among the constellations.

**ecliptic plane** The plane of the Earth's orbit around the Sun.

**ejecta** (from an impact) Debris ejected by the blast of an impact.

**electromagnetic field** An abstract concept used to describe how a charged particle would affect other charged particles at a distance.

**electromagnetic force** One of the four fundamental forces; it is the force that dominates atomic and molecular interactions.

**electromagnetic spectrum** The complete spectrum of light, including radio waves, infrared, visible light, ultraviolet light, X rays, and gamma rays.

**electromagnetic wave** A synonym for light, which consists of waves of electric and magnetic fields.

**electron degeneracy pressure** Degeneracy pressure exerted by electrons, as in brown dwarfs and white dwarfs.

**electrons** Fundamental particles with negative electric charge; the distribution of electrons in an atom gives the atom its size.

**electron-volt (eV)** A unit of energy equivalent to $1.60 \times 10^{-19}$ joule.

**electroweak era** The era of the universe during which only three forces operated (gravity, strong force, and electroweak force), lasting from $10^{-38}$ second to $10^{-10}$ second after the Big Bang.

**electroweak force** The force that exists at high energies when the electromagnetic force and the weak force exist as a single force.

**element** (chemical) A substance made from individual atoms of a particular atomic number.

**ellipse** A type of oval that happens to be the shape of bound orbits. An ellipse can be drawn by moving a pencil along a string whose ends are tied to two tacks; the locations of the tacks are the foci (singular, focus) of the ellipse.

**elliptical galaxies** Galaxies that appear rounded in shape, often longer in one direction, like a football. They have no disks and contain very little cool gas and dust compared to spiral galaxies, though they often contain very hot, ionized gas.

**elongation** (greatest) For Mercury or Venus, the point at which it appears farthest from the Sun in our sky.

**emission** (of light) The process by which matter emits energy in the form of light.

**emission-line spectrum** A spectrum that contains emission lines.

**energy** Broadly speaking, energy is what can make matter move. The three basic types of energy are kinetic, potential, and radiative.

**equation of time** Describes the discrepancies between apparent and mean solar time.

**equivalence principle** The fundamental starting point for general relativity, which states that the effects of gravity are exactly equivalent to the effects of acceleration.

**era of atoms** The era of the universe lasting from about 500,000 years to about 1 billion years after the Big Bang, during which it was cool enough for neutral atoms to form.

**era of galaxies** The present era of the universe, which began with the formation of galaxies when the universe was about 1 billion years old.

**era of nuclei** The era of the universe lasting from about 3 minutes to about 500,000 years after the Big Bang, during which matter in the universe was fully ionized and opaque to light. The cosmic background radiation was released at the end of this era.

**era of nucleosynthesis** The era of the universe lasting from about 0.001 second to about 3 minutes after the Big Bang, by the end of which virtually all of the neutrons and about one-seventh of the protons in the universe had fused into helium.

**erosion** The wearing down or building up of geological features by wind, water, ice, and other phenomena of planetary weather.

**eruption** The process of releasing hot lava on the planet's surface.

**escape velocity** The speed necessary for an object to completely escape the gravity of a large body such as a moon, planet, or star.

**evaporation** The process by which atoms or molecules escape into the gas phase from a liquid.

**event** Any particular point along a world-line represents a particular event; all observers will agree on the reality of an event but may disagree about its time and location.

**event horizon** The boundary that marks the "point of no return" between a black hole and the outside universe; events that occur within the event horizon can have no influence on our observable universe.

**exchange particle** According to the standard model of physics, each of the four fundamental forces is transmitted by the transfer of particular types of exchange particles.

**excited state** (of an atom) Any arrangement of electrons in an atom that has more energy than the ground state.

**exclusion principle** The law of quantum mechanics that states that two fermions cannot occupy the same quantum state at the same time.

**exosphere** The hot, outer layer of an atmosphere, where the atmosphere "fades away" to space.

**exposure time** The amount of time for which light is collected to make a single image.

**extrasolar planet** A planet orbiting a star other than our Sun.

**Fahrenheit** (temperature scale) The temperature scale commonly used in daily activity in the United States. Defined so that, on Earth's surface, water freezes at 32°F and boils at 212°F.

**fall equinox (autumnal equinox)** Refers both to the point in Virgo on the celestial sphere where the ecliptic crosses the celestial equator and to the moment in time when the Sun appears at that point each year (around September 21).

**false-color image** An image displayed in colors that are *not* the true, visible-light colors of an object.

**fault** (geological) A place where rocks slip sideways relative to one another.

**feedback relationships** Processes in which one property amplifies (positive feedback) or counteracts (negative feedback) the behavior of properties.

**fermions** Particles, such as electrons, neutrons, and protons, that obey the exclusion principle.

**field** An abstract concept used to describe how a particle would interact with a force. For example, the idea of a *gravitational field* describes how a particle would react to the local strength of gravity, and the idea of an *electromagnetic field* describes how a charged particle would respond to forces from other charged particles.

**filter** (for light) A material that transmits only particular wavelengths of light.

**fireball** A particularly bright meteor.

**flare star** A small, spectral type M star that displays particularly strong flares on its surface.

**flat (or Euclidean) geometry** Refers to any case in which the rules of geometry for a flat plane hold, such as that the shortest distance between two points is a straight line.

**flat universe** A universe in which the overall geometry of spacetime is flat (Euclidean), as would be the case if the density of the universe is equal to the critical density.

**flybys** (spacecraft) Spacecraft that fly past a target object (such as a planet), usually just once, as opposed to entering a bound orbit of the object.

**focal plane** The place where an image created by a lens or mirror is in focus.

**focus** (of a lens or mirror) The point at which rays of light that were initially parallel (such as light from a distant star) converge.

**force** Anything that can cause a change in momentum.

**formation properties** (of planets) In this book, for the purpose of understanding geological processes, planets are defined to be born with four formation properties: size (mass and radius), distance from the Sun, composition, and rotation rate.

**frame of reference** (in relativity) Two (or more) objects share the same frame of reference if they are *not* moving relative to each other.

**free-fall** Refers to conditions in which an object is falling without resistance; objects are weightless when in free-fall.

**free-float frame** A frame of reference in which all objects are weightless and hence float freely.

**frequency** Describes the rate at which peaks of a wave pass by a point; measured in units of 1/s, often called *cycles per second* or *hertz*.

**frost line** The boundary in the solar nebula beyond which ices could condense; only metals and rocks could condense within the frost line.

**fundamental forces** There are four known fundamental forces in nature: gravity, the electromagnetic force, the strong force, and the weak force.

**fundamental particles** Subatomic particles that cannot be divided into anything smaller.

**galactic disk** (of a spiral galaxy) *See* disk component

**galactic fountain** Refers to a model for the cycling of gas in the Milky Way Galaxy in which fountains of hot, ionized gas rise from the disk into the halo and then cool and form clouds as they sink back into the disk.

**galactic wind** A wind of low-density but extremely hot gas flowing out from a starburst galaxy, created by the combined energy of many supernovae.

**galaxy** A huge collection of anywhere from a few hundred million to more than a trillion stars, all bound together by gravity.

**galaxy cluster** *See* cluster of galaxies

**galaxy evolution** The formation and development of galaxies.

**gamma-ray burst** A sudden burst of gamma rays from deep space; such bursts apparently come from distant galaxies, but their precise mechanism is unknown.

**gamma rays** Light with very short wavelengths (and hence high frequencies)—shorter than those of X rays.

**gas phase** The phase of matter in which atoms or molecules can move essentially independently of one another.

**gas pressure** Describes the force (per unit area) pushing on any object due to surrounding gas. *See also* pressure

**genetic code** The "language" that living cells use to read the instructions chemically encoded in DNA.

**geocentric universe** (ancient belief in) The idea that the Earth is the center of the entire universe.

**geological controlling factors** In this book, for the purpose of understanding geological processes, geology is considered to be influenced primarily by four geological controlling factors: surface gravity, internal temperature, surface temperature, and the presence (and extent) of an atmosphere.

**geological processes** The four basic geological processes are impact cratering, volcanism, tectonics, and erosion.

**geology** The study of surface features (on a moon, planet, or asteroid) and the processes that create them.

**giants** (luminosity class III) Stars that appear just below the supergiants on the H–R diagram because they are somewhat smaller in radius and lower in luminosity.

**global positioning system (GPS)** A system of navigation by satellites orbiting the Earth.

**global wind patterns** (or **global circulation**) Wind patterns that remain fixed on a global scale, determined by the combination of surface heating and the planet's rotation.

**globular cluster** A spherically shaped cluster of up to a million or more stars; globular clusters are found primarily in the halos of galaxies and contain only very old stars.

**gluons** The exchange particles for the strong force.

**grand unified theory (GUT)** A theory that unifies three of the four fundamental forces—the strong force, the weak force, and the electromagnetic force (but not gravity)—in a single model.

**granulation** (on the Sun) The bubbling pattern visible in the photosphere, produced by the underlying convection.

**gravitation** (law of) *See* universal law of gravitation

**gravitational constant** The experimentally measured constant $G$ that appears in the law of universal gravitation;

$$G = 6.67 \times 10^{-11} \frac{m^3}{kg \times s^2}.$$

**gravitational contraction** The process in which gravity causes an object to contract, thereby converting gravitational potential energy into thermal energy.

**gravitational encounter** Occurs when two (or more) objects pass near enough so that each can feel the effects of the other's gravity and can therefore exchange energy.

**gravitational equilibrium** Describes a state of balance in which the force of gravity pulling inward is precisely counteracted by pressure pushing outward.

**gravitational lensing** The magnification or distortion (into arcs, rings, or multiple images) of an image caused by light bending through a gravitational field, as predicted by Einstein's general theory of relativity.

**gravitational redshift** A redshift caused by the fact that time runs slow in gravitational fields.

**gravitational time dilation** The slowing of time that occurs in a gravitational field, as predicted by Einstein's general theory of relativity.

**gravitational waves** Predicted by Einstein's general theory of relativity, these waves travel at the speed of light and transmit distortions of space through the universe. Although not yet observed directly, we have strong indirect evidence that they exist.

**gravitationally bound system** Any system of objects, such as a star system or a galaxy, that is held together by gravity.

**gravitons** The exchange particles for the force of gravity.

**gravity** One of the four fundamental forces; it is the force that dominates on large scales.

**grazing incidence** (in telescopes) Reflections in which light grazes a mirror surface and is deflected at a small angle; commonly used to focus high-energy ultraviolet light and X rays.

**great circle** A circle on the surface of a sphere whose center is at the center of the sphere.

**Great Red Spot** A large, high-pressure storm on Jupiter.

**greenhouse effect** The process by which greenhouse gases in an atmosphere make a planet's surface temperature warmer than it would be in the absence of an atmosphere.

**greenhouse gases** Gases, such as carbon dioxide, water vapor, and methane, that are particularly good absorbers of infrared light but are transparent to visible light.

**Gregorian calendar** Our modern calendar, introduced by Pope Gregory in 1582.

**ground state** (of an atom) The lowest possible energy state of the electrons in an atom.

**group** (of galaxies) A few to a few dozen galaxies bound together by gravity. *See also* cluster of galaxies

**GUT era** The era of the universe during which only two forces operated (gravity and the grand-unified-theory or GUT force), lasting from $10^{-43}$ second to $10^{-38}$ second after the Big Bang.

**GUT force** The proposed force that exists at very high energies when the strong force, the weak force, and the electromagnetic force (but not gravity) all act as one.

**habitable zone** The region around a star in which planets could potentially have surface temperatures at which liquid water could exist.

**half-life** The time it takes for half of the nuclei in a given quantity of a radioactive substance to decay.

**halo** (of a galaxy) The spherical region surrounding the disk of a spiral galaxy.

**Hawking radiation** Radiation predicted to arise from the evaporation of black holes.

**heavy elements** In astronomy, *heavy elements* generally refers to all elements *except* hydrogen and helium.

**helium-capture reactions** Fusion reactions that fuse a helium nucleus into some other nucleus; such reactions can fuse carbon into oxygen, oxygen into neon, neon into magnesium, and so on.

**helium flash** The event that marks the sudden onset of helium fusion in the previously inert helium core of a low-mass star.

**helium fusion** The fusion of three helium nuclei into one carbon nucleus; also called the *triple-alpha reaction.*

**hertz (Hz)** The standard unit of frequency for light waves; equivalent to units of 1/s.

**Hertzsprung–Russell (H–R) diagram** A graph plotting individual stars as points, with stellar luminosity on the vertical axis and spectral type (or surface temperature) on the horizontal axis.

**high-mass stars** Stars born with masses above about $8M_{Sun}$; these stars will end their lives by exploding as supernovae.

**horizon** A boundary that divides what we can see from what we cannot see.

**horizontal branch** The horizontal line of stars that represents helium-burning stars on an H–R diagram for a cluster of stars.

**horoscope** A predictive chart made by an astrologer; in scientific studies, horoscopes have never been found to have any validity as predictive tools.

**hot spot** (geological) A place within a plate of the lithosphere where a localized plume of hot mantle material rises.

**hour angle (HA)** The angle or time (measured in hours) since an object was last on the meridian in the local sky. Defined to be 0 hours for objects that *are* on the meridian.

**Hubble's constant** A number that expresses the current rate of expansion of the universe; designated $H_0$, it is usually stated in units of km/s/Mpc. The reciprocal of Hubble's constant is the age the universe would have *if* the expansion rate had never changed.

**Hubble's law** Mathematically expresses the idea that more distant galaxies move away from us faster; its formula is $v = H_0 \times d$, where $v$ is a galaxy's speed away from us, $d$ is its distance, and $H_0$ is Hubble's constant.

**hydrogen compounds** Compounds that contain hydrogen and were common in the solar nebula, such as water ($H_2O$), ammonia ($NH_3$), and methane ($CH_4$).

**hydrogen-shell burning** Hydrogen fusion that occurs in a shell surrounding a stellar core.

**hydrosphere** Refers to the "layer" of water on the Earth consisting of oceans, lakes, rivers, ice caps, and other liquid water and ice.

**hyperbola** The precise mathematical shape of one type of unbound orbit (the other is a parabola) allowed under the force of gravity; at great distances from the attracting object, a hyperbolic path looks like a straight line.

**hypernova** A term sometimes used to describe a supernova (explosion) of a star so massive that it leaves a black hole behind.

**hyperspace** Any space with more than three dimensions.

**hypothesis** A tentative model proposed to explain some set of observed facts, but which has not yet been rigorously tested and confirmed.

**ices** (in solar system theory) Materials that are solid only at low temperatures, such as the hydrogen compounds water, ammonia, and methane.

**image** A picture of an object made by focusing light.

**imaging** (in astronomical research) The process of obtaining pictures of astronomical objects.

**impact** The collision of a small body (such as an asteroid or comet) with a larger object (such as a planet or moon).

**impact basin** A very large impact crater often filled by a lava flow.

**impact crater** A bowl-shaped depression left by the impact of an object that strikes a planetary surface (as opposed to burning up in the atmosphere).

**impact cratering** The excavation of bowl-shaped depressions (*impact craters*) by asteroids or comets striking a planet's surface.

**impactor** The object responsible for an impact.

**inflation** (of the universe) A sudden and dramatic expansion of the universe thought to have occurred at the end of the GUT era.

**infrared light** Light with wavelengths that fall in the portion of the electromagnetic spectrum between radio waves and visible light.

**inner solar system** Generally considered to encompass the region of our solar system out to about the orbit of Mars.

**intensity** (of light) A measure of the amount of energy coming from light of specific wavelength in the spectrum of an object.

**interferometry** A telescopic technique in which two or more telescopes are used in tandem to produce much better angular resolution than the telescopes could achieve individually.

**intermediate-mass stars** Stars born with masses between about 2–8$M_{Sun}$; these stars end their lives by ejecting a planetary nebula and becoming a white dwarf.

**interstellar cloud** A cloud of gas and dust between the stars.

**interstellar dust grains** Tiny solid flecks of carbon and silicon minerals found in cool interstellar clouds; they resemble particles of smoke and form in the winds of red giant stars.

**interstellar medium** Refers to gas and dust that fills the space between stars in a galaxy.

**intracluster medium** Hot, X-ray-emitting gas found between the galaxies within a cluster of galaxies.

**inverse square law** Any quantity that decreases with the square of the distance between two objects is said to follow an inverse square law.

**inversion** (atmospheric) A local weather condition in which air is colder near the surface than higher up in the troposphere—the opposite of the usual condition, in which the troposphere is warmer at the bottom.

**Io torus** A donut-shaped charged-particle belt around Jupiter that approximately traces Io's orbit.

**ionization** The process of stripping an electron from an atom.

**ionization nebula** A colorful, wispy cloud of gas that glows because neighboring hot stars irradiate it with ultraviolet photons that can ionize hydrogen atoms.

**ionosphere** A portion of the thermosphere in which ions are particularly common (due to ionization by X rays from the Sun).

**ions** Atoms with a positive or negative electrical charge.

**irregular galaxies** Galaxies that look neither spiral nor elliptical.

**isotopes** Each different isotope of an element has the *same* number of protons but a *different* number of neutrons.

**jets** High-speed streams of gas ejected from an object into space.

**joule** The international unit of energy, equivalent to about 1/4,000 of a Calorie.

**jovian nebulae** The clouds of gas that swirled around the jovian planets, from which the moons formed.

**jovian planets** Giant gaseous planets similar in overall composition to Jupiter.

**Julian calendar** The calendar introduced in 46 B.C. by Julius Caesar and used until it was replaced by the Gregorian calendar.

**Kelvin** (temperature scale) The most commonly used temperature scale in science, defined such that absolute zero is 0 K and water freezes at 273.15 K.

**Kepler's first law** States that the orbit of each planet about the Sun is an ellipse with the Sun at one focus.

**Kepler's laws of planetary motion** Three laws discovered by Kepler that describe the motion of the planets around the Sun.

**Kepler's second law** States that, as a planet moves around its orbit, it sweeps out equal areas in equal times. This tells us that a planet moves faster when it is closer to the Sun (near perihelion) than when it is farther from the Sun (near aphelion) in its orbit.

**Kepler's third law** States that the square of a planet's orbital period is proportional to the cube of its average distance from the Sun (semimajor axis), which tells us that more distant planets move more slowly in their orbits. In its original form, written $p^2 = a^3$. *See also* Newton's version of Kepler's third law

**kinetic energy** Energy of motion, given by the formula $\frac{1}{2}mv^2$.

**Kuiper belt** The comet-rich region of our solar system that spans distances of about 30–100 AU from the Sun; Kuiper belt comets have orbits that lie fairly close to the plane of planetary orbits and travel around the Sun in the same direction as the planets.

**Large Magellanic Cloud** One of two small, irregular galaxies (the other is the Small Magellanic Cloud) located about 150,000 light-years away; it probably orbits the Milky Way Galaxy.

**large-scale structure** (of the universe) Generally refers to structure of the universe on size scales larger than that of clusters of galaxies.

**latitude** The angular north-south distance between the Earth's equator and a location on the Earth's surface.

**leap year** A calendar year with 366 rather than 365 days; our current calendar (the Gregorian calendar) has a leap year every 4 years (by adding February 29) except in century years that are not divisible by 400.

**length contraction** Refers to the effect in which you observe lengths to be shortened in reference frames moving relative to you.

**lenticular galaxies** Galaxies that look lens-shaped when seen edge-on, resembling spiral galaxies without arms. They tend to have less cool gas than normal spiral galaxies but more gas than elliptical galaxies.

**leptons** Fermions *not* made from quarks, such as electrons and neutrinos.

**life track** A track drawn on an H–R diagram to represent the changes in a star's surface temperature and luminosity during its life; also called an *evolutionary track.*

**light-collecting area** (of a telescope) The area of the primary mirror or lens that collects light in a telescope.

**light curve** A graph of an object's intensity against time.

**light gases** (in solar system theory) Refers to hydrogen and helium, which never condense under solar nebula conditions.

**light pollution** Human-made light that hinders astronomical observations.

**light-year** The distance that light can travel in 1 year, which is 9.46 trillion km.

**liquid phase** The phase of matter in which atoms or molecules are held together but move relatively freely.

**lithosphere** The relatively rigid outer layer of a planet; generally encompasses the crust and the uppermost portion of the mantle.

**Local Group** The group of over 30 galaxies to which the Milky Way Galaxy belongs.

**local sidereal time (LST)** Sidereal time for a particular location, defined according to the position of the spring equinox in the local sky. More formally, the local sidereal time at any moment is defined to be the hour angle of the spring equinox.

**local sky** The sky as viewed from a particular location on Earth (or another solid object). Objects in the local sky are pinpointed by the coordinates of *altitude* and *direction* (or azimuth).

**Local Supercluster** The supercluster of galaxies to which the Local Group belongs.

**longitude** The angular east-west distance between the prime meridian (which passes through Greenwich) and a location on the Earth's surface.

**lookback time** Refers to the amount of time since the light we see from a distant object was emitted. I.e., if an object has a

**lookback time** of 400 million years, we are seeing it as it looked 400 million years ago.

**low-mass stars** Stars born with masses less than about $2M_{Sun}$; these stars end their lives by ejecting a planetary nebula and becoming a white dwarf.

**luminosity** The total power output of an object, usually measured in watts or in units of solar luminosities ($L_{Sun} = 3.8 \times 10^{26}$ watts).

**luminosity class** Describes the region of the H–R diagram in which a star falls. Luminosity class I represents supergiants, III represents giants, and V represents main-sequence stars; luminosity classes II and IV are intermediate to the others.

**luminosity–distance formula** The formula that relates apparent brightness, luminosity, and distance:

$$\text{apparent brightness} = \frac{\text{luminosity}}{4\pi \times (\text{distance})^2}$$

**lunar eclipse** Occurs when the Moon passes through the Earth's shadow, which can occur only at full moon; may be total, partial, or penumbral.

**lunar maria** The regions of the Moon that look smooth from Earth and actually are impact basins.

**lunar month** *See* synodic month

**lunar phase** Describes the appearance of the Moon as seen from Earth.

**MACHOs** Stands for *massive compact halo objects* and represents one possible form of dark matter in which the dark objects are relatively large, like planets or brown dwarfs.

**magma** Underground molten rock.

**magnetic braking** The process by which a star's rotation slows as its magnetic field transfers its angular momentum to the surrounding nebula.

**magnetic field** Describes the region surrounding a magnet in which it can affect other magnets or charged particles in its vicinity.

**magnetic-field lines** Lines that represent how the needles on a series of compasses would point if they were laid out in a magnetic field.

**magnetosphere** The region surrounding a planet in which charged particles are trapped by the planet's magnetic field.

**magnitude system** A system of describing stellar brightness by using numbers, called *magnitudes,* based on an ancient Greek way of describing the brightnesses of stars in the sky. This system uses *apparent magnitude* to describe a star's apparent brightness and *absolute magnitude* to describe a star's luminosity.

**main sequence** (luminosity class V) The prominent line of points running from the upper left to the lower right on an H–R diagram; main-sequence stars shine by fusing hydrogen in their cores.

**main-sequence fitting** A method for measuring the distance to a cluster of stars by comparing the apparent brightness of the cluster's main sequence with the standard main sequence.

**main-sequence lifetime** The length of time for which a star of a particular mass can shine by fusing hydrogen into helium in its core.

**main-sequence turnoff** A method for measuring the age of a cluster of stars from the point on its H–R diagram where its stars turn off from the main sequence; the age of the cluster is equal to the main-sequence lifetime of stars at the main-sequence turn-off point.

**mantle** (of a planet) The rocky layer that lies between a planet's core and crust.

**Martian meteorite** This term is used to describe meteorites found on Earth that are thought to have originated on Mars.

**mass** A measure of the amount of matter in an object.

**mass-energy** The potential energy of mass, which has an amount $E = mc^2$.

**mass exchange** (in close binary star systems) The process in which tidal forces cause matter to spill from one star to a companion star in a close binary system.

**mass extinction** An event in which a large fraction of the species living on Earth go extinct, such as the event in which the dinosaurs died out about 65 million years ago.

**mass increase** (in relativity) Refers to the effect in which an object moving past you seems to have a mass greater than its rest mass.

**mass-to-light ratio** The mass of an object divided by its luminosity, usually stated in units of solar masses per solar luminosity. Objects with high mass-to-light ratios must contain substantial quantities of dark matter.

**massive-star supernova** A supernova that occurs when a massive star dies, initiated by the catastrophic collapse of its iron core; often called a Type II supernova.

**matter–antimatter annihilation** Occurs when a particle of matter and a particle of antimatter meet and convert all of their mass-energy to photons.

**mean solar time** Time measured by the average position of the Sun in your local sky over the course of the year.

**meridian** A half-circle extending from your horizon (altitude 0°) due south, through your zenith, to your horizon due north.

**metals** (in solar system theory) Elements, such as nickel, iron, and aluminum, that condense at fairly high temperatures.

**meteor** A flash of light caused when a particle from space burns up in our atmosphere.

**meteor shower** A period during which many more meteors than usual can be seen.

**meteorite** A rock from space that lands on Earth.

**Metonic cycle** The 19-year period, discovered by the Babylonian astronomer Meton, over which the lunar phases occur on the same dates.

**Milky Way** Used both as the name of our galaxy and to refer to the band of light we see in the sky when we look into the plane of the Milky Way Galaxy.

**millisecond pulsars** Pulsars with rotation periods of a few thousandths of a second.

**model** (scientific) A representation of some aspect of nature that can be used to explain and predict real phenomena without invoking myth, magic, or the supernatural.

**molecular bands** The tightly bunched lines in an object's spectrum that are produced by molecules.

**molecular clouds** Cool, dense interstellar clouds in which the low temperatures allow hydrogen atoms to pair up into hydrogen molecules ($H_2$).

**molecular dissociation** The process by which a molecule splits into its component atoms.

**molecule** Technically the smallest unit of a chemical element or compound; in this text, the term refers only to combinations of two or more atoms held together by chemical bonds.

**momentum** The product of an object's mass and velocity.

**moon** An object that orbits a planet.

**mutations** Errors in the copying process when a living cell replicates itself.

**natural selection** The process by which mutations that make an organism better able to survive get passed on to future generations.

**nebula** A cloud of gas in space, usually one that is glowing.

**nebular capture** The process by which icy planetesimals capture hydrogen and helium gas to form jovian planets.

**nebular theory** The detailed theory that describes how our solar system formed from a cloud of interstellar gas and dust.

**net force** The overall force to which an object responds; the net force is equal to the rate of change in the object's momentum, or equivalently to the object's mass × acceleration.

**neutrino** A type of fundamental particle that has extremely low mass and responds only to the weak force; neutrinos are leptons and come in three types—electron neutrinos, mu neutrinos, and tau neutrinos.

**neutron degeneracy pressure** Degeneracy pressure exerted by neutrons, as in neutron stars.

**neutron star** The compact corpse of a high-mass star left over after a supernova; typically contains a mass comparable to the mass of the Sun in a volume just a few kilometers in radius.

**neutrons** Particles with no electrical charge found in atomic nuclei, built from three quarks.

**newton** The standard unit of force in the metric system:

$$1 \text{ newton} = 1\,\frac{\text{kg} \times \text{m}}{\text{s}^2}$$

**Newton's first law of motion** States that, in the absence of a net force, an object moves with constant velocity.

**Newton's laws of motion** Three basic laws that describe how objects respond to forces.

**Newton's second law of motion** States how a net force affects an object's motion. Specifically: force = rate of change in momentum, or force = mass × acceleration.

**Newton's third law of motion** States that, for any force, there is always an equal and opposite reaction force.

**Newton's universal law of gravitation** See universal law of gravitation

**Newton's version of Kepler's third law** This generalization of Kepler's third law can be used to calculate the masses of orbiting objects from measurements of orbital period and distance. Usually written as:

$$p^2 = \frac{4\pi^2}{G(M_1 + M_2)} a^3$$

**nodes** (of Moon's orbit) The two points in the Moon's orbit where it crosses the ecliptic plane.

**nonbaryonic matter** Refers to exotic matter that is not part of the normal composition of atoms, such as neutrinos or the hypothetical WIMPs.

**nonscience** As defined in this book, nonscience is any way of searching for knowledge that makes no claim to follow the scientific method, such as seeking knowledge through intuition, tradition, or faith.

**north celestial pole (NCP)** The point on the celestial sphere directly above the Earth's North Pole.

**nova** The dramatic brightening of a star that lasts for a few weeks and then subsides; occurs when a burst of hydrogen fusion ignites in a shell on the surface of an accreting white dwarf in a binary star system.

**nuclear fission** The process in which a larger nucleus splits into two (or more) smaller particles.

**nuclear fusion** The process in which two (or more) smaller nuclei slam together and make one larger nucleus.

**nucleus** (of an atom) The compact center of an atom made from protons and neutrons.

**nucleus** (of a comet) The solid portion of a comet, and the only portion that exists when the comet is far from the Sun.

**observable universe** The portion of the entire universe that, at least in principle, can be seen from Earth.

**Olbers' paradox** Asks the question of how the night sky can be dark if the universe is infinite and full of stars.

**Oort cloud** A huge, spherical region centered on the Sun, extending perhaps halfway to the nearest stars, in which trillions of comets orbit the Sun with random inclinations, orbital directions, and eccentricities.

**opacity** A measure of how much light a material absorbs compared to how much it transmits; materials with higher opacity absorb more light.

**opaque** (material) Describes a material that absorbs light.

**open cluster** A cluster of up to several thousand stars; open clusters are found only in the disks of galaxies and often contain young stars.

**open universe** The universe is open if its average density is less than the critical density, in which case spacetime has an overall shape analogous to the surface of a saddle.

**opposition** The point at which a planet appears opposite the Sun in our sky.

**optical quality** Describes the ability of a lens, mirror, or telescope to obtain clear and properly focused images.

**orbital resonance** Describes any situation in which one object's orbital period is a simple ratio of another object's period, such as 1/2, 1/4, or 5/3. In such cases, the two objects periodically line up with each other, and the extra gravitational attractions at these times can affect the objects' orbits.

**orbiters** (of other worlds) Spacecraft that go into orbit of another world for long-term study.

**outer solar system** Generally considered to encompass the region of our solar system beginning at about the orbit of Jupiter.

**outgassing** The process of releasing gases from a planetary interior, usually through volcanic eruptions.

**oxidation** Refers to chemical reactions, often with the surface of a planet, that remove oxygen from the atmosphere.

**ozone** The molecule $O_3$, which is a particularly good absorber of ultraviolet light.

**ozone depletion** Refers to the declining levels of atmospheric ozone found worldwide on Earth, especially in Antarctica, in recent years.

**ozone hole** A place where the concentration of ozone in the stratosphere is dramatically lower than is the norm.

**pair production** The process in which a concentration of energy spontaneously turns into a particle and its antiparticle.

**parabola** The precise mathematical shape of a special type of unbound orbit allowed under the force of gravity; if an object in a parabolic orbit loses only a tiny amount of energy, it will become bound.

**paradigm** (in science) Refers to general patterns of thought that tend to shape scientific beliefs during a particular time period.

**paradox** A situation that, at least at first, seems to violate common sense or contradict itself. Resolving paradoxes often leads to deeper understanding.

**parallax** The apparent shifting of an object against the background, due to viewing it from different positions. See also stellar parallax

**parallax angle** Half of a star's annual back-and-forth shift due to stellar parallax; related to the star's distance according to the formula

$$\text{distance in parsecs} = \frac{1}{p}$$

where $p$ is the parallax angle in arcseconds.

**parsec (pc)** Approximately equal to 3.26 light-years; it is the distance to an object with a parallax angle of 1 arcsecond.

**partial lunar eclipse** A lunar eclipse in which the Moon becomes only partially covered by the Earth's umbral shadow.

**partial solar eclipse** A solar eclipse during which the Sun becomes only partially blocked by the disk of the Moon.

**particle accelerator** A machine designed to accelerate subatomic particles to high speeds in order to create new particles or to test fundamental theories of physics.

**particle era** The era of the universe lasting from $10^{-10}$ second to 0.001 second after the Big Bang, during which subatomic particles were continually created and destroyed and ending when matter annihilated antimatter.

**peculiar velocity** (of a galaxy) The component of a galaxy's velocity relative to the Milky Way that deviates from the velocity expected by Hubble's law.

**penumbra** The lighter, outlying regions of a shadow.

**penumbral (lunar) eclipse** A lunar eclipse in which the Moon passes only within the Earth's penumbral shadow and does not fall within the umbra.

**perigee** The point at which an object orbiting the Earth is nearest to the Earth.

**perihelion** The point at which an object orbiting the Sun is closest to the Sun.

**period–luminosity relation** The relation that describes how the luminosity of a Cepheid variable star is related to the period between peaks in its brightness; the longer the period, the more luminous the star.

**phase** (of matter) Describes the way in which atoms or molecules are held together; the common phases are solid, liquid, and gas.

**photon** An individual particle of light, characterized by a wavelength and a frequency.

**photosphere** The visible surface of the Sun, where the temperature averages just under 6,000 K.

**pixel** An individual "picture element" on a CCD.

**Planck era** The era of the universe prior to the Planck time.

**Planck time** The time when the universe was $10^{-43}$ second old, before which random energy fluctuations were so large that our current theories are powerless to describe what might have been happening.

**Planck's constant** A universal constant, abbreviated $h$, with value $h = 6.626 \times 10^{-34}$ joule × s.

**planet** An object that orbits a star and that, while much smaller than a star, is relatively large in size; there is no "official" minimum size for a planet, but the nine planets in our solar system all are at least 2,000 km in diameter.

**planetary nebula** The glowing cloud of gas ejected from a low-mass star at the end of its life.

**planetesimals** The building blocks of planets, formed by accretion in the solar nebula.

**plasma** A gas consisting of ions and electrons.

**plasma tail** (of a comet) One of two tails seen when a comet passes near the Sun (the other is the dust tail); composed of ionized gas blown away from the Sun by the solar wind.

**plate tectonics** The geological process in which plates are moved around by stresses in a planet's mantle.

**plates** (on a planet) Pieces of a lithosphere that apparently float upon the denser mantle below.

**potential energy** Energy stored for later conversion into kinetic energy; includes gravitational potential energy, electrical potential energy, and chemical potential energy.

**power** The rate of energy usage, usually measured in watts (1 watt = 1 joule/s).

**precession** The gradual wobble of the axis of a rotating object around a vertical line.

**pressure** Describes the force (per unit area) pushing on an object. In astronomy, we are generally interested in pressure applied by surrounding gas (or plasma). Ordinarily, such pressure is related to the temperature of the gas (*see* thermal pressure). In objects such as white dwarfs and neutron stars, pressure may arise from a quantum effect (*see* degeneracy pressure). Light can also exert pressure. (*See* radiation pressure.)

**primary mirror** The large, light-collecting mirror of a reflecting telescope.

**prime focus** (of a reflecting telescope) The first point at which light focuses after bouncing off the primary mirror; located in front of the primary mirror.

**prime meridian** The meridian of longitude that passes through Greenwich, England, defined to be longitude 0°.

**primitive meteorites** Meteorites that formed at the same time as the solar system itself, about 4.6 billion years ago.

**processed meteorites** Meteorites that apparently once were part of a larger object that "processed" the original material of the solar nebula into another form.

**protogalactic cloud** A huge, collapsing cloud of intergalactic gas from which an individual galaxy formed.

**proton–proton chain** The chain of reactions by which low-mass stars (including the Sun) fuse hydrogen into helium.

**protons** Particles found in atomic nuclei with positive electrical charge, built from three quarks.

**protoplanetary disk** A disk of material surrounding a young star (or protostar) that may eventually form planets.

**protostar** A forming star that has not yet reached the point where sustained fusion can occur in its core.

**protostellar disk** A disk of material surrounding a protostar; essentially the same as a protoplanetary disk, but may not necessarily lead to planet formation.

**protostellar wind** The relatively strong wind from a protostar.

**protosun** The central object in the forming solar system that eventually became the Sun.

**pseudoscience** Something that purports to be science or may appear to be scientific but that does not adhere to the testing and verification requirements of the scientific method.

**pulsar** A neutron star from which we see rapid pulses of radiation as it rotates.

**pulsating variable stars** Stars that alternately grow brighter and dimmer as their outer layers expand and contract in size.

**quantum mechanics** The branch of physics that deals with the very small, including molecules, atoms, and fundamental particles.

**quantum state** Refers to the complete description of the state of a subatomic particle, including its location, momentum, orbital angular momentum, and spin, to the extent allowed by the uncertainty principle.

**quantum tunneling** The process in which, thanks to the uncertainty principle, an electron or other subatomic particle appears on the other side of a barrier that it does not have the energy to overcome in a normal way.

**quarks** The building blocks of protons and neutrons, quarks are one of the two basic types of fermions (leptons are the other).

**quasar** The brightest type of active galactic nucleus.

**radar ranging** A method of measuring distances within the solar system by bouncing radio waves off planets.

**radial motion** The component of an object's motion directed toward or away from us.

**radiation pressure** Pressure exerted by photons of light.

**radiation zone** (of a star) A region of the interior in which energy is transported primarily by radiative diffusion.

**radiative diffusion** The process by which photons gradually migrate from a hot region (such as the solar core) to a cooler region (such as the solar surface).

**radiative energy** Energy carried by light; the energy of a photon is Planck's constant times its frequency, or $h \times f$.

**radio galaxy** A galaxy that emits unusually large quantities of radio waves; thought to contain an active galactic nucleus powered by a supermassive black hole.

**radio waves** Light with very long wavelengths (and hence low frequencies)—longer than those of infrared light.

**radioactive dating** The process of determining the age of a rock (i.e., the time since it solidified) by comparing the present

amount of a radioactive substance to the amount of its decay product.

**radioactive element** (or **radioactive isotope**) A substance whose nucleus tends to fall apart spontaneously.

**recession velocity** (of a galaxy) The speed at which a distant galaxy is moving away from us due to the expansion of the universe.

**recollapsing universe** The possible fate of our universe in which the collective gravity of all its matter eventually halts and reverses the expansion. The galaxies will come crashing back together, and the universe will end in a fiery Big Crunch.

**red giant** A giant star that is red in color.

**red-giant winds** The relatively dense but slow winds from red giant stars.

**redshift** (Doppler) A Doppler shift in which spectral features are shifted to longer wavelengths, caused when an object is moving away from the observer.

**reflecting telescope** A telescope that uses mirrors to focus light.

**reflection** (of light) The process by which matter changes the direction of light.

**refracting telescope** A telescope that uses lenses to focus light.

**rest wavelength** The wavelength of a spectral feature in the absence of any Doppler shift or gravitational redshift.

**retrograde motion** Motion that is backward compared to the norm; e.g., we see Mars in apparent retrograde motion during the periods of time when it moves westward, rather than the more common eastward, relative to the stars.

**revolution** The orbital motion of one object around another.

**right ascension (RA)** Analogous to longitude, but on the celestial sphere; it is the angular east-west distance between the vernal equinox and a location on the celestial sphere.

**rings** (planetary) Consist of numerous small particles orbiting a planet within its Roche zone.

**Roche tidal zone** The region within two to three planetary radii (of any planet) in which the tidal forces tugging an object apart become comparable to the gravitational forces holding it together; planetary rings are always found within the Roche tidal zone.

**rocks** (in solar system theory) Material common on the surface of the Earth, such as silicon-based minerals, that are solid at temperatures and pressures found on Earth but typically melt or vaporize at temperatures of 500–1,300 K.

**rotation** The spinning of an object around its axis.

**rotation curve** A graph that plots rotational (or orbital) velocity against distance from the center for any object or set of objects.

**runaway greenhouse effect** A positive feedback cycle in which heating caused by the greenhouse effect causes more greenhouse gases to enter the atmosphere, which further enhances the greenhouse effect.

**saddle-shaped** (or **hyperbolic**) **geometry** Refers to any case in which the rules of geometry for a saddle-shaped surface hold, such as that two lines that begin parallel eventually diverge.

**Sagittarius Dwarf** A small, dwarf elliptical galaxy that is currently passing through the disk of the Milky Way Galaxy.

**saros cycle** The period over which the basic pattern of eclipses repeats, which is about 18 years $11\frac{1}{3}$ days.

**satellite** Any object orbiting another object.

**scattered light** Light that is reflected into random directions.

**Schwarzschild radius** A measure of the size of the event horizon of a black hole.

**science** The search for knowledge that can be used to explain or predict natural phenomena in a way that can be confirmed by rigorous observations or experiments.

**scientific method** An organized approach to explaining observed facts through science.

**scientific theory** A model of some aspect of nature that has been rigorously tested and has passed all tests to date.

**secondary mirror** A small mirror in a reflecting telescope, used to reflect light gathered by the primary mirror toward an eyepiece or instrument.

**sedimentary rock** A rock that formed from sediments created and deposited by erosional processes.

**seismic waves** Earthquake-induced vibrations that propagate through a planet.

**semimajor axis** Half the distance across the long axis of an ellipse; in this text, it is usually referred to as the *average* distance of an orbiting object, abbreviated *a* in the formula for Kepler's third law.

**SETI** (search for extraterrestrial intelligence) The name given to observing projects designed to search for signs of intelligent life beyond Earth.

**shield volcano** A shallow-sloped volcano made from the flow of low-viscosity basaltic lava.

**shock wave** A wave of pressure generated by gas moving faster than the speed of sound.

**sidereal day** The time of 23 hours 56 minutes 4.09 seconds between successive appearances of any particular star on the meridian; essentially the true rotation period of the Earth.

**sidereal month** About $27\frac{1}{4}$ days, the time required for the Moon to orbit the Earth once (as measured against the stars).

**sidereal period** (of a planet) A planet's actual orbital period around the Sun.

**sidereal time** Time measured according to the position of stars in the sky rather than the position of the Sun in the sky. *See also* local sidereal time

**sidereal year** The time required for the Earth to complete exactly one orbit as measured against the stars; about 20 minutes

longer than the tropical year on which our calendar is based.

**silicate rock** A silicon-rich rock.

**singularity** The place at the center of a black hole where, in principle, gravity crushes all matter to an infinitely tiny and dense point.

**Small Magellanic Cloud** One of two small, irregular galaxies (the other is the Large Magellanic Cloud) located about 150,000 light-years away; it probably orbits the Milky Way Galaxy.

**snowball Earth** Name given to a hypothesis suggesting that, some 600–700 million years ago, the Earth experienced a period in which it became cold enough for glaciers to exist worldwide, even in equatorial regions.

**solar activity** Refers to short-lived phenomena on the Sun, including the emergence and disappearance of individual sunspots, prominences, and flares; sometimes called *solar weather*.

**solar circle** The Sun's orbital path around the galaxy, which has a radius of about 28,000 light-years.

**solar day** Twenty-four hours, which is the average time between appearances of the Sun on the meridian.

**solar eclipse** Occurs when the Moon's shadow falls on the Earth, which can occur only at new moon; may be total, partial, or annular.

**solar flares** Huge and sudden releases of energy on the solar surface, probably caused when energy stored in magnetic fields is suddenly released.

**solar luminosity** The luminosity of the Sun, which is approximately $4 \times 10^{26}$ watts.

**solar maximum** The time during each sunspot cycle at which the number of sunspots is the greatest.

**solar minimum** The time during each sunspot cycle at which the number of sunspots is the smallest.

**solar nebula** The piece of interstellar cloud from which our own solar system formed.

**solar neutrino problem** Refers to the disagreement between the predicted and observed number of neutrinos coming from the Sun.

**solar prominences** Vaulted loops of hot gas that rise above the Sun's surface and follow magnetic-field lines.

**solar system** (or **star system**) Consists of a star (sometimes more than one star) and all the objects that orbit it.

**solar wind** A stream of charged particles ejected from the Sun.

**solid phase** The phase of matter in which atoms or molecules are held rigidly in place.

**sound wave** A wave of alternately rising and falling pressure.

**south celestial pole (SCP)** The point on the celestial sphere directly above the Earth's South Pole.

**spacetime** The inseparable, four-dimensional combination of space and time.

**spacetime diagram** A graph that plots a spatial dimension on one axis and time on another axis.

**spectral lines** Bright or dark lines that appear in an object's spectrum, which we can see when we pass the object's light through a prismlike device that spreads out the light like a rainbow.

**spectral resolution** Describes the degree of detail that can be seen in a spectrum; the higher the spectral resolution, the more detail we can see.

**spectral type** A way of classifying a star by the lines that appear in its spectrum; it is related to surface temperature. The basic spectral types are designated by a letter (OBAFGKM, with O for the hottest stars and M for the coolest) and are subdivided with numbers from 0 through 9.

**spectroscopic binary** A binary star system whose binary nature is revealed because we detect the spectral lines of one or both stars alternately becoming blueshifted and redshifted as the stars orbit each other.

**spectroscopy** (in astronomical research) The process of obtaining spectra from astronomical objects

**spectrum** (of light) *See* electromagnetic spectrum

**speed** The rate at which an object moves. Its units are distance divided by time, such as m/s or km/hr.

**speed of light** The speed at which light travels, which is about 300,000 km/s.

**spherical geometry** Refers to any case in which the rules of geometry for the surface of a sphere hold, such as that lines that begin parallel eventually meet.

**spheroidal component** (of a galaxy) The portion of any galaxy that is spherical (or football-like) in shape and contains very little cool gas; generally contains only very old stars. Elliptical galaxies have only a spheroidal component, while spiral galaxies also have a disk component.

**spin** (quantum) *See* spin angular momentum

**spin angular momentum** Often simply called *spin*, it refers to the inherent angular momentum of a fundamental particle.

**spiral arms** The bright, prominent arms, usually in a spiral pattern, found in most spiral galaxies.

**spiral density waves** Gravitationally driven waves of enhanced density that move through a spiral galaxy and are responsible for maintaining its spiral arms.

**spiral galaxies** Galaxies that look like flat, white disks with yellowish bulges at their centers. The disks are filled with cool gas and dust, interspersed with hotter ionized gas, and usually display beautiful spiral arms.

**spreading centers** (geological) Places where hot mantle material rises upward between plates and then spreads sideways creating new seafloor crust.

**spring equinox (vernal equinox)** Refers both to the point in Pisces on the celestial sphere where the ecliptic crosses the celestial equator and to the moment in time when the Sun appears at that point each year (around March 21).

**standard candle** An object for which we have some means of knowing its true luminosity, so that we can use its apparent brightness to determine its distance with the luminosity–distance formula.

**standard model** (of physics) The current theoretical model that describes the fundamental particles and forces in nature.

**standard time** Time measured according to the internationally recognized time zones.

**star** A large, glowing ball of gas that generates energy through nuclear fusion in its core. The term *star* is sometimes applied to objects that are in the process of becoming true stars (e.g., protostars) and to the remains of stars that have died (e.g., neutron stars).

**star cluster** *See* cluster of stars

**starburst galaxy** A galaxy in which stars are forming at an unusually high rate.

**state** (quantum) *See* quantum state

**steady state theory** A now-discredited theory that held that the universe had no beginning and looks about the same at all times.

**Stefan–Boltzmann constant** constant that appears in the laws of thermal radiation, with value

$$\sigma = 5.7 \times 10^{-8} \, \frac{\text{watt}}{\text{m}^2 \times \text{Kelvin}^4}.$$

**stellar evolution** The formation and development of stars.

**stellar parallax** The apparent shift in the position of a nearby star (relative to distant objects) that occurs as we view the star from different positions in the Earth's orbit of the Sun each year.

**stellar wind** A stream of charged particles ejected from the surface of a star.

**stratosphere** An intermediate-altitude layer of the atmosphere that is warmed by the absorption of ultraviolet light from the Sun.

**stratovolcano** A steep-sided volcano made from viscous lavas that can't flow very far before solidifying.

**stromatolites** Large bacterial "colonies."

**strong force** One of the four fundamental forces; it is the force that holds atomic nuclei together.

**subduction** (of tectonic plates) The process in which one plate slides under another.

**subduction zones** Places where one plate slides under another.

**subgiant** A star that is between being a main-sequence star and being a giant; subgiants have inert helium cores and hydrogen-burning shells.

**sublimation** The process by which atoms or molecules escape into the gas phase from a solid.

**summer solstice** Refers both to the point on the celestial sphere where the ecliptic is farthest north of the celestial equator and to the moment in time when the Sun appears at that point each year (around June 21).

**sunspot cycle** The period of about 11 years over which the number of sunspots on the Sun rises and falls.

**sunspots** Blotches on the surface of the Sun that appear darker than surrounding regions.

**superbubble** Essentially a giant interstellar bubble, formed when the shock waves of many individual bubbles merge to form a single, giant shock wave.

**supercluster** Superclusters consist of many clusters of galaxies, groups of galaxies, and individual galaxies and are the largest known structures in the universe.

**supergiants** (luminosity class I) The very large and very bright stars that appear at the top of an H–R diagram.

**supermassive black hole** Giant black hole, with a mass millions to billions of times that of our Sun, thought to reside in the centers of many galaxies and to power active galactic nuclei.

**supernova** The explosion of a star.

**Supernova 1987A** A supernova witnessed on Earth in 1987; it was the nearest supernova seen in nearly 400 years and helped astronomers refine theories of supernovae.

**supernova remnant** A glowing, expanding cloud of debris from a supernova explosion.

**synchronous rotation** Describes the rotation of an object that always shows the same face to an object that it is orbiting because its rotation period and orbital period are equal.

**synodic month** (or **lunar month**) The time required for a complete cycle of lunar phases, which averages about $29\frac{1}{2}$ days.

**synodic period** (of a planet) The time between successive alignments of a planet and the Sun in our sky; measured from opposition to opposition for a planet beyond Earth's orbit, or from superior conjunction to superior conjunction for Mercury and Venus.

**tangential motion** The component of an object's motion directed across our line of sight.

**tectonics** The disruption of a planet's surface by internal stresses.

**temperature** A measure of the average kinetic energy of particles in a substance.

**terrestrial planets** Rocky planets similar in overall composition to Earth.

**theories of relativity** (*special* and *general*) Einstein's theories that describe the nature of space, time, and gravity.

**thermal emitter** An object that produces a thermal radiation spectrum; sometimes called a "blackbody."

**thermal energy** Represents the collective kinetic energy, as measured by temperature, of the many individual particles moving within a substance.

**thermal escape** The process in which atoms or molecules in a planet's exosphere move fast enough to escape into space.

**thermal pressure** The ordinary pressure in a gas arising from motions of particles that can be attributed to the object's temperature.

**thermal pulses** The predicted upward spikes in the rate of helium fusion, occurring every few thousand years, that occur near the end of a low-mass star's life.

**thermal radiation** The spectrum of radiation produced by an opaque object that depends only on the object's temperature; sometimes called "blackbody radiation."

**thermosphere** A high, hot X-ray-absorbing layer of an atmosphere, just below the exosphere.

**tidal force** A force that is caused when the gravity pulling on one side of an object is larger than that on the other side, causing the object to stretch.

**tidal friction** Friction within an object that is caused by a tidal force.

**tidal heating** A source of internal heating created by tidal friction. It is particularly important for satellites with eccentric orbits such as Io and Europa.

**time dilation** Refers to the effect in which you observe time running slower in reference frames moving relative to you.

**timing** (in astronomical research) The process of tracking how the light intensity from an astronomical object varies with time.

**torque** A twisting force that can cause a change in an object's angular momentum.

**total apparent brightness** *See* apparent brightness. We sometimes say "total apparent brightness" to distinguish it from wavelength-specific measures such as the apparent brightness measured in visible light.

**total luminosity** *See* luminosity. We sometimes say "total luminosity" to distinguish it from wavelength-specific measures such as the luminosity emitted in visible light or the X-ray luminosity.

**total lunar eclipse** A lunar eclipse in which the Moon becomes fully covered by the Earth's umbral shadow.

**total solar eclipse** A solar eclipse during which the Sun becomes fully blocked by the disk of the Moon.

**totality** (eclipse) The portion of either a total lunar eclipse during which the Moon is fully within the Earth's umbral shadow or a total solar eclipse during which the Sun's disk is fully blocked by the Moon.

**transmission** (of light) The process in which light passes through matter without being absorbed.

**transparent** (material) Describes a material that transmits light.

**triple-alpha reaction** *See* helium fusion

**Trojan asteroids** Asteroids found within two stable zones that share Jupiter's orbit but lie 60° ahead of and behind Jupiter.

**tropic of Cancer** The circle on the Earth with latitude 23.5°N. It is the northernmost latitude at which the Sun ever passes directly overhead (at noon on the summer solstice).

**tropic of Capricorn** The circle on the Earth with latitude 23.5°S. It is the southernmost latitude at which the Sun ever passes directly overhead (at noon on the winter solstice).

**tropical year** The time from one spring equinox to the next, on which our calendar is based.

**troposphere** The lowest atmospheric layer, in which convection and weather occur.

**Tully–Fisher relation** A relationship among spiral galaxies showing that the faster a spiral galaxy's rotation speed, the more luminous it is; it is important because it allows us to determine the distance to a spiral galaxy once we measure its rotation rate and apply the luminosity–distance formula.

**turbulence** Rapid and random motion.

**ultraviolet light** Light with wavelengths that fall in the portion of the electromagnetic spectrum between visible light and X rays.

**umbra** The dark central region of a shadow.

**unbound orbits** Orbits on which an object comes in toward a large body only once, never to return; unbound orbits may be parabolic or hyperbolic in shape.

**uncertainty principle** The law of quantum mechanics that states that we can never know both a particle's position and its momentum, or both its energy and the time it has the energy, with absolute precision.

**universal law of gravitation** The law expressing the force of gravity ($F_g$) between two objects, given by the formula

$$F_g = G\frac{M_1 M_2}{d^2}$$

$$\left( G = 6.67 \times 10^{-11}\ \frac{m^3}{kg \times s^2} \right).$$

**universal time (UT)** Standard time in Greenwich (or anywhere on the prime meridian).

**universe** The sum total of all matter and energy.

**up quark** One of the two quark types (the other is the down quark) found in ordinary protons and neutrons. Has a charge of $+\frac{2}{3}$.

**velocity** The combination of speed and direction of motion; it can be stated as a speed in a particular direction, such as 100 km/hr due north.

**virtual particles** Particles that "pop" in and out of existence so rapidly that, according to the uncertainty principle, they cannot be directly detected.

**viscosity** Describes the "thickness" of a liquid in terms of how rapidly it flows; low-viscosity liquids flow quickly (e.g., water), while high-viscosity liquids flow slowly (e.g., molasses).

**visible light** The light our eyes can see, ranging in wavelength from about 400 to 700 nm.

**visual binary** A binary star system in which we can resolve both stars through a telescope.

**voids** Huge volumes of space between superclusters that appear to contain very little matter.

**volatiles** Refers to substances, such as water, carbon dioxide, and methane, that are usually found as gases, liquids, or surface ices on the terrestrial worlds.

**volcanism** The eruption of molten rock, or lava, from a planet's interior onto its surface.

**wavelength** The distance between adjacent peaks (or troughs) of a wave.

**weak bosons** The exchange particles for the weak force.

**weak force** One of the four fundamental forces; it is the force that mediates nuclear reactions; also the only force besides gravity felt by weakly interacting particles.

**weakly interacting particles** Particles, such as neutrinos and WIMPs, that respond only to the weak force and gravity; that is, they do not feel the strong force or the electromagnetic force.

**weather** Describes the ever-varying combination of winds, clouds, temperature, and pressure in a planet's troposphere.

**weight** The net force that an object applies to its surroundings; in the case of a stationary body on the surface of the Earth, weight = mass × acceleration of gravity.

**weightless** A weight of zero, as occurs during free-fall.

**white-dwarf limit** (also called the *Chandrasekhar limit*) The maximum possible mass for a white dwarf, which is about $1.4 M_{Sun}$.

**white dwarf supernova** A supernova that occurs when an accreting white dwarf reaches the white-dwarf limit, ignites runaway carbon fusion, and explodes like a bomb; often called a *Type Ia supernova*.

**white dwarfs** The hot, compact corpses of low-mass stars, typically with a mass similar to the Sun compressed to a volume the size of the Earth.

**WIMPs** Stands for *weakly interacting massive particles* and represents a possible form of dark matter consisting of subatomic particles that are dark because they do not respond to the electromagnetic force.

**winter solstice** Refers both to the point on the celestial sphere where the ecliptic is farthest south of the celestial equator and to the moment in time when the Sun appears at that point each year (around December 21).

**worldline** A line that represents an object on a spacetime diagram.

**wormholes** The name given to hypothetical tunnels through hyperspace that might connect two distant places in our universe.

**X rays** Light with wavelengths that fall in the portion of the electromagnetic spectrum between ultraviolet light and gamma rays.

**X-ray binary** A binary star system that emits substantial amounts of X rays, thought to be from an accretion disk around a neutron star or black hole.

**X-ray burster** An object that emits a burst of X rays every few hours to every few days; each burst lasts a few seconds and is thought to be caused by helium fusion on the surface of an accreting neutron star in a binary system.

**zenith** The point directly overhead, which has an altitude of 90°.

**zodiac** The constellations on the celestial sphere through which the ecliptic passes.

**zones** (on a jovian planet) Bright bands of rising air that encircle a jovian planet at a particular set of latitudes.

# ACKNOWLEDGMENTS

**ILLUSTRATION BY JOE BERGERON**: Figures 1.1, 1.3, 1.15, 1.16, 1.17, 2.6, 2.21, 8.6, 8.7, 8.14, 8.15, 8.16, 11.20, 12.20g, 16.3, 16.23, 16.24, 17.3, 17.9b, 17.14b, 18.1a, 18.18, 20.3, 20.4, 20.21, 20.22, 22.2. S5.2 ©Joe Bergeron, S5.3 ©Joe Bergeron, S5.4 ©Joe Bergeron, S5.5 ©Joe Bergeron

*Part Opener I and Chapter Openers 1–2, S1*: ©Roger Ressmeyer/CORBIS

*Part Opener II and Chapter Openers 3–7*: "An Expanding Bubble in Space": NASA, Donald Walter, South Carolina State Univ., Paul Scowen and Brian Moore, Arizona State Univ.

*Part Opener III and Chapter Openers 8–13*: "Valles Marineris—Point Perspective": Jody Swann, Tammy Becker, and Alfred McEwen of U.S. Geological Survey in Flagstaff, Arizona

*Part Opener IV and Chapter Openers S2–S4*: "Disorder in Stephan's Quintet": Jane C. Charlton (Penn State) et al., HST, ESA, NASA

*Part Opener V and Chapter Openers 14–17*: "Hubble Peeks into a Stellar Nursery in a Nearby Galaxy": Hubble Heritage Team (AURA/STScI/NASA)

*Part Opener VI and Chapter Openers 18–22, S5*: "A Galaxy on the Edge": Hubble Heritage Team (AURA/STScI/NASA)

**All Part Opener backgrounds**, Visual Language Library Antique Celestial Charts and Illustrations, 1680–1880, Volume 3

**CHAPTER 1** **1.2** NASA **1.4** Jerry Lodriguss **1.5** Created by Vincent Ciulla Design. From the Voyage scale model solar system, developed by Challenger Center for Space Science Education, the Smithsonian Institution, and

NASA **1.6** Stan Maddock **Page 12** (*Sun*-left), Big Bear Solar Observatory/New Jersey Institute of Technology and NASA Marshall Space Flight Center; (*Sun*-right) courtesy of SOHO. SOHO is a project of international cooperation between ESA and NASA. **Page 13** (*Mercury*-left) From the Voyage scale model solar system, developed by Challenger Center for Space Science Education, the Smithsonian Institution, and NASA. Image created by ARC Science Simulations, ©2001; (*Mercury*-right) NASA/USGS **Page 14** (*Venus*-left) NASA, courtesy of NSSDC; (*Venus*-right) From the Voyage scale model solar system, developed by Challenger Center for Space Science Education, the Smithsonian Institution, and NASA. ©2001 David P. Anderson, Southern Methodist Univ. **Page 15** (*Earth*-left) From the Voyage scale model solar system, developed by Challenger Center for Space Science Education, the Smithsonian Institution, and NASA. Image created by ARC Science Simulations, ©2001; (*Earth*-right) NASA **Page 16** (*Mars*-top) NASA/USGS, courtesy of NSSDC; (*Mars*-bottom) NASA **Page 17** (*Asteroid*) NEAR Project, John Hopkins Univ./APL, NASA **Page 18** (*Jupiter*) From the Voyage scale model solar system, developed by Challenger Center for Space Science Education, the Smithsonian Institution, and NASA. Image created by ARC Science Simulations, ©2001 **Page 19** (*Saturn*) From the Voyage scale model solar system, developed by Challenger Center for Space Science Education, the Smithsonian Institution, and NASA. Image created by ARC Science Simulations, ©2001 **Page 20** (*Uranus*) From the Voyage scale model solar system, developed by Challenger Center for Space Science Education, the Smithsonian Institution, and NASA. Image created by ARC Science Simulations, ©2001 **Page 21** (*Neptune*) From the Voyage scale model solar system, developed by Challenger Center for Space Science Education, the Smithsonian

Institution, and NASA. Image created by ARC Science Simulations, ©2001 **Page 22** (*Pluto and Charon*) Dr. R. Albrecht (ESA/ESO) and NASA **Page 23** (*Comet Hale–Bopp*) Niescja Turner and Carter Emmart **1.7** Akira Fujii **1.8** Megan Donahue (STScI) **1.9** (**clockwise, starting far-top right**) ©Photo by Corel; ©Christian Jegou/Publiphoto/Photo Researchers, Inc.; ©David Gifford/Science Photo Library/Photo Researchers, Inc.; ©Blakeley Kim; ©Photo by Corel; NASA; Quade Paul/fiVth.com; ©John Eastcott and Yva Momatiuk/Photo Researchers, Inc. **1.19** Quade Paul/fiVth.com, PhotoDisc, and Hubble Space Telescope

**CHAPTER 2** **2.1** Andrea Dupree (Harvard-Smithsonian CFA), Ronald Gilliland (STScI), ESA, and NASA **2.5** Gordon Garradd **2.10** (**c**) Richard Tauber Photography, San Francisco **2.11** (**b**) ©Dennis diCicco **2.13** ©David Nunuk **2.16** ©Dennis diCicco **2.17** ©Husmo-foto **2.19** (**Moons**) Akira Fujii; (**Earth**) NASA **2.23** (**top, bottom**) Akira Fujii; (**center**) Dennis diCicco **2.24, 2.25** Akira Fujii **2.26** Adapted from eclipse map by Fred Espenak, NASA/GSF: (http://sunearth.gsfc.nasa.gov/eclipse/eclipse.html) **2.27** ©Frank Zullo

**CHAPTER S1** **S1.5** Image from TRACE (Transition Region and Coronal Explorer), a mission of the Stanford-Lockheed Institute for Space Research (a joint program of the Lockheed-Martin Advanced Technology Center's Solar and Astrophysics laboratory and Stanford's Solar Observatories Group), and part of the NASA Small Explorer program **S1.6** ©Bernd Wittich/Visuals Unlimited **S1.8** NASA/MSFC **S1.25** (**a, b**) ©Bettmann/CORBIS; (**c**) The Granger Collection, NY; (**d**) ©Science VU/Visuals Unlimited

**CHAPTER 3** **3.2** ©Michael Yamashita/CORBIS **3.3** (a) ©N. Pecnik/Visuals Unlimited **3.4** ©Kenneth Garrett **3.5** (**a**) ©Wm. E. Woolam/Southwest Parks; (**b**) ©2001 Stone/ Richard A. Cooke, III **3.6** ©1987 by Margaret R. Curtis **3.7** ©Richard A. Cooke, III **3.8** ©Loren McIntyre/Woodfin Camp & Assoc. **3.9** (**left**) ©John A. Eddy/Visuals Unlimited; (**right**) ©Jeff Henry/Peter Arnold, Inc. **3.10** ©Oliver Strewe/Wave Productions Pty, Ltd. **3.11** Werner Forman Archive/Art Resource, NY **3.14** Courtesy of Carl Sagan Productions, Inc. From *Cosmos* (Random House), © 1980 Carl Sagan **3.15** ©Bettman/CORBIS **Page 107** The Granger Collection, NY

**CHAPTER 4** **4.1** ©2001 Stone/Dimitri Iundt **4.5** ©Science VU/Visuals Unlimited **Page 117** ©Bettmann/CORBIS

**CHAPTER 5** **Page 134** (**top**) Giraudon/ Art Resource, NY; (**bottom**) Archive Photos **Page 135** (**left**) The Granger Collection, NY; (**right**) ©Erich Lessing/Art Resource, NY **5.13** ©Jerry Lodriguss **Page 138** (**right**) ©Bettmann/CORBIS **Page 139** ©Bettmann/ CORBIS **5.17** NASA **5.19** (**both**) ©Bill Bachmann/Gnass Photo Images

**CHAPTER 6** **6.1** ©Runk/Schoenberger from Grant Heilman Photography

**CHAPTER 7** **7.4** (**a**) Emiko-Rose Koike/ fiVth.com **7.6** ©Craig M. Moore **7.7** (**b**) Yerkes Observatory **7.8** (**b**) Palomar Observatory/Caltech **7.10** (**a**) ©Richard Wainscoat; (**b**) Russ Underwood (W. M. Keck Observatory) **7.12** Mark Voit (STScI) **7.13** ©Anglo-Australian Observatory, photograph by D. Malin **7.15** NASA/CXC/SAO **7.17** ©Richard Wainscoat **7.18** NASA/Ames Research Center **7.19** (**a, b**) Canada-France-Hawaii Telescope Corporation, Hawaii **7.20** (**a**) NASA; (**b**) Don Foley/National Geographic Image Collection **7.21** Jodi Schoemer **7.22** (**c**) Eastman-Kodak **7.23** NASA **7.24** David Parker, 1997/Science Library. *The Arecibo Observatory is part of the National Astronomy and Ionosphere Center, which is operated by Cornell Univ. under a cooperative agreement with the National Science Foundation* **7.26** ©Joel Gordon Photography **7.28** (**right**) NASA/JPL **7.30** NASA/JPL/Caltech

**CHAPTER 8** **8.2** (**left**) Johns Hopkins Univ./APL/NASA **8.3** (**left**) ©1997 H. Mikuz and B. Kambic (Crni Vrh Observatory, Slovenia) **8.4** C. R. O'Dell (Rice Univ.) and NASA **8.8** (**a-left**) NASA/STScI, courtesy of Alfred Schultz and Helen Hart; (**a-right**) JPL/Caltech, Franklin & Marshall College, and NASA at W. M. Keck Observatory; (**b-left**) M. J. McCaughrean (MPIA), C. R. O'Dell (Rice Univ.), and NASA; (**b-right**) J. Bally, D. Devine, and R. Sutherland **8.12** Quade Paul/fiVth.com **8.13** Meteorite specimen courtesy of Robert Haag Meteorites **8.17** (**a, b**) NASA/JPL, courtesy NSSDC **8.18** ©William K. Hartmann **8.22** Data adapted from STARE project: (www. hao.ucar.edu/public/research/stare/hd209458. html)

**CHAPTER 9** **9.1** (**Moon**) Akira Fujii; (**others**) NASA **9.2** (**a**) ©Don Davis; (**b**) NASA, courtesy NSSDC; (**c**) ©Barrie Rokeach; (**d**) Artis Planetarium/The Netherlands; (**e**) NASA/ JPL **9.3** (**both**) ©Roger Ressmeyer/CORBIS **9.9** (**a**) ©Jules Bucher/Photo Researchers,

Inc. **9.11** Don Gault, Peter Schmultz, and NASA Ames Research Center **9.12** (**a**) NASA, from the Apollo 16 crew's mapping camera; (**b**) NASA/USGS **9.13** (**a**) NASA/JPL (Viking Orbiter); (**b**) NASA/USGS; (**c**) NASA /JPL/Malin Space Science Systems **9.14** NASA **9.16** (**b**) ©2001 Stone/Paul Chesley **9.17** (**top**) NASA, courtesy of LPL; (**center**) NASA/JPL; (**bottom**) ©Forest Buchanan/ Visuals Unlimited **9.19** (**left**) NASA/USGS; (**right**) NASA/JPL (Magellan Mission) **9.22** (**all**) NASA **9.23** (**a,c**) NASA/JPL; (**b**) NASA/USGS (Mariner 10 Mission) **9.24** (**a**) NASA, courtesy of Mark Robinson **9.25** Lowell Observatory Photographs **9.26** (**all**) NASA/USGS **9.27** (**a–c**) NASA/JPL; (**d, f**) NASA/JPL/Maline Space Science Systems; (**e**) Dr. David E. Smith, NASA, and MOLA Science Team **9.28** (**all**) NASA/JPL

**CHAPTER 10** **10.1** (*Mercury*-globe) NASA/courtesy NSSDC, (*Mercury*-surface) ©Don Davis; (*Venus*-globe) NASA/JPL, (*Venus*-surface) ©Don Davis; (*Earth*-globe) NASA, (*Earth*-surface) ©Barrie Rokeach; (*Moon*-globe) Akira Fujii, (*Moon*-surface) Artis Planetarium/The Netherlands; (*Mars*-globe) NASA/courtesy of Calvin Hamilton, (*Mars*-surface) NASA/JPL/Caltech **10.2** (**a, b**) NASA **10.10** (**b**) ©Hinrich Baesemann (www.polarfoto.com); (**c**) Dr. L. A. Frank, Univ. of Iowa; (**d**) NASA **10.12** ©Tom Van Sant/ The Geosphere Project/Corbis Stock Market **10.14** (**a**) ©Tom Van Sant/The Geosphere Project/Corbis Stock Market; (**b**) GOES-10 satellite image. Colorization by ARC Science Simulations, ©1998 **10.15** ©Tom Van Sant/ The Geosphere Project/Corbis Stock Market **10.16** (**a, c**) NASA/JPL; (**b**) Malin Space Science Systems and Caltech **10.18** NASA, courtesy NSSDC **10.19** NASA/JPL and Malin Space Science Systems **10.21** ©D. Cavagnaro/ Visuals Unlimited **10.24** (**a**) D. Potter, T. Morgan, and R. Killen; (**b**) M. Mendillo, J. Baumgartner, and J. Wilson of Boston Univ.

**CHAPTER 11** **11.1** NASA **11.3** (**b**) NASA/ JPL **11.6** (**a**) ©Michael Carroll **11.7** (**b**) STScI and R. Beebe and A. Simon (NMSU); (**c**) NASA Infrared Telescope Facility and Glenn Orton **11.8** (**a**) NASA/JPL **11.11** (**Uranus**) E. Karkoscha (Univ. of Arizona and NASA); (**others**) NASA/JPL **11.12** (**b**) J. Clarke (Univ. of Michigan) and NASA **11.13** John Spencer/Lowell Observatory **11.14** Data provided by Fran Bagenal **11.15** Courtesy Tim Parker/JPL **11.16** NASA/JPL **11.17** (**a**) PIRL/Lunar & Planetary Laboratory (Univ. of Arizona) and NASA; (**b**) Univ. of Arizona and NASA; (**c-left**) NASA/JPL; (**c-right**) Univ. of Arizona and NASA; (**d**) PIRL/ Lunar & Planetary Laboratory (Univ. of Arizona) and NASA; (**e**) NASA/USGS; (**f**) NASA/ JPL/Ames Research Center; (**g**) Univ. of Arizona and NASA **11.19** (**a**) DLR/NASA/ JPL; (**b**) Arizona State Univ. and NASA; (**c**) NASA/JPL/Arizona State Univ. **11.21** (**a, c**) NASA/JPL; (**b**) NASA/JPL and Brown Univ. **11.22** (**a**) NASA/JPL; (**b**) NASA/JPL and Arizona State Univ. **11.23** (**a**) NASA/JPL/ Caltech; (**b**) ©Don Davis; (**c**) Seran Gibbard, Bruce Macintosh, Don Gavel, Claire Max (Lawrence Livermore Natonal Laboratory) **11.24**, **11.25** NASA/JPL **11.26** (**a**) NASA/ USGS; (**b**) NASA/JPL; **11.27** (**a**) S. Larson (Univ. of Arizona/LPL); (**b**) NASA/JPL; (**c**)

©William K. Hartmann **11.28** NASA/JPL/ Caltech **11.29** NASA/JPL, courtesy of M. Showalter (Plantary Data Systems Ring Node) **11.30** (**a, b**) NASA/JPL **11.31** (**b**) NASA/JPL, courtesy of M. Showalter (Plantary Data Systems Ring Node) **11.32** (**Uranus**) Erich Karkoschka (Univ. of Arizona/LPL) and NASA; (**others**) NASA/JPL

**CHAPTER 12** **12.1**, **12.2** Data provided by Dave Tholen (Univ. of Hawaii) **12.3** Discovery photograph made January 7, 1976 by Eleanor F. Helin/JPL (Helin then associated with Caltech/Palomar Observatory) **12.4** (**a**) NASA/USGS; (**b**) NASA/JPL; (**c, d**) Johns Hopkins Univ./APL/NASA **12.6** Laird M. Close (Univ. of Arizona) and Wm. J. Merline (Southwest Research Institute, Boulder, Colorado) **12.7** (**b**) Stephen Ostro et al (JPL, Arecibo Radio Telescope, NSF, and NASA) **12.8** (**a**) Geological Survey of Canada; (**b**) courtesy of Calvin Hamilton **12.9** (**a**) Walt Radomski (nyrockman.com); (**b**) PEANUTS reprinted by permission of United Feature Syndicate, Inc. **12.10** Meteorite specimens courtesy of Robert Haag Meteorites **12.11** (**a**) ©Peter Ceravolo; (**b**) Tony and Daphne Hallas **12.12** LASCO, SOHO Consortium, NRL, ESA, and NASA **12.13** (**left**) Astuo Kuboniwa, March 9, 1997, 19:25:00–19:45:out, BISTAR Astronomical Observatory, Japan, Telescope: d = 125mm, f = 500mm refractor, Film: Ektracrome E100S; (**right**) Halley Multicolour Camera Team, Giotto, ESA, ©MPAE **12.17** (**a**) U.S. Naval Observatory; (**b**) Dr. R. Albrecht, ESA/ESO, and NASA **12.18** Eliot Young/Southwest Research Institute **12.19** (**a**) Hal Weaver and T. E. Smith (STScI) and NASA; (**b**) Courtesy of Paul Schenk (Lunar and Planetary Institute) **12.20** (**a**) NASA/JPL/Caltech; (**b**) HST Jupiter Imaging Science Team; (**c**) MSSO, ANU/Science Library/Photo Researchers, Inc.; (**d**) Courtesy of Richard Wainscoat et al (Univ. of Hawaii); (**e**) H. Hammel (MIT) and NASA; (**f**) HST Comet Team and NASA **12.21** (**c**) James W. Young/TMO/JPL/NASA **12.22** Brad Snowder **12.23** Kirk Johnson/ Denver Museum of Natural History **12.24** Image courtesy of Dr. Virgil Sharpton, Univ. of Alaska-Fairbanks **12.25** (**all**) Quade Paul/ fiVth.com **12.26** TASS/Sovfoto

**CHAPTER 13** **13.1** NASA **13.2** (**Venus**) NASA/Magellan data, courtesy Peter Ford (MIT); (**Earth**) NOAA; (**Mars**) NASA/Viking data, courtesy Mike Mellon (Univ. of Colorado) **13.4** ©Tom Van Sant/The Geosphere Project/Corbis Stock Market **13.5** (**a**) ©Gene Ahrens/Bruce Coleman, Inc.; (**b**) ©J. Messerschmidt/Bruce Coleman, Inc.; (**c**) Biological Photo Service; (**d**) ©C. C. Lockwood/DDB Stock Photo **13.7** Digital image by Dr. Peter W. Sloss (NOAA/NESDIS/NGDCO) **13.11** (**a**) NASA; (**b**) Earth Satellite Corp./Science Photo Library/Photo Researchers, Inc. **13.12** (**b**) ©Roger Ressmeyer/CORBIS; (**c**) Mike Yamashita/Woodfin Camp & Assoc. **13.13** (**clockwise from top**) ©Philip Rosenberg; ©Philip Rosenberg; Univ. of Hawaii; R. Shallenberger/Midway Atol National Wildlife Refuge **13.15** ©James L. Amos/Photo Researchers, Inc. **13.16** ©Jeff Greenberg/Visuals Unlimited **13.17** (**a, c**) Biological Photo Services; (**b**) ©Kevin Collins/Visuals Unlimited **13.18** ©Nih R. Feldman/Visuals Unlimited

**13.20** (**a**) Woods Hole Oceanographic Institute; (**b**) ©Barrie Rokeach **13.21** ©Ken Lucas/Visuals Unlimited **13.23** Data obtained from C. D. Keeling and T. P. Whorf, Scripps Institution of Oceanography, Univ. of California, La Jolla: (http://cdiac.esd.ornl.gov/ftp/maunaloa-co2/maunaloa.co2) **13.24** NASA/GSFC (Science Visualization Studio) **13.25** (**a**) NASA; (**b**-both) NASA/Ames Research Center

**CHAPTER S3** **S3.23** (**a**) ESA/NASA; (**b**) HST/MIRLIN/Lindsay King (Univ. of Manchester)

**CHAPTER S4** **S4.1** Fermilab Visual Media Service **S4.5** ©Harold & Esther Edgerton Foundation, 1998. Palm Press, Inc.

**CHAPTER 14** **14.1** Photo by Corel **14.3** National Optical Astronomy Observatories/NSO, Sacramento Peak **14.8** National Optical Astronomy Observatories **14.9** Courtesy of Brookhaven National Laboratory **14.10** (**a**, **b**) ICRR (Institute for Cosmic Ray Research), Univ. of Tokyo **14.12** (**b**) Goram Scharmer/Stanford's Solar Observatories Group **14.13** (**a**, **b**) NOAO/National Solar Observatory **14.15** (**b**) Image from TRACE (Transition Region and Coronal Explorer), a mission of the Stanford-Lockheed Institute for Space Research (a joint program of the Lockheed-Martin Advanced Technology Center's Solar and Astrophysics laboratory and Stanford's Solar Observatories Group), and part of the NASA Small Explorer program **14.16** Courtesy of SOHO. SOHO is a project of international cooperation between ESA and NASA **14.17** Image from TRACE (Transition Region and Coronal Explorer), a mission of the Stanford-Lockheed Institute for Space Research (a joint program of the Lockheed-Martin Advanced Technology Center's Solar and Astrophysics laboratory and Stanford's Solar Observatories Group), and part of the NASA Small Explorer program **14.18** Courtesy of B. Haisch and G, Slater (Lockheed Palo Alto Research Laboratory) **14.19** Data adapted from Marshall Space Flight Center: (http://science.msfc.nasa.gov/ssl/pad/solar) **14.21** (**b**) ©Daniel Hershman

**CHAPTER 15** **Page 475** ©Bettmann/CORBIS **15.3** Hubble Heritage Team (AURA/STScI/NASA) **Table 15.1** (**spectrum**) Roger Bell and Mike Briley, Univ. of Maryland **15.4, 15.5** Harvard College Observatory **15.6** (**photo**-center) Lowell Observatory **15.13** ©Anglo-Australian Observatory/Royal Observatory Edinburgh, photography by D. Malin **15.14** Hubble Heritage Team (AURA/STScI/NASA)

**CHAPTER 16** **16.1** ©Anglo-Australian Observatory, photograph by D. Malin **16.2** IPAC (Infrared Processing and Analysis Center) and Caltech/JPL **16.4** (**b**, **c**) C. Burrows and J. Morse (STScI), J. Hester (Arizona State Univ.), and NASA **16.13** (**a**) Nordic Optical Telescope, La Palma; (**b**) J. P. Harrington, K. J. Borkowski (Univ. of Maryland) and NASA; (**c**) B. Balick (Univ. of Washington), V. Icke (Leiden Univ.), G. Mellema (Stockholm Univ.), and NASA; (**d**) R. Sahai, J. Trauger (JPL), the WFPC2 Science Team, and NASA **16.21** ©ESO (European Southern Observatory) **16.22** ©Anglo-Australian Observatory, photograph by D. Malin

**CHAPTER 17** **17.1** NASA/SAO/CXO **17.4** (**b**) M. Shara, B. Williams, and D. Zurek (STScI); R. Gilmozzi (ESO); D. Prialnik (Tel Aviv Univ.); and NASA **17.6** NASA and F. M. Walter (State Univ., New York at Stony Brook) **17.8** ©ESO (European Southern Observatory) **Pages 556–557** (**Bell**) Copyright is held by CWP/Regents of the Univ. of California: www.physics.ucla.edu/~cwp/Phase2/Burnell,_Jocelyn_Bell@841234567.html); (**others**) Courtesy of Astronomical Institute of Bonn Univ. **17.16** Andrew Fruchter (STScI) and NASA

**CHAPTER 18** **18.2** (**counterclockwise from lower right**) D. Malin (Fig. 18.4); S. L. Snowden (Fig. 18.5); NASA/NSSDC (Fig. 18.13); J. Bally (Fig. 18.10); J. Hester and P. Scowen (Fig. 18.12); D. Malin (Fig. 18.14) **18.3** H. Bond (STScI) and NASA **18.4** ©Anglo-Australian Observatory, photography by D. Malin **18.5** S. L. Snowden (NASA/GSFC) **18.6** (**a**) Tony and Daphne Hallas; (**b**) Jeff Hester (Arizona State Univ.) and NASA **18.7** (**a**) J. Keuhane, B. Koralesky, M. Anderson, L. Rudnick (Univ. of Minnesota) and R. Perley (NRAO); (**b**) NASA/CXO/SAO/Rutgers and J. Hughes **18.8** (**b**) Simulation by D. Strickland and I. Stevens **18.10, 18.11** John Bally (Univ. of Colorado) **18.12** Jeff Hester and Paul Scowen (Arizona State Univ.) and NASA **18.13** Courtesy of NASA's National Space Science Data Center at the Goddard Space Flight Center **18.14** ©Anglo-Australian Observatory/Royal Observatory Edinburgh, photography by D. Malin **18.16, 18.17** ©Anglo-Australian Observatory, photography by D. Malin **18.20** Hubble Heritage Team (AURA/STScI/NASA); Acknowledgments: N. Scoville (Caltech) and T. Rector (NOAO) **18.21** (**photo**) J. Trauger, JPL and NASA **18.22** (**photo**) Hubble Heritage Team (AURA/STScI/NASA); Acknowledgments: N. Scoville (Caltech) and T. Rector (NOAO) **18.23** (**a**) David Talent at the Cerro Tololo Inter-American Observatory, Chile; (**b**) AFRL/BMDO, courtesy of Dr. Mehradad Moshir; (**c**) NRAO/AUI, courtesy of Cornelia Lang (NRAO/UCLA) and Mark Morris (UCLA); (**d**) K. Y. Lo (Univ. of Illinois)

**CHAPTER 19** **19.1** ©Sky Publishing Corporation, reproduced with permission **19.2** (**a**) ©ESO (European Southern Observatory; (**b**, **e**) ©Anglo-Australian Observatory, photography by D. Malin; (**c**) Hubble Heritage Team (AURA/STScI/NASA); (**d**) ©IAC photo from plates taken with the Isaac Newton telescope, photo by D. Malin **19.3, 19.4** ©Anglo-Australian Observatory, photography by D. Malin **19.5** Hubble Heritage Team (AURA/STScI/NASA) **19.6** ©Anglo-Australian Observatory/Royal Observatory Edinburgh, photography by D. Malin **19.7** (**a**, **b**) ©Anglo-Australian Observatory, photography by D. Malin **19.8** (**a**, **b**) ©Anglo-Australian Observatory/Royal Observatory Edinburgh, photography by D. Malin; (**c**) ©Anglo-Australian Observatory, photography by D. Malin **19.11** (**a**) The Observatories of the Carnegie Institution of Washington; (**b**) NASA/STScI **19.12, 19.14** The Observatories of the Carnegie Institution of Washington **19.15** (**a**) J. Trauger, JPL, and NASA; (**b**) Dr. W. L. Freedman (The Observatories of the Carnegie Institution of Washington) and NASA **19.17** Megan Donahue (STScI)

**CHAPTER 20** **20.1** Robert Williams and the HDF Team (STScI) and NASA **20.5** Hyron Spinard, Univ. of California at Berkely et al **20.6** (**a**) Brad Whitmore (STScI) and NASA; (**b**) W. C. Keel (Univ. of Alabama) **20.7** Robert Williams and the HDF Team (STScI) and NASA **20.8** Frank Summers/American Museum of Natural History **20.9** ©Anglo-Australian Observatory, photography by D. Malin **20.10** Dr. Michael J. West/Univ. of Hawaii–Hilo **20.11** (**a**) R. Thompson, M. Rieke, G. Schneider (Univ. of Arizona); N. Scoville (Caltech); and NASA **20.12** (**a**) MPE (Max Plank Institute); (**b**) Subaru Telescope, National Astronomical Observatory of Japan. ©2000 NAOJ **20.13** Data obtained on the 3.9m Anglo-Australian Telescope by G. R. Meurer (JHU) **20.14** Hubble Heritage Team (AURA/STScI/NASA) **20.17** John Bahcall/Institute for Advanced Study and NASA **20.18** NRAO/AUI **20.19** (**a–c**) Alan Bridle (NRAO/AUI); (**d**) NRAO/AUI **20.20** John Biretta (STScI) **20.24** H. Ford (STScI/Johns Hopkins Univ.); L. Dressel, R. Harms, A. Kochhar (Applied Research Corp.); Z. Tsvetanov, A. Davidsen, G. Kriss (Johns Hopkins Univ.); R. Bohlin, G. Hartig (STSci); B. Margon (Univ. of Washington-Seattle); and NASA **20.25** Emiko-Rose Koike/fiVth.com

**CHAPTER 21** **21.3** (**photo**) ©Anglo-Australian Observatory, photography by D. Malin **21.6** Courtesy of Caltech **21.8** (**a**) Omar Lopez-Cruz and Iam Shelton; (**b**) Steve Snowden, NASA/GSFC/USRA **21.9** W. N. Colley and E. Turner (Princeton Univ.), J. A. Tyson (Bell Labs, Lucent Technologies), and NASA **21.11** A. Fruchter, the ERO Team (STScI, ST-ECF), and NASA **21.12** (**inset photos**) Charles Alcock/Lawrence Livermore National Laboratory **21.13** Michael Strauss, Princeton Univ. **21.14** (**a**, **b**) Harvard-Smithsonian Center for Astrophysics; (**c**) Emiko-Rose Koike/fiVth.com **21.15** S. Maddox, G. Efstathiou, and W. Sutherland, MNRAS, 242, 43P **21.16** (**a**, **b**) Ben Moore, Dept. of Physics, Durham Univ., Durham City, England

**CHAPTER 22** **22.5** ©Roger Ressmeyer/CORBIS **22.8** E. Bunn (St. Cloud State Univ.) **22.15** ©BOOMERANG Collaboration **22.16** (**left**) John Kieffer/Peter Arnold, Inc.; (**right**) Joel Gordon Photography

**CHAPTER S5** **S5.1** (**a**, **b**) NASA/JPL **S5.6** ©Seth Shostak

# INDEX